What Is an "Integrated Approach"?

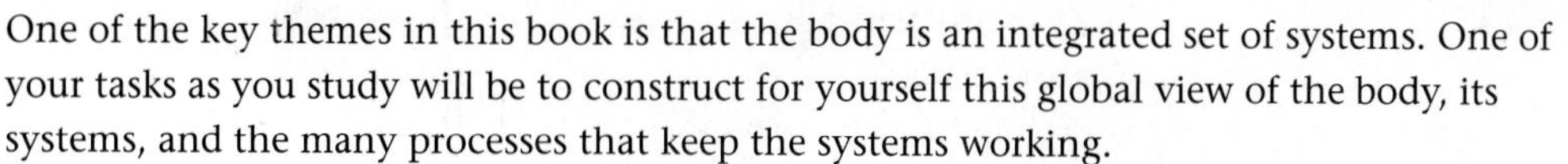

One of the key themes in this book is that the body is an integrated set of systems. One of your tasks as you study will be to construct for yourself this global view of the body, its systems, and the many processes that keep the systems working.

Top Ten Ways to Succeed in Classes that Use Active Learning

By Marilla Svinicki, Ph.D., Director
University of Texas Center for Teaching Effectiveness

1. Make the switch from an authority-based conception of learning to a self-regulated conception of learning. Recognize and accept your own responsibility for learning.
2. Be willing to take risks and go beyond what is presented in class or the text.
3. Be able to tolerate ambiguity and frustration in the interest of understanding.
4. See errors as opportunities to learn rather than failures. Be willing to make mistakes in class or in study groups so that you can learn from them.
5. Engage in active listening to what's happening in class.
6. Trust the instructor's experience in designing class activities and participate willingly if not enthusiastically.
7. Be willing to express an opinion or hazard a guess.
8. Accept feedback in the spirit of learning rather than as a reflection of you as a person.
9. Prepare for class physically, mentally, and materially (do the reading, work the problems, etc.).
10. Provide support for your classmate's attempts to learn. The best way to learn something well is to teach it to someone who doesn't understand.

Dr. Dee's Eleventh Rule:
DON'T PANIC! Pushing yourself beyond the comfort zone is scary, but you have to do it in order to improve.

Word Roots for Physiology

a- or **an-** without, absence
anti- against
ase signifies an enzyme
auto self
bi two
brady slow
cardio- heart
cephalo- head
cerebro- brain
contra- against
-crine a secretion
crypt- hidden
cutan- skin
-cyte or **cyto-** cell
de- without, lacking
di- two
dys- difficult, faulty
-elle small
-emia blood
endo- inside or within
epi- over
erythro- red
exo- outside
extra- outside
gastro- stomach
-gen, -genic produce
gluco-, glyco- sugar or sweet
hemi- half
hemo- blood
hepato- liver
homo- same
hydro- water
hyper- above or excess
hypo- beneath or deficient
inter- between
intra- within
-itis inflammation of
kali- potassium
leuko- white
lipo- fat
lumen inside of a hollow tube
-lysis split apart or rupture
macro- large
micro- small
mono- one
multi- many
myo- muscle
oligo- little, few
para- near, close
patho-, -pathy related to disease
peri- around
poly- many
post- after
pre- before
pro- before
pseudo- false
re- again
retro- backward or behind
semi- half
sub- below
super- above, beyond
supra- above, on top of
tachy- rapid
trans- across, through

HUMAN PHYSIOLOGY

Dee Unglaub Silverthorn

Second Custom Edition for Stony Brook University
State University of New York

Taken from:
Human Physiology: An Integrated Approach, Media Update, Fourth Edition
by Dee Unglaub Silverthorn

Custom Publishing

New York Boston San Francisco
London Toronto Sydney Tokyo Singapore Madrid
Mexico City Munich Paris Cape Town Hong Kong Montreal

Cover Art: Courtesy of Photodisc/Getty Images

Taken from:

Human Physiology: An Integrated Approach, Media Update, Fourth Edition
by Dee Unglaub Silverthorn

Published by Benjamin Cummings
San Francisco, California 94111

This special edition published in cooperation with Pearson Custom Publishing.

Printed in the United States of America

10 9 8 7 6 5 4 3 2 1

2008140605

MP

Pearson
Custom Publishing
is a division of

www.pearsonhighered.com

ISBN 10: 0-558-05501-X
ISBN 13: 978-0-558-05501-1

Contents in Brief

Contents

UNIT 1

BASIC CELL PROCESSES: Integration and Coordination

UNIT 2

HOMEOSTASIS AND CONTROL

UNIT 3

INTEGRATION OF FUNCTION

5

Controversy surrounds the exact arrangements of molecules in cell membranes.

—Robert D. DeVoe, *in Mountcastle's* **Medical Physiology,** *1974*

Cells (green actin and blue DNA) taking up red microspheres by endocytosis.

Membrane Dynamics

BACKGROUND BASICS

Polar and nonpolar molecules: **24** Protein and lipid structure: **29** Cell junctions: **69** Microscopy: **55** Molarity: **36** Solutions: **35** Membrane structure: **53** Cytoskeleton: **62** Types of epithelia: **72** Enzymes **96**

RUNNING PROBLEM

CYSTIC FIBROSIS

Over 100 years ago, midwives performed an unusual test on the infants they delivered: the midwife would lick the infant's forehead. A salty taste meant that the child was destined to die of a mysterious disease that withered the flesh and robbed the breath. Today, a similar "sweat test" will be performed in a major hospital—this time with state-of-the-art techniques—on Daniel Biller, a 2-year-old with a history of weight loss and respiratory problems. The name of the mysterious disease? Cystic fibrosis.

In the 1960s a group of conspiracy theorists obtained a lock of Napoleon Bonaparte's hair and sent it for chemical analysis in an attempt to show that he had been poisoned to death. Somewhere in Manhattan's Little Italy, a group of friends savor a delicious dinner and joke about the garlic odor on their breath that will result. At first glance these two scenarios appear to have little in common, but in fact, Napoleon's hair and garlic breath are both demonstrations of how the human body works to maintain the balance that we call homeostasis.

MASS BALANCE AND HOMEOSTASIS

You learned in the previous chapter that the body is an open system that exchanges heat and materials with the outside environment. To maintain a state of homeostasis—a relatively constant internal environment—the body utilizes the principle of mass balance. The **law of mass balance** says that if the amount of a substance in the body is to remain constant, any gain must be offset by an equal loss (Fig. 5-1■). For example, to maintain constant body concentration, water gain from the external environment and from metabolism must be offset by water loss back to the external environment. Other substances whose concentrations are maintained through mass balance include oxygen and carbon dioxide, salts, and hydrogen ions (pH). The law of mass balance is summarized by the following equation:

Total amount (or **load**) of substance *x* in the body
= intake + production − excretion − metabolism

Although most substances enter the body from the outside environment, some (such as carbon dioxide) can be produced internally through metabolism (Fig. 5-2 ■). In general, intake of water and nutrients into the body comes as food and drink absorbed through the intestine. Oxygen and other gases and volatile molecules enter through the lungs, and a few lipid-soluble chemicals make their way to the internal environment by penetrating the barrier of the skin [p. 83].

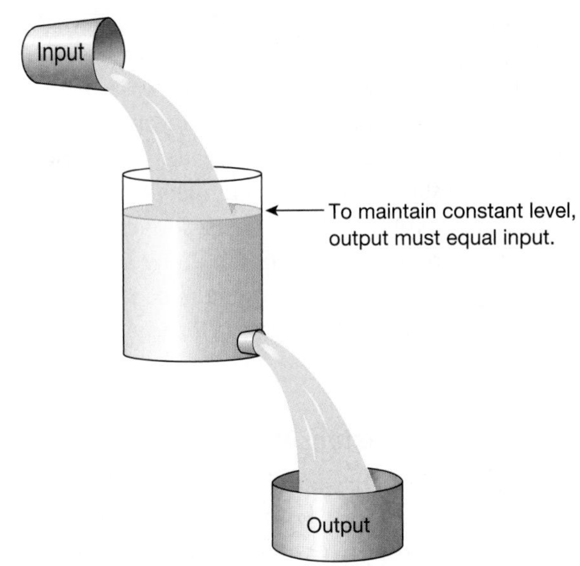

■ **FIGURE 5-1** ***Mass balance in an open system***

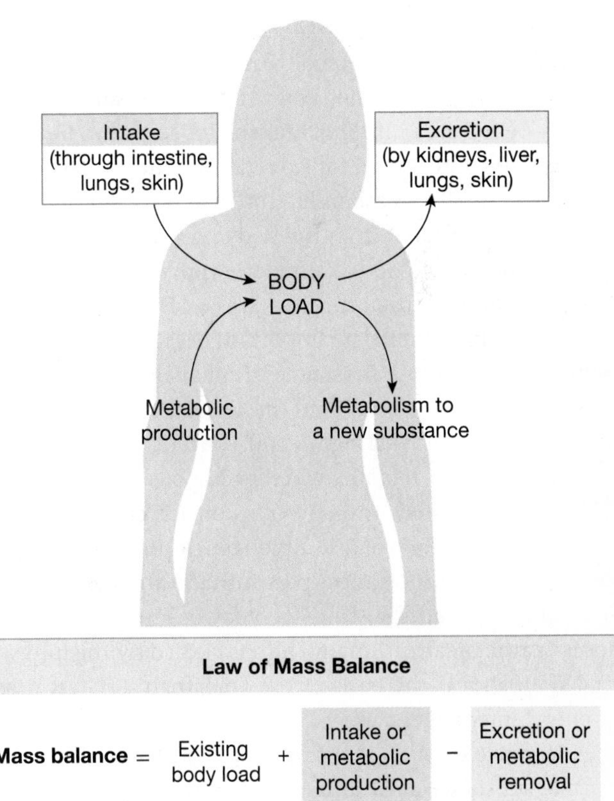

■ **FIGURE 5-2** ***Mass balance in the body***

Materials either enter the body by various routes or are produced through metabolism. Materials leave the body either by excretion or by metabolism.

To maintain mass balance, the body has two options for output. The simplest option is simply to excrete the material. **Excretion** is defined as the elimination of material from the body, and it usually takes place through the urine, feces, lungs, or skin. For example, carbon dioxide produced during metabolism is excreted by the lungs. Many *xenobiotics* [*xenos*, a foreigner] that enter the body, such as drugs or artificial food additives, are excreted by the liver and kidneys.

A second option to maintain mass balance is to metabolize the substance to a different substance. Nutrients that enter the body become the starting substrates in metabolic pathways, as you learned in Chapter 4. Metabolism converts the original nutrient to a different substance but in doing so creates a new mass balance disturbance by adding more of the *metabolite* to the body. (*Metabolite* is the general term for any product created in a metabolic pathway.)

Excretion Clears Substances from the Body

The rate at which a molecule disappears from the body by excretion, metabolism, or both is called the molecule's **clearance**. The quantitative expression of clearance will be introduced in Chapter 19, but it will be easier to understand that discussion if you already know that the kidney is only one organ of several that clear solutes from the body. The liver is the other major organ involved in clearing materials, especially xenobiotics. Hepatocytes [*hepaticus*, pertaining to the liver + *cyte*, cell], or liver cells, metabolize many different types of molecules, including hormones and drugs. The resulting metabolites may be secreted into the intestine for excretion in the feces or released into the blood for excretion by the kidneys.

Saliva, sweat, breast milk, and hair also contain solutes that have been cleared from the body. Salivary secretion of the hormone *cortisol* provides a simple noninvasive source of hormone for monitoring chronic stress. Drugs and alcohol excreted into breast milk are important because a breast-feeding infant will ingest these substances. Hair analysis can be used to test for arsenic in the body, and the 1960s analysis of Napoleon Bonaparte's hair showed significant concentrations of the poison. (The question remains whether Napoleon was murdered, accidentally poisoned, or died from stomach cancer.)

The lungs clear volatile lipid-soluble materials from the blood when these substances pass into the airways and are expelled during breathing. One everyday example of lung clearance is "garlic breath." Ethanol also is cleared by the lungs, and exhaled alcohol is the basis of the "breathalyzer" test used by law enforcement agencies.

Clearance is usually expressed as a volume of blood plasma *cleared* of substance *x* per unit of time. It therefore is only an indirect measure of the movement of substance *x*. A more direct measure is **mass flow**, defined as the rate of intake, production, or output of *x*:

$$\underset{(\text{amount } x/\text{min})}{\text{Mass flow}} = \underset{(\text{amount } x/\text{vol})}{\text{concentration}} \times \underset{(\text{vol/min})}{\text{volume flow}}$$

As an example, suppose a person is given an intravenous infusion of glucose solution that has a concentration of 50 grams of glucose per liter. If the infusion is given at a rate of 2 milliliters per minute, the mass flow of glucose into the body is:

$$50 \text{ g glucose}/1000 \text{ mL solution} \times 2 \text{ mL solution/min} = 0.1 \text{ g glucose/min}$$

Mass flow applies not only to the entry, production, and removal of substances but also to the movement of substances from one compartment in the body to another. Recall from Chapter 3 [p. 52] that we can divide the body into two major compartments: the extracellular fluid and the intracellular fluid. Materials entering the body pass transiently through an epithelium, then become part of the extracellular fluid. How a substance is distributed after that depends on whether or not it crosses the barrier of the cell membrane and enters the cells.

CONCEPT CHECK

1. If a person eats 12 milligrams of salt in a day and excretes 11 milligrams of it in the urine, what happened to the remaining 1 milligram?
2. Glucose is aerobically metabolized to CO_2 and water. Explain the effect of this glucose metabolism on mass balance in the body.

Answers: p. 172

Homeostasis Does Not Mean Equilibrium

When physiologists talk about homeostasis, they are often speaking of the stability of the body's *internal environment*—in other words, the stability of the extracellular fluid. One reason for this is that clinically we are able to monitor the composition of extracellular fluid by the simple act of withdrawing a blood sample and analyzing its fluid matrix, the plasma. It is much more difficult to follow what is taking place inside cells, although cells do maintain *cellular homeostasis*. However, although the composition of both body compartments is relative stable, individual solutes in the two compartments are not in equilibrium. Instead, the extracellular and intracellular fluid compartments usually exist in a state that might best be called a *dynamic disequilibrium*.

Water is essentially the only molecule that moves freely between most cells and the extracellular fluid. Because of this free movement of water, the extracellular and intracellular compartments can reach a state of **osmotic equilibrium** [*osmos*, push or thrust], in which the total amount of solute per volume of fluid is equal on the two sides of the cell membrane. At the same time, however, the body is in a state of **chemical disequilibrium,** in which the major solutes are more concentrated in one of the two body compartments than in the other (Figure 5-3 ■).

For example, sodium, chloride, and bicarbonate (HCO_3^-) ions are more concentrated in extracellular fluid than in intracellular fluid, whereas potassium ions are more concentrated inside the cell. Calcium (not shown in the figure) is more concentrated in the extracellular fluid than in the cytosol, although

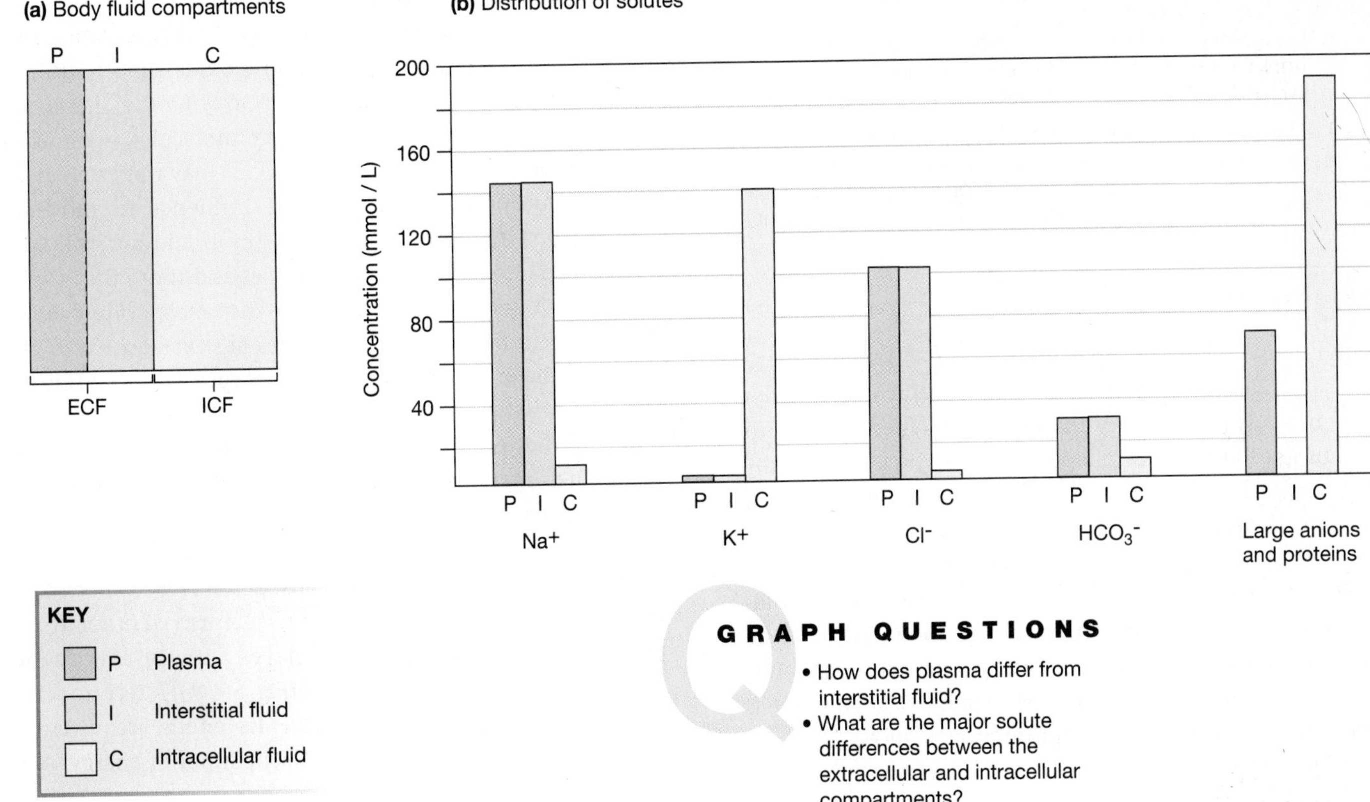

FIGURE 5-3 *Distribution of solutes in the body fluid compartments*

The extracellular fluid is composed of the blood plasma plus interstitial fluid. The compartments of the body are in a state of chemical disequilibrium.

many cells store Ca^{2+} inside organelles such as the endoplasmic reticulum and mitochondria.

Even the extracellular fluid is not at equilibrium between its two subcompartments [Fig. 3-2, p. 52]. A few solutes are more concentrated in the plasma than in the interstitial fluid. Figure 5-3 shows that proteins and other large anions are found both in intracellular fluid and in the plasma but are almost absent from the interstitial fluid.

The concentration differences of chemical disequilibrium are a hallmark of a living organism, as only the continual input of energy keeps the body in this state. If solutes leak across the cell membrane dividing the intracellular and extracellular compartments, energy is required to return them to the compartments they left. For example, K^+ that leak out of the cell and Na^+ that leak into the cell are returned to their original compartments by an energy-utilizing enzyme known as the Na^+-K^+-ATPase. When cells die and cannot use energy, they obey the second law of thermodynamics [p. 93] and return to a state of randomness that is marked by loss of chemical disequilibrium.

Many body solutes mentioned so far are ions, and therefore we must also consider the distribution of electrical charge between the intracellular and extracellular compartments. Although the body as a whole is electrically neutral, a few extra negative ions are found in the intracellular fluid, while their matching positive ions are located in the extracellular fluid. As a result, the inside of cells is slightly negative relative to the extracellular fluid. This electrical difference creates a state of **electrical disequilibrium** in the body, a topic discussed in more detail later in this chapter.

Thus, homeostasis is not the same as equilibrium. The intracellular and extracellular compartments of the body may be in osmotic equilibrium, but they are also in chemical and electrical disequilibrium. Furthermore, osmotic equilibrium and the two disequilibria are dynamic *steady states*. The modifier *dynamic* indicates that materials are constantly moving back and forth between the two compartments, but in a *steady state,* there is no *net* movement of materials between the compartments.

In the remainder of this chapter, we will discuss how the selective permeability of cell membranes is responsible for a body in which the intracellular and extracellular compartments are chemically and electrically different but have the same total concentration of solutes.

CONCEPT CHECK

3. Using what you learned about the naming conventions for enzymes [p. 99], explain what the name *Na^+-K^+-ATPase* tells you about this enzyme's actions.
4. The intracellular fluid can be distinguished from the extracellular fluid by the ICF's high concentration of ________ ion and low concentration of ________, ________, and ________ ions.

Answers: p. 172

DIFFUSION

Although many materials move freely within a body compartment, exchange between the intracellular and extracellular compartments is restricted by the cell membrane. Whether or not a substance enters a cell depends on the properties of the cell membrane and those of the substance. Cell membranes are **selectively permeable**; that is, the lipid and protein composition of a given cell membrane determines which molecules will enter the cell and which will leave [p. 55]. If a membrane allows a substance to pass through it, the membrane is said to be **permeable** to that substance [*permeare*, to pass through]. If a membrane does not allow a substance to pass, the membrane is said to be **impermeable** [*im-*, not] to that substance.

Membrane permeability is variable and can be changed by altering the proteins or lipids of the membrane. Some molecules, such as water, oxygen, carbon dioxide, and lipids, move easily across most cell membranes. On the other hand, ions, most polar molecules, and very large molecules (such as proteins), enter cells with more difficulty or may not enter at all.

Two properties of a molecule influence its movement across cell membranes: the size of the molecule and its lipid solubility [p. 24]. Very small molecules and those that are lipid soluble can cross directly through the phospholipid bilayer. Larger or less lipid-soluble molecules are excluded from crossing the bilayer unless the cell has a specific mechanism for transporting them across. For these molecules, membrane proteins are the usual mediators cells use to transport molecules across their membranes. Very large lipophobic molecules must enter and leave cells in vesicles [p. 66].

There are two ways to categorize how molecules move across membranes. One scheme, just described, separates movement according to physical requirements: whether it takes place through the phospholipid bilayer, with the aid of a membrane protein, or by using vesicles (Fig. 5-4). A second scheme classifies movement according to its energy requirements. **Passive transport** does not require the input of energy. **Active**

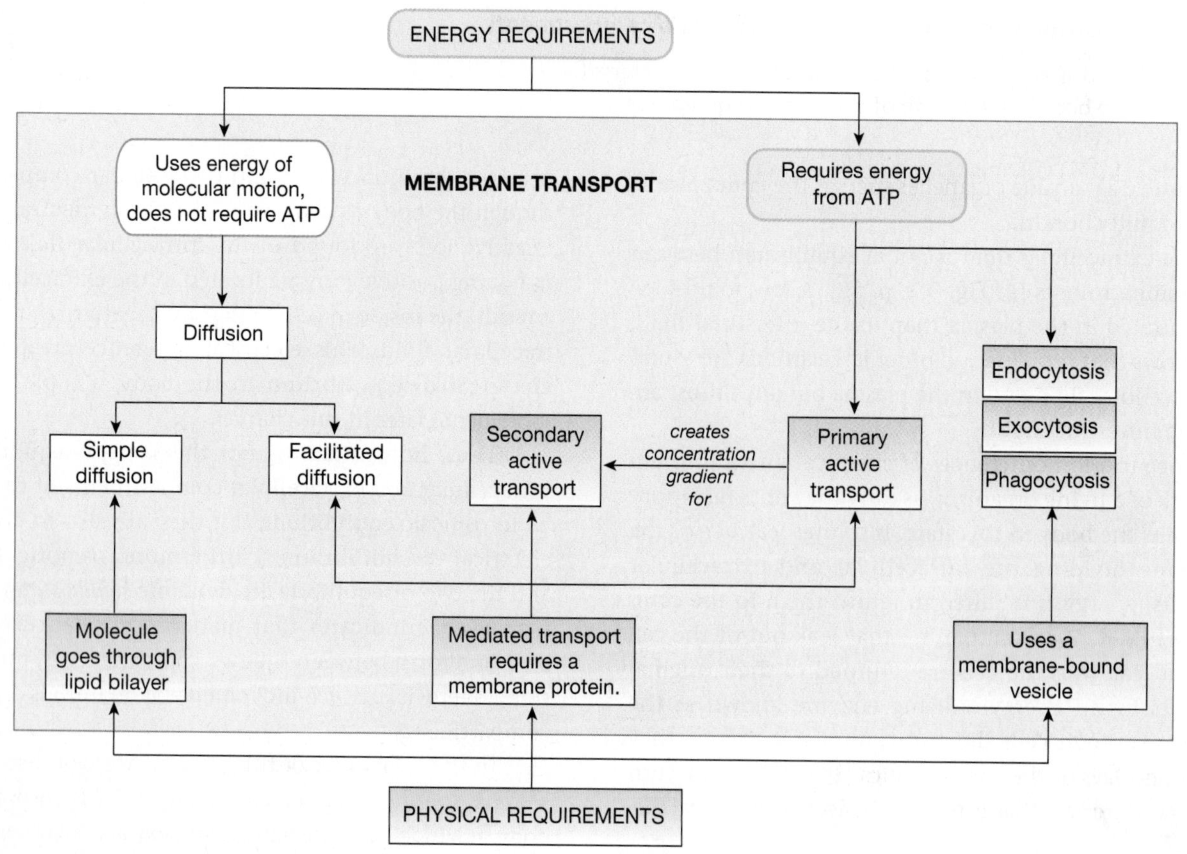

FIGURE 5-4 ***Map of membrane transport***

Movement of substances across cell membranes can be classified either by the energy requirements of transport (top part of map) or according to whether transport uses diffusion, a membrane protein, or a vesicle (bottom part of map).

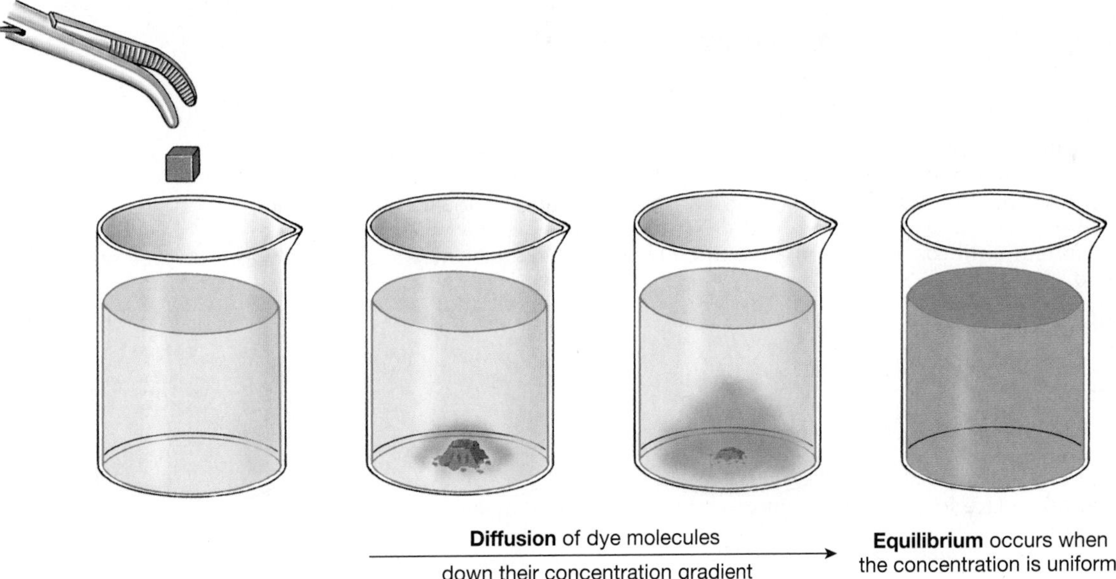
Diffusion of dye molecules
down their concentration gradient
Equilibrium occurs when the concentration is uniform.

■ **FIGURE 5-5** *Diffusion*

When a crystal of dye (such as potassium permanganate) is placed in water, the crystal dissolves, and dye molecules spread outward by diffusion.

transport requires the input of energy from some outside source, such as the high-energy phosphate bond of ATP.

Diffusion Uses Only the Energy of Molecular Movement

Passive transport across membranes uses the kinetic energy [p. 92] inherent in molecules. Gas molecules and molecules in solution constantly move from one place to another, bouncing off other molecules or off the sides of any container holding them. When molecules start out concentrated in one area of an enclosed space, their motion causes them to spread out gradually until they are evenly distributed throughout the available space. This process is known as diffusion.

Diffusion [*diffundere,* to pour out] may be defined as the movement of molecules from an area of higher concentration of the molecules to an area of lower concentration of the molecules.* If you leave a bottle of cologne open and later notice its fragrance across the room, it is because the aromatic molecules in the cologne have diffused from where they are more concentrated (in the bottle) to where they are less concentrated (across the room).

Diffusion has the following seven properties:

1. *Diffusion is a passive process.* By *passive,* we mean that diffusion does not require the input of energy from some outside source. Diffusion uses only the kinetic energy possessed by all molecules.
2. *Molecules move from an area of higher concentration to an area of lower concentration.* A difference in the concentration of a substance between two places is called a concentration gradient [p. 91], also known as a **chemical gradient**. We say that molecules diffuse *down the gradient,* from higher concentration to lower concentration (Fig. 5-5 ■). The rate of diffusion depends on the magnitude of the concentration gradient. The larger the concentration difference, the faster diffusion takes place. For example, when you open a bottle of ammonia, the rate of diffusion is most rapid as the ammonia molecules first escape from the bottle into the air. Later, when the ammonia has spread evenly throughout the room, the rate of diffusion has dropped to zero because there is no longer a concentration gradient.
3. *Net movement of molecules occurs until the concentration is equal everywhere.* Once molecules of a given substance have distributed themselves evenly, the system reaches equilibrium and diffusion stops. Individual molecules are still moving at equilibrium, but for each molecule that exits an area, another one enters. The *dynamic* equilibrium state in diffusion means that the concentration has equalized throughout the system but molecules continue to move.
4. *Diffusion is rapid over short distances but much slower over long distances.* Albert Einstein studied the diffusion of molecules in solution and found that the time required for a molecule to diffuse from point A to point B is proportional to the square of the distance from A to B. In other words, if the distance doubles from 1 to 2, the time needed for diffusion increases from 1^2 to 2^2.

*Some texts use the term *diffusion* to mean any random movement of molecules. These texts call molecular movement along a concentration gradient *net diffusion*. To simplify matters, we will use the term *diffusion* to mean movement down a concentration gradient.

TABLE 5-1 Rules for Diffusion of Uncharged Molecules

General Properties of Diffusion

1. Diffusion uses the kinetic energy of molecular movement and does not require an outside energy source.
2. Molecules diffuse from an area of higher concentration to an area of lower concentration.
3. Diffusion continues until concentrations come to equilibrium. Molecular movement continues, however, after equilibrium has been reached.
4. Diffusion is faster
   - with higher concentration gradients.
   - over shorter distances.
   - at higher temperatures.
   - for smaller molecules.
5. Diffusion can take place in an open system or across a partition that separates two systems.

Simple Diffusion Across a Membrane

6. The rate of diffusion through a membrane is faster if
   - the membrane's surface area is larger.
   - the membrane is thinner.
   - the concentration gradient is larger.
   - the membrane is more permeable to the molecule.
7. Membrane permeability to a molecule depends on
   - the molecule's lipid solubility.
   - the molecule's size.
   - the lipid composition of the membrane.

What does the slow rate of diffusion over long distances mean for biological systems? In humans, nutrients take five seconds to diffuse from the blood to a cell that is 100 μm from the nearest capillary. At that rate, it would take years for nutrients to diffuse from the small intestine to cells in the big toe, and the cells would starve to death. To overcome the limitations of diffusion over distance, organisms have developed various transport mechanisms that speed up the movement of molecules. Most multicellular organisms have some form of circulatory system to bring oxygen and nutrients rapidly from the point at which they enter the body to the cells.

5. *Diffusion is directly related to temperature.* At higher temperatures, molecules move faster. Because diffusion is a result of molecular movement, the rate of diffusion increases as temperature increases. Generally, changes in temperature do not significantly affect diffusion rates in humans because we maintain a relatively constant body temperature.
6. *Diffusion rate is inversely related to molecular size.* Einstein showed that friction between the surface of a particle and the medium through which it diffuses is a source of resistance to movement. He calculated that diffusion is inversely proportional to the radius of the molecule: the larger the molecule, the slower its diffusion through a given medium.
7. *Diffusion can take place in an open system or across a partition that separates two systems.* Diffusion of ammonia or cologne within a room is an example of diffusion taking place in an open system. There are no barriers to molecular movement, and the molecules spread out to fill the entire system. Diffusion can also take place between two systems, such as the intracellular and extracellular compartments, but only if the partition dividing the two compartments allows the diffusing molecules to cross.

For example, if you close the top of an open bottle of ammonia, the ammonia molecules cannot diffuse out into the room because neither the bottle nor the cap is permeable to the ammonia. However, if you replace the metal cap with a plastic bag that has tiny holes in it, you will begin to smell the ammonia in the room because the bag is permeable to the ammonia. Similarly, if a cell membrane is permeable to a molecule, that molecule can enter or leave the cell by diffusion. If the membrane is not permeable to that particular molecule, the molecule cannot cross. Table 5-1 ■ summarizes these points.

An important point to note: ions do not move by diffusion, even though you will read and hear about ions *diffusing across membranes*. Diffusion is random molecular motion down a *concentration* gradient. Ion movement is influenced by *electrical* gradients because of the attraction of opposite charges and repulsion of like charges. Thus, ions move in response to combined electrical and concentration gradients, or *electrochemical gradients*. This electrochemical movement is a more complex process than diffusion resulting solely from a concentration gradient, and the two processes should not be confused. Ions and electrochemical gradients will be discussed in more detail at the end of this chapter.

In summary, diffusion is the passive movement of uncharged molecules down their concentration gradient due to random molecular movement. Diffusion is slower over long distances and slower for large molecules. When the concentration of the diffusing molecules is the same throughout a system, the system has come to chemical equilibrium, although the random movement of molecules continues.

CONCEPT CHECK

5. If the distance over which a molecule must diffuse doubles from 1 to 2, diffusion takes how many times as long? Answers: p. 172

Lipophilic Molecules Can Diffuse Through the Phospholipid Bilayer

Diffusion across membranes is a little more complicated than diffusion in an open system. Water is the primary solvent of the body, and many vital nutrients, ions, and other molecules dissolve in water because of its polar nature. However, substances that are hydrophilic and dissolve in water are lipo*phobic* as a rule: they do not readily dissolve in lipids. For this reason, the hydrophobic lipid core of the cell membrane acts as a barrier that prevents hydrophilic molecules from crossing.

Substances that can pass through the lipid center of a membrane move by diffusion. Diffusion directly across the phospholipid bilayer of a membrane is called **simple diffusion** and has the following properties in addition to the properties of diffusion listed earlier.

1. *The rate of diffusion depends on the ability of the diffusing molecule to dissolve in the lipid layer of the membrane.* Another way to say this is that the diffusion rate depends on how permeable the membrane is to the diffusing molecules. Most molecules in solution can mingle with the polar phosphate-glycerol heads of the bilayer, but only nonpolar molecules that are lipid-soluble (lipophilic) can traverse the central lipid core of the membrane. As a rule, only lipids, steroids, and small lipophilic molecules can move across the membrane by simple diffusion.

   One important exception to this statement concerns water. Water, although a polar molecule, may diffuse slowly across some phospholipid membranes. For years it was thought that the polar nature of the water molecule prevented it from moving through the lipid center of the bilayer, but experiments done with artificial membranes have shown that the small size of the water molecule allows it to slip between the lipid tails in some membranes. How readily water passes through the membrane depends on the composition of the phospholipid bilayer. Membranes with a high cholesterol content are less permeable to water than those with a low cholesterol content, presumably because the cholesterol molecules fill the spaces between the fatty acid tails of the lipid bilayer and thus exclude water. For example, the cell membranes of some sections of the kidney are essentially impermeable to water unless the cells insert special water channel proteins into the phospholipid bilayer.
2. *The rate of diffusion across a membrane is directly proportional to the surface area of the membrane.* In other words, the larger the membrane's surface area, the more molecules can diffuse across per unit time. This fact may seem obvious, but it has important implications in physiology. One striking example of how a change in surface area affects diffusion is the lung disease emphysema. As lung tissue is destroyed, the surface area available for diffusion of oxygen decreases. Consequently, less oxygen can move into the body. In severe cases, the oxygen that reaches the cells is not enough to sustain any muscular activity and the patient is confined to bed.
3. *The rate of diffusion across a membrane is inversely proportional to the thickness of the membrane.* The thicker the membrane, the slower the rate at which diffusion takes place. For most biological membranes, thickness is essentially constant. However, diffusion distance comes into play in certain lung conditions in which the exchange epithelium of the lung is thickened with scar tissue. This slows diffusion so that the oxygen entering the body is not adequate to meet metabolic needs.

The rules for simple diffusion across membranes are summarized in Table 5-1. They can be combined mathematically into an equation known as **Fick's law of diffusion**, a relationship that involves the three factors just mentioned for membrane diffusion plus the factor of concentration gradient from our earlier general discussion of diffusion. In an abbreviated form, Fick's law says that:

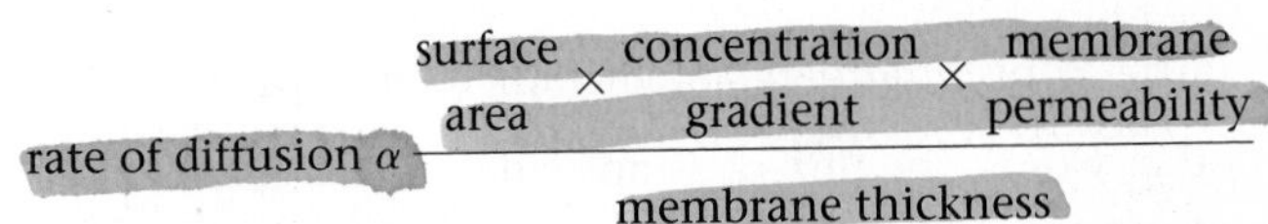

$$\text{rate of diffusion} \propto \frac{\text{surface area} \times \text{concentration gradient} \times \text{membrane permeability}}{\text{membrane thickness}}$$

Figure 5-6 ■ illustrates the principles of Fick's law.

Membrane permeability is the most complex of the four terms in Fick's law because several factors influence it: (1) the size of the diffusing molecule, (2) the lipid-solubility of the molecule, and (3) the composition of the lipid bilayer across

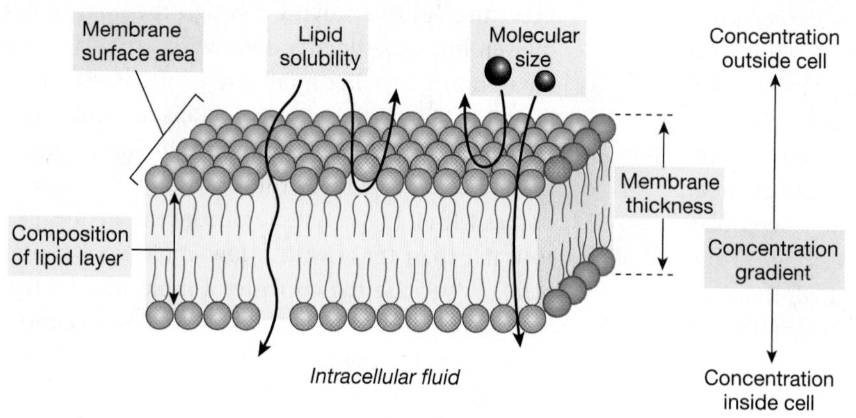

Factors affecting rate of diffusion through a cell membrane:

- Lipid solubility
- Molecular size
- Cell membrane thickness
- Concentration gradient
- Membrane surface area
- Composition of lipid layer

Fick's Law of Diffusion says:

$$\textbf{Rate of diffusion} \propto \frac{\text{surface area} \times \text{concentration gradient} \times \text{membrane permeability}}{\text{membrane thickness}}$$

Membrane permeability

$$\text{Membrane permeability} \propto \frac{\text{lipid solubility}}{\text{molecular size}}$$

Changing the composition of the lipid layer can increase or decrease membrane permeability.

FIGURE 5-6 ***Fick's law of diffusion***

This law mathematically relates factors that influence the rate of simple diffusion across a membrane.

which it is diffusing. As molecular size increases, membrane permeability decreases. As lipid solubility of the diffusing molecule increases, membrane permeability to the molecule increases. Alterations in lipid composition of the membrane change how easily diffusing molecules can slip between the individual phospholipids. For example, cholesterol molecules in membranes pack themselves into the spaces between the fatty acids tails and retard passage of molecules through those spaces [Fig. 3-4, p. 54], making the membrane less permeable.

In most physiological situations, membrane thickness is a constant. In that case, we can remove membrane thickness from our Fick's law equation and rearrange the equation to read:

$$\frac{\text{diffusion rate}}{\text{surface area}} = \frac{\text{concentration}}{\text{gradient}} \times \frac{\text{membrane}}{\text{permeability}}$$

This equation now describes the flux of a molecule across the membrane, because **flux** is defined as the diffusion rate per unit surface area of membrane:

$$\text{flux} = \text{concentration gradient} \times \text{membrane permeability}$$

In other words, the flux of a molecule across a membrane depends on the concentration gradient and the membrane's permeability to the molecule.

One point to remember is that the principles of diffusion just discussed apply to all biological membranes, not just to the cell membrane. Movement of materials in and out of organelles follows the same rules.

CONCEPT CHECK

6. Where does the energy for diffusion come from?
7. Which is more likely to cross a cell membrane by simple diffusion: a fatty acid molecule or a glucose molecule?
8. What happens to the rate of diffusion in each of the following cases?
   (a) membrane thickness increases
   (b) concentration gradient increases
   (c) surface area decreases
9. Two compartments are separated by a membrane that is permeable only to water and to yellow dye molecules. Compartment A is filled with an aqueous solution of yellow dye, and compartment B is filled with an aqueous solution of an equal concentration of blue dye. If the system is left undisturbed for a long time, what color will compartment A be: yellow, blue, or green? (Remember, yellow plus blue makes green.) What color will compartment B be?
10. What keeps atmospheric oxygen from diffusing into our bodies across the skin? (*Hint:* what kind of epithelium is skin?)

Answers: p. 172

PROTEIN-MEDIATED TRANSPORT

In the body, simple diffusion across membranes is limited to lipophilic molecules. The majority of molecules in the body are either lipophobic or electrically charged and therefore cannot

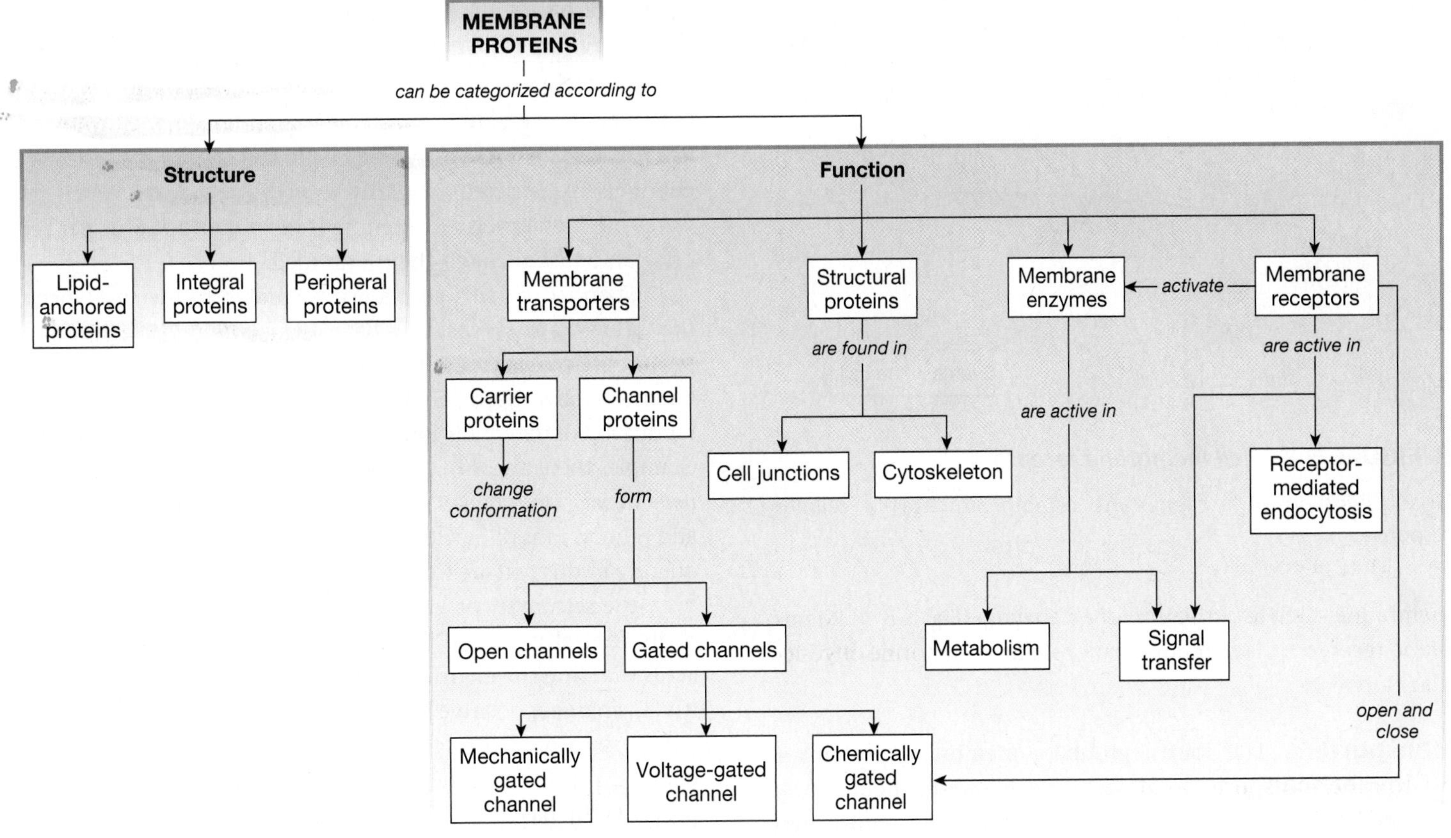

■ **FIGURE 5-7** ***Map of membrane proteins***

Functional categories of membrane proteins include transporters, structural proteins, enzymes, and receptors.

cross membranes by simple diffusion. The vast majority of solutes cross membranes with the help of membrane proteins, a process we call **mediated transport**.

If mediated transport is passive and moves molecules down their concentration gradient, and if net transport stops when concentrations are equal on both sides of the membrane, the process is known as **facilitated diffusion**. If protein-mediated transport requires energy from ATP or another outside source and moves a substance against its concentration gradient, the process is known as **active transport**.

Membrane Proteins Function as Structural Proteins, Enzymes, Receptors, and Transporters

Protein-mediated transport across a membrane is carried out by two groups of membrane-spanning proteins: transporters and receptors. For physiologists, classifying membrane proteins by their function is more useful than classifying them by their structure. Our functional classification scheme recognizes four types of membrane proteins: (1) structural proteins, (2) enzymes, (3) receptors, and (4) transporters. Figure 5-7■ is a map comparing the structural and functional classifications of membrane proteins.

Structural Proteins The **structural proteins** have three major roles. The first is to connect the membrane to the cytoskeleton to maintain the shape of the cell. The microvilli of transporting epithelia [p. 73] are one example of membrane shaping by the cytoskeleton. The second role is to create cell junctions that hold tissues together, such as tight junctions and gap junctions [Fig. 3-21, p. 70]. Finally, the third role is to attach cells to the extracellular matrix by linking cytoskeleton fibers to extracellular collagen and other protein fibers [p. 69].

Enzymes **Membrane enzymes** catalyze chemical reactions that take place either on the cell's external surface or just inside the cell. For example, enzymes on the external surface of cells lining the small intestine are responsible for digesting peptides and carbohydrates. Enzymes attached to the intracellular surface of many cell membranes play an important role in transferring signals from the extracellular environment to the cytoplasm, as you will learn in Chapter 6.

Receptors **Membrane receptor proteins** are part of the body's chemical signaling system. The binding of a receptor with its ligand usually triggers another event at the

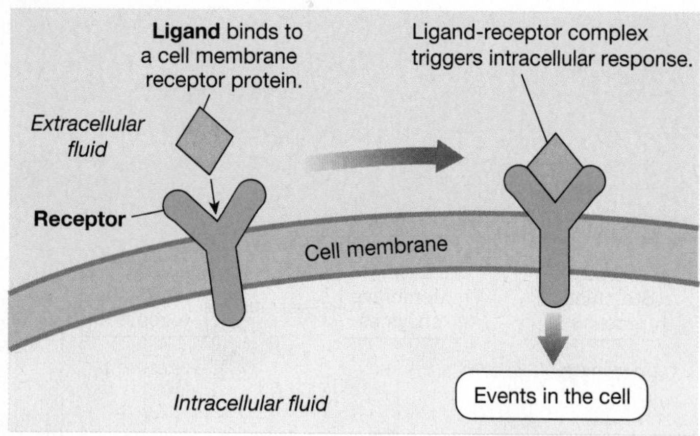
Ligand binds to a cell membrane receptor protein.
Ligand-receptor complex triggers intracellular response.
Extracellular fluid
Receptor
Cell membrane
Intracellular fluid
Events in the cell

■ **FIGURE 5-8** ***Cell membrane receptors***

Ligand binding to a membrane receptor initiates a cellular response.

membrane, such as activation of an enzyme (Fig. 5-8 ■). Membrane receptors play an important role in some forms of vesicular transport.

Transporters The fourth group of membrane proteins—**membrane transporters**—move molecules across membranes. We can further subdivide transporter proteins into two categories: channels and carriers. **Channel proteins** create water-filled passageways that directly link the intracellular and extracellular compartments (Fig. 5-9a ■). **Carrier proteins** bind to the substrates that they carry but never form a direct connection between the intracellular fluid and extracellular fluid. As Figure 5-9b shows, carriers are open to one side of the membrane or the other, but not to both at once the way channel proteins are.

Why do cells need both channels and carriers? The answer lies in the different properties of the two transporters. Channel proteins allow more rapid transport across the membrane but are not as selective about what they transport. Carriers, while slower, are better at discriminating between closely related molecules. Carriers can also move larger molecules than channels can.

Channel Proteins Form Open, Water-Filled Passageways

Channel proteins are made of membrane-spanning protein subunits that create a cluster of cylinders that surround a narrow, water-filled pore (Fig. 5-10 ■). Movement through channels is restricted primarily to water and ions. When the water-filled channels are open, tens of millions of ions per second can whisk through them unimpeded.

Channel proteins are named according to the substance(s) they allow to pass. Most cells have **water channels** made from a protein called *aquaporin*. In addition, more than 100 types of **ion channels** have been identified. Ion channels may be specific for one ion or may allow ions of similar size and charge to pass. For example, there are Na^+ channels, K^+ channels, and nonspecific *monovalent* ("one charge") cation channels that transport Na^+, K^+, and lithium ions (Li^+). Other ion channels you will encounter frequently in this text are Ca^{2+} channels and Cl^- channels.

The selectivity of a channel is determined by the diameter of its central pore and by the electrical charge of the amino acids that line the channel. If the channel amino acids are positively charged, positive ions will be repelled and negative ions will pass through the channel. On the other hand, a cation channel must have a negative charge that attracts cations but prevents the passage of Cl^- or other anions.

Channel proteins are like narrow doorways into the cell. If the door is closed, nothing can go through. If the door is open, there is a continuous passage between the two rooms connected by the doorway. The open or closed state of a channel is determined by regions of the protein molecule that act like swinging "gates."

According to current models, many channel gates are part of the cytoplasmic side of the membrane protein (Fig. 5-11 ■). Such a gate can be envisioned as a ball on a chain that swings up and blocks the mouth of the channel. A few channels have a gate in the middle of the protein, and one type of channel in nerve cells has two different gates.

Channels can be classified according to whether their gates are usually open or usually closed. **Open channels** spend most of their time with their gate open, allowing ions to move back

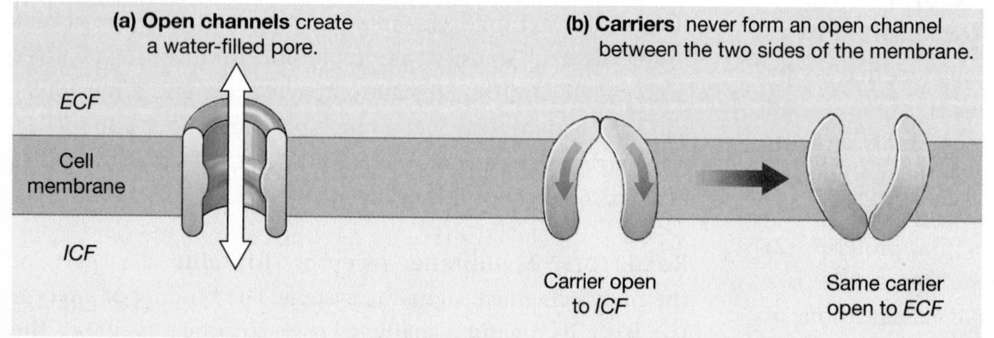
(a) Open channels create a water-filled pore.
(b) Carriers never form an open channel between the two sides of the membrane.
ECF
Cell membrane
ICF
Carrier open to ICF
Same carrier open to ECF

■ **FIGURE 5-9** ***Membrane transport proteins***

Many channels are made of multiple protein subunits that assemble in the membrane.

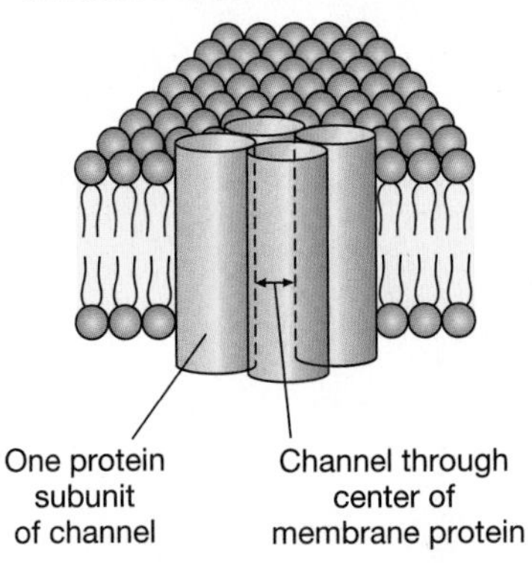

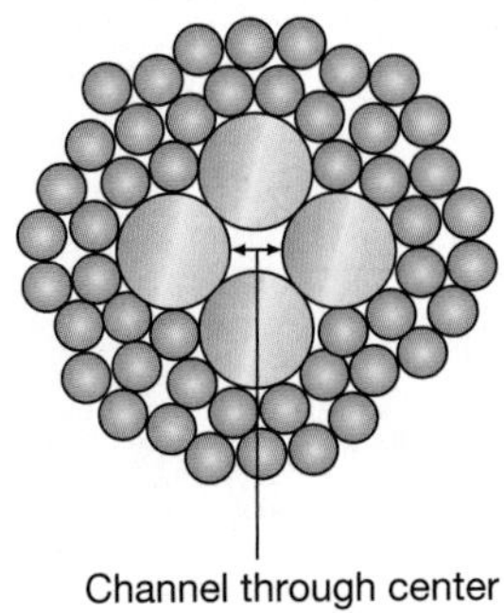

■ **FIGURE 5-10** ***Structure of channel proteins***

Hydrophilic amino acids in the protein line the channel, creating a water-filled passage that allows ions and very small molecules, such as water, to pass through.

and forth across the membrane without regulation. These gates may occasionally flicker closed, but for the most part these channels behave as if they have no gates. Open channels are sometimes called either *leak channels* or *pores,* as in *water pores.*

Gated channels spend most of their time in a closed state, which allows these channels to regulate the movement of ions through them. When a gated channel opens, ions move through the channel just as they move through open channels. When a gated channel is closed, which it may be much of the time, it allows no ion movement between the intracellular and extracellular fluid.

What controls the opening and closing of gated channels? The gating can be controlled by intracellular messenger molecules or extracellular ligands (**chemically gated channels**), by the electrical state of the cell (**voltage-gated channels**), or by a physical change, such as increased temperature or a force that puts tension on the membrane and pops the channel open (**mechanically gated channels**). You will encounter many variations of these channel types as you study physiology.

Gated channels are usually closed. They open in response to chemical, mechanical, or electrical signals.

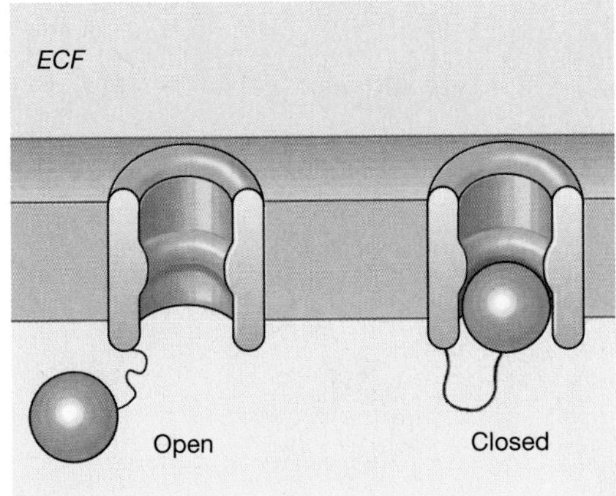

■ **FIGURE 5-11** ***Gating of channel proteins***

RUNNING PROBLEM

Cystic fibrosis is a debilitating disease caused by a defect in a gated channel protein that normally transports chloride ions (Cl^-). The channel protein—called the cystic fibrosis transmembrane conductance regulator, or CFTR—is located in epithelia lining the airways, sweat glands, and pancreas. The opening and closing of this channel are regulated through the binding of nucleotides to specific regions of the channel. In people with cystic fibrosis, the CFTR is nonfunctional or absent. As a result, chloride transport across the epithelium is impaired.

Question 1:

Is the CFTR a chemically gated, a voltage-gated, or a mechanically gated channel protein?

CONCEPT CHECK

11. Positively charged ions are called ________, and negatively charged ions are called ________.

Answers: p. 172

Carrier Proteins Change Conformation to Move Molecules

The second type of transport protein is the carrier protein. Carrier proteins bind with specific substrates and carry them across the membrane by changing conformation. Small organic molecules (such as glucose and amino acids), which are too large to pass through channels, cross membranes using carriers. Ions such as Na^+ and K^+ may move by carriers as well as through channels.

Some carrier proteins move only one kind of molecule and are known as **uniport carriers** (Fig. 5-12a ■). However, it is common to find carriers that move two or even three kinds of molecules. A carrier that moves more than one kind of molecule at one time is called a **cotransporter**. If the molecules being transported are moving in the same direction, whether into or out of the cell, the carrier proteins are **symport carriers** [*sym-,* together + *portare,* to carry]. If the molecules are being carried in opposite directions, the carrier proteins are **antiport carriers** [*anti,* opposite + *portare,* to carry]. Symport and antiport carriers are shown in Figure 5-12b and c.

Carriers are large, complex proteins with multiple subunits. The conformation change required of a carrier protein makes this mode of transmembrane transport much slower than movement

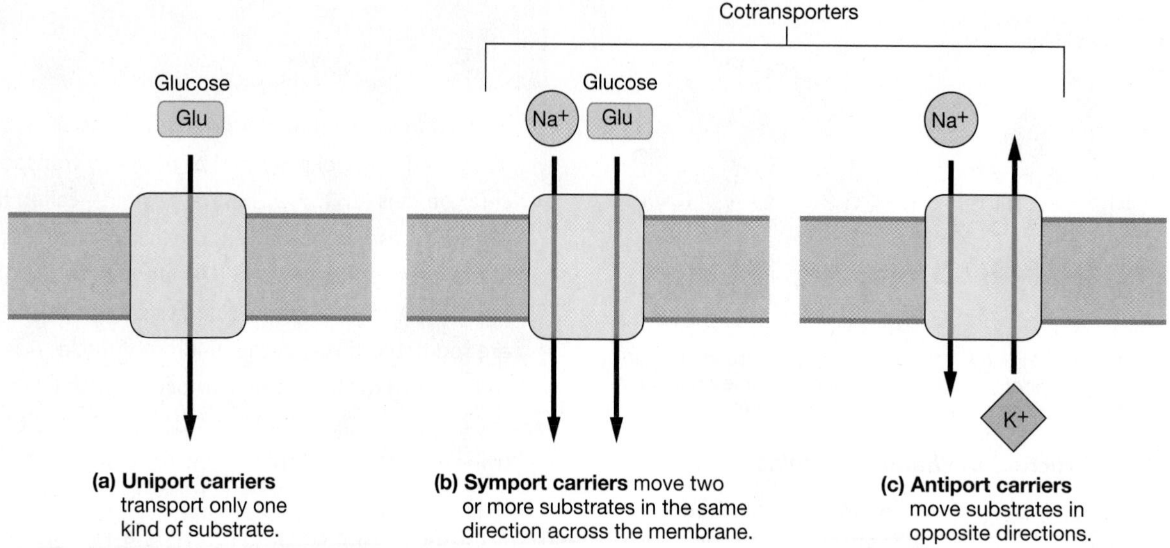

FIGURE 5-12 ***Types of carrier-mediated transport***

In the illustrations for this book, carrier proteins are represented by solid shapes in the cell membrane.

through channel proteins. Only 1000 to 1,000,000 molecules per second can be moved by a carrier protein, whereas tens of millions of ions per second move through a channel protein.

Carrier proteins differ from channel proteins in another way: carriers never create a continuous passage between the inside and outside of the cell. If channels are like doorways, then carriers are like revolving doors that allow movement between inside and outside without ever creating an open hole. Carrier proteins can transport molecules across a membrane in both directions, like a revolving door at a hotel, or they can restrict their transport to one direction, like the turnstile at an amusement park that allows you out of the park but not back in.

Carriers form passageways, but these openings are never open to both sides at the same time. One side is always closed, preventing free exchange across the membrane. In this respect, carrier proteins are like the Panama Canal (Fig. 5-13a ■). Picture

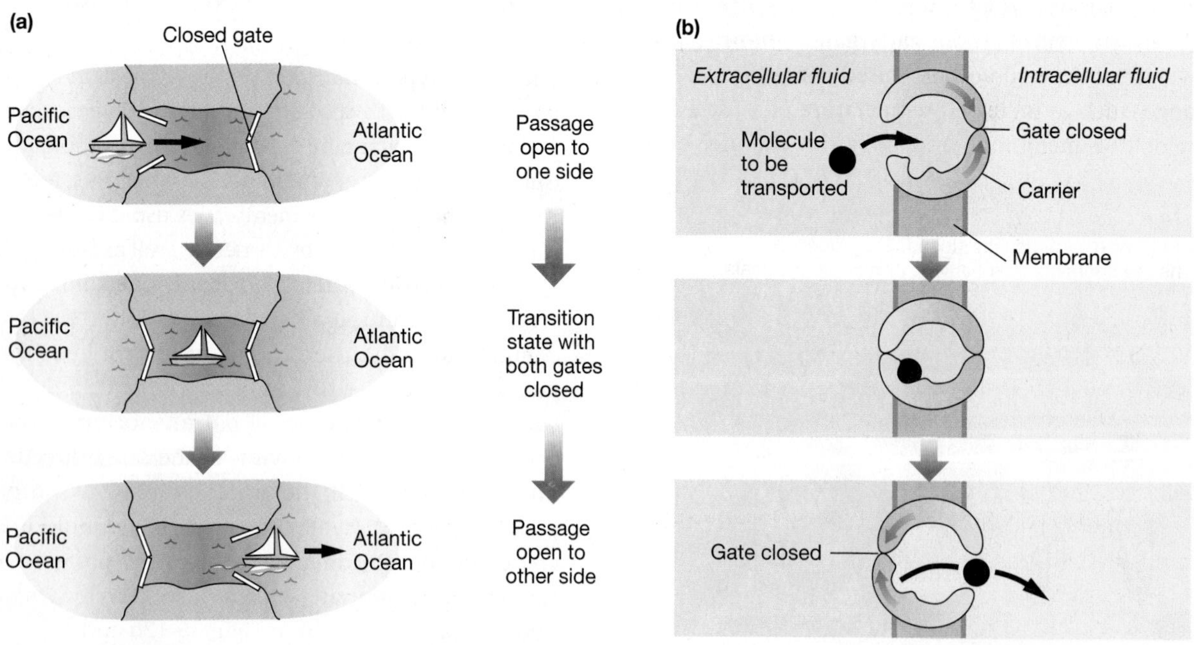

FIGURE 5-13 ***Facilitated diffusion by means of a carrier protein***

Carrier proteins, like the canal illustrated, never form a continuous passageway between the extracellular and intracellular fluids.

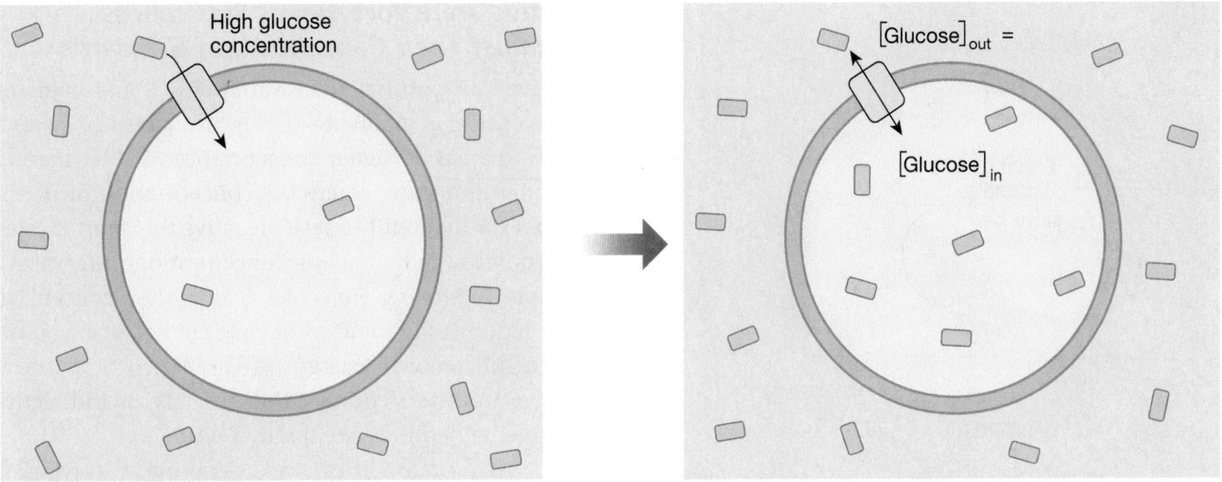

Facilitated diffusion brings glucose into the cell down its concentration gradient.

Diffusion reaches equilibrium when the glucose concentrations inside and outside the cell are equal.

■ **FIGURE 5-14** ***Net movement of molecules stops when facilitated diffusion reaches equilibrium***

This figure shows glucose transport using a GLUT carrier protein.

the canal with only two gates, one on the Atlantic side and one on the Pacific side. Only one gate at a time is open. When the Atlantic gate is closed, the canal opens into the Pacific. A ship enters the canal from the Pacific, and the gate closes behind it. Now the canal is isolated from both oceans with the ship trapped in the middle. Then the Atlantic gate opens, making the canal continuous with the Atlantic Ocean. The ship sails out of the gate and off into the Atlantic, having crossed the barrier of the land without the canal ever forming a continuous connection between the two oceans.

Movement across the membrane through a carrier protein is similar (Fig. 5-13b). The molecule to be transported binds to the carrier on one side of the membrane (the extracellular side in our example). This binding changes the conformation of the carrier so that the opening closes. After a brief transition in which both sides are closed, the opposite side of the carrier opens to the other side of the membrane. The carrier then releases the molecule being transported into the opposite compartment, having brought it through the membrane without creating a continuous connection between the extracellular and intracellular compartments.

CONCEPT CHECK

12. Name four functions of membrane proteins.
13. Which kinds of particles pass through open channels?
14. Name three ways channels differ from carriers.
15. If a channel is lined with amino acids that have a net positive charge, which of the following ions is/are likely to move freely through the channel? Na^+, Cl^-, K^+, Ca^{2+}.
16. Why doesn't glucose cross the cell membrane through open channels?

Answers: p. 172

Facilitated Diffusion Uses Carrier Proteins

As noted earlier, facilitated diffusion is protein-mediated transport in which no outside source of energy is needed to move molecules across the cell membrane, and active transport is protein-mediated transport that requires an outside energy source. Let us look first at facilitated diffusion.

Some polar molecules appear to move into and out of cells by diffusion, even though we know from their chemical properties that they are unable to pass easily through the lipid core of the cell membrane. The solution to this seeming contradiction is that these polar molecules cross the cell membrane by facilitated diffusion, with the aid of specific carriers. Sugars and amino acids are examples of molecules that enter or leave cells using facilitated diffusion. For example, a family of carrier proteins known as the GLUT transporters move glucose and related hexose sugars across membranes.

Facilitated diffusion has the same properties as simple diffusion (Table 5-1). The transported molecules move down their concentration gradient, the process requires no input of energy, and net movement stops at equilibrium, when the concentration inside the cell equals the concentration outside the cell (Fig. 5-14 ■):

$$[\text{glucose}]_{ECF} = [\text{glucose}]_{ICF}^*$$

Cells in which facilitated diffusion takes place can avoid reaching equilibrium by keeping the concentration of substrate in the cell low. With glucose, for example, this is accomplished by

*In this book the presence of brackets around a solute's name indicates concentration.

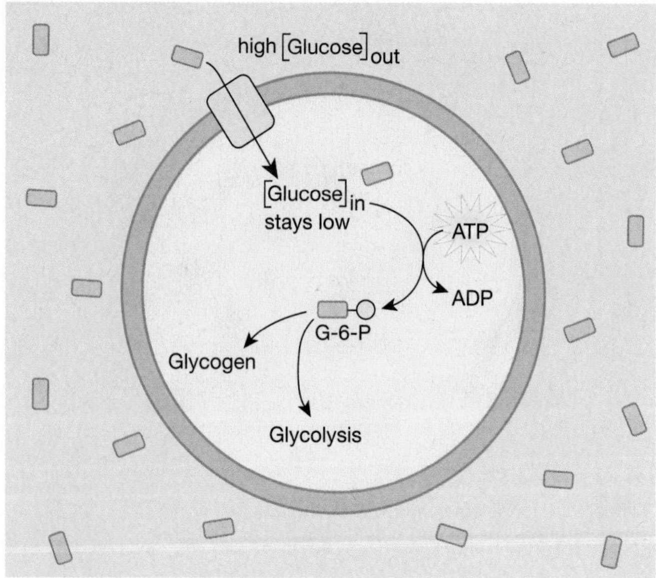

■ **FIGURE 5-15** ***Diffusion of glucose into cells***

In many cells facilitated diffusion of glucose does not reach equilibrium because the cell converts glucose to glucose 6-phosphate (G-6-P), keeping the intracellular glucose concentration low.

phosphorylation (Fig. 5-15■). As soon as a glucose molecule enters the cell, it is phosphorylated to glucose 6-phosphate, the first step of glycolysis [p. 104]. Addition of the phosphate group prevents build-up of glucose inside the cell and also prevents glucose from leaving the cell.

CONCEPT CHECK

17. Liver cells are able to convert glycogen to glucose, thereby making the intracellular glucose concentration higher than the extracellular glucose concentration. What do you think happens to facilitated diffusion of glucose when this occurs? Answers: p. 172

Active Transport Moves Substances Against Their Concentration Gradients

Active transport is a process that moves molecules *against* their concentration gradient—that is, from areas of lower concentration to areas of higher concentration. Rather than creating an equilibrium state, where the concentration of the molecule is equal throughout the system, active transport creates a state of *dis*equilibrium by making concentration differences more pronounced. Moving molecules against their concentration gradient requires the input of outside energy, just as pushing a ball up a hill requires energy [Fig. 4-2, p. 92]. The energy for active transport comes either directly or indirectly from the high-energy phosphate bond of ATP.

Active transport can be divided into two types. In **primary (direct) active transport**, the energy to push molecules against their concentration gradient comes directly from the high-energy phosphate bond of ATP. **Secondary (indirect) active transport** uses potential energy [p. 92] stored in the concentration gradient of one molecule to push other molecules against their concentration gradient. All secondary active transport ultimately depends on primary active transport because the concentration gradients that drive secondary transport are created using energy from ATP.

The mechanism for both types of active transport appears to be similar to that for facilitated diffusion. A substrate to be transported binds to a membrane carrier and the carrier then changes conformation, releasing the substrate into the opposite compartment. Active transport differs from facilitated diffusion because the conformation change in the carrier protein requires energy input.

Primary Active Transport Because primary active transport uses ATP as its energy source, many primary active transporters are known as **ATPases**. You may recall from Chapter 4 that the suffix *-ase* signifies an enzyme, and the stem (ATP) is the

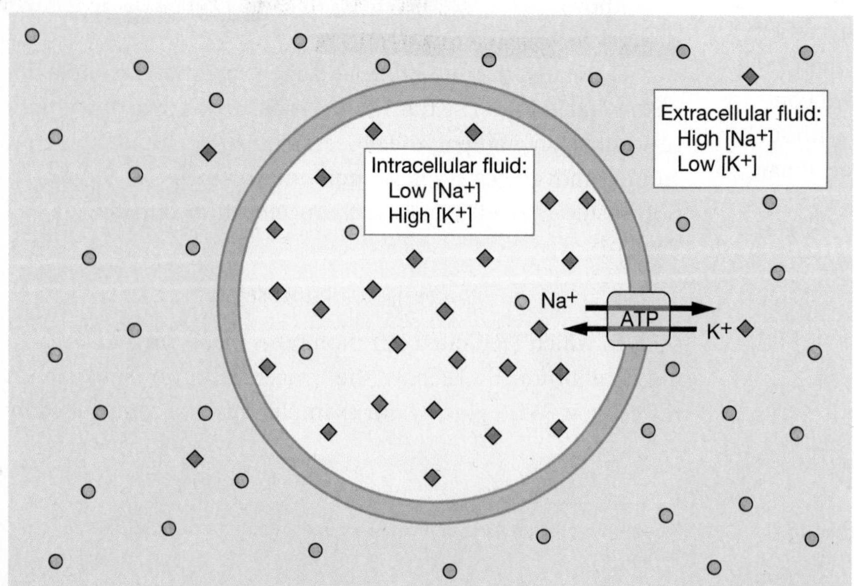

The Na^+-K^+-ATPase uses energy from ATP to pump Na^+ out of the cell and K^+ into the cell.

■ **FIGURE 5-16** ***The sodium-potassium pump, Na^+-K^+-ATPase***

In this book, carrier proteins that hydrolyze ATP have the letters *ATP* written on the membrane protein.

substrate upon which the enzyme is acting [p. 99]. These enzymes hydrolyze ATP to ADP and inorganic phosphate (P_i), releasing usable energy in the process. Most of the ATPases you will encounter in your study of physiology are listed in Table 5-2 ■. ATPases are sometimes called *pumps*, as in the sodium-potassium pump, Na^+-K^+-ATPase, mentioned earlier in this chapter.

The sodium-potassium pump is probably the single most important transport protein in animal cells because it maintains the concentration gradients of Na^+ and K^+ across the cell membrane (Fig. 5-16 ■). The transporter is arranged in the cell membrane so that it pumps 3 Na^+ out of the cell and 2 K^+ into the cell for each ATP consumed. In some cells, the energy needed to move these ions uses 30% of all the ATP produced by the cell. The current model of how the Na^+-K^+-ATPase works is illustrated in Figure 5-17 ■.

TABLE 5-2 Primary Active Transporters

NAMES	TYPE OF TRANSPORT
Na^+-K^+-ATPase or sodium-potassium pump	Antiport
Ca^{2+}-ATPase	Uniport
H^+-ATPase or proton pump	Uniport
H^+-K^+-ATPase	Antiport

5

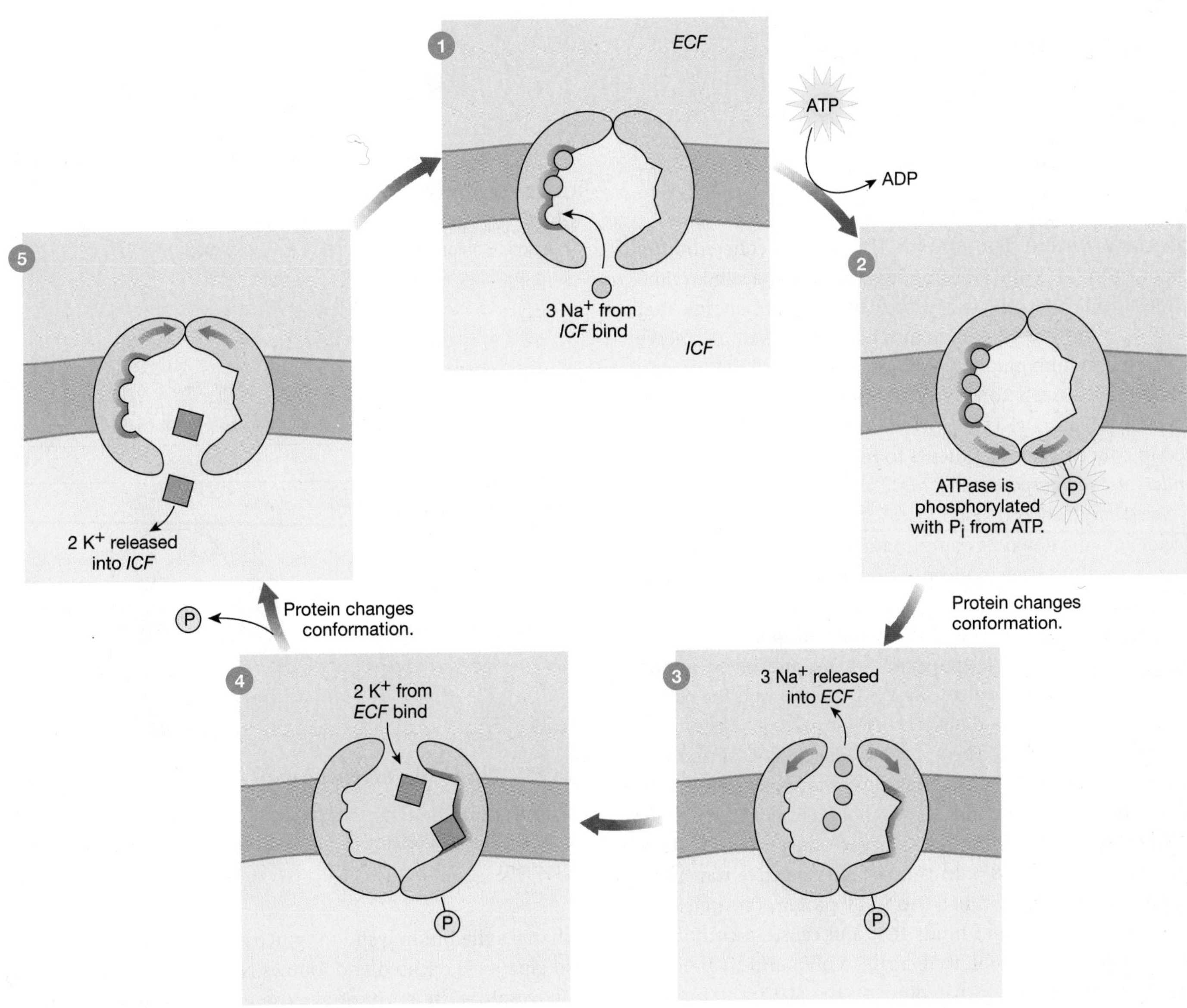

■ **FIGURE 5-17** ***Mechanism of the Na^+-K^+-ATPase***

This figure presents one model of how the Na^+-K^+-ATPase uses energy and inorganic phosphate from ATP to move ions across a membrane.

TABLE 5-3 Common Secondary Active Transporters

SYMPORT CARRIERS	ANTIPORT CARRIERS
Sodium-dependent transporters	
Na^+-glucose (SGLT)	Na^+-H^+
Na^+-amino acids (several types)	Na^+-Ca^{2+}
Na^+-K^+-2 Cl^- (NKCC)	
Na^+-bile salts (small intestine)	
Na^+-choline uptake (nerve cells)	
Na^+-neurotransmitter uptake (nerve cells)	
Nonsodium-dependent transporters	
	HCO_3^--Cl^-
	H^+-K^+

Secondary Active Transport The sodium concentration gradient, with Na^+ concentration high in the extracellular fluid and low inside the cell, is a source of potential energy that the cell can harness for other functions. For example, nerve cells use the sodium gradient to transmit electrical signals, and epithelial cells use it to drive the uptake of nutrients, ions, and water. Membrane transporters that use potential energy stored in concentration gradients to move molecules are called *secondary active transporters*.

Secondary active transport uses the kinetic energy of one molecule moving down its concentration gradient to push other molecules against their concentration gradient. The cotransported molecules may go in the same direction across the membrane (symport) or in opposite directions (antiport). The most common secondary active transport systems are driven by the sodium concentration gradient. As a Na^+ moves into the cell, it either brings one or more molecules with it or trades places with molecules exiting the cell. The major Na^+-dependent transporters are listed in Table 5-3■. Notice that the cotransported molecules may be either other ions or uncharged molecules, such as glucose.

The mechanism of the Na^+-glucose transporter (SGLT) is illustrated in Figure 5-18■. In this secondary active transport, both Na^+ and glucose bind to the SGLT protein on the extracellular fluid side. Sodium binds first and causes a conformational change in the protein that creates a high-affinity binding site for glucose. When glucose binds to the SGLT, the protein changes conformation again and opens its channel to the intracellular fluid side. Sodium is released as it moves down its concentration gradient. The loss of Na^+ from the protein changes the binding site for glucose back to a low-affinity site, so glucose is released and follows Na^+ into the cytoplasm. The net result is the entry of glucose into the cell against its concentration gradient, coupled to the movement of Na^+ into the cell down its concentration gradient.

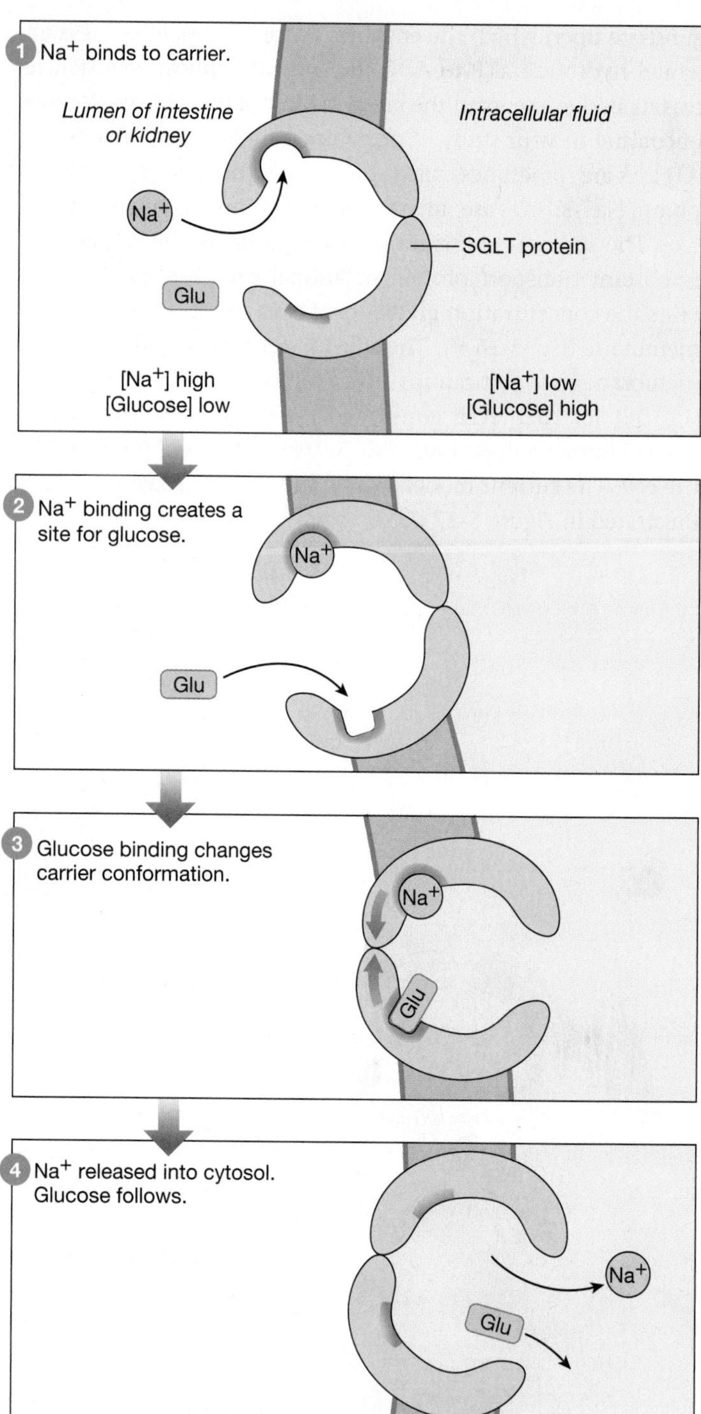
1 Na+ binds to carrier.
Lumen of intestine or kidney
Intracellular fluid
Na+
SGLT protein
Glu
[Na+] high
[Glucose] low
[Na+] low
[Glucose] high
2 Na+ binding creates a site for glucose.
Na+
Glu
3 Glucose binding changes carrier conformation.
Na+
Glu
4 Na+ released into cytosol. Glucose follows.
Na+
Glu

■ **FIGURE 5-18** ***Mechanism of the SGLT transporter***

This transporter uses the potential energy stored in the Na^+ concentration gradient to move glucose against its concentration gradient.

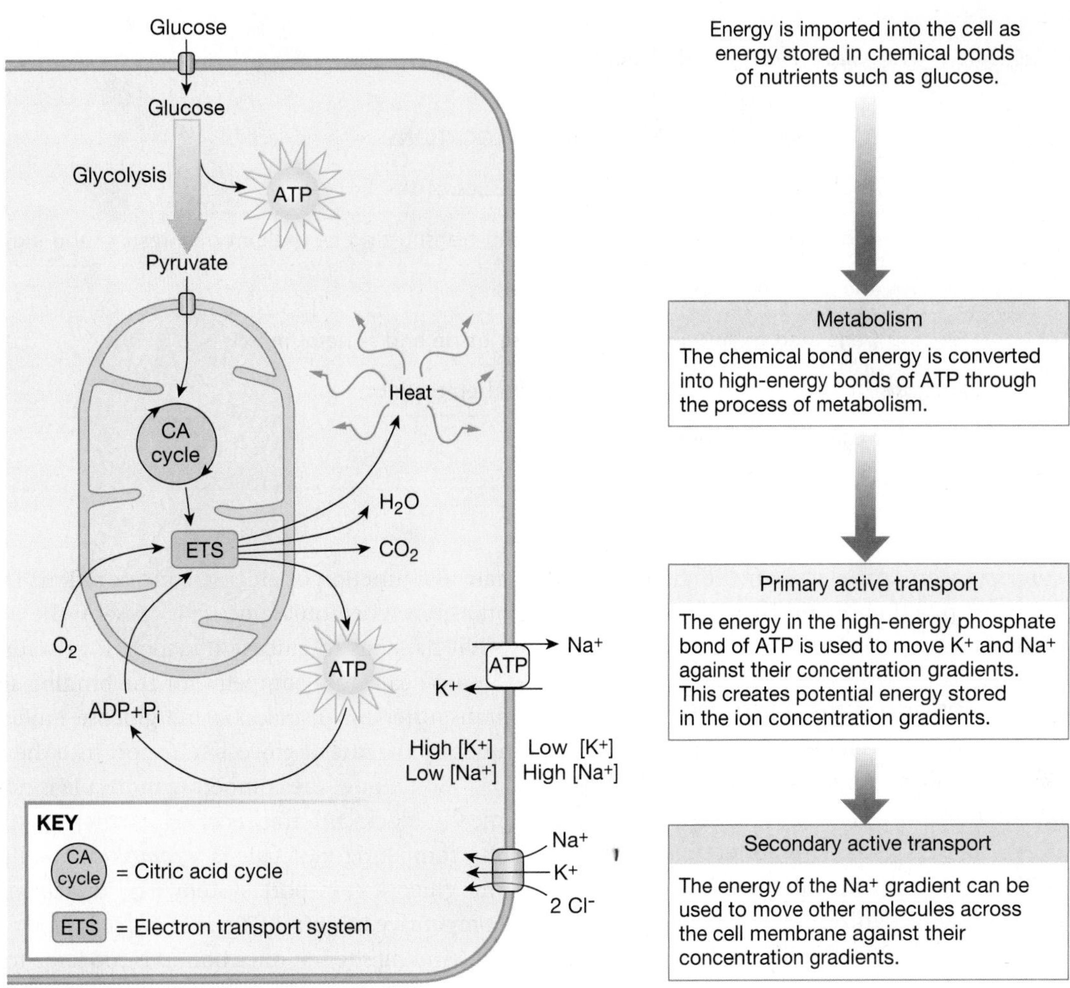

FIGURE 5-19 *Energy transfer in living cells*

Why does the body have both a facilitated diffusion GLUT carrier and a SGLT Na^+-glucose symporter? The simple answer is that GLUT carriers are found on all cells, but Na^+-glucose symporters are restricted to cells that are bringing glucose into the body from the external environment. GLUT transporters move glucose into or out of the cells depending on the concentration gradient. For example, when blood glucose levels are high, GLUT transporters on liver cells bring glucose into those cells. During times of fasting, when blood glucose levels fall, liver cells convert their glycogen stores to glucose. When the glucose concentration inside the liver cells builds up and exceeds the glucose concentration in the plasma, glucose leaves the cells on the reversible GLUT transporters. In contrast, the SGLT transporter can move substrate only into the cell because glucose must follow the Na^+ gradient. Consequently, SGLT transporters are found on epithelial cells that bring glucose into the body from the external environment.

The use of energy to drive active transport is summarized in Figure 5-19■. The organism imports energy from the environment in the chemical bonds of nutrients such as glucose. This energy is transferred to the high-energy bonds of ATP through oxidative phosphorylation in the mitochondria [p. 108]. The energy in ATP is then used either to fuel primary active transport or to create ion concentration gradients for secondary active transport. For example, the Na^+-K^+-ATPase pushes sodium out of the cell and potassium into it. As this happens, the energy from ATP is transformed into potential energy stored in the ion concentration gradients. This potential energy can be harnessed by various sodium-dependent cotransporters, such as the Na^+-K^+-$2Cl^-$ transporter (NKCC). The kinetic energy of Na^+ moving into the cell down its concentration gradient is linked to the uphill movement of K^+ and Cl^- into the cell. As you study the different systems of the body, you will find these secondary active transporters taking part in many physiological processes.

CONCEPT CHECK

18. Name two ways active transport by the Na^+-K^+-ATPase (Fig. 5-17) differs from secondary transport by the SGLT (Fig. 5-18). Answers: p. 172

Carrier-Mediated Transport Exhibits Specificity, Competition, and Saturation

Both passive and active forms of carrier-mediated transport demonstrate three properties: specificity, competition, and

TABLE 5-4: The GLUT Family* of Glucose Transporters

	SUBSTANCES TRANSPORTED	TISSUE LOCATIONS
GLUT1	Glucose and other hexoses	Most tissues of the body
GLUT2	Glucose and other hexoses	Liver and transporting epithelium of intestine and kidney
GLUT3	Glucose and other hexoses	Neurons
GLUT4	Glucose (regulated by insulin)	Adipose tissue and skeletal muscle
GLUT5	Fructose	Intestinal epithelium

*GLUT6 through GLUT12 remain under investigation.

saturation. These concepts were introduced in the discussion on protein interactions [p. 43] and reflect the binding of a substrate to the protein.

Specificity As noted in Chapter 2, specificity refers to the ability of a carrier to move only one molecule or only a group of closely related molecules. One example of specificity is found in the GLUT family of transporters, which move only six-carbon sugars (*hexoses*), such as glucose, mannose, galactose, and fructose [p. 27], across cell membranes. GLUT transporters have binding sites that recognize and transport hexoses, but they will not transport the disaccharide maltose or any form of glucose that is not normally found in nature. Thus we can say that GLUT transporters are specific for naturally occurring six-carbon monosaccharides.

For many years, scientists assumed that there must be different isoforms of the glucose carrier because they had observed that glucose transport was regulated by hormones in some cells but not in others. However, it was not until the 1980s that the first glucose transporter was isolated. To date, about 12 glucose facilitated diffusion carrier genes have been identified, and five GLUT proteins have been studied in detail (Table 5-4 ■). The proteins named GLUT6 through GLUT12 are still being investigated. The restriction of different GLUT transporters to different tissues is an important feature in the metabolism and homeostasis of glucose.

Competition The property of competition is closely related to specificity. A transporter may move several members of a related group of substrates, but those substrates will compete with one another for the binding sites on the transporter. For example, GLUT transporters move the family of hexose sugars, but each different GLUT transporter has a "preference" for one or more hexoses, based on its binding affinity.

The results of an experiment demonstrating competition are shown in Figure 5-20 ■. The graph shows glucose transport rate as a function of glucose concentration. The top line shows transport when only glucose is present; the bottom line shows what happens to glucose transport if galactose is also present. Because galactose competes for the binding sites on the GLUT transporters, it displaces some glucose molecules, and consequently the rate of glucose transport into the cell decreases.

Sometimes the competing molecule is not transported but merely blocks the transport of another substrate. In this case, the competing molecule is a *competitive inhibitor* [p. 41]. In the glucose transport system, the disaccharide maltose is a competitive inhibitor (Fig. 5-21 ■). It competes with glucose for the binding site but once bound is too large to be moved across the membrane.

Competition between transported substrates has been put to good use in medicine. An example involves gout, a disease caused by elevated levels of uric acid in the plasma. One method of decreasing plasma uric acid is to enhance its excretion in the

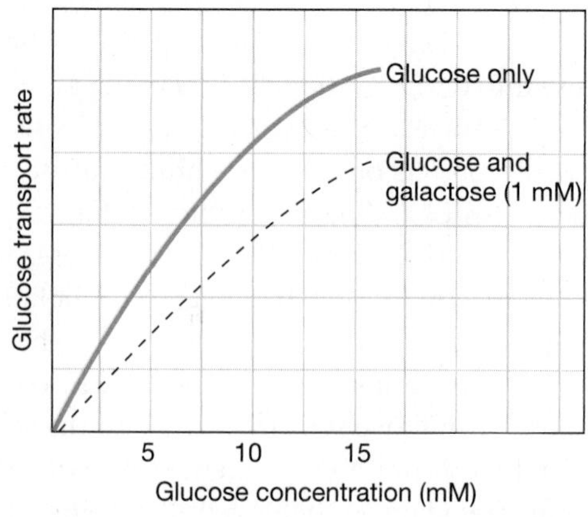

■ **FIGURE 5-20** ***Graph of transport competition***

This graph shows glucose transport rate as a function of glucose concentration. In one experiment, only glucose was present. In the second experiment a constant concentration of galactose was present.

(a)

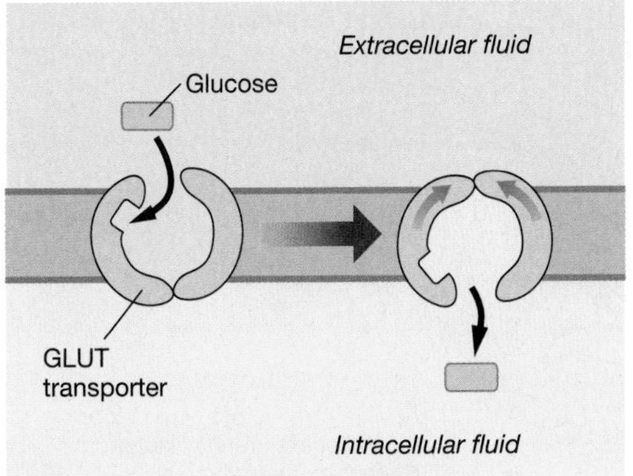

The **GLUT transporter** brings glucose across cell membranes.

(b)

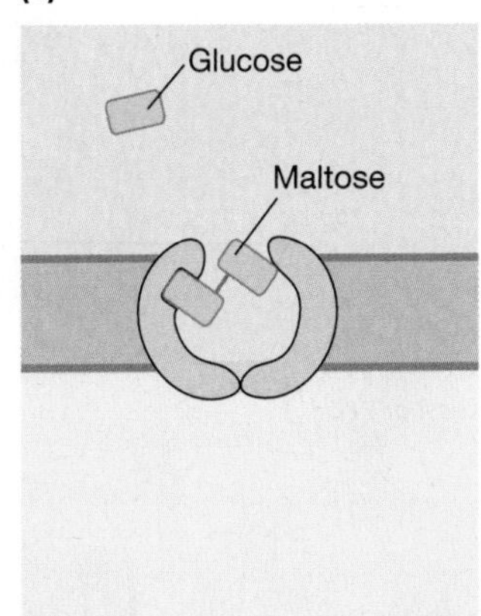

Maltose is a competitive inhibitor that binds to the GLUT transporter but is not itself carried across the membrane.

■ **FIGURE 5-21** ***Competitive inhibition of glucose transport***

The inhibitor in this case is the disaccharide maltose, a molecule much larger than glucose.

urine. Normally, the kidney's organic anion transporter (OAT) reclaims uric acid from the urine and returns the acid to the plasma. However, if an organic acid called probenecid is administered to the patient, the OAT binds to probenecid instead of to uric acid, preventing the reabsorption of uric acid. As a result, more uric acid leaves the body in the urine, lowering the uric acid concentration in the plasma.

Saturation The rate of substrate transport depends on both the substrate concentration and the number of carrier molecules, a property that is shared by enzymes [p. 98]. For a fixed number of carriers, however, as substrate concentration increases, the transport rate increases up to a maximum, the point at which all carrier binding sites are filled with substrate. At this point, the carriers are said to have reached saturation. At saturation, the carriers are working at their maximum rate, and a further increase in substrate concentration will have no effect. Figure 5-22 ■ shows saturation represented graphically.

For an analogy, think of the carriers as doors into a concert hall. Each door has a maximum number of people that it can allow to enter the hall in a given period of time. Suppose all the doors together can allow a maximum of 100 people per minute to enter the hall. This is the maximum transport rate, also called the **transport maximum**. When the concert hall is empty, three maintenance people enter the doors every hour. The transport rate is 3 people/60 minutes, or 0.05 people/minute, well under the maximum. For a local dance recital, about 50 people per minute go through the doors, still well under the maximum. When the most popular rock group of the day appears in concert, however, thousands of people gather outside. When the doors open, thousands of people are clamoring to get in, but the doors will allow only 100 people/minute into the hall. The doors are working at the maximum rate, so it does not matter whether there are 1000 or 3000 people trying to get in. The transport rate is saturated at 100 people/minute.

How can cells increase their transport capacity and avoid saturation? One way is to increase the number of carriers in the membrane. This would be like opening more doors into the concert hall. Under some circumstances, cells are able to insert additional carriers into their membranes. Under other circumstances, a cell may withdraw carriers to decrease movement of a molecule into or out of the cell.

All forms of carrier-mediated transport show specificity, competition, and saturation, but as we learned earlier in the chapter, they also differ in one important way: passive mediated transport—better known as facilitated diffusion—requires no input of energy from an outside source. Active transport requires energy input from ATP, either directly or indirectly.

GRAPH QUESTION

On the *x*-axis, mark the substrate concentration at which the carriers first become saturated.

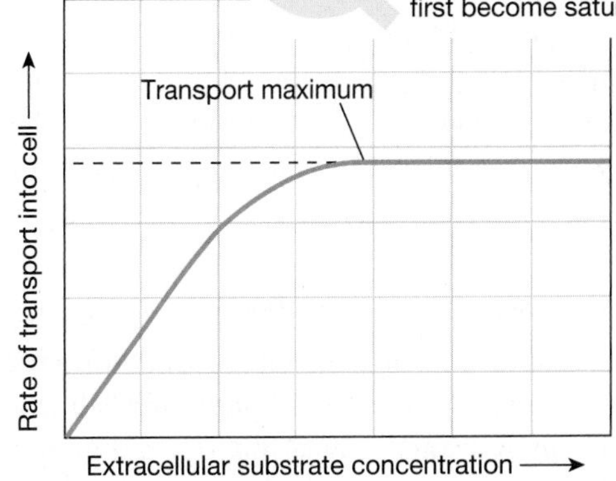

Transport rate is proportional to substrate concentration until the carriers are saturated.

■ **FIGURE 5-22** ***Graph showing saturation of carrier-mediated transport***

CONCEPT CHECK

19. What would you call a carrier that moves two substrates in opposite directions across a membrane?
20. In the concert-hall door analogy, we described how the maximum transport rate might be increased by increasing the number of doors leading into the hall. Using the same analogy, can you think of another way a cell might increase its maximum transport rate?

Answers: p. 172

VESICULAR TRANSPORT

What happens to the many macromolecules that are too large to enter or leave cells through protein channels or carriers? They move in and out of the cell with the aid of bubble-like vesicles created from the cell membrane. Cells use two basic mechanisms to import large molecules and particles: phagocytosis and endocytosis. Phagocytosis once was considered a type of endocytosis, but as scientists learned more about the mechanisms behind the two processes, they decided that phagocytosis was fundamentally different. Material leaves cells by the process known as exocytosis, a process that is similar to endocytosis run in reverse.

Phagocytosis Creates Vesicles Using the Cytoskeleton

If you studied *Amoeba* in your biology laboratory, you may have watched these one-cell creatures ingest their food by surrounding it and enclosing it within a vesicle that is brought into the cytoplasm. **Phagocytosis** [*phagein,* to eat + *cyte,* cell + *-sis,* process] is the actin-mediated process by which a cell engulfs a bacterium or other particle into a large membrane-bound vesicle called a **phagosome** [*soma,* body]. The phagosome pinches off from the cell membrane and moves to the interior of the cell, where it fuses with a lysosome [p. 66], whose digestive enzymes destroy the bacterium. Phagocytosis requires energy from ATP for the movement of the cytoskeleton and for the intracellular transport of the vesicles. In humans, phagocytosis occurs only in certain types of white blood cells called *phagocytes,* which specialize in "eating" bacteria and other foreign particles (Fig. 5-23 ■).

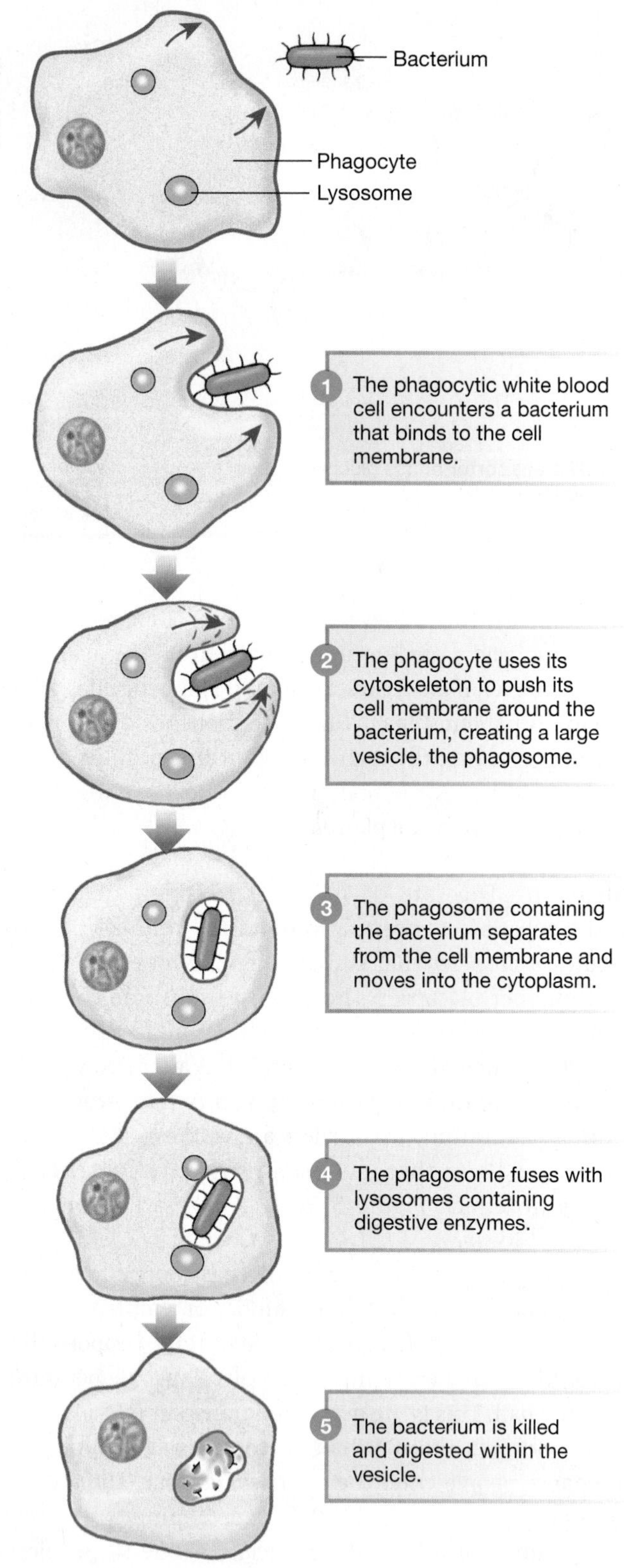

Bacterium
Phagocyte
Lysosome
1 The phagocytic white blood cell encounters a bacterium that binds to the cell membrane.
2 The phagocyte uses its cytoskeleton to push its cell membrane around the bacterium, creating a large vesicle, the phagosome.
3 The phagosome containing the bacterium separates from the cell membrane and moves into the cytoplasm.
4 The phagosome fuses with lysosomes containing digestive enzymes.
5 The bacterium is killed and digested within the vesicle.

■ **FIGURE 5-23** ***Phagocytosis***

Endocytosis Creates Smaller Vesicles

Endocytosis, the second pathway by which large molecules or particles move into cells, differs from phagocytosis in that in endocytosis, the membrane surface indents rather than pushes out, and the vesicles formed are much smaller. In addition, some endocytosis is *constitutive;* that is, it is an essential function that is always taking place. In contrast, phagocytosis must be triggered by the presence of a substance to be ingested.

Endocytosis is an active process that requires energy from ATP. It can be nonselective, allowing extracellular fluid to enter the cell—a process called **pinocytosis** [*pino-,* drink]—or it can be highly selective, allowing only specific molecules to enter the cell. Two types of endocytosis require a ligand to bind to a

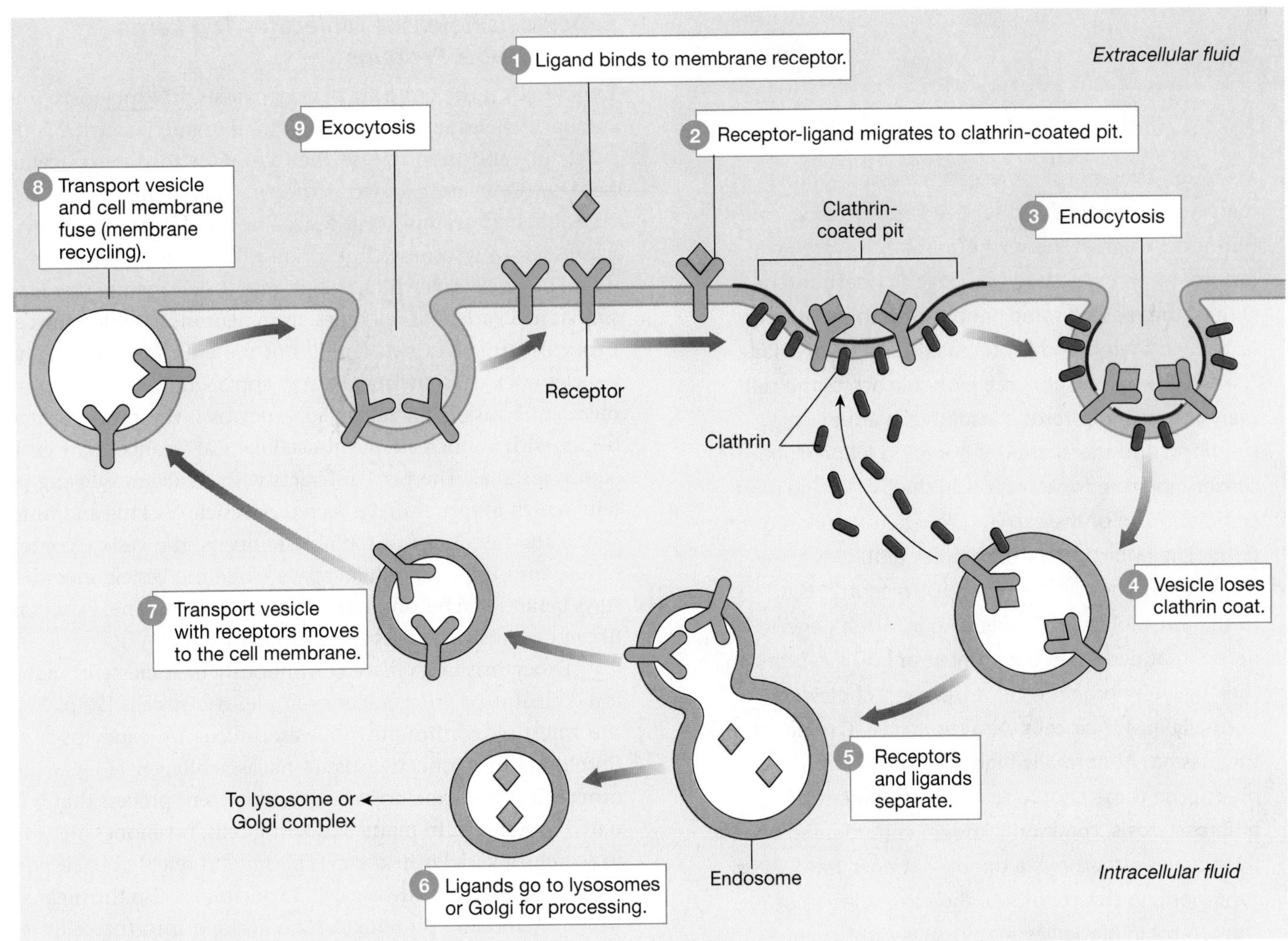
1 Ligand binds to membrane receptor.
Extracellular fluid
9 Exocytosis
2 Receptor-ligand migrates to clathrin-coated pit.
8 Transport vesicle and cell membrane fuse (membrane recycling).
Clathrin-coated pit
3 Endocytosis
Receptor
Clathrin
4 Vesicle loses clathrin coat.
7 Transport vesicle with receptors moves to the cell membrane.
5 Receptors and ligands separate.
To lysosome or Golgi complex
6 Ligands go to lysosomes or Golgi for processing.
Endosome
Intracellular fluid

■ **FIGURE 5-24** ***Receptor-mediated endocytosis and exocytosis***

Steps 1–4 illustrate endocytosis; steps 7–9 show exocytosis.

membrane receptor protein: receptor-mediated endocytosis and potocytosis.

Receptor-Mediated Endocytosis **Receptor-mediated endocytosis** takes place in regions of the cell membrane known as **clathrin-coated pits**, indentations where the cytoplasmic side of the membrane has high concentrations of the protein *clathrin* (Fig. 5-24 ■). In the first step of the process, extracellular ligands that will be brought into the cell bind to their membrane receptors (step ① in Fig. 5-24). The receptor-ligand complex migrates along the cell surface until it encounters a coated pit ②. Once the receptor-ligand complex is in the coated pit, the membrane draws inward, or *invaginates* ③, then pinches off from the cell membrane and becomes a cytoplasmic vesicle. The clathrin molecules are released and recycle back to the membrane ④. In the vesicle, the receptor and ligand separate, leaving the ligand inside an *endosome* ⑤. The endosome moves to a lysosome if the ligand is to be destroyed, or to the Golgi complex if the ligand is to be processed ⑥.

Meanwhile, the ligand's receptors may be reused in a process known as **membrane recycling**. The vesicle with the receptors moves to the cell membrane ⑦ and fuses with it ⑧. The vesicle membrane then is incorporated back into the cell membrane by exocytosis ⑨. Notice in Figure 5-24 that the cytoplasmic face of the membrane remains the same throughout endocytosis and recycling. The extracellular surface of the cell membrane becomes the inside face of the vesicle membrane.

Receptor-mediated endocytosis transports a variety of substances into the cell, including protein hormones, growth factors, antibodies, and plasma proteins that serve as carriers for iron and cholesterol. Abnormalities in receptor-mediated removal of cholesterol from the blood are associated with elevated plasma cholesterol levels and cardiovascular disease.

Potocytosis and Caveolae The form of endocytosis known as **potocytosis** is distinguished from receptor-mediated endocytosis by the fact that potocytosis uses **caveolae** ("little caves")

CLINICAL FOCUS

LDL

THE LETHAL LIPOPROTEIN

Although cholesterol molecules are essential for membrane structure and for the synthesis of steroid hormones (such as the sex hormones), elevated cholesterol levels in the body can lead to heart disease. One of the reasons some people have too much cholesterol in their blood (*hypercholesterolemia*) is failure of cells to transport the molecule across the cell membrane. Cholesterol is insoluble in aqueous solutions, and therefore it is bound to a lipoprotein carrier molecule for transport in the blood. The most common form of the carrier is *low-density lipoprotein (LDL)*. The LDL-cholesterol complex (LDL-C) is taken into cells by endocytosis when LDL receptors bind to the LDL molecule. People who inherit a genetic defect that decreases the number of LDL receptors on their cell membranes cannot transport cholesterol normally into their cells. As a result, LDL-C remains in the plasma. Abnormally high blood levels of LDL-C predispose these people to the development of **atherosclerosis**, commonly known as hardening of the arteries [*atheroma*, a tumor + *skleros*, hard + *-sis*, condition]. In this condition, the accumulation of cholesterol in blood vessels blocks blood flow and contributes to heart attacks.

rather than clathrin-coated pits to concentrate and bring receptor-bound molecules into the cell. Caveolae are membrane regions with lipid rafts [p. 57], membrane receptor proteins, and a family of unique membrane proteins named *caveolins*. The receptors in caveolae are lipid-anchored proteins. In many cells, caveolae appear as small indented pockets on the cell membrane, which is how they acquired their name.

Caveolae have several functions: to concentrate and internalize small molecules, to help in the transfer of macromolecules across the capillary endothelium (see Fig. 5-27), and to participate in cell signaling. Caveolae appear to be involved in some disease processes, including viral and parasitic infections. Two forms of the disease *muscular dystrophy* are associated with abnormalities in the protein caveolin. Scientists are currently trying to discover more details about the role of caveolae in normal physiology and pathophysiology.

Exocytosis Releases Molecules Too Large for Transport Proteins

Exocytosis is the opposite of endocytosis. In exocytosis, intracellular vesicles move to the cell membrane, fuse with it (Fig. 5-24, ⑧), and then release their contents to the extracellular fluid ⑨. Cells use exocytosis to export large lipophobic molecules, such as proteins synthesized in the cell, and to get rid of wastes left in lysosomes from intracellular digestion.

The process by which the cell and vesicle membranes fuse is similar in a variety of cell types, from neurons to endocrine cells. Exocytosis involves two families of proteins: *Rabs*, which help vesicles dock onto the membrane, and *SNAREs*, which facilitate membrane fusion. In regulated exocytosis, the process usually begins with an increase in intracellular Ca^{2+} concentration that acts as a signal. The Ca^{2+} interacts with a calcium-sensing protein, which in turn initiates secretory vesicle docking and fusion. When the fused area of membrane opens, the vesicle contents diffuse into the extracellular space while the vesicle membrane stays behind and becomes part of the cell membrane. Exocytosis, like endocytosis, requires energy in the form of ATP.

Exocytosis takes place continuously in some cells, making it a constitutive process. For example, goblet cells [p. 75] in the intestine continuously release mucus by exocytosis, and fibroblasts in connective tissue release collagen [p. 77]. In other cell types, exocytosis is an intermittent process that is initiated by a signal. In many endocrine cells, hormones are stored in secretory vesicles in the cytoplasm and released in response to a signal from outside the cell. Exocytosis is also the means by which membrane proteins can be inserted into the cell membrane, as shown in Figure 5-24. You will encounter many examples of exocytosis in your study of physiology.

CONCEPT CHECK

21. How does phagocytosis differ from endocytosis?
22. Name the two membrane protein families associated with endocytosis.
23. How do cells move large proteins into the cell? Out of the cell?

Answers: p. 172

TRANSEPITHELIAL TRANSPORT

All the transport processes described in the previous sections deal with the movement of molecules across a single membrane, that of the cell. However, any molecules entering and leaving the body across an epithelium must cross two cell membranes. Molecules cross the first membrane when they move into an epithelial cell from the external environment, and cross the second when they leave the epithelial cell to enter the extracellular fluid. Movement across epithelial cells, **transepithelial transport**, uses a combination of active and passive transport.

The transporting epithelia of the intestine and kidney are specialized to selectively transport molecules into and out of

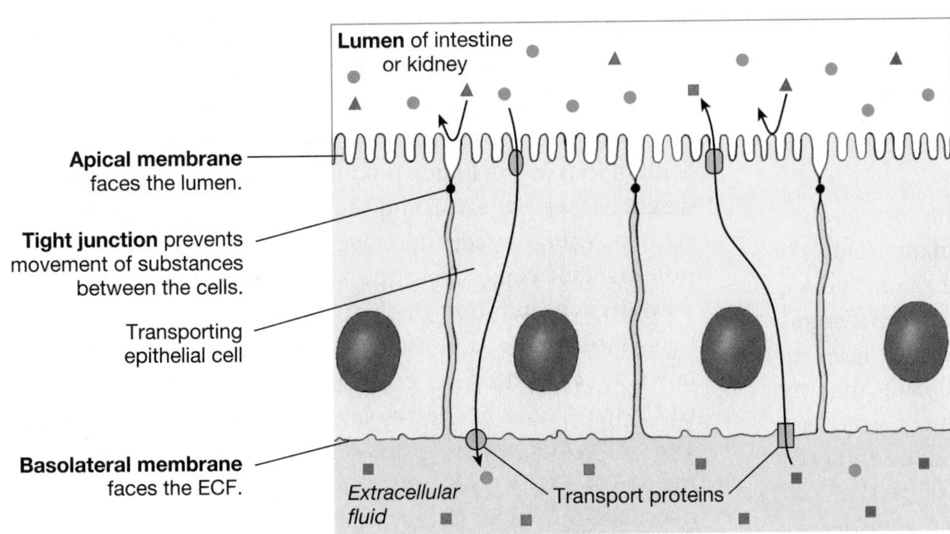

Polarized epithelia have different transport proteins on apical and basolateral membranes. This allows selective directional transport across the epithelium. Transport from lumen to ECF is called **absorption**. Transport from ECF to lumen is called **secretion**.

■ **FIGURE 5-25** ***Polarized cells of transporting epithelia***

The apical membrane and the basolateral membrane are the two poles of the cell.

the body. These epithelial cells are connected to one another by adhesive junctions and tight junctions [p. 69] that act as barriers to minimize the unregulated diffusion of material between the cells. The tight junctions also mark the separation of the cell membrane into two regions, or poles. The surface of the epithelial cell that faces the lumen of an organ is called the *apical* [*apex,* the highest point] membrane (Fig. 5-25 ■; p. 51). It is often folded into microvilli that increase its surface area. The apical membrane is separated from the remainder of the cell membrane by tight junctions. The three surfaces of the cell that face the extracellular fluid are collectively called the *basolateral* membrane [*basal,* base + *latus,* side]. The apical membrane is also called the *mucosal* membrane; the corresponding term for the basolateral membrane is *serosal* membrane.

Transporting epithelial cells are said to be *polarized* because their apical and basolateral membranes have very different properties. Certain transport proteins, such as the Na^+-K^+-ATPase, are almost always found only on the basolateral membrane, whereas others, like the Na^+-glucose symporter, are localized to the apical membrane. This polarized distribution of transporters results in the one-way movement of certain molecules across the epithelium. Transport of material from the lumen of an organ to the extracellular fluid is called **absorption**. This process is the opposite of *secretion,* which is the movement of material from the ECF to the lumen.

The cells of transporting epithelia can alter their permeability by selectively inserting or withdrawing membrane proteins. Transporters pulled out of the membrane may be destroyed in lysosomes, or they may be stored in vesicles inside the cell, ready to be reinserted into the membrane in response to a signal (another example of membrane recycling).

The transepithelial movement of molecules requires that the molecules first enter an epithelial cell and then leave it. If the molecule can be transported through a protein channel or on transport carriers, then the two-step process usually has one "uphill" step that requires energy and one "downhill" step in which the molecule moves passively down its gradient. Molecules that

RUNNING PROBLEM

The sweat test that Daniel will undergo analyzes levels of the salt NaCl in sweat. Sweat—a mixture of ions and water—is secreted into sweat ducts by the epithelial cells of sweat glands. As sweat moves toward the skin's surface through the sweat ducts, CFTR allows chloride ions to move out of the sweat and back into the epithelial cells. Sodium ions are also reabsorbed, following the Cl^-. This epithelium is not permeable to water, and so normal reabsorption of NaCl creates sweat with a low salt content. However, in the absence of CFTRs in the epithelium, salt is not reabsorbed. "Normally, sweat contains about 120 millimoles of salt per liter," says Beryl Rosenstein, M.D., of the Cystic Fibrosis Center at the Johns Hopkins Medical Institutions. "In cystic fibrosis, salt concentrations in the sweat can be four times the normal amount."

Question 2:

Based on the information given, is CFTR on the apical or basolateral surface of the sweat gland epithelium?

are too large to be moved by membrane proteins can be transported across the cell in vesicles.

Transepithelial Transport of Glucose Uses Membrane Proteins

The movement of glucose from the lumen of the kidney tubule or intestine to the extracellular fluid is an important example of directional movement across a transporting epithelium. Transepithelial movement of glucose involves three transport systems: the secondary active transport of glucose with Na^+ from the lumen into the epithelial cell at the apical membrane, followed by the movement of both Na^+ and glucose out of the cell and into the extracellular fluid on the basolateral side of the cell. Sodium moves out by primary active transport via a Na^+-K^+-ATPase, and glucose leaves the cell by facilitated diffusion.

Figure 5-26 ■ shows the process in detail. The glucose concentration in the transporting epithelial cell is higher than the glucose concentration in either the extracellular fluid or the lumen of the kidney or intestine. Therefore, moving glucose from the lumen into the cell requires the input of energy—in this case, energy stored in the Na^+ concentration gradient. Sodium ions in the lumen bind to the symporter, as previously described (see Fig. 5-18), and bring glucose with them into the cell. The energy needed to move glucose against its concentration gradient comes from the kinetic energy of Na^+ moving down its concentration gradient.

Once glucose is in the epithelial cell, it leaves by moving down its concentration gradient on the facilitated diffusion GLUT transporter in the basolateral membrane (② Fig. 5-26). The Na^+ is pumped out of the cell on the basolateral side using the Na^+-K^+-ATPase ③. Sodium is more concentrated in the extracellular fluid than in the cell; therefore, this step requires energy provided by ATP.

The removal of Na^+ from the cell is essential if glucose is to continue to be absorbed from the lumen because the

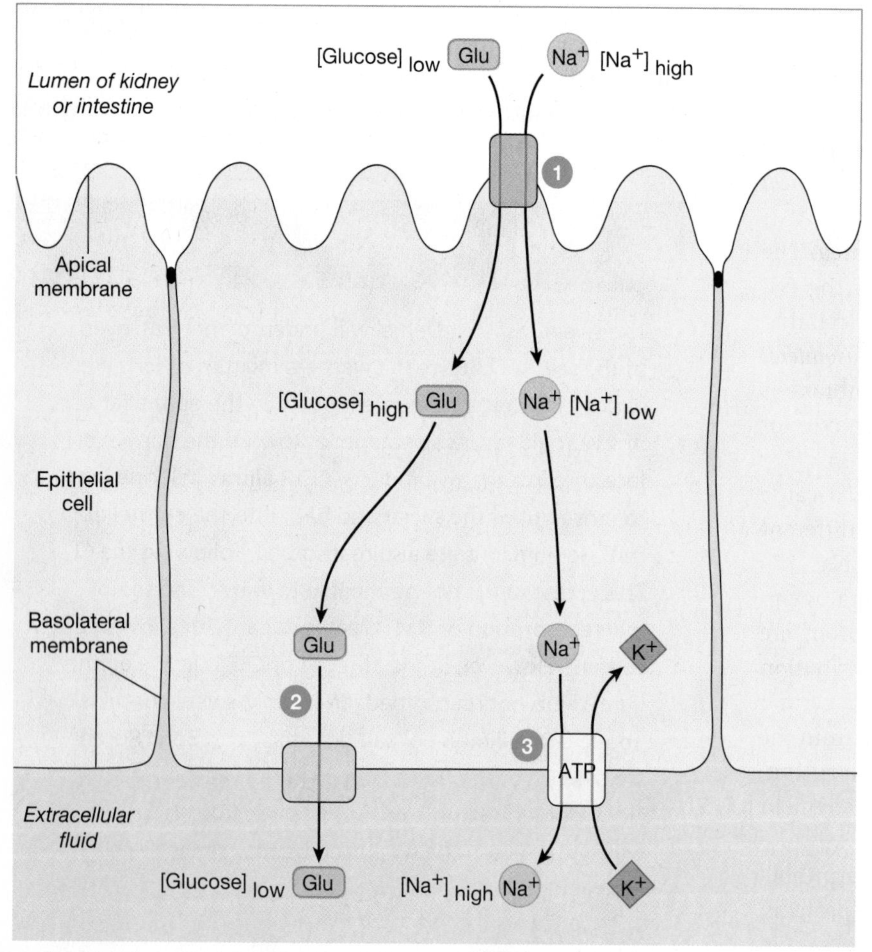

① **Na^+- glucose symporter** brings glucose into cell against its gradient using energy stored in the Na^+ concentration gradient.

② **GLUT transporter** transfers glucose to ECF by facilitated diffusion.

③ **Na^+-K^+- ATPase** pumps Na^+ out of the cell, keeping ICF Na^+ concentration low.

FIGURE QUESTIONS

- Match each transporter to its location.
  1. GLUT — a) apical membrane
  2. Na^+-glucose symporter — b) basolateral membrane
  3. Na^+-K^+-ATPase
- Is glucose movement across the basolateral membrane active or passive? Explain.
- Why doesn't Na^+ movement at the apical membrane require ATP?

■ **FIGURE 5-26** ***Transepithelial transport of glucose***

This process involves indirect (secondary) active transport of glucose across the apical membrane and glucose diffusion across the basolateral membrane.

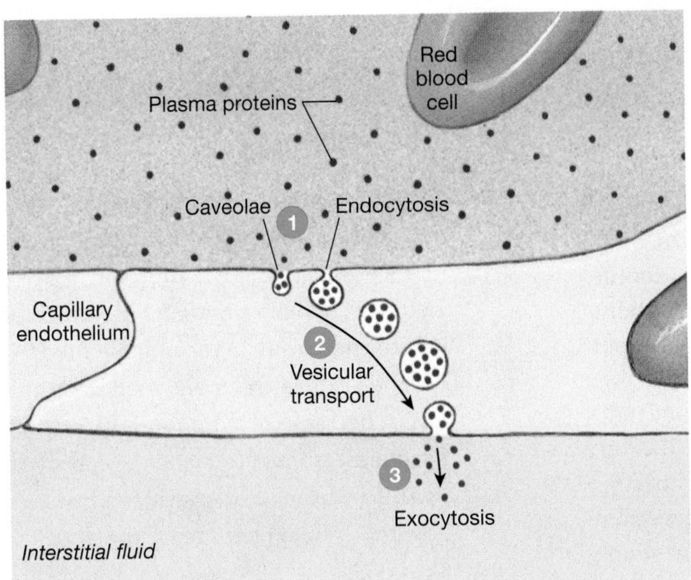

■ **FIGURE 5-27** *Transcytosis across the capillary endothelium*

Na^+-glucose symporter depends on low intracellular concentrations of Na^+. If the basolateral Na^+-K^+-ATPase is poisoned with *ouabain* (pronounced wah-bane—a compound related to the heart drug digitalis), Na^+ that enters the cell cannot be pumped out. The Na^+ concentration inside the cell gradually increases until it is equal to that in the lumen. Without a sodium gradient, there is no energy source to run the Na^+-glucose symporter, and the movement of glucose across the epithelium stops.

Transepithelial transport can use ion movement through channels in addition to carrier-mediated transport. For example, the apical membrane of a transporting epithelium may use the Na^+-K^+-2 Cl^- (NKCC) symporter to bring K^+ into the cell against its concentration gradient, using energy from the Na^+ gradient. Because the K^+ concentration inside the cell is higher than in the extracellular fluid, the K^+ can move out of the cell on the basolateral side through open K^+ leak channels. The Na^+ must be pumped out by the Na^+-K^+-ATPase. By this simple mechanism the body can absorb Na^+ and K^+ at the same time from the lumen of the intestine or the kidney.

CONCEPT CHECK

24. Why does Na^+ movement from the cytoplasm to the extracellular fluid require energy?
25. Ouabain, an inhibitor of the Na^+-K^+-ATPase, cannot pass through cell membranes. What would happen to the transepithelial glucose transport shown in Figure 5-26 if ouabain were applied to the apical side of the epithelium? To the basolateral side of the epithelium?
26. Which GLUT transporter is illustrated in Figure 5-26? (*Hint:* see Table 5-4.)

Answers: p. 173

Transcytosis Uses Vesicles to Cross an Epithelium

Some molecules, such as proteins, are too large to cross epithelia on membrane transporters. Instead they are moved across epithelia by **transcytosis**, which is a combination of endocytosis, vesicular transport across the cell, and exocytosis (Fig. 5-27 ■). In this process, the molecule is brought into the epithelial cell via receptor-mediated endocytosis or potocytosis. The resulting vesicle attaches to microtubules in the cell's cytoskeleton and is transported across the cell by a process known as **vesicular transport**. At the opposite side of the epithelium, the contents of the vesicle are expelled into the interstitial fluid by exocytosis.

Transcytosis makes it possible for large proteins to move across an epithelium and remain intact. It is the means by which infants absorb maternal antibodies in breast milk. The antibodies are absorbed on the apical surface of the infant's intestinal epithelium and then released into the extracellular fluid.

CONCEPT CHECK

27. If a poison that disassembles microtubules is applied to a capillary endothelial cell, what happens to transcytosis?

Answers: p. 173

Now that we have considered how solutes cross cell membranes, we will turn to the movement of water between the body's compartments.

OSMOSIS AND TONICITY

The distribution of solutes in the body depends on whether a substance can cross the cell membrane, either by simple diffusion, protein-mediated transport, or vesicular transport. Water, on the other hand, is able to move freely in and out of nearly every cell in the body by traversing water-filled ion channels and special water channels created by the protein aquaporin. In this section we examine the relationship between solute movement and water movement across cell membranes, a topic that provides the foundation for clinical use of intravenous (IV) fluid therapy.

The Body Is Mostly Water

Water is the most important molecule in the human body because it is the solvent for all living matter. As we look for life in distant parts of the solar system, one of the first questions scientists ask about a planet is, "Does it have water?" Without water, life as we know it cannot exist.

How much water is in the human body? Because one individual differs from the next, there is no single answer. However, in human physiology we often speak of standard values for physiological functions, based on "the 70-kg man." These standard values are derived from data obtained by studying young white males whose average weight was 70 kg. Thus, when we speak of standard or average values in physiology, remember that these numbers need to be adjusted for an individual's age, sex, weight, and ethnic origin.

The "standard" 70-kilogram (154-pound) male has 60% of his total body weight, or 42 kg (92.4 lb), in the form of water. Each kilogram of water has a volume of 1 liter, so his **total body water** is 42 liters. This is the equivalent of 21 two-liter soft drink bottles! Women have less water per kilogram of body mass than men because women have more adipose tissue. Look back at Figure 3-31 [p. 79] and note how the large fat droplets in adipose tissue occupy most of the cell, displacing the more aqueous cytoplasm. Age also influences body water content. Infants have relatively more water than adults, and water content decreases as people grow older than 60.

Table 5-5 ■ shows water content as a percentage of total body weight in people of various ages and both sexes. In clinical practice, it is necessary to allow for the variability of body water content when prescribing drugs. Because women and older people have less body water, they will have a higher concentration of a drug in the plasma than will young men if all are given an equal dose per kilogram of body mass.

TABLE 5-5 Water Content as Percentage of Total Body Weight by Age and Sex

AGE	MALE	FEMALE
Infant	65%	65%
1–9	62%	62%
10–16	59%	57%
17–39	61%	51%
40–59	55%	47%
60+	52%	46%

Adapted from Edelman and Leibman, *American Journal of Medicine 27;* 256–277, 1959.

CLINICAL FOCUS

ESTIMATING BODY WATER

Clinicians estimate a person's fluid loss in dehydration by equating weight loss to water loss. Because 1 liter of pure water weighs 1 kilogram, a decrease in body weight of 1 kilogram (or 2.2 lb) is considered equivalent to the loss of 1 liter of body fluid. A baby with diarrhea can easily be weighed to estimate its fluid loss. A decrease of 1.1 pounds (0.5 kg) of body weight is assumed to mean the loss of 500 mL of fluid. This calculation provides a quick estimate of how much fluid needs to be replaced.

The distribution of water among body compartments is less variable. When we look at the relative volumes of the body compartments, the intracellular compartment contains about two-thirds (67%) of the body's water (Fig. 5-28 ■). The remaining third (33%) is split between the interstitial fluid (which contains about 75% of the extracellular water) and the plasma (which contains about 25% of the extracellular water).

The Body Is in Osmotic Equilibrium

Water is able to move freely between cells and the extracellular fluid, and will distribute itself until water concentrations are equal throughout the body—in other words, until the body is in a state of osmotic equilibrium. The movement of water across a membrane in response to a solute concentration gradient is called **osmosis**. In osmosis, water moves to dilute the more concentrated solution. Once concentrations are equal, net movement of water stops.

Look at the example shown in Figure 5-29 ■, in which two compartments of equal volume are separated by a selectively permeable membrane that is permeable to water but that does not allow glucose to cross. In ①, compartments A and B contain equal volumes of glucose solution. Compartment B has more solute (glucose) per volume of solution and therefore is the more concentrated solution. A concentration gradient across the membrane exists for glucose, but the membrane is not permeable to glucose, so glucose cannot diffuse to equalize its distribution.

Water, on the other hand, can cross the membrane freely. It will move by osmosis from compartment A, which contains

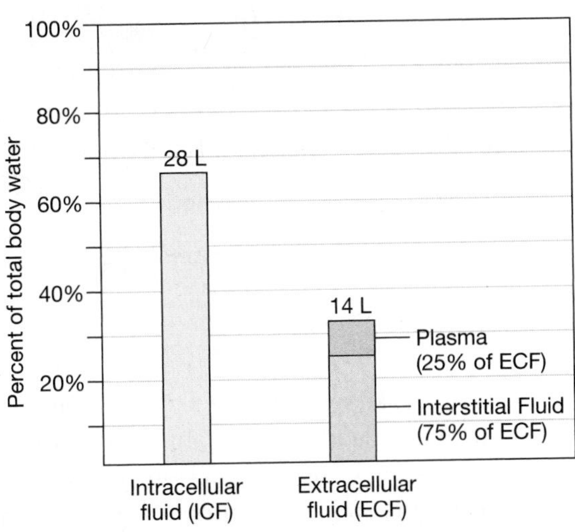

GRAPH QUESTIONS

- Using the ECF volume shown, calculate the volumes of the plasma and interstitiial fluid.
- What is this person's total body water volume?
- Use your answers from the two previous questions to calculate the percentage of total body water in the plasma and interstitial fluid.

■ **FIGURE 5-28** ***Distribution of water volume in the three body fluid compartments***

This figure shows the compartment volumes for the "standard" 70-kg man.

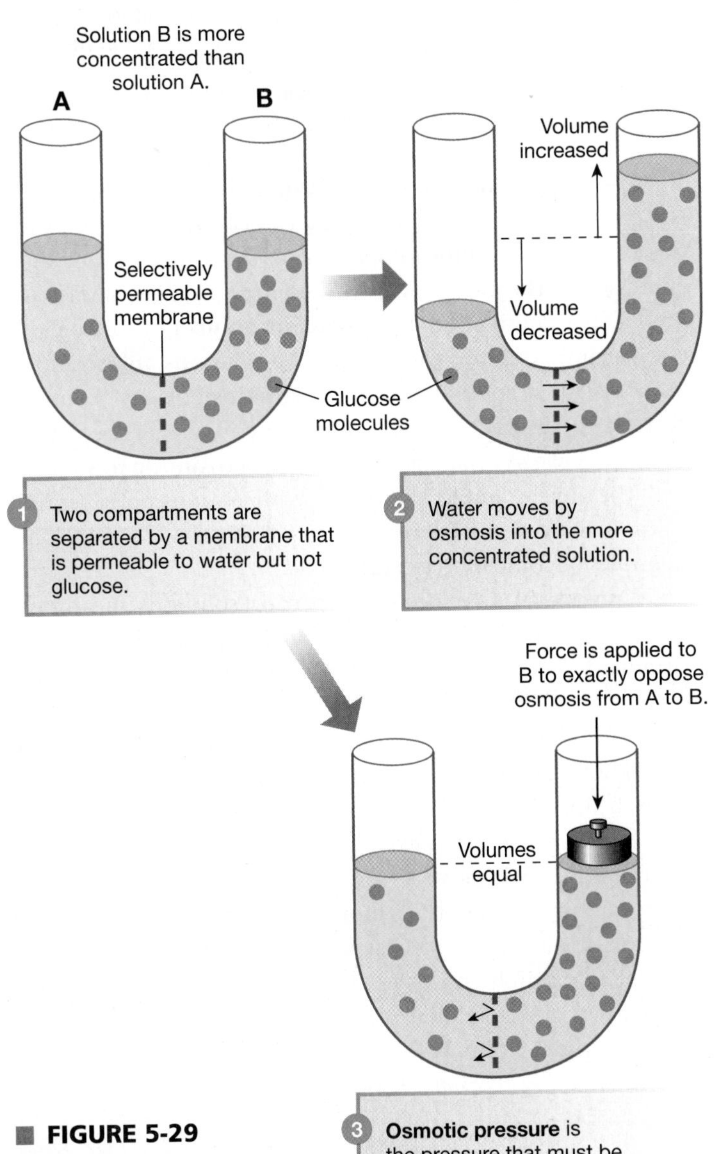

■ **FIGURE 5-29** ***Osmosis and osmotic pressure***

the dilute glucose solution, to compartment B, which contains the more concentrated glucose solution. Thus, water moves to dilute the more concentrated solution (Fig. 5-29, ②).

How can we make quantitative measurements of osmosis? One method is shown in Figure 5-29, ③. Place a piston into compartment B, which has a higher solute concentration than compartment A. By pushing down on the piston, you can keep water from flowing from A to B. The pressure that must be applied to the piston to exactly oppose the osmotic movement of water into compartment B is known as the **osmotic pressure** of solution B. The units for osmotic pressure, just as with other pressures in physiology, are *atmospheres* (atm) or *millimeters of mercury* (mm Hg).*

Osmolarity Describes the Number of Particles in Solution

Another way to predict the osmotic movement of water quantitatively is to know the concentrations of the solutions with which we are dealing. In chemistry, concentrations are usually expressed as *molarity* (*M*), which is defined as number of moles of dissolved solute per liter of solution (mol/L). Recall from Chapter 2 that a *mole* is 6.02×10^{23} molecules [p. 36].

However, using molarity to describe biological concentrations can be misleading. The important factor for osmosis is the number of *particles* in a given volume of solution, not the number of molecules. Because some molecules dissociate into ions when they dissolve in a solution, the number of particles in solution is not always the same as the number of molecules. For example, one glucose molecule dissolved in

*A pressure of 1 mm Hg is equivalent to the hydrostatic pressure exerted on a 1-cm^2 area by a 1-mm-high column of mercury.

TABLE 5-6 Comparing Osmolarities

SOLUTION A = 1 OsM GLUCOSE	SOLUTION B = 2 OsM GLUCOSE	SOLUTION C = 1 OsM NaCl
A is hyposmotic to B	B is hyperosmotic to A	C is isosmotic to A
A is isosmotic to C	B is hyperosmotic to C	C is hyposmotic to B

water yields one particle, but one NaCl dissolved in water yields two ions (particles): Na^+ and Cl^-. Water will move osmotically in response to the total concentration of *particles* in the solution. The particles may be ions, uncharged molecules, or a mixture of both.

Consequently, we express the concentration of biological solutions as **osmolarity**, the number of particles (ions or intact molecules) per liter of solution. Osmolarity is expressed in *osmoles* per liter (osmol/L or OsM) or, for very dilute physiological solutions, milliosmoles/liter (mOsM). To convert between molarity and osmolarity, use the following equation:

$$\text{molarity (mol/L)} \times \text{number of particles/molecule} = \text{osmolarity (osmol/L)}$$

Let us look at two examples, glucose and sodium chloride, and compare their molarity with their osmolarity.

One mole of glucose molecules dissolved in enough water to create 1 liter of solution yields a 1 molar solution (1 M). Because glucose does not dissociate in solution, the solution has only one mole of osmotically active particles:

$$\text{1 M glucose} \times \text{1 particle per glucose molecule} = \text{1 OsM glucose}$$

Unlike glucose, sodium chloride dissociates into two ions when placed in solution.* Thus, one mole of NaCl dissociates in solution to yield two moles of particles: one mole of Na^+ and one mole of Cl^-. The result is a 2 OsM solution:

$$\text{1 M NaCl} \times \text{2 ions per NaCl} = \text{2 OsM NaCl}$$

Osmolarity describes only the number of particles in the solution. It says nothing about the composition of the particles. A 1 OsM solution could be composed of pure glucose or pure Na^+ and Cl^- or a mixture of the three.

The normal osmolarity of the human body ranges from 280 to 296 milliosmoles per liter (mOsM). In this book, to simplify calculations we will round that number up slightly to 300 mOsM.

A term related to osmolarity that you may hear used is osmolality. **Osmolality** is concentration expressed as osmoles of solute per kilogram of water. Because biological solutions are dilute and little of their weight comes from solute, physiologists sometimes use the terms *osmolarity* and *osmolality* interchangeably. Osmolality is usually used in clinical situations because it is easy to estimate people's body water content by weighing them.

CONCEPT CHECK

28. A mother brings her baby to the Emergency Room because he has had diarrhea and vomiting for two days. The staff weighs the baby and finds that he has lost 2 pounds. If you assume that all the weight loss is water loss, what volume of water has the baby lost? (2.2 pounds = 1 kilogram) Answers: p. 173

Comparing Osmolarities of Two Solutions Osmolarity is a property of every solution. You can compare the osmolarities of different solutions so long as the concentrations are expressed in the same units—for example, as milliosmoles per liter. If two solutions contain the same number of solute particles per unit volume, we say that the solutions are **isosmotic** [*iso-*, equal]. If solution A has a higher osmolarity (contains more particles per unit volume, is more concentrated) than solution B, we say that solution A is **hyperosmotic** to solution B. In the same example, solution B, with fewer osmoles per unit volume, is **hyposmotic** to solution A. Table 5-6 ■ shows some examples of comparative osmolarities.

Osmolarity is a *colligative* property of solutions, meaning it depends strictly on the *number* of particles per liter of solution. Osmolarity says nothing about what the particles are or how they behave. Before we can predict whether osmosis will take place between any two solutions divided by a membrane, we must know the properties of the membrane and of the solutes on each side of it.

If the membrane is permeable only to water and not to any solutes, water will move by osmosis from a less concentrated (hyposmotic) solution into a more concentrated (hyperosmotic) solution, as illustrated in Figure 5-29. Most biological systems are not this simple, however. Biological membranes are selectively permeable and allow some solutes to cross in addition to water. To predict the movement of water into and out of cells, you must know the *tonicity* of the solution, explained in the next section.

*For the purposes of this discussion, we will assume that all solutes that can dissociate do so completely (complete dissociation). The actual dissociation constant for NaCl is about 1.8.

RUNNING PROBLEM

Daniel's medical history tells a frightening story of almost constant medical problems since birth: recurring bouts of respiratory infections, digestive ailments, and, for the past six months, a history of weight loss. Then, last week, when Daniel began having trouble breathing, his mother rushed him to the hospital. A culture taken from Daniel's lungs raised a red flag for cystic fibrosis: the mucus from his airways was unusually thick and dehydrated. In cystic fibrosis, this thick mucus causes life-threatening respiratory congestion and provides a perfect breeding ground for infection-causing bacteria. The thickened mucus is a direct result of faulty CFTRs. Normally these proteins in the lungs transport chloride ions out of the epithelial cells and into the airways.

Question 3:

Why would failure to transport chloride ions into the lumen of the airways cause the secreted mucus to be thick? (Hint: remember that water moves to dilute the more concentrated region.)

Tonicity of a Solution Describes the Volume Change of a Cell Placed in That Solution

Tonicity [*tonikos,* pertaining to stretching] is a physiological term used to describe a solution and how that solution affects cell volume. If a cell placed in the solution gains water and swells, we say that the solution is **hypotonic** to the cell. If the cell loses water and shrinks when placed in the solution, the solution is said to be **hypertonic**. If the cell does not change size in the solution, the solution is **isotonic** (Table 5-7 ■). By convention, we always describe the tonicity of the solution relative to the cell. Tonicity describes the cell volume once the cell has come to equilibrium with the solution.

TABLE 5-7 Tonicity of Solutions

SOLUTION	CELL BEHAVIOR WHEN PLACED IN THE SOLUTION	DESCRIPTION OF THE SOLUTION RELATIVE TO THE CELL
A	Cell swells	Solution A is hypotonic
B	Cell doesn't change size	Solution B is isotonic
C	Cell shrinks	Solution C is hypertonic

How, then, does tonicity differ from osmolarity?

1. Osmolarity describes the number of solute particles dissolved in a volume of solution. It has units, such as osmoles/liter. The osmolarity of a solution can be measured by a machine called an *osmometer*. Tonicity has no units; it is only a comparative term.
2. Osmolarity can be used to compare any two solutions, and the relationship is reciprocal (solution A is hyperosmotic to solution B; therefore, solution B is hyposmotic to solution A). Tonicity always compares a solution and a cell, and by convention, tonicity is used to describe only the solution—for example, "Solution A is hypotonic to red blood cells."
3. Osmolarity alone will not tell you what happens to a cell placed in a solution. Tonicity by definition tells you what happens to cell volume when the cell is placed in the solution.

This third point is the one that is most confusing to students. Why can't osmolarity be used to predict tonicity? The reason is that the tonicity of a solution depends not only on its concentration (osmolarity) but also on the *nature* of the solutes in the solution. By nature of the solutes, we mean whether the solute particles can cross the cell membrane. If the solute particles (ions or molecules) can enter the cell, we call them **penetrating solutes**. We call particles that cannot cross the cell membrane **nonpenetrating solutes**. Tonicity depends on the concentration of nonpenetrating solutes only. Let's see why this is true.

First, some preliminary information. The most important nonpenetrating solute in physiology is NaCl. If a cell is placed in a solution of NaCl, the Na^+ and Cl^- will not cross the membrane into the cell. (In reality, a few Na^+ ions may leak across, but they are immediately transported back to the extracellular fluid by the Na^+-K^+-ATPase. NaCl is therefore considered a *functionally* nonpenetrating solute.) By convention, we assume that cells are filled with other types of nonpenetrating solutes. In other words, the solutes inside the cell are unable to leave so long as the cell membrane remains intact.

Now we are ready to see why osmolarity alone cannot be used to predict tonicity. Suppose you know the composition and osmolarity of a solution. How can you figure out the tonicity of the solution without actually putting a cell in it? The key lies in knowing *the relative concentrations of nonpenetrating solutes in the cell and in the solution.*

Here are the rules for predicting tonicity:

1. *If the cell has a higher concentration of nonpenetrating solutes than the solution,* there will be net movement of water into the cell. The cell swells, and the solution is *hypotonic.*

(a)

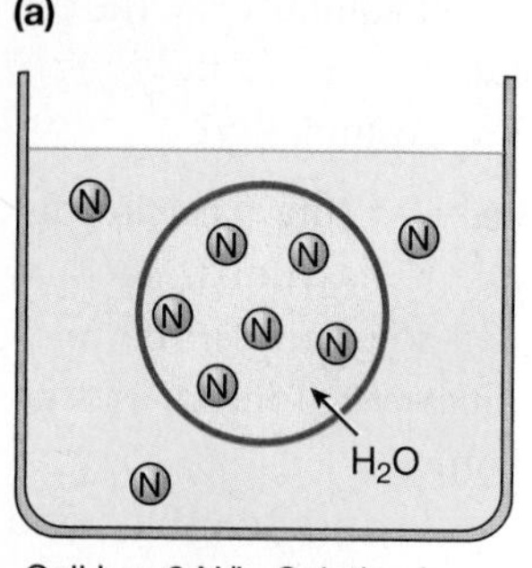

Cell has 6 N/L. Solution has 3 N/L. Water moves into the cell.

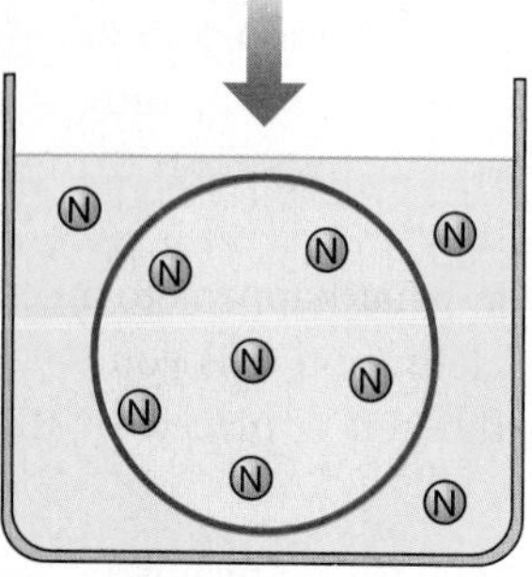

At equilibrium, the cell gained volume. Therefore, the solution was hypotonic.

(b)

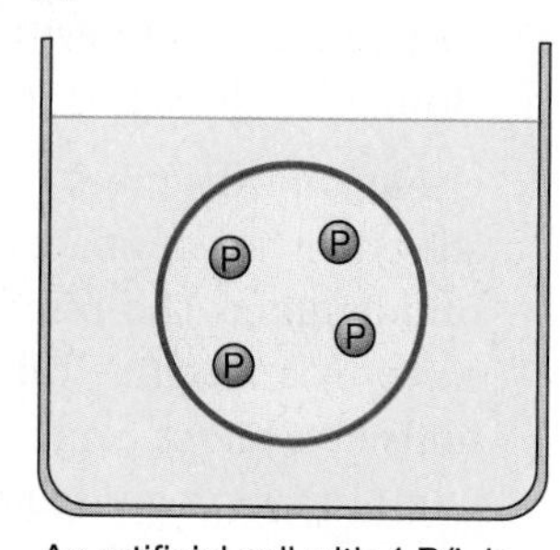

An artificial cell with 4 P/L is placed in 1 L of pure water.

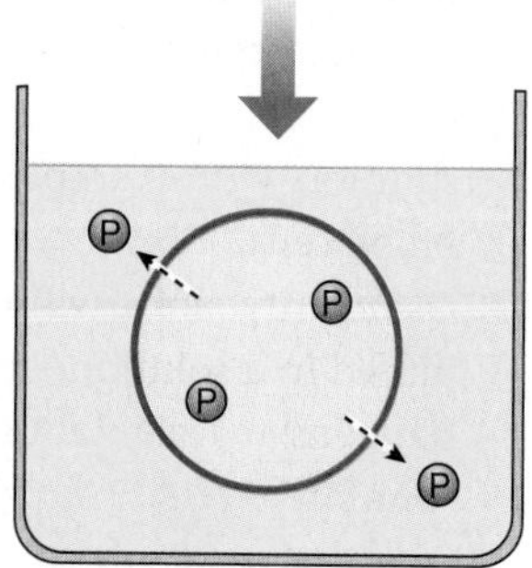

The penetrating solutes leave the cell by diffusion, reaching equilibrium at 2 P/L. No water moves, so the solution is isotonic.

■ **FIGURE 5-30** ***Tonicity depends on the relative concentrations of nonpenetrating solutes***

Water and penetrating solutes can cross the cell membrane and come to equilibrium, but nonpenetrating solutes cannot cross. The "cell" and the solution are each 1 liter in the top figures.

2. *If the cell has a lower concentration of nonpenetrating solutes than the solution,* there will be net movement of water out of the cell. The cell shrinks, and the solution is *hypertonic*.
3. *If the concentrations of nonpenetrating solutes are the same in the cell and the solution,* there is no net movement of water at equilibrium. The solution is *isotonic* to the cell.

Let's look at three examples of how this works. The first two examples will be simple because they use only nonpenetrating solutes or penetrating solutes. The third example will show how combining penetrating and nonpenetrating solutes can complicate the situation.

The artificial cell at the top of Figure 5-30a ■, contains six particles of nonpenetrating solute in 1 liter of cell volume. The 1 liter of solution contains three particles of nonpenetrating solute per liter. As in the tube example of Figure 5-29, there is a concentration gradient for the solute, but the solute cannot cross the cell membrane to equilibrate. There is also an osmotic gradient, however, and because water *can* cross the membrane, water moves into the cell until the solute concentrations have equilibrated (bottom of Fig. 5-30a). The cell gains volume at equilibrium, which means the solution was hypotonic to the cell. We could have predicted this by using rule 1: if the cell has a higher concentration of nonpenetrating solutes than the solution, there will be net movement of water into the cell.

Now let's consider a situation in which an artificial cell with a volume of 1 liter has four particles of penetrating solute and is placed in 1 liter of pure water (top of Fig. 5-30b). Based on osmolarity alone, you might think that water would move into the cell because the cell is more concentrated. However, there is a concentration gradient for the solute, and the solute is able to cross the cell membrane. Solute therefore moves out of the cell by diffusion until solute concentrations in the cell and the solution reach equilibrium (bottom of Fig. 5-30b). Once the penetrating solute is at equilibrium, the cell and solution have equal osmolarities (two particles/liter), and the net movement of water is zero. The solution in this instance was isotonic. You could have predicted this from rule 3 above: if the concentrations of nonpenetrating solutes are the same in the cell and the solution, there is no net movement of water at equilibrium and the solution is isotonic. In this example, the concentrations of nonpenetrating solute in cell and solution were both zero. Remember, however, that we assume that real cells always contain only nonpenetrating solutes.

Now let's look at a complex example that mixes penetrating and nonpenetrating solutes. In Figure 5-31a ■, the artificial cell contains six particles of nonpenetrating solute in a 1 liter volume. The 1 liter of solution also contains six particles of solute: three nonpenetrating and three penetrating. Because cell and solution have the same concentrations (six particles per liter), they are isosmotic, and no water will move initially when the two are placed together (Fig. 5-31b).

Using the tonicity rules above, let us compare the concentrations of nonpenetrating solutes in the solution and cell. The nonpenetrating solutes are more concentrated in the cell than in the solution (six versus three). We therefore predict that water will move from the solution into the cell, increasing cell volume. However, the solution is isosmotic to the cell, and so what will cause osmosis?

You have learned that penetrating solutes move freely into and out of cells. In this example, there is a concentration gradient for the penetrating solute: 3/L in the solution versus 0/L in the cell. The penetrating solute therefore will diffuse down its concentration gradient and move into the cell. As soon as one particle moves in, we have a total of five solutes outside the cell but seven inside. This solute imbalance disturbs the osmotic balance and creates an osmotic gradient (Fig. 5-31c). Once this osmotic gradient exists, water moves into the cell and cell volume increases (solute movement has no significant effect on cell volume). Water movement continues until the concentrations of *nonpenetrating* solutes are equal, as in Figure 5-31d. Thus, in this example, an isosmotic solution is hypotonic because cell volume increased (rule 1).

If accepting the rules makes you uneasy, let's look at this example mathematically. We began with 1 L of solution in the cell and 1 L outside, a total of 2 L, and a total of 12 particles,

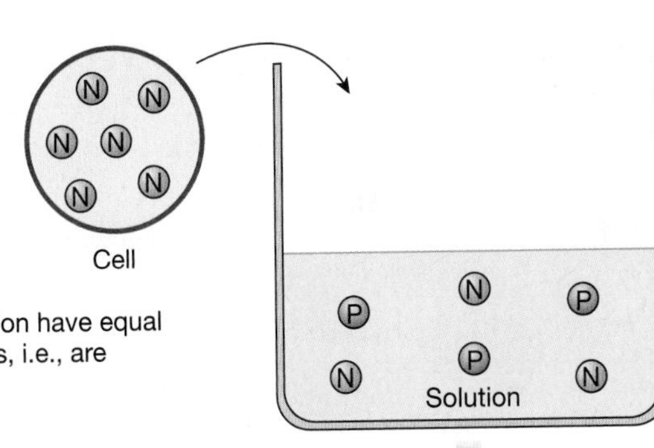

(a) Cell and solution have equal concentrations, i.e., are isosmotic.

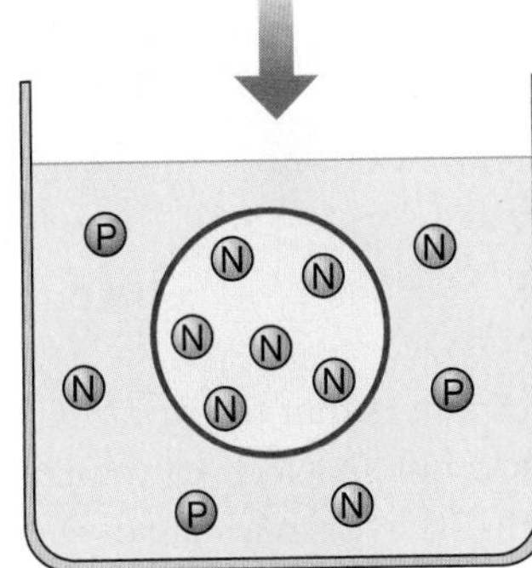

(b) When the cell is placed in the solution, no water moves initially because the cell and solution are in osmotic equilibrium.

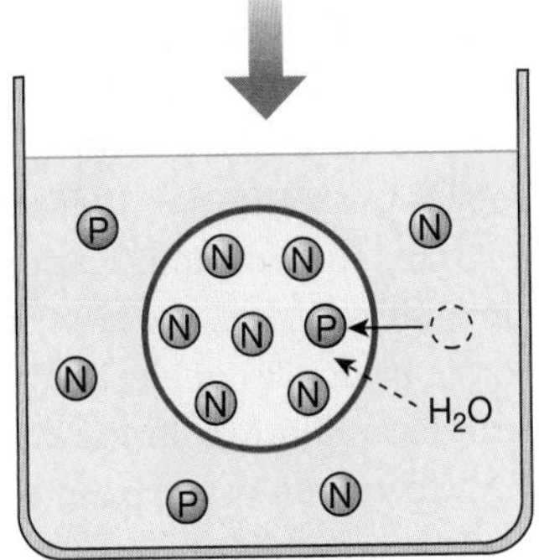

(c) However, there is a concentration gradient for the penetrating solute (P), which diffuses into the cell. This disrupts the osmotic equilibrium, so water follows the solute into the cell.

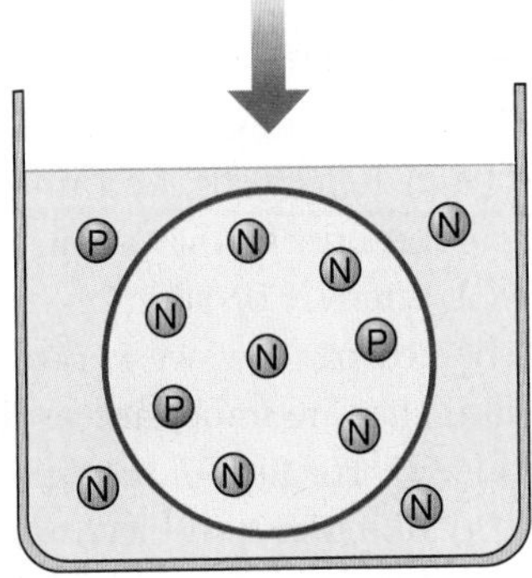

(d) Equilibrium is restored when the concentrations of nonpenetrating solutes (N) are equal in the cell and the solution. The cell gained volume at equilibrium; therefore, the solution was hypotonic.

FIGURE QUESTION

Using the same cell, give the relative osmolarity and the tonicity of the following solutions, if the solution has
(a) 6 nonpenetrating particles
(b) 6 nonpenetrating and 3 penetrating particles or
(c) 3 nonpenetrating and 6 penetrating particles

■ **FIGURE 5-31** ***In a solution of mixed solutes, only the concentration of nonpenetrating solutes contributes to the tonicity of the solution***

TABLE 5-8 Rules for Osmolarity and Tonicity
1. Assume that all intracellular solutes are nonpenetrating.
2. Compare osmolarities before the cell and solution are put together, because at equilibrium, the cell contents and the solution outside the cell will be isosmotic.
3. Tonicity of a solution describes the volume change of a cell at equilibrium (Table 5-7).
4. Determine tonicity by comparing nonpenetrating solute concentrations in the cell and the solution. Net water movement will be into the compartment that has the higher concentration of nonpenetrating solutes.
5. A solution that is hyposmotic to a cell will always be hypotonic.

giving a concentration of 6 particles/L. The system will not gain or lose solute or water, so the overall concentration will remain 6 particles/L. When the cell is placed in the solution, the two penetrating solutes move into the cell, disturbing the osmotic balance. Water has to enter the cell so that the concentration remains at 6 particles/L:

$$8 \text{ particles}/? \text{ liters} = 6 \text{ particles/L}$$

The cell volume at equilibrium will be 1.33 liters: 8 particles/1.33 L = 6 particles/L. The solution has lost 0.33 liter of water that moved into the cell:

$$4 \text{ particles}/(1 - 0.33) \text{ L} = 6 \text{ particles/L}$$

At equilibrium, the concentrations of the cell and the solution will always be the same.

Learning the rules rather than depending on mathematical calculations is important for clinical situations, when you will not know exact volumes for the person needing fluids. Table 5-8 ■ lists some rules to help you distinguish between osmolarity and tonicity.

Understanding the difference between the two properties is critical to making good clinical decisions about intravenous (IV) fluid therapy. In medicine, the tonicity of a solution is an important consideration. One purpose of IV fluids is to get water into dehydrated cells (in which case, a hypotonic IV solution is used) or to keep fluid in the extracellular fluid to replace blood loss (in which case, an isotonic IV solution is used). The choice of fluid depends on how the clinician wants the solutes and water to distribute between the extracellular and intracellular fluid compartments. Table 5-9 ■ lists the most common IV solutions and their approximate osmolarity and tonicity relative to the normal human cell.

TABLE 5-9 Intravenous Solutions

SOLUTION	ALSO KNOWN AS	OSMOLARITY	TONICITY
0.9% saline*	Normal saline	Isosmotic	Isotonic
D_5—0.9% saline	5% dextrose** in normal saline	Hyperosmotic	Isotonic
D_5W	5% dextrose in water	Isosmotic	Hypotonic
0.45% saline	Half-normal saline	Hyposmotic	Hypotonic
D_5—0.45% saline	5% dextrose in half-normal saline	Hyperosmotic	Hypotonic

* Saline = NaCl. **Dextrose = glucose.

5

CONCEPT CHECK

29. Which of the following solutions has/have the most water per unit volume: 1 M glucose, 1 M NaCl, or 1 OsM NaCl?
30. Two compartments are separated by a membrane that is permeable to water and urea but not to NaCl. Which way will water move when the following solutions are placed in the two compartments?

Compartment A	Membrane	Compartment B
(a) 1 M NaCl	|	1 OsM NaCl
(b) 1 M urea	|	2 M urea
(c) 1 OsM NaCl	|	1 OsM urea

31. You have a patient who lost 1 liter of blood, and you need to restore volume quickly while waiting for a blood transfusion to arrive from the blood bank.
    (a) Which would be better to administer: 5% dextrose (another name for glucose) in water or 0.9% NaCl in water? (Hint: think about how these solutes distribute in the body.) Defend your choice.
    (b) How much of your solution of choice would you have to administer to return blood volume to normal?

Answers: p. 173

THE RESTING MEMBRANE POTENTIAL

Many of the body's solutes, including organic compounds such as pyruvate and lactate, are ions and therefore carry a net electrical charge. Potassium (K^+) is the major cation within cells, and sodium (Na^+) dominates the extracellular fluid (see Fig. 5-3, p. 131). Chloride ions (Cl^-) mostly remain with Na^+ in the extracellular fluid, whereas phosphate ions and negatively charged proteins are the major anions of the intracellular fluid.

However, the intracellular compartment is not electrically neutral: there are some protein anions inside cells that do not have matching cations, giving the cells a net negative charge. At the same time, the extracellular compartment has a net positive charge: some cations in the extracellular fluid do not have matching anions. One consequence of this uneven distribution of ions is that the intracellular and extracellular compartments are not in electrical equilibrium. Instead, the two compartments exist in a state of electrical disequilibrium [page 131].

The concept of electrical disequilibrium has traditionally been taught in chapters on nerve and muscle function because those tissues generate electrical signals known as action potentials. Yet one of the most exciting recent discoveries in physiology is the realization that other kinds of cells also use electrical signals for communication. In fact, all living organisms, including plants, use electrical signals! This section reviews the basic principles of electricity and discusses what creates electrical disequilibrium in the body. The chapter ends with a look at how beta cells of the pancreas use changes in the distribution of ions across cell membranes to trigger insulin secretion.

Electricity Review Atoms are electrically neutral [p. 20]. They are composed of positively charged protons, negatively charged electrons, and uncharged neutrons, but in balanced proportions, so that an atom is neither positive nor negative. The removal or addition of electrons to an atom creates the charged particles we know as ions. We have discussed several ions that are important in the human body, such as Na^+, K^+, and H^+. For each of these positive ions, somewhere in the body there is a matching electron, usually found as part of a negative ion. For example, when Na^+ in the body enters in the form of NaCl, the "missing" electron from Na^+ can be found on the Cl^-.

The following principles are important to remember when dealing with electricity in physiological systems:

1. The **law of conservation of electrical charge** states that the net amount of electrical charge produced in any process is zero. This means that for every positive charge on an ion, there is an electron on another ion. Overall, the human body is electrically neutral.
2. Opposite charges (+ and −) are attracted to each other, but two charges of the same type (+ and +, or − and −) repel each other. The protons and electrons in an atom exhibit this attraction.

3. Separating positive charges from negative charges requires energy. For example, energy is needed to separate the protons and electrons of an atom.
4. If separated positive and negative charges can move freely toward each other, the material through which they are moving is called a **conductor**. Water is a good conductor of electrical charge. If separated charges are unable to move through the material that separates them, the material is known as an **insulator**. The phospholipid bilayer of the cell membrane is a good insulator, as is the plastic coating on electrical wires.

The word *electricity* comes from the Greek word *elektron,* meaning "amber," the fossilized resin of trees. The Greeks discovered that if they rubbed a rod of amber with cloth, the amber acquired the ability to attract hair and dust. This attraction (called static electricity) arises from the separation of electrical charge that occurs when electrons move from the amber atoms to the cloth. To separate these charged particles, energy (work) must be put into the system. In the case of the amber, work was done by rubbing the rod. In the case of biological systems, the work is usually done by energy stored in ATP and other chemical bonds.

The Cell Membrane Enables Separation of Electrical Charge in the Body

In the body, separation of electrical charge takes place across the cell membrane. This process is shown in Figure 5-32 ■. The diagram shows an artificial cell filled with molecules that dissociate into positive and negative ions, represented by the plus and

RUNNING PROBLEM

Three days after Daniel's sweat test, the lab returns the grim results: salt levels in his sweat are more than twice the normal concentration. Daniel is diagnosed with cystic fibrosis. Now, along with antibiotics to prevent lung infections and therapy to loosen the mucus in his airways, Daniel must begin a regimen of pancreatic enzymes to be taken whenever he eats, for the rest of his life. In cystic fibrosis, thick mucus in the pancreatic ducts blocks the secretion of digestive enzymes into the intestine. Without artificial enzymes, he would starve. Yet even with these treatments, Daniel will probably die before the age of 30.

Question 4:
Why will Daniel starve if he does not take artificial pancreatic enzymes?

129 139 151 157 161 168

(a) Cell and solution are electrically and chemically at equilibrium.

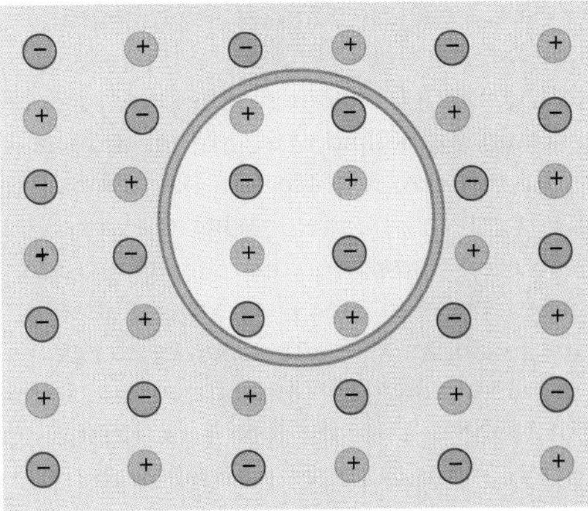

(b) Cell and solution in chemical and electrical disequilbrium. Energy is used to pump one cation out of the cell, leaving a net charge of -1 in the cell and +1 outside the cell.

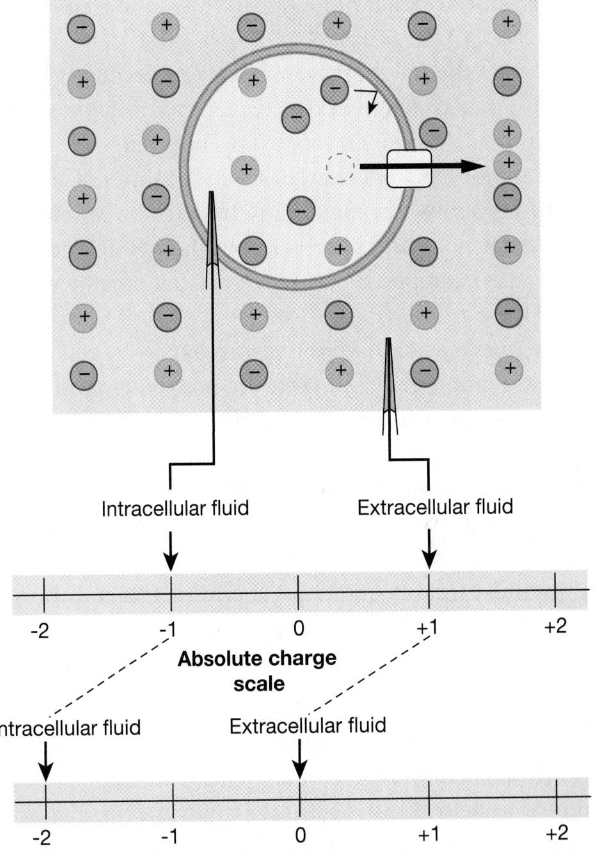

(c) On an absolute charge scale, the extracellular fluid (ECF) would be at +1 and the intracellular fluid (ICF) at -1. Physiological measurements, however, are always on a relative scale, on which the extracellular fluid is assigned a value of zero. This shifts the scale to the left and gives the inside of the cell a relative charge of -2.

■ **FIGURE 5-32** ***Separation of electrical charge***

The cell membrane acts as an insulator to prevent free movement of ions between the intracellular and extracellular compartments.

minus signs. Because the molecules were electrically neutral to begin with, there are equal numbers of positive and negative ions inside the cell. The cell is placed in an aqueous solution, also electrically neutral, that contains the same types of cations and anions. The phospholipid bilayer of the artificial cell, like the bilayer of a real cell, is not permeable to ions. Water can freely cross this cell membrane, making the extracellular and intracellular ion concentrations equal. In Figure 5-32a, the system is at osmotic, chemical, and electrical equilibrium.

In Figure 5-32b, an active transport carrier protein is inserted into the membrane. This carrier uses energy to move positive ions out of the cell against their concentration gradient. The negative ions in the cell attempt to follow the positive ions because of the attraction of positive and negative charges. Because the membrane is impermeable to negative ions, however, they remain trapped in the cell. Positive ions outside the cell might try to move into the cell, attracted by the net negative charge of the intracellular fluid, but the membrane does not allow these cations to leak across it.

As soon as the first positive ion leaves the cell, the electrical equilibrium between the extracellular fluid and intracellular fluid is disrupted: the cell's interior has a net charge of -1 while the cell's exterior has a net charge of $+1$. The input of energy to transport ions across the membrane has created an **electrical gradient**—that is, a difference between the net charge in two regions. In this example, the inside of the cell became negative relative to the outside.

The active transport of positive ions out of the cell also creates a concentration gradient: there are now more positive ions outside the cell than inside. The combination of electrical and concentration gradients is called an **electrochemical gradient**. The cell remains in osmotic equilibrium because water can move freely across the membrane in response to solute movement.

An electrical gradient between the extracellular fluid and the intracellular fluid is known as the **resting membrane potential difference**, or **membrane potential** for short. Although the name sounds intimidating, we can break it apart to see what it means.

1. The *resting* part of the name comes from the fact that this electrical gradient is seen in all living cells, even those that appear to be without electrical activity. In these "resting" cells, the membrane potential has reached a steady state and is not changing.
2. The *potential* part of the name comes from the fact that the electrical gradient created by active transport of ions across the cell membrane is a form of stored, or potential, energy, just as concentration gradients are a form of potential energy. When oppositely charged molecules come back together, they release energy that can be used to do work, in the same way that molecules moving down their concentration gradient can do work. The work done by electrical energy includes opening voltage-gated membrane channels and sending electrical signals.
3. The *difference* part of the name is to remind you that the membrane potential represents a difference in the amount of electrical charge inside and outside the cell. The word *difference* is usually dropped from the name, as noted earlier.

In living systems, we measure electrical gradients on a relative scale rather than an absolute scale. Figure 5-32c compares the two scales. On the absolute scale, the extracellular fluid in our simple example has a net charge of $+1$ from the positive ion it gained, and the intracellular fluid has a net charge of -1 from the now-unbalanced negative ion that was left behind.

However, in real life we cannot measure the charges as numbers of electrons gained or lost. Instead we use a device that measures the *difference* in electrical charge between two points. This device artificially sets the net electrical charge of one side of the membrane at zero and measures the net charge of the second side relative to the first. In our example, resetting the extracellular fluid net charge to zero gives the intracellular fluid a net charge of -2, and we call this value the cell's resting membrane potential.

The equipment for measuring a cell's membrane potential is depicted in Figure 5-33 ■. *Electrodes* are created from hollow glass tubes drawn to very fine points. These *micropipets* are filled with a liquid that conducts electricity and then connected to a *voltmeter,* which measures the electrical difference between two points in units of either volts (V) or millivolts (mV). A *recording electrode* is inserted through the cell membrane into the cytoplasm of the cell. A *reference electrode* is placed in the external bath, which represents the extracellular fluid.

In living systems, by convention, the extracellular fluid is designated as the *ground* and assigned a charge of 0 mV (Fig. 5-32c). When the recording electrode is placed inside a living cell, the voltmeter measures the membrane potential—in other words, the electrical difference between the intracellular fluid and the extracellular fluid. A chart recorder connected to the voltmeter can make a recording of the membrane potential versus time.

For nerve and muscle cells, the voltmeter will record a resting membrane potential between -40 and -90 mV, indicating that the intracellular fluid is negative relative to the extracellular fluid (0 mV). (Throughout this discussion, remember that, as you saw in Figure 5-32c, the extracellular fluid is not really neutral because it has excess positive charges that exactly balance the excess negative charges inside the cell. The total body remains electrically neutral at all times.)

The Resting Membrane Potential Is Due Mostly to Potassium

Which ions create the resting membrane potential in animal cells? The artificial cell shown in Figure 5-32b used an active transport protein to move an unspecified positively charged ion across a membrane that was otherwise impermeable to ions. But what processes go on in living cells to create an electrical gradient?

Real cells are not completely impermeable to all ions. They have open channels and protein transporters that allow ions to

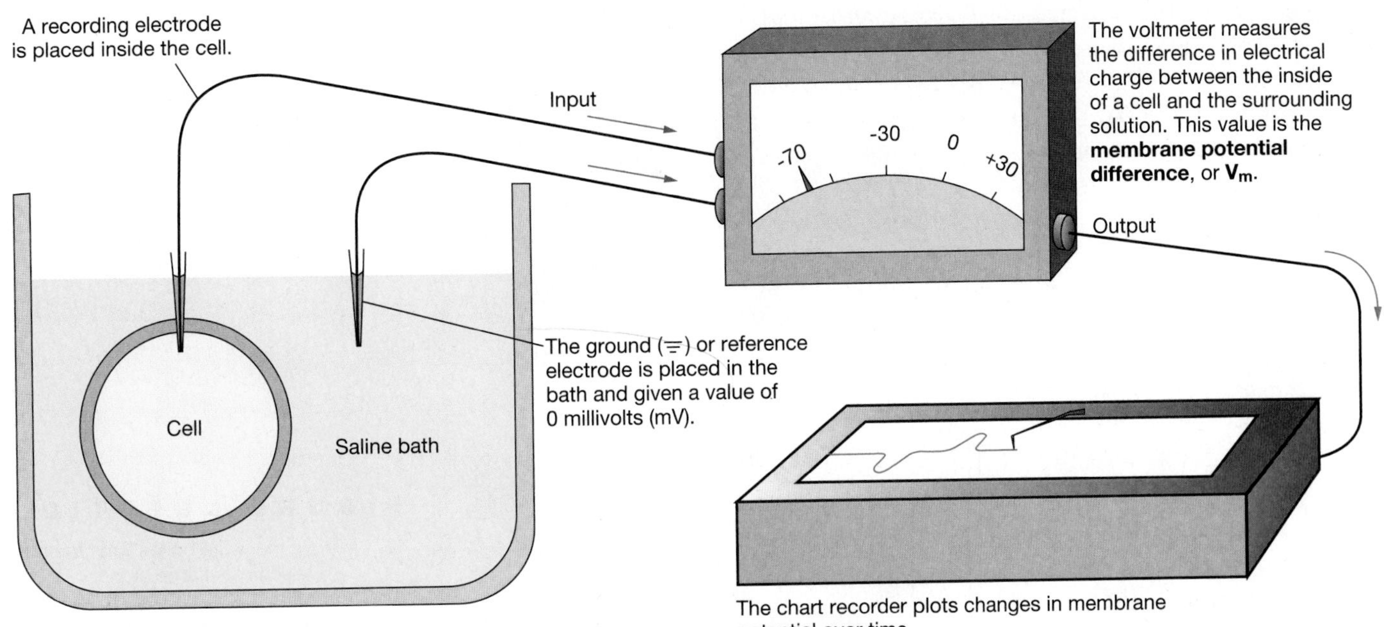
A recording electrode is placed inside the cell.
Input
-70
-30
0
+30
The voltmeter measures the difference in electrical charge between the inside of a cell and the surrounding solution. This value is the membrane potential difference, or V_m.
Output
The ground (⏚) or reference electrode is placed in the bath and given a value of 0 millivolts (mV).
Cell
Saline bath
The chart recorder plots changes in membrane potential over time.

FIGURE 5-33 ***Measuring membrane potential difference***

In the laboratory, a voltmeter measures the difference in electrical charge between the inside of a cell and the surrounding solution.

move between the cytoplasm and the extracellular fluid. We can use a different artificial cell to show how the resting membrane potential arises in a typical living cell.

The artificial cell in Figure 5-34a ■ has a membrane that is impermeable to ions. The cell contains K^+ and large negatively charged proteins, represented by Pr^-. The cell is placed in a solution of Na^+ and Cl^-. Both the cell and the solution are electrically neutral, and the system is in electrical equilibrium. However, it is not in chemical equilibrium. There are concentration gradients for all four types of ions in the system, and they would all diffuse down their respective concentration gradients if they could cross the cell membrane.

In Figure 5-34b, a K^+ leak channel is inserted into the membrane, making it permeable only to K^+. Because there is no K^+ in the extracellular fluid initially, some K^+ will leak out of the cell, moving down their concentration gradient. As K^+ leaves the cell, the negatively charged proteins, Pr^-, are unable to follow because the cell membrane is not permeable to them. The proteins gradually build up a negative charge inside the cell as more and more K^+ diffuses out of the cell.

If the only force acting on K^+ were the concentration gradient, K^+ would leak out of the cell until the K^+ concentration inside the cell equaled the K^+ concentration outside. The loss of positive ions from the cell creates an electrical gradient, however. Because opposite charges attract each other, the negative Pr^- inside the cell try to pull K^+ back into the cell. At some point in this process, the electrical force attracting K^+ into the cell becomes equal in magnitude to the chemical concentration gradient driving K^+ out of the cell. At that point, net movement of K^+ across the membrane stops (Fig. 5-34c). The rate at which K^+ move out of the cell down the concentration gradient is exactly equal to the rate at which K^+ move into the cell down the electrical gradient.

In a cell that is permeable to only one ion, such as the artificial cell just described, the membrane potential that exactly opposes the concentration gradient of the ion is known as the **equilibrium potential**, or E_{ion} (where the subscript *ion* is replaced by the symbol for whichever ion we are looking at). For example, when the concentration gradient is 150 mM K^+ inside and 5 mM K^+ outside the cell, the equilibrium potential for potassium, or E_K, is −90 mV. The equilibrium potential for any ion at 37° C (human body temperature) can be calculated using the Nernst equation:

$$E_{ion} = \frac{61}{z} \log \frac{[\text{ion}]_{out}}{[\text{ion}]_{in}}$$

where 61 is 2.303 RT/F at 37° C,*
z is the electrical charge on the ion (+1 for K^+), and
$[\text{ion}]_{out}$ and $[\text{ion}]_{in}$ are the ion concentration outside and inside the cell.

Now we will use the same artificial cell (K^+ and Pr^- inside, Na^+ and Cl^- outside), but this time we will make the membrane permeable only to Na^+ (Fig. 5-35■). Because Na^+ is more concentrated outside the cell, some Na^+ moves into the cell and accumulates there. Meanwhile, Cl^- left behind in the extracellular

*R is the ideal gas constant, T is absolute temperature, and F is the Faraday constant. For additional information, see Appendix B.

(a) An artificial cell whose membrane is impermeable to ions is filled with K+ and large protein anions. It is placed in a solution of Na+ and Cl⁻. Both cell and solution are electrically neutral.

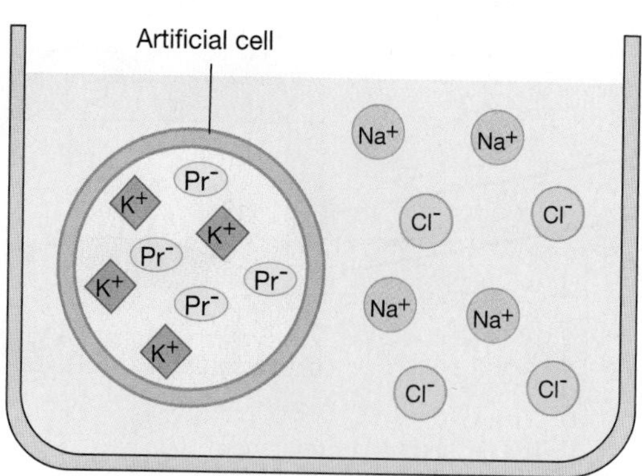

(b) A K+ leak channel is inserted into the membrane. K+ leaks out of the cell because there is a K+ concentration gradient.

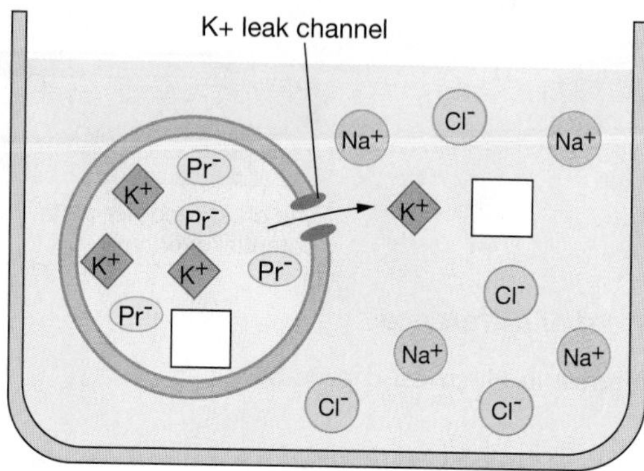

FIGURE QUESTION

In the white boxes write the net electrical charge of the intracellular and extracellular compartments as shown.

(c) The negative membrane potential attracts K+ back into the cell. When the electrical gradient exactly opposes the K+ concentration gradient, the resting membrane potential is the **equilibrium potential** for K+ (E_K).

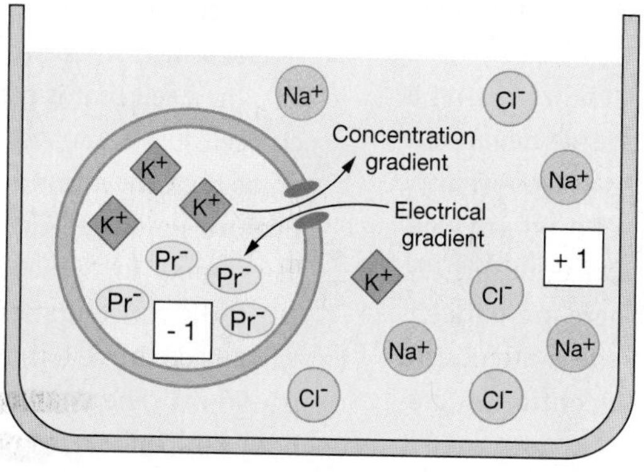

FIGURE QUESTION

Why don't Na+, Cl⁻, and the proteins (Pr⁻) cross the membrane?

■ **FIGURE 5-34** ***Potassium equilibrium potential***

The potassium equilibrium potential, or E_K, is the membrane potential at which the chemical and electrical gradients are equal in magnitude and opposite in direction, resulting in no net movement of K^+.

fluid gives that compartment a net negative charge. This imbalance creates an electrical gradient that tends to drive Na^+ back out of the cell. When the Na^+ concentration is 150 mM outside and 15 mM inside, the equilibrium potential for Na^+ (E_{Na}) is +60 mV. In other words, the concentration gradient moving Na^+ into the cell (150 mM outside, 15 mM inside) is exactly opposed by a positive membrane potential of +60 mV.

In reality, living cells are not permeable to only one ion. The situation in real cells is similar to a combination of the two artificial systems just described. If a cell is permeable to several ions, we cannot use the Nernst equation to calculate membrane potential. Instead we must use a related equation called the *Goldman equation* that considers concentration gradients of the permeable ions and the relative permeability of the cell to each ion. For more detail on the Goldman equation, see Chapter 8.

The cell illustrated in Figure 5-36 ■ has a resting membrane potential of −70 mV. Most cells are about 40 times more permeable to K^+ than to Na^+, and as a result a cell's resting membrane potential is closer to the E_K of −90 mV than to the E_{Na} of +60 mV. A small amount of Na^+ leaks into the cell, making the

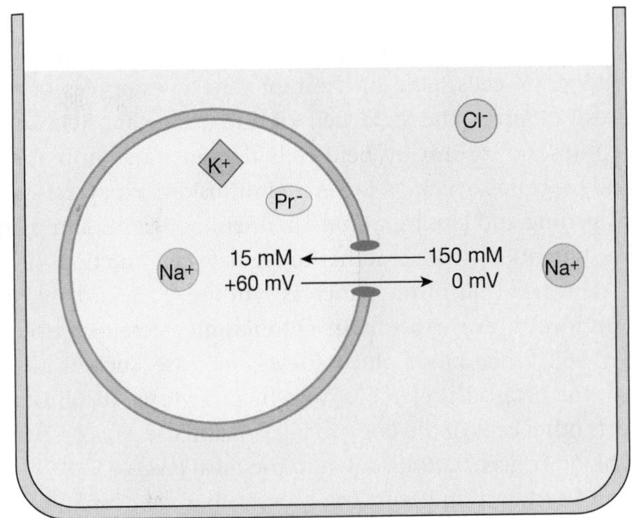

■ **FIGURE 5-35** ***Sodium equilibrium potential***

In this book, ion channels will be represented by open pores on the membrane.

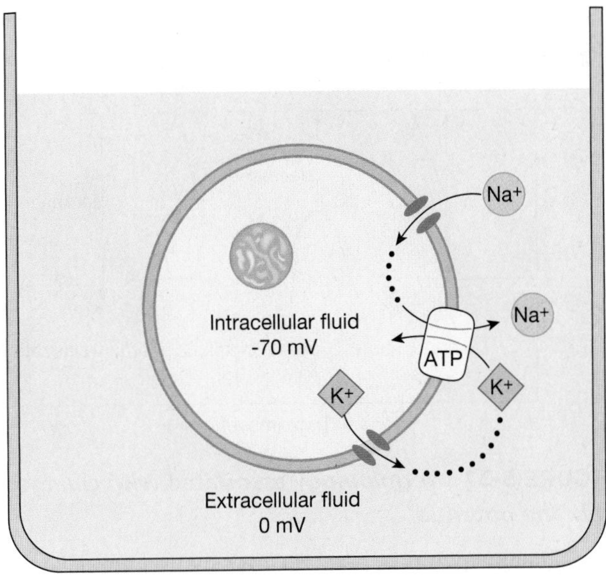

FIGURE QUESTIONS

- What force(s) promote(s) Na^+ leak into the cell?
- What force(s) promote(s) K^+ leak out of the cell?

■ **FIGURE 5-36** ***Resting membrane potential in an actual cell***

Most cells in the human body are about 40 times more permeable to K^+ than to Na^+, and the resting membrane potential is about −70 mV.

inside of the cell less negative than it would be if Na^+ were totally excluded. Additional Na^+ that leaks in is promptly pumped out by the Na^+-K^+-ATPase, as described earlier. At the same time, K^+ ions that leak out of the cell are pumped back in. The pump contributes to the membrane potential by pumping 3 Na^+ out for every 2 K^+ pumped in. Because the Na^+-K^+-ATPase helps maintain the electrical gradient, it is called an *electrogenic* pump.

Not all ion transport creates an electrical gradient. Many transporters, like the Na^+-K^+-2 Cl^- (NKCC) symporter, are electrically neutral. Some make an even exchange: for each charge that enters the cell, the same charge leaves. An example is the HCO_3^--Cl^- antiporter of red blood cells, which transports these ions in a one-for-one, electrically neutral exchange. Electrically neutral transporters have little effect on the resting membrane potential of the cell.

CONCEPT CHECK

32. Add a Cl^- leak channel to the artificial cell shown in Figure 5-34a, and then figure out which way Cl^- will move along the concentration and electrical gradients. Will the Cl^- equilibrium potential be positive or negative?
33. What would happen to the resting membrane potential of a cell poisoned with ouabain (an inhibitor of the Na^+-K^+-ATPase)? Answers: p. 173

Changes in Ion Permeability Change the Membrane Potential

As you have just learned, two factors influence a cell's membrane potential: (1) the concentration gradients of different ions across the membrane and (2) the permeability of the membrane to those ions. If the cell's permeability to an ion changes, the cell's membrane potential changes. We monitor changes in membrane potential using the same intracellular recording electrodes that we use to record resting membrane potential (Fig. 5-33).

Figure 5-37 ■ shows a recording of membrane potential plotted against time. The membrane potential (V_m) begins at a steady resting value of −70 mV. When the trace moves upward (becomes less negative), the potential difference between the inside of the cell and the outside (set at 0 mV) decreases, and the cell is said to have *depolarized*. A return to the resting membrane potential is termed *repolarization*. If the resting potential moves away from 0 mV, the membrane potential becomes more negative, the potential difference has increased, and the cell has *hyperpolarized*.

A major point of confusion when talking about changes in membrane potential is the use of the phrases "the membrane potential decreased" or "the membrane potential increased." Normally, we associate "increase" with becoming more positive and "decrease" with becoming more negative—the opposite of what is happening in our cell discussion. One way to avoid confusion is to add the word *difference* after *membrane potential*. If the membrane potential *difference* is *increasing*, the value of V_m must be moving away from the ground value of zero and becoming *more negative*. If the membrane potential *difference* is

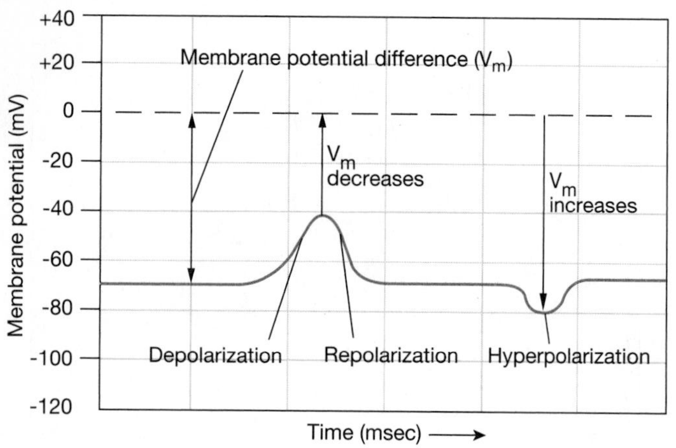

■ **FIGURE 5-37** ***Terminology associated with changes in membrane potential***

If the membrane potential becomes less negative, the cell depolarizes. If the membrane potential becomes more negative than the resting potential, the cell hyperpolarizes.

decreasing, the value of V_m is moving closer to the ground value of 0 mV and is becoming *less negative.*

Four ions usually contribute the most to changes in membrane potential: Na^+, Ca^{2+}, Cl^-, and K^+. The first three are more concentrated in the extracellular fluid than in the cytosol, and the resting cell is minimally permeable to them. If a cell suddenly becomes more permeable to any one of these ions, then those ions will move across the membrane into the cell. Entry of Ca^{2+} or Na^+ will depolarize the cell (make the membrane potential more positive). Entry of Cl^- will hyperpolarize the cell (make the membrane potential more negative).

Most resting cells are fairly permeable to K^+, but making them more permeable will allow even more K^+ to leak out. The cell will hyperpolarize until it approaches the equilibrium potential for K^+. Making the cell *less* permeable to K^+ allows fewer K^+ to leak out of the cell. When the cell retains K^+, it becomes more positive and depolarizes. You will encounter instances of all these permeability changes as you study physiology.

It is important to remember that a significant change in membrane potential requires the movement of very few ions. *You need not reverse the concentration gradient to change the membrane potential.* For example, to change the membrane potential by 100 mV, only one of every 100,000 K^+ must enter or leave the cell. This is such a tiny fraction of the total number of K^+ in the cell that the concentration of K^+ remains essentially unchanged.

INTEGRATED MEMBRANE PROCESSES: INSULIN SECRETION

The movement of Na^+ and K^+ across cell membranes has been known to play a role in generating electrical signals in excitable tissues for many years. You will study these processes in detail in the chapters on the nervous and muscular systems. Recently, however, we have come to understand that small changes in membrane potential act as signals in nonexcitable tissues, such as endocrine cells. One of the best-studied examples of this process involves the beta cell of the pancreas. Release of the hormone insulin by beta cells demonstrates how membrane processes—such as facilitated diffusion, exocytosis, and the opening and closing of ion channels by ligands and membrane potential—work together to regulate cell function.

The beta cells of the pancreas synthesize the protein hormone insulin and store it in cytoplasmic secretory vesicles [p. 66]. When blood glucose levels increase, such as after a meal, the beta cells release insulin by exocytosis. Insulin then directs other cells of the body to take up and use glucose, bringing blood concentrations down to pre-meal levels.

A key question about the process that went unanswered until recently was, "How does a beta cell 'know' that glucose levels have gone up and that it needs to release insulin?" The answer, we have now learned, links the beta cell's metabolism to its electrical activity.

Figure 5-38a ■ shows a beta cell at rest. Recall from earlier sections in this chapter that the gates of membrane channels can be opened or closed by chemical or electrical signals. The beta cell has two such channels that help control insulin release. One is a **voltage-gated Ca^{2+} channel**. This channel is closed at the cell's resting membrane potential (⑤ in Fig. 5-38a). The other is a K^+ leak channel (that is, the channel is usually open) that closes when ATP binds to it. It is called an **ATP-gated K^+ channel**, or **K_{ATP} channel**. In the resting cell, when glucose concentrations are low, the cell makes less ATP ① through ③. There is little ATP to bind to the K_{ATP} channel, and the channel remains open, allowing K^+ to leak out of the cell ④. At the resting membrane potential, the voltage-gated Ca^{2+} channels are closed, and there is no insulin secretion ⑤.

Figure 5-38b shows a beta cell secreting insulin. Following a meal, plasma glucose levels increase as glucose is absorbed from the intestine ①. Glucose reaching the beta cell diffuses into the cell with the aid of a GLUT transporter. Increased glucose in the cell stimulates the metabolic pathways of glycolysis and the citric acid cycle [p. 103], and ATP production increases ②, ③. When ATP binds to the K_{ATP} channel, the gate to the channel closes, preventing K^+ from leaking out of the cell ④. Retention of K^+ depolarizes the cell ⑤, which then causes the voltage-sensitive Ca^{2+} channels to open ⑥. Calcium ions enter the cell from the extracellular fluid, moving down their electrochemical gradient. The Ca^{2+} binds to proteins that initiate exocytosis of the insulin-containing vesicles, and insulin is released into the extracellular space ⑦.

The discovery that cells other than nerve and muscle cells use changes in membrane potential as signals for physiological responses changes our traditional thinking about the role of the resting membrane potential. In the next chapter, we will describe some other types of signals that the body uses for communication and coordination.

(a) Beta cell at rest. The K_{ATP} channel is open and the cell is at its resting membrane potential.

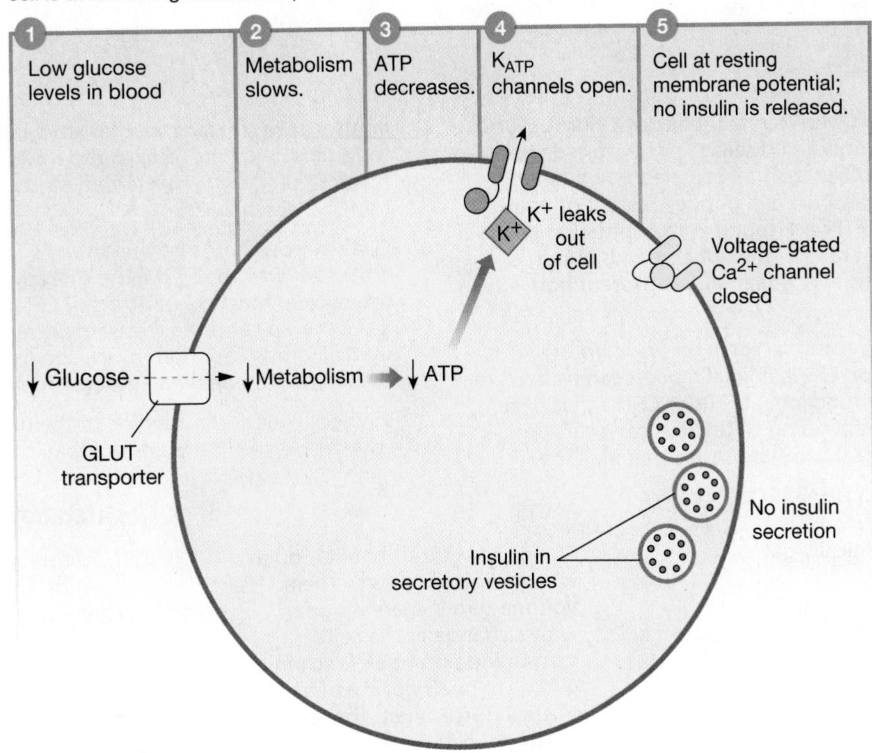
1
Low glucose levels in blood
2
Metabolism slows.
3
ATP decreases.
4
KATP channels open.
5
Cell at resting membrane potential; no insulin is released.
K+
K+ leaks out of cell
Voltage-gated Ca2+ channel closed
↓ Glucose
↓ Metabolism
↓ ATP
GLUT transporter
No insulin secretion
Insulin in secretory vesicles

(b) Beta cell secreting insulin. Closure of the K_{ATP} channel depolarizes the cell, triggering exocytosis of insulin.

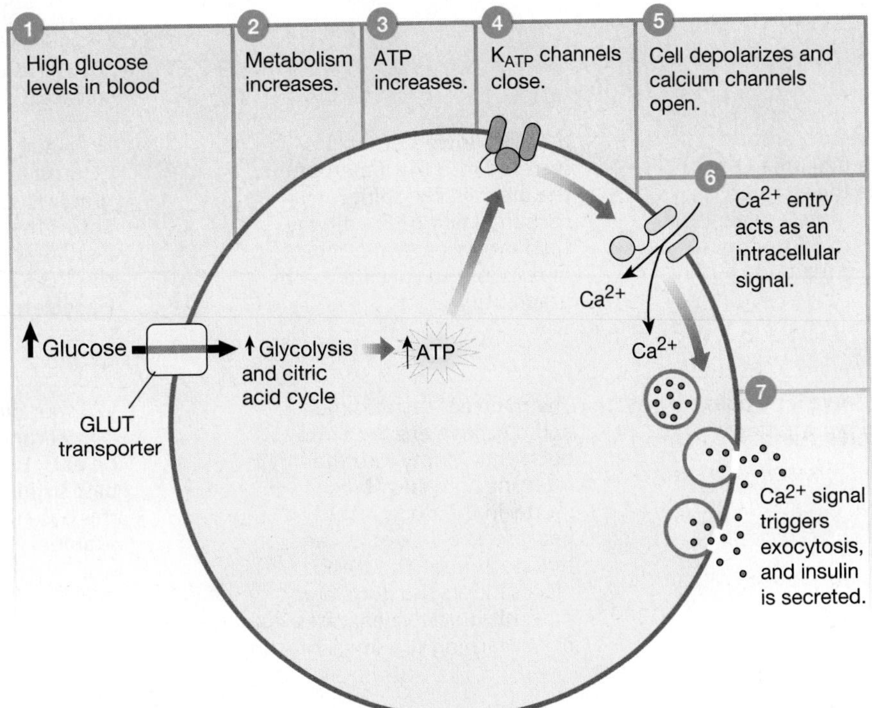
1
High glucose levels in blood
2
Metabolism increases.
3
ATP increases.
4
KATP channels close.
5
Cell depolarizes and calcium channels open.
6
Ca2+ entry acts as an intracellular signal.
Ca2+
Ca2+
↑ Glucose
↑ Glycolysis and citric acid cycle
↑ ATP
GLUT transporter
7
Ca2+ signal triggers exocytosis, and insulin is secreted.

■ **FIGURE 5-38** ***Insulin secretion and membrane transport processes***

RUNNING PROBLEM CONCLUSION

CYSTIC FIBROSIS

In this running problem, you learned that cystic fibrosis, one of the most common inherited diseases in the United States, is caused by a defect in the channel protein known as CFTR, which regulates the transport of chloride ions out of epithelial cells. Because CFTRs are found in the epithelial cell membranes of several organs—the sweat glands, lungs, and pancreas—cystic fibrosis may affect many different body processes.

Some of the most interesting research on cystic fibrosis uses genetically altered mice. These animal models can be bred to have either totally nonfunctional CFTRs or CFTRs that have altered functions corresponding to the mutations of the CFTR gene in humans. An excellent review paper, "The CF mouse: an important tool for studying cystic fibrosis," can be found in the online journal *Expert Reviews in Molecular Medicine* at *http://www-ermm.cbcu.cam.ac.uk/ 01002551h.htm* (12 March 2001).

Cystic fibrosis is one of the diseases for which clinical trials are under way to see if gene therapy can successfully restore the normal function of affected CFTRs. To learn more about gene therapy and the status of current research, go to the Cystic Fibrosis Foundation website (*www.cff.org*) and click on the link to Research and Clinical Trials.

To check your understanding of the running problem, compare your answers with the information in the following table.

	QUESTION	FACTS	INTEGRATION AND ANALYSIS
1	Is the CFTR a chemically gated, a voltage-gated, or a mechanically gated channel protein?	Chemically gated channels open when a ligand binds to them. Voltage-gated channels open with a change in the cell's membrane potential. Mechanically gated channels open when a physical force opens the channel. CFTRs open in response to the binding of nucleotides.	Nucleotides are chemical ligands; therefore,CFTRs are chemically gated channel proteins.
2	Based on the information given, is the CFTR on the apical or basolateral surface of the sweat gland epithelium?	In normal people, the CFTRs move Cl^- from sweat into epithelial cells.	The epithelial surface that faces the lumen of the sweat gland, which contains sweat, is the apical membrane. Therefore, the CFTRs are on the apical surface.
3	Why would failure to transport chloride ions into the lumen of the airways cause the secreted mucus to be thick? (*Hint*: remember that water moves to dilute the more concentrated region.)	If Cl^- (followed by Na^+) is secreted into the lumen of the airways, the solute concentration of the airway fluid increases. Water moves in response to concentration gradients.	Normally, the movement of Cl^- and Na^+ creates an osmotic gradient so that water also enters the airway lumen, creating a saline solution that thins the thick mucus. If Cl^- cannot be secreted into the airways, there will be no fluid movement to thin the mucus.
4	Why will Daniel starve if he does not take artificial pancreatic enzymes?	The pancreas secretes mucus and digestive enzymes into ducts that empty into the small intestine. In cystic fibrosis, mucus in the ducts is thick because of a lack of Cl^- and fluid secretion. This thick mucus blocks the ducts and prevents digestive enzymes from reaching the small intestine.	Without digestive enzymes, Daniel cannot digest the food he eats. His weight loss over the past six months suggests that this has already became a problem.Taking artificial enzymes will enable him to digest his food.

129 139 151 157 161 168

CHAPTER SUMMARY

In this chapter you learned how the cell membrane acts as a barrier to create distinct intracellular and extracellular compartments, repeating the theme of *compartmentation* that was introduced in Chapters 3 and 4. Movement of materials from one compartment to another illustrates a new theme, *mass flow*. Mass flow across cell membranes occurs in response to osmotic, chemical (concentration), or electrical gradients. The selectively permeable cell membrane creates resistance to mass flow that can be overcome by changing the composition of the membrane lipids or by inserting membrane proteins that act as channels or transporters. *Movement of substances* in the body requires energy from different sources: molecular motion, concentration gradients, or chemical bonds. Finally, the theme of *protein interactions* is exemplified in the binding of substrates to transporters.

Mass Balance and Homeostasis

IP Fluids and Electrolytes: Introduction to Body Fluids

1. The **law of mass balance** says that if the amount of a substance in the body is to remain constant, any input must be offset by an equal loss. (p. 129; Fig. 5-1)
2. Input of a substance into the body comes from metabolism or from the outside environment. Output occurs through metabolism or **excretion**. (p. 130; Fig. 5-2)
3. **Clearance** is the rate at which a material is removed from the blood by excretion, metabolism, or both. The liver, kidneys, lungs, and skin all clear substances from the blood. (p. 130)
4. The rate of intake, production, or output of a substance x is expressed as **mass flow**, where mass flow = concentration × volume flow. (p. 130)
5. Cells and the extracellular fluid both maintain homeostasis, but without being in equilibrium with each other. Most solutes are concentrated in either one compartment or the other, creating a state of **chemical disequilibrium**. (p. 130; Fig. 5-3)
6. Cations and anions are not distributed equally between the body compartments, creating a state of **electrical disequilibrium**. (p. 131)
7. Water moves freely between the cells and extracellular fluid, resulting in a state of **osmotic equilibrium**. (p. 130)

Diffusion

8. The cell membrane is a selectively permeable barrier that restricts free exchange between the cell and the interstitial fluid. The movement of a substance across the membrane depends on the **permeability** of the membrane to that substance. (p. 132)
9. Movement of molecules across membranes can be classified either by energy requirements or by the physical means the molecule uses to cross the membrane. (p. 132; Fig. 5-4)
10. Lipid-soluble substances can diffuse through the phospholipid bilayer. Less lipid-soluble molecules require the assistance of a membrane protein to cross the membrane. (p. 132)
11. **Passive transport** does not require the input of energy. (p. 132)
12. **Diffusion** is the passive movement of molecules down a chemical (concentration) gradient from an area of higher concentration to an area of lower concentration. Net movement stops when the system reaches **equilibrium**, although molecular movement continues. (p. 133; Fig. 5-5)
13. Diffusion rate depends on the magnitude of the concentration gradient. Diffusion is slow over long distances, is directly related to temperature, and is inversely related to molecular size. (p. 135)
14. **Simple diffusion** across a membrane is directly proportional to membrane surface area, concentration gradient, and membrane permeability, and inversely proportional to membrane thickness. (p. 135; Fig. 5-6)

Protein-Mediated Transport

15. Most molecules cross membranes with the aid of membrane proteins. (p. 137)
16. Membrane proteins have four functional roles: **structural proteins** maintain cell shape and form cell junctions; **membrane-associated enzymes** catalyze chemical reactions and help transfer signals across the membrane; **receptor proteins** are part of the body's signaling system; and **transport proteins** move many molecules into or out of the cell. (pp. 137–138; Fig. 5-7)
17. **Channel proteins** form water-filled channels that link the intracellular and extracellular compartments. **Gated channels** regulate movement of substances through them by opening and closing. Gated channels are regulated by ligands, by the electrical state of the cell, or by physical changes such as pressure. (pp. 138–139; Fig. 5-11)
18. **Carrier proteins** never form a continuous connection between the intracellular and extracellular fluid. They bind to substrates, then change conformation. (p. 138; Fig. 5-9b)
19. Protein-mediated diffusion is called **facilitated diffusion**. It has the same properties as simple diffusion. (p. 141; Tbl. 5-1; Figs. 5-13, 5-14)
20. **Active transport** moves molecules against their concentration gradient and requires an outside source of energy. In **primary (direct) active transport**, the energy comes directly from ATP. **Secondary (indirect) active transport** uses the potential energy stored in a concentration gradient and is indirectly driven by energy from ATP. (p. 142)
21. The most important primary active transporter is the **sodium-potassium ATPase** (Na^+-K^+-ATPase), which pumps Na^+ out of the cell and K^+ into the cell. (pp. 142–143; Fig. 5-16)
22. Most secondary active transport systems are driven by the sodium concentration gradient. (p. 144; Tbl. 5-3; Fig. 5-17)
23. All carrier-mediated transport demonstrates **specificity**, **competition**, and **saturation**. Specificity refers to the ability of a transporter to move only one molecule or a group of closely related molecules. Related molecules may compete for a single transporter. Saturation occurs when a group of membrane transporters are working at their maximum rate. (pp. 145–147; Fig. 5-20, 5-22)

Vesicular Transport

24. Large macromolecules and particles are brought into cells by **phagocytosis** and **endocytosis**. Material leaves cells by **exocytosis**. When vesicles that come into the cytoplasm by endocytosis are returned to the cell membrane, the process is called **membrane recycling**. (p. 148; Figs. 5-23, 5-24)

25. In **receptor-mediated endocytosis**, ligands bind to membrane receptors that concentrate in **clathrin-coated pits**, the site of endocytosis. In **potocytosis**, receptors are located in **caveolae** that have a nonclathrin protein coating. (pp. 149–150; Fig. 5-24)
26. In exocytosis, the vesicle membrane fuses with the cell membrane before releasing its contents into the extracellular space. Exocytosis requires ATP. (p. 150)

Transepithelial Transport

27. Transporting epithelia in the intestine and kidney have different membrane proteins on their **apical** and **basolateral** surfaces. This polarization allows one-way movement of molecules across the epithelium. (pp. 150–151; Figs. 5-25, 5-26)
28. Larger molecules cross epithelia by **transcytosis**, which includes **vesicular transport**. (p. 153; Fig. 5-27)

Osmosis and Tonicity

29. The movement of water across a membrane in response to a concentration gradient is called **osmosis**. (p. 154; Fig. 5-29)
30. To compare solution concentrations, we express the concentration in terms of **osmolarity**, the number of particles (ions or intact molecules) per liter of solution, expressed as milliosmoles per liter (mOsM). (p. 156)
31. **Tonicity** of a solution describes the cell volume change that occurs when the cell is placed in that solution. Cells swell in **hypotonic solutions** and shrink in **hypertonic solutions**. If the cell does not change size at equilibrium, the solution is **isotonic**. (p. 157)
32. The osmolarity of a solution cannot be used to determine the tonicity of the solution. The relative concentrations of **nonpenetrating solutes** in the cell and in the solution determine tonicity. **Penetrating solutes** contribute to the osmolarity of a solution but not to its tonicity. (p. 157; Fig. 5-30, 5-31)

The Resting Membrane Potential

IP Nervous I: The Membrane Potential

33. Although the total body is electrically neutral, diffusion and active transport of ions across the cell membrane create an **electrical gradient**, with the inside of cells negative relative to the extracellular fluid. (p. 162; Fig. 5-33)
34. The electrical gradient between the extracellular fluid and the intracellular fluid is known as the **resting membrane potential difference.** (p. 162)
35. The movement of an ion across the cell membrane is influenced by the **electrochemical gradient** for that ion. (p. 162)
36. The membrane potential that exactly opposes the concentration gradient of an ion is known as the **equilibrium potential** (E_{ion}). The equilibrium potential for any ion can be calculated using the Nernst equation. (p. 163; Fig. 5-34)
37. In most living cells, K^+ is the primary ion that determines the resting membrane potential. (p. 163)
38. Changes in membrane permeability to ions such as K^+, Na^+, Ca^{2+}, or Cl^- will alter membrane potential and create electrical signals. (p. 166)

Integrated Membrane Processes: Insulin Secretion

39. The use of electrical signals to initiate a cellular response is a universal property of living cells. Pancreatic beta cells release insulin in response to a change in membrane potential. (p. 166; Fig. 5-38)

QUESTIONS

(Answers to the Review Questions begin on page A1.)

The Physiology Place

Access more review material online at **The Physiology Place** website. There you'll find review questions, problem-solving activities, case studies, flashcards, and direct links to both *InterActive Physiology®* and PhysioEx™. To access the site, go to *www.physiologyplace.com* and select Human Physiology, Fourth Edition.

LEVEL ONE REVIEWING FACTS AND TERMS

1. List the four functions of membrane proteins, and give an example of each.
2. Distinguish between active transport and passive transport.
3. Which of the following processes are examples of active transport, and which are examples of passive transport? Simple diffusion, phagocytosis, facilitated diffusion, exocytosis, osmosis, endocytosis, potocytosis.
4. List four factors that will increase the rate of diffusion.
5. Match the membrane channels with the appropriate description(s). Answers may be used once, more than once, or not at all.
   - (a) chemically gated channel
   - (b) open pore
   - (c) voltage-gated channel
   - (d) mechanically gated channel

   1. channel that spends most of its time in the open state
   2. channel that opens in response to a signal
   3. channel that opens when resting membrane potential changes
   4. channel that opens when a ligand binds to it
   5. channel that opens in response to membrane stretch
   6. channel through which water can pass
6. List the three physical methods by which materials enter cells.
7. A cotransporter is a protein that moves more than one molecule at a time. If the molecules are moved in the same direction, the cotransporters are called __________ carriers; if the molecules are transported in opposite directions, the cotransporters are called __________ carriers. A transport protein that moves only one substrate is called a __________ carrier.
8. The two types of active transport are __________, which derives energy directly from ATP, and __________, which couples the kinetic energy of one molecule moving down its concentration gradient to the movement of another molecule against its concentration gradient.

9. A molecule that moves freely between the intracellular and extracellular compartments is said to be a __________ solute. A molecule that is not able to enter cells is called a __________ solute.
10. Rank the following individuals in order of how much body water they contain, from highest to lowest: (a) a 25-year-old, 70-kg male; (b) a 25-year-old, 50-kg female; (c) a 65-year-old, 50-kg female; and (d) a 1-year-old male toddler.
11. What determines the osmolarity of a solution? In what units is body osmolarity usually given?
12. What does it mean if we say that a solution is hypotonic to a cell? Hypertonic to the same cell? What determines the tonicity of a solution relative to a cell?
13. In your own words, state the four principles of electricity important in physiology.
14. Match each of the following items with its primary role in cellular activity.

(a) Na^+-K^+-ATPase	1. ion channel
(b) proteins	2. extracellular cation
(c) unit of measurement for membrane potential	3. source of energy
(d) K^+	4. intracellular anion
(e) Cl^-	5. intracellular cation
(f) ATP	6. millivolts
(g) Na^+	7. electrogenic pump
	8. extracellular anion
	9. milliosmoles

15. The membrane potential at which the electrical gradient exactly opposes the concentration gradient for an ion is known as the __________.
16. A material that allows free movement of electrical charges is called a(n) __________, whereas one that prevents this movement is called a(n) __________.

LEVEL TWO REVIEWING CONCEPTS

17. Create a map of transport across cell membranes using the following terms. You may add additional terms if you wish.

active transport	Na^+-K^+-ATPase
carrier	passive transport
caveolae	phospholipid bilayer
channel	potocytosis
clathrin-coated pit	receptor
concentration gradient	receptor-mediated endocytosis
electrochemical gradient	secondary active transport
exocytosis	simple diffusion
facilitated diffusion	small polar molecule
glucose	transcytosis
GLUT transporter	vesicle
ion	vesicular transport
large polar molecule	water
ligand	
osmosis	

18. Draw a large rectangle to represent the total body volume. Using the information in Figure 5-28, divide the box proportionately into compartments to represent the different body compartments. Use the information in Figure 5-3 and add solutes to the compartments. Use large letters for solutes with higher concentrations, and small letters for solutes with low concentrations. Label the cell membranes and the endothelial membrane.
19. What factors influence the rate of diffusion across a membrane? Briefly explain each one.
20. Define the following terms and explain how they differ from one another: specificity, competition, saturation. Apply these terms in a short explanation of facilitated diffusion of glucose.
21. Red blood cells are suspended in a solution of NaCl. The cells have an osmolarity of 300 mOsM, and the solution has an osmolarity of 250 mOsM. (a) The solution is (hypertonic, isotonic, or hypotonic) to the cells. (b) Water would move (into the cells, out of the cells, or not at all).
22. Two compartments are separated by a membrane that is permeable to glucose. Each compartment is filled with 1 M glucose. After 6 hours, compartment A contains 1.5 M glucose and compartment B contains 0.5 M glucose. What kind of transport occurred?
23. A 2 M NaCl solution and a 2 M glucose solution are placed into two compartments separated by a membrane that is permeable to water but not to NaCl or glucose. Are the following statements true or false? Defend each answer with a short statement.
    (a) The salt solution is isosmotic to the glucose solution.
    (b) The salt solution is hyperosmotic to the glucose solution.
    (c) Water will move from the salt solution to the sugar solution.
    (d) The volume will increase on the glucose side of the membrane.
24. Referring to the previous question, change the molarity of the salt and sugar solutions so that each false statement would become true.
25. Explain the differences between a chemical gradient, an electrical gradient, and an electrochemical gradient.

LEVEL THREE PROBLEM SOLVING

26. Sweat glands secrete into their lumen a fluid that is identical to interstitial fluid. As the fluid moves through the lumen on its way to the surface of the skin, the cells of the sweat gland's epithelium make the fluid hypotonic by removing Na^+ and leaving water behind. Design an epithelial cell that will reabsorb Na^+ but not water. You may place water pores, Na^+ leak channels, K^+ leak channels, and the Na^+-K^+-ATPase in the apical membrane, basolateral membrane, or both.
27. Insulin is a hormone that promotes the movement of glucose into many types of cells, thereby lowering blood glucose concentration. Propose a mechanism that explains how this occurs, using your knowledge of cell membrane transport.
28. The following terms have been applied to membrane transport molecules: specificity, competition, saturation. These terms can also be applied to enzymes. How does the application of these terms change in the two situations? What chemical characteristics do enzymes and transport molecules share that allow these terms to be applied to both?
29. NaCl is a nonpenetrating solute and urea is a penetrating solute for cells. Red blood cells are placed in each of the solutions below. The intracellular concentration of nonpenetrating solute is 300 mOsM. What will happen to the cell volume in each solution? Label each solution with all the terms that apply: hypertonic, isotonic, hypotonic, hyperosmotic, hyposmotic, isosmotic.
    (a) 150 mM NaCl plus 150 mM urea
    (b) 100 mM NaCl plus 50 mM urea
    (c) 100 mM NaCl plus 100 mM urea
    (d) 150 mM NaCl plus 100 mM urea
    (e) 100 mM NaCl plus 150 mM urea
30. Integral membrane glycoproteins have their sugars added as the proteins pass through the lumen of the endoplasmic reticulum and Golgi complex [p. 119]. Based on this information, where would

5

you predict finding the sugar "tails" of the proteins: on the cytoplasmic side of the membrane, the extracellular side, or both? Explain your reasoning.

LEVEL FOUR QUANTITATIVE PROBLEMS

31. The addition of dissolved solutes to water lowers the freezing point of water. A 1 OsM solution depresses the freezing point of water 1.86° C. If a patient's plasma shows a freezing-point depression of 0.550° C, what is her plasma osmolarity? (Assume that 1 kg water = 1 L.)
32. The patient in the previous question is found to have total body water volume of 42 L, ECF volume of 12.5 L, and plasma volume of 2.7 L.
    (a) What is her intracellular fluid (ICF) volume? Her interstitial fluid volume?
    (b) How much solute (osmoles) exists in her whole body? ECF? ICF? plasma? (*Hint*: concentration = solute amount / volume of solution)
33. What is the osmolarity of half-normal saline (= 0.45% NaCl)? [p. 36] Assume that all NaCl molecules dissociate into two ions.
34. If you give 1 L of half-normal saline (see question 33) to the patient in question 32, what happens to each of the following at equilibrium? (*Hint:* NaCl is a nonpenetrating solute.)
    (a) her total body volume
    (b) her total body osmolarity
    (c) her ECF and ICF volumes
    (d) her ECF and ICF osmolarities
35. The following graph shows the results of an experiment in which a cell was placed in a solution of glucose. The cell had no glucose in it at the beginning, and its membrane can transport glucose. Which of the following processes is/are illustrated by this experiment?
    (a) simple diffusion
    (b) saturation
    (c) competition
    (d) active transport

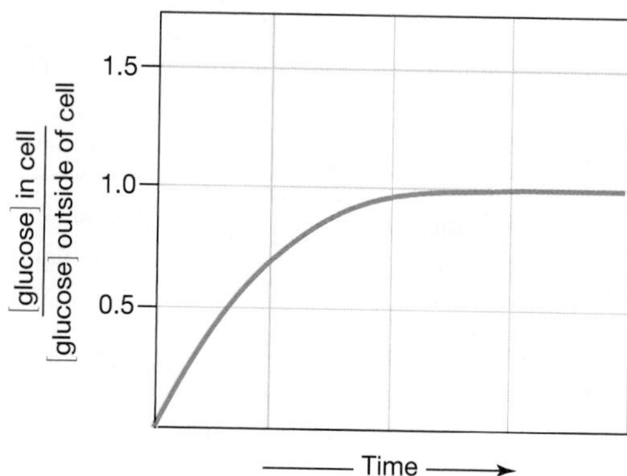

ANSWERS

Answers to Concept Check Questions

Page 130

1. The remaining 1 milligram of salt remains in the body.
2. Glucose metabolism adds CO_2 and water to the body, disturbing the mass balance of these two substances. To maintain mass balance, both metabolites must be either excreted or further metabolized.

Page 132

3. The stem preceding the suffix *–ase* is the name of the substrate on which the enzyme acts; therefore ATP is a substrate for this enzyme.
4. Intracellular fluid has a high K^+ concentration and low Na^+, Cl^-, and Ca^{2+} concentrations.

Page 135

5. If distance doubles, diffusion takes four times as long.

Page 136

6. Energy for diffusion comes from molecular motion.
7. Because it is lipophilic, the fatty acid is more likely to cross by simple diffusion.
8. The diffusion rate (a) decreases, (b) increases, (c) decreases.
9. Compartment A remains yellow, and compartment B turns green.
10. The skin's thick extracellular matrix is generally impermeable to oxygen. Also, oxygen needs a moist surface to effectively diffuse across a membrane.

Page 139

11. Positive ions are cations, and negative ions are anions.

Page 141

12. Membrane proteins serve as structural proteins, receptors, enzymes, and transporters.
13. Ions and water molecules move through open channels.
14. Channel proteins form continuous connections between the two sides of a membrane, transport molecules more quickly, and bind less tightly to their substrates.
15. A channel lined with positive charges will attract anions, which in this instance means Cl^-.
16. Glucose is too large to pass through a channel.

Page 142

17. The direction of facilitated diffusion of glucose reverses, and glucose leaves the cell.

Page 145

18. The ATPase is an antiporter, but the SGLT is a symporter. The ATPase requires energy from ATP to change conformation, whereas the SGLT uses energy stored in the Na^+ concentration gradient.

Page 148

19. An antiporter moves substrates in opposite directions.
20. Larger doors could move more people. This would be analogous to a cell's synthesizing a new isoform of the transporter that would let the transporter move more substrate per second.

Page 150

21. In phagocytosis, the cytoskeleton pushes the membrane out to engulf a particle in a large vesicle. In endocytosis, the membrane surface indents and the vesicle is much smaller.
22. The proteins associated with endocytosis are clathrin and caveolin.
23. Proteins move into cells by endocytosis and out of cells by exocytosis.

Page 153

24. Sodium movement out of the cell requires energy because the direction of ion flow is against the concentration gradient.
25. Ouabain applied to the apical side would have no effect because there are no Na^+-K^+-ATPase molecules on that side. Ouabain applied to the basolateral side will stop the pump. Glucose transport will continue for a time until the Na^+ gradient between the cell and the lumen disappears due to Na^+ entry into the cell.
26. The GLUT2 transporter is illustrated.

Page 153

27. Transcytosis will stop because vesicular transport by the cytoskeleton depends on functioning microtubules.

Page 156

28. The baby has lost 0.91 kg of water, which is 0.91 liter.

Page 160

29. 1 M NaCl = 2 OsM NaCl. The 1 M (= 1 OsM) glucose and 1 OsM NaCl have the most water.
30. (a) Water moves into A because A is 2 OsM; (b) no net movement occurs because urea will diffuse across the membrane until it reaches equilibrium; (c) water moves into A, because A has a higher concentration of nonpenetrating solutes.
31. (a) The NaCl solution is better, even though both solutions are isosmotic to the body (Tbl. 5-9). Because, blood is lost from the extracellular compartment, the best replacement solution would remain in the ECF. Thus glucose is not as good a choice because it slowly enters cells, taking water with it. (b) If 1 L has been lost, you should replace at least 1 L.

Page 165

32. Cl^- will move into the cell down its concentration gradient, which would make the inside of the cell negative. The positive charges left outside would attract Cl^- back outside. The equilibrium potential would be negative.
33. Over time, Na^+ would leak into the cell, and the resting membrane potential would become more positive.

Answers to Figure and Graph Questions

Page 131

Fig. 5-3: 1. Plasma contains proteins and large anions not present in interstitial fluid. 2. The extracellular compartment contains more Na^+, Cl^-, and bicarbonate than the intracellular compartment, and fewer K^+.

Page 147

Fig. 5-22: You should mark the *x*-axis at the point where the curve levels off to a horizontal line.

Page 152

Fig. 5-26: (a) 1 = b; 2 = a; 3 = b. (b) Basolateral glucose transport is passive because the glucose moves down its concentration gradient. (c) Na^+ movement across the apical membrane does not require ATP because Na^+ is moving down its concentration gradient.

Page 155

Fig. 5-28: (1) 25% of 14 L = 3.5 L plasma. 75% = 10.5 L interstitial fluid. (2) Total body water = 42 L. (3) 3.5 L/42 L = 8.3% plasma; 10.5 L/42 L = 25% interstitial volume.

Page 159

Fig. 5-31: (a) isosmotic and isotonic; (b) hyperosmotic and isotonic; (c) hyperosmotic and hypotonic.

Page 164

Fig. 5-34: ICF = −1 and ECF = +1. The cell membrane is not permeable to Na^+, Cl^-, and proteins.

Page 165

Fig. 5-36: (1) Na^+ leak, into the cell is promoted by concentration and electrical gradients. (2) K^+ leaks out of the cell are promoted by the concentration gradient.

6
Future progress in medicine will require a quantitative understanding of the many interconnected networks of molecules that comprise our cells and tissues, their interactions, and their regulation.
—Overview of the NIH Roadmap, 2003

Communication, Integration, and Homeostasis

BACKGROUND BASICS

Homeostasis: **3** Nucleotides: **32** Cell junctions: **69** Extracellular matrix: **68** Endocrine glands: **75** Membrane structure: **53** Membrane proteins: **55, 137** Diffusion: **133** Exocytosis: **148**

RUNNING PROBLEM

DIABETES MELLITUS

It is 8:00 A.M., and Marvin Garcia, age 20, is hungry. He came to his family physician's office before breakfast to have a fasting blood glucose test as part of a routine physical examination. In this test, blood is drawn after an overnight fast, and the glucose concentration in the blood is measured. Because he knows he is in good condition, Marvin isn't worried about the results. He is surprised, then, when the nurse practitioner in the doctor's office calls two days later. "Your fasting blood sugar is a bit elevated, Marvin. It is 150 milligrams per deciliter, and normal is 110 or less. Does anyone in your family have diabetes?" "Well, yeah—my dad has it. What exactly is diabetes?"

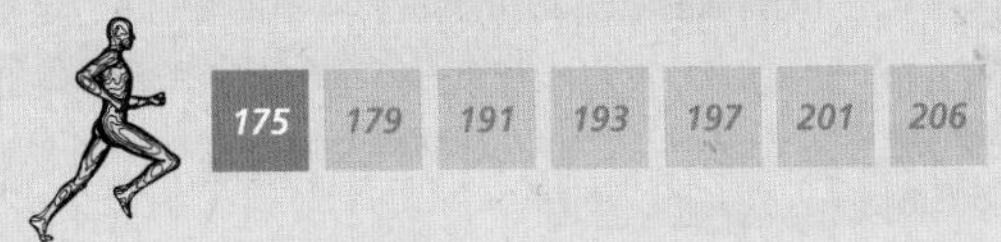

In 2003 the United States National Institutes of Health embarked on an ambitious project to promote translation of basic research into new medical treatments and strategies for disease prevention. Contributors to the NIH Roadmap (*http://nihroadmap.nih.gov*) are compiling information on biological pathways in an effort to understand how cells communicate with one another and maintain the body in a healthy state. This chapter examines the basic patterns of cell-to-cell communication and shows how the coordination of function resides in chemical and electrical signals. A combination of simple diffusion across small distances, widespread distribution of molecules through the circulatory system, and rapid, specific delivery of messages by the nervous system enables each cell in the body to communicate with most other cells and maintain homeostasis.

CELL-TO-CELL COMMUNICATION

In recent years the amount of information available about cell-to-cell communication has mushroomed as a result of advances in research technology. Signal pathways that once seemed fairly simple and direct are now known to be incredibly complex networks and webs of information transfer. In the sections that follow, we distill what is known about cell-to-cell communication into some basic patterns that you can learn and recognize when you encounter them again in your study of physiology.

By most estimates the human body is composed of about 75 *trillion* cells. Those cells face a daunting task—to communicate with one another in a manner that is rapid and yet conveys a tremendous amount of information. Surprisingly, there are only two basic types of physiological signals: electrical and chemical. **Electrical signals** are changes in a cell's membrane potential [p. 162]. **Chemical signals** are molecules secreted by cells into the extracellular fluid. Chemical signals are responsible for most communication within the body. The cells that receive electrical or chemical signals are called **target cells**, or **targets** for short.

Our bodies use four basic methods of cell-to-cell communication: (1) **gap junctions**, which allow direct cytoplasmic transfer of electrical and chemical signals between adjacent cells; (2) **contact-dependent signals**, which occur when surface molecules on one cell membrane bind to surface molecules on another cell membrane; (3) **local communication** by chemicals that diffuse through the extracellular fluid; and (4) **long-distance communication** through a combination of electrical signals carried by nerve cells and chemical signals transported in the blood. A given molecule can function as a signal by more than one method. For example, a molecule can act close to the cell that released it (local communication) as well as in distant parts of the body (long-distance communication).

6

Gap Junctions Create Cytoplasmic Bridges

The simplest form of cell-to-cell communication is the direct transfer of electrical and chemical signals through **gap junctions**, protein channels that create cytoplasmic bridges between adjacent cells (Fig. 6-1a ■) [p. 69]. A gap junction forms from

(a) Gap junctions form direct cytoplasmic connections between adjacent cells.

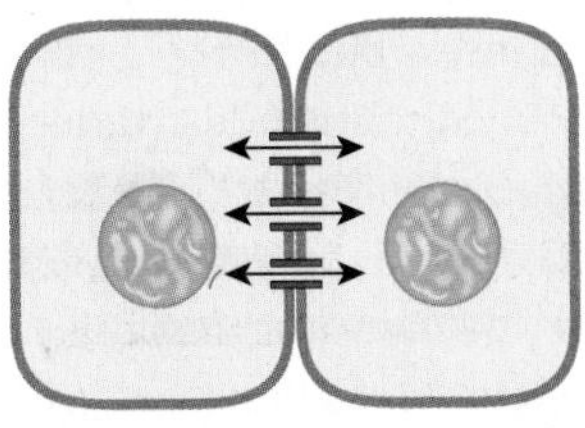

(b) Contact-dependent signals require interaction between membrane molecules on two cells.

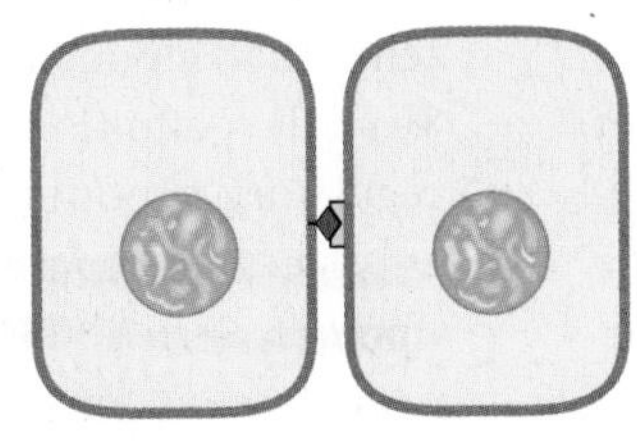

(c) Autocrine signals act on the same cell that secreted them. **Paracrine signals** are secreted by one cell and diffuse to adjacent cells.

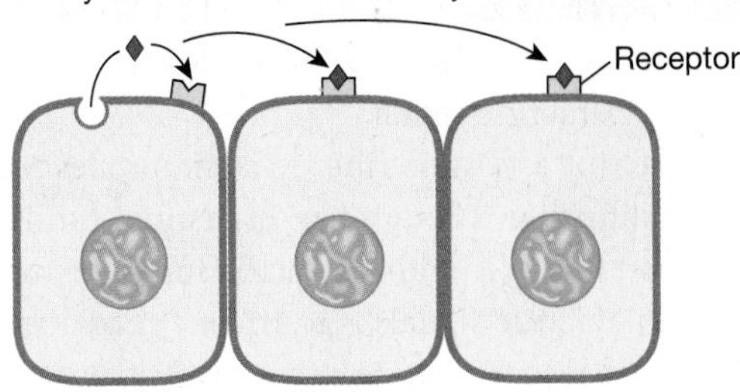

■ **FIGURE 6-1** ***Direct contact and local cell-to-cell communication***

Local communication can be either by autocrine signals or by paracrine signals.

the union of membrane-spanning proteins, called *connexins*, on two adjacent cells. The united connexins create a protein channel (*connexon*) that can open and close. When the channel is open, the connected cells function like a single cell that contains multiple nuclei (a *syncytium*).

When gap junctions are open, ions and small molecules such as amino acids, ATP, and cyclic AMP diffuse directly from the cytoplasm of one cell to the cytoplasm of the next. As with other membrane channels, larger molecules cannot pass through gap junctions. In addition, gap junctions are the only means by which electrical signals can pass *directly* from cell to cell. Movement of molecules through gap junctions can be modulated or shut off completely.

Gap junctions are not all alike. Scientists have discovered more than 20 different isoforms of connexins that may mix or match to form gap junctions. The variety of connexin isoforms allows gap junction selectivity to vary from tissue to tissue. In mammals, gap junctions are found in almost every cell type, including heart muscle, some types of smooth muscle, lung, liver, and neurons of the brain.

Contact-Dependent Signals Require Cell-to-Cell Contact

Some cell-to-cell communication requires that surface molecules on one cell membrane bind to a membrane protein of another cell (Fig. 6-1b). Such *contact-dependent signaling* occurs in the immune system and during growth and development, such as when nerve cells send out long extensions that must grow from the central axis of the body to the *distal* (distant) ends of the limbs. **CAMs**, cell adhesion molecules first known for their role in cell-to-cell adhesion [p. 69], have now been shown to act as receptors in cell-to-cell signaling. CAMs are linked to the cytoskeleton and to intracellular enzymes. Through these linkages, CAMs transfer signals in both directions across cell membranes.

Paracrine and Autocrine Signals Carry Out Local Communication

Local communication is accomplished by paracrine and autocrine signaling. A **paracrine signal** [*para-*, beside + *krinen*, to secrete] is a chemical that acts on cells in the immediate vicinity of the cell that secreted the signal. If a chemical signal acts on the cell that secreted it, it is called an **autocrine signal** [*auto-*, self]. In some cases a molecule may act as both an autocrine signal and a paracrine signal.

Paracrine and autocrine signal molecules reach their target cells by diffusing through the interstitial fluid (Fig. 6-1c). Because distance is a limiting factor for diffusion, the effective range of paracrine signals is restricted to adjacent cells. A good example of a paracrine molecule is *histamine*, a chemical released from damaged cells. When you scratch yourself with a pin, the red, raised *wheal* that results is due in part to the local release of histamine from the injured tissue. The histamine acts as a paracrine signal, diffusing to the capillaries in the immediate area of the injury and making them more permeable to white blood cells and antibodies in the plasma. Fluid also leaves the blood vessels and collects in the interstitial space, causing swelling around the area of injury.

Several important classes of molecules act as local signals. *Cytokines* are regulatory peptides that usually act close to the site where they are secreted. *Eicosanoids* [p. 29] are lipid-derived paracrine and autocrine signal molecules. Cytokines and eicosanoids will be discussed in more detail below.

Neural Signals, Hormones, and Neurohormones Carry Out Long-Distance Communication

All cells in the body can release paracrine signals, but most long-distance communication between cells is the responsibility of the nervous and endocrine systems. The endocrine system communicates by using **hormones** [*hormon*, to excite], chemical signals that are secreted into the blood and distributed all over the body by the circulation. Hormones come in contact with most cells of the body, but only those cells with receptors for the hormone are target cells (Fig. 6-2a ■).

The nervous system uses a combination of chemical signals and electrical signals to communicate over long distances. An electrical signal travels along a nerve cell (*neuron*) until it reaches the very end of the cell, where it is translated into a chemical signal secreted by the neuron (a **neurocrine**). If a neurocrine molecule diffuses from the neuron across a narrow extracellular space to a target cell and has a rapid effect, it is called a **neurotransmitter** (Fig. 6-2b). If a neurocrine acts more slowly as an autocrine or paracrine signal, it is called a **neuromodulator**. If a neurocrine released by a neuron diffuses into the blood for distribution, it is called a **neurohormone** (Fig. 6-2c). The similarities between neurohormones and classic hormones secreted by the endocrine system blur the distinction between the nervous and endocrine systems, making them a continuum rather than two distinct systems (see Fig. 6-31, p. 204).

Cytokines May Act as Both Local and Long-Distance Signals

Cytokines are among the most recently identified communication molecules. Initially the term *cytokine* referred only to proteins that modulate immune responses, but in the past few years the definition has been broadened to include a variety of regulatory peptides. All nucleated cells synthesize and secrete cytokines in response to stimuli. Cytokines control cell development, cell differentiation, and the immune response. In development and differentiation, cytokines function as autocrine or paracrine signals. In stress and inflammation, some

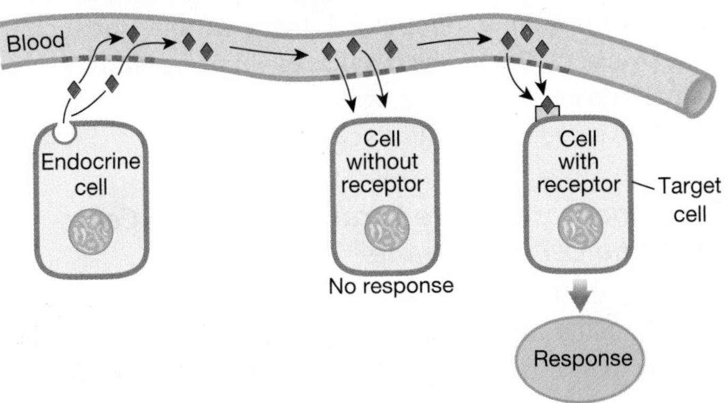
(a) Hormones are secreted by endocrine glands or cells into the blood. Only target cells with receptors for the hormone will respond to the signal.
Blood
Endocrine cell
Cell without receptor
Cell with receptor
Target cell
No response
Response

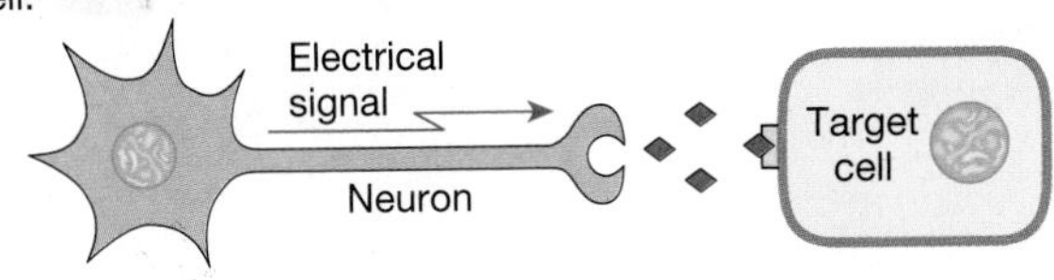
(b) Neurotransmitters are chemicals secreted by neurons that diffuse across a small gap to the target cell. Neurons use electrical signals as well.
Electrical signal
Neuron
Target cell

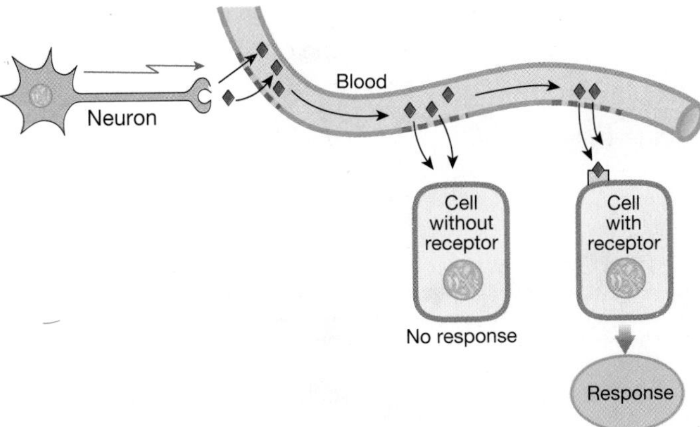
(c) Neurohormones are chemicals released by neurons into the blood for action at distant targets.
Neuron
Blood
Cell without receptor
Cell with receptor
No response
Response

■ **FIGURE 6-2** ***Long distance cell-to-cell communication***

cytokines may act on relatively distant targets and may be transported through the circulation just as hormones are.

How do cytokines differ from hormones? In general, cytokines act on a broader spectrum of target cells. In addition, cytokines are not produced by specialized glands the way hormones are, and they are made on demand. In contrast, most protein or peptide hormones are made in advance and stored in the endocrine cell until needed. However, the distinction between cytokines and hormones is sometimes blurry. For example, erythropoietin, the molecule that controls synthesis of red blood cells, is by tradition considered a hormone but functionally fits the definition of a cytokine.

CONCEPT CHECK

1. Match the communication method on the left with its property on the right.

	Communication occurs by:
(a) autocrine	1. electrical signals
(b) cytokine	2. chemical signals
(c) gap junction	3. both electrical and chemical signals
(d) hormone	
(e) neurohormone	
(f) neurotransmitter	
(g) paracrine	

2. Which signal molecules listed in the previous question are transported through the circulatory system? Which are associated with neurons?

3. A cat sees a mouse and pounces on it. Do you think the internal signal to pounce could have been transmitted by a paracrine signal? Give two reasons to explain why or why not.

Answers: p. 209

6

SIGNAL PATHWAYS

Chemical signals in the form of paracrine and autocrine molecules and hormones are released from cells into the extracellular compartment. This is not a very specific way for these signals to find their targets because substances that travel through the blood reach nearly every cell in the body. Yet cells do not respond to every signal that reaches them. Why do some cells respond to a chemical signal while other cells ignore it? The answer lies in the target-cell **receptor proteins** to which chemical signals bind

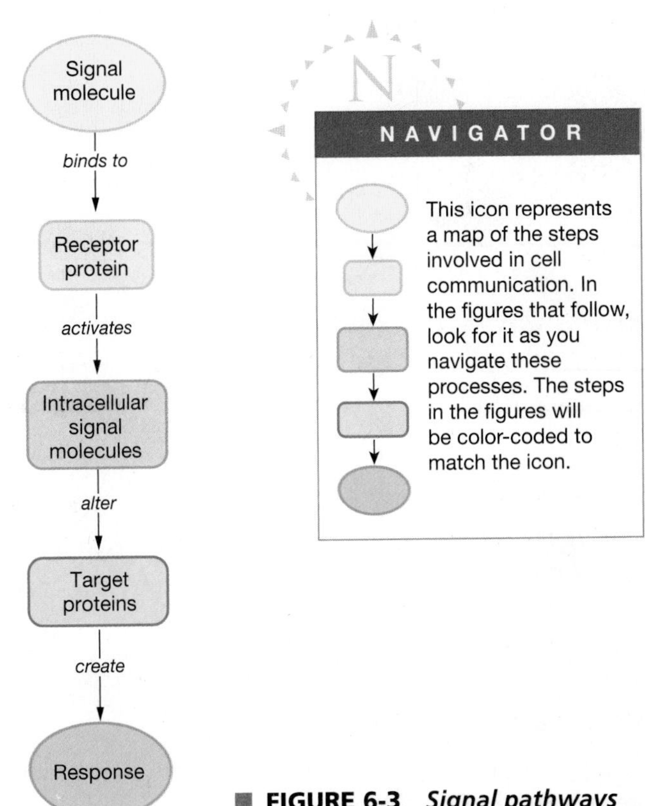
Signal molecule
binds to
Receptor protein
activates
Intracellular signal molecules
alter
Target proteins
create
Response
N
NAVIGATOR
This icon represents a map of the steps involved in cell communication. In the figures that follow, look for it as you navigate these processes. The steps in the figures will be color-coded to match the icon.

■ **FIGURE 6-3** ***Signal pathways***

[p. 137]. *A cell cannot respond to a chemical signal if the cell lacks the appropriate receptor proteins for that signal* (Fig. 6-2a).

If a target cell has a receptor for a signal molecule, binding of the signal to the receptor protein will initiate a response. All signal pathways share the following common features (Fig. 6-3 ■):

1. The signal molecule is a *ligand* that binds to a receptor. The ligand is also known as a *first messenger* because it brings information to its target cell.
2. Ligand-receptor binding activates the receptor.
3. The receptor in turn activates one or more intracellular signal molecules.
4. The last signal molecule in the pathway initiates synthesis of target proteins or modifies existing target proteins to create a response.

In the following sections, we will describe some basic signal pathways. They may seem complex at first, but they follow patterns that you will encounter over and over as you study the systems of the body. Most physiological processes, from the beating of your heart to learning and memory, use some variation of these pathways. One of the wonders of physiology is the fundamental importance of these signal pathways and the way they have been conserved in animals ranging from worms to humans.

Receptor Proteins Are Located Inside the Cell or on the Cell Membrane

Chemical signals fall into two broad categories based on their lipid solubility: lipophilic or lipophobic. Target-cell receptors may be found in the nucleus, in the cytosol, or on the cell membrane as integral proteins. Where a chemical signal binds to its receptor largely depends on whether the signal molecule can enter the cell (Fig. 6-4 ■).

Lipophilic signal molecules can diffuse through the phospholipid bilayer of the cell membrane [p. 135] and bind to *cytosolic*

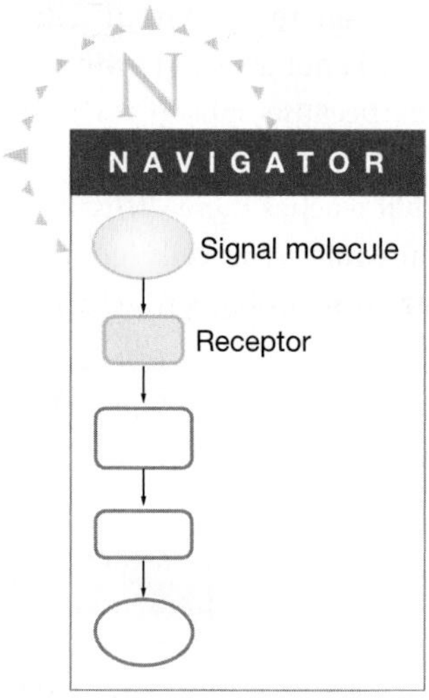

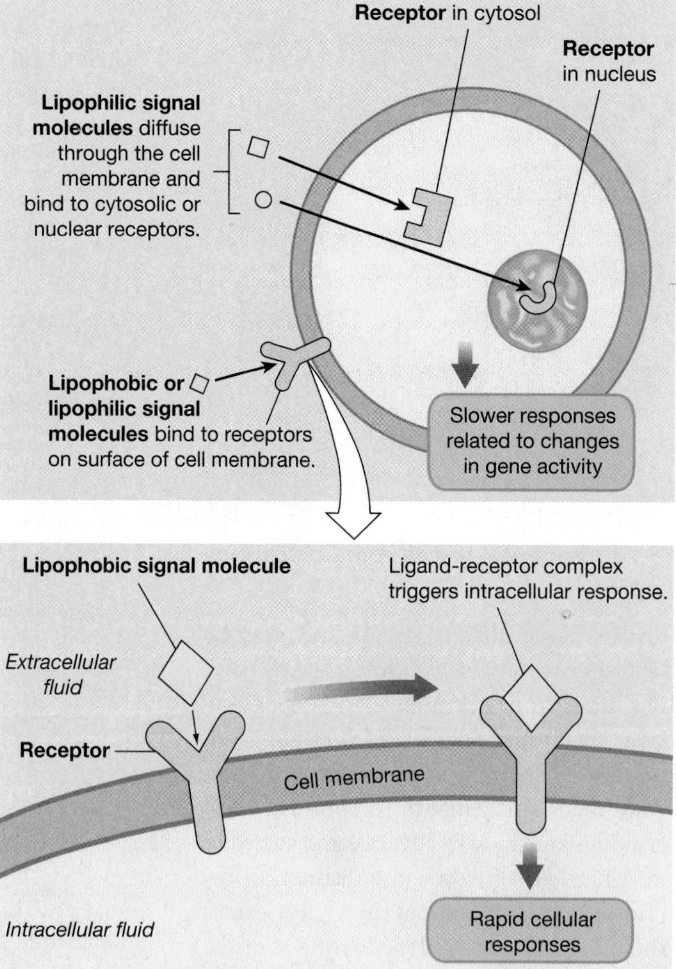

■ **FIGURE 6-4** ***Target cell receptors***

Receptors are either membrane proteins or are located in the cytosol or nucleus.

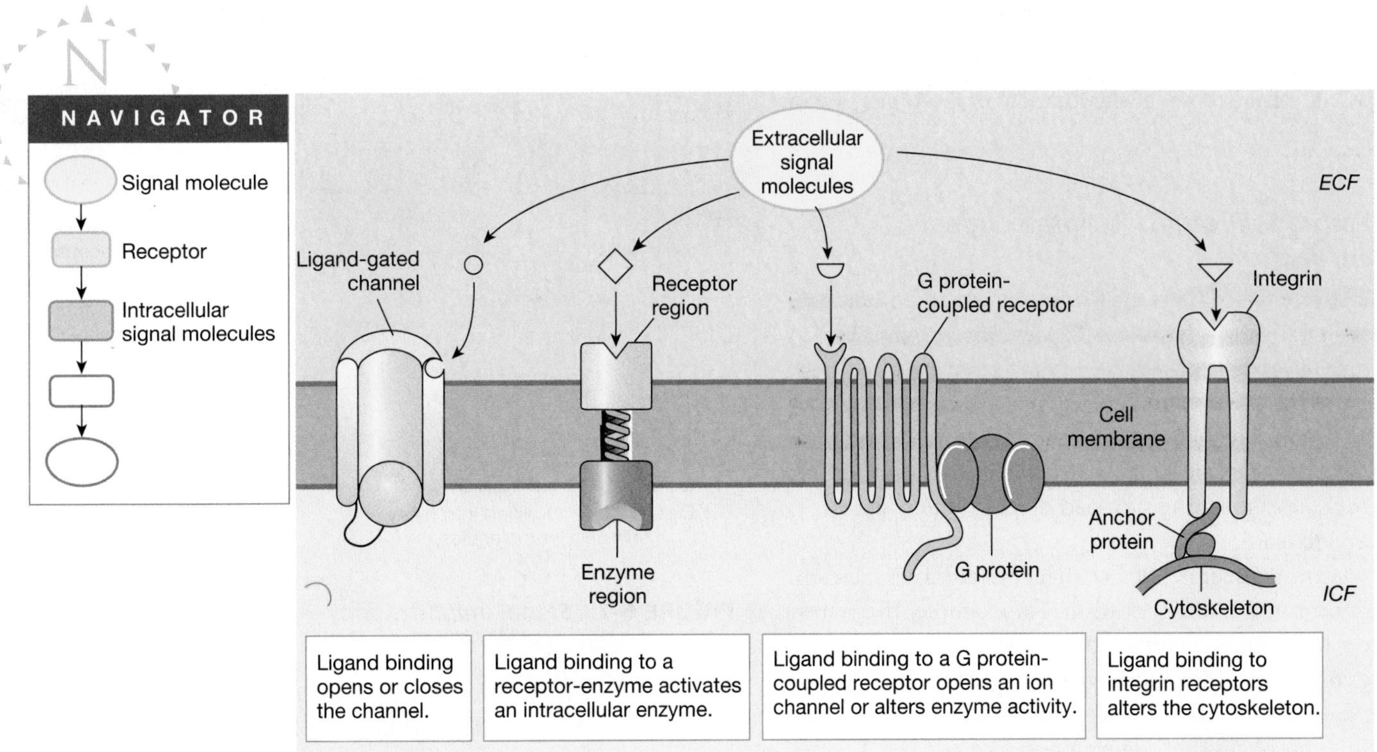

■ **FIGURE 6-5** ***Four categories of membrane receptors***

receptors or *nuclear receptors*. In these cases, receptor activation often turns on a gene and directs the nucleus to make new mRNA (transcription, [p. 115]). The mRNA then provides a template for synthesis of new proteins (translation, [p. 118]). This is a relatively slow process, and the cell's response may not be noticeable for an hour or longer. In some instances the activated receptor can also turn off, or repress, gene activity. Many lipophilic signal molecules that follow this pattern are hormones, so we will defer further discussion of their action to the next chapter.

Lipophobic signal molecules are unable to diffuse through the phospholipid bilayer of the cell membrane. Instead, these signal molecules remain in the extracellular fluid and bind to receptor proteins on the cell membrane. (Some lipophilic signal molecules also bind to cell membrane receptors.) In general, the response time for pathways linked to membrane receptor proteins is very rapid, and responses can be seen within milliseconds to minutes.

Protein receptors for signal molecules play an important role in physiology and medicine. About half of all drugs currently in use act on receptor proteins. We can group membrane receptors into four major categories, illustrated in Figure 6-5 ■. The simplest receptors are chemically gated (*ligand-gated*) ion channels called *receptor-channels* [p. 139]. Ligand binding opens or closes the channel and alters ion flow across the membrane.

Three other receptor types are shown in Figure 6-5: *receptor-enzymes, G protein-coupled receptors,* and *integrin receptors*. For all three, information from the signal molecule must be passed across the membrane to initiate an intracellular response. This transmission of information from one side of a membrane to the other using membrane proteins is known as *signal transduction*. We will take a closer look at signal transduction before returning to the four receptor types that participate in it.

RUNNING PROBLEM

Later that day in the physician's office, the nurse practitioner explains diabetes to Marvin. Diabetes mellitus is a family of metabolic disorders caused by defects in the homeostatic pathways that regulate glucose metabolism. Several forms of diabetes exist, and some can be inherited. One form, called type 1 diabetes mellitus, is caused by deficient production of insulin, a protein hormone made in the pancreas. In another form, called type 2 diabetes mellitus, insulin is often present in normal or above-normal levels. However, the insulin-sensitive cells of the body do not respond normally to the hormone.

Question 1:

In which type of diabetes is the signal pathway for insulin more likely to be defective?

CONCEPT CHECK

4. List four components of signal pathways.
5. Name three cellular locations of receptors.

Answers: p. 209

Membrane Proteins Facilitate Signal Transduction

Signal transduction is the process by which an extracellular signal molecule activates a membrane receptor that in turn alters intracellular molecules to create a response. The extracellular signal molecule is the first messenger, and the intracellular molecules form a *second messenger system*. The term *signal transduction* comes from the verb *to transduce,* meaning "to lead across" [*trans,* across + *ducere,* to lead].

A **transducer** is a device that converts a signal from one form into a different form. For example, the transducer in a radio converts radio waves into sound waves (Fig. 6-6 ■). In biological systems, transducers convert the message of extracellular signal molecules into intracellular messages that trigger a response.

Signal transduction converts one form of signal into a different form.

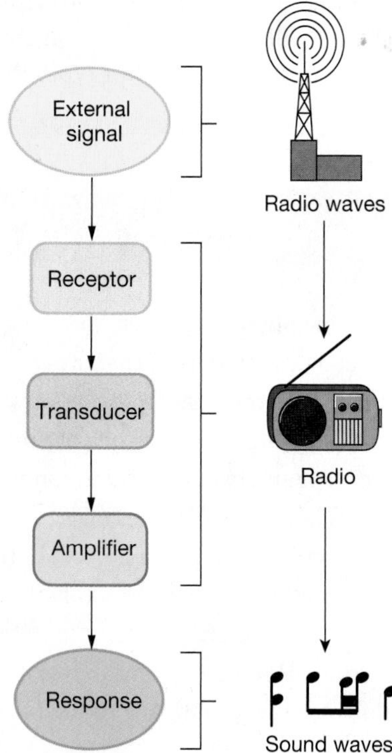

■ **FIGURE 6-6** ***Signal transduction***

An example of signal transduction in the physical world is the process that takes place in a radio. The radio contains a transducer that converts radio waves into sound waves.

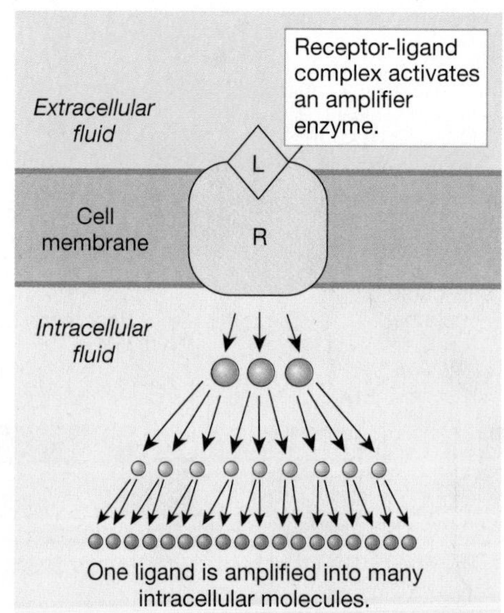

■ **FIGURE 6-7** ***Signal amplification***

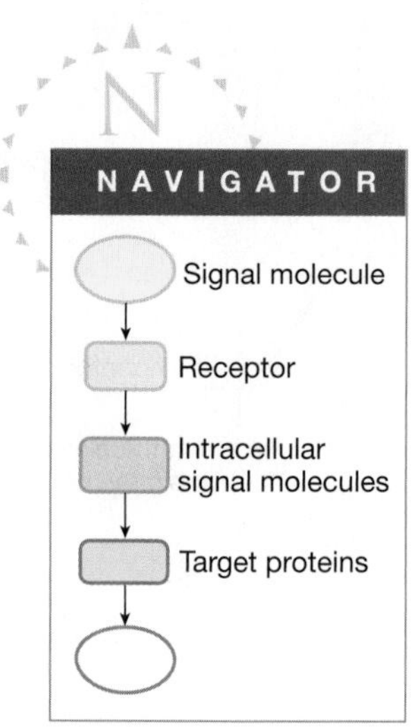

In biological systems, as in a radio, the original signal is not only transformed but also amplified [*amplificare,* to make larger]. In cells, **signal amplification** turns one signal molecule into multiple second messenger molecules. The process begins when the ligand combines with its receptor (Fig. 6-7 ■). The receptor-ligand complex then turns on an **amplifier enzyme**, an enzyme that activates several more molecules. By the end of the process, the effects of the ligand have been amplified much more than if there were a 1:1 ratio between each step. Amplification gives the body "more bang for the buck" by enabling a small amount of ligand to create a large effect.

The basic pattern of a biological signal transduction pathway is shown in Figure 6-8 ■ and can be broken down into the following events.

1. An extracellular signal molecule binds to and activates a protein or glycoprotein membrane receptor.
2. The activated membrane receptor turns on its associated proteins. These proteins then may:
   (a) activate **protein kinases**, which are enzymes that transfer a phosphate group from ATP to a protein [p. 100]. Phosphorylation is an important biochemical method of regulating cellular processes.
   (b) activate amplifier enzymes that create intracellular **second messengers**. The most common amplifier enzymes and second messengers are listed in Tables 6-1 ■ and 6-2 ■.
3. Second messenger molecules in turn
   (a) alter the gating of ion channels. Opening or closing ion channels creates electrical signals by altering the cell's membrane potential [p. 162].
   (b) increase intracellular calcium. Calcium binding to proteins changes their function, creating a cellular response.

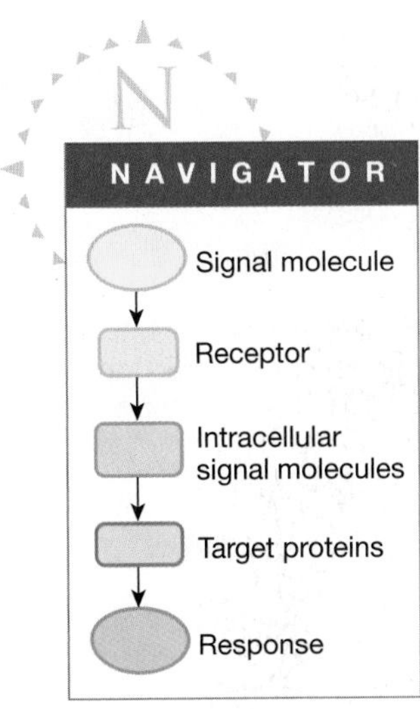

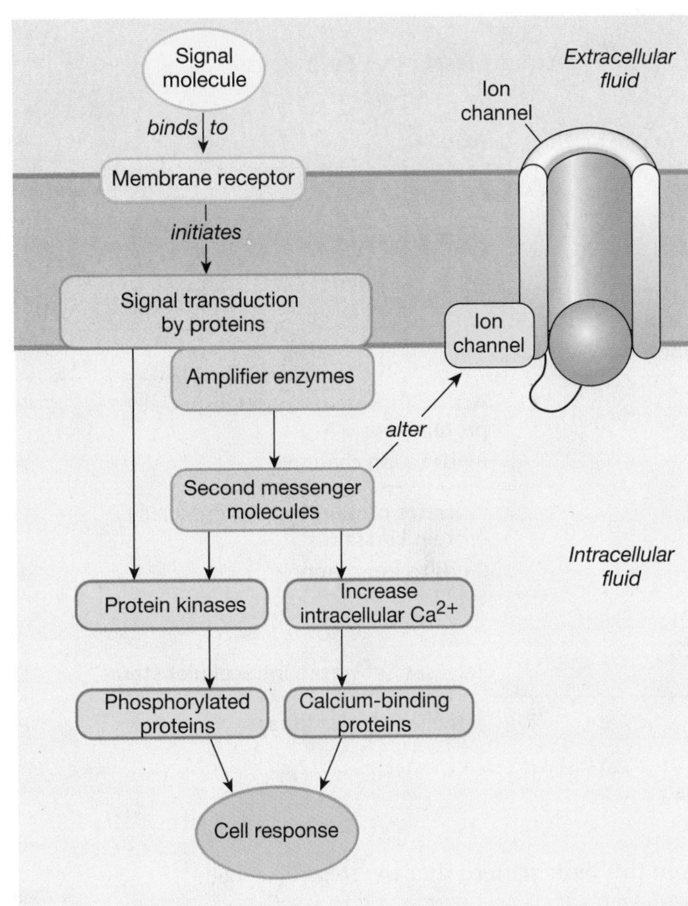

■ **FIGURE 6-8** ***Biological signal transduction***

(c) change enzyme activity, especially of protein kinases or **protein phosphatases**, enzymes that remove a phosphate group. The phosphorylation or *dephosphorylation* of a protein can change its configuration and create a response. Examples of changes that occur with phosphorylation include increased or decreased enzyme activity and opening or closing gated ion channels.

4. The proteins modified by calcium binding and phosphorylation control one or more of the following:
   (a) metabolic enzymes,
   (b) motor proteins for muscle contraction and cytoskeletal movement,
   (c) proteins that regulate gene activity and protein synthesis, and
   (d) membrane transport and receptor proteins.

If you think this list includes almost everything a cell does, you're right!

TABLE 6-1 **Amplifier Enzymes**

AMPLIFIER ENZYME	CELLULAR LOCATION	ACTIVATED BY	CONVERTS	TO
Adenylyl cyclase	Membrane	G protein-coupled receptor	ATP	cAMP
Guanylyl cyclase	Membrane Cytosol	Receptor-enzyme Nitric oxide (NO)	GTP	cGMP
Phospholipase C	Membrane	G protein-coupled receptor	Membrane phospholipids	IP_3 and DAG*

*IP_3 = Inositol trisphosphate; DAG = diacylglycerol

TABLE 6-2 Second Messenger Pathways

SECOND MESSENGER	ACTION	EFFECTS
Ions		
Ca^{2+}	Binds to calmodulin Binds to other proteins	Alters enzyme activity Exocytosis, muscle contraction, cytoskeleton movement, channel opening
Nucleotides		
cAMP	Activates protein kinases, especially protein kinase A Binds to ion channels	Phosphorylates proteins Alters channel opening
cGMP	Activates protein kinases, especially protein kinase G Binds to ion channels	Phosphorylates proteins Alters channel opening
Lipid-derived		
IP_3	Releases Ca^{2+} from intracellular stores	See Ca^{2+} effects above
DAG	Activates protein kinase C	Phosphorylates proteins

You can see from this basic pattern that the steps of a signal transduction pathway form a **cascade** (Fig. 6-9 ■) that starts when a stimulus (the signal molecule) converts inactive molecule A (the receptor) to an active form. Active A then converts inactive molecule B into active B, active molecule B in turn converts inactive molecule C into active C, and so on, until at the final step a substrate is converted into a product. Many intracellular signal pathways are cascades. Blood clotting is an important example of an extracellular cascade.

In the sections that follow, we will examine in more detail the four major types of membrane receptors (see Fig. 6-5). Keep in mind that these receptors may be responding to any of the different kinds of signal molecules—hormones, neurohormones, neurotransmitters, cytokines, paracrines, or autocrines.

CONCEPT CHECK

6. What are the four steps of signal transduction?
7. What happens during amplification?
8. Why do steroid hormones not require signal transduction and second messengers to exert their action? (*Hint:* are steroids lipophobic or lipophilic? [p. 17])

Answers: p. 209

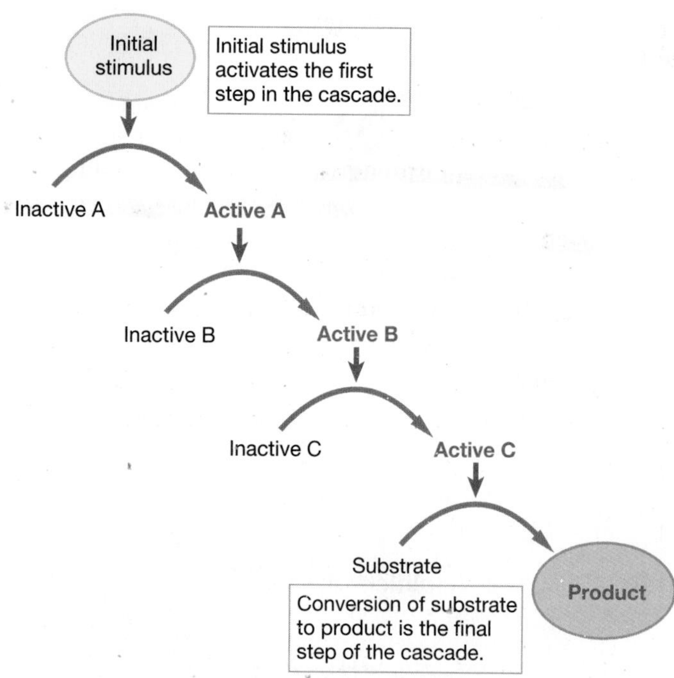

FIGURE QUESTION

Using Tables 6-1 and 6-2, create a cascade that includes ATP, cAMP, adenylyl cyclase, a phosphorylated protein, and protein kinase A. Match these molecules to the steps shown in the figure above.

■ **FIGURE 6-9** *Steps of a cascade*

Receptor-Enzymes Have Protein Kinase or Guanylyl Cyclase Activity

Receptor-enzymes have two regions: a receptor region on the extracellular side of the cell membrane, and an enzyme region

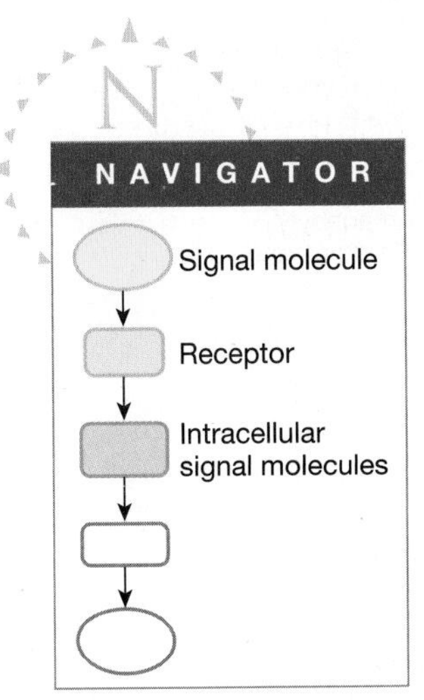

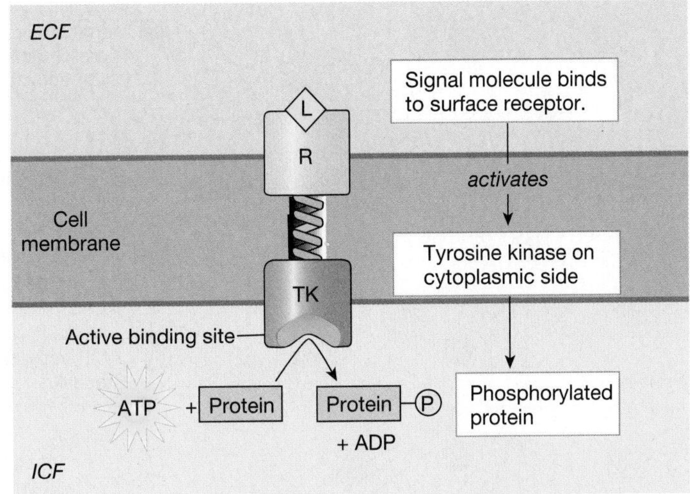

■ **FIGURE 6-10** ***Tyrosine kinase, an example of a receptor-enzyme***

Tyrosine kinase (TK) transfers a phosphate group from ATP to a tyrosine (an amino acid) of a protein.

on the cytoplasmic side (see Fig. 6-5). In some instances, the receptor region and enzyme region are parts of the same protein molecule. In other cases, the enzyme region is a separate protein. Ligand binding to the receptor activates the enzyme. The enzymes of receptor-enzymes are either protein kinases, such as *tyrosine kinase* (Fig. 6-10 ■), or *guanylyl cyclase,* the amplifier enzyme that converts GTP to **cyclic GMP (cGMP)** [p. 32]. Ligands for receptor-enzymes include many growth factors and cytokines, as well as the hormone insulin.

CLINICAL FOCUS

INSULIN'S SIGNAL TRANSDUCTION PATHWAY

In people with type 2 diabetes mellitus, the hormone insulin binds to its receptor, but the cell fails to respond normally to the signal. As a result, researchers have been investigating the insulin receptor and its signal pathways in an effort to uncover the causes of type 2 diabetes. Insulin does not use the well-studied cAMP second messenger system, and so for many years the insulin receptor pathway was a "black box." In 1982 scientists discovered that the insulin receptor is a tyrosine kinase receptor-enzyme. Their next step was to discover what substrates tyrosine kinase was phosphorylating. This search is still ongoing. At least eight different substrates for the insulin receptor kinase have been identified, but the downstream steps of their cascades are still under investigation. Although we know what effects insulin has on glucose transport and metabolism, we still do not fully understand the pathways through which these effects take place.

Most Signal Transduction Uses G Proteins

The **G protein-coupled receptors (GPCR)** are a large and complex family of membrane-spanning proteins that cross the phospholipid bilayer seven times (see Fig. 6-5). The cytoplasmic tail of the receptor protein is linked to a three-part membrane transducer molecule known as a **G protein.** Hundreds of G protein-coupled receptors have been identified, and the list continues to grow. The types of ligands that bind to G protein-coupled receptors include hormones, growth factors, olfactory molecules, visual pigments, and neurotransmitters. In 1994 Alfred G. Gilman and Martin Rodbell received a Nobel prize for the discovery of G proteins and their role in cell signaling.

G proteins get their name from the fact that they bind guanosine nucleotides [p. 32]. Inactive G proteins are bound to guanosine diphosphate (GDP). Exchanging the GDP for guanosine triphosphate (GTP) activates the G protein. When G proteins are activated, they either (1) open an ion channel in the membrane or (2) alter enzyme activity on the cytoplasmic side of the membrane.

G proteins linked to amplifier enzymes make up the bulk of all known signal transduction mechanisms. The two most common amplifier enzymes for G protein-coupled receptors are adenylyl cyclase and phospholipase C. The pathways for these amplifier enzymes are described next.

Adenylyl Cyclase-cAMP Is the Signal Transduction System for Many Lipophobic Hormones

The **G protein-coupled adenylyl cyclase-cAMP system** was the first identified signal transduction pathway (Fig. 6-11 ■). It was discovered in the 1950s by Earl Sutherland when he was studying the effects of hormones on carbohydrate metabolism. This discovery proved so significant to our understanding of signal transduction that in 1971 Sutherland was awarded a Nobel prize for his work.

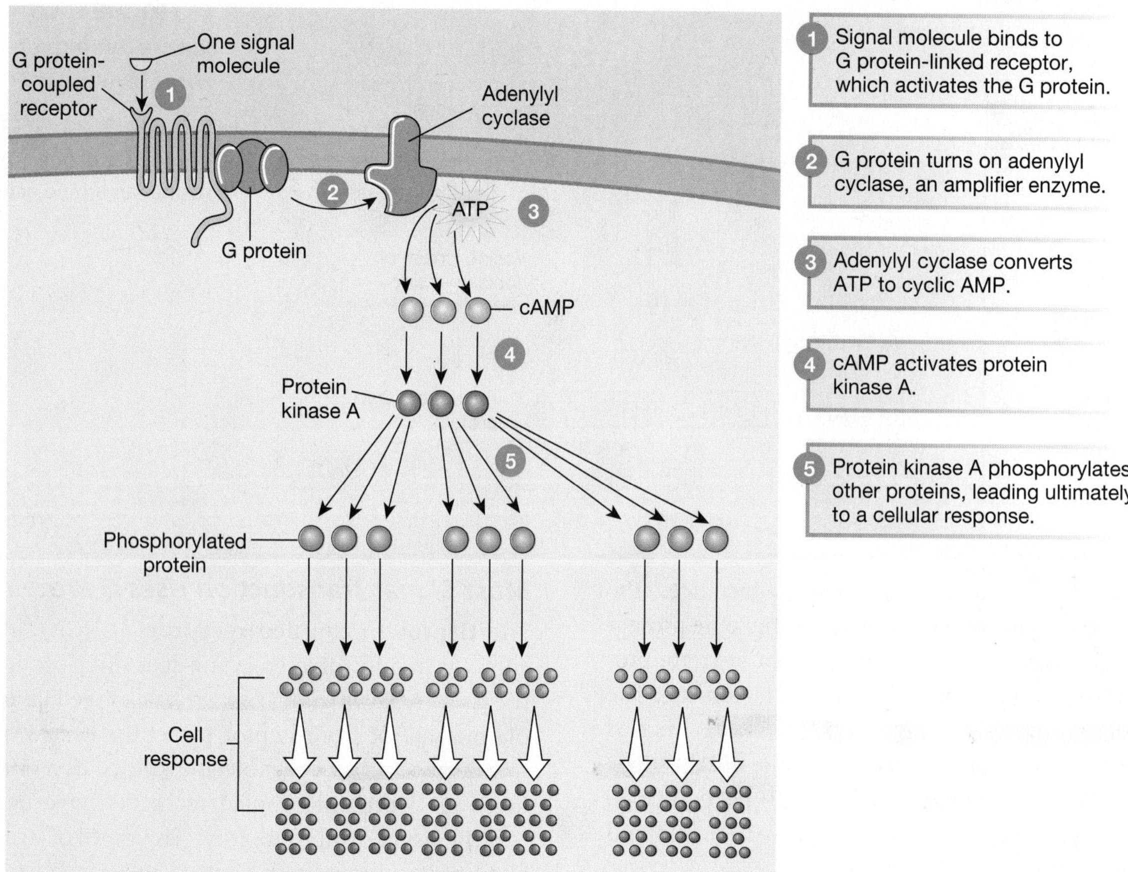

■ **FIGURE 6-11** ***The G protein-coupled adenylyl cyclase-cAMP system***

This was the first second messenger system described.

In the adenylyl cyclase-cAMP system, *adenylyl cyclase* is the amplifier enzyme that converts ATP to the second messenger molecule *cyclic AMP* (cAMP). Cyclic AMP then activates *protein kinase A* (PK-A), which in turn phosphorylates other intracellular proteins as part of the signal cascade. The G protein-coupled adenylyl cyclase-cAMP system is the signal transduction system for many protein hormones.

G Protein-Coupled Receptors Also Use Lipid-Derived Second Messengers

Some G protein-coupled receptors are linked to a different amplifier enzyme: phospholipase C (Fig. 6-12 ■). When a signal molecule activates this G protein-coupled pathway, **phospholipase C (PL-C)** converts a membrane phospholipid (*phosphatidylinositol bisphosphate*) into two different second messenger molecules: diacylglycerol and inositol trisphosphate.

Diacylglycerol (DAG) is a nonpolar diglyceride that remains in the lipid portion of the membrane and interacts with **protein kinase C** (PK-C), a Ca^{2+}-activated enzyme associated with the cytoplasmic face of the cell membrane. Protein kinase C phosphorylates cytosolic proteins that continue the signal cascade.

Inositol trisphosphate (IP_3) is a water-soluble messenger molecule that enters the cytoplasm. There it binds to a calcium channel on the endoplasmic reticulum (ER). IP_3 binding opens the Ca^{2+} channel, allowing Ca^{2+} to diffuse out of the ER and into the cytosol. Calcium is itself an important signal molecule, as discussed below.

Integrin Receptors Transfer Information from the Extracellular Matrix

The membrane-spanning proteins called integrins [p. 70] mediate blood clotting, wound repair, cell adhesion and recognition in the immune response, and cell movement during development. On the extracellular side of the membrane, integrin receptors bind either to proteins of the extracellular matrix [p. 68] or to ligands such as antibodies and molecules involved in blood clotting. Inside the cell, integrins attach to the cytoskeleton via *anchor proteins* (Fig. 6-5). Ligand binding to the receptor causes integrins to activate intracellular enzymes or alter the organization of the cytoskeleton.

The importance of integrin receptors is illustrated by inherited conditions in which the receptor is absent. In one condition, platelets—cell fragments that play a key role in blood clotting—lack an integrin receptor. As a result, blood clotting is defective in these individuals.

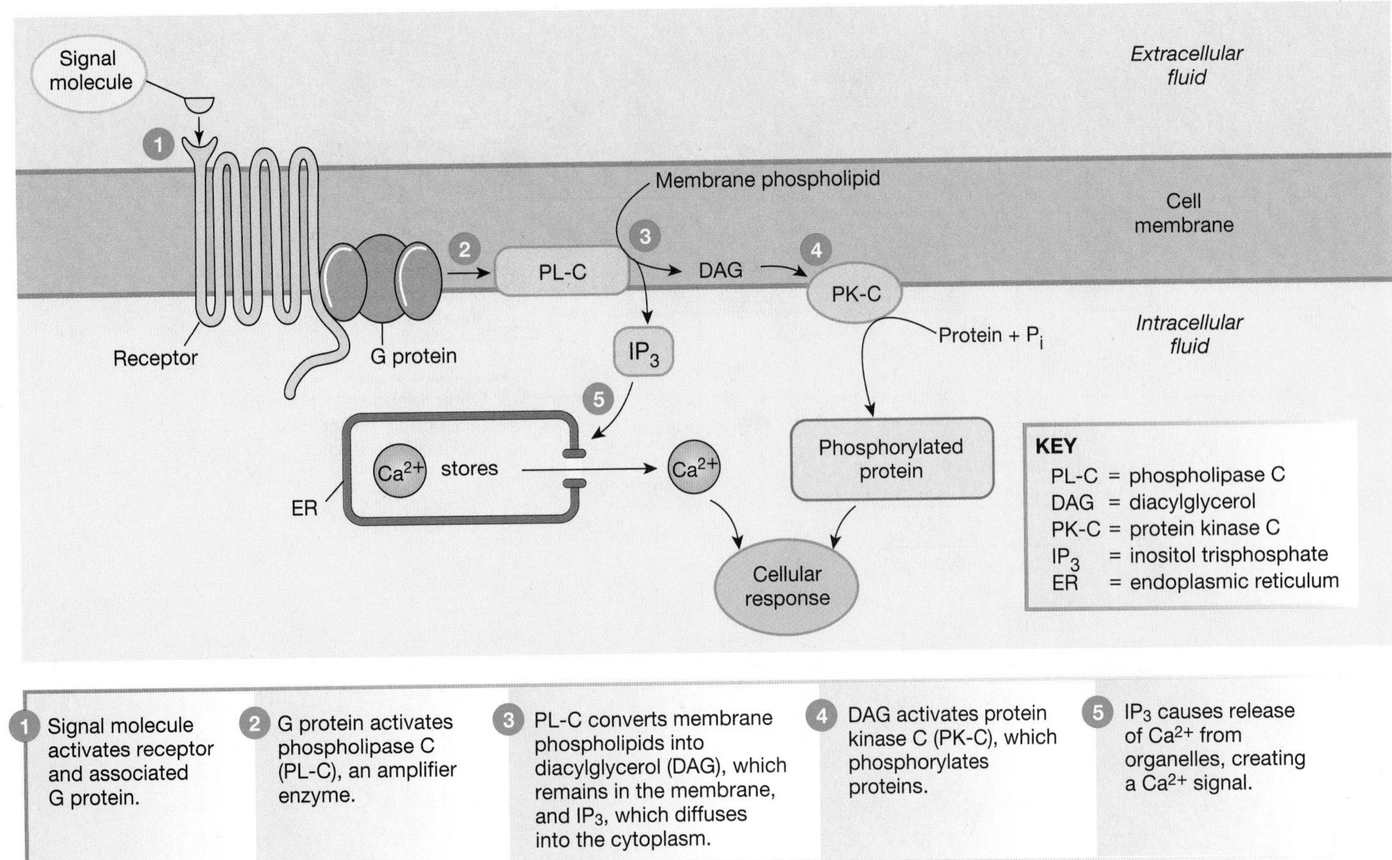

FIGURE 6-12 ***The phospholipase C system***

In this system—another G protein-coupled second messenger system—phospholipase C (PL-C) converts membrane lipids into two second messengers: diacylglycerol (DAG) and inositol trisphosphate (IP_3).

The Most Rapid Signal Pathways Change Ion Flow Through Channels

Ligand-gated ion channels are the simplest receptors, and the activation of a **receptor-channel** initiates the most rapid intracellular responses. For that reason these receptors are often located in the excitable tissues of nerve and muscle. When an extracellular signal molecule binds to the receptor-channel protein, a channel gate opens or closes, changing the cell's permeability to an ion. One example of a receptor-channel is the acetylcholine-gated cation channel of skeletal muscle. The neurotransmitter *acetylcholine* from an adjacent neuron binds to the acetylcholine receptor and opens the channel, creating a cascade that initiates muscle contraction.

Increasing or decreasing the permeability of an ion channel changes the cell's membrane potential [p. 165]. For example, opening the acetylcholine-gated cation channel just described allows Na^+ to enter the cytosol down that ion's electrochemical gradient. Net entry of cations depolarizes the cell, creating an electrical signal that alters voltage-sensitive proteins (Fig. 6-13).

Note that not all ligand-gated ion channels are receptor-channels that are directly activated by extracellular signal molecules. Some ligand-gated channels are controlled by intracellular second messengers, such as cAMP. Others are indirectly linked to receptors by G proteins.

CONCEPT CHECK

9. Name the four categories of membrane receptors.
10. What is the difference between a first messenger and a second messenger?
11. Place the following terms in the correct order for a signal transduction pathway:
    (a) cell response, receptor, second messenger, ligand
    (b) amplifier enzyme, cell response, phosphorylated protein, protein kinase, second messenger
12. In each of the following situations, will a cell depolarize or hyperpolarize?
    (a) Cl^- channel opens
    (b) K^+ channel opens
    (c) Na^+ channel opens

Answers: p. 209

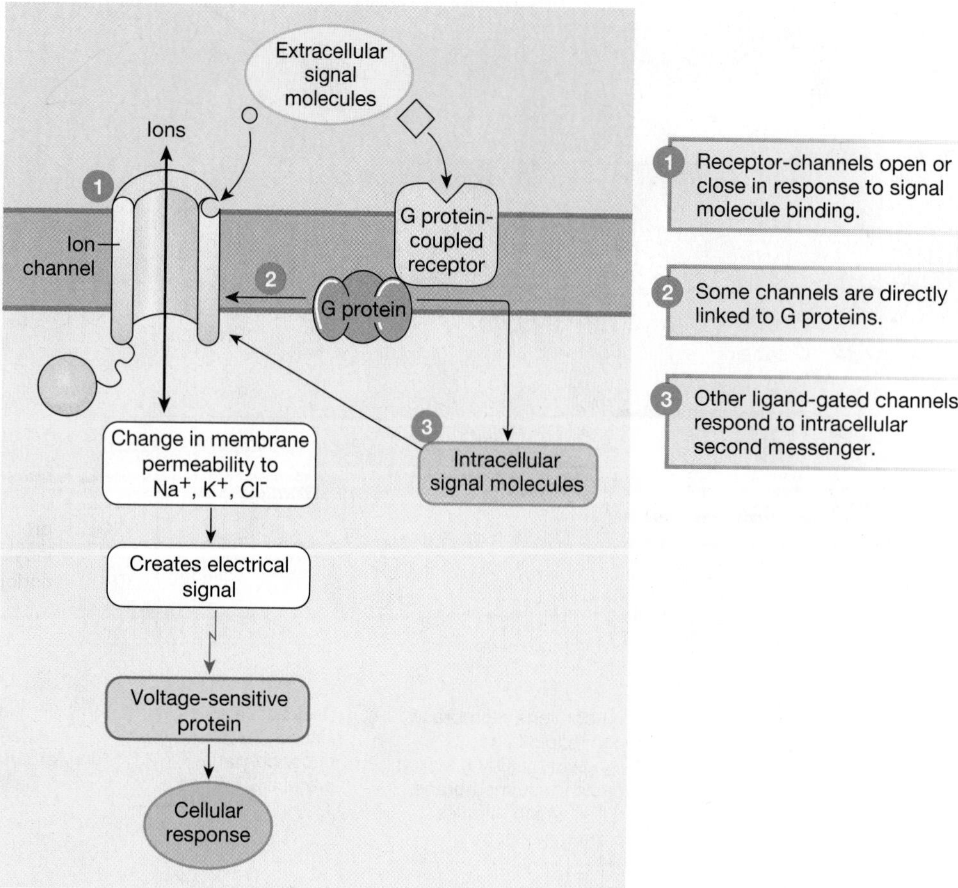

■ **FIGURE 6-13** ***How ions create electrical signals***

Figure 6-14 ■ is a summary map of basic signal transduction, showing the general relationships among first messengers, membrane receptors, second messengers, and cell responses.

NOVEL SIGNAL MOLECULES

In Chapters 7 and 8, you will learn more about hormones and neurotransmitters and their signal pathways. The following sections introduce you to some unusual signal molecules that are important in physiology and medicine. They include an ion (Ca^{2+}), two gases, and a family of lipid-derived messengers. The processes controlled by these signal molecules have been known for years, but the control signals themselves were discovered only relatively recently.

Calcium Is an Important Intracellular Signal

Calcium ions are the most versatile ionic messengers (Fig. 6-15 ■). Calcium enters the cytosol either through voltage-gated Ca^{2+} channels or through ligand-gated or mechanically gated channels. Calcium can also be released from intracellular compartments by second messengers, such as IP_3. Most intracellular Ca^{2+} is stored in the endoplasmic reticulum [p. 67], where it is concentrated by active transport.

Release of Ca^{2+} into the cytosol (from any of the sources just mentioned) creates a Ca^{2+} signal, or Ca^{2+} "spark," that can be recorded using special Ca^{2+}-imaging techniques (see Biotechnology box: "Measuring Calcium Signals"). The calcium ions combine with cytoplasmic calcium-binding proteins to exert various effects. Several types of calcium-dependent events occur in the cell:

1. Ca^{2+} binds to the protein **calmodulin**, found in all cells, and alters enzyme or transporter activity or the gating of ion channels.
2. Calcium binds to other regulatory proteins and alters movement of contractile or cytoskeletal proteins such as microtubules. For example, Ca^{2+} binding to the regulatory protein *troponin* initiates muscle contraction in a skeletal muscle cell.
3. Ca^{2+} binds to regulatory proteins to trigger exocytosis of secretory vesicles [p. 148]. This was illustrated in Chapter 5 in the description of pancreatic beta cell release of insulin.

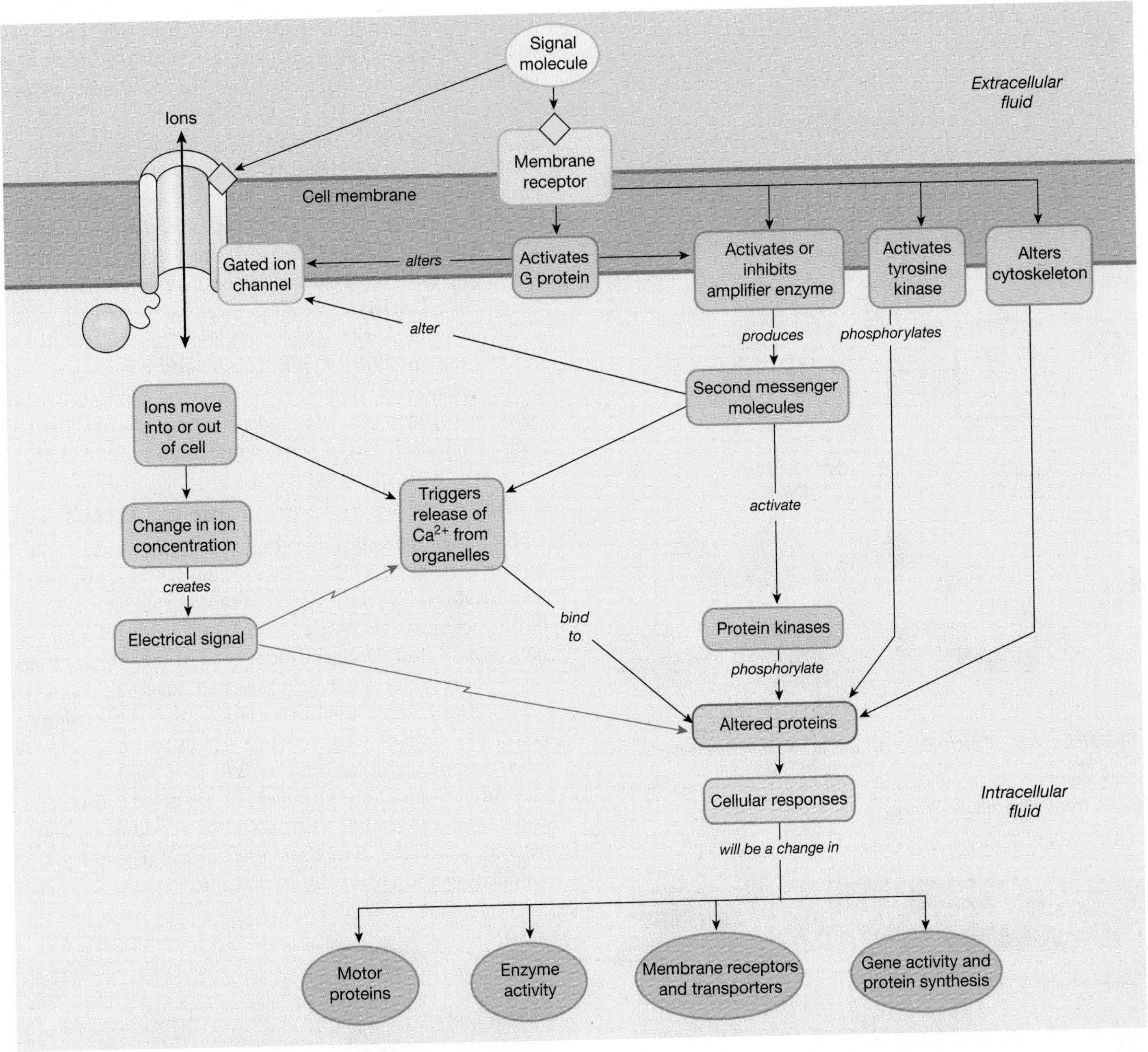

FIGURE 6-14 ***Summary map of signal transduction systems***

4. Ca^{2+} binds directly to ion channels to alter their gating state. An example of this target is a Ca^{2+}-activated K^+ channel found in nerve cells.
5. Ca^{2+} entry into a fertilized egg initiates development of the embryo.

CONCEPT CHECK

13. The concentration of extracellular Ca^{2+} averages 2.5 mmol/L. Free cytosolic Ca^{2+} concentration is about 0.001 mmol/L. If a cell is going to move calcium ions from its cytosol to the extracellular fluid, will it use passive or active transport? Explain. Answers: p. 209

Gases Are Ephemeral Signal Molecules

Nitric oxide (NO), a soluble gas, is a novel short-acting paracrine/autocrine signal that acts close to where it is produced. Nitric oxide took years to identify because it is rapidly broken down, with a half-life of only 2 to 30 seconds. (*Half-life* is the time required for the signal to lose half of its activity.) In tissues, NO is synthesized by the action of the enzyme *nitric oxide synthase* (NOS) on the amino acid arginine:

$$\text{Arginine} + O_2 \xrightarrow{\textit{nitric oxide synthase}} \text{NO} + \text{citrulline (an amino acid)}$$

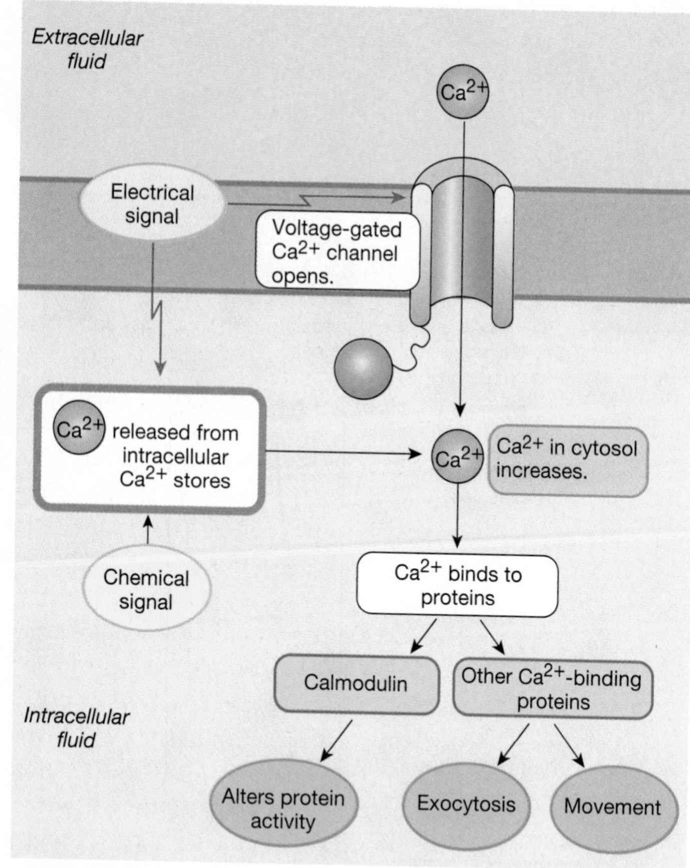

■ **FIGURE 6-15** ***Calcium as an intracellular messenger***

Calcium signals occur in the cytosol when Ca^{2+} enter the cell or are released from intracellular stores.

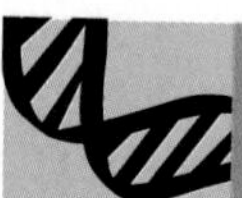

BIOTECHNOLOGY

MEASURING CALCIUM SIGNALS

If you've ever run your hand through a tropical ocean at night and seen the glow of bioluminescent jellyfish, you've seen a calcium signal. Aequorin, a protein complex isolated from jellyfish, is one of the molecules that scientists use to monitor the presence of calcium ions during a cellular response. When aequorin combines with calcium, it releases light that can be measured by electronic detection systems. Since the first use of aequorin in 1967, researchers have been designing better and better indicators that allow them to follow calcium signals in cells. With the help of molecules called fura, Oregon green, BAPTA, and chameleons, we can now watch calcium ions diffuse through gap junctions and flow out of intracellular organelles.

The NO produced in this reaction diffuses into target cells, where it binds to a receptor that activates the cytosolic form of guanylyl cyclase and causes formation of the second messenger cGMP.

Nitric oxide in the brain acts as a neurotransmitter and a neuromodulator. In blood vessels, NO is produced by endothelial cells lining the vessels. It then diffuses into adjacent smooth muscle cells, causing them to relax and dilate the blood vessel. In 1998 the Nobel prize for physiology and medicine was awarded jointly to Robert Furchgott, Louis Ignarro, and Ferid Murad for their work on NO as a signal molecule in the cardiovascular system.

Carbon monoxide (CO), a gas known mostly for its toxic effects, is also produced in minute amounts to be a signal molecule in certain cells. Like NO, CO activates guanylyl cyclase and cGMP, but it may also work independently to exert its effects. Carbon monoxide targets smooth muscle and neural tissue.

Some Lipids Are Important Paracrine Signals

One of the interesting developments from sequencing the human genome and using genes to find proteins has been the identification of *orphan receptors,* receptors that have no known ligand. Scientists are trying to work backwards through signal pathways to find the ligands that bind to these orphan receptors. As a result of this type of research, investigators have recently recognized the importance and universality of *eicosanoids,* lipid-derived paracrine signals that play important roles in many physiological processes.

All eicosanoid signal molecules are derived from arachidonic acid, a 20-carbon fatty acid. The synthesis process is a network called the *arachidonic acid cascade* (Fig. 6-16 ■). For simplicity, we will break the cascade into steps.

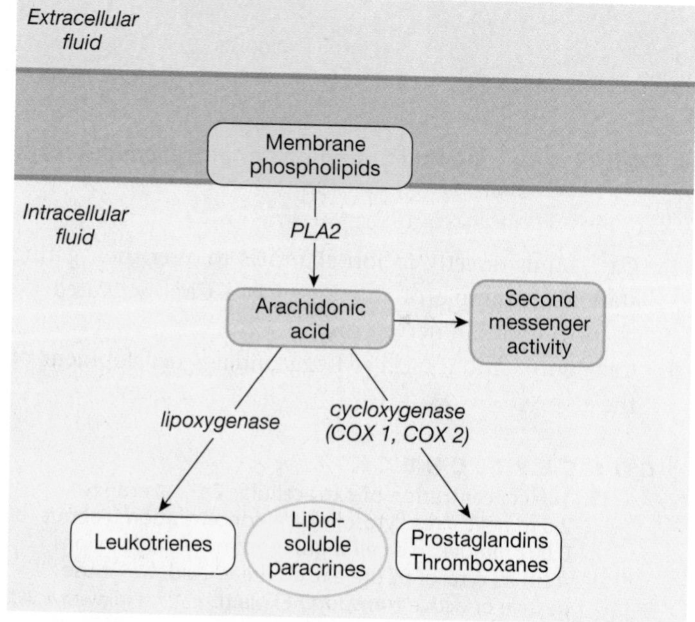

■ **FIGURE 6-16** ***The arachidonic acid cascade produces lipid messengers***

Arachidonic acid is produced from membrane phospholipids by the action of an enzyme, **phospholipase A_2** (PLA2). The activity of phospholipase A_2 is controlled by hormones and other signals. Arachidonic acid itself may act directly as a second messenger, altering ion channel activity and intracellular enzymes. It may also be converted into one of several classes of eicosanoid paracrines. These lipid-soluble molecules can diffuse out of the cell and combine with receptors on neighboring cells to exert their action.

There are two major groups of arachidonic acid-derived paracrines to be aware of:

1. **Leukotrienes** are molecules produced by the action of the enzyme *lipoxygenase* on arachidonic acid [*leuko-*, white + *triene*, a molecule with three double bonds between carbon atoms]. Leukotrienes are secreted by certain types of white blood cells. They play a significant role in asthma, a lung condition in which the smooth muscle of the airways constricts, making it difficult to breathe, and in the severe allergic reaction known as *anaphylaxis*. For this reason, pharmaceutical companies have been actively developing drugs to block leukotriene synthesis or action.
2. **Prostanoids** are molecules produced when the enzyme **cyclooxygenase (COX)** acts on arachidonic acid. Prostanoids include **prostaglandins** and **thromboxanes**. These eicosanoids act on many tissues of the body, including smooth muscle in various organs, platelets, kidney, and bone. In addition, prostaglandins are involved in sleep, inflammation, pain, and fever.

The nonsteroidal anti-inflammatory drugs (NSAIDs), such as aspirin and ibuprofen, help prevent inflammation by inhibiting COX enzymes and decreasing prostaglandin synthesis. However, NSAIDs are not specific and may have serious unwanted side effects, such as bleeding in the stomach. The discovery of two COX isozymes, COX1 and COX2, enabled the design of drugs that target a specific COX isozyme. By inhibiting only COX2, the enzyme that produces inflammatory prostaglandins, physicians hoped to treat inflammation with fewer side effects. However, recently studies showed that patients who took COX2 inhibitors for extended periods had increased risk of heart attacks and strokes, so whether use of those drugs should continue is still a matter of debate.

CONCEPT CHECK

14. Based on what you have learned about signal molecules, where might a drug that blocks leukotriene action act? How might a drug that blocks leukotriene synthesis act?

Answers: p. 209

MODULATION OF SIGNAL PATHWAYS

As you have just learned, signal pathways in the cell can be very complex. To complicate matters, different cells may respond differently to a given signal molecule. How can one molecule trigger response A in tissue 1 and response B in tissue 2? *For most signal molecules, the target cell response is determined by the receptor and its associated intracellular pathways, not by the ligand.* Because of the importance of signal pathways, cells use receptors to maintain flexibility in their responses.

Receptors Exhibit Saturation, Specificity, and Competition

Receptors are proteins; therefore, receptor-ligand binding exhibits the protein-binding characteristics of specificity, competition, and saturation [p. 43]. You have learned about similar protein-binding properties in the enzymes discussed in Chapter 4 [p. 96] and the transporters discussed in Chapter 5 [p. 138].

6

Specificity and Competition: Multiple Ligands for One Receptor Receptors have binding sites for their ligands, just as enzymes and transporters do. As a result, different molecules with similar structures may be able to bind to the same receptor. A classic example of this principle involves two neurocrines responsible for the fight-or-flight response: the neurotransmitter *norepinephrine* and its cousin the neurohormone *epinephrine* (also called *adrenaline*). Both molecules bind to a class of receptors called *adrenergic receptors*. (*Adrenergic* is the adjective relating to adrenaline.) The ability of adrenergic receptors to bind these neurocrines, but not others, demonstrates specificity of the receptors.

Epinephrine and norepinephrine also compete for a single receptor type. Both neurocrines bind to subtypes of adrenergic receptors designated alpha (α) and beta (β). However, α-receptors have a higher binding affinity for norepinephrine, whereas the β_2-receptor subtype has a higher affinity for epinephrine.

Agonists and Antagonists When a ligand combines with a receptor, one of two events follows. Either the ligand turns the receptor on and elicits a response, or the ligand occupies the binding site and prevents the receptor from responding (Fig. 6-17 ■). Ligands that turn receptors on are known as *agonists*, and ligands that block receptor activity are called *antagonists*.

Pharmacologists use the principle of competing agonists [p. 40] to design drugs that are longer-acting and more resistant to enzymatic degradation than the endogenous ligand. One example is the family of modified estrogens (female sex hormones) in birth control pills. These drugs are agonists of naturally occurring estrogens but have chemical groups added to protect them from breakdown and extend their active life.

Multiple Receptors for One Ligand For many years physiologists were unable to explain the observation that a single signal molecule could have different effects in different tissues. For example, epinephrine, the neurohormone previously described, dilates blood vessels in skeletal muscle but constricts blood vessels in the intestine. How can one chemical have opposite effects? The answer became clear when scientists discovered that receptors, like other proteins, come as families of related isoforms [p. 40].

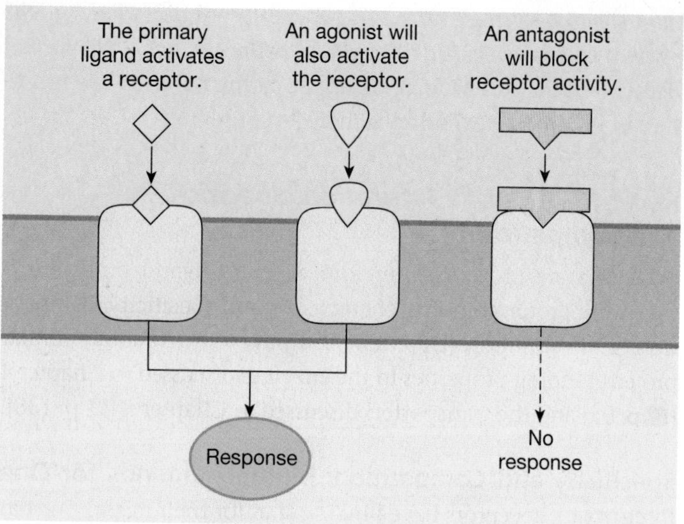

The primary ligand activates a receptor.
An agonist will also activate the receptor.
An antagonist will block receptor activity.
Response
No response

■ **FIGURE 6-17** ***Agonists and antagonists***

The cellular response that follows binding of a signal molecule to a receptor depends on which isoform of the receptor is involved. For example, the α- and β-adrenergic receptors for epinephrine described earlier are isoforms of each other. When epinephrine binds to α-receptors on smooth muscle in intestinal blood vessels, the vessels constrict (Fig. 6-18 ■). When epinephrine binds to β-receptors on certain skeletal muscle blood vessels, the vessels dilate. In other words, the response of the blood vessel to epinephrine depends on the receptor isoform, not on the ligand that activates the receptor. Many drugs now are designed so that they are specific for only one receptor isoform.

CONCEPT CHECK

15. What common property of receptors, enzymes, and transporters explains why they all exhibit saturation, specificity, and competition?
16. Insulin increases the number of glucose transporters on a skeletal muscle cell but not on the membrane of a liver cell. List two possible mechanisms that could explain how this one hormone can have these two different effects.

Answers: p. 209

Up-Regulation and Down-Regulation Enable Cells to Modulate Responses

Saturation of proteins refers to the fact that protein activity reaches a maximum rate because cells contain limited numbers of protein molecules [p. 43]. This phenomenon can be observed with enzymes, transporters, and receptors. A cell's ability to respond to a chemical signal therefore can be limited by the finite number of receptors for that signal.

A single cell contains between 500 and 100,000 receptors on the surface of its cell membrane, with additional receptors in the cytosol and nucleus. In any given cell, the number of receptors may change over time. Old receptors are withdrawn from the membrane by endocytosis and are broken down in lysosomes. New receptors are inserted into the membrane by exocytosis. Intracellular receptors are also made and broken down. This flexibility permits a cell to vary its responses to chemical signals depending on the extracellular conditions and the internal needs of the cell.

What happens when a signal molecule is present in the body in abnormally high concentrations for a sustained period of time? Initially the increased signal level creates an enhanced response. As this enhanced response continues, the target cells may attempt to bring their response back to normal by *down-regulation* of the receptors for the signal [p. 43].

Down-regulation takes two forms: either a decrease in receptor number or a decrease in binding affinity. The cell can physically remove receptors from the membrane through endocytosis [Fig. 5-24, p. 149]. A quicker and more easily reversible type of down-regulation, called *desensitization,* can be achieved by binding a chemical modulator to the receptor protein. For example, the β-adrenergic receptors described in the previous section can be desensitized by phosphorylation of the receptor. The result of decreased receptor number or decreased binding affinity is a diminished response of the target cell even though the concentration of the signal molecule remains high.

Down-regulation is one explanation for the development of *drug tolerance,* a condition in which the response to a given dose

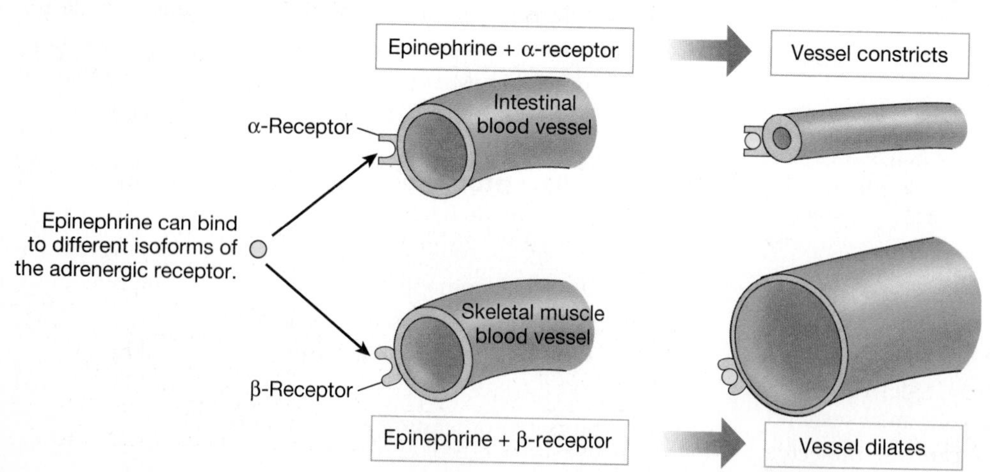

■ **FIGURE 6-18** ***Target response depends on the target receptor***

In this example, epinephrine will either dilate or constrict blood vessels depending on the receptor found on the blood vessel.

RUNNING PROBLEM

"My dad takes insulin shots for his diabetes," Marvin says. "What does insulin do?" The nurse practitioner replies that normally insulin helps many cells take up and utilize glucose. In both types of diabetes, however, fasting blood glucose concentrations are elevated because the cells are not taking up and using glucose normally. If people with type 1 diabetes are given shots of insulin, their blood glucose levels decline. If people with type 2 diabetes are given insulin, blood glucose levels may change very little.

Question 2:
In which form of diabetes are the insulin receptors more likely to be up-regulated?

decreases despite continuous exposure to the drug. The development of tolerance to opiates, such as morphine and codeine, occurs when the receptors for these drugs down-regulate.

If the concentration of a ligand decreases, the target cell may use up-regulation to insert more receptors into the cell membrane in an attempt to keep its response at a normal level. For example, if a nerve cell is damaged and unable to release normal amounts of neurotransmitter, its target cell will up-regulate its receptors. This up-regulation makes the target cell more sensitive to whatever neurotransmitters are present. Up-regulation is also programmed during development as a mechanism that allows cells to vary their responsiveness to growth factors and other signal molecules.

CONCEPT CHECK

17. To down-regulate a receptor's binding affinity, a cell might (select all that apply):
    (a) synthesize a new isoform of the receptor
    (b) withdraw receptors from the membrane
    (c) insert new receptors into the membrane
    (d) use a covalent modulator (*Hint:* p. 41)

Answers: p. 209

Cells Must Be Able to Terminate Signal Pathways

In the body, signals turn on and off, so cells must be able to tell when a signal is over. This requires that signaling processes have built-in termination mechanisms. For example, to stop the response to a calcium signal, a cell removes Ca^{2+} from the cytosol by pumping it either back into the endoplasmic reticulum or out into the extracellular fluid.

Receptor activity can be stopped in a variety of ways. The extracellular first messenger can be degraded by enzymes in the extracellular space. An example of this is the breakdown of the neurotransmitter acetylcholine. Other first messengers, particularly neurotransmitters, can be removed from the extracellular fluid by being transported into neighboring cells. A widely used class of antidepressant drugs called *selective serotonin reuptake inhibitors,* or SSRIs, extends the active life of the neurotransmitter serotonin by slowing its removal from the extracellular fluid.

Once a ligand is bound to its receptor, activity can also be terminated by endocytosis of the receptor-ligand complex. This process was illustrated in Figure 5-24 [p. 149]. After the vesicle is in the cell, the ligand is removed, and the receptors can be returned to the membrane by exocytosis.

Many Diseases and Drugs Target the Proteins of Signal Transduction

As we learn more about cell signaling, scientists are realizing how many diseases are linked to problems with signal pathways. Diseases can be caused by alterations in receptors or by problems with G proteins or second messenger pathways (see Table 6-3 ■ for some examples). A single change in the amino acid sequence of a receptor protein can alter the shape of the receptor's binding site, thereby either destroying or modifying its activity.

Pharmacologists are using information about signaling mechanisms to design drugs to treat disease. Some of the alphabet soup of drugs in widespread use are ARBs (angiotensin receptor blockers), beta-adrenergic receptor blockers, and calcium-channel blockers for treating high blood pressure; SERMs (selective estrogen receptor modulators) for treating estrogen-dependent cancers; and H_2 (histamine type 2) receptor antagonists for decreasing acid secretion in the stomach. We will encounter many of these drugs again when we study the systems in which they are effective.

CONTROL PATHWAYS: RESPONSE AND FEEDBACK LOOPS

In Chapter 1 you learned that homeostasis is the ability of the body to maintain a relatively stable internal environment [p. 3]. Homeostasis is a continuous process that uses a **physiological control system** to monitor key functions, or **regulated variables**.

In its simplest form, any control system has three components: (1) an input signal; (2) a controller, which is programmed to respond to certain input signals; and (3) an output signal [Fig. 1-6, p. 9]. Physiological control systems are a little more complex. The input signal consists of the regulated variable and a specialized **sensor**. If the variable moves out of its desirable range, the sensor is activated and sends a signal to the

6

TABLE 6-3 Some Diseases or Conditions Linked to Abnormal Signaling Mechanisms

Genetically inherited abnormal receptors		
RECEPTOR	**PHYSIOLOGICAL ALTERATION**	**DISEASE OR CONDITION THAT RESULTS**
Vasopressin receptor (X-linked defect)	Shortens half-life of the receptor	Congenital diabetes insipidus
Calcium sensor in parathyroid gland	Fails to respond to increase in plasma Ca^{2+}	Familial hypercalcemia
Rhodopsin receptor in retina of eye	Improper protein folding	Retinitis pigmentosa
Toxins affecting signal pathways		
TOXIN	**PHYSIOLOGICAL EFFECT**	**CONDITION THAT RESULTS**
Bordetella pertussis toxin	Blocks inhibition of adenylate cyclase (i.e., keeps it active)	Whooping cough
Cholera toxin	Blocks enzyme activity of G proteins; cell keeps making cAMP	Ions secreted into lumen of intestine, causing massive diarrhea

controller (Fig. 6-19 ■). The controller acts as an **integrating center** [*integrare,* to restore] that evaluates information coming from the sensor and initiates a response that is designed to bring the regulated variable back into the desired range. The integrating center is often a nerve cell or an endocrine cell. The muscles and other tissues controlled by integrating centers are known as **effectors** [*effectus,* the carrying out of a task] because they effect a change.

Cannon's Postulates Describe Regulated Variables and Physiological Control Systems

Walter Cannon, the father of American physiology, described a number of properties of homeostatic control systems in the 1920s based on his observations of the body in health and disease states.* You will encounter these properties repeatedly as you study the various organ systems of the body. Cannon's four postulates are:

1. **The nervous system has a role in preserving the "fitness" of the internal environment.** *Fitness* in this instance means conditions that are compatible with normal function. The nervous system coordinates and integrates blood volume, blood osmolarity, blood pressure, and body temperature, among other regulated variables.
2. **Some systems of the body are under tonic control [*tonos,* tone].** To quote Cannon, "An agent may exist which has a moderate activity which can be varied up and down." This type of control is like the volume control on a radio, which enables you to make the sound level louder or softer by turning a single knob. A physiological example of a tonically controlled system is the neural regulation of diameter in certain blood vessels, in which increased input from the nervous system decreases diameter, and decreased input from the nervous system increases diameter (Fig. 6-20 ■). *Tonic control* is one of the more difficult concepts in physiology because we have a tendency to think of responses stopping and starting when a controller turns off or on rather than as responses increasing and decreasing.
3. **Some systems of the body are under antagonistic control.** Cannon wrote, "When a factor is known which can shift a homeostatic state in one direction, it is reasonable to look for a factor or factors having an opposing effect." Systems that are not under tonic control are usually under *antagonistic control,* either by hormones or the nervous system. For example,

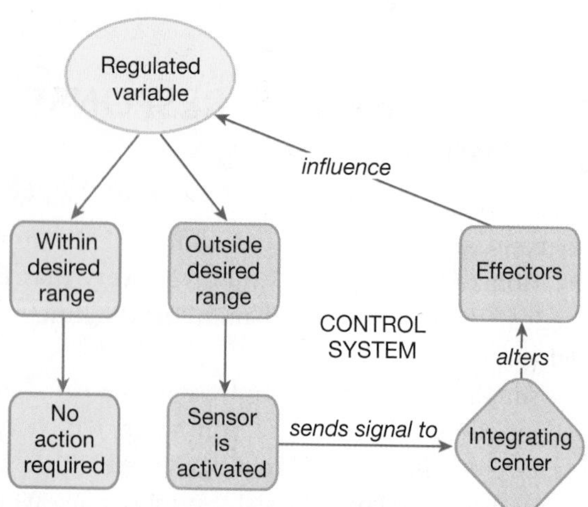

■ **FIGURE 6-19** ***Physiological control systems keep regulated variables within a desired range during homeostasis***

*"Organization for Physiological Homeostasis," *Physiological Reviews* 9: 399–443, 1929.

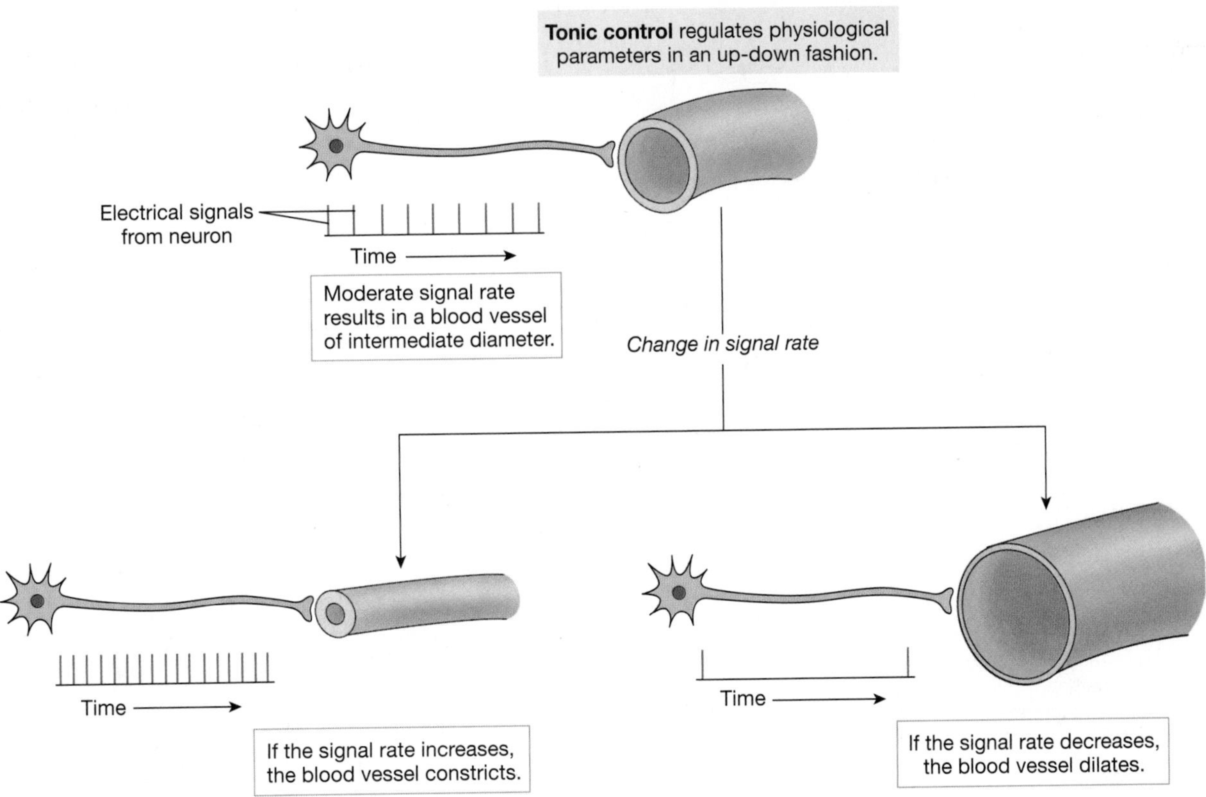

Tonic control regulates physiological parameters in an up-down fashion.
Electrical signals from neuron
Time
Moderate signal rate results in a blood vessel of intermediate diameter.
Change in signal rate
Time
If the signal rate increases, the blood vessel constricts.
Time
If the signal rate decreases, the blood vessel dilates.

■ **FIGURE 6-20** *Tonic control of blood vessel diameter*

insulin and glucagon are antagonistic hormones. Insulin decreases the concentration of glucose in the blood; glucagon increases it. In pathways controlled by the nervous system, the sympathetic and parasympathetic divisions often have opposing effects. For example, chemical signals from a sympathetic neuron increase heart rate, but chemical signals from a parasympathetic neuron decrease it (Fig. 6-21 ■).

4. **One chemical signal can have different effects in different tissues.** Cannon observed correctly that "homeostatic agents antagonistic in one region of the body may be cooperative in another region." However, it was not until we learned about cell receptors that the basis for the seemingly contradictory actions of some hormones or nerves became clear. As you learned in the first part of this chapter, a single chemical signal can have different effects depending on the receptor at the target cell. For example, epinephrine constricts or dilates blood vessels, depending on whether the vessel has α- or β-adrenergic receptors (see Fig. 6-18).

The remarkable accuracy of Cannon's postulates, now confirmed with cellular and molecular data, is a tribute to the observational skills of scientists in the nineteenth and early twentieth centuries.

CONCEPT CHECK

18. What is the difference between tonic control and antagonistic control?
19. How can one chemical signal have opposite effects in two different tissues?

Answers: p. 209

RUNNING PROBLEM

"Why is an elevated blood glucose concentration bad?" Marvin asks. "The elevated blood glucose itself is not bad," says the nurse practitioner, "but when it is high after an overnight fast, it suggests that there is something wrong with the way your body is regulating its glucose metabolism." When a normal person absorbs a meal containing carbohydrates, blood glucose levels increase and stimulate insulin release. When cells have taken up the glucose from the meal and blood glucose levels fall, secretion of another pancreatic hormone, glucagon, increases. Glucagon raises blood glucose and helps keep the level within the homeostatic range.

Question 3:

The homeostatic regulation of blood glucose levels by the hormones insulin and glucagon is an example of which of Cannon's postulates?

175 179 191 193 197 201 206

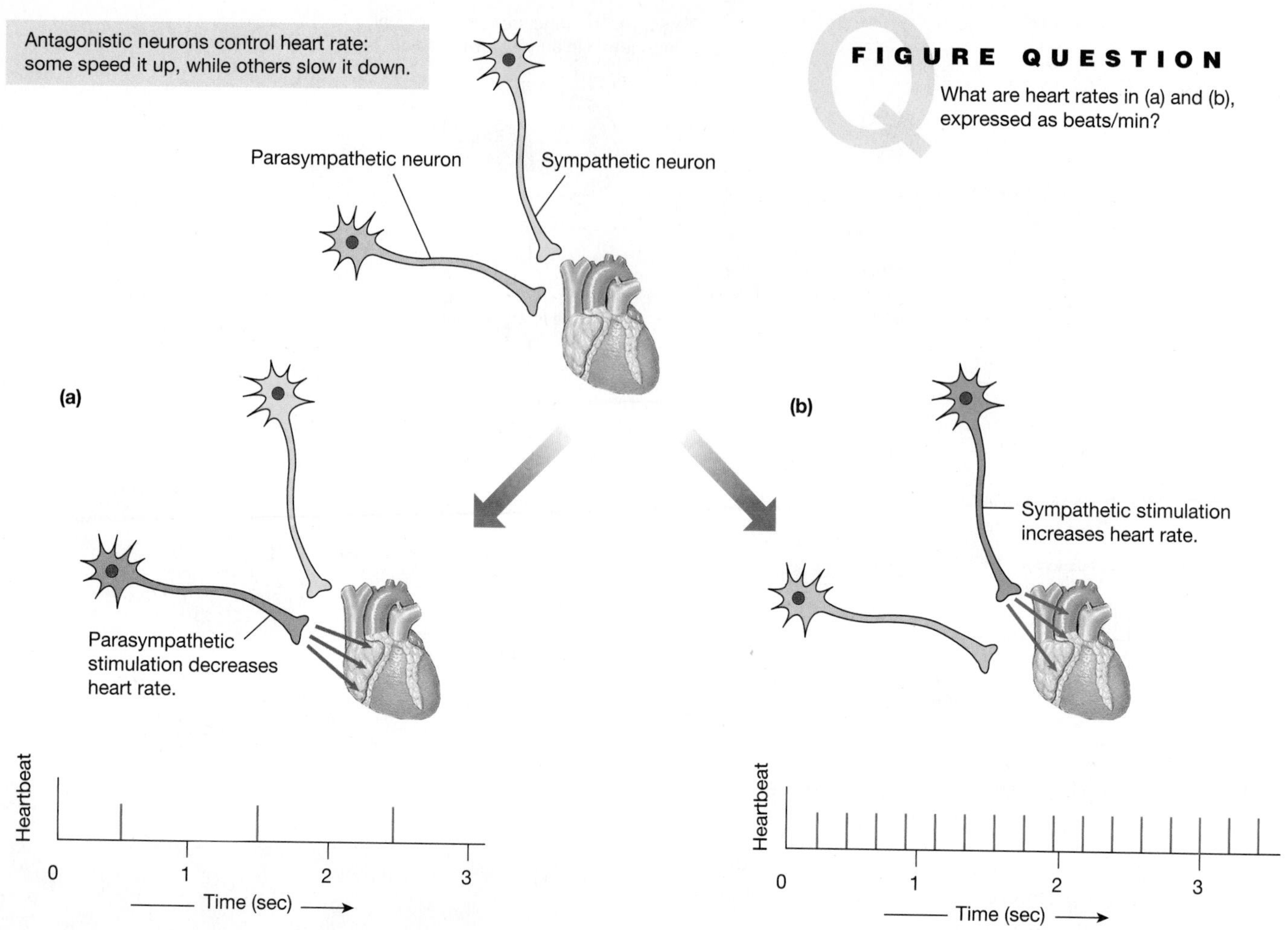

Antagonistic neurons control heart rate: some speed it up, while others slow it down.

Parasympathetic neuron

Sympathetic neuron

FIGURE QUESTION

What are heart rates in (a) and (b), expressed as beats/min?

(a)

Parasympathetic stimulation decreases heart rate.

Heartbeat

0 1 2 3

Time (sec)

(b)

Sympathetic stimulation increases heart rate.

Heartbeat

0 1 2 3

Time (sec)

FIGURE 6-21 ***Antagonistic control of heart rate***

The heart is controlled by antagonistic neurons. One set of neurons speeds up heart rate, and the other set slows it down.

Homeostasis May Be Maintained by Local or Long-Distance Pathways

The simplest control takes place at the tissue or cell involved. In **local control**, a relatively isolated change occurs in the vicinity of a cell or tissue and evokes a paracrine or autocrine response (Fig. 6-22 ■). More complicated **reflex control pathways** respond to changes that are widespread throughout the body or *systemic* in nature. In a reflex pathway, an integrating center located away from the affected cell or tissue receives information, evaluates it, and decides whether to send a chemical or electrical signal to initiate a response.

Long-distance reflex pathways are traditionally considered to involve two control systems: the nervous system and the endocrine system. However, cytokines [p. 176] are now known to be involved in some long-distance pathways. During stress and systemic inflammatory responses, cytokines work together with the nervous and endocrine systems to integrate information from all over the body into coordinated responses.

Local Control Paracrine and autocrine signals are responsible for the simplest control systems. In local control, a cell or tissue senses a change in its immediate vicinity and responds. The response is restricted to the region where the change took place—hence the term *local control*.

One example of local control can be observed when oxygen concentration in a tissue decreases. The cells lining the small blood vessels bringing blood to that area sense the fall in oxygen concentration and respond by secreting a paracrine signal. The paracrine molecule relaxes muscles in the blood vessel wall, dilating the blood vessel and bringing more blood and therefore more oxygen to the area. Paracrine signal molecules involved in this response include carbon dioxide and metabolic products such as lactic acid.

Reflex Control In a reflex control pathway, coordination of the reaction lies outside the organ that carries out the response. We will use the term *reflex* to mean any long-distance pathway that uses the nervous system, endocrine system, or both to receive

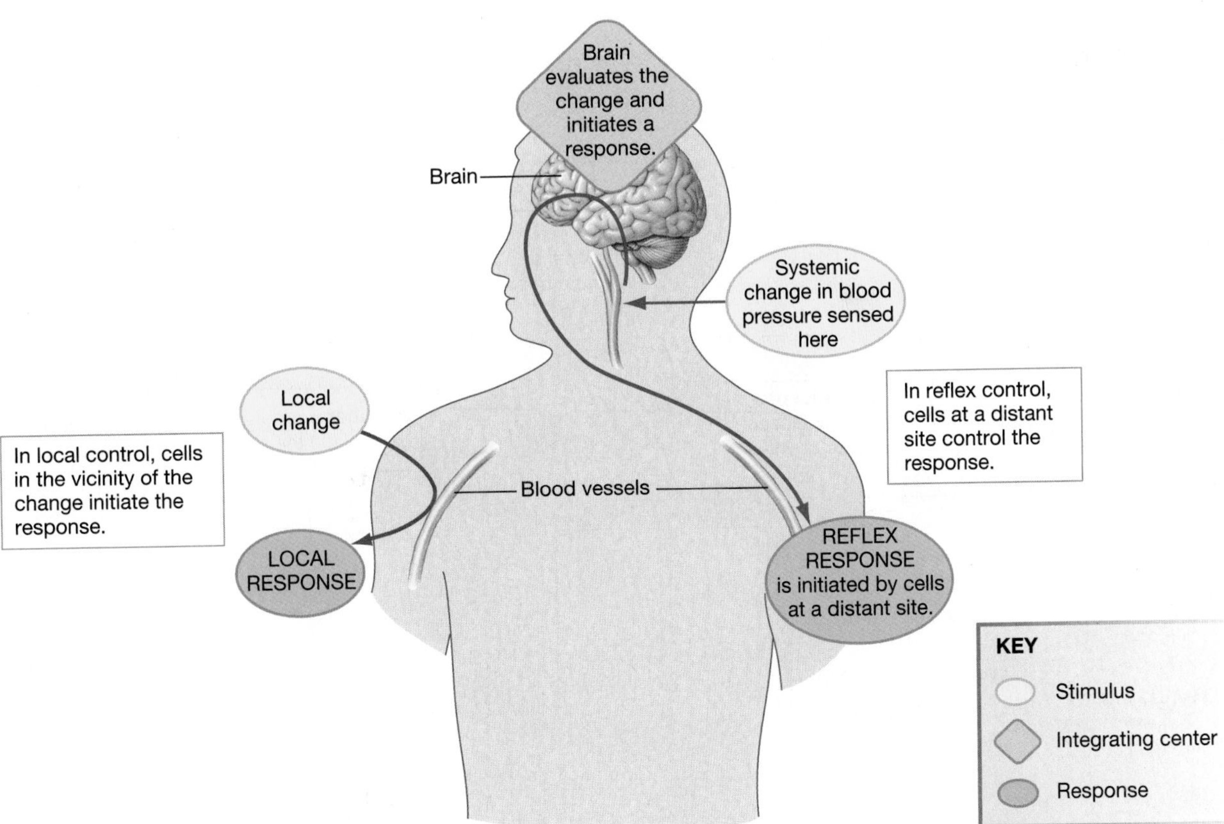

■ **FIGURE 6-22** ***Comparison of local and reflex control***

input about a change, integrate the information, and react appropriately. A reflex pathway can be broken down into two parts: a response loop and a feedback loop (Fig. 6-23 ■). The response loop begins with a stimulus and ends with the response of the target cell. We will discuss response loops first and then consider how they interact with feedback loops.

As with any other control system, a **response loop** has three primary components: an *input signal, integration of the signal,* and an *output signal*. These three components can be broken down into the following sequence of seven steps to form a pattern that is found with slight variations in all reflex pathways:

Stimulus → sensor or receptor → afferent pathway → integrating center → efferent pathway → target or effector → response

The input signal of a homeostatic reflex pathway consists of a stimulus, its sensory receptor, and an afferent (or incoming) pathway. (1) A **stimulus** is the disturbance or change that sets the pathway in motion. The stimulus may be a change in temperature, oxygen content, blood pressure, or any one of a myriad of other variables. The stimulus is sensed by (2) a **sensor** or sensory receptor that is continuously monitoring its environment. When alerted to a change, the receptor sends (3) a signal, or **afferent** (incoming) **pathway**, that links the receptor to (4) an integrating center. The integrating center then evaluates the incoming signal, compares it with the **setpoint**, or desired

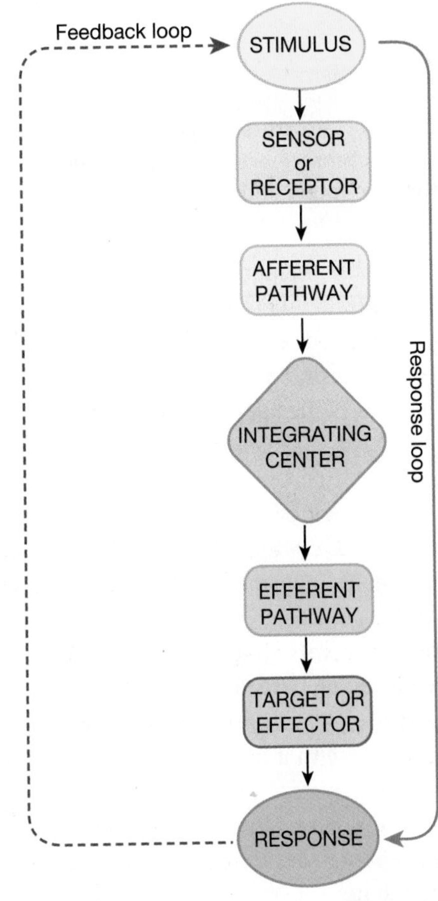

■ **FIGURE 6-23** ***Steps in a reflex control pathway***

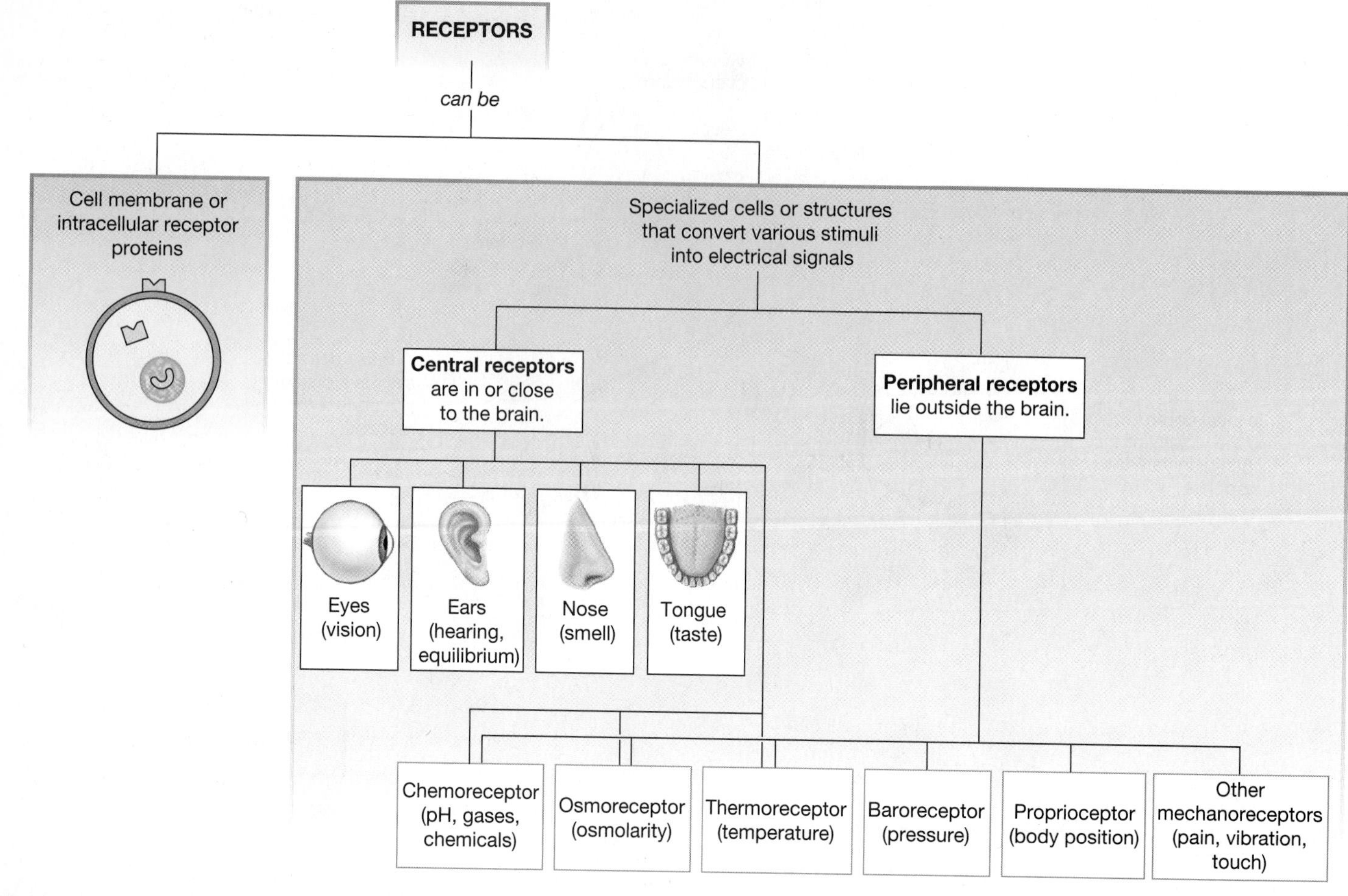

FIGURE 6-24 ***Multiple meanings of the word* receptor**

The word *receptor* may mean a protein that binds to a ligand. Receptor can also mean a specialized cell or structure for transduction of stimuli into electrical signals (a *sensory receptor*). Sensory receptors are classified as central or peripheral, depending on whether they are found in the brain or outside the brain.

value, and decides on an appropriate response. The integrating center then initiates (5) the output signal, or **efferent** (outgoing) **pathway**. This is an electrical and/or chemical signal that travels to (6) the effector. The effector, or target, is the cell or tissue that carries out (7) the appropriate response to bring the situation back to within normal limits.

Receptor The first step in a physiological response loop is activation of a sensor or receptor by the stimulus. NOTICE! This is a new and different application of the word *receptor*. Like many other terms in physiology, *receptor* can have different meanings (Fig. 6-24 ■). The sensory receptors of a neural reflex are not protein receptors that bind to signal molecules, like those involved in signal transduction. Rather, sensory receptors are specialized cells, parts of cells, or complex multicellular receptors such as the eye that respond to changes in the environment around them.

There are many sensory receptors in the body, each located where it is in the best position to monitor the variable it detects. The eyes, ears, and nose are receptors that sense light, sound and motion, and odors, respectively. Your skin is covered with less complex receptors that sense touch, temperature, vibration, and pain. Other sensory receptors are internal: receptors in the joints of the skeleton that send information to the brain about body position, or blood pressure and oxygen receptors in blood vessels that monitor conditions in the circulatory system. The sensory receptors involved in neural reflexes are divided into *central receptors,* located in or closely linked to the brain, and *peripheral receptors,* which reside elsewhere in the body.

All sensory receptors have a **threshold**, a minimum stimulus that must be achieved to set the reflex response in motion. If a stimulus is below the threshold, no response loop will be initiated. You can demonstrate threshold easily by touching the back of your hand with a sharp, pointed object, such as a pin. If you touch the point to your skin lightly enough, you can see the contact between the point and your skin even though you do not feel anything. In this case, the stimulus (pressure from the point of the pin) is below threshold, and the pressure receptors of the skin are not responding. As you press harder, the stimulus reaches threshold, and the receptors respond by sending a signal through the afferent pathway, causing you to feel the pin.

Endocrine reflexes that are not associated with the nervous system do not use sensory receptors to initiate their pathways. Instead, endocrine cells act both as sensor and integrating center for the reflex. You were introduced to an example of this in Chapter 5, when we discussed how the pancreatic beta cells sense and respond to changes in blood glucose concentrations [p. 166].

Afferent pathway The afferent pathway in a reflex varies depending on the type of reflex. In a neural reflex, such as the pin touch above, the afferent pathway is the electrical and chemical signals carried by a nerve cell. In an endocrine reflex, there is no afferent pathway because the stimulus comes directly into the endocrine cell, which serves as both sensor and integrating center.

Integrating center The integrating center in a reflex pathway is the cell that receives information about the change and is programmed to initiate an appropriate response. In endocrine reflexes, the integrating center is the endocrine cell. In neural reflexes, the integrating center usually lies within the central nervous system, which is composed of the brain and the spinal cord.

If information is coming from a single stimulus, it is a relatively simple task for an integrating center to compare that information with the setpoint and initiate a response (if necessary). Integrating centers really "earn their pay," however, when two or more conflicting signals come in from different sources. The center must evaluate each signal on the basis of its strength and importance and must come up with an appropriate response that integrates information from all contributing receptors. This is similar to the kind of decision making you must do when on one evening your parents want to take you to dinner, your friends are having a party, there is a television program you want to watch, and you have a major physiology test in three days. It is up to you to rank those items in order of importance and decide how you will act on them.

Efferent pathway Efferent pathways are relatively simple. In the nervous system, the efferent pathway is always the electrical and chemical signals transmitted by an efferent neuron. Because all electrical signals traveling through the nervous system are identical, the distinguishing characteristic of the signal is the anatomical route taken by the nerve cell through which the signal goes. For example, the vagus nerve carries a neural signal to the heart, and the phrenic nerve carries one to the diaphragm. Because the nature of the electrical message is always the same and because there are relatively few types of neurotransmitters, nervous system efferent pathways are named using the anatomical description of the nerve that carries the signal.

In the endocrine system, the anatomical routing of the efferent pathway is always the same because all hormones travel in the blood to get to their target. Hormonal efferent pathways are distinguished by the chemical nature of the signal and are therefore named for the hormone that carries the message. For example, the efferent pathway for a reflex integrated through the pancreas will be either the hormone insulin or the hormone glucagon, depending on the stimulus and the appropriate response.

RUNNING PROBLEM

Marvin is fascinated by the ability of the body to keep track of glucose. "How does the pancreas know which hormone to secrete?" he wonders. Special cells in the pancreas called beta cells sense an increase in blood glucose concentrations after a meal, and they release insulin in response. Insulin then acts on many tissues of the body so that they take up and utilize glucose.

Question 4:

In the insulin reflex pathway that regulates blood glucose levels, what are the stimulus, the sensor, the integrating center, the efferent pathway, the effector(s), and the response(s)?

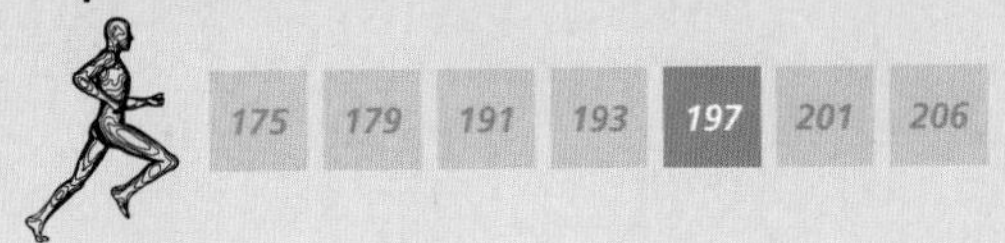

Effectors The effectors of reflex control pathways are the cells or tissues that carry out the response. The targets of neural pathways are muscles, glands, and some adipose tissue. The targets of endocrine pathways are any cells that have the proper receptor for the hormone.

Responses There are two levels of response for any reflex control pathway. One is the very specific *cellular response* that takes place in the target cell. The more general *systemic response* describes what those specific cellular events mean either to the tissue or to the organism as a whole. For example, when the hormone epinephrine combines with β_2-adrenergic receptors on the walls of certain blood vessels, the cellular response is relaxation of the smooth muscle. The systemic response to relaxation of the blood vessel wall is increased blood flow through the vessel.

CONCEPT CHECK

20. What is the difference between local control and reflex control?
21. Name the seven steps in a reflex control pathway in their correct order.

Answers: p. 209

Response Loops Begin with a Stimulus and End with a Response

To illustrate response loops, we will now apply the concept to nonbiological and biological examples. A simple nonbiological analogy to a homeostatic reflex pathway is an aquarium whose

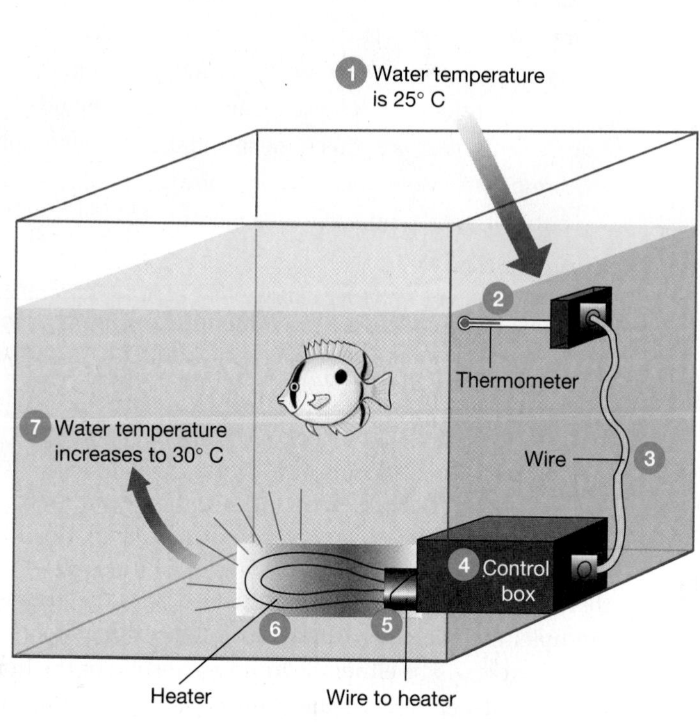

1 Water temperature is 25° C
2
Thermometer
Wire
3
7 Water temperature increases to 30° C
4 Control box
6
5
Heater
Wire to heater

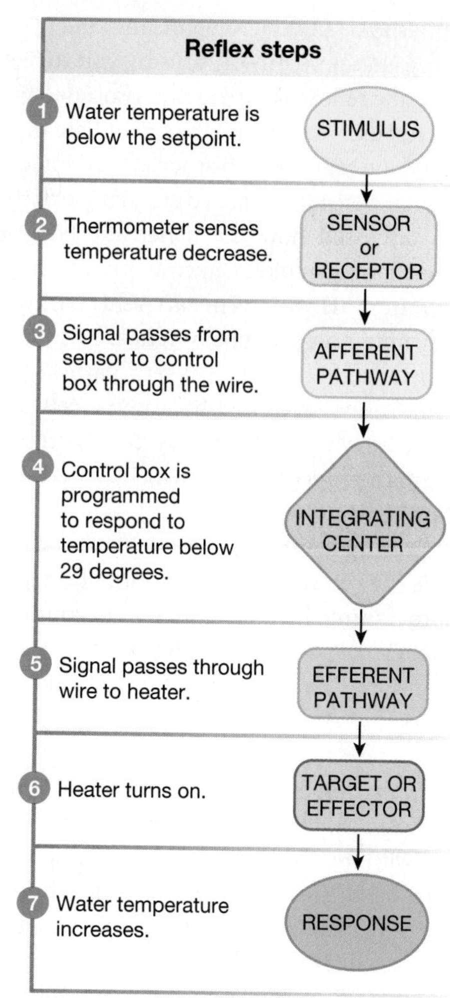

Reflex steps
1 Water temperature is below the setpoint.
STIMULUS
2 Thermometer senses temperature decrease.
SENSOR or RECEPTOR
3 Signal passes from sensor to control box through the wire.
AFFERENT PATHWAY
4 Control box is programmed to respond to temperature below 29 degrees.
INTEGRATING CENTER
5 Signal passes through wire to heater.
EFFERENT PATHWAY
6 Heater turns on.
TARGET OR EFFECTOR
7 Water temperature increases.
RESPONSE

■ **FIGURE 6-25** ***A nonbiological response loop***

The control box of the aquarium is set to maintain a water temperature of 30° ± 1° C.

heater is programmed to maintain the water temperature at 30° C in a room whose temperature is 25° C (Fig. 6-25 ■). The desired water temperature (30° C) is the *setpoint* for the regulated variable.

Assume that initially the aquarium water is at room temperature, 25° C. When you turn the control box on, you set the response loop in motion. The thermometer (sensor) registers a temperature of 25° C. It sends this information via a wire (afferent path) to the control box (integrating center). The control box evaluates the incoming temperature signal, compares it with the setpoint for the system (30° C), and "decides" that a response is needed to bring the water temperature up to the setpoint. The control box sends a signal via another wire (efferent path) to the heater (effector), which turns on and starts heating the water (response). This sequence—from stimulus to response—is the response loop.

This aquarium example involves a variable (temperature) that is under *tonic control* (see p. 197) by a single control system (the heater). We can also describe a nonbiological analogy that illustrates Cannon's postulate of *antagonistic control*. For example, think of a house that has both heating and air-conditioning. The owner would like the house to remain at 70° F (about 21° C). On chilly autumn mornings, the heater turns on to warm the house. Then, as the day warms up, the heater is no longer needed. When the sun heats the house above the setpoint, the air-conditioner turns on to cool the house back to 70° F. The heater and air-conditioner have antagonistic control over house temperature. A similar physiological example would be the hormones insulin and glucagon, which exert antagonistic control over glucose metabolism, as noted earlier.

CONCEPT CHECK

22. What is the drawback of having only a single control system (a heater) for maintaining aquarium water temperature in some desired range? Answers: p. 209

Setpoints Can Be Varied

In physiological systems, the setpoint for any given regulated variable can vary from person to person, or even for the same individual over a period of time. Factors that influence an individual's setpoint for a given variable include inheritance and the conditions to which the person has become accustomed. The adaptation of physiological processes to a given set of environmental conditions is known as **acclimatization** if it occurs

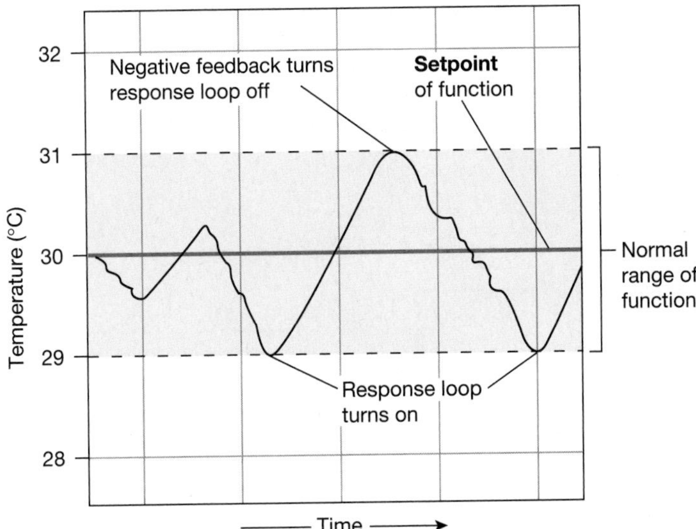

FIGURE 6-26 *Oscillation around the setpoint*

Most functions that are controlled homeostatically have a setpoint, or normal value. The response loop that controls the function is activated when the function moves outside a predetermined normal range.

naturally, and as **acclimation** if the process is induced artificially in a laboratory setting. Each winter, northerners go south in February, hoping to escape the bitter subzero temperatures and snows of the northern climate. As they walk around in 40° F weather in short-sleeve shirts, the southerners, all bundled up in coats and gloves, think they are crazy: the weather is cold! The difference in behavior is due to different temperature acclimatization, a difference in the setpoint for body temperature regulation that is a result of prior conditioning.

Physiological setpoints also vary within individuals in response to external cues, such as the daily light-dark cycles and the seasons. These changing setpoints cause certain variables to vary in predictable ways over a period of time, forming patterns of change known as biorhythms (discussed later in this chapter).

Feedback Loops Modulate the Response Loop

The response loop is only part of a reflex. For example, in the aquarium just described, the sensor sends temperature information to the control box, which recognizes that the water is too cold. The control box responds by turning on the heater to warm the water. Once the response starts, though, what keeps the heater from sending the temperature up to, say, 50° C?

The answer is a **feedback loop**, where the response "feeds back" to influence the input portion of the pathway. In the aquarium example, turning on the heater increases the temperature of the water. The sensor continuously monitors the temperature and sends that information to the control box. When the temperature warms up to the maximum acceptable value, the control box shuts off the heater, thus ending the reflex response.

Negative Feedback Loops Are Homeostatic For most reflexes, feedback loops are homeostatic—that is, designed to keep the system at or near a setpoint so that the variable being regulated will be relatively stable. How well an integrating center succeeds in maintaining stability depends on the *sensitivity* of the system. In the case of our aquarium, the control box is programmed to have a sensitivity of ±1° C. If the water temperature drops from 30° C to 29.5° C, it is still within the acceptable range, and no response is triggered. If the water temperature drops below 29° C (30° − 1°), the control box turns the heater on (Fig. 6-26 ■). As the water heats up, the control box constantly receives information about the water temperature from the sensor. When the water reaches 31° C (30° + 1°), the upper limit for the acceptable range, the feedback loop causes the control box to turn the heater off. The water then gradually cools off until the cycle starts all over again. The end result is a regulated variable that *oscillates* [*oscillare,* to swing] around the setpoint.

In physiological systems, some sensors are more sensitive than others. For example, the sensors for osmolarity trigger reflexes to conserve water when blood osmolarity increases only 3% above normal, but the sensors for low oxygen in the blood will not respond until oxygen has decreased by 40%.

A pathway in which the response opposes or removes the signal is known as **negative feedback** (Fig. 6-27a ■). Negative feedback loops *stabilize* the variable being regulated and thus aid the system in maintaining homeostasis. In the aquarium example, the heater warms the water (the response) and removes the stimulus (low water temperature). With loss of the stimulus for the pathway, the response loop shuts off. All homeostatic reflexes are controlled by negative feedback so that the variable being regulated will stay within a normal range. *Negative feedback loops can restore the normal state but cannot prevent the initial disturbance.*

Positive Feedback Loops Are Not Homeostatic A few reflex pathways are not homeostatic. In a **positive feedback loop**, the response *reinforces* the stimulus rather than decreasing or removing it. In positive feedback, the response sends the variable being regulated even farther from its normal value, triggering a vicious cycle of ever-increasing response and sending the system temporarily out of control (Fig. 6-27b). Because positive feedback escalates the response, this type of feedback requires some intervention or event outside the loop to stop the response.

One example of a positive feedback loop involves the hormonal control of uterine contractions during childbirth (Fig. 6-28 ■). When the baby is ready to be delivered, it drops lower in the uterus and begins to put pressure on the *cervix,* the opening of the uterus. Sensory signals from the cervix to the brain cause release of the hormone *oxytocin,* which causes the uterus to contract and push the baby's head even harder against the cervix, further stretching it. The increased stretch causes more oxytocin release, which causes more contractions that push the baby harder against the cervix. This cycle continues until finally the baby is delivered, releasing the stretch on the cervix and stopping the positive feedback loop.

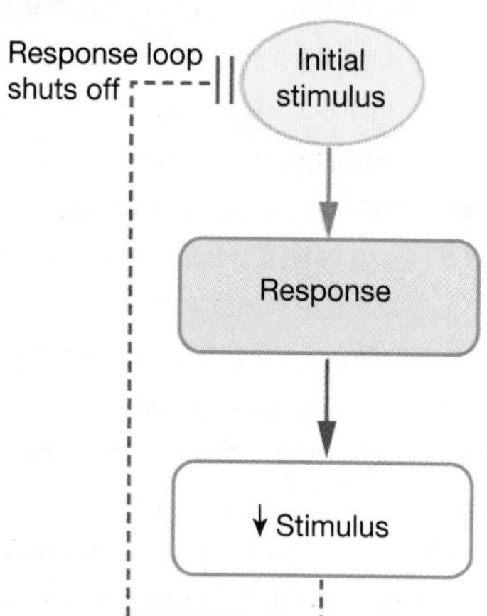

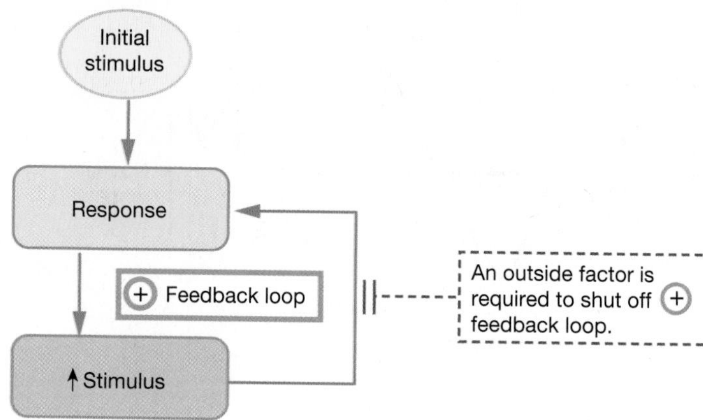

■ **FIGURE 6-27** ***Negative and positive feedback***

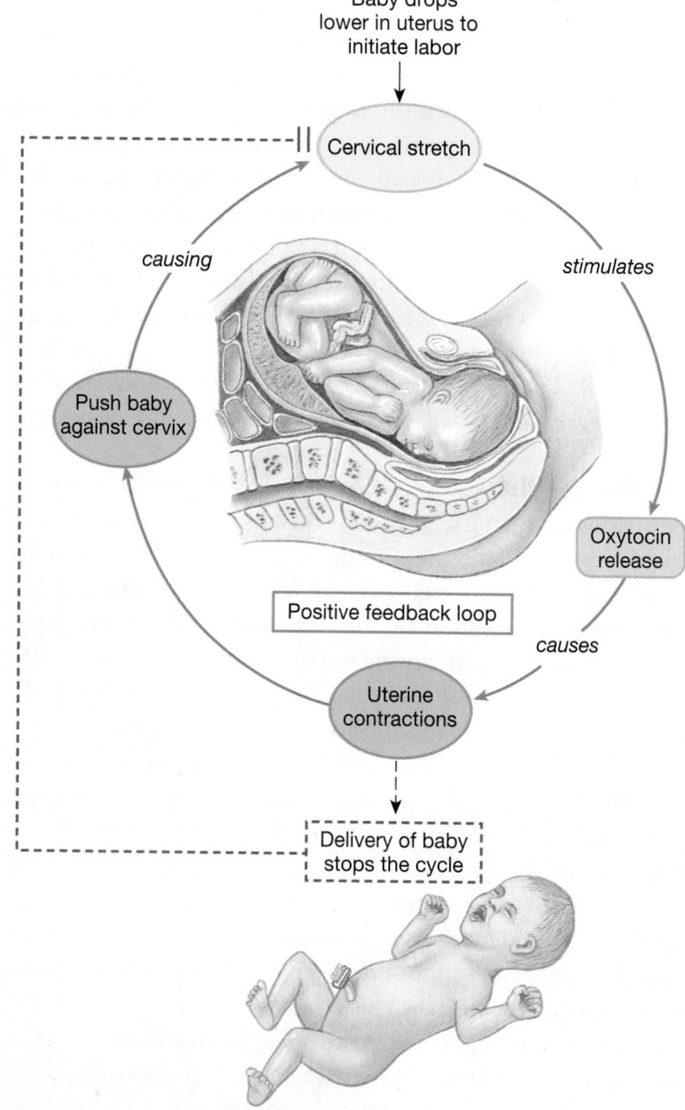

■ **FIGURE 6-28** ***A positive feedback loop***

CONCEPT CHECK

23. Does the aquarium heating system in Figure 6-25 function using positive feedback or negative feedback? Draw in the appropriate feedback loop on the reflex steps in the figure, using either a solid arrow accompanied by a plus sign inside a circle for positive feedback, or two short, parallel "stop" lines at the end of a dashed line for negative feedback, as illustrated in Figure 6-27.

Answers: p. 210

Feedforward Control Allows the Body to Anticipate Change and Maintain Stability

Negative feedback loops can stabilize a function and maintain it within a normal range but are unable to prevent the change that triggered the reflex in the first place. A few reflexes have evolved that enable the body to predict that a change is about to occur and start the response loop in anticipation of the change. These anticipatory responses are called **feedforward control**.

An easily understood physiological example of feedforward control is the reflex of salivation. The sight, smell, or even the thought of food is enough to start our mouths watering. The saliva is present in expectation of the food that will soon be eaten. This reflex extends even further, because the same stimuli can start the secretion of hydrochloric acid as the stomach anticipates food on the way. One of the most complex feedforward reflexes appears to be the body's response to exercise, to be discussed in Chapter 25.

Biological Rhythms Result from Changes in a Setpoint

In many reflex pathways, the stimuli are obviously related to the function of the reflex. In the aquarium example, a change in temperature is the stimulus to ensure that temperature is maintained within the desired range. This is not true of all reflexes, however. Many hormones, for example, are secreted continuously, with

(a)

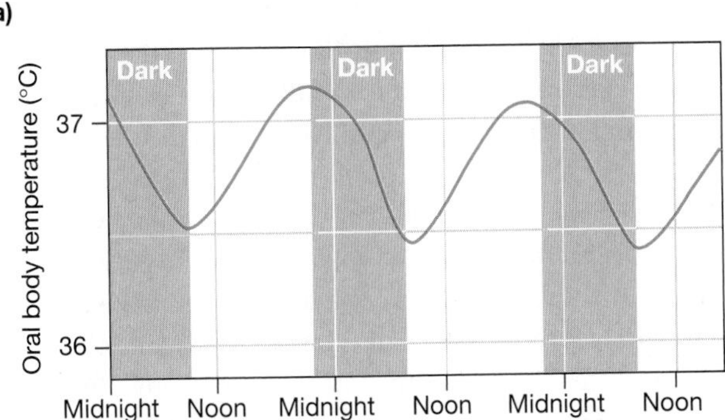

(b)

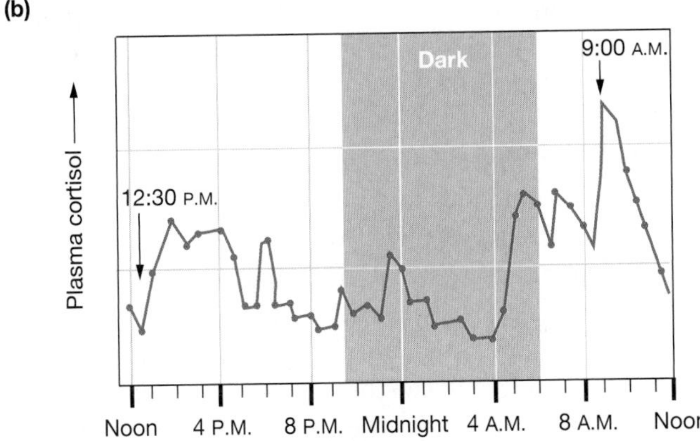

■ **FIGURE 6-29** *Circadian rhythms*

levels that rise and fall throughout the day. Most examples of these apparently spontaneous reflexes occur in a predictable manner and are often timed to coincide with a predictable environmental change, such as light-dark cycles or the seasons.

All animals exhibit some form of daily biological rhythm, called a **circadian rhythm** [*circa,* about + *dies,* day]. Humans have circadian rhythms for many body functions, including blood pressure, body temperature, and metabolic processes. Body temperature peaks in the late afternoon and declines dramatically in the early hours of the morning (Fig. 6-29a ■). Have you ever been studying late at night and noticed that you feel cold? This is not because of a drop in environmental temperature but because your thermoregulatory reflex has turned down your internal thermostat.

Many hormones in humans are secreted so that their concentration in the blood fluctuates predictably through a 24-hour cycle as their setpoints change. Cortisol, growth hormone, and the sex hormones are among the most noted examples. If an abnormality in hormone secretion is suspected, it is important to know at what time of day the body fluid used for testing was taken from the patient. A cortisol value that is normal in a 9:00 A.M. sample would be abnormally high for a blood sample taken at noon (Fig. 6-29b). One strategy for avoiding this type of error uses a 24-hour collection period that results in an average value for the hormone over the course of a day. For example, cortisol secretion is monitored indirectly by measuring all urinary cortisol metabolites excreted in 24 hours.

What is the adaptive significance of functions that vary with a circadian rhythm? Our best answer is that biological rhythms create an anticipatory response to a predictable environmental variable. There are seasonal rhythms of reproduction in many mammalian and non-mammalian vertebrates and invertebrates, rhythms timed so that the offspring have food and other favorable conditions to maximize survival. Circadian rhythms cued by the light-dark cycle may correspond to our rest-activity cycles. These rhythms allow our bodies to anticipate behavior and coordinate body processes accordingly. You may hear someone who is accustomed to eating dinner at 6 P.M. say that he cannot digest his food if he waits until 10 P.M. to eat because his digestive system has "shut down" in anticipation of going to bed.

One of the interesting correlations between circadian rhythms and behavior involves body temperature. Researchers found that self-described "morning people" have temperature rhythms that cause body temperature to climb before they awaken in the morning, so that they get out of bed prepared to face the world. On the other hand, "night people" may be forced by school and work schedules to get out of bed while their body temperature is still at its lowest point, before their bodies are prepared for activity. These night people are still going strong and working productively in the early hours of the morning when the morning peoples' body temperatures are dropping and they are fast asleep.

Circadian rhythms arise from special groups of cells in the brain and are reinforced by information about the light-dark cycle that comes in through the eyes. Research in simpler animals such as flies is beginning to explain the molecular basis for biological rhythms. We will discuss the cellular and molecular basis for circadian rhythms in Chapter 9.

Now that you have been introduced to response loops and feedback loops, we turn to an analysis of the different control systems.

RUNNING PROBLEM

"OK, just one more question," says Marvin. "You said that people with diabetes have high blood glucose levels. If glucose is so high, why can't it just leak into the cells?"

Question 5:

Why can't glucose always diffuse into cells when the blood glucose concentration is higher than the intracellular glucose concentration?

Question 6:

What do you think happens to the rate of insulin secretion when blood glucose levels fall? What kind of feedback loop is operating?

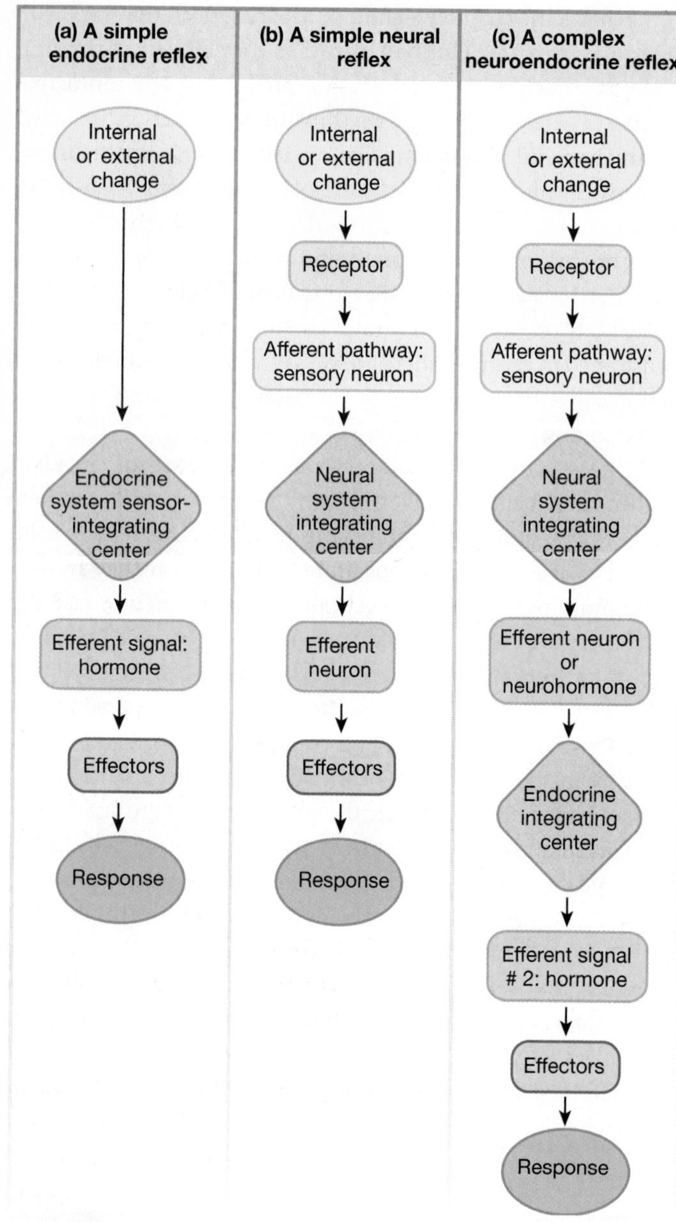

■ **FIGURE 6-30** ***Endocrine, neural, and neuroendocrine control pathways***

Control Systems Vary in Their Speed and Specificity

Physiological reflex control pathways are mediated by the nervous system, the endocrine system, or a combination of the two (Fig. 6-30 ■). A reflex mediated solely by the nervous system or solely by the endocrine system is relatively simple, but combination reflex pathways can be quite complex. In the most complex pathways, signals pass through three different integrating centers before finally reaching the target tissue. With so much overlap between pathways controlled by the nervous and endocrine systems, it makes sense to consider these systems as parts of a continuum rather than as two discrete systems.

Why does the body need different types of control systems? To answer that question, let us compare endocrine control with neural control to see what the differences are. Five major differences are summarized in Table 6-4 ■ and discussed next.

Specificity Neural control is very specific because each nerve cell has a specific target cell or cells to which it sends its message. Anatomically, we can isolate a neuron and trace it from its origin to where it terminates on its target cell(s). Endocrine control is more general because the chemical messenger is released into the blood and can reach virtually every cell in the body. As you learned in the first half of this chapter, the body's response to a specific hormone depends on which cells have receptors for that hormone. Multiple tissues in the body can respond to a hormone simultaneously.

Nature of the Signal The nervous system uses both electrical and chemical signals to send information throughout the body. Electrical signals travel long distances through nerve cells, releasing chemical signals (neurotransmitters) that diffuse across the small gap between the neuron and its target (Fig. 6-31,① ■). In a limited number of instances, electrical signals pass directly from cell to cell through gap junctions.

The endocrine system uses only chemical signals: hormones secreted by endocrine glands or cells into the blood (Fig. 6-31,⑥). The neurohormone pathway (Fig. 6-31,②) represents a hybrid of the neural and endocrine reflexes. In a neurohormone pathway, a nerve cell creates an electrical signal, but the chemical the cell releases is a neurohormone that goes into the blood for general distribution.

CONCEPT CHECK

24. (a) In the simple neural reflex shown in Figure 6-30b, which box or boxes represent(s) the brain and spinal cord? (b) Which box or boxes represent(s) the central and peripheral sense organs? (c) In Figure 6-30b, add a dashed line connecting boxes to show how a negative feedback loop would shut off the reflex.

Answers: p. 210

Speed Neural reflexes are much faster than endocrine reflexes. The electrical signals of the nervous system cover great distances very rapidly, with speeds of up to 120 m/sec. Neurotransmitters also create very rapid responses, on the order of milliseconds.

Hormones are much slower than neural reflexes. Their distribution through the circulatory system and diffusion from capillary to receptors take considerably longer than signals through nerve cells. In addition, hormones have a slower onset of action. In target tissues, the response may take minutes to hours before it can be measured.

Why do we need the speedy reflexes of the nervous system? Consider this example. A mouse ventures out of his hole and sees a cat ready to pounce on him and eat him. A signal must go from the mouse's eyes and brain down to his feet, telling him to run back into the hole. If his brain and feet were only 5 micrometers

TABLE 6-4 Comparison of Neural and Endocrine Control

PROPERTY	NEURAL REFLEX	ENDOCRINE REFLEX
Specificity	Each neuron terminates on a single target cell or on a limited number of adjacent target cells.	Most cells of the body are exposed to a hormone. The response depends on which cells have receptors for the hormone.
Nature of the signal	Electrical signal passes through neuron, then chemical neurotransmitters pass the signal from cell to cell. In a few cases, cell-to-cell communication takes place through gap junctions.	Chemical signals are secreted in the blood for distribution throughout the body.
Speed	Very rapid.	Distribution of the signal and onset of action are much slower than in neural responses.
Duration of action	Usually very short. Responses of longer duration are mediated by neuromodulators.	Duration of action is usually much longer than in neural responses.
Coding for stimulus intensity	Each signal is identical in strength. Stimulus intensity is correlated with increased frequency of signaling.	Stimulus intensity is correlated with amount of hormone secreted.

6

(5 μm = 1/200 millimeter) apart, it would take a chemical signal 20 milliseconds (msec) to diffuse across the space; the mouse could escape. If the brain and feet were 50 μm (1/20 millimeter) apart, diffusion would take 2 seconds; the mouse might get caught. But because the head and tail of a mouse are *centimeters* apart, it would take a chemical signal *three weeks* to diffuse from the mouse's head to his feet. Poor mouse! Even if the distribution of the chemical were accelerated by help from the circulatory system, the chemical message would still take 10 seconds to get to the feet, and the mouse would become cat food. The moral of this tale is that reflexes requiring a speedy response are mediated by the nervous system because they are so much more rapid.

Duration of Action Neural control is of shorter duration than endocrine control. The neurotransmitter released by a nerve cell combines with a receptor on the target cell and initiates a response. The response is usually very brief, however, because the neurotransmitter is rapidly removed from the vicinity of the receptor by various mechanisms. To get a sustained response, multiple repeating signals must be sent through the nerve cell.

Endocrine reflexes are slower to start, but they are of longer duration. This means that most of the ongoing, long-term functions of the body, such as metabolism and reproduction, fall under the control of the endocrine system.

Coding for Stimulus Intensity As a stimulus increases in intensity, control systems must have a mechanism for conveying this information to the integrating center. The signal strength from any one neuron is constant in magnitude and therefore cannot reflect stimulus intensity. Instead, the frequency of signaling through the afferent neuron increases. In the endocrine system, stimulus intensity is reflected by the amount of hormone released: the stronger the stimulus, the greater the amount of hormone released.

Complex Reflex Control Pathways Have Several Integrating Centers

Figure 6-31 summarizes variations in the neural, neuroendocrine, and endocrine reflex control pathways.

In a simple endocrine reflex pathway (Fig. 6-30a; Fig. 6-31, ⑥), the endocrine cell acts as both sensor and integrating center; there is no afferent pathway. The efferent pathway is the hormone, and the target is any cell having the appropriate receptor protein.

An example of a simple endocrine reflex is the secretion of the hormone insulin in response to changes in blood glucose level. The endocrine cells that secrete insulin monitor blood glucose concentrations by using ATP production in the cell as an indicator [Fig. 5-38, p. 167]. When blood glucose increases, intracellular ATP production exceeds the threshold level, and the endocrine cells respond by secreting insulin into the blood. Any target cell in the body that has insulin receptors will respond to the hormone and initiate processes that take glucose out of the blood. The removal of the stimulus acts in a negative feedback manner, and the response loop shuts off when blood glucose levels fall below a certain concentration.

In a simple neural reflex, all the steps of the pathway are present, from receptor to target (Fig. 6-30b, Fig. 6-31, ①). The neural reflex is represented in its simplest form by the knee jerk (or patellar tendon) reflex (see Fig. 13-7). A blow to the knee (the stimulus) activates a stretch receptor. An electrical and chemical signal travels through an afferent neuron to the

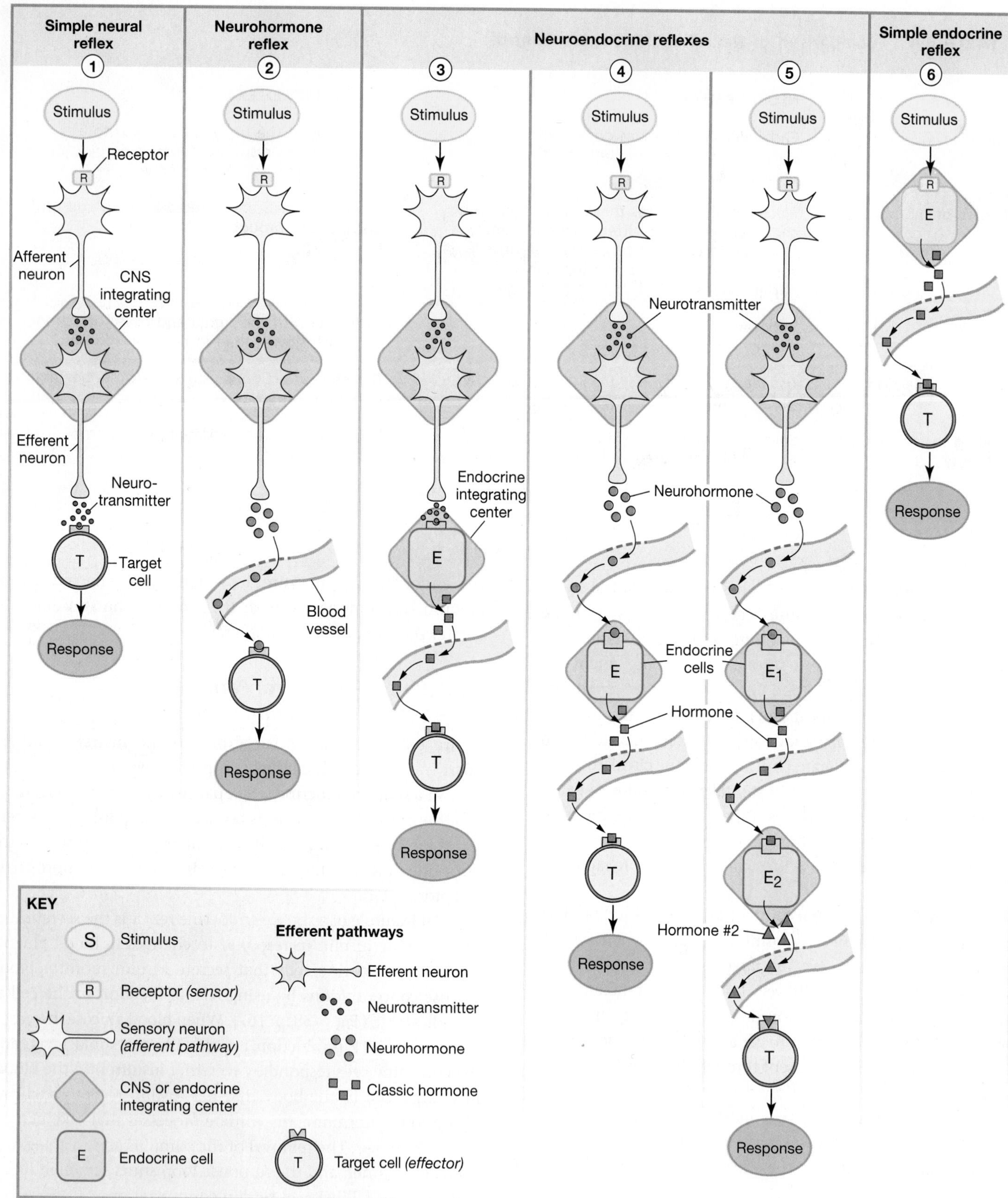

■ **FIGURE 6-31** ***Some basic patterns of neural, endocrine, and neuroendocrine control pathways***

An example of pathway ① is the knee jerk reflex. An example of ② is secretion of oxytocin in response to suckling. An example of ③ is the secretion of insulin in response to a signal from the brain. ⑥ shows insulin release in response to an increase in blood glucose.

TABLE 6-5 Comparison of Neural, Neuroendocrine, and Endocrine Reflexes

	NEURAL	NEUROENDOCRINE	ENDOCRINE
Sensor or receptor	Special and somatic sensory receptors	Special and somatic sensory receptors	Endocrine cell
Afferent pathway	Afferent sensory neuron	Afferent sensory neuron	None
Integrating center	Brain or spinal cord	Brain or spinal cord	Endocrine cell
Efferent pathway	Efferent neuron (electrical signal and neurotransmitter)	Efferent neuron (electrical signal and neurohormone)	Hormone
Effector(s)	Muscles and glands, some adipose tissue	Most cells of the body	Most cells of the body
Response	Contraction and secretion primarily; may have some metabolic effects.	Change in enzymatic reactions, membrane transport, or cell proteins	Change in enzymatic reactions or membrane transport or cell proteins

spinal cord (the integrating center). If the blow is strong enough (exceeds threshold), a signal travels from the spinal cord through an efferent neuron to the muscles of the thigh (the target or effector). In response, the muscles contract, causing the lower leg to kick outward (the knee jerk).

CONCEPT CHECK

25. Match the following terms for parts of the knee jerk reflex to the parts of the simple neural reflex shown in Figure 6-30b: blow to knee, leg muscles, neuron to leg muscles, sensory neuron, brain and spinal cord, stretch receptor, muscle contraction. Answers: p. 210

The neurohormone reflex, shown in Figure 6-31, ②, is identical to the neural reflex except that the neurohormone released by the neuron travels in the blood to its target, just like a hormone. A simple neurohormone reflex is the release of breast milk in response to a baby's suckling. The baby's mouth on the nipple stimulates sensory signals that travel through sensory neurons to the brain (integrating center). An electrical signal in the efferent neuron triggers the release of the neurohormone oxytocin from the brain into the circulation. Oxytocin is carried to the breast, where it causes contraction of smooth muscles in the breast (effectors), with the resultant ejection of milk.

In complex pathways, there may be more than one integrating center. Figure 6-31 shows three examples of complex neuroendocrine pathways. The simplest of these, pattern ③, combines a neural reflex with a classic endocrine reflex. The target of the neural reflex is an endocrine cell that releases a hormone. An example of this pattern can be found in the control of insulin release by the nervous system, in which both excitatory and inhibitory neurons terminate on the endocrine cells of the pancreas. The endocrine cells must integrate information from three sources: the two antagonistic inputs from the nervous system and their direct detection of blood glucose levels.

CONCEPT CHECK

26. Match the following terms with the appropriate parts of the simple neuroendocrine reflex in Figure 6-31, ③ (terms may be used more than once): food in stomach following a meal, brain and spinal cord, endocrine cells of pancreas, stretch receptors, efferent neuron to pancreas, insulin, adipose cell, blood, sensory neuron. Answers: p. 210

Another complex reflex (Fig. 6-31, ④) uses a neurohormone to control the release of a classic hormone. The secretion of growth hormone is an example of this pathway. The most complex neuroendocrine pathways, shown as Figure 6-31, ⑤, include a neurohormone and two classic hormones. This pattern is typical of some hormones released by the anterior pituitary, an endocrine gland located just below the brain (see Chapter 7 for details).

In describing complex neuroendocrine reflex pathways, we identify only one receptor and afferent pathway, as indicated in Figure 6-31. In the three complex pathways shown, the brain is the first integrating center and the neurohormone is the first efferent pathway. In Figure 6-31, ⑤ the endocrine target (E_1) of the neurohormone is the second integrating center, and its hormone is the second efferent pathway. The second endocrine gland in the pathway (E_2) is the third integrating center, and its hormone is the third efferent pathway. The target of the last signal in the sequence is the effector.

Table 6-5 ■ compares the various steps in neural, neuroendocrine, and endocrine reflexes. In the remainder of the text, we will use the general patterns shown in Figure 6-31 as a tool for classifying complex reflex pathways. The next chapter looks in detail at some of the pathways of the endocrine system and the roles these pathways play in homeostasis.

6

RUNNING PROBLEM CONCLUSION

DIABETES MELLITUS

Marvin underwent further tests and was diagnosed with type 2 diabetes. With careful attention to his diet and with a regular exercise program, he has managed to keep his blood glucose levels under control. Diabetes is becoming a major health issue in the United States. To learn more about diabetes, see the American Diabetes Association website (*www.diabetes.org*) or the Centers for Disease Control and Prevention (*www.cdc.gov*).

In this running problem, you learned about glucose homeostasis and how it is maintained by insulin and glucagon. The disease diabetes mellitus is an indication that glucose homeostasis has been disrupted. Check your understanding of this running problem by comparing your answers to the information in the summary table.

	QUESTION	FACTS	INTEGRATION AND ANALYSIS
1	In which type of diabetes is the signal pathway for insulin more likely to be defective?	Insulin is a peptide hormone that uses membrane receptors linked to second messengers to transmit its signal to cells [p. 183]. People with type 1 diabetes lack insulin; people with type 2 diabetes have normal-to-elevated insulin levels.	Normal or high insulin levels suggest that the problem is not with amount of insulin but with the action of the insulin at the cell. The problem in type 2 diabetes could be a defective signal transduction mechanism.
2	In which form of diabetes are the insulin receptors more likely to be up-regulated?	Up-regulation of receptors usually occurs if a signal molecule is present in unusually low concentrations [p. 191]. In type 1 diabetes, insulin is not secreted by the pancreas.	In type 1 diabetes, insulin levels are low. Therefore, type 1 is more likely to cause up-regulation of the insulin receptors.
3	The homeostatic regulation of blood glucose levels by the hormones insulin and glucagon is an example of which of Cannon's postulates?	Cannon's postulates describe the role of the nervous system in maintaining homeostasis, and the concepts of tonic activity, antagonistic control, and different effects of signals in different tissues.	Insulin decreases blood glucose levels, and glucagon increases them. Therefore, the two hormones are an example of an antagonistic control.
4	In the insulin pathway that regulates blood glucose levels, what are the stimulus, the sensor, the integrating center, the efferent pathway, the effector(s), and the response(s)?	See the steps of reflex pathways [p. 195].	*Stimulus:* increase in blood glucose levels; *sensor:* beta cells of the pancreas that sense the change; *integrating center:* beta cells; *efferent pathway* (the signal): insulin; *effectors:* any tissues of the body that respond to insulin; *responses:* cellular uptake and use of glucose.
5	Why can't glucose always diffuse into cells when the blood glucose concentration is higher than the intracellular glucose concentration?	Glucose is lipophobic. Simple diffusion goes across the phospholipid bilayer. Facilitated diffusion uses protein carriers [p. 141].	Because glucose is lipophobic, it must cross the membrane by facilitated diffusion. If a cell lacks the necessary protein carriers, facilitated diffusion cannot take place.
6	What do you think happens to the rate of insulin secretion when blood glucose levels fall? What kind of feedback loop is operating?	The stimulus for insulin release is an increase in blood glucose levels. In negative feedback, the response offsets the stimulus. In positive feedback, the response enhances the stimulus.	An increase in blood glucose concentration stimulates insulin release; therefore, a decrease in blood glucose should decrease insulin release. In this example, the response (lower blood glucose) offsets the stimulus (increased blood glucose), so a negative feedback loop is operating.

175 179 191 193 197 201 206

CHAPTER SUMMARY

This chapter focuses on two of the major themes in physiology: *homeostasis and control systems*, and *communication*. The sensors, integrating centers, and effectors of physiological control systems are described in the context of reflex control pathways, which vary from simple to complex. Functional control systems require efficient communication that uses various combinations of chemical and electrical signals. Those signals that cannot cross cell membranes must use membrane receptor proteins and signal transduction to transfer their information into the cell. The interaction of signal molecules with protein receptors illustrates another fundamental theme of physiology, *molecular interactions*.

Cell-to-Cell Communication

1. There are two basic types of physiological signals: chemical and electrical. Chemical signals are the basis for most communication within the body. (p. 175)
2. There are four methods of cell-to-cell communication: (1) direct cytoplasmic transfer through gap junctions, (2) contact-dependent signaling, (3) local chemical communication, and (4) long-distance communication. (p. 175; Figs. 6-1 and 6-2)
3. **Gap junctions** are protein channels that connect two adjacent cells. When they are open, chemical and electrical signals pass directly from one cell to the next. (p. 175)
4. **Contact-dependent signals** require direct contact between surface molecules of two cells. (p. 176)
5. Local communication is accomplished by **paracrine signals**, chemicals that act on cells in the immediate vicinity of the cell that secreted the paracrine. A chemical that acts on the cell that secreted it is called an **autocrine signal**. The activity of paracrine and autocrine signal molecules is limited by diffusion distance. (p. 176)
6. Long-distance communication is accomplished by **neurocrine molecules** and electrical signals in the nervous system, and by **hormones** in the endocrine system. Only cells that possess receptors for a hormone will be **target cells.** (p. 176)
7. **Cytokines** are regulatory molecules that control cell development, differentiation, and the immune response. They function as both local and long-distance signals. (p. 176)

Signal Pathways

8. Chemical signals bind to **receptors** and change intracellular signal molecules that direct the response. (p. 177; Fig. 6-3)
9. Lipophilic signal molecules enter the cell and combine with cytoplasmic or nuclear receptors. Lipophobic signal molecules and some lipophilic molecules combine with membrane receptors. (p. 178; Fig. 6-4)
10. **Signal transduction** pathways use membrane receptor proteins and intracellular second messenger molecules to translate signal information into an intracellular response. (p. 179)
11. Some signal transduction pathways activate **protein kinases**. Others activate **amplifier enzymes** that create **second messenger** molecules. (p. 180)
12. Signal pathways create intracellular **cascades** that amplify the original signal. (p. 180; Figs. 6-7 and 6-9)
13. **Receptor-enzymes** activate protein kinases, such as **tyrosine kinase** (Fig. 6-10), or the amplifier enzyme **guanylyl cyclase**, which produces the second messenger **cGMP**. (p. 182)
14. **G proteins** linked to amplifier enzymes are the most prevalent signal transduction system. **G protein-coupled receptors** also alter ion channels. (p. 183)
15. The **G protein-coupled adenylyl cyclase-cAMP-protein kinase A** pathway is the most common pathway for protein and peptide hormones. (p. 183; Fig. 6-11)
16. The amplifier enzyme **phospholipase C** creates two second messengers: **IP_3** and **diacylglycerol**. IP_3 causes Ca^{2+} release from intracellular stores. Diacylglycerol activates **protein kinase C**. (p. 184; Fig. 6-12)
17. **Integrin** receptors link the extracellular matrix to the cytoskeleton. (p. 184; Fig. 6-5)
18. **Ligand-gated ion channels** open or close to create electrical signals. (p. 185; Fig. 6-13)

6

Novel Signal Molecules

19. Calcium is an important signal molecule that binds to **calmodulin** to alter enzyme activity. It also binds to other cell proteins to alter movement and initiate exocytosis. (p. 186; Fig. 6-15)
20. **Nitric oxide (NO)** and **carbon monoxide (CO)** are short-lived gaseous signal molecules. NO activates guanylyl cyclase directly. (p. 187)
21. The arachidonic acid cascade creates lipid paracrines, such as **leukotrienes**, **prostaglandins**, and **thromboxanes**. (p. 188; Fig. 6-16)

Modulation of Signal Pathways

22. The response of a cell to a signal molecule is determined by the cell's receptor for the signal. (p. 189)
23. Receptor proteins exhibit specificity, competition, and saturation. (p. 189)
24. A receptor may have multiple ligands. **Agonists** mimic the action of a signal molecule. **Antagonists** block the signal pathway. (p. 189; Fig. 6-17)
25. Receptors come in related forms called **isoforms**. One ligand may have different effects when binding to different isoforms. (p. 189; Fig. 6-18)
26. Cells exposed to abnormally high concentrations of a signal for a sustained period of time attempt to bring their response back to normal by decreasing the number of receptors or decreasing the binding affinity of the receptors. This is known as **down-regulation** of the receptors. **Up-regulation** is the opposite of down-regulation. (p. 190)
27. Cells have mechanisms for terminating signal pathways, such as removing the signal molecule or breaking down the receptor-ligand complex. (p. 191)
28. Many diseases have been linked to defects with various aspects of signal pathways, such as missing or defective receptors. (p. 191)

Control Pathways: Response and Feedback Loops

29. Walter Cannon first described four basic postulates of homeostasis: (1) The nervous system plays an important role in maintaining homeostasis. (2) Some parameters are under **tonic control**, which allows the parameter to be increased or decreased by a single signal

(Fig. 6-20). (3) Other parameters are under **antagonistic control**, in which one hormone or neuron increases the parameter while another decreases it (Fig. 6-21). (4) Chemical signals can have different effects in different tissues of the body, depending on the type of receptor present at the target cell. (p. 192)

30. The simplest homeostatic control takes place at the tissue or cell level and is known as **local control**. (p. 194)
31. In **reflex** control pathways, the decision that a response is needed is made away from the cell or tissue. A chemical or electrical signal to the cell or tissue then initiates the response. Long-distance reflex pathways involve the nervous and endocrine systems and cytokines. (p. 194; Fig. 6-22)
32. Reflex pathways can be broken down into **response loops** and **feedback loops**. A response loop begins when a **stimulus** is sensed by a sensor or **sensory receptor**. The sensor is linked by an **afferent pathway** to an **integrating center** that decides on an appropriate response. An **efferent pathway** travels from the integrating center to an **effector** that carries out the appropriate **response**. (p. 194; Fig. 6-23)
33. In **negative feedback**, a homeostatic response is turned off when the response of the system opposes or removes the original stimulus. (p. 199; Fig. 6-27a)
34. In **positive feedback** loops, the response reinforces the stimulus rather than decreasing or removing it. This destabilizes the system until some intervention or event outside the loop stops the response. (p. 199; Fig. 6-27b)
35. **Feedforward control** allows the body to predict that a change is about to occur and start the response loop in anticipation of the change. (p. 200)
36. Apparently spontaneous reflexes that occur in a predictable manner are called **biological rhythms**. Those that coincide with light-dark cycles are called **circadian rhythms**. (p. 200)
37. Neural control is faster and more specific than endocrine control but is usually of shorter duration. Endocrine control is less specific and slower to start but is longer lasting and is usually amplified. (p. 202; Tbl. 6-4)
38. Many reflex pathways are combinations of neural and endocrine control mechanisms. (p. 203; Fig. 6-31)

6

QUESTIONS

(Answers to the Review Questions begin on page A1.)

THE PHYSIOLOGY PLACE

Access more review material online at **The Physiology Place** website. There you'll find review questions, problem-solving activities, case studies, flashcards, and direct links to both *Inter Active Physiology®* and PhysioEx™. To access the site, go to *www.physiologyplace.com* and select Human Physiology, Fourth Edition.

LEVEL ONE REVIEWING FACTS AND TERMS

1. What are the two routes for long-distance signal delivery in the body?
2. Which two body systems are charged with maintaining homeostasis by responding to changes in the environment?
3. What two types of physiological signals are used to send messages through the body? Of these two types, which is available to all cells?
4. The process of maintaining a relatively stable internal environment is called __________.
5. List at least three parameters maintained by homeostasis.
6. Distinguish between the "target" and the "receptor" in physiological systems.
7. In a signal pathway, the signal ligand, also called a __________ __________, binds to a __________, which activates and changes intracellular __________.
8. The three main amplifier enzymes are (a) __________, which forms cAMP; (b) __________, which forms cGMP; and (c) __________, which converts a phospholipid from the cell's membrane into two different second messenger molecules.
9. An enzyme known as protein kinase adds the functional group __________ to its substrate, by transferring it from a(n) __________ molecule.
10. Put the following parts of a reflex in the correct order for a physiological response loop: efferent pathway, afferent pathway, effector, stimulus, response, integrating center.
11. Distinguish between central and peripheral receptors.
12. Match each of the following terms with its description:

(a) threshold	1. the desired target value for a parameter
(b) setpoint	2. the distance allowed away from the setpoint before a response starts
(c) effector	3. the minimum stimulus to trigger a response
(d) oscillation	4. the organ or gland that performs the change
(e) sensitivity	5. movement of a parameter within the desired range

13. Receptors for signal pathways may be found in the __________, __________, or __________ of the cell.
14. The name for the daily fluctuations of body functions, including blood pressure, temperature, and metabolic processes, is __________ __________. These cycles arise in special cells in the __________.
15. Down-regulation results in a(n) __________(increased or decreased?) sensitivity to a prolonged signal.
16. List the two ways that down-regulation may be achieved.
17. In a negative feedback loop, the effector moves the system in the __________ (same/opposite) direction as the stimulus.

LEVEL TWO REVIEWING CONCEPTS

18. Explain the relationships of the terms in each of the following sets. Give a physiological example or location if applicable.
    (a) gap junctions, connexins, syncytium, connexon
    (b) autocrine, paracrine, cytokine, neurocrine, hormone
    (c) agonist, antagonist
    (d) transduction, amplification, cascade
19. List and compare the four classes of membrane receptors for signal pathways. Give an example of each.
20. Who was Walter Cannon? Restate his four postulates in your own words.

21. Briefly define the following terms and give an anatomical example when applicable: efferent pathway, afferent pathway, effector, stimulus, response, integrating center.
22. Explain the differences among positive feedback, negative feedback, and feedforward mechanisms. Under what circumstances would each be advantageous?
23. Compare and contrast the advantages and disadvantages of neural versus endocrine control mechanisms.
24. Label each of the following systems as positive or negative feedback.
    (a) glucagon secretion in response to declining blood glucose
    (b) increasing milk letdown and secretion in response to more suckling
    (c) urgency in emptying one's urinary bladder
    (d) sweating in response to rising body temperature
25. Identify the effector organ for each example in question 24.
26. Now identify the integrating center for each example in question 24.

LEVEL THREE PROBLEM SOLVING

27. In each of the following situations, identify the components of the reflex.
    (a) You are sitting quietly at your desk, studying, when you become aware of the bitterly cold winds blowing outside at 30 mph, and you begin to feel a little chilly. You start to turn up the thermostat, remember last month's bill, and reach for an afghan to pull around you instead. Pretty soon you are toasty warm again.
    (b) While you are strolling through the shopping district, the aroma of cinnamon sticky buns reaches you. You inhale appreciatively, but remind yourself that you're not hungry, because you just had lunch an hour ago. You go about your business, but 20 minutes later you're back at the bakery, sticky bun in hand, ravenously devouring its sweetness, saliva moistening your mouth.

LEVEL FOUR QUANTITATIVE PROBLEMS

28. In a signal cascade for rhodopsin, a photoreceptor molecule, one rhodopsin activates 1000 molecules of transducin, the next molecule in the signal cascade. Each transducin activates one phosphodiesterase, and each phosphodiesterase converts 4000 cGMP to GMP.
    (a) What is the name of the phenomenon described in this paragraph?
    (b) Activation of one rhodopsin will result in the production of how many GMP molecules?

6

ANSWERS

Answers to Concept Check Questions

Page 177

1. All the communication methods listed are chemical signals except for (c) gap junctions, which transfer both chemical and electrical signals. Neurohormones (e) and neurotransmitters (f) are associated with electrical signaling in neurons but are themselves chemicals.
2. Cytokines, hormones, and neurohormones travel through the blood. Neurohormones and neurotransmitters are released by neurons.
3. The signal to pounce could not have been a paracrine signal because the eyes are too far away from the legs and because the response was too rapid for it to have taken place by diffusion.

Page 180

4. The components of signal pathways are signal molecule, receptor, intracellular signal molecule(s), and target proteins.
5. The cellular locations of receptors are cell membrane, cytosol, and nucleus.

Page 182

6. The steps of signal transduction are (1) signal molecule binds to receptor that (2) activates a protein that (3) creates second messengers that (4) create a response.
7. Amplification turns one signal molecule (first messenger) into multiple second messenger molecules.
8. Steroids are lipophilic, so they can enter cells to bind to intracellular receptors.

Page 185

9. Receptors are either ligand-gated ion channels, receptor-enzymes, G protein-coupled receptors, or integrins.
10. First messengers are extracellular; second messengers are intracellular.
11. (a) ligand, receptor, second messenger, cell response; (b) amplifier enzyme, second messenger, protein kinase, phosphorylated protein, cell response
12. (a) Cl^- channel opens: cell hyperpolarizes; (b) K^+ channel opens: cell hyperpolarizes; (c) Na^+ channel opens: cell depolarizes.

Page 187

13. The cell must use active transport to move Ca^{2+} against their concentration gradient.

Page 189

14. A drug that blocks leukotriene action could act at the receptor or at any step downstream. A drug that blocks leukotriene synthesis might inhibit lipoxygenase.

Page 190

15. Receptors, enzymes, and transporters are all proteins.
16. Insulin could be using different second messenger systems or binding to different receptors.

Page 191

17. Choices (a) and (d) would down-regulate binding affinity. Changing receptor number would not affect binding affinity.

Page 193

18. Tonic control usually involves one control system, but antagonistic control uses two.
19. A signal can have opposite effects by using different receptors or different signal pathways.

Page 197

20. Local control takes place in or very close to the target cell. Reflex control is mediated by a distant integrating center.
21. Stimulus, sensor or receptor, afferent pathway, integrating center, efferent pathway, target or effector, response (tissue and systemic)

Page 198

22. If the aquarium water became overheated, there is no control mechanism for bringing it back into the desired range.

Page 200

23. Negative feedback shuts off the heater. This feedback loop is shown as a dashed line going from the response back to the stimulus, with parallel "stop" lines at the stimulus end.

Page 202

24. (a) The "neural system integrating center" is the brain and spinal cord. (b) "Receptor" represents the sense organs. (c) The dashed line indicating negative feedback runs from "Response" back to "Internal or external change."

Page 205

25. blow to knee = internal or external change; leg muscles = effectors; neuron to leg muscles = efferent neuron; sensory neuron = afferent pathway; brain and spinal cord = integrating center; stretch receptor = receptor; muscle contraction = response.

Page 205

26. food in stomach = stimulus; brain and spinal cord = CNS integrating center; endocrine cells of pancreas = E (integrating center); stretch receptors = receptor; efferent neuron to pancreas = efferent neuron; insulin = classic hormone; adipose cell = target cell; sensory neuron = afferent neuron.

Answers to Figure Questions

Page 182

Fig. 6-9: A (inactive and active) = adenylyl cyclase; inactive B = ATP; active B = cAMP; C (inactive and active) = protein kinase A; product = phosphorylated protein.

Page 194

Fig. 6-21: (a) 60 beats/min (b) 280 beats/min.

7

The separation of the endocrine system into isolated subsystems must be recognized as an artificial one, convenient from a pedagogical point of view but not accurately reflecting the interrelated nature of all these systems.

—Howard Rasmussen, *in Williams' Textbook of Endocrinology, 1974*

Radioactive scan of the thyroid gland.

Introduction to the Endocrine System

BACKGROUND BASICS

Receptors: **178** Peptides and proteins: **31** Comparison of endocrine and nervous systems: **202**
Signal transduction: **180** Steroids: **27** Specificity: **39**

RUNNING PROBLEM

GRAVES' DISEASE

The ball slid by the hole and trickled off the green: another bogey. Ben Crenshaw's golf game was falling apart. The 33-year-old professional had won the Masters Tournament only a year ago, but now something was not right. He was tired and weak, had been losing weight, and felt hot all the time. He attributed his symptoms to stress, but his family thought otherwise. At their urging, he finally saw a physician. The diagnosis? Graves' disease, which results in an overactive thyroid gland.

David was seven years old when the symptoms first appeared. His appetite at meals increased, and he always seemed to be in the kitchen looking for food. Despite eating more, however, he was losing weight. When he started asking for water instead of soft drinks, David's mother became concerned, and when he wet the bed three nights in a row, she knew something was wrong. The doctor confirmed the suspected diagnosis after running tests to determine the concentration of glucose in David's blood and urine. David had diabetes mellitus. In his case, the disease was due to lack of insulin, a hormone produced by the pancreas. David was placed on insulin injections, a treatment he would continue for the rest of his life.

One hundred years ago, David would have died not long after the onset of symptoms. The field of **endocrinology**, the study of hormones, was then in its infancy. Most hormones had not been discovered, and the functions of known hormones were not well understood. There was no treatment for diabetes, no birth control pill for contraception. Babies born with inadequate secretion of thyroid hormone did not grow or develop normally.

Today, all that has changed. We have identified a long and growing list of hormones. The endocrine diseases that once killed or maimed can now be controlled by synthetic hormones and sophisticated medical procedures. Although physicians do not hesitate to use these treatments, we are still learning exactly how hormones act on their target cells. This chapter provides an introduction to the basic principles of hormone structure and function. You will learn more about individual hormones as you encounter them in your study of the various systems.

■ **FIGURE 7-1** ***An endocrine disorder in ancient art***

This pre-Colombian stone carving of a woman shows a mass at her neck. This mass is an enlarged thyroid gland, a condition known as goiter. It was considered a sign of beauty among the people who lived high in the Andes mountains.

HORMONES

As you learned in Chapter 6, hormones are chemical messengers secreted into the blood by specialized cells. Hormones are responsible for many functions that we think of as long-term, ongoing functions of the body. Processes that fall mostly under hormonal control include growth and development, metabolism, regulation of the internal environment (temperature, water balance, ions), and reproduction. Hormones act on their target cells in one of three basic ways: (1) by controlling the rates of enzymatic reactions, (2) by controlling the transport of ions or molecules across cell membranes, or (3) by controlling gene expression and the synthesis of proteins.

Hormones Have Been Known Since Ancient Times

Although the scientific field of endocrinology is relatively young, diseases of the endocrine system have been documented for more than a thousand years. Evidence of endocrine abnormalities can even be seen in ancient art. For example, one pre-Colombian statue of a woman shows a mass on the front of her neck (Fig. 7-1 ■). The mass is an enlarged thyroid gland, or *goiter*, a common condition high in the Andes, where the dietary iodine needed to make thyroid hormones was lacking.

The first association of endocrine structure and function was probably the link between the testes and male sexuality. Castration of animals and men was a common practice in both Eastern and Western cultures because it was known to decrease the sex drive and render males infertile.

In 1849, A. A. Berthold performed the first classic experiment in endocrinology. He removed the testes from roosters and observed that the castrated birds had smaller combs, less aggressiveness, and less sex drive than uncastrated roosters. If the testes were surgically placed back into the donor cock or into another castrated bird, normal male behavior and comb development resumed. Because the reimplanted testes were not connected to nerves, Berthold concluded that the glands must be secreting something into the blood that affected the entire body.

Experimental endocrinology did not receive much attention, however, until 1889, when the 72-year-old French physician Charles Brown-Séquard made a dramatic announcement of his sexual rejuvenation after injecting himself with extracts made from bull testes ground up in water. An international uproar followed, and physicians on both sides of the Atlantic began to inject their patients with extracts of many different endocrine organs, a practice known as *organotherapy*.

We now know that the increased virility Brown-Séquard reported was most likely a placebo effect because testosterone is a hydrophobic steroid that cannot be extracted by an aqueous preparation. His research opened the door to hormone therapy, however, and in 1891 organotherapy had its first true success: a woman was treated for low thyroid hormone levels with glycerin extracts of sheep thyroid glands.

As the study of "internal secretions" grew, Berthold's experiments became a template for endocrine research. Once a gland or structure was suspected of secreting hormones, the classic steps for identifying an endocrine gland became:

1. Remove the suspected gland and monitor the animal for anatomical, behavioral, or physiological abnormalities. This is equivalent to inducing a state of *hormone deficiency*.
2. Either place the gland back in the animal or administer an extract of the gland and see if the abnormalities disappear. Such *replacement therapy* should eliminate the symptoms of hormone deficiency.
3. Either implant the gland in a normal animal or administer an extract from the gland to a normal animal, and see if symptoms characteristic of *hormone excess* appear.
4. Once a gland is identified as a potential source of hormones, purify extracts of the gland to isolate the active substance. The test for hormone activity is usually a biological assay in which an animal is injected with the purified extract and monitored for a response.

Hormones identified by this technique are sometimes called *classic hormones*. They include hormones of the pancreas, thyroid, adrenal glands, pituitary, and gonads, all discrete endocrine glands that could be easily identified and surgically removed. Not all hormones come from identifiable glands, however, and we have been slower to discover them.

The Anatomy Summary in Figure 7-2 ■ lists the major hormones of the body and the glands or cells that secrete them, along with the major properties of each hormone.

What Makes a Chemical a Hormone?

In 1905, the term *hormone* was coined from the Greek verb meaning "to excite or arouse." The traditional definition of a **hormone** is a chemical secreted by a cell or group of cells into the blood for transport to a distant target, where it exerts its effect at very low concentrations. However, as scientists learn more about chemical communication in the body, this definition is continually being challenged.

CLINICAL FOCUS

DIABETES

THE DISCOVERY OF INSULIN

Diabetes mellitus, the metabolic condition associated with pathologies of insulin function, has been known since ancient times. Detailed clinical descriptions of insulin-deficient diabetes were available to physicians, but they had no means of treating the disease, and patients invariably succumbed. However, in a series of classic experiments in endocrine physiology, researchers finally identified the cause of diabetes. In 1889, Oscar Minkowski at the University of Strasbourg (Germany) pinpointed the relationship between diabetes and the pancreas. Minkowski surgically removed the pancreas from dogs (*pancreatectomy*) and noticed that they developed symptoms that mimicked diabetes. He also found that implanting pieces of pancreas under the dogs' skin would prevent development of diabetes. Subsequently, in 1921 Fredrick G. Banting and Charles H. Best (Toronto, Canada) identified an antidiabetic substance in pancreas extracts. Banting and Best and others injected pancreatic extracts into diabetic animals and found that the extracts reversed the elevated blood glucose levels of diabetes. From there, it was a relatively short process until, in 1922, purified insulin was used in the first clinical trials.

ANATOMY SUMMARY
HORMONES

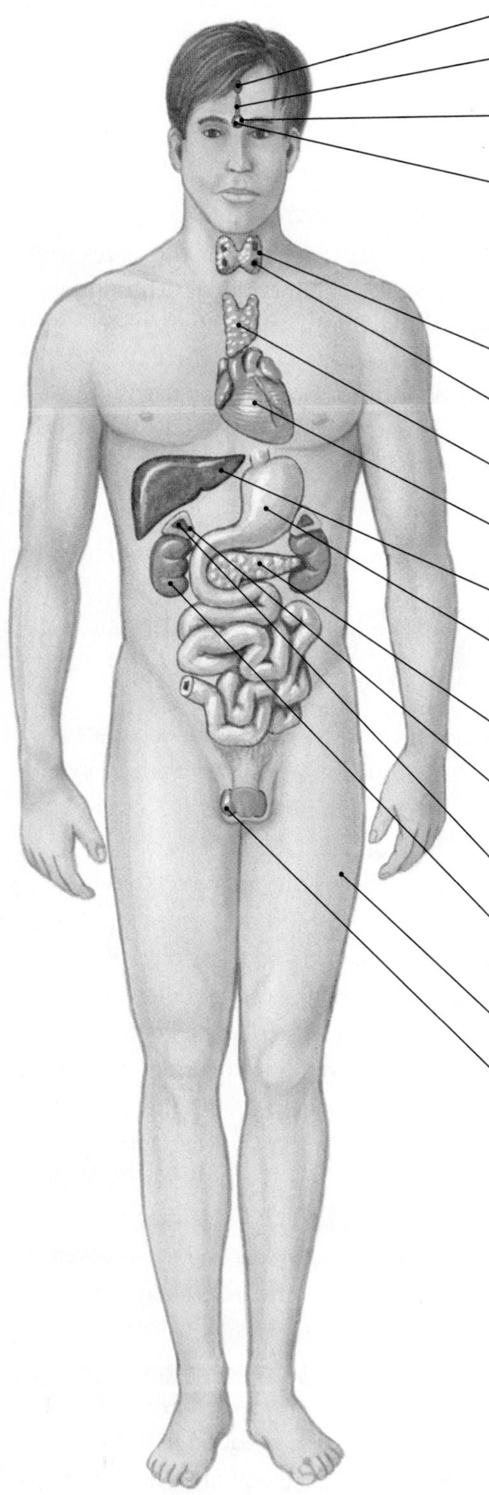

Location	Gland or cell?	Chemical class
Pineal gland	Gland	Amine
Hypothalamus	Clusters of neurons	Peptides
Posterior pituitary	Extensions of hypothalamic neurons	Peptides
Anterior pituitary	Gland	Peptides
Thyroid	Gland	Iodinated amines Peptide
Parathyroid	Gland	Peptide
Thymus	Gland	Peptides
Heart	Cells	Peptide
Liver	Cells	Peptides
Stomach and small intestine	Cells	Peptides
Pancreas	Gland	Peptide
Adrenal cortex	Gland	Steroids
Adrenal medulla	Gland	Amines
Kidney	Cells	Peptide Steroid
Skin	Cells	Steroid
Testes (male)	Glands	Steroids Peptide
Ovaries (female)	Glands	Steroids Peptide
Adipose tissue	Cells	Peptide
Placenta (pregnant females only)	Gland	Steroids Peptide

FIGURE 7-2

Hormones	*Targets*	*Main Effects*
Melatonin	Unclear in humans	Circadian rhythms; other effects uncertain
Trophic hormones (see Fig. 7-13); see posterior pituitary	Anterior pituitary	Release or inhibit pituitary hormones
Oxytocin (OT) Vasopressin (ADH)	Breast and uterus Kidney	Milk ejection; labor and delivery; behavior Water reabsorption
Prolactin (PRL) Growth hormone (GH, somatotropin) Corticotropin (ACTH) Thyrotropin (TSH) Follicle stimulating hormone (FSH) Luteinizing hormone (LH)	Breast Many tissues Adrenal cortex Thyroid gland Gonads Gonads	Milk production Growth and metabolism Cortisol release Thyroid hormone synthesis and release Egg or sperm production; sex hormone production Sex hormone production; egg or sperm production
Triiodothyronine and thyroxine (T_3, T_4) Calcitonin (CT)	Many tissues Bone	Metabolism; growth and development Plasma calcium levels (minimal effect in humans)
Parathyroid hormone (PTH)	Bone, kidney	Regulates plasma calcium and phosphate levels
Thymosin, thymopoietin	Lymphocytes	Lymphocyte development
Atrial natriuretic peptide (ANP)	Kidneys	Increases sodium excretion
Angiotensinogen Insulin-like growth factors (IGF)	Adrenal cortex, blood vessels, brain Many tissues	Aldosterone secretion; increases blood pressure Growth
Gastrin, cholecystokinin (CCK), secretin, and others	GI tract and pancreas	Assist digestion and absorption of nutrients
Insulin, glucagon, somatostatin (SS), pancreatic polypeptide	Many tissues	Metabolism of glucose and other nutrients
Aldosterone Cortisol Androgens	Kidney Many tissues Many tissues	Na^+ and K^+ homeostasis Stress response Sex drive in females
Epinephrine, norepinephrine	Many tissues	Fight-or-flight response
Erythropoietin (EPO) 1,25 Dihydroxy-vitamin D_3 (calciferol)	Bone marrow Intestine	Red blood cell production Increases calcium absorption
Vitamin D_3	Intermediate form of hormone	Precursor of 1,25 dihydroxy-vitamin D_3
Androgen Inhibin	Many tissues Anterior pituitary	Sperm production, secondary sex characteristics Inhibit FSH secretion
Estrogens and progesterone Ovarian inhibin Relaxin (pregnancy)	Many tissues Anterior pituitary Uterine muscle	Egg production; secondary sex characteristics Inhibits FSH secretion Relaxes muscle
Leptin and others	Hypothalamus, other tissues	Food intake, metabolism, reproduction
Estrogens and progesterone (P) Chorionic somatomammotropin (CS) Chorionic gonadotropin (CG)	Many tissues Many tissues Corpus luteum of ovary	Fetal and maternal development Metabolism Hormone secretion

Hormones Are Secreted by a Cell or Group of Cells Traditionally, the field of endocrinology has focused on chemical messengers secreted by endocrine *glands*, the discrete and readily identifiable tissues derived from epithelial tissue [p. 75]. However, we now know that molecules that act as hormones are secreted not only by classic endocrine glands but also by isolated endocrine cells (hormones of the *diffuse endocrine system*), by neurons *(neurohormones)*, and by cells of the immune system *(cytokines)*.

Hormones Are Secreted into the Blood Secretion, first presented in Chapter 3 [p. 53], is the movement of a substance from the intracellular compartment either to the extracellular compartment or to the external environment. According to the traditional definition, hormones are secreted into the blood. However, the term *ectohormone* [*ektos*, outside] has been given to signal molecules secreted into the external environment.

Pheromones [*pherein*, to bring] are specialized ectohormones that act on other organisms of the same species to elicit a physiological or behavioral response. For example, sea anemones secrete alarm pheromones when danger threatens, and ants release trail pheromones to attract fellow workers to food sources. Pheromones are also used to attract members of the opposite sex for mating purposes. Sex pheromones can be found throughout the animal kingdom, in animals from fruit flies to dogs, but do humans have pheromones? This is still a matter of debate. Some studies have shown that human *axillary* (armpit) sweat glands secrete volatile steroids related to sex hormones that may serve as human sex pheromones. In one study, when female students were asked to rate the odors of T-shirts worn by male students, each woman preferred the odor of men who were genetically dissimilar from her. In another study, female axillary secretions rubbed on the upper lip of young women altered the timing of their menstrual cycles. How humans might sense pheromones will be discussed in Chapter 10.

Hormones Are Transported to a Distant Target By the traditional definition, a hormone must be transported by the blood to a distant target cell. Experimentally, this property is sometimes difficult to demonstrate. Molecules that are suspected of being hormones but not fully accepted as such are called *candidate hormones*. They are usually identified by the word *factor*. For example, in the early 1970s, the hypothalamic regulating hormones were known as "releasing factors" and" inhibiting factors" rather than releasing and inhibiting hormones.

Currently, **growth factors**, a large group of substances that influence cell growth and division, are being studied to determine if they meet all the criteria for hormones. Although many growth factors have been shown to act locally as *autocrines* or *paracrines* [p. 176], evidence is lacking for their widespread distribution via the circulation. A similar situation exists with the lipid-derived signal molecules called *eicosanoids* [p. 29].

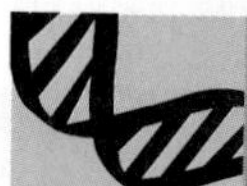

BIOTECHNOLOGY

IMMUNOCYTOCHEMISTRY

Traditionally, physiologists thought that each hormone came from a single gland (even though some glands secrete multiple hormones), but the research technique called *immunocytochemistry* has turned that view of endocrinology upside down. Immunocytochemistry begins when an animal is injected with a foreign molecule (an antigen), such as a hormone. The animal's immune system recognizes the injected molecule as "not self" and produces specific antibodies against it. The antibodies are extracted from the host animal and combined with a radioactive, fluorescent, or enzymatic marker. The tagged antibodies are applied to cells in tissue culture or to sections of freshly excised tissue, then examined under the microscope. If the original antigen is present in the tissue, the antibodies bind to it and become visible under the microscope. By screening multiple tissues with the antibodies against different hormones, investigators discovered that many hormones are made in multiple sites, often far from the tissue from which they were originally isolated.

Complicating the classification of signal molecules is the fact that a molecule may act as a hormone when secreted from one location but as a paracrine or autocrine signal when secreted from a different location. For example, in the 1920s scientists discovered that *cholecystokinin* (CCK) in extracts of intestine caused contraction of the gall bladder. For many years thereafter, CCK was known only as an intestinal hormone. Then in the mid-1970s, CCK was found in neurons of the brain, where it acts as a neurotransmitter or neuromodulator. In recent years, CCK has become famous for its possible role in controlling hunger.

Hormones Exert Their Effect at Very Low Concentrations One hallmark of a hormone is its ability to act at concentrations in the nanomolar (10^{-9} M) to picomolar (10^{-12} M) range. Some chemical signals transported in the blood to distant targets are not considered hormones because they must be present in relatively high concentrations before an effect is noticed. For example, histamine released during allergic reactions may act on cells throughout the body, but its concentration exceeds the accepted range for a hormone.

As researchers discover new signal molecules and new receptors, the boundary between hormones and nonhormonal signal molecules continues to be challenged, just as the distinction between the nervous and endocrine systems has blurred. Many *cytokines* [p. 176] seem to meet the previously stated definition of a hormone. However, experts in cytokine research do not consider cytokines to be hormones because peptide cytokines are synthesized and released on demand, in contrast to classic peptide hormones, which are made in advance and stored in the parent endocrine cell. A few cytokines—for example, *erythropoietin,* the molecule that controls red blood cell production—were classified as hormones before the term *cytokine* was coined, contributing to the overlap between the two groups of signal molecules.

Hormones Act by Binding to Receptors

All hormones bind to target cell receptors and initiate biochemical responses. These responses are known as the **cellular mechanism of action** of the hormone. As you can see in Figure 7-2, one hormone may act on multiple tissues. To complicate matters, the effects may vary in different tissues or at different stages of development. Or a hormone may have no effect at all in a particular cell. Insulin is an example of a hormone with varied effects. In muscle and adipose tissues, it alters glucose transport proteins and enzymes for glucose metabolism. In the liver, it modulates enzyme activity but has no direct effect on glucose transport proteins. In the brain and certain other tissues, glucose metabolism is totally independent of insulin.

CONCEPT CHECK

1. Name the membrane transport process by which glucose moves from the extracellular fluid into cells.

Answers: p. 241

The variable responsiveness of a cell to a hormone depends primarily on the cell's receptor and signal transduction pathways [p. 180]. If there are no hormone receptors in a tissue, its cells cannot respond. If tissues have different receptors and receptor-linked pathways for the same hormone, they will respond differently.

Hormone Action Must Be Terminated

Signal activity by hormones and other chemical signals must be of limited duration if the body is to respond to changes in its internal state. For example, insulin is secreted when blood glucose concentrations increase following a meal. As long as insulin is present, glucose leaves the blood and enters cells. However, if insulin activity continues too long, blood glucose levels could fall so low that the nervous system becomes unable to function properly—a potentially fatal situation. Normally the body avoids this situation in several ways: by limiting insulin secretion, by removing or inactivating insulin circulating in the blood, and by terminating insulin activity in target cells.

In general, hormones in the bloodstream are *degraded* (broken down) into inactive metabolites by enzymes found primarily in the liver and kidneys. The metabolites are then excreted in either the bile or the urine. The rate of hormone breakdown is indicated by a hormone's **half-life** in the circulation, the amount of time required to reduce the concentration of hormone by one-half. Half-life is one indicator of how long a hormone is active in the body.

Hormones bound to target membrane receptors have their activity terminated in several ways. Enzymes are always present in the plasma and can degrade peptide hormones bound to cell membrane receptors. In some cases, the receptor-hormone complex is brought into the cell by endocytosis, and the hormone is then digested in lysosomes [Fig. 5-24, p. 149]. Intracellular enzymes metabolize hormones that enter cells.

CONCEPT CHECK

2. What is the suffix in a chemical name that tells you a molecule is an enzyme? [*Hint:* p. 99] Use that suffix to name an enzyme that digests peptides.

Answers: p. 241

THE CLASSIFICATION OF HORMONES

Hormones can be classified according to different schemes. The scheme used in Figure 7-2 groups them according to their source. A different scheme divides hormones into those whose release is controlled by the brain, and those whose release in not controlled by the brain. Another scheme groups hormones according to whether they bind to G protein-coupled receptors, tyrosine kinase-linked receptors, or intracellular receptors, and so on.

A final scheme divides hormones into three main chemical classes: peptide/protein hormones, steroid hormones, and amine hormones (Table 7-1 ■). The peptide hormones are composed of linked amino acids. The steroid hormones are all derived from cholesterol [p. 30]. The amine hormones are all derivatives of one of two amino acids: tryptophan or tyrosine.

CONCEPT CHECK

3. What is the classic definition of a hormone?
4. Based on what you know about the organelles involved in protein and steroid synthesis [p. 66], what would be the major differences between the organelle composition of a steroid-producing cell and that of a protein-producing cell?

Answers: p. 241

Most Hormones Are Peptides or Proteins

The peptide/protein hormones range from small peptides of only three amino acids to large proteins and glycoproteins. Despite the size variability among hormones in this group, all of them are usually called peptide hormones for the sake of simplicity. You can remember which hormones fall into this category by exclusion: if a hormone is not a steroid and not an amine, then it is probably a peptide.

7

TABLE 7-1 Comparison of Peptide, Steroid, and Amine Hormones

	PEPTIDE HORMONES	STEROID HORMONES	AMINES: CATECHOLAMINES	AMINES: THYROID HORMONES
Synthesis and storage	Made in advance; stored in secretory vesicles	Synthesized on demand from precursors	Made in advance; stored in secretory vesicles	Made in advance; precursor stored in secretory vesicles
Release from parent cell	Exocytosis	Simple diffusion	Exocytosis	Simple diffusion
Transport in blood	Dissolved in plasma	Bound to carrier proteins	Dissolved in plasma	Bound to carrier proteins
Half-life	Short	Long	Short	Long
Location of receptor	Cell membrane	Cytoplasm or nucleus; some have membrane receptors also	Cell membrane	Nucleus
Response to receptor-ligand binding	Activation of second messenger systems; may activate genes	Activation of genes for transcription and translation; may have nongenomic actions	Activation of second messenger systems	Activation of genes for transcription and translation
General target response	Modification of existing proteins and induction of new protein synthesis	Induction of new protein synthesis	Modification of existing proteins	Induction of new protein synthesis
Examples	Insulin, parathyroid hormone	Estrogen, androgens, cortisol	Epinephrine, norepinephrine	Thyroxine (T_4)

Peptide Hormone Synthesis, Storage, and Release

The synthesis and packaging of peptide hormones into membrane-bound secretory vesicles is similar to that of other proteins. The initial peptide that comes off the ribosome is a large inactive protein known as a preprohormone (Fig. 7-3 ■). **Preprohormones** contain one or more copies of a peptide hormone, a *signal sequence* that directs the protein into the lumen of the rough endoplasmic reticulum, and other peptide sequences that may or may not have biological activity.

As an inactive preprohormone moves through the endoplasmic reticulum and Golgi complex, the signal sequence is removed, creating a smaller, still-inactive molecule called a **prohormone** (Fig. 7-3). In the Golgi complex, the prohormone is packaged into secretory vesicles along with *proteolytic* [*proteo-*, protein + *lysis*, rupture] enzymes that chop the prohormone into active hormone and other fragments. This process is called *post-translational modification* [p. 120].

The secretory vesicles containing peptides are stored in the cytoplasm of the endocrine cell until the cell receives a signal for secretion. At that time, the vesicles move to the cell membrane and release their contents by calcium-dependent exocytosis [p. 148]. All of the peptide fragments created from the prohormone are released together into the extracellular fluid, in a process known as *co-secretion*.

Post-Translational Modification of Prohormones Studies of prohormone processing have led to some interesting discoveries. Some prohormones, such as that for *thyrotropin-releasing hormone* (TRH), contain multiple copies of the hormone (Fig. 7-4a ■). Another interesting prohormone is called *proopiomelanocortin* (Fig. 7-4b). This prohormone is split into three active peptides plus an inactive fragment. In some instances, even the fragments are clinically useful. For example, proinsulin is cleaved into active insulin and an inactive fragment known as *C-peptide* (Fig. 7-4c). Clinicians measure the levels of C-peptide in the blood of diabetics to monitor how much insulin the patient's pancreas is producing.

Transport in the Blood and Half-Life of Peptide Hormones Peptide hormones are water soluble and therefore generally dissolve easily in the extracellular fluid for transport throughout the body. The half-life for peptide hormones is

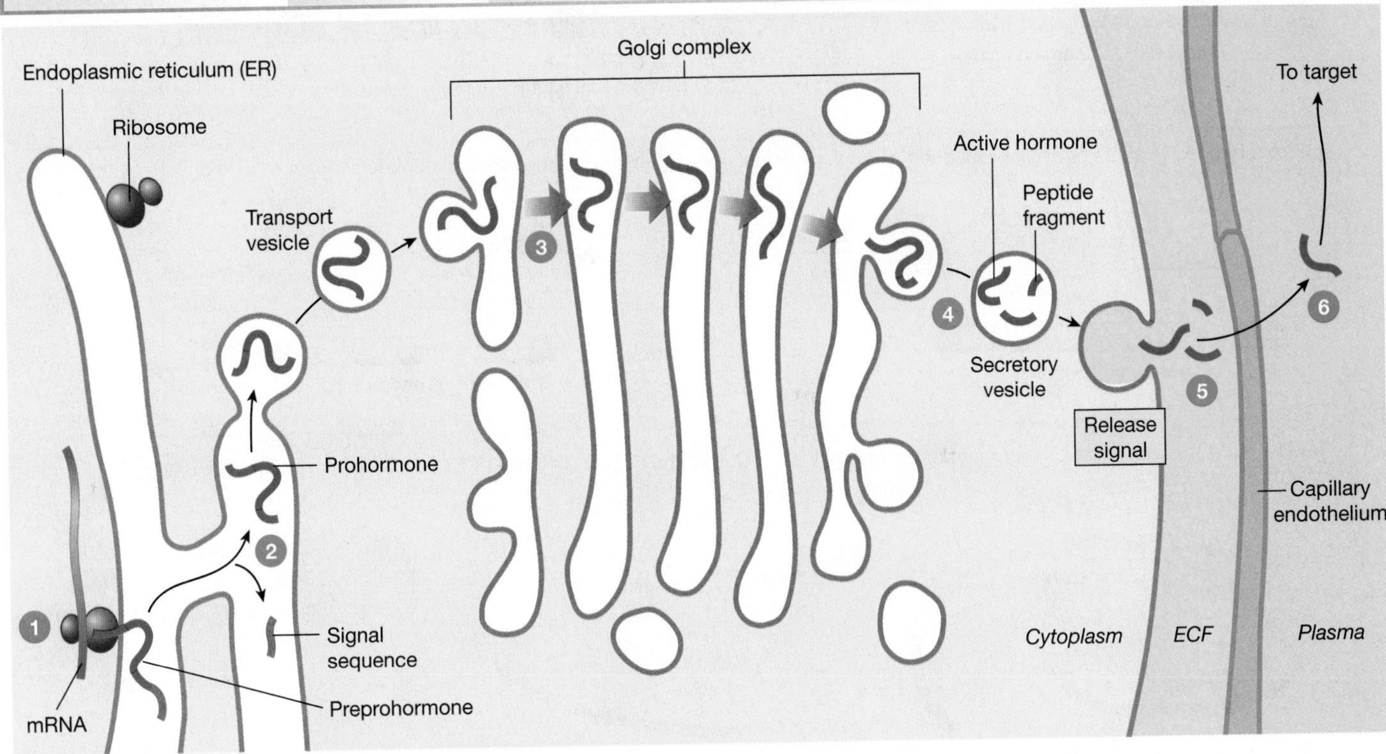

1 Messenger RNA on the ribosomes binds amino acids into a peptide chain called a preprohormone. The chain is directed into the ER lumen by a signal sequence of amino acids.
2 Enzymes in the ER chop off the signal sequence, creating an inactive prohormone.
3 The prohormone passes from the ER through the Golgi complex.
4 Secretory vesicles containing enzymes and prohormone bud off the Golgi. The enzymes chop the prohormone into one or more active peptides plus additional peptide fragments.
5 The secretory vesicle releases its contents by exocytosis into the extracellular space.
6 The hormone moves into the circulation for transport to its target.
Endoplasmic reticulum (ER)
Ribosome
Golgi complex
Transport vesicle
Active hormone
Peptide fragment
To target
Secretory vesicle
Release signal
Prohormone
Capillary endothelium
Signal sequence
Preprohormone
mRNA
Cytoplasm
ECF
Plasma

FIGURE 7-3 ***Peptide hormone synthesis, packaging, and release***

usually quite short, in the range of several minutes. If the response to a peptide hormone must be sustained for an extended period of time, the hormone must be secreted continually.

Cellular Mechanism of Action of Peptide Hormones

Because peptide hormones are lipophobic, they are usually unable to enter the target cell. Instead, they bind to surface membrane receptors. The hormone-receptor complex initiates the cellular response by means of a *signal transduction* system (Fig. 7-5 ■). Many peptide hormones work through cAMP second messenger systems [p. 183]. A few peptide hormone receptors, such as that of insulin, have tyrosine kinase activity [p. 183] or work through other signal transduction pathways.

The response of cells to peptide hormones is usually rapid because second messenger systems modify existing proteins. The changes triggered by peptide hormones include opening or closing membrane channels and modulating metabolic enzymes or transport proteins. Researchers have recently discovered that some peptide hormones also have longer-lasting effects when their second messenger systems activate genes and direct the synthesis of new proteins.

Steroid Hormones Are Derived from Cholesterol

The steroid hormones have a similar chemical structure because they are all derived from cholesterol (Fig. 7-6 ■). Unlike peptide hormones, which are made in tissues all over the body, steroid hormones are made in only a few organs. Three types of steroid hormones are made in the adrenal cortex, the outer portion of the adrenal glands [*cortex*, bark]. One adrenal gland sits atop each kidney [*ad-*, upon + *renal*, kidney]. The gonads produce the sex steroids (estrogens, progesterone, and androgens). In pregnant women, the placenta is also a source of steroid hormones.

Steroid Hormone Synthesis and Release Cells that secrete steroid hormones have unusually large amounts of smooth endoplasmic reticulum, the organelle in which steroids are synthesized. Steroids are lipophilic and diffuse easily across membranes, both out of their parent cell and into their target cell. This property also means that steroid-secreting cells cannot store hormones in secretory vesicles. Instead, they synthesize their hormone as it is needed. When a stimulus activates the endocrine cell, precursors in the cytoplasm are rapidly

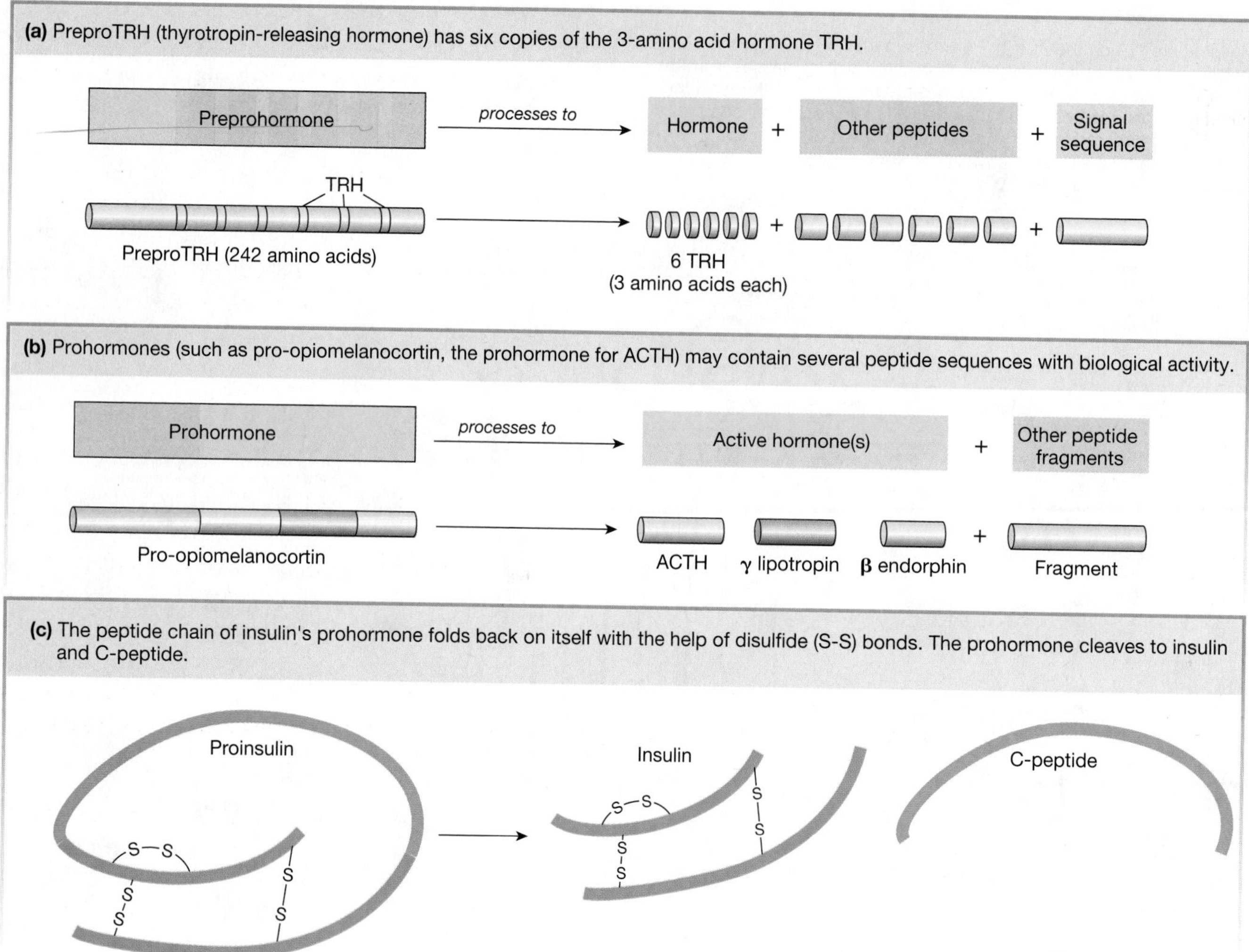
(a) PreproTRH (thyrotropin-releasing hormone) has six copies of the 3-amino acid hormone TRH.
Preprohormone
processes to
Hormone
Other peptides
Signal sequence
TRH
PreproTRH (242 amino acids)
6 TRH
(3 amino acids each)
(b) Prohormones (such as pro-opiomelanocortin, the prohormone for ACTH) may contain several peptide sequences with biological activity.
Prohormone
processes to
Active hormone(s)
Other peptide fragments
Pro-opiomelanocortin
ACTH
γ lipotropin
β endorphin
Fragment
(c) The peptide chain of insulin's prohormone folds back on itself with the help of disulfide (S-S) bonds. The prohormone cleaves to insulin and C-peptide.
Proinsulin
Insulin
C-peptide
S—S

FIGURE 7-4 ***Peptide hormone processing***

Peptide hormones are made as large, inactive preprohormones that include a signal sequence, one or more copies of the hormone, and additional peptide fragments.

converted to active hormone. The hormone concentration in the cytoplasm rises, and the hormones move out of the cell by simple diffusion.

Transport in the Blood and Half-Life of Steroid Hormones Like their parent cholesterol, steroid hormones are not very soluble in plasma and other body fluids. For this reason, most of the steroid hormone molecules found in the blood are bound to protein carrier molecules. Some hormones have specific carriers, such as *corticosteroid-binding globulin*. Others simply bind to general plasma proteins, such as *albumin*.

The binding of a steroid hormone to a carrier protein protects the hormone from enzymatic degradation and results in an extended half-life. For example, **cortisol**, a hormone produced by the adrenal cortex, has a half-life of 60–90 minutes. (Compare this with epinephrine, an amine hormone whose half-life is measured in seconds.)

Although binding steroid hormones to protein carriers extends their half-life, it also blocks their entry into target cells. The carrier-steroid complex remains outside the cell because the carrier proteins are lipophobic and cannot diffuse through the membrane. Only unbound hormone molecule can diffuse into the target cell (Fig. 7-7 ■). As unbound hormone leaves the plasma, the carriers obey the law of mass action and release hormone so that the ratio of unbound to bound hormone in the plasma remains constant [the K_d; p. 39].

Fortunately, hormones are active in minute concentrations, and only a tiny amount of unbound steroid is enough to produce a response. As unbound hormone leaves the blood and enters cells, additional carriers release their bound steroid so that some unbound hormone is always in the blood and ready to enter a cell.

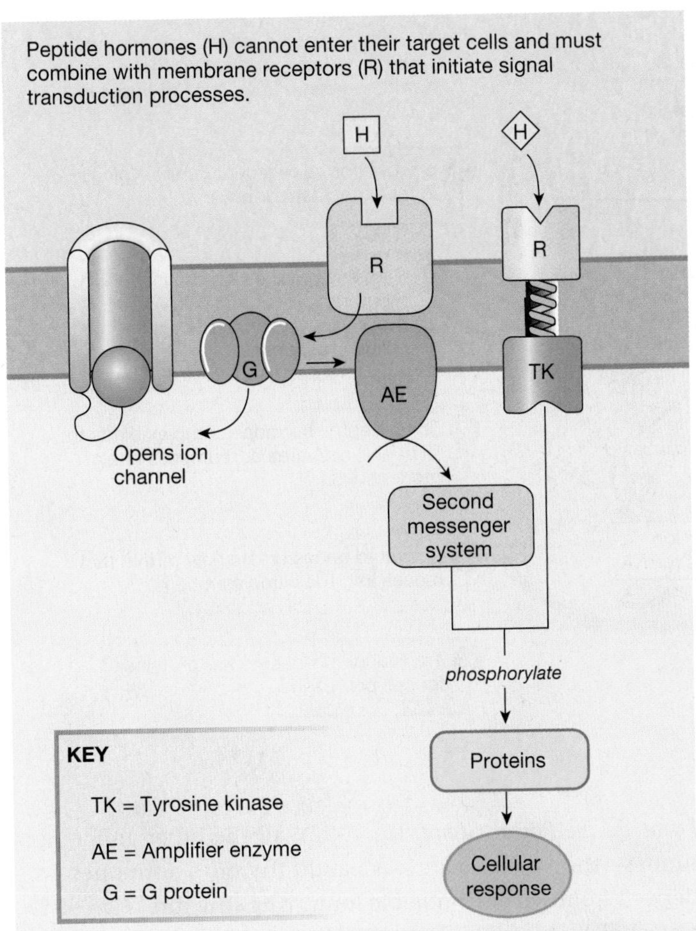

■ **FIGURE 7-5** ***Membrane receptors and signal transduction for peptide hormones***

Cellular Mechanism of Action of Steroid Hormones

The best-studied steroid hormone receptors are found within cells, either in the cytoplasm or in the nucleus. The ultimate destination of steroid receptor-hormone complexes is the nucleus, where the complex acts as a *transcription factor,* binding to DNA and either activating or *repressing* (turning off) one or more genes (Fig. 7-7,③). Activated genes create new mRNA that directs the synthesis of new proteins. Any hormone that alters gene activity is said to have a *genomic effect* on the target cell.

When steroid hormones activate genes to direct the production of new proteins, there is usually a lag time between hormone-receptor binding and the first measurable biological effects. This lag can be as much as 90 minutes. Consequently, steroid hormones do not mediate reflex pathways that require rapid responses.

In recent years researchers have discovered that several steroid hormones, including estrogens and aldosterone, have cell membrane receptors linked to signal transduction pathways, just as peptide hormones do. These receptors enable those steroid hormones to initiate rapid **nongenomic responses** in addition to their slower genomic effects. With the discovery of nongenomic effects of steroid hormones, the functional differences between steroid and peptide hormones seem almost to have disappeared.

CONCEPT CHECK

5. What are the three chemical classes of hormones?
6. The steroid hormone aldosterone has a short half-life for a steroid hormone—only about 20 minutes. What would you predict about the degree to which aldosterone is bound to blood proteins?

Answers: p. 242

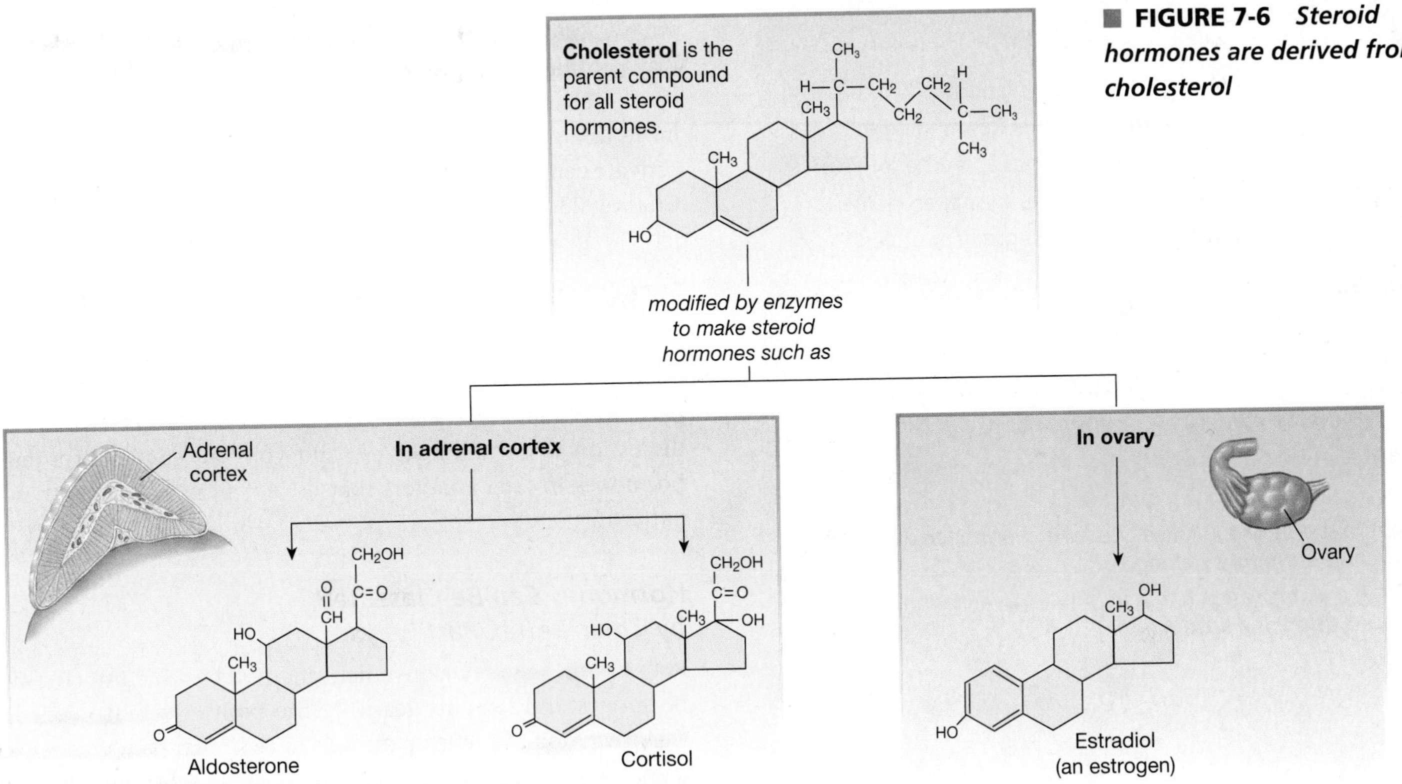

Cholesterol is the parent compound for all steroid hormones.

modified by enzymes to make steroid hormones such as

In adrenal cortex

Adrenal cortex

Aldosterone

Cortisol

In ovary

Ovary

Estradiol (an estrogen)

■ **FIGURE 7-6** ***Steroid hormones are derived from cholesterol***

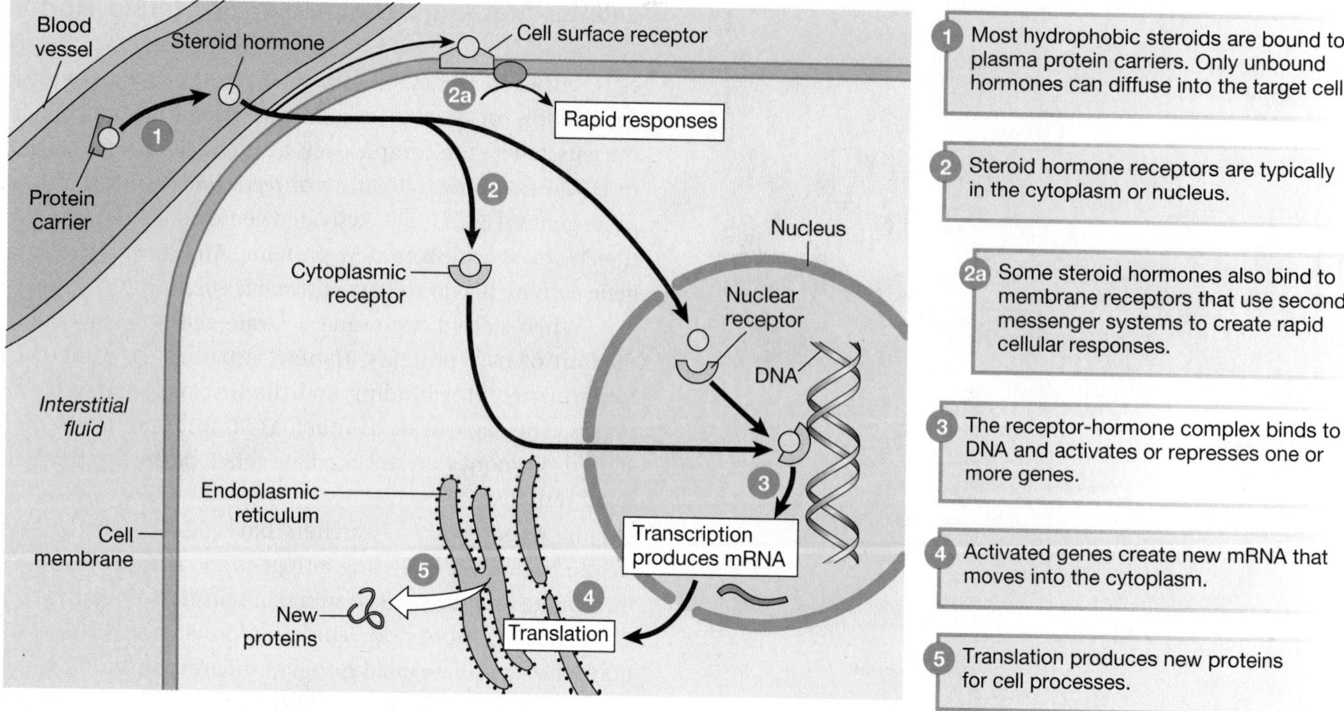

■ **FIGURE 7-7** ***Steroid hormone action***

Amine Hormones Are Derived from One of Two Amino Acids

The amine hormones are small molecules created from either the amino acid tryptophan or the amino acid tyrosine. The amine hormone **melatonin** is derived from tryptophan (see *Focus on the Pineal Gland,* Fig. 7-22); all the other amine hormones—the catecholamines and thyroid hormones—are derived from tyrosine, notable for its ring structure (Fig. 7-8 ■). Catecholamines have one tyrosine molecule; the thyroid hormones have two tyrosines plus iodine atoms.

Despite a common precursor, the two groups of tyrosine-based amine hormones have little in common. The **catecholamines** (epinephrine, norepinephrine, and dopamine) are neurohormones that bind to cell membrane receptors the way peptide hormones do. The **thyroid hormones**, produced by the butterfly-shaped thyroid gland in the neck, behave more like steroid hormones, with intracellular receptors that activate genes. Thyroid hormones will be discussed in detail in Chapter 23.

RUNNING PROBLEM

Shaped like a butterfly, the thyroid gland straddles the trachea just below the Adam's apple. Responding to hormonal signals from the hypothalamus and anterior pituitary, the thyroid gland concentrates iodine, an element found in food (most notably as an ingredient added to salt), and combines it with the amino acid tyrosine to make two thyroid hormones, thyroxine and triiodothyronine. These thyroid hormones perform many important functions in the body, including the regulation of growth and development, oxygen consumption, and the maintenance of body temperature.

Question 1:

a. ***To which of the three classes of hormones do the thyroid hormones belong?***
b. ***If a person's diet is low in iodine, predict what happens to thyroxine production.***

CONTROL OF HORMONE RELEASE

Reflex pathways that help maintain homeostasis were introduced in Chapter 6. The sections that follow apply the basic patterns of reflexes to the control pathways for hormones. This discussion is not all-inclusive, and you will encounter a few hormones in later chapters that do not fit exactly into these patterns.

Hormones Can Be Classified by Their Reflex Pathways

Reflex pathways are a convenient method by which to classify hormones and simplify learning the pathways that regulate their secretion. All reflex pathways have similar components: a stimulus, an input signal, integration of the signal, an output

Tyrosine
is the parent amino acid for catecholamines and thyroid hormones.
Catecholamines
are made by modifying the side groups of tyrosine.
Dopamine
Norepinephrine
Epinephrine
Thyroid hormones
are synthesized from two tyrosines and iodine (I) atoms.
Thyroxine (Tetraiodothyronine, T_4)
Triiodothyronine (T_3)

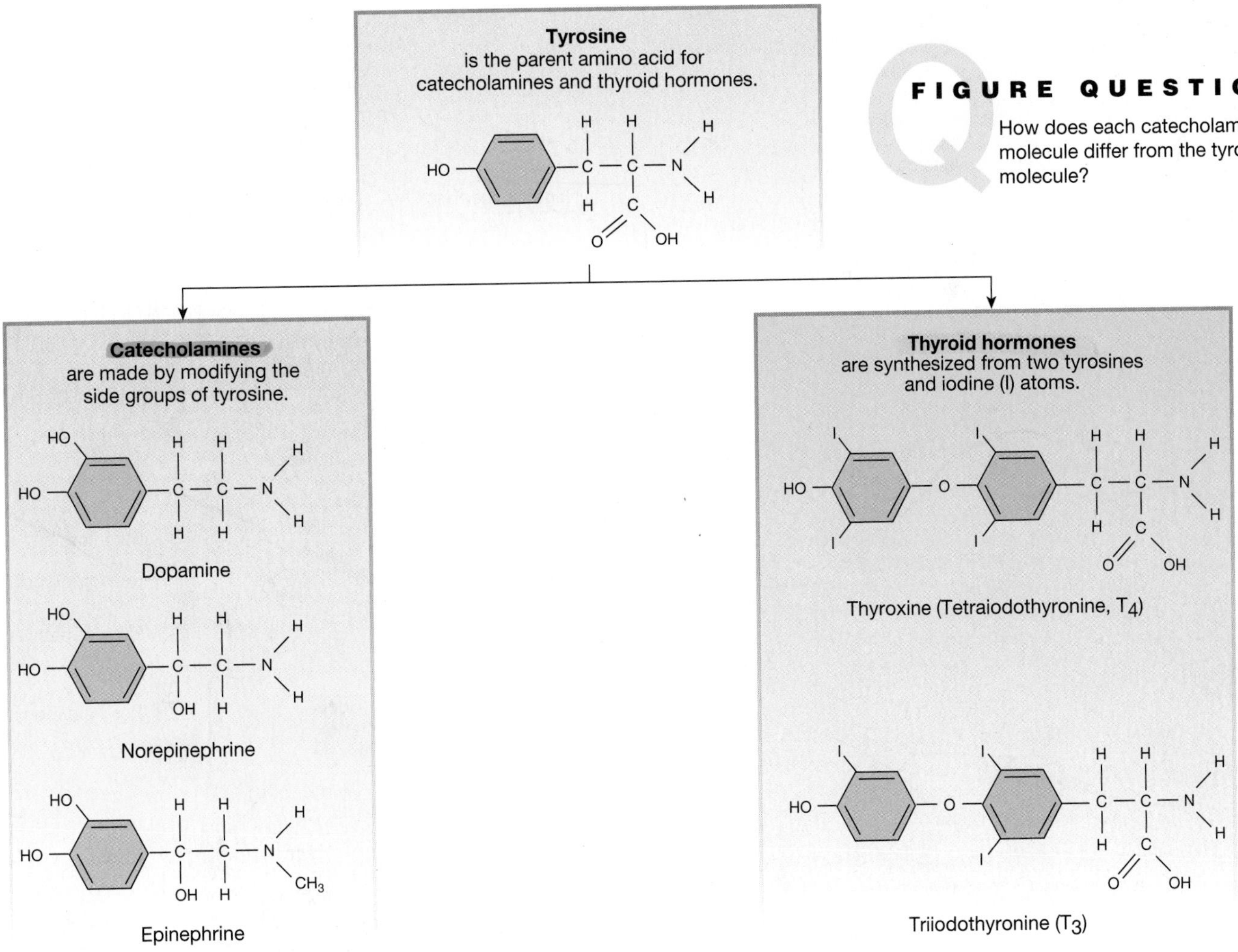

FIGURE QUESTION

How does each catecholamine molecule differ from the tyrosine molecule?

■ **FIGURE 7-8** ***Tyrosine-derived amine hormones***

signal, and a response [Fig. 6-25, p. 198]. In endocrine and neuroendocrine reflexes, the output signal is a hormone or a neurohormone.

In a simple reflex pathway, the response of the pathway usually serves as the *negative feedback* signal that turns off the reflex [Fig. 6-27a, p. 200]. For example, an increase in blood glucose concentration initiates insulin secretion by the pancreas (Fig. 7-9 ■). Once released from the pancreas, insulin travels through the blood to its target tissues, which increase their glucose uptake and metabolism. The resultant decrease in blood glucose concentration acts as a negative feedback signal and turns off the reflex, ending release of insulin.

Hormones are not restricted to following only one reflex pathway pattern, however. For example, insulin secretion can also be triggered by input signals from the nervous system (Fig. 7-9) or by a hormone secreted from the digestive tract as a meal is eaten (not shown). The pancreatic endocrine cells—the integrating center for this reflex—thus must evaluate input signals from three different sources when "deciding" whether to secrete insulin.

CONCEPT CHECK

7. In Figure 6-23 (p. 195), which reflex step(s) represent(s) the input signal? Integration of the signal? The output signal?
8. In the blood glucose example, the increase in blood glucose corresponds to which step of a reflex pathway? Insulin secretion and the decrease in blood glucose correspond to which steps?
9. Which three reflex pathways in Figure 6-31 (p. 204) match insulin release by the three different mechanisms just described?

Answers: p. 242

The Endocrine Cell Is the Sensor in the Simplest Endocrine Reflexes

The simplest reflex control pathways in the endocrine system are those in which an endocrine cell directly senses a stimulus and responds by secreting its hormone [Fig. 6-31, pattern 6, p. 204]. In this type of pathway, the endocrine cell acts as both sensor (receptor) and integrating center. **Parathyroid hormone** (PTH) is an example of a hormone that operates via this simple

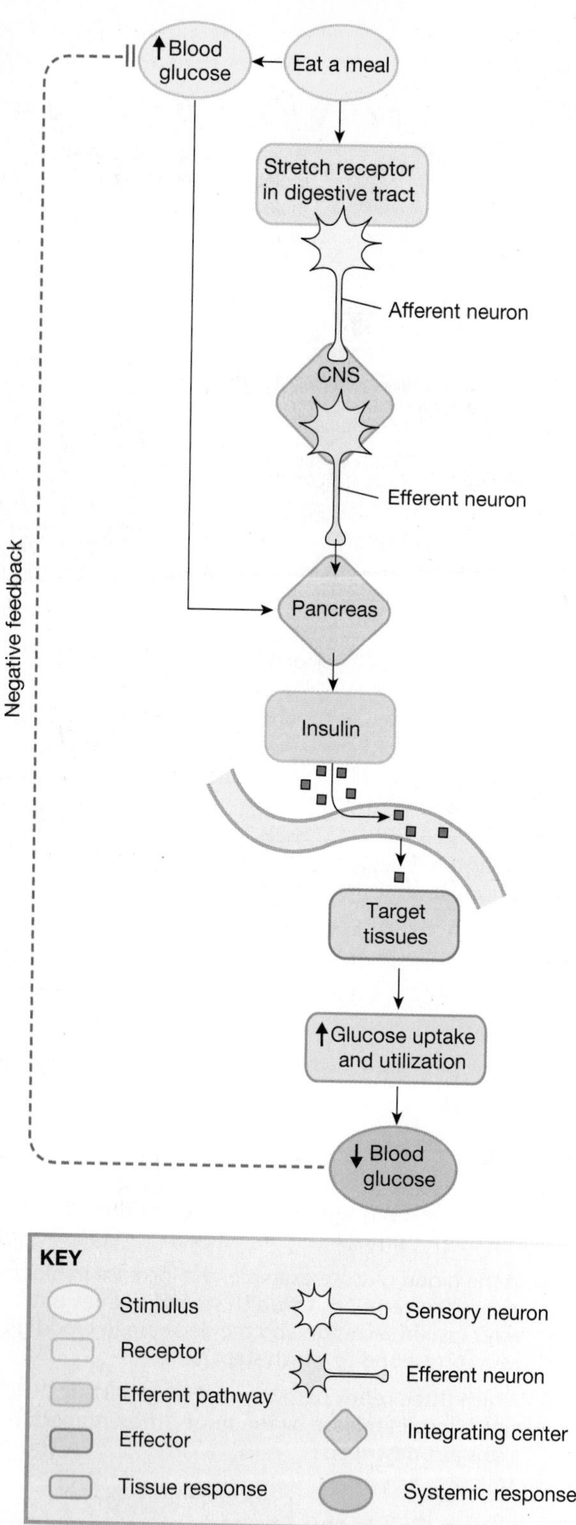

KEY

Stimulus
Receptor
Efferent pathway
Effector
Tissue response
Sensory neuron
Efferent neuron
Integrating center
Systemic response

FIGURE QUESTION

What shuts off the pathway that begins with the stimulus of "eat a meal?"

■ **FIGURE 7-9** ***Hormones may have multiple stimuli for their release***

Insulin can be released directly by an increase in blood glucose levels, or through nervous stimulation triggered by ingestion of a meal.

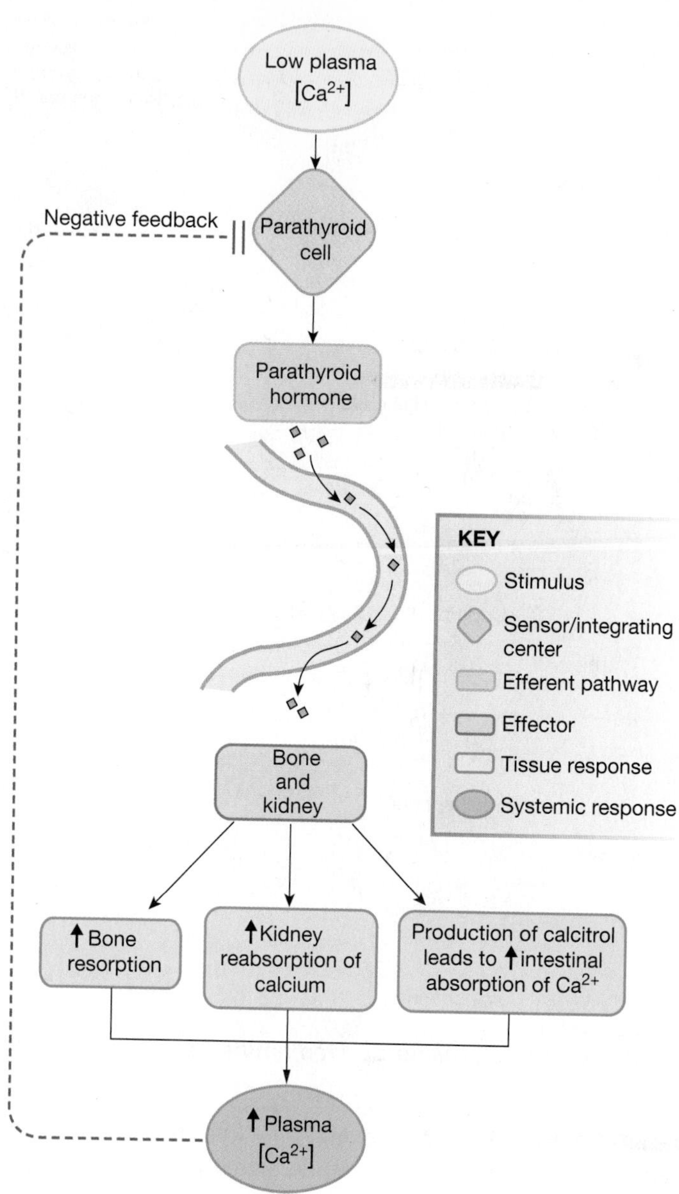

■ **FIGURE 7-10** ***A simple endocrine reflex: parathyroid hormone***

endocrine reflex. Other hormones that follow a simple reflex pattern include the classic hormones insulin and glucagon, as well as some hormones of the diffuse endocrine system.

Parathyroid endocrine cells are clustered in four small glands that lie behind the thyroid gland. They monitor plasma Ca^{2+} concentration with the aid of G protein-coupled Ca^{2+} receptors on their cell membrane. When a certain number of receptors are bound to Ca^{2+}, PTH secretion is inhibited. If the plasma Ca^{2+} concentration falls below a certain level and fewer receptors are bound, inhibition ceases and the parathyroid cells secrete PTH (Fig. 7-10 ■). Parathyroid hormone travels through the blood to act on its target tissues, initiating responses that increase the concentration of Ca^{2+} in the plasma. The increase in plasma Ca^{2+} is a negative feedback signal that turns off the reflex, ending the release of parathyroid hormone.

CONCEPT CHECK

10. Draw a reflex pathway for parathyroid hormone as described in the previous paragraph. Answers: p. 242

Many Endocrine Reflexes Involve the Nervous System

The nervous system and the endocrine system overlap in both structure and function. Stimuli that are integrated by the central nervous system influence the release of many hormones through efferent neurons, as previously described for insulin. In addition, specialized groups of neurons secrete neurohormones, and two endocrine structures are incorporated in the anatomy of the brain: the pineal gland (discussed in a *Focus* box on p. 237) and the pituitary gland.

One of the most fascinating links between the brain and the endocrine system is the influence of emotions over hormone secretion and function. Physicians for centuries have recorded instances in which emotional state has influenced health or normal physiological processes. Women today know that the timing of their menstrual periods may be altered by stressors such as travel or final exams. The condition known as "failure to thrive" in infants can often be linked to environmental or emotional stress that increases secretion of some pituitary hormones and decreases production of others. The interactions among stress, the endocrine system, and the immune system are receiving intense study, and we will discuss them further in Chapter 24.

Neurohormones Are Secreted into the Blood by Neurons

As noted in Chapter 6, neurohormones are chemical signals released into the blood by a neuron [Fig. 6-31, reflex 2]. The human nervous system produces three major groups of neurohormones: (1) catecholamines made by modified neurons in the adrenal medulla, (2) hypothalamic neurohormones secreted from the posterior pituitary, and (3) hypothalamic neurohormones that control hormone release from the anterior pituitary. Because the latter two groups of neurohormones are associated with the pituitary gland, we will first describe that important endocrine structure.

CONCEPT CHECK

11. Catecholamines belong to which chemical class of hormone? Answers: p. 242

The Pituitary Gland Is Actually Two Fused Glands

The **pituitary gland** is a lima-bean-sized structure that extends downward from the brain, connected to it by a thin stalk and cradled in a protective pocket of bone (Fig. 7-11 ■). The first accurate description of the function of the pituitary gland came from Richard Lower (1631–1691), an experimental physiologist at Oxford University. Using observations and some experiments, he theorized that substances produced in the brain passed down the stalk into the gland and from there into the blood.

Lower did not realize that the pituitary gland is actually two different tissue types that merged during embryonic development. The **anterior pituitary** is a true endocrine gland of epithelial origin, derived from embryonic tissue that formed the roof of the mouth [Fig. 3-28, p. 77]. It is also called the *adenohypophysis* [*adeno-*, gland + *hypo-*, beneath + *phyein*, to grow], and its hormones are *adenohypophyseal* secretions. The **posterior pituitary**, or *neurohypophysis*, is an extension of the neural tissue of the brain. It secretes neurohormones made in the hypothalamus.

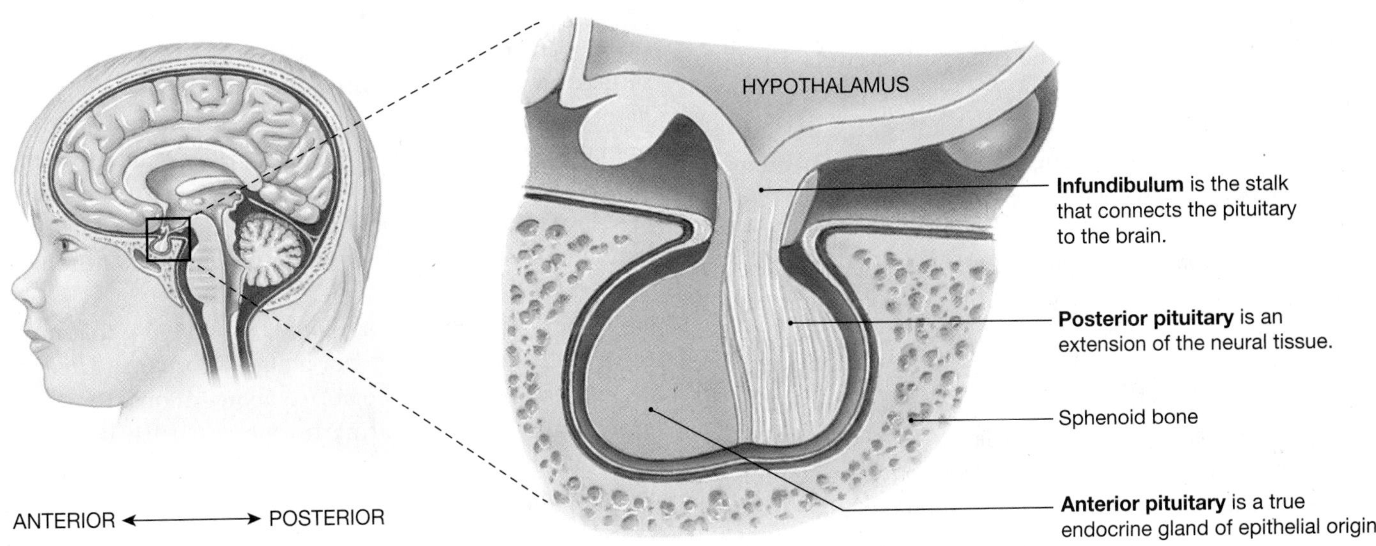
HYPOTHALAMUS
Infundibulum is the stalk that connects the pituitary to the brain.
Posterior pituitary is an extension of the neural tissue.
Sphenoid bone
Anterior pituitary is a true endocrine gland of epithelial origin
ANTERIOR ⟷ POSTERIOR

■ **FIGURE 7-11** *Pituitary gland anatomy*

The pituitary gland sits in a protected pocket of bone, connected to the brain by a thin stalk.

7

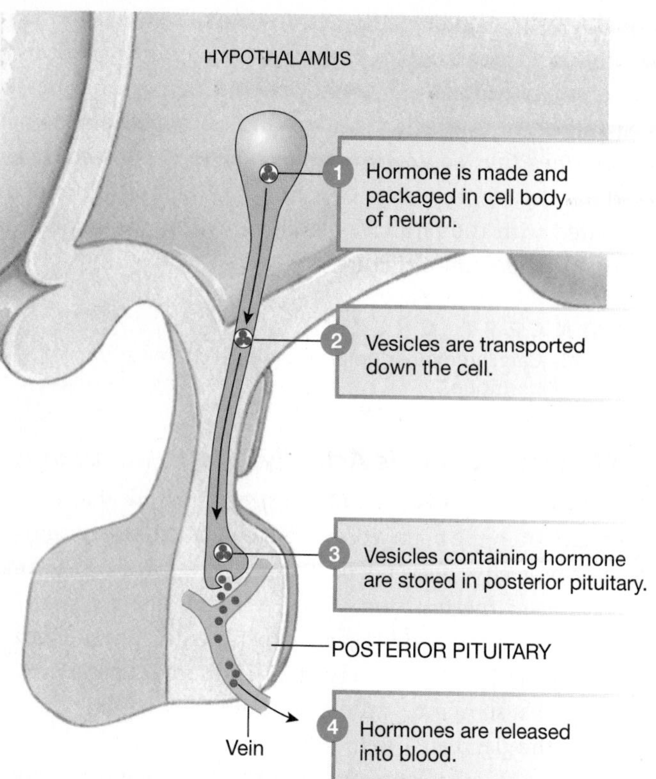

HYPOTHALAMUS
1 Hormone is made and packaged in cell body of neuron.
2 Vesicles are transported down the cell.
3 Vesicles containing hormone are stored in posterior pituitary.
POSTERIOR PITUITARY
4 Hormones are released into blood.
Vein

■ **FIGURE 7-12** ***Synthesis, storage, and release of posterior pituitary hormones***

The Posterior Pituitary Stores and Releases Two Neurohormones

The posterior pituitary is the storage and release site for two neurohormones: oxytocin and vasopressin. These small peptide hormones are synthesized in the cell bodies of neurons in the hypothalamus, a region of the brain that controls many homeostatic functions (Fig. 7-12 ■). Each hormone is made in a separate cell type.

Hypothalamic neurohormones follow the standard pattern for peptide synthesis, storage, and release described earlier in this chapter. However, secretory vesicles containing hormone are transported down long extensions of the neurons into the posterior pituitary, where they are stored in the cell terminals. When a stimulus reaches the hypothalamus, an electrical signal passes from the neuron cell body to the distal end of the cell in the posterior pituitary, and the vesicle contents are released into the circulation.

The two posterior pituitary neurohormones are composed of nine amino acids each. **Vasopressin** (also known as antidiuretic hormone) regulates water balance in the body. In women, **oxytocin** released from the posterior pituitary controls the ejection of milk during breast-feeding and contractions of the uterus during labor and delivery.

A few neurons release oxytocin as a neurotransmitter or neuromodulator onto neurons in other parts of the brain. A number of animal experiments plus a few human experiments suggest that oxytocin plays an important role in social, sexual, and maternal behaviors. Some investigators postulate that *autism,* a developmental disorder in which patients are unable to form normal social relationships, may be related to defects in the normal oxytocin-modulated pathways of the brain.

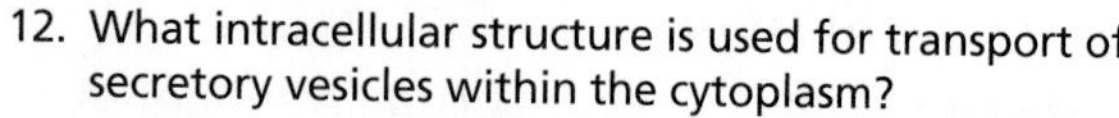

CONCEPT CHECK

12. What intracellular structure is used for transport of secretory vesicles within the cytoplasm?
13. Name the membrane process by which the contents of secretory vesicles are released into the extracellular fluid.

Answers: p. 242

The Anterior Pituitary Secretes Six Hormones

As late as 1889, it was being said in reviews of physiological function that the pituitary was of little or no use to higher vertebrates! By the early 1900s, however, researchers had discovered that animals with their anterior pituitary glands surgically removed were unable to survive more than a day or two. This observation, combined with the clinical signs associated with pituitary tumors, made scientists realize that the anterior pituitary is a major endocrine gland that secretes not one but six physiologically significant hormones: prolactin, thyrotropin, adrenocorticotropin, growth hormone, follicle-stimulating hormone, and luteinizing hormone. Secretion of all the anterior pituitary hormones is controlled by hypothalamic neurohormones.

The anterior pituitary hormones, their associated hypothalamic neurohormones, and their targets are illustrated in Figure 7-13 ■. Notice that all but one of the anterior pituitary hormones have another endocrine gland or cell as one of their targets. A hormone that controls the secretion of another hormone is known as a **trophic hormone**.

The adjective *trophic* comes from the Greek word *trophikós,* which means "pertaining to food or nourishment" and refers to the manner in which the trophic hormone "nourishes" the target cell. Trophic hormones often have names that end with the suffix *-tropin,* as in *gonadotropin.** The root word to which the suffix is attached is the target tissue: the gonadotropins are hormones that are trophic to the gonads. The hypothalamic neurohormones that control release of the anterior pituitary hormones are also trophic hormones, but for historical reasons they are described as either *releasing hormones* (e.g., thyrotropin-releasing hormone) or *inhibiting hormones* (e.g., growth hormone-inhibiting hormone).

One complication you should be aware of is that many of the hypothalamic and anterior pituitary hormones have multiple names as well as standardized abbreviations. For example, **growth hormone-inhibiting hormone** (GHIH) is also called *somatostatin.* The abbreviations and alternate names are listed in the caption of Figure 7-13.

---

*A few hormones whose names end in *-tropin* do not have endocrine cells as their targets. For example, melanotropin acts on pigment-containing cells in many animals.

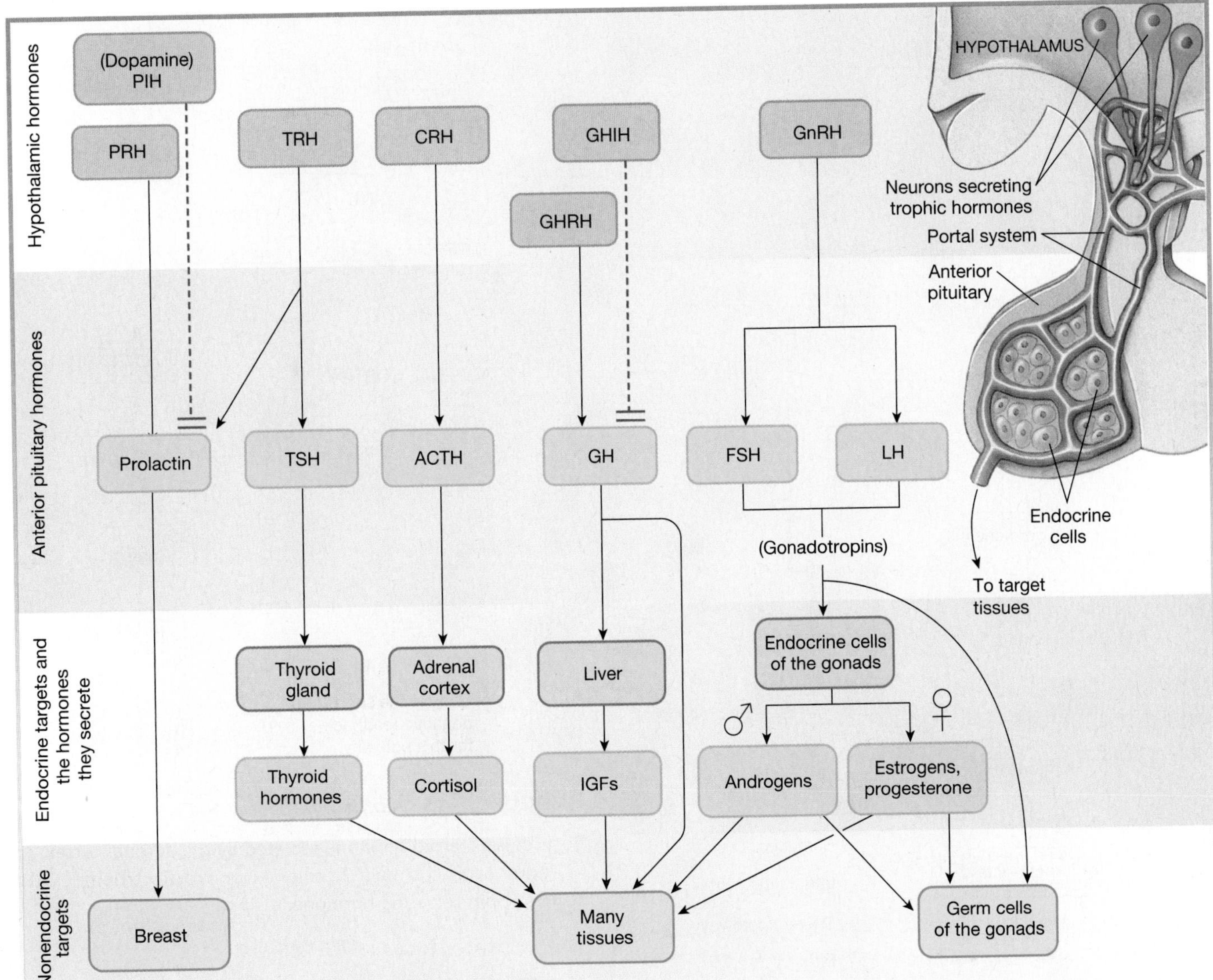

FIGURE 7-13 ***Hormones of the hypothalamic-anterior pituitary pathway***

The hypothalamus secretes releasing hormones (-RH) and inhibiting hormones (-IH) that act on endocrine cells of the anterior pituitary to influence secretion of their hormones. Anterior pituitary hormones act either on additional endocrine glands or directly on target cells. ACTH = adrenocorticotropic hormone (corticotropin); CRH = corticotropin-releasing hormone; FSH = follicle-stimulating hormone; GH = growth hormone; GHIH = growth hormone-inhibiting hormone (somatostatin); GHRH = growth hormone-releasing hormone; GnRH = gonadotropin-releasing hormone; IGFs = insulin-like growth factors; LH = luteinizing hormone; PIH = prolactin-inhibiting hormone; PRH = prolactin-releasing hormone; TRH = thyrotropin-releasing hormone; TSH = thyroid-stimulating hormone (thyrotropin).

Feedback Loops Are Different in the Hypothalamic-Pituitary Pathway

The pathways in which anterior pituitary hormones act as trophic hormones are among the most complex endocrine reflexes because they involve three integrating centers: the hypothalamus, the anterior pituitary, and the endocrine target of the pituitary hormone (Fig. 7-14 ■). Feedback in these complex pathways follows a pattern that is different from the pattern described previously. Instead of the response acting as the negative feedback signal, the hormones themselves are the signal. Each hormone in the pathway feeds back to suppress hormone secretion by integrating centers earlier in the reflex pathway.

When secretion of one hormone in a complex pathway increases or decreases, the secretion of other hormones also changes because of the feedback loops that link the hormones. In pathways with two or three hormones in sequence, the "downstream" hormone usually feeds back to suppress the hormone(s) that controlled its secretion. (A major exception to this is feedback by ovarian hormones, as you will learn in Chapter 26.) For example, cortisol secreted from the adrenal cortex feeds back to suppress secretion of the trophic hormones corticotropin-releasing hormone and adrenocorticotropic hormone (Fig. 7-15 ■). This relationship is called **long-loop negative feedback**. In **short-loop**

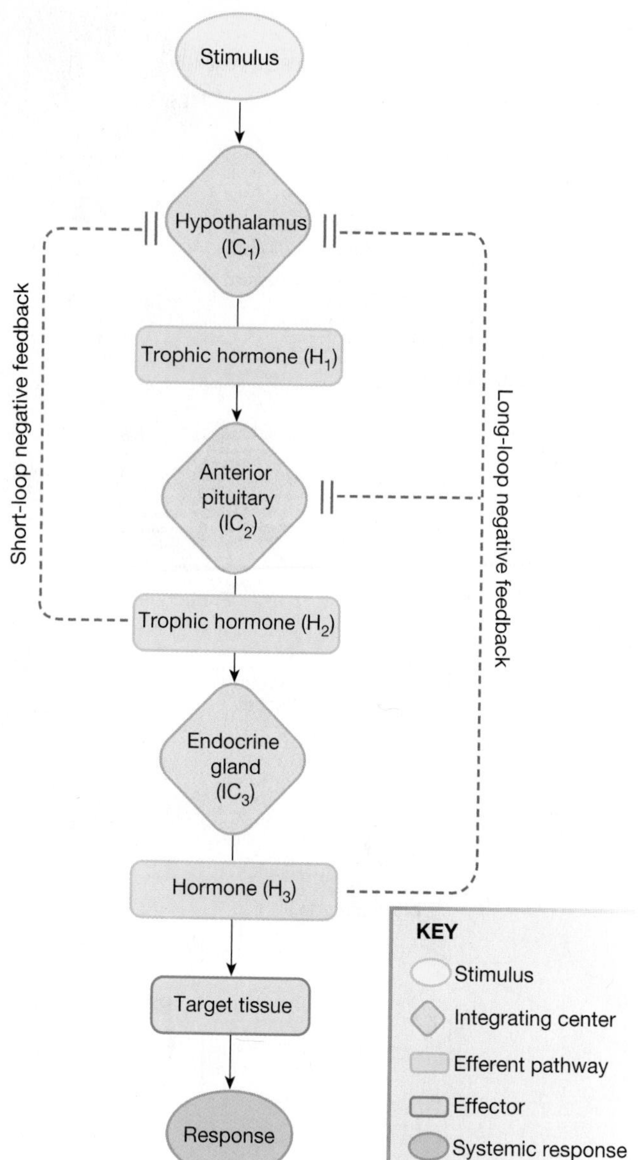

■ **FIGURE 7-14** ***Negative feedback loops in the hypothalamic-anterior pituitary pathway***

In complex endocrine pathways, the hormones of the pathway serve as negative feedback signals.

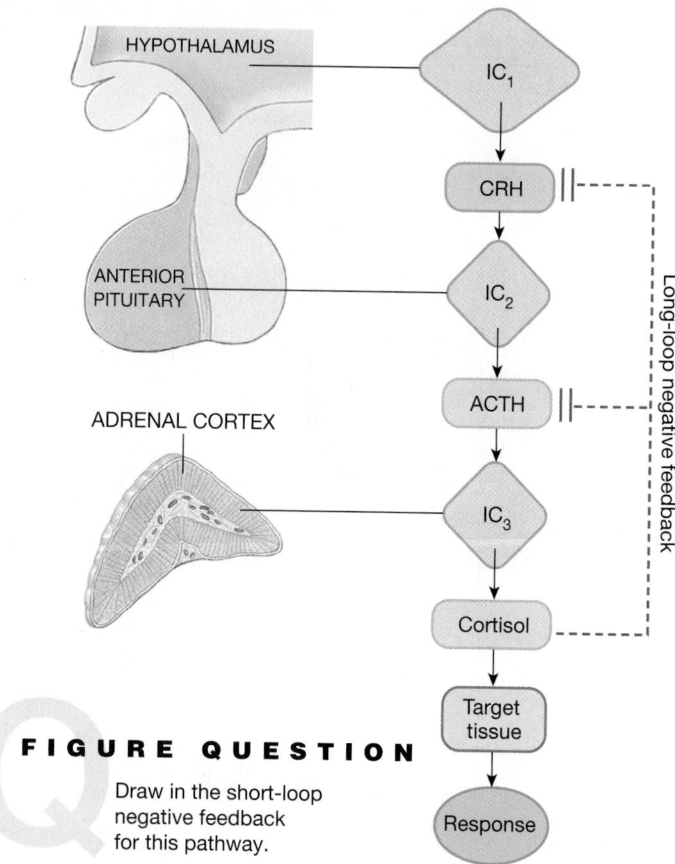

■ **FIGURE 7-15** ***Control pathway for cortisol secretion***

Cortisol is a steroid hormone secreted by the adrenal cortex. ACTH = adrenocorticotropic hormone or corticotropin; CRH = corticotropin-releasing hormone.

negative feedback, pituitary hormones feed back to decrease hormone secretion by the hypothalamus. We see this type of feedback in the cortisol secretion in Figure 7-15, where ACTH exerts short-loop negative feedback on the secretion of CRH. With this system of negative feedback, the hormones normally stay within the range needed for an appropriate response. Feedback patterns are important in the diagnosis of endocrine pathologies, to be discussed later in the chapter.

CONCEPT CHECK

14. Which pathway in Figure 6-31 (p. 204) fits the pituitary hormone pattern just described, in which there are three integrating centers?

Answers: p. 242

RUNNING PROBLEM

Thyroid hormone production is regulated by thyroid-stimulating hormone (TSH), a hormone secreted by the anterior pituitary. The production of TSH is in turn regulated by the neurohormone thyrotropin-releasing hormone (TRH) from the hypothalamus.

Question 2:

a. ***In a normal person, when thyroid hormone levels in the blood increase, will negative feedback increase or decrease the secretion of TSH?***

b. ***In a person with a hyperactive gland that is producing too much thyroid hormone, would you expect the level of TSH to be higher or lower than in a normal person?***

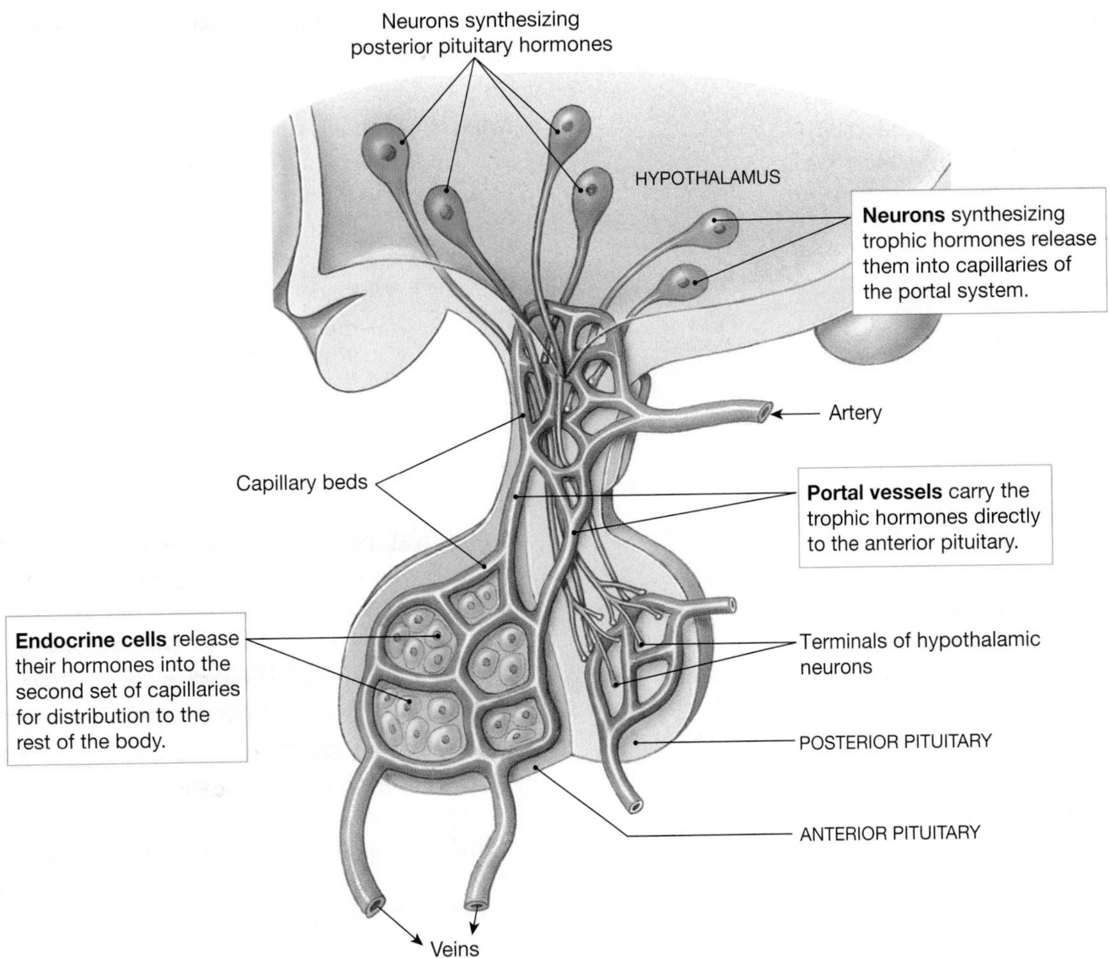
Neurons synthesizing posterior pituitary hormones
HYPOTHALAMUS
Neurons synthesizing trophic hormones release them into capillaries of the portal system.
Artery
Capillary beds
Portal vessels carry the trophic hormones directly to the anterior pituitary.
Endocrine cells release their hormones into the second set of capillaries for distribution to the rest of the body.
Terminals of hypothalamic neurons
POSTERIOR PITUITARY
ANTERIOR PITUITARY
Veins

■ **FIGURE 7-16** ***The hypothalamic-hypophyseal portal system***

The Hypothalamic-Hypophyseal Portal System Directs Trophic Hormone Delivery

The hypothalamic trophic hormones that regulate secretion of anterior pituitary hormones are transported directly to the pituitary through a special set of blood vessels known as the **hypothalamic-hypophyseal portal system** (Fig. 7-16 ■). A **portal system** is a specialized region of the circulation consisting of two sets of capillaries directly connected by a set of blood vessels. There are three portal systems in the body: one in the kidneys, one in the digestive system, and this one in the brain.

Hormones secreted into a portal system have a distinct advantage over hormones secreted into the general circulation because with a portal system, a much smaller amount of hormone can be secreted to elicit a given level of response. A dose of hormone secreted into the general circulation will be rapidly diluted by the total blood volume, which is typically more than 5 L. The same dose secreted into the tiny volume of blood flowing through the portal system remains concentrated while it is taken directly to its target. Thus, a small number of neurosecretory neurons in the hypothalamus can effectively control the anterior pituitary.

The minute amounts of hormone secreted into the hypothalamic-hypophyseal portal system posed a great challenge to the researchers who first isolated these hormones. Because such tiny quantities of hypothalamic-releasing hormones are secreted, Roger Guillemin and Andrew Shalley had to work with huge amounts of tissue to obtain enough hormone to analyze. Guillemin and his colleagues processed more than 50 tons of sheep hypothalami, and a major meat packer donated more than 1 million pig hypothalami to Shalley and his associates. For the final analysis, they needed 25,000 hypothalami to isolate and identify the amino acid sequence of just 1 mg of thyrotropin-releasing hormone, a tiny peptide made of three amino acids (see Fig. 7-4a). For their discovery, Guillemin and Shalley shared a Nobel prize in 1977.

Anterior Pituitary Hormones Control Growth, Metabolism, and Reproduction

The hormones of the anterior pituitary control so many vital functions that the pituitary is often called the master gland of the body. In general, we can say that the anterior pituitary hormones control metabolism, growth, and reproduction, all very complex processes.

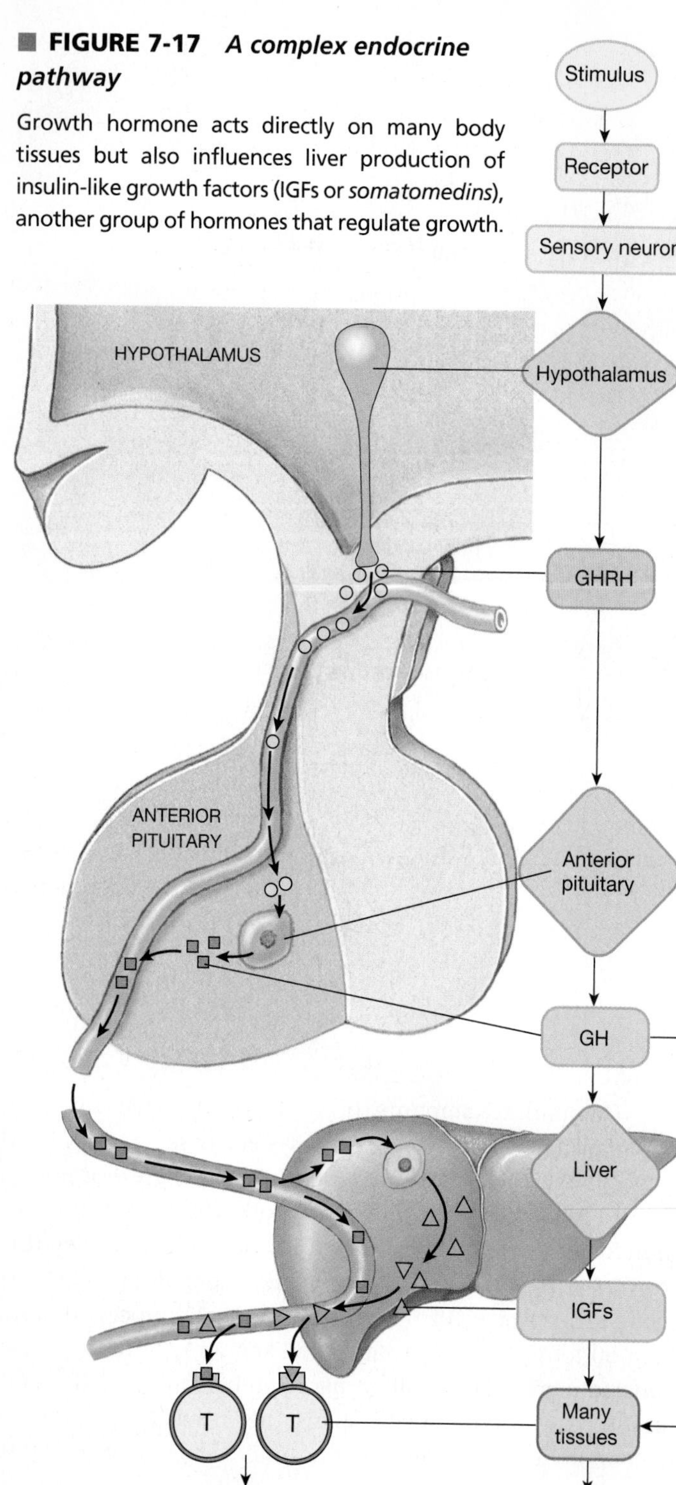

■ FIGURE 7-17 ***A complex endocrine pathway***

Growth hormone acts directly on many body tissues but also influences liver production of insulin-like growth factors (IGFs or *somatomedins*), another group of hormones that regulate growth.

One anterior pituitary hormone, **prolactin** (PRL), controls milk production in the female breast. In both sexes, prolactin appears to play a role in regulation of the immune system. **Growth hormone** (GH; also called *somatotropin*) affects metabolism of many tissues in addition to stimulating hormone production by the liver (Fig. 7-17 ■). Prolactin and growth hormone are the only two anterior pituitary hormones whose secretion is controlled by both releasing hormones and inhibiting hormones, as you can see in Figure 7-13 on page 227. We will discuss these hormones in detail in Chapters 26 and 23, respectively.

CONCEPT CHECK

15. Which pathway(s) in Figure 6-31 (p. 204) fit(s):
    (a) the hypothalamic trophic hormone-prolactin-breast pattern just described?
    (b) the growth hormone pathway shown in Figure 7-17?

Answers: p. 242

The remaining four anterior pituitary hormones all have another endocrine gland as their primary target. **Follicle-stimulating hormone** (FSH) and **luteinizing hormone** (LH), known collectively as the **gonadotropins**, were originally named for their effects on the ovaries, but both hormones are trophic on male testes as well. **Thyroid-stimulating hormone** (TSH, or *thyrotropin*) controls hormone synthesis and secretion in the thyroid gland. **Adrenocorticotrophic hormone** (ACTH, or *corticotropin*) acts on certain cells of the adrenal cortex to control synthesis and release of the steroid hormone cortisol.

The hormones of the anterior and posterior pituitary will be discussed in more detail in later chapters.

CONCEPT CHECK

16. What is the target tissue of a hypothalamic hormone secreted into the hypothalamic-hypophyseal portal system?
17. Look at the pathway in Figure 7-9 for insulin release as the result of eating a meal. What event serves as the negative feedback signal to shut off insulin release?

Answers: p. 242

HORMONE INTERACTIONS

One of the most complicated and confusing aspects of endocrinology is the way hormones interact at their target cells. It would be simple if each endocrine reflex were a separate entity and if each cell were under the influence of only a single hormone. In many instances, however, cells and tissues are controlled by multiple hormones that may be present at the same time. Complicating the picture is the fact that multiple hormones acting on a single cell can interact in ways that cannot be predicted by knowing the individual effects of the hormone. In this section, we examine three types of hormone interaction: synergism, permissiveness, and antagonism.

In Synergism, the Effect of Interacting Hormones Is More Than Additive

Sometimes different hormones have the same effect on the body, although they may accomplish that effect through different

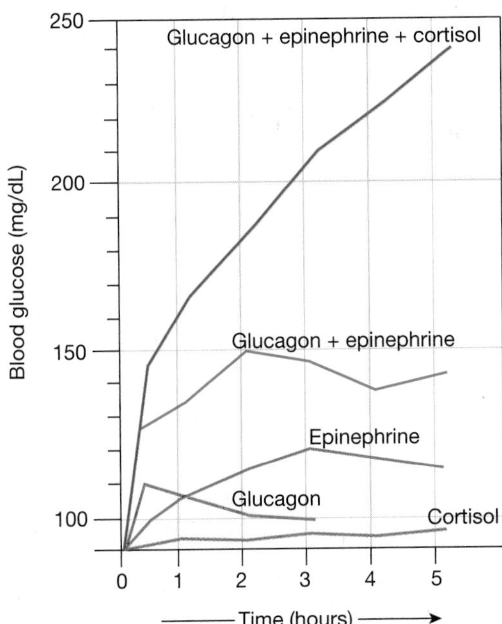

■ **FIGURE 7-18** ***Synergism***

This graph shows the effect of hormone infusions on blood glucose levels. The effects of combined hormones are greater than the summed effects of the individual hormones, indicating synergistic relationships. (Data adapted from Eigler et al., *J. Clin. Invest.* 63: 114, 1979.)

cellular mechanisms. One example is the hormonal control of blood glucose levels. Glucagon from the pancreas is the hormone primarily responsible for elevating blood glucose levels, but it is not the only hormone that has that effect. Cortisol raises blood glucose concentration, as does epinephrine.

What happens if two of these hormones are present in a target cell at the same time, or if all three hormones are secreted at the same time? You might expect their effects to be additive. In other words, if a given amount of epinephrine elevates blood glucose 5 mg/100 mL blood, and glucagon elevates blood glucose 10 mg/100 mL blood, you might expect both hormones acting at the same time to elevate blood glucose 15 mg/100 mL blood (5 + 10).

Frequently, however, two (or more) hormones interact at their targets so that the combination yields a result that is greater than additive. This type of interaction is called **synergism**. For our epinephrine/glucagon example, a synergistic reaction would be:

epinephrine	elevates blood glucose	5 mg/100 mL blood
glucagon	elevates blood glucose	10 mg/100 mL blood
epinephrine + glucagon	elevate blood glucose	22 mg/100 mL blood

That is, the combined effect of the two hormones is greater than the sum of the effects of the two hormones individually. Synergism is sometimes known as *potentiation,* as in "Epinephrine potentiates glucagon's effect on blood glucose."

An example of synergism involving epinephrine, glucagon, and cortisol is shown in Figure 7-18 ■. The cellular mechanisms that underlie synergistic effects are not always clear, but with peptide hormones, synergism is often linked to overlapping effects on second messenger systems.

Synergism is not limited to hormones. It can occur with any two (or more) chemicals in the body. Pharmacologists have developed drugs with synergistic components. For example, the effectiveness of the antibiotic penicillin is enhanced by the presence of clavulanic acid in the same pill.

A Permissive Hormone Allows Another Hormone to Exert Its Full Effect

In **permissiveness**, one hormone cannot fully exert its effects unless a second hormone is present. For example, maturation of the reproductive system is controlled by gonadotropin-releasing hormone from the hypothalamus, gonadotropins from the anterior pituitary, and steroid hormones from the gonads. However, if thyroid hormone is not present in sufficient amounts, maturation of the reproductive system is delayed. Because thyroid hormone by itself cannot stimulate maturation of the reproductive system, thyroid hormone is considered to have a permissive effect on sexual maturation.

RUNNING PROBLEM

Ben Crenshaw was diagnosed with Graves' disease, one form of hyperthyroidism. The goal of treatment is to reduce thyroid hormone activity, and Ben's physician offered him several alternatives. One treatment involves drugs that prevent the thyroid gland from using iodine. Another treatment is a single dose of radioactive iodine that destroys the thyroid tissue. A third treatment is surgical removal of all or part of the thyroid gland. Ben elected initially to use the thyroid-blocking drug. Several months later he was given radioactive iodine.

Question 3:
Why is radioactive iodine (rather than some other radioactive element, such as cobalt) used to destroy thyroid tissue?

The results of this interaction can be summarized as follows:

thyroid hormone alone	no development of reproductive system
reproductive hormones alone	delayed development of reproductive system
reproductive hormones with adequate thyroid hormone	normal development of reproductive system

The molecular mechanisms responsible for permissiveness are not well understood in most instances.

Antagonistic Hormones Have Opposing Effects

In some situations, two molecules work against each other, one diminishing the effectiveness of the other. This tendency of one substance to oppose the action of another is called *antagonism*. Recall from Chapter 6 that antagonism may result when two molecules compete for the same receptor [p. 44]. When one molecule binds to the receptor but does not activate it, that molecule acts as a competitive inhibitor, or antagonist, to the other molecule. This type of receptor antagonism has been put to use in the development of pharmaceutical compounds, such as the estrogen receptor antagonist *tamoxifen*.

In endocrinology, two hormones are considered functional antagonists if they have opposing physiological actions. For example, glucagon and growth hormone, both of which raise the concentration of glucose in the blood, are antagonistic to insulin, which lowers the concentration of glucose in the blood. Hormones with antagonistic actions do not necessarily compete for the same receptor. Instead, they may act through different metabolic pathways, or one hormone may decrease the number of receptors for the opposing hormone. For example, evidence suggests that growth hormone decreases the number of insulin receptors, providing part of its functional antagonistic effects on blood glucose concentration.

The synergistic, permissive, and antagonistic interactions of hormones make the study of endocrinology both challenging and intriguing. With this brief survey of hormone interactions, you have built a solid foundation for learning more about hormone interactions in later chapters.

ENDOCRINE PATHOLOGIES

As one endocrinologist said, "There are no good or bad hormones. A balance of hormones is important for a healthy life. . . . Unbalance leads to diseases."* We can learn much about the normal functions of a hormone by studying the diseases caused by hormone imbalances. There are three basic patterns of endocrine pathology: hormone excess, hormone deficiency, and abnormal responsiveness of target tissues to a hormone.

*W. König, preface to *Peptide and Protein Hormones* (New York: VCH Publishers, 1993).

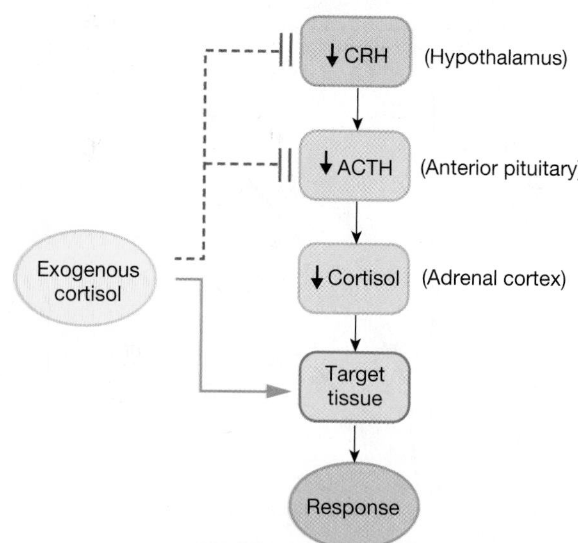

■ **FIGURE 7-19** ***Negative feedback by exogenous cortisol***

Hormone administered to a person for medical reasons will have the same negative feedback effect as the endogenous hormone.

To illustrate endocrine pathologies, we will use a single example, that of cortisol production by the adrenal cortex (see Fig. 7-15). This is a complex reflex pathway that starts with the secretion of corticotropin-releasing hormone (CRH) from the hypothalamus. CRH stimulates release of adrenocorticotropin (ACTH) from the anterior pituitary. ACTH in turn controls the synthesis and release of cortisol from the adrenal cortex. As in all other homeostatic reflex pathways, negative feedback shuts off the pathway. As cortisol increases, it acts as a negative feedback signal, causing the pituitary and hypothalamus to decrease their output of ACTH and CRH, respectively.

Hypersecretion Exaggerates a Hormone's Effects

If a hormone is present in excessive amounts, the normal effects of the hormone are exaggerated. Most instances of hormone excess are due to **hypersecretion**. There are numerous causes of hypersecretion, including benign tumors (*adenomas*) and cancerous tumors of the endocrine glands. Occasionally, nonendocrine tumors secrete hormones.

Any substance coming from outside the body is referred to as *exogenous* [*exo-*, outside + *-gen,* to be born], and sometimes a patient may exhibit signs of hypersecretion as the result of medical treatment with an exogenous hormone or agonist. In this case, the condition is said to be *iatrogenic,* or physician caused [*iatros,* healer + *-gen,* to be born]. It seems simple enough to correct the hormone imbalance by stopping treatment with the exogenous hormone, but this is not always the case.

In our example, exogenous cortisol in the body acts as a negative feedback signal, just as cortisol produced within the body would, shutting off the production of CRH and ACTH (Fig. 7-19 ■). Without the trophic "nourishing" influence of

ACTH, the body's own cortisol production shuts down. If the pituitary remains suppressed and the adrenal cortex is deprived of ACTH long enough, the cells of both glands shrink and lose their ability to manufacture ACTH and cortisol. The loss of cell mass is known as **atrophy** [*a-*, without + *trophikós,* nourishment].

If the cells of an endocrine gland atrophy because of exogenous hormone administration, they may be very slow or totally unable to regain normal function when the treatment with exogenous hormone is stopped. As you may know, steroid hormones can be used to treat poison ivy and severe allergies. However, when treatment is complete, the dosage must be tapered off gradually to allow the pituitary and adrenal gland to work back up to normal hormone production. As a result, packages of steroid pills direct patients ending treatment to take six pills one day, five the day after that, and so on. Low-dose, over-the-counter steroid creams usually do not pose a risk of feedback suppression when used as directed.

Hyposecretion Diminishes or Eliminates a Hormone's Effects

Symptoms of hormone deficiency occur when too little hormone is secreted (**hyposecretion**). Hyposecretion may occur anywhere along the endocrine control pathway, in the hypothalamus, pituitary, or other endocrine glands. The most common cause of hyposecretion syndromes is atrophy of the gland due to some disease process. For example, hyposecretion of thyroid hormone may occur if there is insufficient dietary iodine for the thyroid gland to manufacture the iodinated hormone.

Negative feedback pathways are affected in hyposecretion, but in the opposite direction from hypersecretion. The absence of negative feedback causes trophic hormone levels to rise as the trophic hormones attempt to make the defective gland increase its hormone output. For example, if the adrenal cortex atrophies as a result of tuberculosis, cortisol production diminishes. The hypothalamus and anterior pituitary sense that cortisol levels are below normal, so they increase secretion of CRH and ACTH, respectively, in an attempt to stimulate the adrenal gland into making more cortisol.

CONCEPT CHECK

18. Draw a reflex pathway similar to the one in Figure 7-19 to illustrate what happens to hormone levels and feedback when the adrenal cortex atrophies and cortisol secretion is below normal.

Answers: p. 242

Receptor or Second Messenger Problems Cause Abnormal Tissue Responsiveness

Endocrine diseases do not always arise from problems with endocrine glands. They may also be triggered by changes in the responsiveness of target tissues to the hormones. In these situations, the target tissues show abnormal responses even though the hormone levels may be within the normal range. Changes in the target tissue response are usually caused by abnormal interactions between the hormone and its receptor or by alterations in signal transduction pathways. These concepts were covered for signal molecules in general in Chapter 6 [p. 190], so we will restrict this discussion to some typical examples of abnormal tissue responsiveness in the endocrine system.

Down-Regulation If hormone secretion is abnormally high for an extended period of time, target cells may *down-regulate* (decrease the number of) their receptors in an effort to diminish their responsiveness to excess hormone. **Hyperinsulinemia** [*hyper-,* elevated + insulin + *-emia,* in the blood] is a classic example of down-regulation in the endocrine system. In this disorder, sustained high levels of insulin in the blood cause target cells to remove insulin receptors from the cell membrane. Patients suffering from hyperinsulinemia may show signs of diabetes despite their high blood insulin levels.

Receptor and Signal Transduction Abnormalities

Many forms of inherited endocrine pathologies can be traced to problems with hormone action in the target cell. Endocrinologists once believed that these problems were rare, but they are being recognized more and more as scientists increase their understanding of receptors and signal transduction mechanisms.

Some pathologies are due to problems with the hormone receptor. If a mutation alters the protein sequence of the receptor, the cellular response to receptor-hormone binding may be altered. In other mutations the receptors may be absent or completely nonfunctional. For example, in *testicular feminizing syndrome,* androgen receptors are nonfunctional in the male fetus because of a genetic mutation. As a result, androgens produced by the developing fetus are unable to influence development of the genitalia. The result is a child who appears to be female but lacks a uterus and ovaries.

Genetic alterations in signal transduction pathways can lead to symptoms of hormone excess or deficiency. In the disease called *pseudohypoparathyroidism* [*pseudo-,* false + *hypo-,* decreased + parathyroid + *-ism,* condition or state of being], patients show signs of low parathyroid hormone even though blood levels of the hormone are normal or elevated. These patients have inherited a defect in the G protein that links the hormone receptor to the cAMP amplifier enzyme, adenylyl cyclase. Because the signal transduction pathway does not function, the cells are unable to respond to parathyroid hormone, and signs of hormone deficiency appear.

7

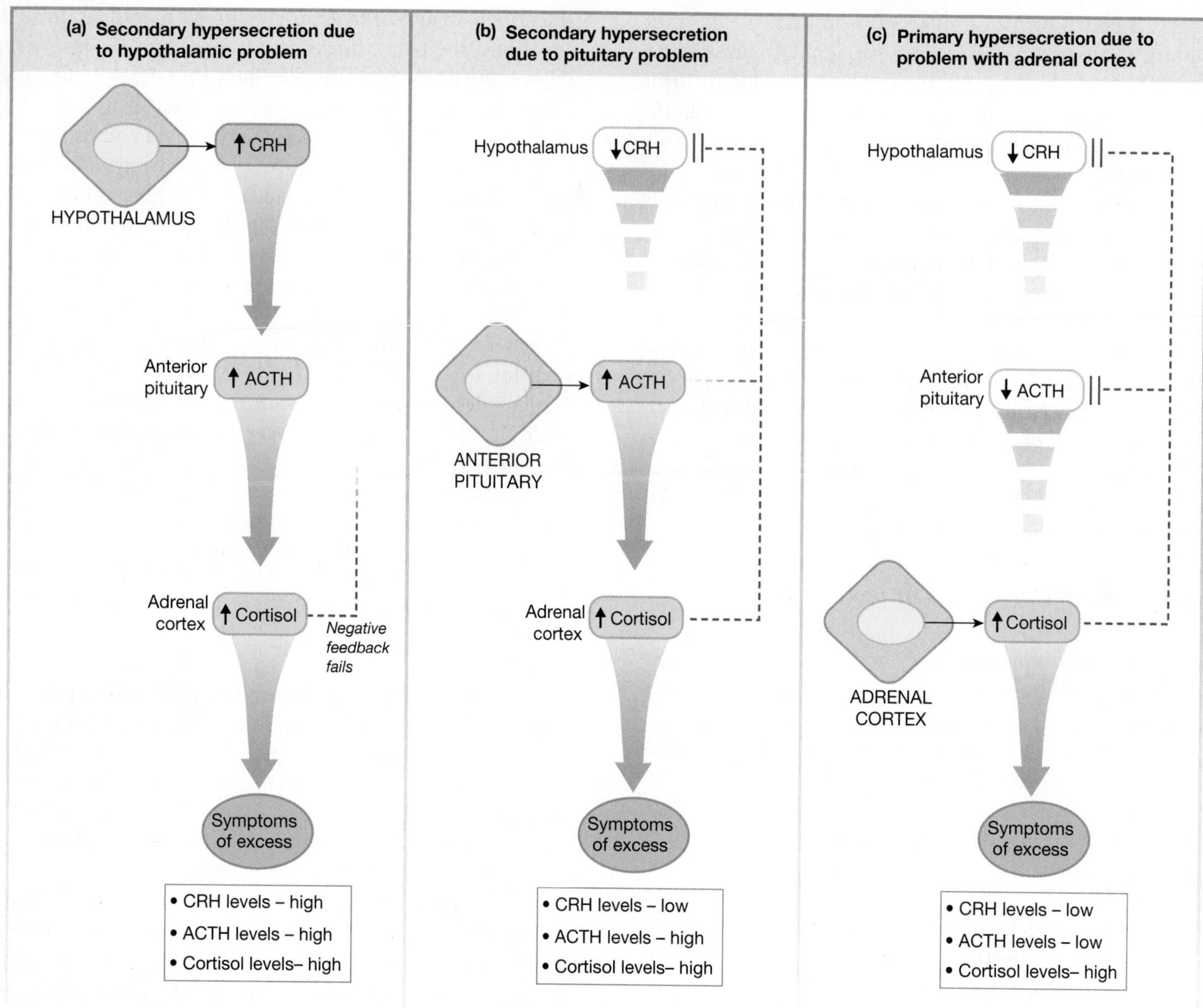

■ **FIGURE 7-20** ***Primary and secondary hypersecretion of cortisol***

When there is a pathology in an endocrine gland, negative feedback fails.

Diagnosis of Endocrine Pathologies Depends on the Complexity of the Reflex

Diagnosis of endocrine pathologies may be simple or complicated, depending on the complexity of the reflex. In the simplest endocrine reflex, such as that for parathyroid hormone, if there is too much or too little hormone, there is only one location where the problem can arise: the parathyroid glands (see Fig. 7-10). However, with complex hypothalamic-pituitary-endocrine gland reflexes, the diagnosis can be much more difficult.

If a pathology (deficiency or excess) arises in the last endocrine gland in a reflex, the problem is considered to be a **primary pathology**. For example, if a tumor in the adrenal cortex begins to produce excessive amounts of cortisol, the resulting condition is called *primary hypersecretion*. If dysfunction occurs in one of the tissues producing trophic hormones, the problem is a **secondary pathology**. For example, if the pituitary is damaged because of head trauma and ACTH secretion diminishes, the resulting cortisol deficiency is considered to be *secondary hyposecretion* of cortisol.

The diagnosis of pathologies in complex endocrine pathways depends on understanding negative feedback in the control pathway. Figure 7-20 ■ shows three possible causes of excess cortisol secretion. To determine which is the correct *etiology* (cause) of the disease in a particular patient, the clinician must assess the levels of the three hormones in the control pathway.

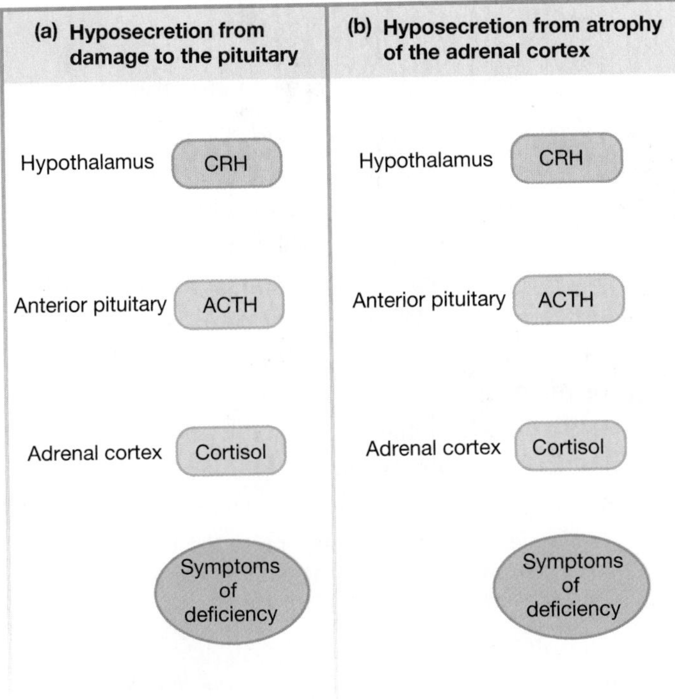

FIGURE QUESTION

For each condition, use arrows to indicate whether levels of the three hormones in the pathway will be increased, decreased, or unchanged. Draw in negative feedback loops or indicate where feedback has failed.

■ **FIGURE 7-21** ***Patterns of hormone secretion in hypocortisolism***

If the problem is overproduction of CRH by the hypothalamus (Fig. 7-20a), CRH levels will be higher than normal. High CRH in turn causes high ACTH, which in turn causes high cortisol. This is therefore secondary hypersecretion arising from a problem in the hypothalamus. In clinical practice, this type of pathology is very rare.

Figure 7-20b shows a secondary hypersecretion of cortisol due to an ACTH-secreting tumor of the pituitary. Once again, the high levels of ACTH cause high cortisol production, but in this example the high cortisol level has a negative feedback effect on the hypothalamus, decreasing production of CRH. The combination of low CRH and high ACTH isolates the problem to the pituitary. This pathology is responsible for about two-thirds of cortisol hypersecretion *syndromes* [*syn-*, together + *-drome*, running; a combination of symptoms characteristic of a particular pathology].

If cortisol levels are high but levels of both trophic hormones are low, the problem must be a primary disorder (Fig. 7-20c). There are two possible explanations: *endogenous* [*endo-*, within + *-gen*, to be born] cortisol hypersecretion or the exogenous administration of cortisol for therapeutic reasons (see Fig. 7-19).

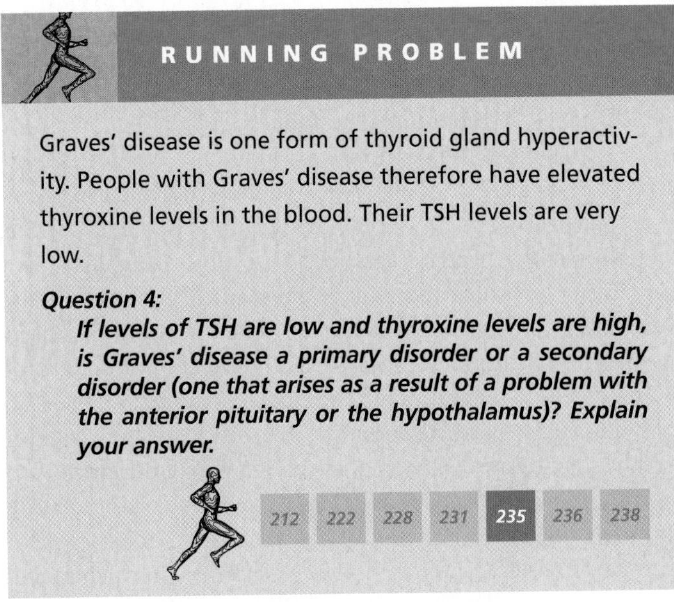

RUNNING PROBLEM

Graves' disease is one form of thyroid gland hyperactivity. People with Graves' disease therefore have elevated thyroxine levels in the blood. Their TSH levels are very low.

Question 4:

If levels of TSH are low and thyroxine levels are high, is Graves' disease a primary disorder or a secondary disorder (one that arises as a result of a problem with the anterior pituitary or the hypothalamus)? Explain your answer.

212 222 228 231 235 236 238

In either case, high levels of cortisol act as a negative feedback signal that shuts off production of CRH and ACTH. The pattern of high cortisol with low trophic hormone levels points to a primary disorder.

When the problem is an adrenal tumor that is secreting cortisol in an unregulated fashion, the normal control pathways are totally ineffective. Although negative feedback shuts off production of the trophic hormones, the tumor is not dependent on them for cortisol production, so cortisol secretion continues in their absence. The tumor must be removed or suppressed before cortisol secretion can be controlled.

Figure 7-21 ■ shows two possible etiologies for hyposecretion of cortisol. You can apply your understanding of negative feedback in the hypothalamic-pituitary control pathway to predict whether the levels of CRH, ACTH, and cortisol will be high or low in each case.

HORMONE EVOLUTION

Chemical signaling is an ancient method for communication and the maintenance of homeostasis. As scientists sequence the genomes of diverse species, they are discovering that in many cases hormone structure and function have changed amazingly little from the most primitive vertebrates through the mammals. In fact, hormone signaling pathways that were once considered exclusive to vertebrates, such as those for thyroid hormones and insulin, have now been shown to play physiological or developmental roles in invertebrates such as echinoderms and insects. This *evolutionary conservation* of hormone function is also demonstrated by the fact that some hormones from other organisms have biological activity when administered to humans. By studying which portions of a hormone molecule do not change from species to species, scientists have acquired important clues to aid in the design of agonist and antagonist drugs.

The ability of nonhuman hormones to work in humans was a critical factor in the birth of endocrinology. When Best and Banting discovered insulin in 1921 and the first diabetic patients were treated with the hormone, the insulin was extracted from cow, pig, or sheep pancreases. Until recently, slaughterhouses were the major source of insulin for the medical profession. Now, with genetic engineering, the human gene for insulin has been inserted into bacteria, which then synthesize the hormone, providing us with a plentiful source of human insulin.

Although many hormones have the same function in most vertebrates, a few hormones that play a significant role in the physiology of lower vertebrates seem to be evolutionarily "on their way out" in humans. Calcitonin is a good example of such a hormone. Although it plays a major role in calcium metabolism in fish, calcitonin apparently has no significant influence on daily calcium balance in adult humans. Neither calcitonin deficiency nor calcitonin excess is associated with any pathological condition or symptom.

Although calcitonin is not a significant hormone in humans, the calcitonin gene does code for a biologically active protein. Cells in the brain process calcitonin gene mRNA to make a peptide known as *calcitonin gene-related peptide* (CGRP), which apparently acts as a neurotransmitter. CGRP can act as a powerful dilator of blood vessels, and one recent study found that a CGRP receptor antagonist effectively treated migraine headaches, which are caused by cerebral blood vessel dilation (vasodilation). The ability of one gene to produce multiple peptides is one reason research is shifting from genomics to physiology and proteomics (the study of the role of proteins in physiological function) [p. 122].

Some endocrine structures that are important in lower vertebrates are *vestigial* [*vestigium,* trace] in humans, meaning that in humans these structures are present as minimally functional glands. For example, *melanocyte-stimulating hormone* (MSH) from the intermediate lobe of the pituitary controls pigmentation in reptiles and amphibians. However, adult humans have only a vestigial intermediate lobe and normally do not have measurable levels of MSH in their blood.

In the research arena, *comparative endocrinology*—the study of endocrinology in nonhuman organisms—has made significant contributions to our quest to understand the human body. Many of our models of human physiology are based on research carried out in fish or frogs or rats, to name a few. For example, the pineal gland hormone *melatonin* (Fig. 7-22) was discovered through research using tadpoles. Many small nonhuman vertebrates have short life cycles that facilitate studying aging or reproductive physiology. Genetically altered mice (transgenic or knockout mice) have provided researchers valuable information about proteomics.

Opponents of animal research argue that scientists should not experiment with animals at all and should use only cell cultures and computer models. Although cultures and models are valuable tools and can be helpful in the initial stages of medical research, at some point new drugs and procedures must be tested on intact organisms prior to clinical trials in humans. Responsible scientists follow guidelines for appropriate animal use and limit the number of animals killed to the minimum needed to provide valid data.

In this chapter we have examined how the endocrine system with its hormones helps regulate the slower processes in the body. In the next chapter, you will learn how the nervous system can take care of the more rapid responses needed to maintain homeostasis.

RUNNING PROBLEM

Researchers have learned that Graves' disease is an autoimmune disorder in which the body fails to recognize its own tissue. In this condition, the body produces antibodies that mimic TSH and bind to the TSH receptor, turning it on. This false signal "fools" the thyroid gland into overproducing thyroid hormone. More women than men are diagnosed with Graves' disease, perhaps because of the influence of female hormones on thyroid function. Stress and other environmental factors have also been implicated in hyperthyroidism.

Question 5:

Antibodies are proteins that bind to the TSH receptor. From that information, what can you conclude about the cellular location of the TSH receptor?

Question 6:

In Graves' disease, why doesn't negative feedback shut off thyroid hormone production before it becomes excessive?

FOCUS ON . . . THE PINEAL GLAND

THE PINEAL GLAND

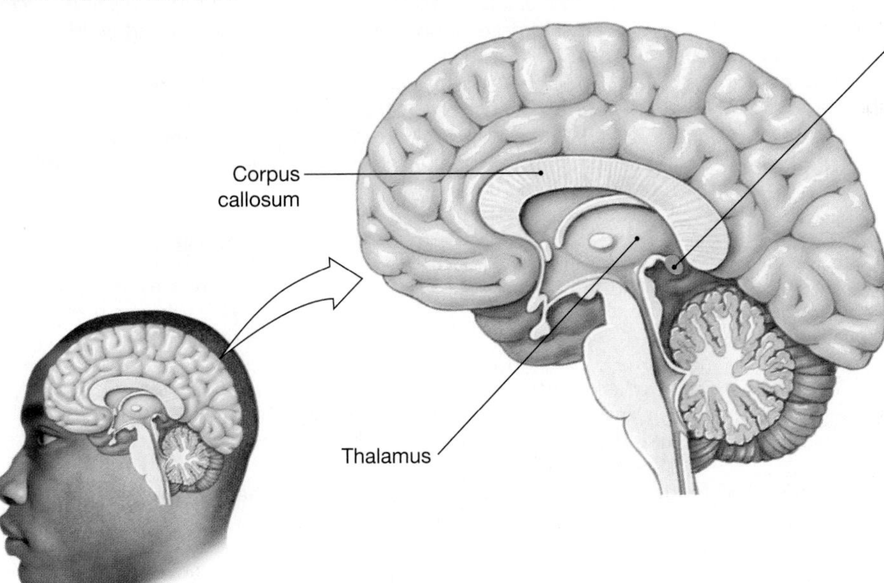

The pineal gland is a pea-sized structure buried deep in the brain of humans. Nearly 2000 years ago, this "seat of the soul" was thought to act as a valve that regulated the flow of vital spirits and knowledge into the brain. By 1950, however, scientists had decided that it was a vestigial structure with no known function.

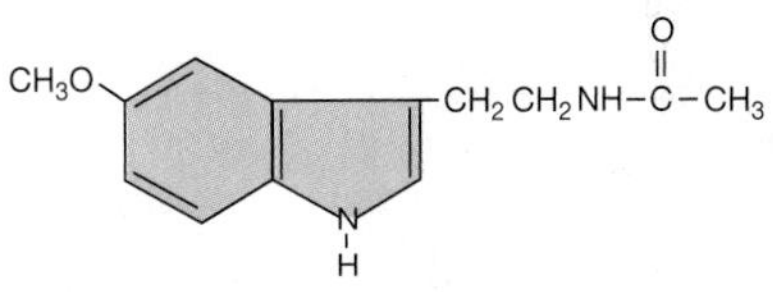

Melatonin is an amine hormone derived from the amino acid tryptophan.

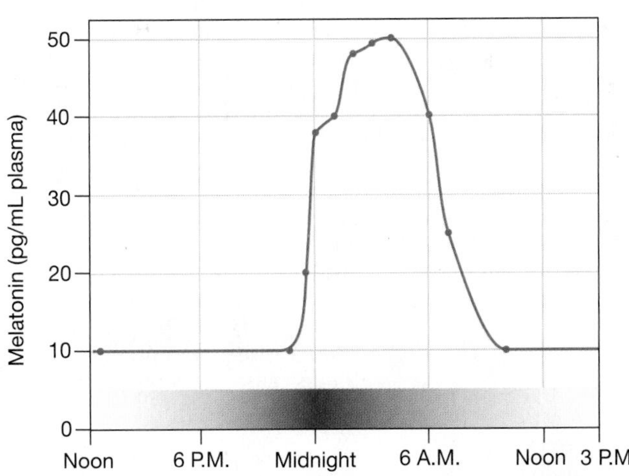

Melatonin is the "darkness hormone," secreted at night as we sleep. It is the chemical messenger that transmits information about light-dark cycles to the brain center that governs the body's biological clock.

(Adapted from J. Arendt, *Clin. Endocrinol.* 29: 205–229, 1988.)

About 1957 one of the wonderful coincidences of scientific research occurred. An investigator heard about a factor in beef pineal glands that could lighten the skin of amphibians. Using the classical methodology of endocrinology, he obtained pineal glands from a slaughterhouse and started making extracts. His biological assay consisted of dropping pineal extracts into bowls of live tadpoles to see if their skin color blanched. Several years and hundreds of thousands of pineal glands later, he had isolated a small amount of melatonin.

Ten years ago scientists and the popular press were trying to link melatonin to sexual function, the onset of puberty, seasonal affective depressive disorder (SADD) in the darker winter months, and sleep-wake cycles. At that time, the only function supported with scientific evidence was the hormone's ability to help shift timing of the body's internal clock, making it useful in overcoming jet lag. Now there is evidence that melatonin is a powerful antioxidant that has the potential to protect the body from the damage caused by free radicals. For a review, see "Melatonin: lowering the high price of free radicals," *News in Physiological Sciences* 15: 246–250, Oct. 2000 (*http://nips.physiology.org*).

FIGURE 7-22 ***The pineal gland and melatonin***

RUNNING PROBLEM CONCLUSION

GRAVES' DISEASE

In this running problem, you learned that in Graves' disease, thyroid hormone levels are high because an immune-system protein mimics TSH. You also learned that the thyroid gland concentrates iodine for synthesis of thyroid hormones and that radioactive iodine can concentrate in the gland and destroy the thyroid cells.

Graves' disease is the most common form of hyperthyroidism. Other famous people who have suffered from it include former U.S. President George H. W. Bush and First Lady Barbara Bush. To learn more about Graves' disease and other thyroid conditions, check out the Thyroid Foundation of America website at *www.tsh.org*. Check your answers to the problem questions by comparing them to the information in the summary table below.

	QUESTION	FACTS	INTEGRATION AND ANALYSIS
1a	To which of the three classes of hormones do thyroid hormones belong?	The three classes of hormones are peptides, steroids, and amines.	Thyroid hormones are made from the amino acid tyrosine; therefore, they are amines.
1b	If a person's diet is low in iodine, predict what happens to thyroxine production.	The thyroid gland concentrates iodine and combines it with the amino acid tyrosine to make thyroid hormones.	If iodine is lacking in the diet, a person will be unable to make thyroid hormones.
2a	In a normal person, when thyroid hormone levels in the blood increase, will negative feedback increase or decrease the secretion of TSH?	Negative feedback shuts off response loops.	Normally negative feedback will decrease TSH secretion.
2b	In a person with a hyperactive gland that is producing too much thyroid hormone, would you expect the level of TSH to be higher or lower than in a normal person?		If thyroid hormone is high, you would expect strong negative feedback and even lower levels of TSH.
3	Why is radioactive iodine (rather than some other radioactive element, such as cobalt) used to destroy thyroid tissue?	The thyroid gland concentrates iodine to make thyroid hormones.	Radioactive iodine will be concentrated in the thyroid gland and therefore will selectively destroy that tissue. Other radioactive elements would distribute more widely throughout the body and might harm normal tissues.
4	If levels of TSH are low and thyroxine levels are high, is Graves' disease a primary disorder or a secondary disorder (one that arises as a result of a problem with the anterior pituitary or the hypothalamus)? Explain your answer.	In secondary hypersecretion disorders, you would expect the levels of the hypothalamic and/or anterior pituitary trophic hormones to be elevated.	In Graves' disease, TSH from the anterior pituitary is very low. Therefore, the oversecretion of thyroid hormones is not the result of elevated TSH. This means that Graves' disease is a primary disorder that is caused by a problem in the thyroid gland itself.
5	Antibodies are proteins that bind to the TSH receptor. From that information, what can you conclude about the cellular location of the TSH receptor?	Receptors may be membrane receptors or intracellular receptors. Proteins cannot cross the cell membrane.	The TSH receptor is a membrane receptor. It uses the cAMP second messenger pathway for signal transduction.
6	In Graves' disease, why doesn't negative feedback shut off thyroid hormone production before it becomes excessive?	In normal negative feedback, increasing levels of thyroid hormone shut off TSH secretion. Without TSH stimulation, the thyroid stops producing thyroid hormone.	In Graves' disease, high levels of thyroid hormone have shut off TSH production. However, the thyroid gland still produces hormone in response to the binding of antibody to the TSH receptor. In this situation, negative feedback has failed.

212 222 228 231 235 236 238

CHAPTER SUMMARY

This chapter introduced you to the endocrine system and the role it plays in *communication* and *control* of physiological processes. As you've seen before, the fact that the body is *compartmentalized* into intracellular and extracellular compartments means that special mechanisms are required to enable signals to pass from one compartment to the other. The chapter also presented basic patterns that you will encounter again as you study various organ systems: differences among the three chemical classes of hormones, reflex pathways for hormones, types of hormone interaction, and endocrine pathologies.

Hormones

IP Endocrine System: Endocrine System Review

1. The specificity of a hormone depends on its receptors and their associated signal transduction pathways. (p. 216)
2. A **hormone** is a chemical secreted by a cell or group of cells into the blood for transport to a distant target, where it is effective at very low concentrations. (p. 212)
3. **Pheromones** are chemical signals secreted into the external environment. (p. 216)
4. Hormones bind to receptors to initiate responses known as the **cellular mechanism of action**. (p. 217)
5. Hormone activity is limited by terminating secretion, removing hormone from the blood, or terminating activity at the target cell. (p. 217)
6. The rate of hormone breakdown is indicated by a hormone's **half-life**. (p. 217)

The Classification of Hormones

IP Endocrine System: Biochemistry, Secretion and Transport of Hormones, and the Actions of Hormones on Target Cells

7. There are three types of hormones: **peptide/protein hormones**, composed of three or more amino acids; **steroid hormones**, derived from cholesterol; and **amine hormones**, derived from either tyrosine (e.g., melatonin) or tryptophan (e.g., catecholamines and thyroid hormones). (p. 217)
8. Peptide hormones are made as inactive **preprohormones** and processed to **prohormones**. Prohormones are chopped into active hormone and peptide fragments that are co-secreted. (p. 218; Figs. 7-3, 7-4)
9. Peptide hormones dissolve in the plasma and have a short half-life. They bind to surface receptors on their target cells and initiate rapid cellular responses through signal transduction. In some instances, peptide hormones also initiate synthesis of new proteins. (p. 218; Fig. 7-5)
10. Steroid hormones are synthesized as they are needed. They are hydrophobic, and most steroid hormones in the blood are bound to protein carriers. Steroids have an extended half-life. (p. 220)
11. Traditional steroid receptors are inside the target cell, where they turn genes on or off and direct the synthesis of new proteins. Cell response is slower than with peptide hormones. Steroid hormones may bind to membrane receptors and have nongenomic effects. (p. 221; Fig. 7-7)
12. Amine hormones may behave like typical peptide hormones or like a combination of a steroid hormone and a peptide hormone. (p. 222; Fig. 7-8)

Control of Hormone Release

IP Endocrine System: The Hypothalamic-Pituitary Axis

13. Classic endocrine cells act as both sensor and integrating center in the simple reflex pathway. (p. 223; Fig. 7-10)
14. Many endocrine reflexes involve the nervous system, either through **neurohormones** or through neurons that influence hormone release. (p. 225)
15. The pituitary gland is composed of the anterior pituitary (a true endocrine gland) and the posterior pituitary (an extension of the brain). (p. 225; Fig. 7-11)
16. The posterior pituitary releases two neurohormones, oxytocin and vasopressin, that are made in the hypothalamus. (p. 226; Fig. 7-12)
17. **Trophic hormones** control the secretion of other hormones. (p. 226)
18. Anterior pituitary hormones are controlled by releasing hormones and inhibiting hormones from the hypothalamus. (p. 226; Fig. 7-13)
19. In complex endocrine reflexes, hormones of the pathway act as negative feedback signals. (p. 227; Fig. 7-14)
20. The hypothalamic trophic hormones reach the pituitary through the **hypothalamic-hypophyseal portal system**. (p. 229; Fig. 7-16)
21. There are six anterior pituitary hormones: prolactin, growth hormone, follicle-stimulating hormone, luteinizing hormone, thyroid-stimulating hormone, and adrenocorticotrophic hormone. (p. 226; Fig. 7-13)

Hormone Interactions

22. If the combination of two or more hormones yields a result that is greater than additive, the interaction is **synergism**. (p. 231; Fig. 7-18)
23. If one hormone cannot exert its effects fully unless a second hormone is present, the second hormone is said to be **permissive** to the first. (p. 231)
24. If one hormone opposes the action of another, the two are **antagonistic** to each other. (p. 232)

Endocrine Pathologies

25. Diseases of hormone excess are usually due to **hypersecretion**. Symptoms of hormone deficiency occur when too little hormone is secreted (**hyposecretion**). **Abnormal tissue responsiveness** may result from problems with hormone receptors or signal transduction pathways. (p. 232)
26. **Primary pathologies** arise in the last endocrine gland in a reflex. A **secondary pathology** is a problem with one of the tissues producing trophic hormones. (p. 234; Fig. 7-20)

Hormone Evolution

27. Many human hormones are similar to hormones found in other vertebrate animals. (p. 235)

QUESTIONS

(Answers to the Review Questions begin on page A1.)

THE PHYSIOLOGY PLACE

Access more review material online at **The Physiology Place** website. There you'll find review questions, problem-solving activities, case studies, flashcards, and direct links to both *InterActive Physiology®* and PhysioEx™. To access the site, go to *www.physiologyplace.com* and select Human Physiology, Fourth Edition.

LEVEL ONE REVIEWING FACTS AND TERMS

1. The study of hormones is called __________.
2. List the three basic ways hormones act on their target cells.
3. List five endocrine glands, and name one hormone secreted by each. Give one effect of each hormone you listed.
4. Match the following researchers with their experiments:

(a) Lower	1. isolated trophic hormones from the hypothalami of pigs and sheep
(b) Berthold	2. claimed sexual rejuvenation after he injected himself with testicular extracts
(c) Guillemin and Shalley	3. isolated insulin
(d) Brown-Séquard	4. accurately described the function of the pituitary gland
(e) Banting and Best	5. studied comb development in castrated roosters

5. Put the following steps for identifying an endocrine gland in order:
   (a) Purify the extracts and separate the active substances.
   (b) Perform replacement therapy with the gland or its extracts and see if the abnormalities disappear.
   (c) Implant the gland or administer the extract from the gland to a normal animal and see if symptoms characteristic of hormone excess appear.
   (d) Put the subject into a state of hormone deficiency by removing the suspected gland, and monitor the development of abnormalities.
6. For a chemical to be defined as a hormone, it must be secreted into the__________for transport to a__________and take effect at__________concentrations.
7. What is meant by the term *half-life* in connection with the activity of hormone molecules?
8. Metabolites are inactivated hormone molecules, broken down by enzymes found primarily in the__________and __________, to be excreted in the__________and__________, respectively.
9. Candidate hormones often have the word__________as part of their name.
10. List and define the three chemical classes of hormones. Name one hormone in each class.
11. Decide if each of the following characteristics applies best to peptide hormones, steroid hormones, amine hormones, all of these, or none of these.
    (a) are lipophobic and must use a signal transduction system
    (b) have a short half-life, measured in minutes
    (c) often have a lag time of 90 minutes before effects are noticeable
    (d) are water-soluble, and thus easily dissolve in the extracellular fluid for transport
    (e) most hormones belong to this class
    (f) are all derived from cholesterol
    (g) consist of three or more amino acids linked together
    (h) are released into the blood to travel to a distant target organ
    (i) are transported in the blood bound to protein carrier molecules
    (j) are all lipophilic, so diffuse easily across membranes
12. Why do steroid hormones usually take so much longer to act than peptide hormones?
13. When steroid hormones act on a cell nucleus, the hormone-receptor complex acts as a/an__________factor, binds to DNA, and activates one or more__________, which create mRNA to direct the synthesis of new__________.
14. Researchers have discovered that some cells have additional steroid hormone receptors on their__________, enabling a faster response.
15. The amino acids that give rise to the amine hormones are__________, the basis for melatonin, and__________, from which the catecholamines and thyroid hormones are made.
16. A hormone that controls the secretion of another hormone is known as a __________hormone.
17. In reflex control pathways involving trophic hormones and multiple integrating centers, the hormones themselves act as__________ __________signals, suppressing trophic hormone secretion earlier in the reflex.
18. What characteristic defines neurohormones?
19. List the two hormones secreted by the posterior pituitary gland. To what chemical class do they belong?
20. What is the hypothalamic-hypophyseal portal system? Why is it important?
21. List the six hormones of the anterior pituitary gland; give an action of each. Which ones are trophic hormones?
22. How do long-loop negative feedback and short-loop negative feedback differ? Give an example of each type in the body's endocrine system.
23. When two hormones work together to create a result that is greater than additive, that interaction is called__________. When two hormones must both be present to achieve full expression of an effect, that interaction is called__________. When hormone activities oppose each other, that effect is called__________.

LEVEL TWO REVIEWING CONCEPTS

24. Map the following groups of terms. Add additional terms if you like.

List 1	List 2
co-secretion	ACTH
endoplasmic reticulum	anterior pituitary
exocytosis	blood
Golgi complex	endocrine cell
hormone receptor	gonadotropins
peptide hormone	growth hormone
preprohormone	hypothalamus
prohormone	inhibiting hormone
secretory vesicle	neurohormone
signal sequence	neuron

synthesis	oxytocin
target cell response	peptide/protein
	peripheral endocrine gland
	portal system
	posterior pituitary
	prolactin
	releasing hormone
	trophic hormone
	TSH
	vasopressin

25. Compare and contrast the terms in each of the following sets:
    (a) paracrine, hormone, cytokine
    (b) primary and secondary endocrine pathologies
    (c) hypersecretion and hyposecretion
    (d) anterior and posterior pituitary
26. Compare and contrast the three chemical classes of hormones.

LEVEL THREE PROBLEM SOLVING

27. You encountered the terms *specificity, receptors,* and *down-regulation* in other chapters in this text. Do their meanings change when applied to the endocrine system? What chemical and physical characteristics do hormones, enzymes, transport proteins, and receptors have in common that makes specificity important?
28. Dexamethasone is a drug used to suppress the secretion of adrenocorticotrophic hormone (ACTH) from the anterior pituitary. Two patients with hypersecretion of cortisol are given dexamethasone. Patient A's cortisol secretion level falls to normal levels as a result, but patient B's cortisol secretion level remains elevated. Draw maps of the reflex pathways for these two patients (see Fig. 7-15 for a template) and use the maps to determine which patient has primary hypercortisolism. Explain your reasoning.
29. Some early experiments for male birth control pills used drugs that suppressed gonadotropin (FSH and LH) release. However, men given these drugs stopped taking them because the drugs decreased testosterone secretion, which decreased the men's sex drive and caused impotence.
    (a) Use the information given in Figure 7-13 to draw the GnRH-FSH/LH-testosterone reflex pathway. Use the pathway to show how suppressing gonadotropins decreases sperm production and testosterone secretion.
    (b) Researchers subsequently suggested that a better treatment would be to give men extra testosterone. Draw another copy of the reflex pathway to show how testosterone could suppress sperm production without the side effect of impotence.

LEVEL FOUR QUANTITATIVE PROBLEMS

30. The following graph represents the disappearance of a drug from the blood as the drug is metabolized and excreted. Based on the graph, what is the half-life of the drug?

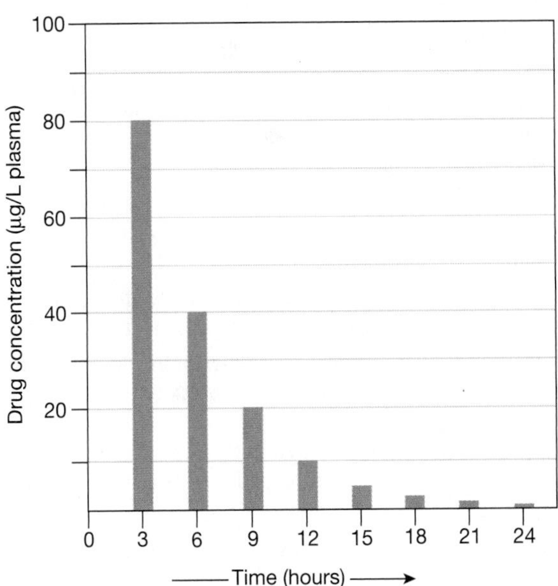

31. The following graph shows plasma TSH concentration in three groups of subjects. Pattern A is the normal subjects. Which pattern would be consistent with the following pathologies? Explain your reasoning.
    (a) primary hypothyroidism
    (b) primary hyperthyroidism
    (c) secondary hyperthyroidism
32. Based on what you have learned about the pathway for insulin secretion, draw and label a graph showing the effect of plasma glucose concentration on insulin secretion.

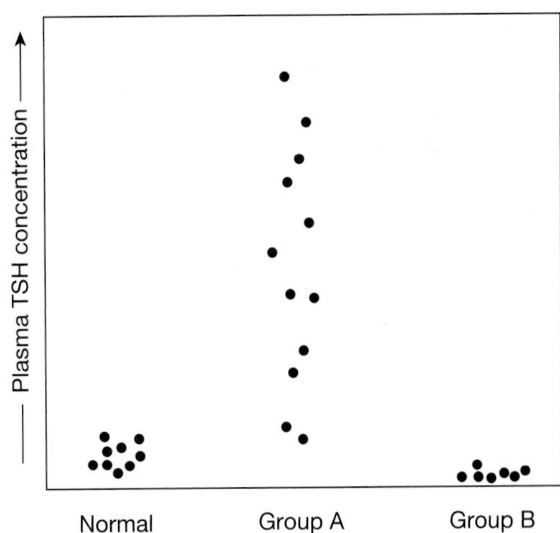

ANSWERS

Answers to Concept Check Questions

Page 217

1. Glucose enters cells by facilitated diffusion (GLUT transporters).

Page 217

2. The suffix *-ase* indicates an enzyme. A *peptidase* digests peptides.

Page 217

3. A hormone is a chemical that is secreted into the blood and acts on a distant target in very low concentrations.
4. A steroid-producing cell would have extensive smooth endoplasmic reticulum; a protein-producing cell would have lots of rough endoplasmic reticulum.

Page 221

5. The three chemical classes of hormones are peptide, steroid, and amine.
6. The short half-life suggests that aldosterone is not bound to plasma proteins as much as other steroid hormones are.

Page 223

7. The input signal is the stimulus, receptor, and afferent pathway. Integration of the signal takes place in the integrating center. The output signal is the efferent pathway.
8. Increased blood glucose is the stimulus. Insulin secretion is the efferent pathway; decrease in blood glucose is the response.
9. Insulin release by blood glucose is reflex 6. Insulin release triggered by a neural signal following a meal is reflex 3. Insulin release in response to a digestive hormone is closest to reflex 4, although the question does not indicate whether the hormone is neurosecretory. If it is not, there is no matching pathway in Figure 6-31.

Page 225

10. Stimulus: decreased Ca^{2+}; sensor/integrating center: parathyroid cells; efferent path: PTH; effector: target tissues; response: increased Ca^{2+}.

Page 225

11. Catecholamines are amine hormones.

Page 226

12. Microtubules of the cytoskeleton move secretory vesicles.
13. Contents of secretory vesicles are released by exocytosis.

Page 228

14. Pathway 5 in Figure 6-31 fits the complex pattern described.

Page 230

15. (a) Pathway 4; (b) pathway 4 for GH acting directly on targets, and pathway 5 for GH acting on the liver.

Page 230

16. The target is endocrine cells of the anterior pituitary.
17. The pathway shuts off when food is no longer present in the intestine to create stretch. A decrease in blood glucose can also serve as a negative feedback signal.

Page 233

18. Cortisol level is low; low negative feedback makes CRH and ACTH levels high.

Answers to Figure Questions

Page 223

Fig. 7-8: The conversion of tyrosine to dopamine adds a hydroxyl (—OH) group to the 6-carbon ring and changes the carboxyl (—COOH) group to a hydrogen. Norepinephrine is made from dopamine by changing one hydrogen to a hydroxyl group. Epinephrine is made from norepinephrine by changing one hydrogen attached to the nitrogen to a methyl (—CH_3) group.

Page 224

Fig. 7-9: The pathway begun by eating a meal shuts off when the stretch stimulus disappears as the meal is digested and absorbed from the digestive tract.

Page 228

Fig. 7-15: In short-loop negative feedback, ACTH inhibits CRH.

Page 235

Fig. 7-21: (a) CRH high, ACTH low, cortisol low. No negative feedback loops are functioning. (b) CRH normal/high, ACTH high, cortisol low. Absence of negative feedback by cortisol increases trophic hormones. Short-loop negative feedback from ACTH may keep CRH within the normal range.

12

A muscle is...an engine, capable of converting chemical energy into mechanical energy. It is quite unique in nature, for there has been no artificial engine devised with the great versatility of living muscle.

—Ralph W. Stacy and John A. Santolucito,
in Modern College Physiology, 1966

One somatic motor neuron branches to innervate several skeletal muscle fibers.

Muscles

BACKGROUND BASICS

Glucose and glycogen: **27** Gap junctions: **175** Tendons: **79** Kinases and phosphatases: **100** Isozymes: **96** Anaerobic and aerobic metabolism: **106** Glycolysis: **104** Fatty acid metabolism: **111** Tonic control: **192** Nitric oxide: **187** Threshold: **254** Summation: **278** Autonomic neurons: **379** Somatic motor neurons: **390** Neuromuscular junction: **390**

RUNNING PROBLEM

PERIODIC PARALYSIS

This morning, Paul Leong, age 6, gave his mother the fright of her life. One minute he was happily playing in the backyard with his new beagle puppy. The next minute, after sitting down to rest, he could not move his legs. In answer to his screams, his mother came running and found her little boy unable to walk. Panic-stricken, she scooped him up, brought him into the house, and dialed 9-1-1. But as she hung up the phone and prepared to wait for the paramedics, Paul got to his feet and walked over to her. "I'm OK now, Mom," he announced. "I'm going outside."

It was his first time to be the starting pitcher. As he ran from the bullpen onto the field, his heart was pounding and his stomach felt as if it were tied in knots. He stepped onto the mound and gathered his thoughts before throwing his first practice pitch. Gradually, as he went through the familiar routine of throwing and catching the baseball, his heart slowed and his stomach relaxed. It was going to be a good game.

The pitcher's pounding heart, queasy stomach, and movements as he runs and throws are all the results of muscle contraction. Our muscles have two common functions: to generate motion and to generate force. Our skeletal muscles also generate heat and contribute significantly to the homeostasis of body temperature. When homeostasis is threatened by cold conditions, the brain may direct our muscles to shiver, creating additional heat.

Three types of muscle tissue occur in the human body: skeletal muscle, cardiac muscle, and smooth muscle. Most **skeletal muscles** are attached to the bones of the skeleton, enabling these muscles to control body movement. **Cardiac muscle** [*kardia,* heart] is found only in the heart and is responsible for moving blood through the circulatory system. Skeletal and cardiac muscles are classified as **striated muscles** [*stria,* groove] because of their alternating light and dark bands under the light microscope (Fig. 12-1a, 1b ■).

Smooth muscle is the primary muscle of internal organs and tubes, such as the stomach, urinary bladder, and blood vessels. Its primary function is to influence the movement of material into, out of, and within the body. An example is the passage of food through the gastrointestinal tract. Under the microscope, smooth muscle lacks the obvious cross-bands of striated muscles (Fig. 12-1c). Its lack of banding results from the less organized arrangement of contractile fibers within the muscle cells.

(a) Skeletal muscle

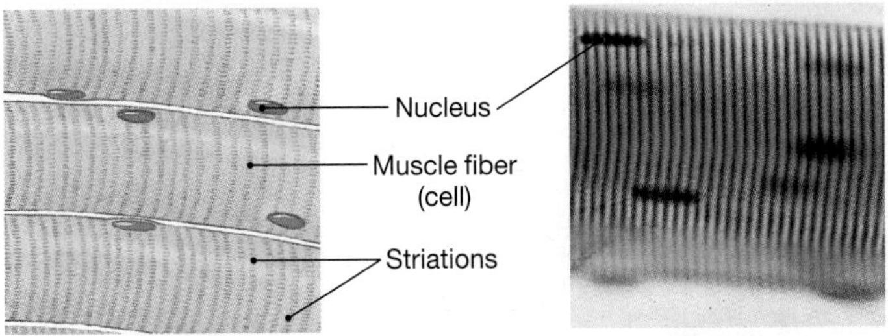

(b) Cardiac muscle

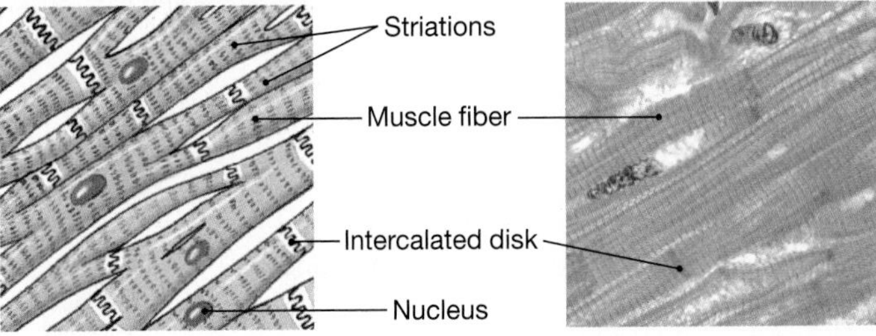

(c) Smooth muscle

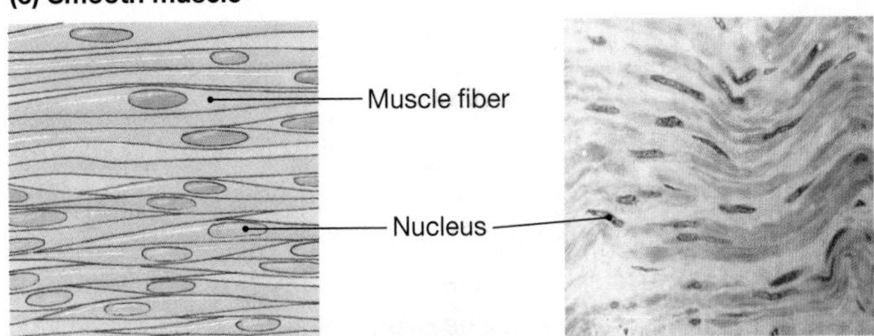

■ **FIGURE 12-1** ***The three types of muscles***

Skeletal muscles are often described as voluntary muscles, and smooth and cardiac muscle as involuntary. However, this is not a precise classification. Skeletal muscles can contract without conscious direction, and we can learn a certain degree of conscious control over some smooth and cardiac muscle [p. 377].

Skeletal muscles are unique in that they contract only in response to a signal from a somatic motor neuron. They cannot initiate their own contraction, nor is their contraction influenced directly by hormones. In contrast, cardiac and smooth muscle have multiple levels of control. Although their primary extrinsic control arises through autonomic innervation, some types of smooth and cardiac muscle can contract spontaneously, without signals from the central nervous system. In addition, the activity of cardiac and some smooth muscle is subject to modulation by the endocrine system. Despite these differences, smooth and cardiac muscle share many properties with skeletal muscle.

This chapter discusses skeletal and smooth muscle anatomy and contraction, and then concludes by comparing the properties of skeletal muscle, smooth muscle, and cardiac muscle. We will look at the details of cardiac muscle in Chapter 14 when we study the heart. The metabolism and endocrinology of skeletal muscle will be covered in Chapters 22, 23, and 25.

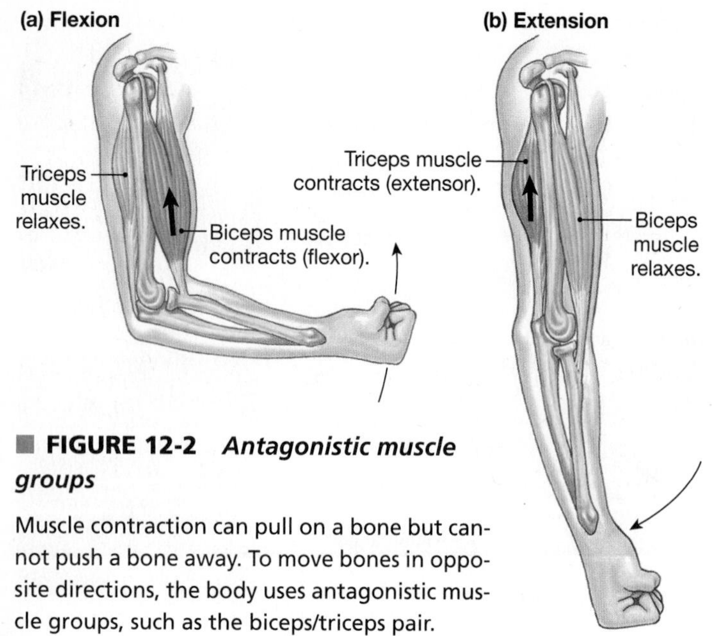
(a) Flexion
(b) Extension
Triceps muscle relaxes.
Biceps muscle contracts (flexor).
Triceps muscle contracts (extensor).
Biceps muscle relaxes.

■ **FIGURE 12-2** ***Antagonistic muscle groups***

Muscle contraction can pull on a bone but cannot push a bone away. To move bones in opposite directions, the body uses antagonistic muscle groups, such as the biceps/triceps pair.

SKELETAL MUSCLE

Skeletal muscles make up the bulk of muscle in the body and constitute about 40% of total body weight. They are responsible for positioning and moving the skeleton, as their name suggests. Skeletal muscles are usually attached to bones by **tendons** made of collagen [p. 79]. The **origin** of a muscle is the end of the muscle that is attached closest to the trunk or to the more stationary bone. The **insertion** of the muscle is the more *distal* [*distantia,* distant] or more mobile attachment.

When the bones attached to a muscle are connected by a flexible joint, contraction of the muscle moves the skeleton. If the centers of the connected bones are brought closer together when the muscle contracts, the muscle is called a **flexor**, and the movement is called *flexion.* If the bones move away from each other when the muscle contracts, the muscle is called an **extensor**, and the movement is called *extension.*

Most joints in the body have both flexor and extensor muscles, because a contracting muscle can pull a bone in one direction but cannot push it back. Flexor-extensor pairs are called **antagonistic muscle groups** because they exert opposite effects. Figure 12-2 ■ shows a pair of antagonistic muscles in the arm: the *biceps brachii* [*brachion,* arm], which acts as the flexor, and the *triceps brachii,* which acts as the extensor. When the biceps muscle contracts, the hand and forearm move toward the shoulder. When the triceps contracts, the flexed forearm moves away from the shoulder. In each case, when one muscle contracts and shortens, the antagonistic muscle must relax and lengthen.

CONCEPT CHECK

1. Identify as many pairs of antagonistic muscle groups in the body as you can. If you cannot name them, point out the probable location of the flexor and extensor of each group.

Answers: p. 434

Skeletal Muscles Are Composed of Muscle Fibers

Muscles function together as a unit. A skeletal muscle is a collection of muscle cells, or **muscle fibers** (see Anatomy Summary, Fig. 12-3 ■), just as a nerve is a collection of neurons. Each skeletal muscle fiber is a long, cylindrical cell with up to several hundred nuclei on the surface of the fiber. Skeletal muscle fibers are the largest cells in the body, created by the fusion of many individual embryonic muscle cells.

The fibers in a given muscle are arranged with their long axes in parallel (Fig. 12-3a), and each skeletal muscle fiber is sheathed in connective tissue. Groups of adjacent fibers are bundled together into units called **fascicles.** Collagen, elastic fibers, nerves, and blood vessels are found between the fascicles. The entire muscle is enclosed in a connective tissue sheath that is continuous with the connective tissue around the muscle fibers and fascicles and with the tendons holding the muscle to underlying bones.

Muscle Fiber Anatomy Muscle physiologists, like neurobiologists, have adopted a specialized vocabulary (Table 12-1 ■). The cell membrane of a muscle fiber is called the **sarcolemma** [*sarkos,* flesh + *lemma,* shell], and the cytoplasm is called the **sarcoplasm**. The main intracellular structures in striated muscles are **myofibrils** [*myo-,* muscle], highly organized bundles of contractile and elastic proteins that carry out the work of contraction. Skeletal muscles also contain extensive **sarcoplasmic reticulum** (SR), a form of modified endoplasmic reticulum that wraps around each myofibril like a piece of lace (Figs. 12-3b, 12-4 ■). The sarcoplasmic reticulum consists of longitudinal tubules, which release Ca^{2+} ions, and the **terminal cisternae**, which concentrate and sequester Ca^{2+} [*sequestrare,* to put in the hands of a trustee].

A branching network of **transverse tubules**, also known as **t-tubules**, is closely associated with the terminal cisternae. One t-tubule with its two flanking terminal cisternae is known as a *triad* (Fig. 12-4). The membranes of t-tubules are a continuation of the muscle fiber membrane. This makes the lumen of the t-tubules continuous with the extracellular fluid.

TABLE 12-1 Muscle Terminology

GENERAL TERM	MUSCLE EQUIVALENT
Muscle cell	Muscle fiber
Cell membrane	Sarcolemma
Cytoplasm	Sarcoplasm
Modified endoplasmic reticulum	Sarcoplasmic reticulum

To understand how this network of tubules in the heart of the muscle fiber communicates with the outside, take a lump of soft clay and poke your finger into the middle of it. Notice how the outside surface of the clay (analogous to the cell membrane of the muscle fiber) is now continuous with the sides of the hole that you poked in the clay (the membrane of the t-tubule).

T-tubules rapidly move action potentials that originate at the neuromuscular junction on the cell surface into the interior of the fiber. Without t-tubules, the action potential could reach the center of the fiber only by the diffusion of positive charge through the cytosol, a slower process that would delay the response time of the muscle fiber.

The cytosol between the myofibrils contains many glycogen granules and mitochondria. Glycogen, the storage form of glucose found in animals, is a reserve source of energy. Mitochondria provide much of the ATP for muscle contraction through oxidative phosphorylation of glucose and other biomolecules.

Myofibrils Are the Contractile Structures of a Muscle Fiber

One muscle fiber contains a thousand or more myofibrils that occupy most of the intracellular volume, leaving little space for cytosol and organelles (Fig. 12-3b). Each myofibril is composed of several types of proteins: the contractile proteins *myosin* and *actin,* the regulatory proteins *tropomyosin* and *troponin,* and the giant accessory proteins *titin* and *nebulin.*

Myosin [*myo-,* muscle] is the motor protein of the myofibril. Various isoforms of myosin occur in different types of muscle and help determine the muscle's speed of contraction. Each myosin molecule is composed of protein chains that intertwine to form a long tail and a pair of tadpolelike heads (Fig. 12-3e). In skeletal muscle, about 250 myosin molecules join to create a **thick filament**. Each thick filament is arranged so that the myosin heads are clustered at the ends of the filament, and the central region of the filament is a bundle of myosin tails. The rodlike core of the thick filament is stiff, but the protruding myosin heads have an elastic hinge region where the heads join the rods. This hinge region allows the heads to swivel around their point of attachment.

Actin [*actum,* to do] is a protein that makes up the **thin filaments** of the muscle fiber. One actin molecule is a globular protein (*G-actin*), represented in Figure 12-3f by a round ball. Usually, multiple G-actin molecules polymerize to form long chains or filaments, called *F-actin.* In skeletal muscle, two F-actin polymers twist together like a double strand of beads, creating the thin filaments of the myofibril.

Most of the time, the parallel thick and thin filaments of the myofibril are connected by **crossbridges** that span the space between the filaments. These crossbridges form when myosin heads of the thick filaments bind loosely to actin in the thin filaments (Fig. 12-3d). Each G-actin molecule has a single binding site for a myosin head.

Under a light microscope, the arrangement of thick and thin filaments in a myofibril creates a repeating pattern of alternating light and dark bands (Figs. 12-1a, 12-3c). One repeat of the pattern forms a **sarcomere** [*sarkos,* flesh + *-mere,* a unit or segment], which has the following elements (Fig. 12-5 ■):

1. **Z disks**: One sarcomere is composed of two Z disks and the filaments found between them. Z disks are zigzag protein structures that serve as the attachment site for thin filaments. The abbreviation *Z* comes from *zwischen,* the German word for "between."
2. **I band**: These are the lightest color bands of the sarcomere and represent a region occupied only by thin filaments. The abbreviation *I* comes from *isotropic,* a description from early microscopists meaning that this region reflects light uniformly under a polarizing microscope. A Z disk runs through the middle of every I band, so each half of an I band belongs to a different sarcomere.
3. **A band**: This is the darkest of the sarcomere's bands and encompasses the entire length of a thick filament. At the outer edges of the A band, the thick and thin filaments overlap. The center of the A band is occupied by thick filaments only. The abbreviation *A* comes from *anisotropic* [*an-,* not], meaning that the protein fibers in this region scatter light unevenly.
4. **H zone**: This central region of the A band is lighter than the outer edges of the A band because the H zone is occupied by thick filaments only. The *H* comes from *helles,* the German word for "clear."
5. **M line**: This band represents proteins that form the attachment site for thick filaments, equivalent to the Z disk for the thin filaments. Each M line divides an A band in half. *M* is the abbreviation for *mittel,* the German word for "middle."

In three-dimensional array, the actin and myosin molecules form a lattice of parallel, overlapping thin and thick filaments, held in place by their attachments to the Z-disk and M-line proteins, respectively (Fig. 12-5b). When viewed end-on, each thin filament is surrounded by three thick filaments, and six thin filaments encircle each thick filament (Fig. 12-5c, rightmost circle).

The proper alignment of filaments within a sarcomere is ensured by two types of proteins: titin and nebulin (Fig. 12-6 ■). **Titin** is a huge elastic molecule and the largest known protein, composed of more than 25,000 amino acids. A single titin molecule stretches from one Z disk to the neighboring M line. To get an idea of the immense size of titin, imagine that one titin molecule is an 8-foot-long piece of the very thick rope used to tie ships to a wharf. By comparison, a single actin molecule would be about the length and weight of a single eyelash.

Titin has two functions: (1) it stabilizes the position of the contractile filaments and (2) its elasticity returns stretched muscles to their resting length. Titin is helped by **nebulin**, an inelastic

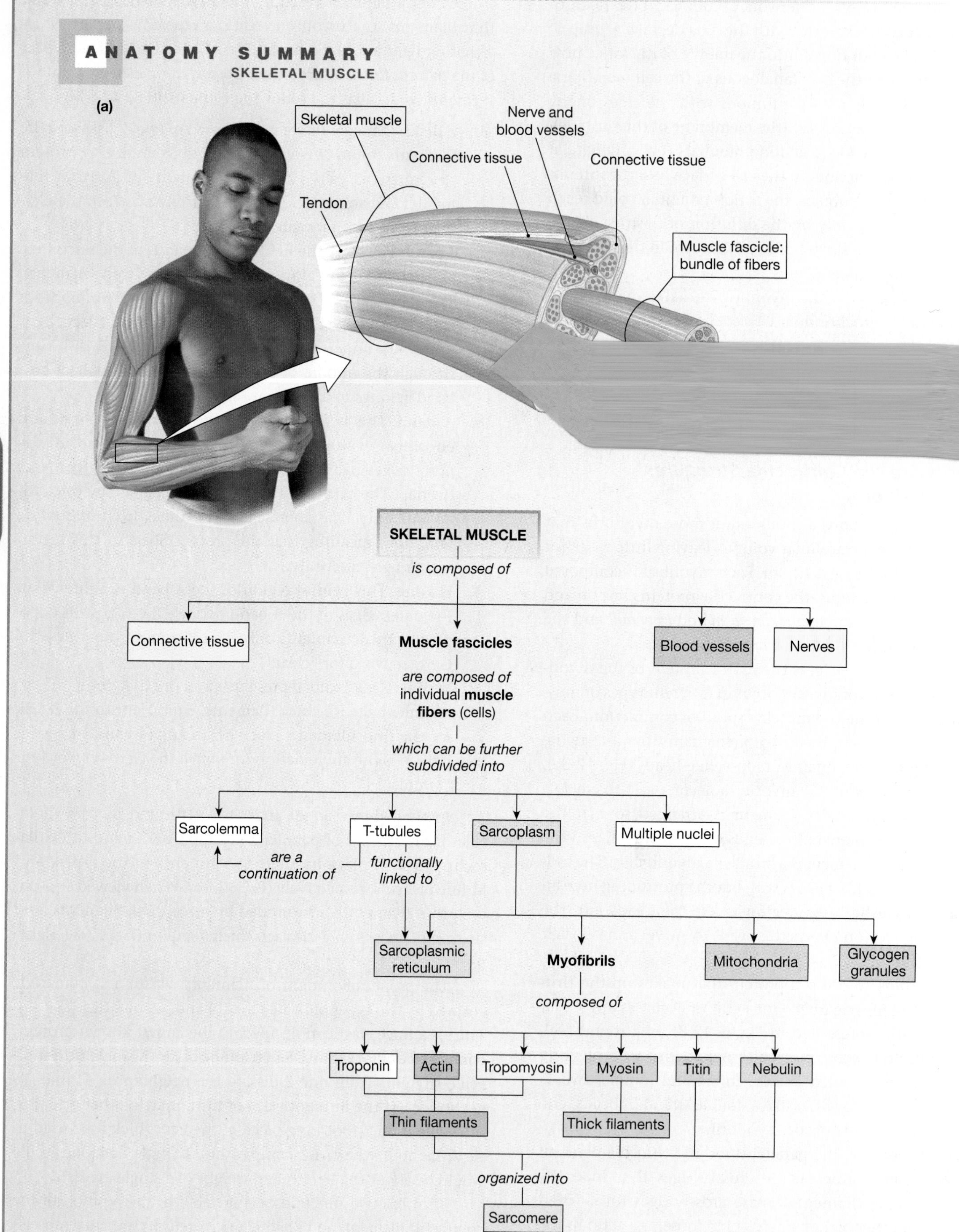
ANATOMY SUMMARY
SKELETAL MUSCLE
(a)
Skeletal muscle
Nerve and blood vessels
Connective tissue
Connective tissue
Tendon
Muscle fascicle: bundle of fibers
SKELETAL MUSCLE
is composed of
Connective tissue
Muscle fascicles
Blood vessels
Nerves
are composed of individual muscle fibers (cells)
which can be further subdivided into
Sarcolemma
T-tubules
Sarcoplasm
Multiple nuclei
are a continuation of
functionally linked to
Sarcoplasmic reticulum
Myofibrils
Mitochondria
Glycogen granules
composed of
Troponin
Actin
Tropomyosin
Myosin
Titin
Nebulin
Thin filaments
Thick filaments
organized into
Sarcomere

■ **FIGURE 12-3**

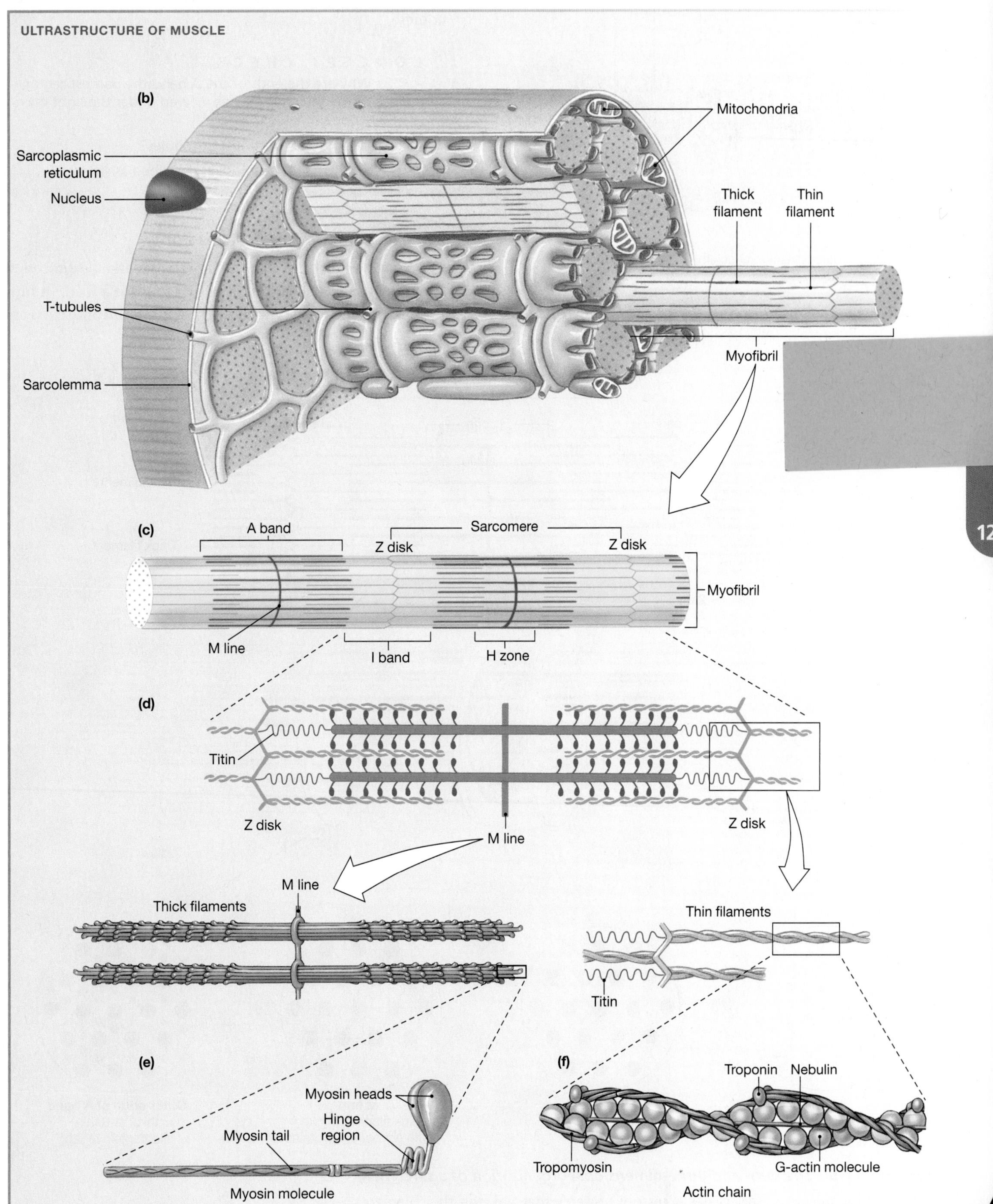

■ **FIGURE 12-3** ***(continued)***

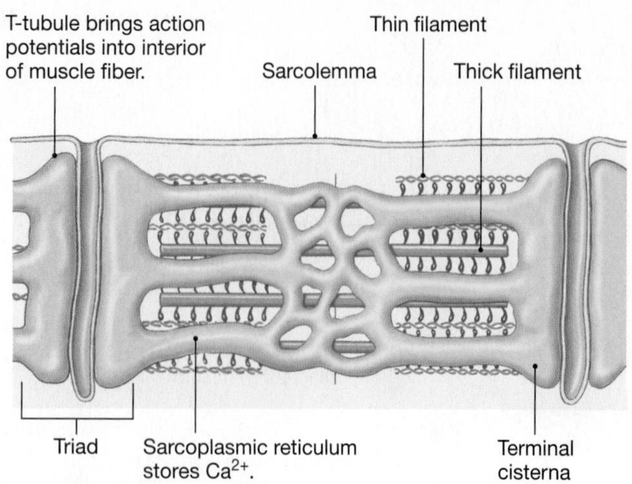

FIGURE 12-4 ***T-tubules and the sarcoplasmic reticulum***

giant protein that lies alongside thin filaments and attaches to the Z disk. Nebulin helps align the actin filaments of the sarcomere.

CONCEPT CHECK

2. Why are the ends of the A band the darkest region of the sarcomere when viewed under the light microscope?
3. What is the function of t-tubules?
4. Why are skeletal muscles described as striated?

Answers: p. 434

Muscle Contraction Creates Force

The contraction of muscle fibers is a remarkable process that enables us to create force to move or to resist a load. In muscle physiology, the force created by the contracting muscle is called

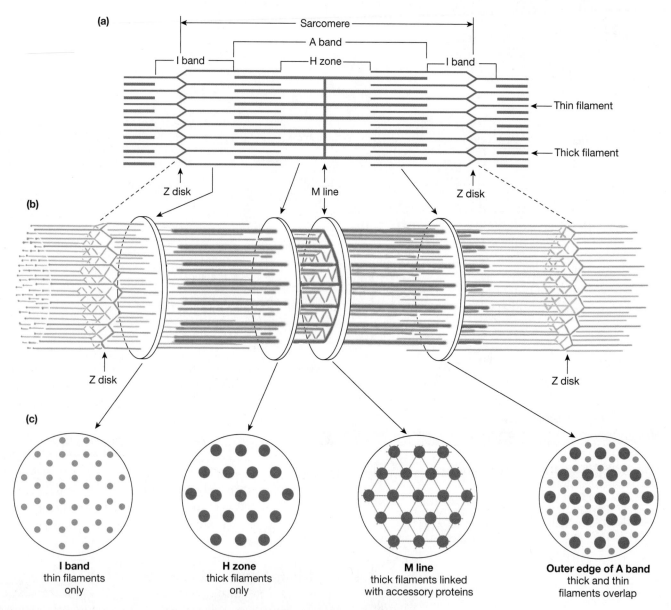

(a) Sarcomere, A band, I band, H zone, I band, Thin filament, Thick filament, Z disk, M line, Z disk

(b) Z disk, Z disk

(c)

I band thin filaments only

H zone thick filaments only

M line thick filaments linked with accessory proteins

Outer edge of A band thick and thin filaments overlap

FIGURE 12-5 ***The two- and three-dimensional organization of a sarcomere***

The Z disk (not shown in part c) has accessory proteins that link the thin filaments together, similar to the accessory proteins shown for the M line.

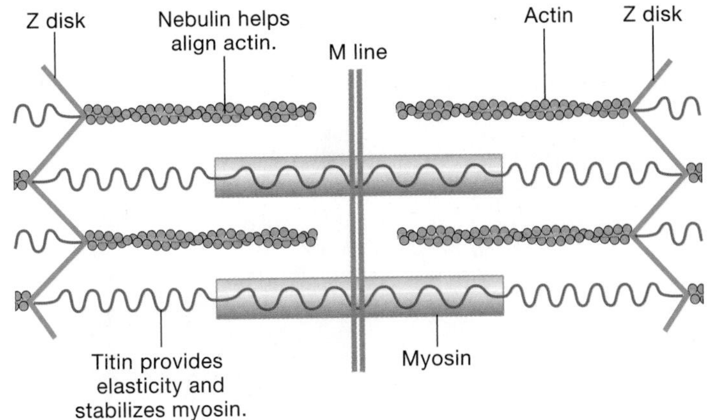

■ **FIGURE 12-6** ***Titin and nebulin***

Titin spans the distance from one Z disk to the neighboring M line. Nebulin, lying along the thin filaments, attaches to a Z disk but does not extend to the M line.

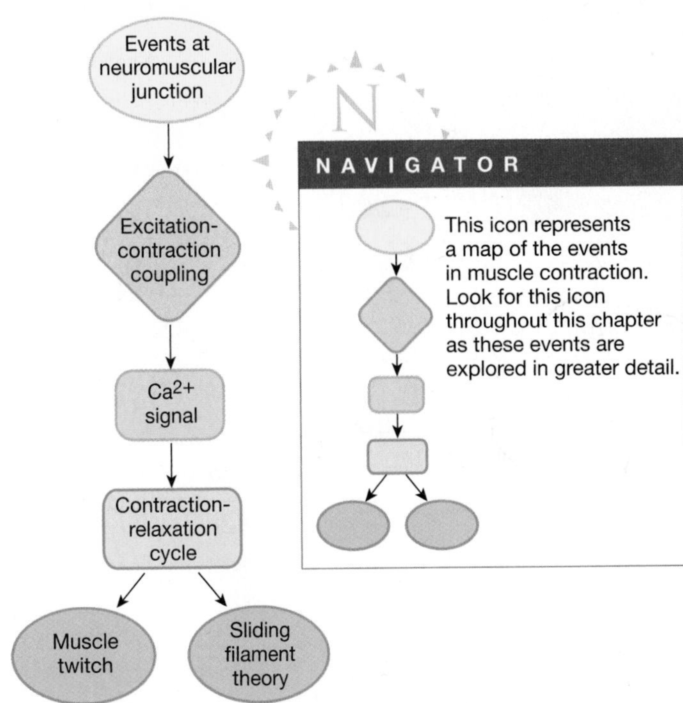

■ **FIGURE 12-7** ***Summary of muscle contraction***

the **muscle tension**. The **load** is a weight or force that opposes contraction of a muscle. **Contraction**, the creation of tension in a muscle, is an active process that requires energy input from ATP. **Relaxation** is the release of tension created by a contraction.

Figure 12-7 ■ summarizes the major steps leading up to skeletal muscle contraction.

1. **Events at the neuromuscular junction** convert a chemical signal from a somatic motor neuron into an electrical signal in the muscle fiber. These events were described in Chapter 11 [p. 391].
2. **Excitation-contraction coupling** is the process in which muscle action potentials initiate calcium signals that in turn activate a contraction-relaxation cycle.
3. At the molecular level, a **contraction-relaxation cycle** can be explained by the *sliding filament theory of contraction*. In intact muscles, one contraction-relaxation cycle is called a muscle *twitch*.

In the sections that follow, we will examine each of these steps. We start with the molecular basis for muscle contraction that is the heart of the process. From there, we go to the integrated function of a muscle fiber as it undergoes excitation-contraction coupling. The skeletal muscle section ends with a discussion of the organization of intact muscles and how they move bones around joints.

CONCEPT CHECK

5. What are the three anatomical elements of a neuromuscular junction?
6. What is the chemical signal at a neuromuscular junction?

Answers: p. 434

Muscles Shorten When They Contract

In previous centuries, scientists observed that when muscles move a load, they shorten. This observation led to early theories of contraction, which proposed that muscles were made of molecules that curled up and shortened when active, then relaxed and stretched at rest, like elastic in reverse. The theory received support when myosin was found to be a helical molecule that shortened upon heating (the reason meat shrinks when you cook it).

In 1954, however, scientists Andrew Huxley and Rolf Niedeigerke discovered that the length of the A band of a myofibril remains constant during contraction. Because the A band represents the myosin filament, Huxley and Niedeigerke realized that shortening of the myosin molecule could not be responsible for contraction. Subsequently, they proposed an alternative model, the **sliding filament theory of contraction**. In this model, overlapping actin and myosin filaments of fixed length slide past one another in an energy-requiring process, resulting in muscle contraction.

The sliding filament theory explains how a muscle can contract and create force without creating movement. For example, if you push on a wall, you are creating tension in many muscles of your body without moving the wall. According to the sliding filament theory, tension generated in a muscle fiber is directly proportional to interaction between the thick and thin filaments.

Sliding Filament Theory of Contraction If you examined a myofibril at its resting length, you would see that within each sarcomere, the ends of the thick and thin filaments overlap slightly. As the muscle contracts, the thick and thin filaments slide past each other, moving the Z disks of the sarcomere closer together. This phenomenon can be seen in light micrographs of

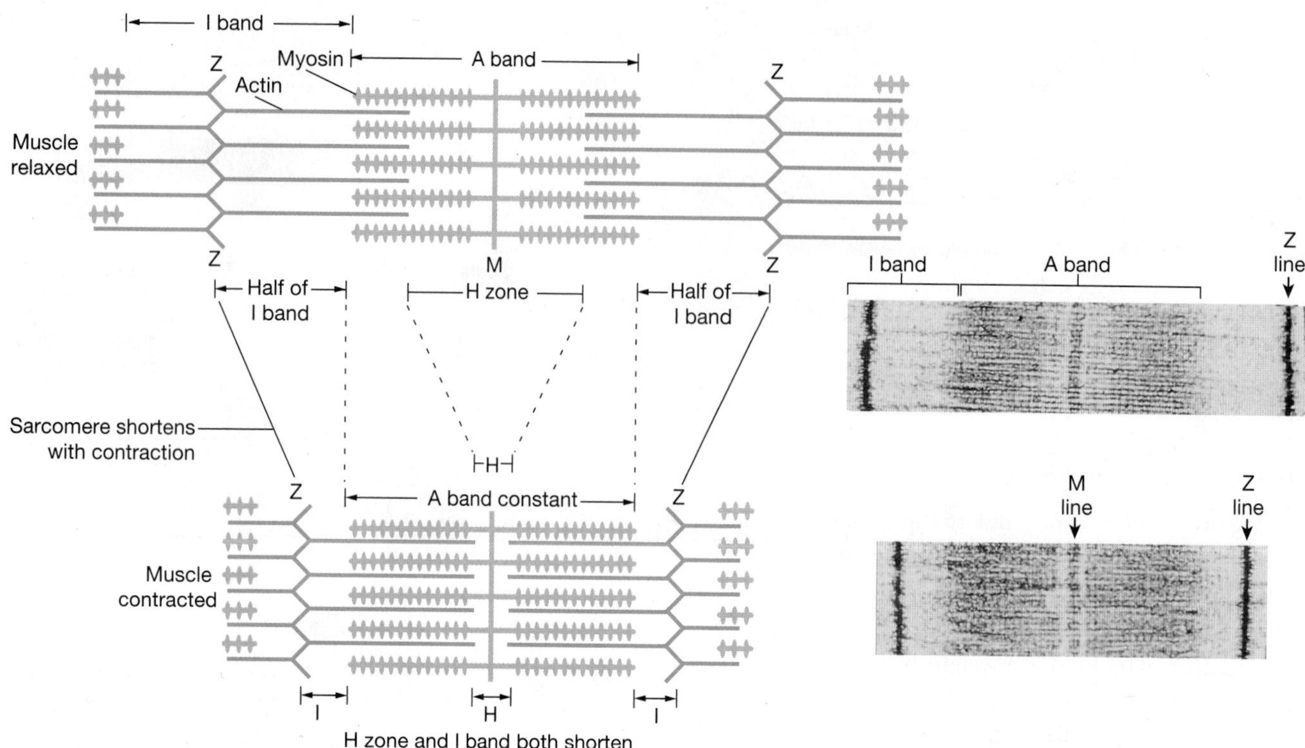

■ **FIGURE 12-8** ***Changes in sarcomere length during contraction***

As contraction takes place, the thick and thin filaments do not change length but instead slide past one another.

relaxed and contracted muscle (Fig. 12-8 ■). In the relaxed state, a sarcomere has a large I band (thin filaments only) and an A band whose length is the length of the thick filament. As contraction occurs, the sarcomere shortens. The two Z disks at each end move closer together while the I band and H zone—regions where actin and myosin do not overlap in resting muscle—almost disappear.

Despite the shortening of the sarcomere, the length of the A band remains constant. These changes are consistent with the sliding of thin actin filaments along the thick myosin filaments as the actin filaments move toward the M line in the center of the sarcomere. It is from this process that the sliding filament theory of contraction derives its name.

The force that pushes the actin filament is the movement of myosin crossbridges that link actin and myosin. Each myosin head has two binding sites on it: one for an ATP molecule and one for actin. The actin molecules serve as the "rope" to which the myosin heads bind.

During the **power stroke** that is the basis for muscle contraction, movement of the flexible myosin crossbridges pushes actin filaments toward the center of the sarcomere. At the end of a power stroke, each myosin head releases its bound actin, then swings back and binds to a new actin molecule, ready to start another cycle. This process repeats many times as a muscle fiber contracts. The myosin heads repeatedly bind and release actin molecules as myosin pushes the thin filaments toward the center of the sarcomere. An analogy that may help you visualize this is to think of a tug-of-war team holding onto one end of a long rope. When the order comes, each person begins pulling on the rope, hand over hand, grabbing, pulling, and releasing as the rope moves past.

In a muscle fiber, what causes movement of the myosin molecules? The answer is energy from ATP. Myosin is a motor protein with the ability to create movement [p. 63]. It accomplishes this task by converting the chemical bond energy of ATP into the mechanical energy of motion. Each myosin molecule is an ATPase (*myosin ATPase*) that binds ATP and hydrolyzes it to ADP and inorganic phosphate (P_i), releasing energy. The released energy is trapped and stored as potential energy in the angle between the myosin head and the long axis of the myosin filament. This potential energy then fuels the power stroke that moves actin.

Figure 12-9 ■ shows the molecular events of a contractile cycle.

1. **The rigor state.** Myosin heads create crossbridges by tightly binding to G-actin molecules. In this state, no nucleotide (ATP or ADP) occupies the second binding site on the myosin head. In living muscle, the rigor state [*rigere,* to be stiff] occurs for only a very brief period.
2. **ATP binds and myosin detaches.** An ATP molecule binds to the myosin head. This changes the actin-binding affinity of myosin, and the head releases from the G-actin molecule.

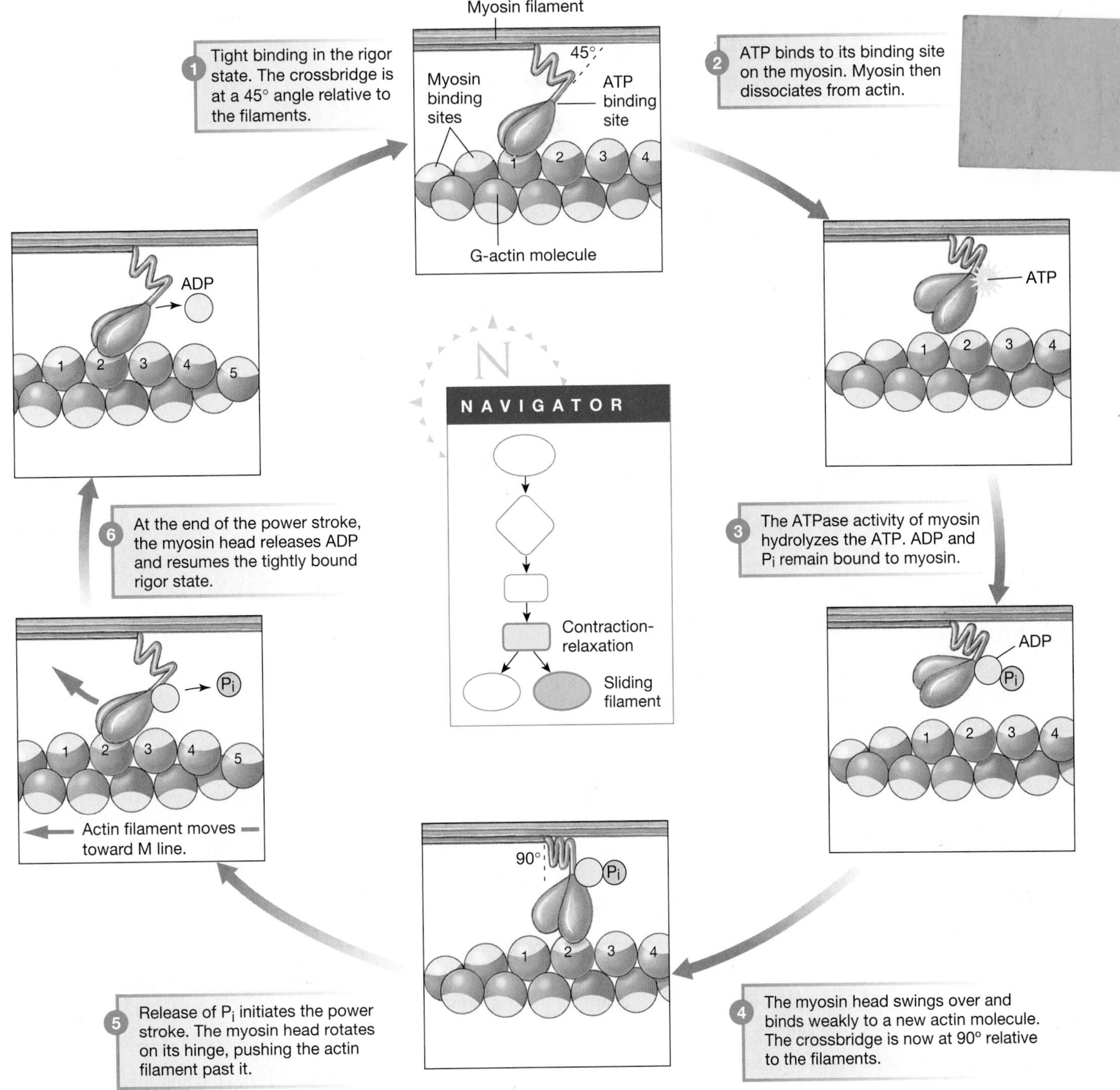

Myosin filament
1 Tight binding in the rigor state. The crossbridge is at a 45° angle relative to the filaments.
45°
Myosin binding sites
ATP binding site
G-actin molecule
2 ATP binds to its binding site on the myosin. Myosin then dissociates from actin.
ATP
3 The ATPase activity of myosin hydrolyzes the ATP. ADP and Pi remain bound to myosin.
ADP
Pi
90°
4 The myosin head swings over and binds weakly to a new actin molecule. The crossbridge is now at 90° relative to the filaments.
5 Release of Pi initiates the power stroke. The myosin head rotates on its hinge, pushing the actin filament past it.
Actin filament moves toward M line.
6 At the end of the power stroke, the myosin head releases ADP and resumes the tightly bound rigor state.
NAVIGATOR
Contraction-relaxation
Sliding filament

■ **FIGURE 12-9** ***The molecular basis of contraction***

To review actin and myosin structure, see Figure 12-3(d–f).

3. **ATP hydrolysis.** The ATP-binding site on the myosin head closes around ATP and hydrolyzes it to ADP and inorganic phosphate (P_i). Both products remain bound to the head.
4. **Myosin reattaches: weak binding.** The energy released from ATP causes the myosin head to swing and bind weakly to a new G-actin molecule, one or two positions away from the G-actin to which it was previously bound. At this point, the myosin has potential energy, like a stretched spring, and is ready to execute the power stroke that will move the actin filament past it. ADP and P_i are still bound to myosin.
5. **P_i release and the power stroke.** The power stroke begins when inorganic phosphate is released from its myosin binding site. As the myosin head swings toward the M line, it pushes the attached actin filament in the same direction. The power stroke is also called *crossbridge tilting* because the myosin head and hinge region tilt from a 90° angle relative to the thick and thin filaments to a 45° angle.
6. **Release of ADP.** In the last step of the contractile cycle, myosin releases ADP, the second product of ATP hydrolysis.

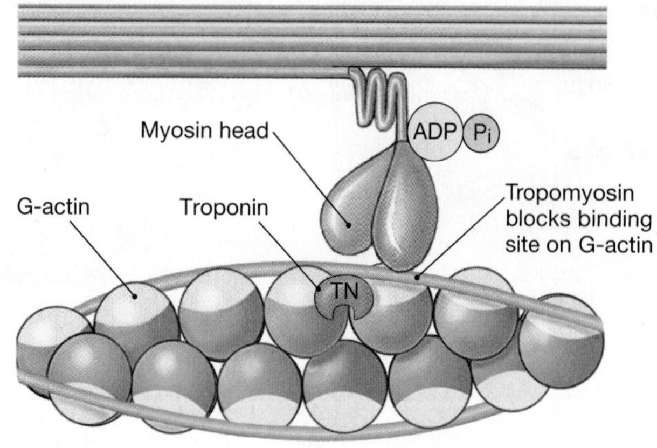

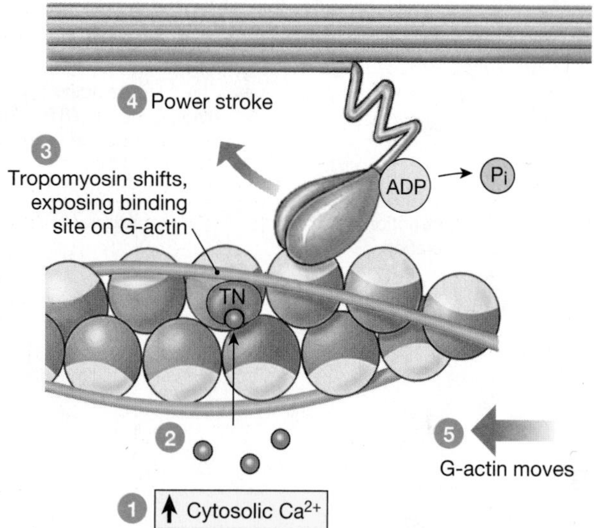

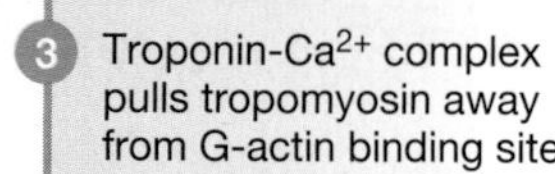

3 Troponin-Ca^{2+} complex pulls tropomyosin away from G-actin binding site.

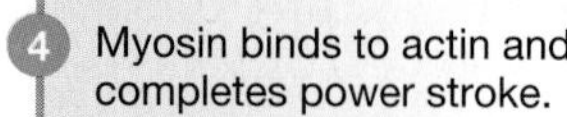

4 Myosin binds to actin and completes power stroke.
5 Actin filament moves.

FIGURE 12-10 ***Regulatory role of tropomyosin and troponin***

At this point, the myosin head is again tightly bound to actin in the rigor state. The cycle is ready to begin again when a new ATP binds to myosin.

Although the contractile cycle began with the rigor state in which no ATP or ADP was bound to myosin, relaxed muscle fibers remain mostly in step 4. The rigor state in living muscle is normally brief because the muscle fiber has a sufficient supply of ATP that binds to myosin when ADP is released in step 6.

After death, however, when metabolism stops and ATP supplies are exhausted, muscles are unable to bind more ATP, so they remain in the tightly bound state described in step 1. In the condition known as *rigor mortis,* the muscles "freeze" owing to immovable crossbridges. The tight binding of actin and myosin persists for a day or so after death, until enzymes within the decaying fiber begin to break down the muscle proteins.

Actin-myosin binding and crossbridge tilting explain how actin filaments slide past myosin filaments during contraction. But what regulates this process? If ATP is always available in the living muscle fiber, what keeps the filaments from continuously interacting? The answer lies with the two regulatory proteins tropomyosin and troponin.

CONCEPT CHECK

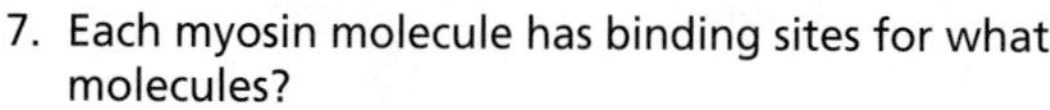

7. Each myosin molecule has binding sites for what molecules?
8. What is the difference between F-actin and G-actin?

Answers: p. 434

Contraction Is Regulated by Troponin and Tropomyosin

In skeletal muscle, the thin actin filaments of the myofibril are associated with two regulatory proteins that prevent myosin heads from completing their power stroke, much as the safety latch on a gun keeps the cocked trigger from being pulled. **Tropomyosin** [*tropos,* to turn] is an elongated protein polymer that wraps around the actin filament and partially blocks the myosin-binding sites (Fig. 12-10a ■). **Troponin** (TN) is a calcium-binding protein that controls the position of tropomyosin.

When tropomyosin is in its blocking (or "off") position, weak actin-myosin binding can take place, but myosin is blocked from completing its power stroke. For contraction to occur, tropomyosin must be shifted to an "on" position that uncovers the remainder of the binding site. This allows the power stroke to take place.

The off-and-on positioning of tropomyosin is regulated by troponin, a complex of three proteins associated with tropomyosin. As contraction begins in response to a calcium signal (① in Fig. 12-10b), one protein of the complex—**troponin C**—binds reversibly to Ca^{2+} (②). Calcium binding pulls tropomyosin toward the groove of the actin filament and unblocks the myosin-binding sites (③). This "on" position enables the myosin heads to carry out their power strokes and move the actin filament (④ and ⑤). Contractile cycles repeat as long as the binding sites are uncovered.

For relaxation to occur, Ca^{2+} concentrations in the cytosol must decrease so that Ca^{2+} unbinds from troponin. Without Ca^{2+}, the troponin-tropomyosin complex returns to its "off" position, covering most of the myosin-binding site. During the portion of the relaxation phase when actin and myosin are not bound to each other, the filaments of the sarcomere slide back to their original positions with the aid of titin and elastic connective tissues within the muscle.

Although the preceding discussion sounds as if we know everything there is to know about the molecular basis of muscle contraction, in reality this is simply our current model. The process is more complex than presented here, and it now appears that myosin influences Ca^{2+}-troponin binding, depending on whether the myosin is bound to actin in a strong (rigor) state, bound to actin in a weak state, or not bound at all. The details of this influence are still being worked out.

Studying contraction and the movement of molecules in a myofibril has proved very difficult. Many research techniques rely on crystallized molecules, electron microscopy, and other tools that cannot be used with living tissues. Often we can see the thick and thin filaments only at the beginning and end of contraction. Progress is being made, however, and perhaps in the next decade you will see a "movie" of muscle contraction, constructed from photographs of sliding filaments.

CONCEPT CHECK

9. Name an elastic fiber in the sarcomere that aids relaxation.
10. In the sliding filament theory of contraction, what prevents the filaments from sliding back to their original position each time a myosin head releases to bind to the next actin binding site? (*Hint:* what would happen if all crossbridges released simultaneously?)

Answers: p. 434

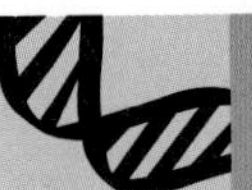

BIOTECHNOLOGY

THE *IN VITRO* MOTILITY ASSAY

One big step forward in understanding the power stroke of myosin was the development of the *in vitro* motility assay in the 1980s. In this assay, isolated myosin molecules are randomly bonded to a specially coated glass coverslip. A fluorescently labeled actin molecule is placed on top of the myosin molecules. With ATP as a source of energy, the myosin heads bind to the actin and move it across the coverslip, marked by a fluorescent trail as it goes. In even more ingenious experiments, developed in 1995, a single myosin molecule is bound to a tiny bead that elevates it above the surface of the cover slip. An actin molecule is placed on top of the myosin molecule, like the balancing pole of a tightrope walker. As the myosin "motor" moves the actin molecule, lasers measure the nanometer movements and piconewton forces created with each cycle of the myosin head. Because of this technique, researchers can now measure the mechanical work being done by a single myosin molecule!

Acetylcholine Initiates Excitation-Contraction Coupling

Now that you have been introduced to the molecular basis of muscle contraction, we will start at the neuromuscular junction and follow the contraction process as it begins at that point. It can be broken down into the following basic steps:

1. Acetylcholine (ACh) is released from the somatic motor neuron.
2. ACh initiates an action potential in the muscle fiber.
3. The muscle action potential triggers calcium release from the sarcoplasmic reticulum.
4. Calcium combines with troponin and initiates contraction.

As you learned earlier in the chapter, this combination of electrical and mechanical events in a muscle fiber is called excitation-contraction coupling. Now let's look at the process in detail.

Acetylcholine released into the synapse at a neuromuscular junction binds to ACh receptor-channels on the motor end plate of the muscle fiber (Fig. 12-11 ■) [p. 390]. When these channels open, they allow both Na^+ and K^+ to cross the membrane. However, Na^+ influx exceeds K^+ efflux because the electrochemical driving force is greater for Na^+ [p. 135]. The addition of net positive charge to the muscle fiber depolarizes the membrane, creating an **end-plate potential (EPP)**. Normally, end-plate potentials always reach threshold and initiate a muscle action potential.

The action potential is conducted across the surface of the muscle fiber and into the t-tubules by the opening of voltage-gated

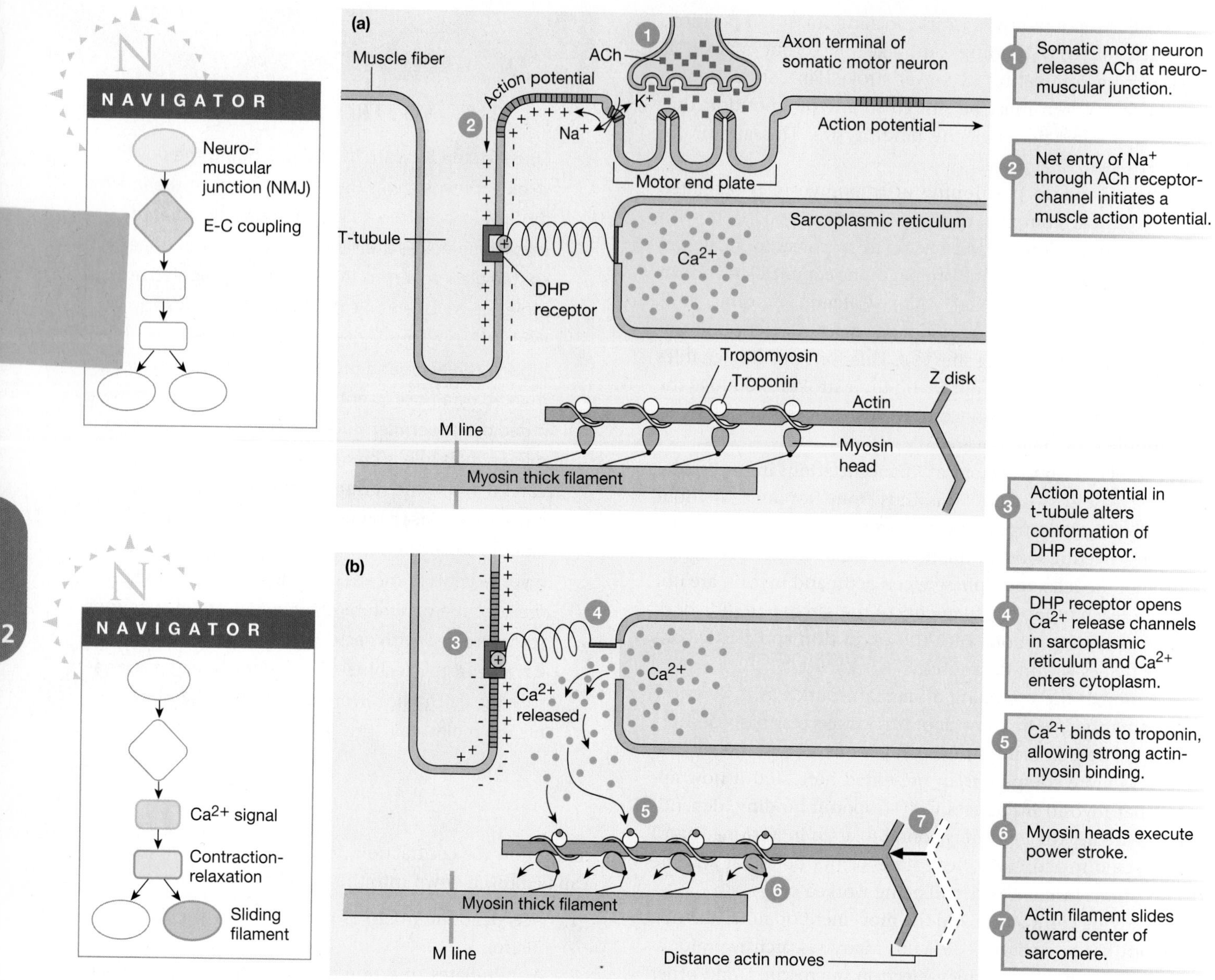

FIGURE 12-11 ***Excitation-contraction coupling***

Na^+ channels. The process is similar to the conduction of action potentials in axons, although action potentials in skeletal muscle are conducted more slowly than action potentials in neurons [p. 257].

The action potential that moves across the membrane and down the t-tubules causes Ca^{2+} release from the sarcoplasmic reticulum (Fig. 12-11b). The t-tubule membrane contains voltage-sensing receptors (**dihydropyridine**, or **DHP**, receptors) that are mechanically linked to **Ca^{2+} release channels** in the adjacent sarcoplasmic reticulum. (These channels are also called **ryanodine receptors**, or **RyR**). When a wave of depolarization reaches a DHP receptor, its conformation changes, opening Ca^{2+} release channels in the sarcoplasmic reticulum. Stored Ca^{2+} then moves down its electrochemical gradient into the cytosol, where it initiates contraction as depicted in Figure 12-10b.

Free cytosolic Ca^{2+} levels in a resting muscle are normally quite low, but after an action potential, they increase about 100-fold. When cytosolic Ca^{2+} levels are high, Ca^{2+} binds to troponin, tropomyosin moves to the "on" position, and contraction occurs.

Relaxation occurs when the sarcoplasmic reticulum pumps Ca^{2+} back into its lumen using **Ca^{2+}-ATPase** [p. 142]. As the free cytosolic Ca^{2+} concentration decreases, Ca^{2+} releases from troponin, tropomyosin slides back to block the myosin-binding site, and the fiber relaxes.

The discovery that Ca^{2+}, not the action potential, is the signal for contraction was the first piece of evidence suggesting that calcium acts as a messenger inside cells. For years it was thought that calcium signals occurred only in muscles, but we now know that calcium is an almost universal second messenger [p. 186].

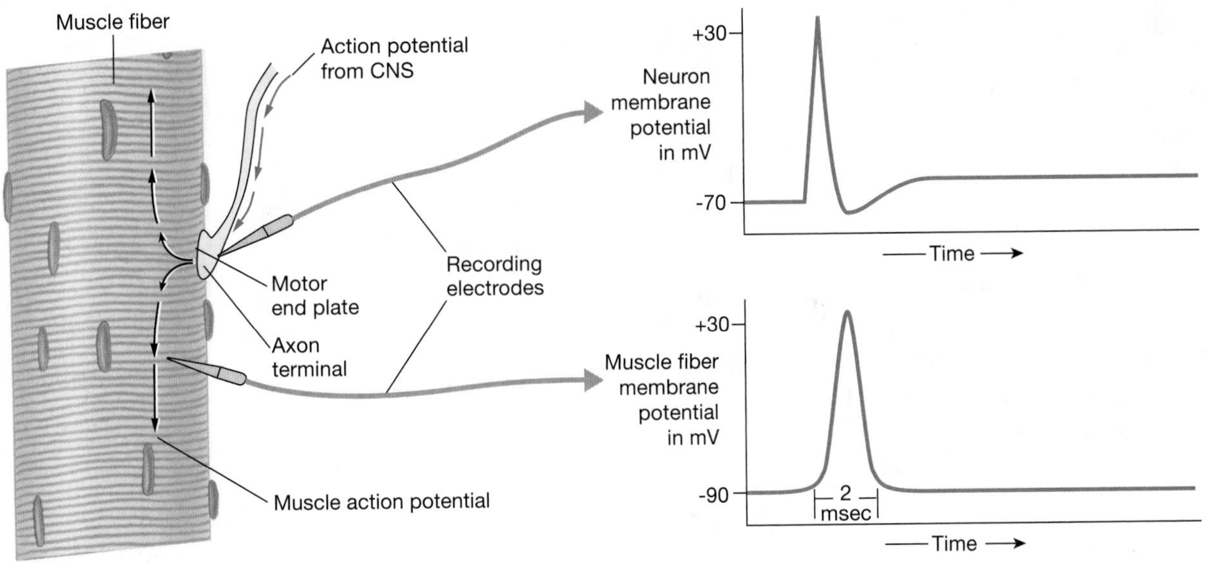

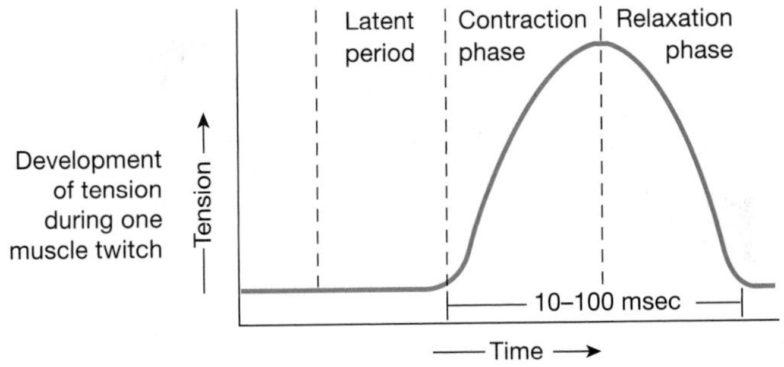

Muscle fiber
Action potential from CNS
Neuron membrane potential in mV
+30
-70
Time →
Motor end plate
Recording electrodes
Axon terminal
Muscle fiber membrane potential in mV
+30
-90
2 msec
Time →
Muscle action potential
Latent period
Contraction phase
Relaxation phase
Development of tension during one muscle twitch
Tension →
10–100 msec
Time →

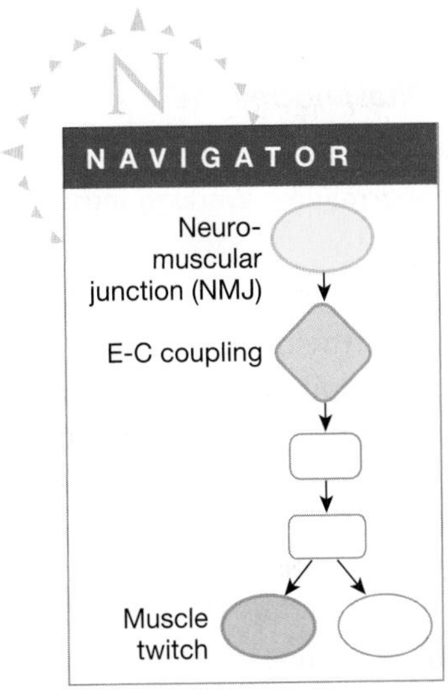

NAVIGATOR
Neuro-muscular junction (NMJ)
E-C coupling
Muscle twitch

FIGURE QUESTIONS

- Compare the resting membrane potential of the motor neuron and the muscle fiber.
- Movement of what ion(s) in what direction(s) creates the muscle action potential?

FIGURE 12-12 ***Electrical and mechanical events in muscle contraction***

Action potentials in the axon terminal (top graph) and in the muscle fiber (middle graph) are followed by a muscle twitch (bottom graph).

Figure 12-12 ■ shows the timing of electrical and mechanical events during excitation-contraction coupling. The somatic motor neuron action potential is followed by the skeletal muscle action potential, which in turn is followed by contraction. A single contraction-relaxation cycle in a skeletal muscle fiber is known as a **twitch**. Notice that there is a short delay—the **latent period**—between the muscle action potential and the beginning of muscle tension development. This delay represents the time required for excitation-contraction coupling to take place.

Once contraction begins, muscle tension increases steadily to a maximum value as crossbridge interaction increases. Tension then decreases in the relaxation phase of the twitch. During relaxation, elastic elements of the muscle return the sarcomeres to their resting length.

A single action potential in a muscle fiber evokes a single twitch (Fig. 12-12, bottom graph). However, muscle twitches vary from fiber to fiber in the speed with which they develop tension (the rising slope of the twitch curve), the maximum tension they achieve (the height of the twitch curve), and the duration of the twitch (the width of the twitch curve). We will discuss factors that affect these parameters in upcoming sections. First we will discuss how muscles produce ATP to provide energy for contraction and relaxation.

CONCEPT CHECK

11. Which part of contraction requires ATP? Does relaxation require ATP?
12. What events are taking place during the latent period before contraction begins? Answers: p. 434

RUNNING PROBLEM

Paul had experienced mild attacks of muscle weakness in his legs before, usually in the morning. Twice the weakness had come on after exposure to cold. Each attack had disappeared within minutes, and Paul seemed to suffer no lasting effects. On the advice of Paul's family doctor, Mrs. Leong took her son to see a specialist in muscle disorders, who diagnosed a condition called periodic paralysis. This condition is caused by a genetic defect in the double-gated Na^+ channels in the membranes of skeletal muscle fibers. Under certain conditions, the defective Na^+ channels fail to inactivate after they open and continuously admit Na^+ into the interior of the muscle cells.

Question 1:

What effect does the continuous influx of Na^+ have on the membrane potential of Paul's muscle fibers?

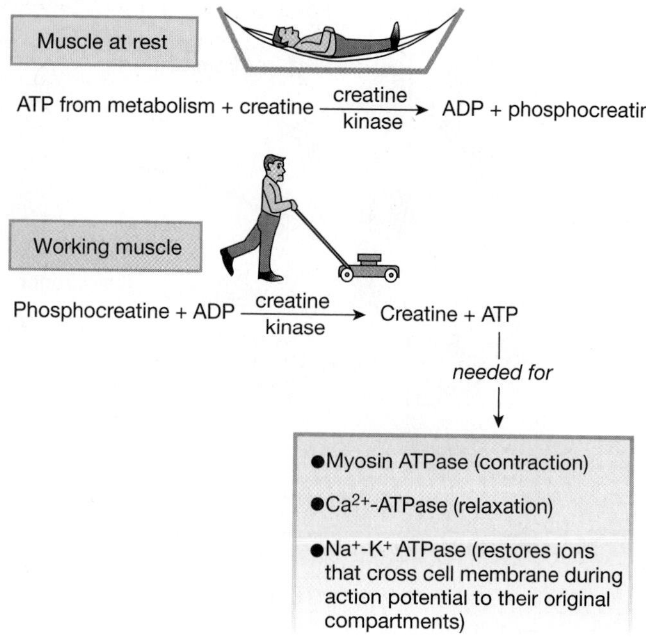

■ **FIGURE 12-13** ***Phosphocreatine***

Resting muscle stores energy from ATP in the high-energy phosphate bonds of phosphocreatine. Working muscle then uses that stored energy.

Skeletal Muscle Contraction Requires a Steady Supply of ATP

The muscle fiber's use of ATP is a key feature of muscle physiology. Muscles require energy constantly: during contraction for crossbridge movement and release, during relaxation to pump Ca^{2+} back into the sarcoplasmic reticulum, and after excitation-contraction coupling to restore Na^+ and K^+ to the extracellular and intracellular compartments, respectively. Where do muscles get the ATP they need for this work?

The amount of ATP in a muscle fiber at any one time is sufficient for only about eight twitches. As a backup energy source, muscles contain **phosphocreatine**, a molecule whose high-energy phosphate bonds are created from creatine and ATP when muscles are at rest (Fig. 12-13 ■). When muscles become active, such as during exercise, the high-energy phosphate group of phosphocreatine is transferred to ADP, creating more ATP to power the muscles.

The enzyme responsible for transferring the phosphate group from phosphocreatine to ADP is **creatine kinase** (CK), also known as *creatine phosphokinase* (CPK). Muscle cells contain large amounts of this enzyme. Consequently, elevated blood levels of creatine kinase usually indicate damage to skeletal or cardiac muscle. Because the two muscle types contain different isozymes [p. 96], clinicians can distinguish cardiac tissue damage during a heart attack from skeletal muscle damage.

Because energy stored in high-energy phosphate bonds is very limited, muscle fibers must use metabolism to transfer energy from the chemical bonds of nutrients to ATP. Carbohydrates, particularly glucose, are the most rapid and efficient source of energy for ATP production. Glucose is metabolized through glycolysis to pyruvate [p. 104]. In the presence of adequate oxygen, pyruvate goes into the citric acid cycle, producing about 30 ATP for each molecule of glucose.

When oxygen concentrations are too low to maintain aerobic metabolism, the muscle fiber shifts to *anaerobic glycolysis*. In this pathway, glucose is metabolized to lactic acid with a yield of only 2 ATP per glucose. Anaerobic metabolism of glucose is a quicker source of ATP but produces many fewer ATP per glucose. When muscle energy demands outpace the amount of ATP that can be produced through anaerobic metabolism of glucose, muscles can function for only a short time without fatiguing.

Muscle fibers also obtain energy from fatty acids, although this process always requires oxygen [p. 111]. During rest and light exercise, skeletal muscles burn fatty acids along with glucose, one reason that modest exercise programs of brisk walking are an effective way to reduce body fat. However, *beta-oxidation*—the process by which fatty acids are converted to acetyl CoA—is a slow process and cannot produce ATP rapidly enough to meet the energy needs of muscle fibers during heavy exercise. Under these conditions, muscle fibers rely more on glucose.

Proteins normally are not a source of energy for muscle contraction. Most amino acids found in muscle fibers are used to synthesize proteins rather than to produce ATP.

Do muscles ever run out of ATP? You might think so if you have ever exercised to the point of fatigue, the point at which you feel that you cannot continue or your limbs refuse to obey commands from your brain. Most studies show, however, that even intense exercise uses only 30% of the ATP in a muscle fiber. The condition we call fatigue must come from other changes in the exercising muscle.

CONCEPT CHECK

13. According to the convention for naming enzymes, what does the name *creatine kinase* tell you about this enzyme's function? [*Hint:* p. 99]
14. The reactions in Figure 12-13 show that creatine kinase catalyzes the creatine-phosphocreatine reaction in both directions. What then determines the direction that the reaction goes at any given moment? [*Hint:* p. 39] Answers: p. 434

Muscle Fatigue Has Multiple Causes

The physiological term **fatigue** describes a condition in which a muscle is no longer able to generate or sustain the expected power output. Fatigue is highly variable. It is influenced by the intensity and duration of the contractile activity, by whether the muscle fiber is using aerobic or anaerobic metabolism, by the composition of the muscle, and by the fitness level of the individual.

Multiple factors have been proposed as playing a role in fatigue (Fig. 12-14 ■). They can be classified into **central fatigue** mechanisms, which arise in the central nervous system, and **peripheral fatigue** mechanisms, which arise anywhere between the neuromuscular junction and the contractile elements of the muscle. Most experimental evidence suggests that muscle fatigue arises from excitation-contraction failure in the muscle fiber rather than from failure of control neurons or neuromuscular transmission.

Central fatigue includes subjective feelings of tiredness and a desire to cease activity. Several studies have shown that this psychological fatigue precedes physiological fatigue in the muscles and therefore may be a protective mechanism. Low pH from acid production during ATP hydrolysis is often mentioned as a possible cause of fatigue, and some evidence suggests that acidosis may influence the sensation of fatigue perceived by the brain. However, homeostatic mechanisms for pH balance maintain blood pH at normal levels until exertion is nearly maximal, so pH as a factor in central fatigue probably applies only in cases of maximal exertion.

Neural causes of fatigue could arise either from communication failure at the neuromuscular junction or from failure of the CNS command neurons. For example, if ACh is not synthesized in the axon terminal fast enough to keep up with neuron firing rate, neurotransmitter release at the synapse will decrease. Consequently, the muscle end-plate potential may fail to reach the threshold value needed to trigger a muscle fiber action potential, resulting in contraction failure. This type of fatigue is associated with some neuromuscular diseases, but it is probably not a factor in normal exercise.

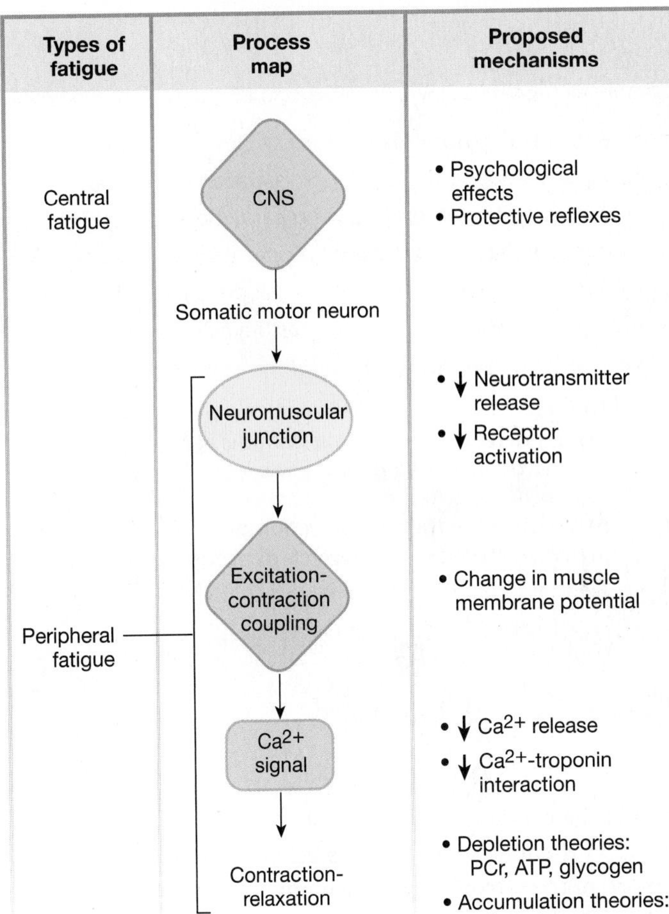

■ **FIGURE 12-14** ***Locations and possible causes of muscle fatigue***

There appears to be no single cause for muscle fatigue during exercise, and the study of this phenomenon is quite complex. Fatigue within the muscle fiber can occur in any of several sites. In extended submaximal exertion, fatigue is associated with the depletion of muscle glycogen stores. Because most studies show that lack of ATP is not a limiting factor, glycogen depletion may be affecting some other aspect of contraction, such as the release of Ca^{2+} from the sarcoplasmic reticulum.

The cause of fatigue in short-duration maximal exertion seems to be different. It apparently results from increased levels of inorganic phosphate (P_i) produced when ATP and phosphocreatine are used for energy in the muscle fiber. Elevated inorganic phosphate levels may slow P_i release from myosin and thereby alter the power stroke (Fig. 12-9, ⑤). Another theory suggests that elevated phosphate levels decrease Ca^{2+} release because the phosphate combines with Ca^{2+} to become calcium phosphate. Some investigators feel that phosphate alters the dynamics of Ca^{2+} release from the sarcoplasmic reticulum.

Potassium is another factor implicated in fatigue. During maximal exercise, K^+ leaves the muscle fiber with each action potential, and as a result K^+ concentrations rise in the extracellular

RUNNING PROBLEM

Two forms of periodic paralysis exist. One form, called *hypokalemic periodic paralysis,* is characterized by decreased blood levels of K^+ during paralytic episodes. The other form, *hyperkalemic periodic paralysis,* is characterized by either normal or increased blood levels of K^+ during episodes. Results of a blood test revealed that Paul has the hyperkalemic form.

Question 2:

In people with hyperkalemic periodic paralysis, attacks tend to occur after a period of exercise (that is, after a period of repeated muscle contractions). What ion is responsible for the repolarization phase of the muscle action potential, and in which direction does this ion move across the muscle fiber membrane?

fluid of the t-tubules. The shift in K^+ alters the membrane potential of the muscle fiber and is believed to decrease Ca^{2+} release from the sarcoplasmic reticulum.

CONCEPT CHECK

15. If K^+ concentration increases in the extracellular fluid surrounding a cell but does not change significantly in the cell's cytoplasm, the cell membrane will ________ (*depolarize/hyperpolarize*) and become ________ (*more/less*) negative.

Answers: p. 434

Skeletal Muscle Fibers Are Classified by Contraction Speed and Resistance to Fatigue

Skeletal muscle fibers can be classified on the basis of their speed of contraction and their resistance to fatigue with repeated stimulation. The groups include slow-twitch fibers (also called ST or type I), fast-twitch oxidative-glycolytic fibers (FOG or type IIA), and fast-twitch glycolytic fibers (FG or type IIB).

Fast-twitch muscle fibers (type II) develop tension two to three times faster than **slow-twitch fibers** (type I). The speed with which a muscle fiber contracts is determined by the isoform of myosin ATPase present in the fiber's thick filaments. Fast-twitch fibers split ATP more rapidly and can therefore complete multiple contractile cycles more rapidly than slow-twitch fibers. This speed translates into faster tension development in the fast-twitch fibers.

The duration of contraction also varies according to fiber type. Twitch duration is determined largely by how fast the sarcoplasmic reticulum removes Ca^{2+} from the cytosol. As cytosolic Ca^{2+} concentrations fall, Ca^{2+} unbinds from troponin, allowing tropomyosin to move into position to partially block the myosin-binding sites. With the power stroke inhibited in this way, the muscle fiber relaxes.

Fast-twitch fibers pump Ca^{2+} into their sarcoplasmic reticulum more rapidly than slow-twitch fibers do, so fast-twitch fibers have quicker twitches. The twitches in fast-twitch fibers last only about 7.5 msec, making these muscles useful for fine, quick movements, such as playing the piano. Contractions in slow-twitch muscle fibers may last more than 10 times as long. Fast-twitch fibers are used occasionally, but slow-twitch fibers are used almost constantly for maintaining posture, standing, or walking.

The second major difference between muscle fiber types is their ability to resist fatigue. Glycolytic fibers (fast-twitch type IIB) rely primarily on anaerobic glycolysis to produce ATP. However, the accumulation of H^+ from ATP hydrolysis contributes to acidosis, a condition implicated in the development of fatigue, as noted previously. As a result, glycolytic fibers fatigue more easily than do oxidative fibers, which do not depend on anaerobic metabolism. Oxidative fibers rely primarily on oxidative phosphorylation [p. 108] for production of ATP—hence their descriptive name. These fibers, which include slow-twitch fibers and fast-twitch oxidative-glycolytic fibers, have more mitochondria (the site of enzymes for the citric acid cycle and oxidative phosphorylation) than glycolytic fibers. They also have more blood vessels in their connective tissue to bring oxygen to the cells (Fig. 12-15 ■).

The efficiency with which muscle fibers obtain oxygen is a factor in their preferred method of glucose metabolism. Oxygen in the blood must diffuse into the interior of muscle fibers in order to reach the mitochondria. This process is facilitated by the presence of **myoglobin**, a red oxygen-binding pigment with a high affinity for oxygen. This affinity allows myoglobin to act as a transfer molecule, bringing oxygen more rapidly to the interior of the fibers. Because oxidative fibers contain more myoglobin, oxygen diffusion is faster than in glycolytic fibers. Oxidative fibers are described as *red muscle* because large amounts of myoglobin give them their characteristic color.

In addition to myoglobin, oxidative fibers have smaller diameters, so the distance through which oxygen must diffuse before reaching the mitochondria is shorter. Because oxidative fibers have more myoglobin and more capillaries to bring blood to the cells and are smaller in diameter, they maintain a better supply of oxygen and are able to use oxidative phosphorylation for ATP production.

Glycolytic fibers, in contrast, are described as *white muscle* because of their lower myoglobin content. These muscle fibers are also larger in diameter than slow-twitch fibers. The combination of larger size, less myoglobin, and fewer blood vessels means that glycolytic fibers are more likely to run out of oxygen after repeated contractions. Glycolytic fibers therefore rely primarily on anaerobic glycolysis for ATP synthesis and fatigue most rapidly.

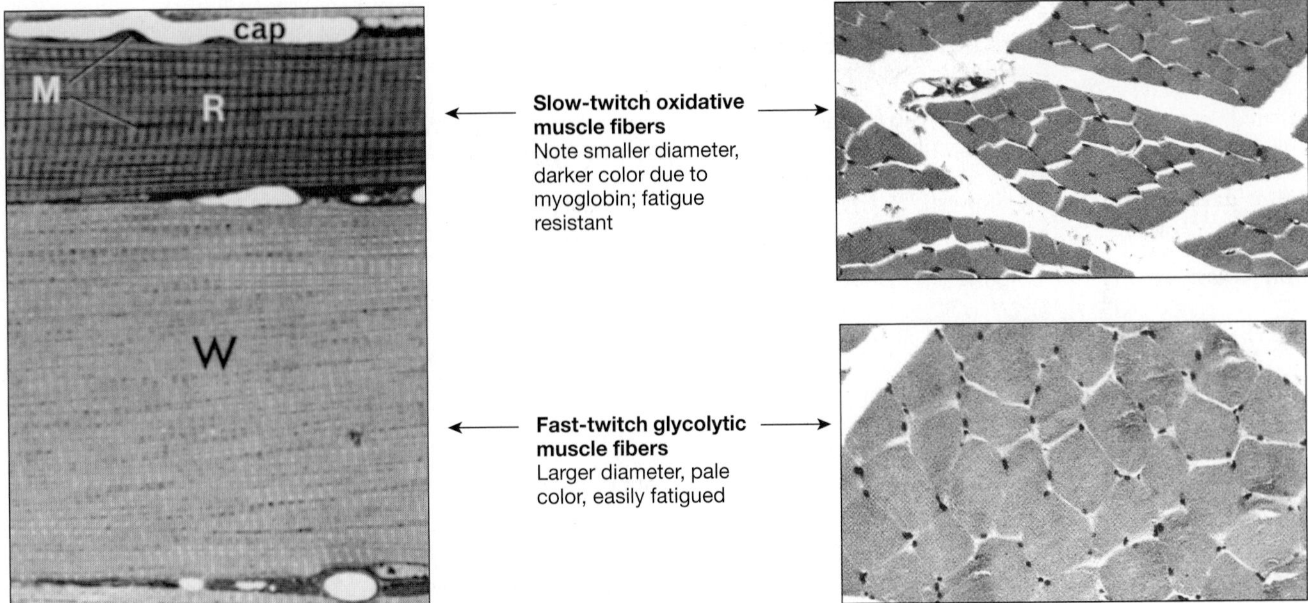

■ **FIGURE 12-15** ***Fast-twitch glycolytic and slow-twitch oxidative muscle fibers***

Large amounts of red myoglobin, numerous mitochondria (M), and extensive capillary blood supply (cap) distinguish slow-twitch oxidative muscle (labeled R here for red muscle) from fast-twitch glycolytic muscle (labeled W for white muscle).

Fast-twitch oxidative-glycolytic fibers exhibit properties of both oxidative and glycolytic fibers. They are smaller than fast-twitch glycolytic fibers and use a combination of oxidative and glycolytic metabolism to produce ATP. Because of their intermediate size and the use of oxidative phosphorylation for ATP synthesis, fast-twitch oxidative-glycolytic fibers are more fatigue resistant than their fast-twitch glycolytic cousins. Fast-twitch oxidative-glycolytic fibers, like slow-twitch fibers, are classified as red muscle because of their myoglobin content.

Human muscles are a mixture of fiber types, with the ratio of types varying from muscle to muscle and from one individual to another. For example, who would have more fast-twitch fibers in leg muscles, a marathon runner or a high-jumper? Characteristics of the three muscle fiber types are compared in Table 12-2 ■.

Tension Developed by Individual Muscle Fibers Is a Function of Fiber Length

In a muscle fiber, the tension developed during a twitch is a direct reflection of the length of individual sarcomeres before contraction begins (Fig. 12-16 ■). Each sarcomere will contract with optimum force if it is at optimum length (neither too long nor too short) before the contraction begins. Fortunately, the normal resting length of skeletal muscles usually ensures that sarcomeres are at optimum length when they begin a contraction.

At the molecular level, sarcomere length reflects the overlap between the thick and thin filaments. The sliding filament theory predicts that *the tension a muscle fiber can generate is directly proportional to the number of crossbridges formed between the thick and thin filaments*. If the fibers start a contraction at a very long sarcomere length, the thick and thin filaments are barely overlapping, forming few crossbridges (Fig. 12-16e). This means that in the initial part of the contraction, the sliding filaments can interact only minimally and therefore cannot generate much force.

At the optimum sarcomere length (Fig. 12-16c), the filaments begin contracting with numerous crossbridges between the thick and thin filaments, allowing the fiber to generate optimum force in that twitch. If the sarcomere is shorter than optimum length at the beginning of the contraction (Fig. 12-16b), the thick and thin fibers have too much overlap before the contraction begins. Consequently, the thick filaments can move the thin filaments only a short distance before the thin actin filaments from opposite ends of the sarcomere start to overlap. This overlap prevents crossbridge formation. If the sarcomere is so short that the thick filaments run into the Z disks (Fig. 12-16a), myosin is unable to find new binding sites for crossbridge formation, and tension decreases rapidly. Thus the development of single-twitch tension in a muscle fiber is a passive property that depends on filament overlap and sarcomere length.

Force of Contraction Increases with Summation of Muscle Twitches

Although we have just seen that single-twitch tension is determined by the length of the sarcomere, it is important to note that a single twitch does not represent the maximum force that

TABLE 12-2 Characteristics of Muscle Fiber Types

	SLOW-TWITCH OXIDATIVE; RED MUSCLE	FAST-TWITCH OXIDATIVE-GLYCOLYTIC; RED MUSCLE	FAST-TWITCH GLYCOLYTIC; WHITE MUSCLE
Speed of development of maximum tension	Slowest	Intermediate	Fastest
Myosin ATPase activity	Slow	Fast	Fast
Diameter	Small	Medium	Large
Contraction duration	Longest	Short	Short
Ca^{2+}-ATPase activity in SR	Moderate	High	High
Endurance	Fatigue resistant	Fatigue resistant	Easily fatigued
Use	Most used: posture	Standing, walking	Least used: jumping
Metabolism	Oxidative; aerobic;	Glycolytic but becomes more oxidative with endurance training	Glycolytic; more anaerobic than fast-twitch oxidative-glycolytic type
Capillary density	High	Medium	Low
Mitochondria	Numerous	Moderate	Few
Color	Dark red (myoglobin)	Red	Pale

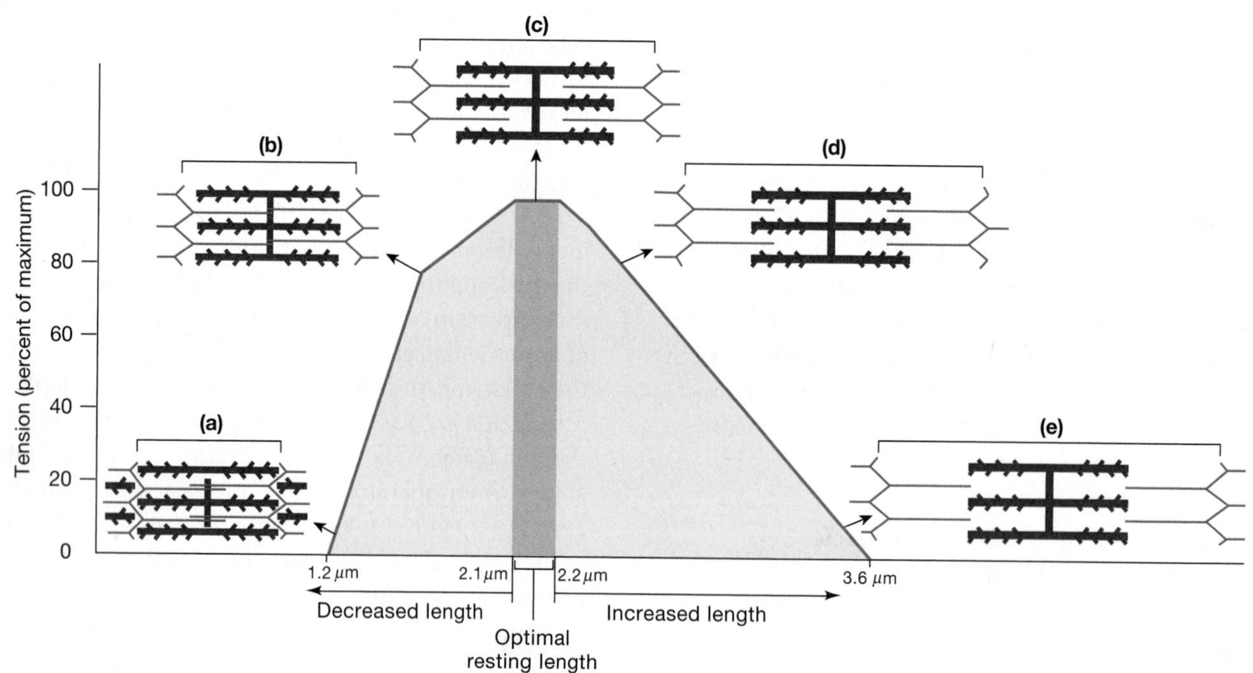

■ **FIGURE 12-16** ***Length-tension relationships in contracting skeletal muscle***

The graph plots tension generated by a skeletal muscle at various resting lengths before contraction starts.

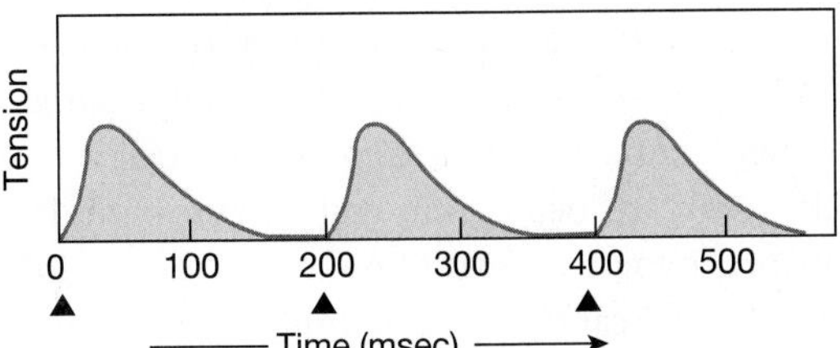
(a) Single twitches: Muscle relaxes completely between stimuli (▲).
Tension
0
100
200
300
400
500
Time (msec)

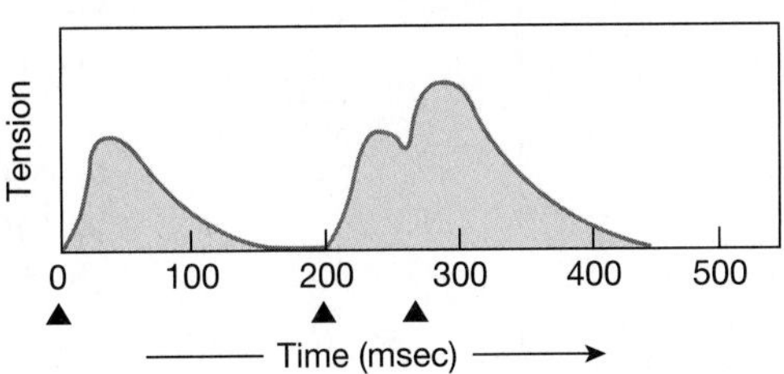
(b) Summation: Stimuli closer together do not allow muscle to relax fully.
Tension
0
100
200
300
400
500
Time (msec)

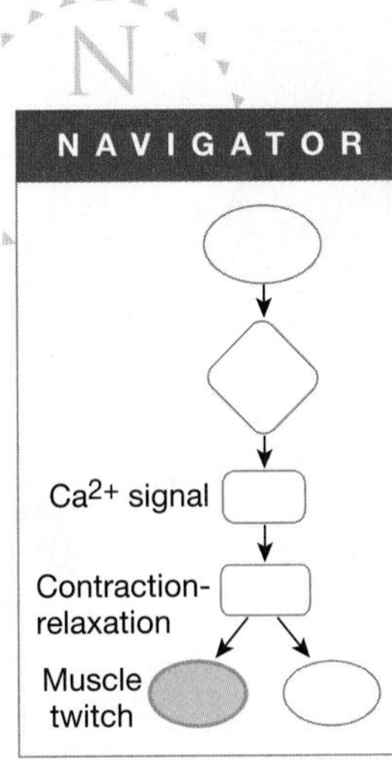
NAVIGATOR
Ca^{2+} signal
Contraction-relaxation
Muscle twitch

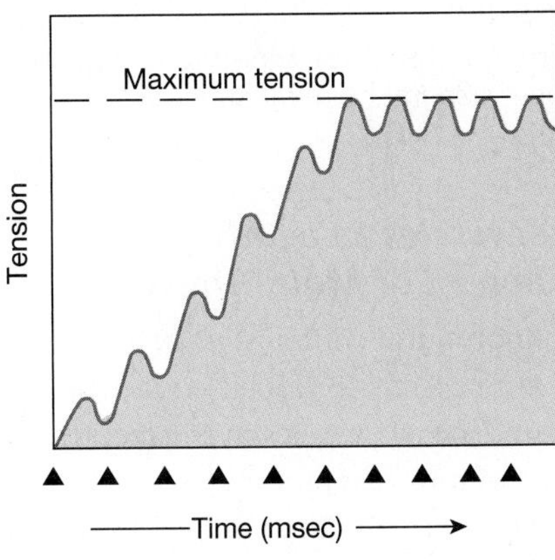
(c) Summation leading to unfused tetanus: Stimuli are far enough apart to allow muscle to relax slightly between stimuli.
Maximum tension
Tension
Time (msec)

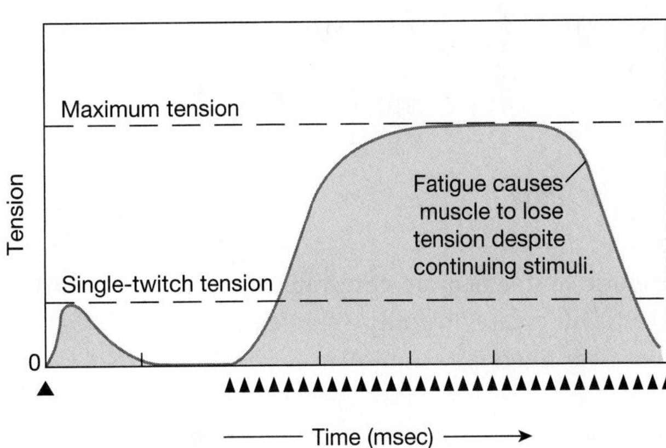
(d) Summation leading to complete tetanus: Muscle reaches steady tension.
Maximum tension
Fatigue causes muscle to lose tension despite continuing stimuli.
Single-twitch tension
Tension
0
Time (msec)

■ **FIGURE 12-17** ***Summation of contractions***

a muscle fiber can develop. The force generated by the contraction of a single muscle fiber can be increased by increasing the rate (frequency) at which muscle action potentials stimulate the muscle fiber.

A typical muscle action potential lasts between 1 and 3 msec, while the muscle contraction may last 100 msec (see Fig. 12-12). If repeated action potentials are separated by long intervals of time, the muscle fiber has time to relax completely between stimuli (Fig. 12-17a ■). If the interval of time between action potentials is shortened, the muscle fiber does not have time to relax completely between two stimuli, resulting in a more forceful contraction (Fig. 12-17b). This process is known as **summation** and is similar to the temporal summation of graded potentials that takes place in neurons [p. 278].

If action potentials continue to stimulate the muscle fiber repeatedly at short intervals (high frequency), relaxation between contractions diminishes until the muscle fiber achieves a state of maximal contraction known as **tetanus**. There are two types of tetanus. In *incomplete* (or *unfused*) *tetanus,* the stimulation rate of the muscle fiber is not at a maximum value, and consequently the fiber relaxes slightly between stimuli (Fig. 12-17c). In *complete* (or *fused*) *tetanus,* the stimulation rate is fast enough that the muscle fiber does not have time to relax. Instead, it reaches maximum tension and remains there (Fig. 12-17d).

Thus it is possible to increase the tension developed in a single muscle fiber by changing the rate at which action potentials occur in the fiber. Muscle action potentials are initiated by the somatic motor neuron that controls the muscle fiber.

CONCEPT CHECK

16. Summation in muscle fibers means that the ________ of the fiber increases with repeated action potentials.
17. Temporal summation in neurons means that the ________ of the neuron increases when two depolarizing stimuli occur close together in time.

Answers: p. 434

A Motor Unit Is One Somatic Motor Neuron and the Muscle Fibers It Innervates

The basic unit of contraction in an intact skeletal muscle is a **motor unit**, composed of a group of muscle fibers that function together and the somatic motor neuron that controls them (Fig. 12-18 ■). When the somatic motor neuron fires an action potential, all muscle fibers in the motor unit contract. Note

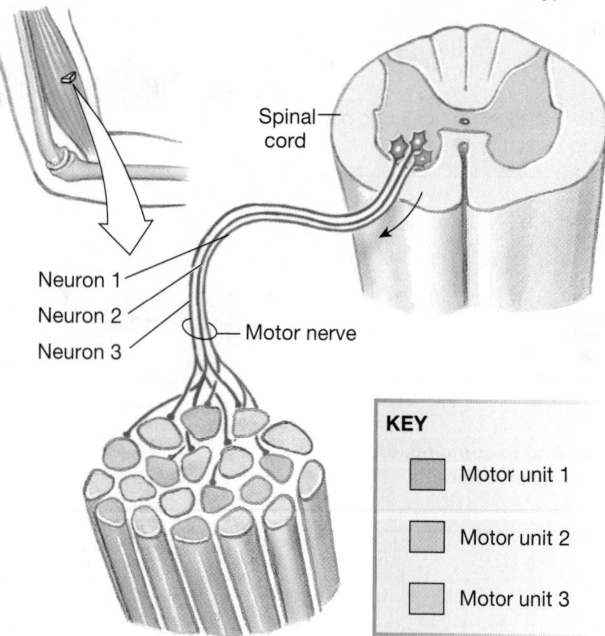

■ **FIGURE 12-18** ***Motor units***

that although one somatic motor neuron innervates multiple fibers, each muscle fiber is innervated by only a single neuron.

The number of muscle fibers in a motor unit varies. In muscles used for fine motor actions, such as the muscles that move the eyes or the muscles of the hand, a motor unit contains as few as three to five muscle fibers. If one such motor unit is activated, only a few fibers contract, and the muscle response is quite small. If additional motor units are activated, the response increases by small increments because only a few more muscle fibers contract with the addition of each motor unit. This arrangement allows fine gradations of movement.

In muscles used for gross motor actions such as standing or walking, each motor unit may contain hundreds or even thousands of muscle fibers. The gastrocnemius muscle in the calf of the leg, for example, has about 2000 muscle fibers in each motor unit. Each time an additional motor unit is activated in these muscles, many more muscle fibers contract, and the muscle response jumps by correspondingly greater increments.

All muscle fibers in a single motor unit are of the same fiber type. Thus, there are fast-twitch motor units and slow-twitch motor units. Which kind of muscle fiber associates with a particular neuron appears to be a function of the neuron. During embryological development, each somatic motor neuron secretes a growth factor that directs the differentiation of all muscle fibers in its motor unit so that they develop into the same fiber type.

Intuitively, it would seem that people who inherit a predominance of one fiber type over another would excel in certain sports. They do, to some extent. Endurance athletes, such as distance runners and cross-country skiers, have a predominance of slow-twitch fibers, whereas sprinters, ice hockey players, and weight lifters tend to have larger percentages of fast-twitch fibers. Inheritance is not the only determining factor for fiber composition in the body, however, because the metabolic characteristics of muscle fibers can be changed to some extent. With endurance training, the aerobic capacity of some fast-twitch fibers can be enhanced until they are almost as fatigue-resistant as slow-twitch fibers. Since the conversion occurs only in those muscles that are being trained, a neuromodulator chemical is probably involved. In addition, endurance training increases the number of capillaries and mitochondria in the muscle tissue, allowing more oxygen-carrying blood to reach the contracting muscle and contributing to the increased aerobic capacity of the muscle fibers.

CONCEPT CHECK

18. Which type of runner would you expect to have more slow-twitch fibers, a sprinter or a marathoner?

Answers: p. 434

Contraction in Intact Muscles Depends on the Types and Numbers of Motor Units

In a skeletal muscle, each motor unit contracts in an all-or-none manner. How then can muscles create graded contractions of varying force and duration? The answer lies in the fact that intact muscles are composed of multiple motor units of different types (Fig. 12-18). This diversity allows the muscle to vary contraction by (1) changing the types of motor units that are active or (2) changing the number of motor units that are responding at any one time.

The force of contraction in a skeletal muscle can be increased by recruiting additional motor units. **Recruitment** is controlled by the nervous system and proceeds in a standardized sequence. A weak stimulus directed onto a pool of somatic motor neurons in the central nervous system activates only the neurons with the lowest thresholds [p. 254]. Studies have shown that these low-threshold neurons control fatigue-resistant slow-twitch fibers, which generate minimal force.

As the stimulus onto the motor neuron pool increases in strength, additional motor neurons with higher thresholds begin to fire. These neurons in turn stimulate motor units composed of fatigue-resistant fast-twitch oxidative-glycolytic fibers. Because more motor units (and thus more muscle fibers) are participating in the contraction, greater force is generated in the muscle.

As the stimulus increases to even higher levels, somatic motor neurons with the highest thresholds begin to fire. These neurons stimulate motor units composed of glycolytic fast-twitch fibers. At this point, the muscle contraction is approaching its maximum force. Because of differences in myosin and crossbridge formation, fast-twitch fibers can generate more force than slow-twitch fibers. However, because fast-twitch fibers fatigue more rapidly, it is impossible to hold a muscle contraction at maximum force for an extended period of time. You can demonstrate this by clenching your fist as hard as you can: how long can you hold it before some of the muscle fibers begin to fatigue?

Sustained contractions in a muscle require a continuous train of action potentials from the central nervous system to the muscle. As you learned earlier, however, increasing the stimulation rate of a muscle fiber results in summation of its contractions. If the muscle fiber is easily fatigued, summation will lead to fatigue and diminished tension (Fig. 12-17d).

One way the nervous system avoids fatigue in sustained contractions is by **asynchronous recruitment** of motor units. The nervous system modulates the firing rates of the motor neurons so that different motor units take turns maintaining muscle tension. The alternation of active motor units allows some of the motor units to rest between contractions, preventing fatigue.

Asynchronous recruitment will prevent fatigue only in submaximal contractions, however. In high-tension, sustained contractions, the individual motor units may reach a state of unfused tetanus, in which the muscle fibers cycle between contraction and partial relaxation. In general, we do not notice this cycling because the different motor units in the muscle are contracting and relaxing at slightly different times. As a result, the contractions and relaxations of the motor units average out and appear to be one smooth contraction. But as different motor units fatigue, we are unable to maintain the same amount of tension in the muscle, and the force of the contraction gradually decreases.

CONCEPT CHECK

19. What is the response of a muscle fiber to an increase in the firing rate of the somatic motor neuron?
20. How does the nervous system increase the force of contraction in a muscle composed of many motor units?

Answers: p. 434

MECHANICS OF BODY MOVEMENT

Because one main role of skeletal muscles is to move the body, we now turn to the mechanics of body movement. The term *mechanics* refers to how muscles move loads and how the anatomical relationship between muscles and bones maximizes the work the muscles can do.

Isotonic Contractions Move Loads, but Isometric Contractions Create Force Without Movement

When we described the function of muscles earlier in this chapter, we noted that they can create force to generate movement but can also create force without generating movement. You can demonstrate both properties with a pair of heavy weights. Pick up one weight in each hand and then bend your elbows so that the weights touch your shoulders. You have just performed an **isotonic contraction** [*iso*, equal + *teinein*, to stretch]. Any contraction that creates force and moves a load is an isotonic contraction.

When you bent your arms at the elbows and brought the weights to your shoulders, the biceps muscles shortened in a **concentric action**. If you now slowly extend your arms, resisting the tendency of the weights to pull them down, you are performing another type of isotonic contraction known as an **eccentric** (or lengthening) **action** [*ec-*, out of + *centrum*, center]. Eccentric motion is thought to contribute most to cellular damage after exercise and to lead to delayed muscle soreness.

If you pick up the weights and hold them stationary in front of you, the muscles of your arms are creating tension (force) to overcome the load of the weights but are not creating movement. Contractions that create force without moving a load are called **isometric** (static) **contractions** [*iso*, equal + *metric*, measurement]. Isotonic and isometric contractions are illustrated in Figure 12-19 ■. To demonstrate an isotonic contraction experimentally, we hang a weight (the load) from the muscle in Figure 12-19a and electrically stimulate the muscle to contract. The muscle contracts, lifting the weight. The graph on the right shows the development of force throughout the contraction.

To demonstrate an isometric contraction experimentally, we attach a heavier weight to the muscle, as shown in Figure 12-19b. When the muscle is stimulated, it develops tension, but the force created is not enough to move the load. In isometric contractions, muscles create force without shortening significantly. For example, when your exercise instructor yells at you to "tighten those glutes," your response is isometric contraction of the gluteal muscles in your buttocks.

How can an isometric contraction create force if the length of the muscle does not change significantly? The elastic elements of the muscle provide the answer. All muscles contain elastic fibers in the tendons and other connective tissues that attach muscles to bone, and in the connective tissue between muscle fibers. In muscle fibers, elastic cytoskeletal proteins occur between the myofibrils and as part of the sarcomere. All of these elastic components behave collectively as if they were connected in series (one after the other) to the contractile elements of the muscle. Consequently, they are often called the **series elastic elements** of the muscle (Fig. 12-20 ■).

When the sarcomeres shorten in an isometric contraction, the elastic elements stretch. This stretching of the elastic elements allows the fibers to maintain a relatively constant length even though the sarcomeres are shortening and creating tension (Fig. 12-20, ②). Once the elastic elements have been stretched and the force generated by the sarcomeres equals the load, the muscle shortens in an isotonic contraction and lifts the load.

Bones and Muscles Around Joints Form Levers and Fulcrums

The anatomical arrangement of muscles and bones in the body is directly related to how muscles work. The body uses its bones and joints as levers and fulcrums on which muscles exert force

(a) Isotonic contraction: muscle contracts, shortens, and creates enough force to move the load.

Muscle contracts

Muscle relaxes

20 kg

20 kg

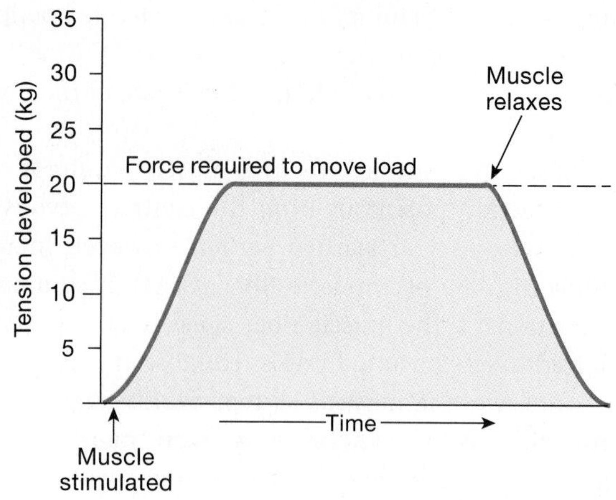

(b) Isometric contraction: muscle contracts but does not shorten. Force cannot move the load.

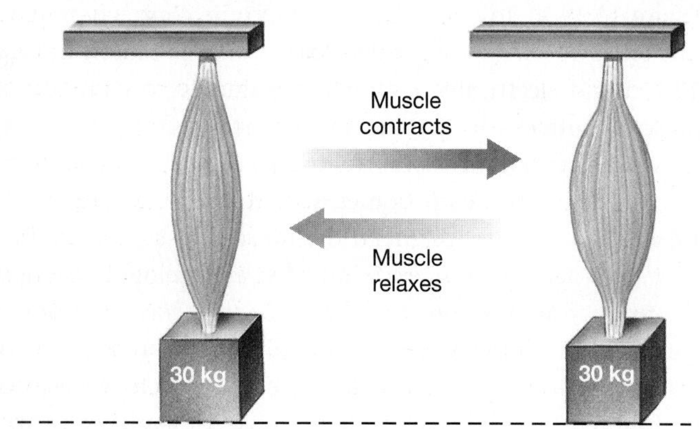

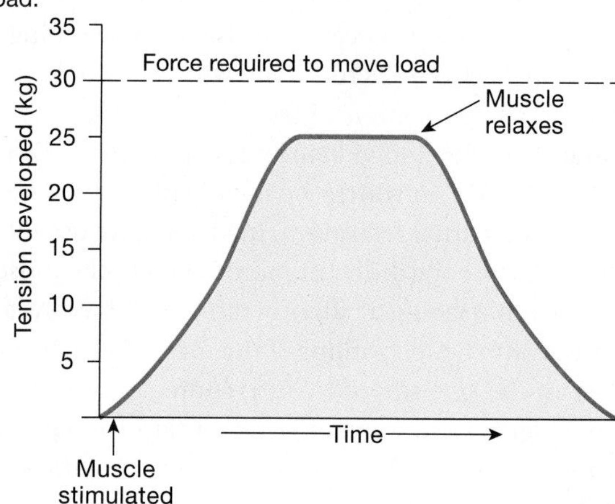

■ **FIGURE 12-19** ***Isotonic and isometric contractions***

to move or resist a load. A **lever** is a rigid bar that pivots around a point known as the **fulcrum** (Fig. 12-21a ■). In the body, bones form levers, flexible joints form the fulcrums, and muscles attached to bones create force by contracting. Most lever systems in the body are similar to the one shown in Figure 12-21a, where the fulcrum is located at one end of the lever, the load is near the other end of the lever, and the muscle attaches between the fulcrum and the load. This arrangement maximizes the distance and speed with which the lever can move the load but also requires that the muscles do more work. We will use the flexion of the forearm to illustrate how this lever system functions.

In the lever system of the forearm, the elbow joint acts as the fulcrum around which rotational movement of the forearm (the lever) takes place (Fig. 12-21a). The biceps muscle is attached at its origin at the shoulder and inserts onto the radius bone of the forearm a few centimeters away from the elbow joint. When the biceps contracts, it creates the upward force F_1 (Fig. 12-21b) as it pulls on the bone. The total rotational force* created by the biceps depends on the force of muscle contraction and on the distance between the fulcrum and the point at which the muscle inserts onto the radius.

If the biceps is to hold the forearm stationary and flexed at a 90° angle, the muscle must exert enough upward rotational force to exactly oppose the downward rotational force exerted by gravity on the forearm (Fig. 12-21b). The downward rotational force on the forearm is proportional to the weight of the forearm (F_2) times the distance from the fulcrum to the forearm's center of gravity (the point along the lever at which the forearm load exerts its force). For the arm illustrated in Figure 12-21b, the biceps must exert 6 kg of force to hold the arm at a 90° angle. Because the muscle is not shortening, this is an isometric contraction.

Now what happens if a 7-kg weight is placed in the hand? This weight places an additional load on the lever that is farther from the fulcrum than the forearm's center of gravity (Fig. 12-21c). Unless the biceps can create additional upward force to offset the downward force created by the weight, the hand will fall. If you know the force exerted by the added weight and its distance from the elbow, you can calculate the additional muscle force needed to keep the arm from dropping the 7-kg weight.

*In physics, rotational force is expressed as *torque,* and the force of contraction is expressed in newtons (mass × acceleration due to gravity). For simplicity, we will ignore the contribution of gravity in this discussion and use the mass unit "kilograms" for force of contraction.

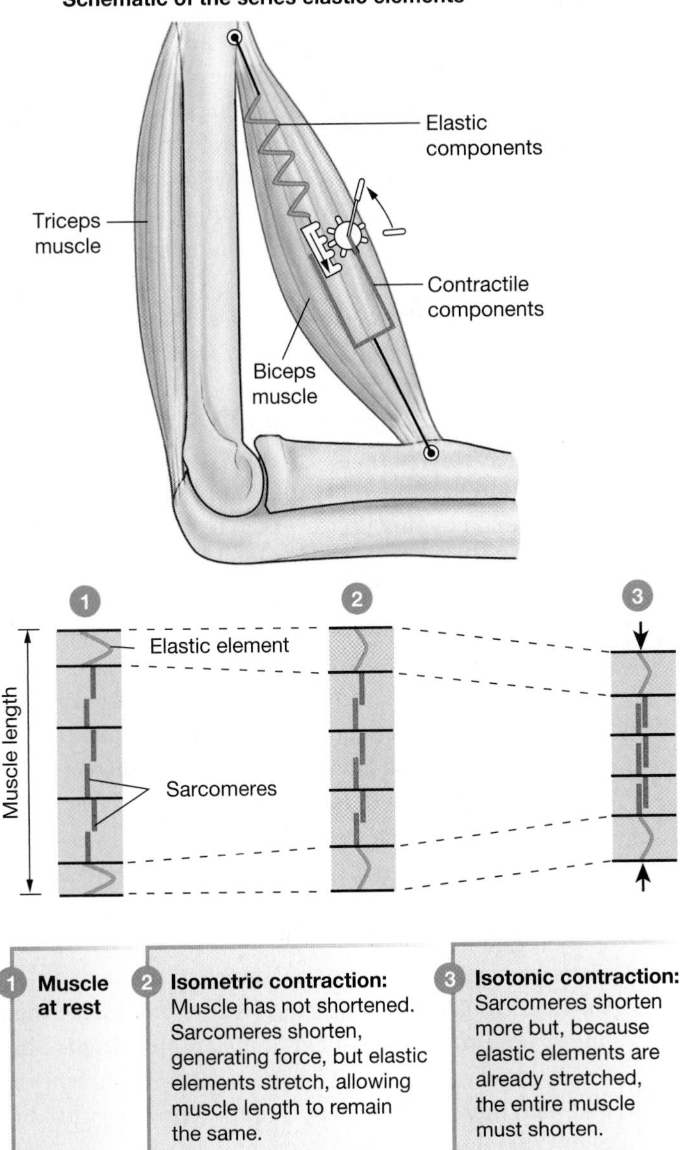

Schematic of the series elastic elements
Elastic components
Triceps muscle
Contractile components
Biceps muscle
1
2
3
Elastic element
Muscle length
Sarcomeres
1 Muscle at rest
2 Isometric contraction: Muscle has not shortened. Sarcomeres shorten, generating force, but elastic elements stretch, allowing muscle length to remain the same.
3 Isotonic contraction: Sarcomeres shorten more but, because elastic elements are already stretched, the entire muscle must shorten.

■ **FIGURE 12-20** ***Series elastic elements in muscle***

A muscle has both contractile components (sarcomeres, shown here as a gear and ratchet) and elastic components (shown here as a spring).

What happens to the force required of the biceps to support a weight if the distance between the fulcrum and the muscle insertion point changes? Genetic variability in the insertion point can have a dramatic effect on the force required to move or resist a load. For example, if the biceps in Figure 12-21b inserted 6 cm from the fulcrum instead of 5 cm, it would only need to generate 5 kg of force to offset the weight of the arm. Some studies have shown a correlation between muscle insertion points and success in certain athletic events.

In the example so far, we have assumed that the load is stationary and that the muscle is contracting isometrically. What happens if we want to flex the arm and lift the load? To move the load from its position, the biceps must exert a force that exceeds the force created by the stationary load.

The disadvantage of a lever system in which the fulcrum is positioned near one end of the lever is that the muscle is required to create large amounts of force to move or resist a small load, as we just saw. However, the advantage of this type of lever-fulcrum system is that it maximizes speed and mobility. A small movement of the forearm at the point where the muscle inserts becomes a much larger movement at the hand (Fig. 12-22 ■). In addition, the two movements occur in the same amount of time, and so the speed of contraction at the insertion point is amplified at the hand. Thus, the lever-fulcrum system of the arm amplifies both the distance the load is moved and the speed at which this movement takes place.

In muscle physiology, the speed with which a muscle contracts depends on the type of muscle fiber (fast-twitch or slow-twitch) and on the load that is being moved. Intuitively, you can see that you can flex your arm much faster with nothing in your hand than you can while holding a 7-kg weight in your hand. The relationship between load and velocity of contraction in a muscle fiber, determined experimentally, is graphed in Figure 12-23 ■. Contraction is fastest when the load on the muscle is zero. When the load on the muscle equals the ability of the muscle to create force, the muscle is unable to move the load and the velocity drops to zero. The muscle can still contract, but the contraction becomes isometric instead of isotonic. Because speed is a function of load and muscle fiber type, it cannot be regulated by the body except through recruitment of faster muscle fiber types. However, the arrangement of muscles, bones, and joints allows the body to amplify speed so that regulation at the cellular level becomes less important.

RUNNING PROBLEM

Paul's doctor explained to Mrs. Leong that the paralytic attacks associated with hyperkalemic periodic paralysis last only a few minutes to a few hours and generally involve only the muscles of the extremities. "Is there any treatment?" asked Mrs. Leong. The doctor replied that although the condition is incurable, attacks may be prevented with drugs. Diuretics, for example, increase the rate at which the body excretes water and ions (including Na^+ and K^+), and these medications have been shown to prevent attacks of paralysis in people with this condition.

Question 3:

Why does a Na^+ channel that will not inactivate cause paralysis?

397 410 412 419 423 430

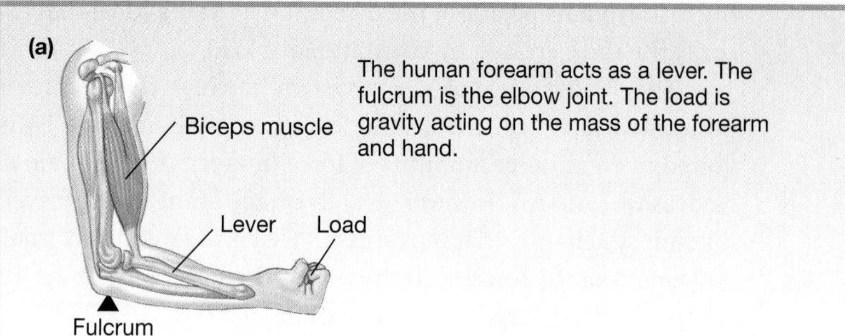

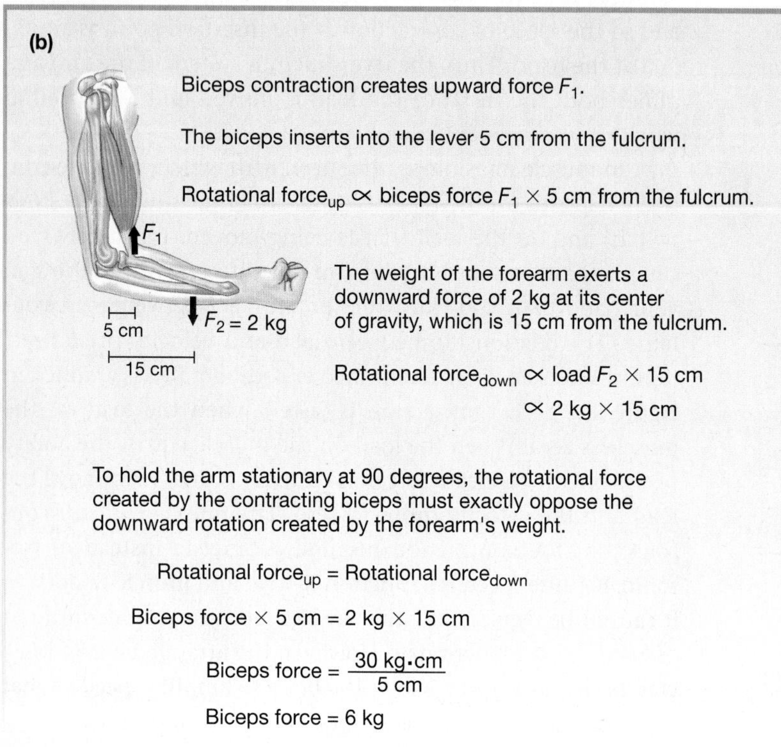

(b)
Biceps contraction creates upward force F_1.
The biceps inserts into the lever 5 cm from the fulcrum.
Rotational force$_{up}$ ∝ biceps force F_1 × 5 cm from the fulcrum.
F_1
The weight of the forearm exerts a downward force of 2 kg at its center of gravity, which is 15 cm from the fulcrum.
5 cm
F_2 = 2 kg
15 cm
Rotational force$_{down}$ ∝ load F_2 × 15 cm
∝ 2 kg × 15 cm
To hold the arm stationary at 90 degrees, the rotational force created by the contracting biceps must exactly oppose the downward rotation created by the forearm's weight.
Rotational force$_{up}$ = Rotational force$_{down}$
Biceps force × 5 cm = 2 kg × 15 cm
Biceps force = 30 kg·cm / 5 cm
Biceps force = 6 kg

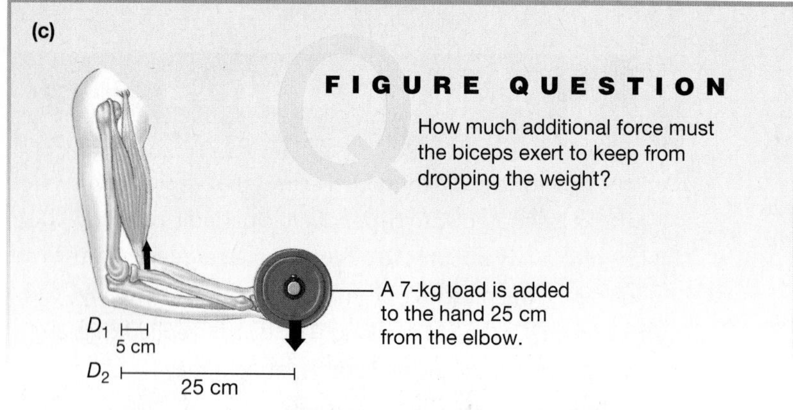

(c)
FIGURE QUESTION
How much additional force must the biceps exert to keep from dropping the weight?
A 7-kg load is added to the hand 25 cm from the elbow.
D_1
5 cm
D_2
25 cm

■ **FIGURE 12-21** ***The arm is a lever and fulcrum system***

CONCEPT CHECK

21. One study found that many world-class athletes have muscle insertions that are farther from the joint than in the average person. Why would this trait translate into an advantage for a weight lifter?

Answers: p. 434

Muscle Disorders Have Multiple Causes

Dysfunction in skeletal muscles can arise from a problem with the signal from the nervous system, from miscommunication at the neuromuscular junction, or from defects in the muscle. Unfortunately, in many muscle conditions, even the simple ones, we do not fully understand the mechanism of the primary defect. As a result, we can treat the symptoms but may not be able to cure the problem.

One common muscle disorder is a "charlie horse," or *muscle cramp*—a sustained painful contraction of skeletal muscles. Many muscle cramps are caused by hyperexcitability of the somatic motor neurons controlling the muscle. As the neuron fires repeatedly, the muscle fibers of its motor unit go into a state of painful sustained contraction. Sometimes muscle cramps can be relieved by forcibly stretching the muscle. Apparently, stretching sends sensory information to the central nervous system that inhibits the somatic motor neuron, relieving the cramp.

The simplest muscle disorders arise from overuse. Most of us have exercised too long or too hard and suffered from muscle fatigue or soreness as a result. Trauma to muscles can cause muscle fibers, the connective tissue sheath, or the union of muscle and tendon to tear.

Disuse of muscles can be as traumatic as overuse. With prolonged inactivity, such as may occur when a limb is immobilized in a cast, the skeletal muscles will atrophy. Blood supply to the muscle diminishes, and the muscle fibers get smaller. If activity is resumed in less than a year, the fibers usually will regenerate. Atrophy of longer than one year is usually permanent. If the atrophy results from somatic motor neuron dysfunction, therapists now try to maintain muscle function by administering electrical impulses that directly stimulate the muscle fibers.

Acquired disorders that affect the skeletal muscle system include infectious diseases, such as influenza, that lead to weakness and achiness, and poisoning by toxins, such as those produced in botulism (*Clostridium botulinus*) and tetanus (*Clostridium tetani*). Botulinum toxin acts by decreasing the release of acetylcholine from the somatic motor neuron. Clinical investigators have successfully used injections of botulinum toxin as a treatment for writer's cramp, a disabling cramp of the hand that apparently arises as a result of hyperexcitability in the distal portion of the somatic motor neuron. You may also have heard of Botox® injections for cosmetic wrinkle reduction. Botulinum toxin injected under the skin temporarily paralyzes facial muscles that pull the skin into wrinkles.

Inherited muscular disorders are the most difficult to treat. These conditions include various forms of muscular dystrophy as well as biochemical defects in glycogen and lipid storage. In **Duchenne's muscular dystrophy**, the structural protein **dystrophin**, which links actin to proteins in the cell membrane, is

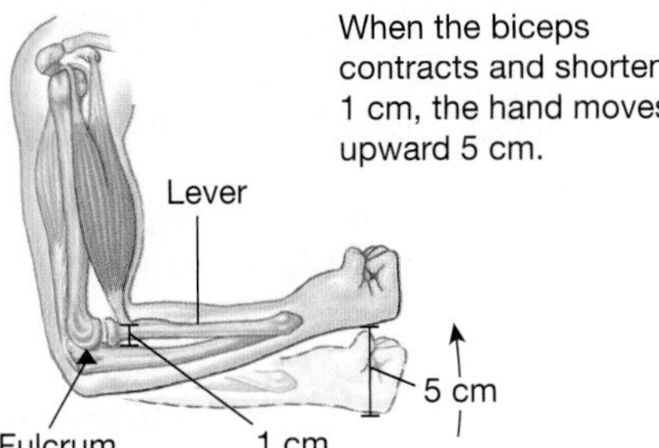
Because the insertion of the biceps is close to the fulcrum, a small movement of the biceps becomes a much larger movement of the hand.
When the biceps contracts and shortens 1 cm, the hand moves upward 5 cm.
Lever
Fulcrum
1 cm
5 cm

FIGURE QUESTION

If the biceps shortens 1 cm in 1 second, how fast does the hand move upward?

■ **FIGURE 12-22** ***The arm amplifies speed of movement of the load.***

absent. In muscle fibers that lack dystrophin, tiny tears in the membrane allow extracellular Ca^{2+} to enter the fiber. Consequently, intracellular enzymes are activated, resulting in breakdown of the fiber components. The major symptom of Duchenne dystrophy is progressive muscle weakness, and patients usually die before age 30 from failure of the respiratory muscles.

McArdle's disease, also known as *myophosphorylase deficiency glycogenosis,* is a condition in which the enzyme that converts glycogen to glucose 6-phosphate is absent in muscles. As a result, muscles lack a usable glycogen energy supply, and exercise tolerance is limited.

One way we are trying to learn more about muscle diseases is by using animal models, such as genetically engineered mice that lack the genes for certain muscle proteins. Researchers are trying to correlate the absence of protein with particular disruptions in function.

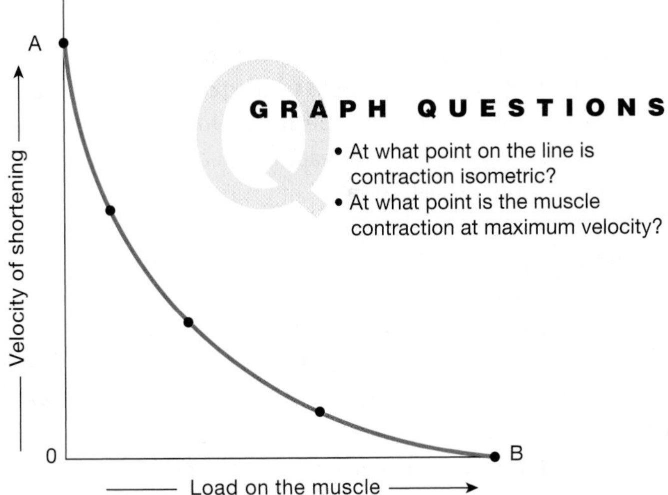
A
B
0
Velocity of shortening
Load on the muscle

GRAPH QUESTIONS

- At what point on the line is contraction isometric?
- At what point is the muscle contraction at maximum velocity?

■ **FIGURE 12-23** ***Load-velocity relationship in skeletal muscle***

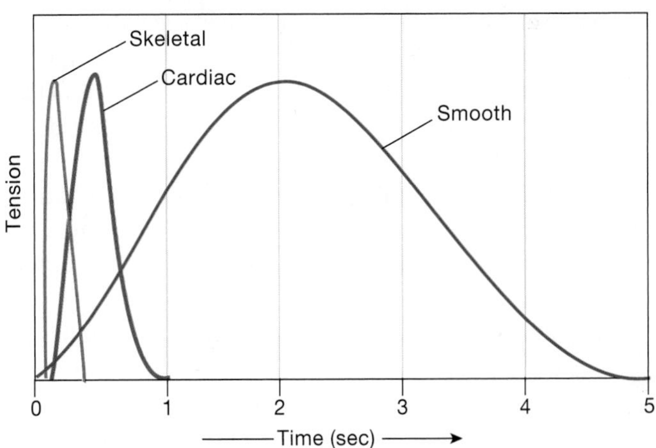
Skeletal
Cardiac
Smooth
Tension
0
1
2
3
4
5
Time (sec)

■ **FIGURE 12-24** ***Duration of muscle contraction in the three types of muscle***

SMOOTH MUSCLE

Although skeletal muscle has the most muscle mass in the body, cardiac and smooth muscle are more important in the maintenance of homeostasis. Smooth muscle is found predominantly in the walls of hollow organs and tubes, where its contraction changes the shape of the organ. Often smooth muscle generates force to move material through the lumen of the organ. For example, sequential waves of smooth muscle contraction in the intestinal tract move ingested material from the esophagus to the colon.

Smooth muscle is noticeably different from striated muscle in the way it develops tension. In a smooth muscle twitch, contraction and relaxation occur much more slowly than in either skeletal or cardiac muscle (Fig. 12-24 ■). At the same time, smooth muscle uses less energy to generate a given amount of force, and it can maintain its force for long periods. By one estimate, for example, a smooth muscle cell can generate maximum tension with only 25–30% of its crossbridges active. We still do not fully understand the mechanisms through which this is accomplished.

In addition, smooth muscle has low oxygen consumption rates yet can sustain contractions for extended periods without fatiguing. This property allows organs such as the bladder to maintain tension despite a continued load. It also allows some smooth muscles to be tonically contracted and maintain tension most of the time. The esophageal and urinary bladder **sphincters** [*sphingein,* to close] are examples of tonically contracted muscles whose function is to close off the opening to a hollow organ. These sphincters relax when it is necessary to allow material to enter or leave the organ.

Until recently, smooth muscle had not been studied as extensively as skeletal muscle for many reasons:

1. **Smooth muscle has more variety**. Many types of smooth muscle with widely differing properties are found throughout the animal kingdom, making a single model of smooth muscle function impossible. In humans, smooth muscle

can be divided into six major groups: *vascular* (blood vessel walls), *gastrointestinal* (walls of digestive tract and associated organs, such as the gall bladder), *urinary* (walls of bladder and ureters), *respiratory* (airway passages), *reproductive* (uterus in females and other reproductive structures in both females and males), and *ocular* (eye). These muscles have different functions in the body, and their physiology is a reflection of their specialized functions. In contrast, skeletal muscle is relatively uniform throughout the body.

2. **Smooth muscle anatomy makes functional studies difficult**. The contractile fibers of smooth muscle are arranged in oblique bundles rather than in parallel sarcomeres. Consequently, a contraction pulls on the cell membrane in many directions at once. In addition, within an organ the layers of smooth muscle may run in several directions. For example, the intestine has one layer that encircles the lumen and a perpendicular layer that runs the length of the intestine. It is difficult to measure tension developing in both layers at once.
3. **Smooth muscle contraction is controlled by hormones and paracrines in addition to neurotransmitters.** Unlike skeletal muscle, which is controlled only by acetylcholine from somatic motor neurons, smooth muscle activity may be controlled by acetylcholine, norepinephrine, and a variety of other neurotransmitters, hormones, and paracrines.
4. **Smooth muscle has variable electrical properties.** Normal skeletal muscles always respond to an action potential with a twitch, but smooth muscles exhibit a variety of electrical behaviors. They may hyperpolarize as well as depolarize, and they can depolarize without firing action potentials. Contraction may take place after an action potential, after a subthreshold graded potential, or without any change in membrane potential.
5. **Multiple pathways influence contraction and relaxation of smooth muscle.** Skeletal muscles contract in response to acetylcholine from a somatic motor neuron, and relax when the stimulus for contraction ceases. In marked contrast, multiple neurotransmitters, hormones, and paracrines acting on a smooth muscle fiber can inhibit contraction as well as stimulate it. And because several different signals might reach the muscle fiber simultaneously, smooth muscle fibers must act as integrating centers. For example, sometimes blood vessels receive contradictory messages from two sources: one message signals for contraction, the other for relaxation. The smooth muscle fibers must integrate the two signals and execute an appropriate response. The complexity of overlapping regulatory pathways influencing smooth muscle tone makes the tissue difficult to work with in the laboratory.

Because of the variability in smooth muscle types, we will introduce only their general features in this chapter. Properties that are specific to a certain type will be dealt with when you learn about the different muscles in later chapters.

CLINICAL FOCUS

SMOOTH MUSCLE AND ATHEROSCLEROSIS

For years, it was believed that mature smooth muscle cells had lost the ability to undergo mitosis. Recent studies, however, have shown otherwise. Not only can smooth muscle cells reproduce themselves, but their proliferation may also play a significant role in *atherosclerosis,* a disease of blood vessels in which the vessel lumen narrows as the vessel wall thickens. Calcified fatty deposits are found in the extracellular matrix, leading to the hardened state that gives atherosclerosis its popular name; hardening of the arteries. As part of the disease process, smooth muscle cells in the blood vessel wall convert from a contractile state to a proliferative state. During proliferation, the muscle cells migrate toward the lumen, divide, and accumulate cholesterol. This change in smooth muscle function is regulated by growth factors and cytokines released by white blood cells in the region of the atherosclerotic lesion. Researchers are trying to unravel the complex story behind the smooth muscle changes in atherosclerosis so that they can develop drugs to help prevent the disease.

Smooth Muscles Are Much Smaller than Skeletal Muscle Fibers

Smooth muscles are small, spindle-shaped cells with a single nucleus, in contrast to the large multinucleated fibers of skeletal muscles. In neurally controlled smooth muscle, neurotransmitter is released from autonomic neuron varicosities [p. 383] close to the surface of the muscle fibers. Smooth muscle lacks specialized receptor regions such as the motor end plates found in skeletal muscle synapses. Instead, the neurotransmitter simply diffuses across the cell surface until it finds a receptor.

Most smooth muscle is **single-unit smooth muscle** (*unitary smooth muscle*), so called because the individual muscle cells contract as a single unit. Single-unit smooth muscle is also called **visceral smooth muscle** because it forms the walls of internal organs (viscera), such as blood vessels and the intestinal tract. All the fibers of single-unit smooth muscle are electrically connected to one another, so an action potential in one cell will spread rapidly through gap junctions to make the entire sheet of tissue contract (Fig. 12-25a ■). Because all fibers contract every time, no reserve units are left to be recruited to increase contraction force. Instead, the amount of Ca^{2+} that enters the cell determines the force of contraction, as you will learn in the discussion that follows.

(a) Single-unit smooth muscle cells are connected by gap junctions, and the cells contract as a single unit.

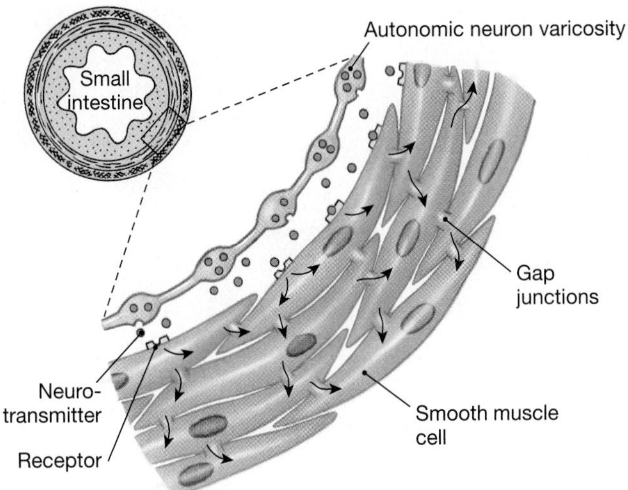

(b) Multi-unit smooth muscle cells are not electrically linked, and each cell must be stimulated independently.

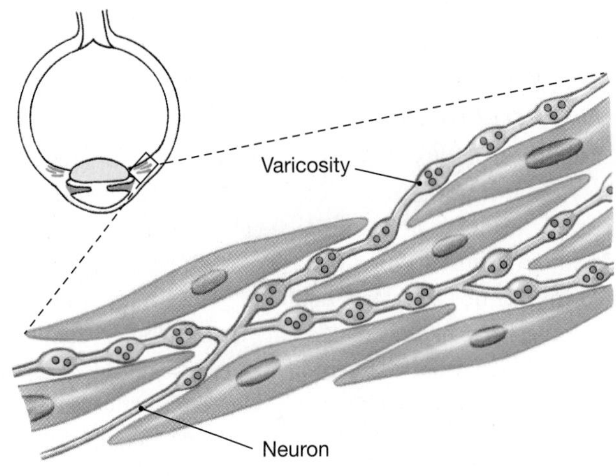

■ **FIGURE 12-25** *Types of smooth muscle*

Multi-unit smooth muscle consists of cells that are not linked electrically. Consequently, each individual muscle cell must be closely associated with an axon terminal or varicosity and stimulated independently (Fig. 12-25b). This arrangement allows fine control of contractions in these muscles through selective activation of individual muscle cells. As in skeletal muscle, increasing the force of contraction requires recruitment of additional fibers.

Multi-unit smooth muscle is found in the iris and ciliary body of the eye, in part of the male reproductive tract, and in the uterus except just prior to labor and delivery. Interestingly, the multi-unit smooth muscle of the uterus changes and becomes single-unit during the final stages of pregnancy. Genes for synthesis of gap junction connexin proteins turn on, apparently under the influence of pregnancy hormones. The addition of gap junctions to the uterine muscle cells synchronizes electrical signals, allowing the uterine muscle to contract more effectively while expelling the baby.

CONCEPT CHECK

22. What is the difference in how contraction force is varied in multi-unit and single-unit smooth muscle?

Answers: p. 434

Smooth Muscle Has Longer Actin and Myosin Filaments

Smooth muscle uses many of the same contractile elements as skeletal muscle: actin-myosin crossbridges, sarcoplasmic reticulum with Ca^{2+} release channels, and a Ca^{2+} signal that initiates the process. However, details of the structural elements and the contraction process differ in the two muscle types.

Smooth muscles have longer actin and myosin filaments than skeletal muscles, and the myosin isoform in smooth muscle is different from that in skeletal muscle. Smooth muscle myosin ATPase activity is much slower, decreasing the rate of crossbridge cycling and lengthening the contraction phase. In addition, one of the smaller protein chains in the myosin head plays a regulatory role in controlling contraction and relaxation. This small regulatory protein chain is called a **myosin light chain**.

Actin is more plentiful in smooth muscle than in striated muscle, with an actin-to-myosin ratio of 10–15 to 1, compared with 2–4 to 1 in striated muscle. Smooth muscle actin is associated with tropomyosin, as in skeletal muscle. However, unlike skeletal muscle, smooth muscle lacks troponin.

Smooth muscle has less sarcoplasmic reticulum than skeletal muscle, although the amount varies from one type of smooth muscle to another. The primary Ca^{2+} release channel in smooth muscle sarcoplasmic reticulum is an **IP_3-receptor channel**. Inositol trisphosphate (IP_3) is a second messenger created in the phospholipase C pathway [p. 184]. The calcium-storage

RUNNING PROBLEM

Three weeks later, Paul had another attack of paralysis, this time at kindergarten after a game of tag. He was rushed to the hospital and given glucose by mouth. Within minutes, he was able to move his legs and arms and asked for his mother.

Question 4:

Explain why oral glucose might help bring Paul out of his paralysis. (Hint: cells use glucose to produce ATP for active transport. The Na^+-K^+-ATPase actively exchanges K^+ and Na^+ across the cell membrane. What happens to the extracellular K^+ level when Paul is given glucose?)

397 410 412 419 423 430

function of the sarcoplasmic reticulum may be supplemented by *caveolae* [p. 149], small vesicles that cluster close to the cell membrane (Fig. 12-26 ■).

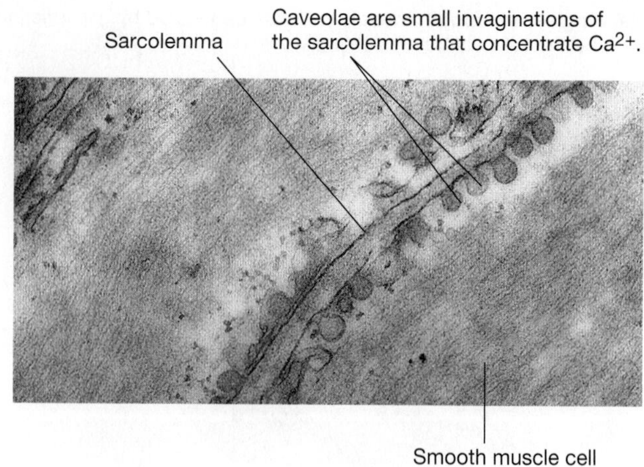

Sarcolemma
Caveolae are small invaginations of the sarcolemma that concentrate Ca^{2+}.
Smooth muscle cell

■ **FIGURE 12-26** ***Caveolae in smooth muscle***

Smooth Muscle Contractile Filaments Are Not Arranged in Sarcomeres

Smooth muscle gets its name from the homogeneous appearance of its cytoplasm under the microscope (Figs. 12-1c and 12-26). The contractile fibers are not arranged in sarcomeres, which is the reason smooth muscle does not have distinct banding patterns as striated muscle does. Instead, actin and myosin are arranged in long bundles that extend diagonally around the cell periphery, forming a lattice around a central nucleus (Fig. 12-27a ■). The oblique arrangement of contractile elements beneath the cell membrane causes smooth muscle fibers to become globular when they contract (Fig. 12-27b), rather than simply shortening as skeletal muscles do.

The long actin filaments of smooth muscle attach to **dense bodies** of protein in the cytoplasm and terminate at protein *attachment plaques* in the cell membrane (Fig. 12-27a, c). The less numerous myosin filaments lie bundled between the long actin filaments and are arranged so that their entire surface is covered by myosin heads (Fig. 12-27d). (Recall that in the sarcomere of skeletal muscles, the center of the myosin filament lacks myosin heads.)

The continuous line of myosin heads allows actin to slide along the myosin for longer distances. This unique organization enables smooth muscle to be stretched more while still maintaining enough overlap to create optimum tension. This is

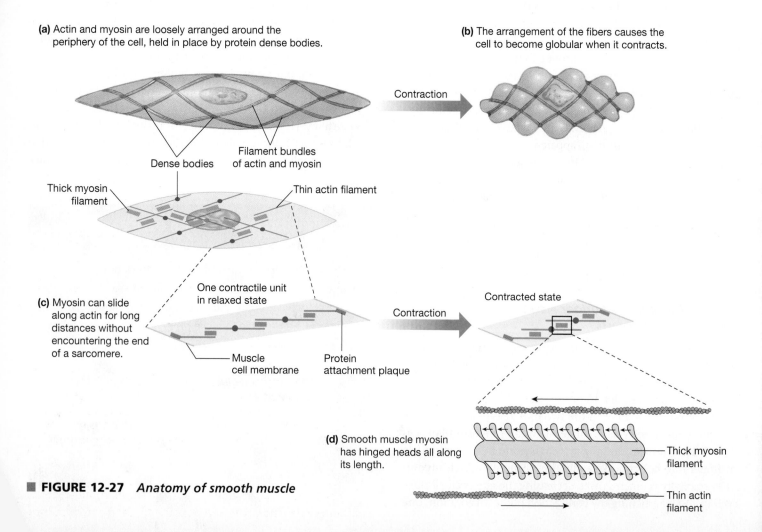

(a) Actin and myosin are loosely arranged around the periphery of the cell, held in place by protein dense bodies.
(b) The arrangement of the fibers causes the cell to become globular when it contracts.
Contraction

Filament bundles of actin and myosin
Thick myosin filament
Thin actin filament
(c) Myosin can slide along actin for long distances without encountering the end of a sarcomere.
One contractile unit in relaxed state
Contraction
Contracted state
Muscle cell membrane

(d) Smooth muscle myosin has hinged heads all along its length.
Thick myosin filament
Thin actin filament

■ **FIGURE 12-27** ***Anatomy of smooth muscle***

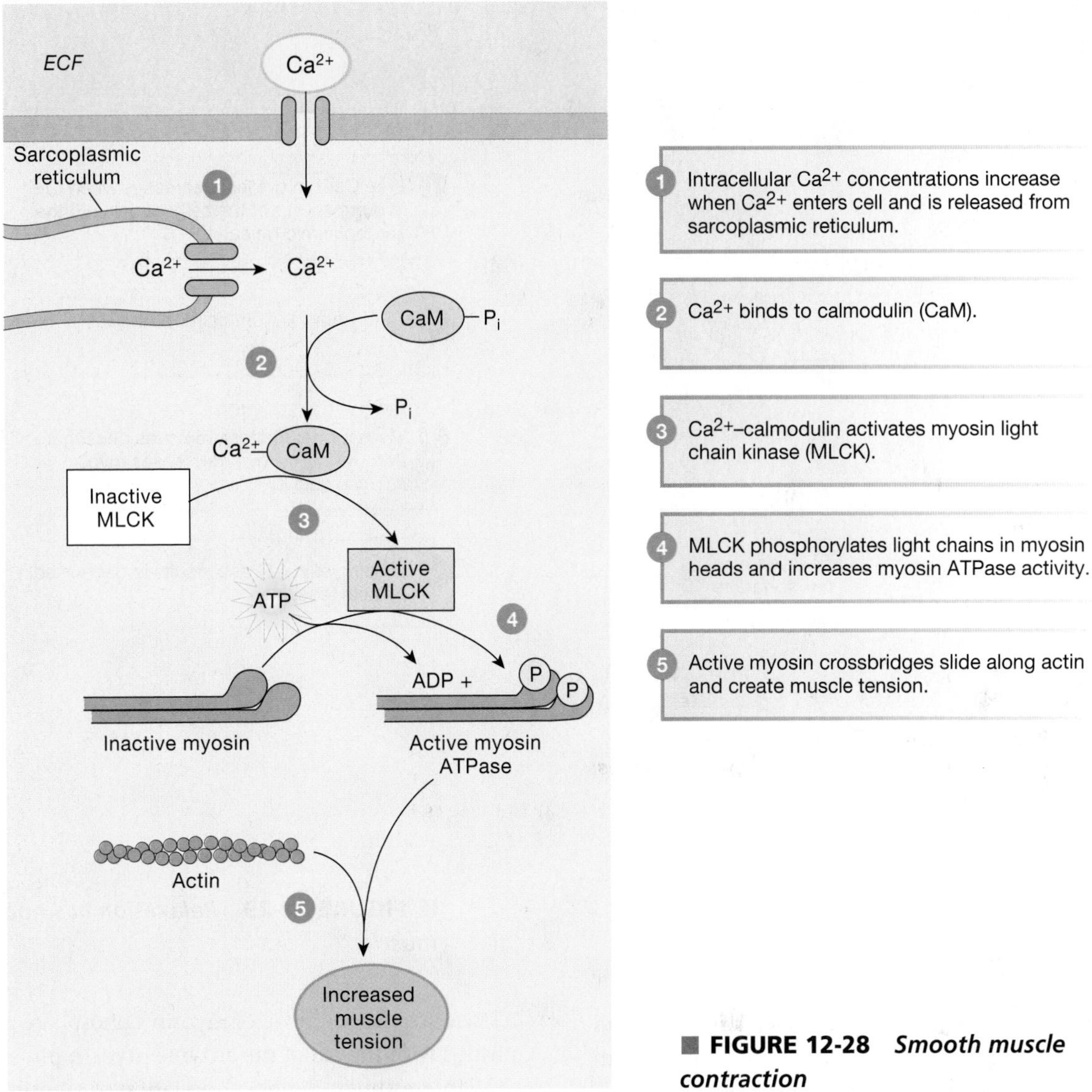

1. Intracellular Ca^{2+} concentrations increase when Ca^{2+} enters cell and is released from sarcoplasmic reticulum.
2. Ca^{2+} binds to calmodulin (CaM).
3. Ca^{2+}–calmodulin activates myosin light chain kinase (MLCK).
4. MLCK phosphorylates light chains in myosin heads and increases myosin ATPase activity.
5. Active myosin crossbridges slide along actin and create muscle tension.

■ **FIGURE 12-28** ***Smooth muscle contraction***

an important property for internal organs, such as the bladder, whose volume varies as it alternately fills and empties.

CONCEPT CHECK

23. The dense bodies that anchor smooth muscle actin are analogous to what structure in a sarcomere? (*Hint:* see Fig. 12-5.)
24. Name three ways smooth muscle myosin differs from skeletal muscle myosin.
25. Name one way actin and its associated proteins differ in skeletal and smooth muscle. Answers: p. 434

Phosphorylation of Proteins Plays a Key Role in Smooth Muscle Contraction

The molecular events of smooth muscle contraction are similar in many ways to those in skeletal muscle, but some important differences exist. The primary difference is the role of phosphorylation in the regulation of contraction. Here is a summary of our current understanding of the key points of smooth muscle contraction. In smooth muscle:

1. An increase in cytosolic Ca^{2+} initiates contraction. Ca^{2+} is released from the sarcoplasmic reticulum and also enters from the extracellular fluid.
2. Ca^{2+} binds to **calmodulin**, a binding protein found in the cytosol. (In skeletal muscle, Ca^{2+} binds to troponin, which smooth muscle lacks.)
3. Ca^{2+} binding to calmodulin is the first step in a cascade that ends in contraction. (In skeletal muscle, Ca^{2+} binding initiates contraction immediately.)
4. Phosphorylation of proteins is an essential step in contraction.
5. The primary control of contraction resides in the regulation of myosin ATPase activity.

CONCEPT CHECK

26. Compare list items 1, 3, 4, and 5 above with what happens during skeletal muscle contraction. (*Hint:* see Fig. 12-11.) Answers: p. 434

Figure 12-28 ■ illustrates the steps of smooth muscle contraction. Contraction begins when cytosolic Ca^{2+} concentrations

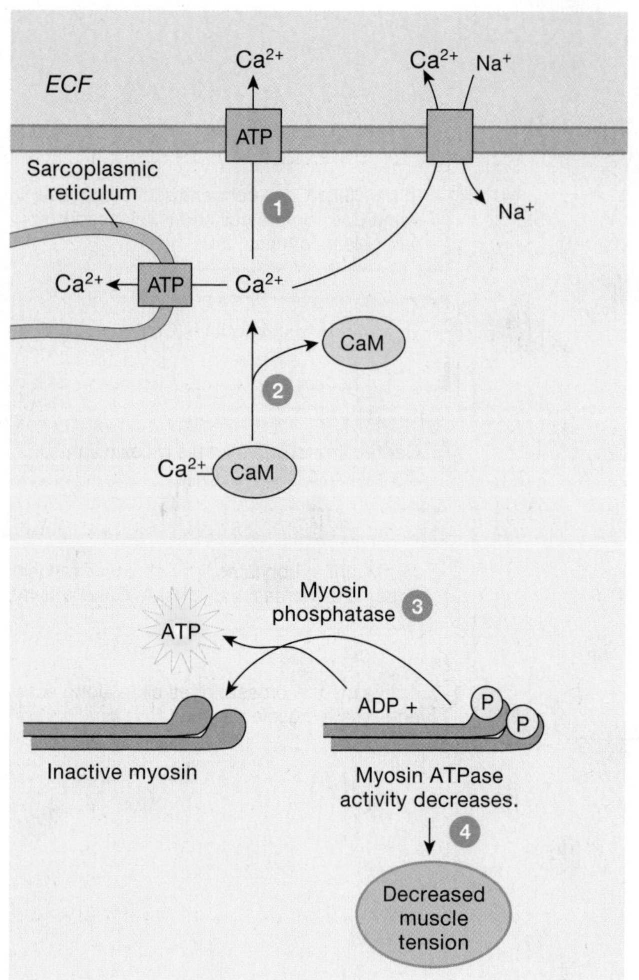
ECF
Ca2+
Ca2+ Na+
ATP
Sarcoplasmic reticulum
Na+
Ca2+ ATP Ca2+
CaM
Ca2+ CaM
Myosin phosphatase
ATP
ADP +
P
P
Inactive myosin
Myosin ATPase activity decreases.
Decreased muscle tension
1 Free Ca2+ in cytosol decreases when Ca2+ is pumped out of the cell or back into the sarcoplasmic reticulum.
2 Ca2+ unbinds from calmodulin (CaM).
3 Myosin phosphatase removes phosphate from myosin, which decreases myosin ATPase activity.
4 Less myosin ATPase results in decreased muscle tension.

■ **FIGURE 12-29** ***Relaxation in smooth muscle***

increase following Ca^{2+} entry from the extracellular fluid and Ca^{2+} release from the sarcoplasmic reticulum. The calcium ions bind to calmodulin (CaM), obeying the law of mass action [p. 39]. The Ca^{2+}-calmodulin complex then activates an enzyme called **myosin light chain kinase (MLCK)**. This enzyme enhances myosin ATPase activity by phosphorylating light protein chains in the myosin head. When myosin ATPase activity is high, actin binding and crossbridge cycling increase tension in the muscle. Thus, smooth muscle contraction is primarily controlled through myosin-linked regulatory processes rather than the actin-linked regulation of skeletal muscle.

Relaxation in Smooth Muscle Has Several Steps

Relaxation in a smooth muscle fiber is a multistep process (Fig. 12-29 ■). As in skeletal muscle, free Ca^{2+} is removed from the cytosol when Ca^{2+}-ATPase pumps it back into the sarcoplasmic reticulum. In addition, some of the Ca^{2+} is pumped out of the cell with the help of a Ca^{2+}-Na^{+} antiport exchanger [p. 139] and Ca^{2+}-ATPase. By the law of mass action, a decrease in free cytosolic Ca^{2+} causes Ca^{2+} to unbind from calmodulin. In the absence of Ca^{2+}-calmodulin, myosin light chain kinase inactivates.

The additional step in smooth muscle relaxation is dephosphorylation of the myosin light chain, which decreases myosin ATPase activity. Removal of myosin's phosphate group is accomplished with the aid of the enzyme **myosin phosphatase**.

Interestingly, dephosphorylation of myosin does not automatically result in relaxation. Under conditions that we do not fully understand, dephosphorylated myosin may remain attached to actin for a period of time in what is known as a **latch state**. This condition maintains tension in the muscle fiber without consuming ATP. It is a significant factor in the ability of smooth muscle to sustain contraction without fatiguing. The hinge muscles of certain bivalve mollusks such as oysters can enter a similar latch state that allows them to remain tightly closed under anaerobic conditions.

CONCEPT CHECK

27. What happens to contraction if a smooth muscle is placed in a saline bath from which all calcium has been removed?

Answers: p. 434

Calcium Entry Is the Signal for Smooth Muscle Contraction

In smooth muscle, an increase in cytosolic Ca^{2+} concentration is the signal to initiate contraction. As you saw in Figure 12-28, Ca^{2+} enters the cell from the extracellular fluid and is released from the sarcoplasmic reticulum. However, because Ca^{2+} stores

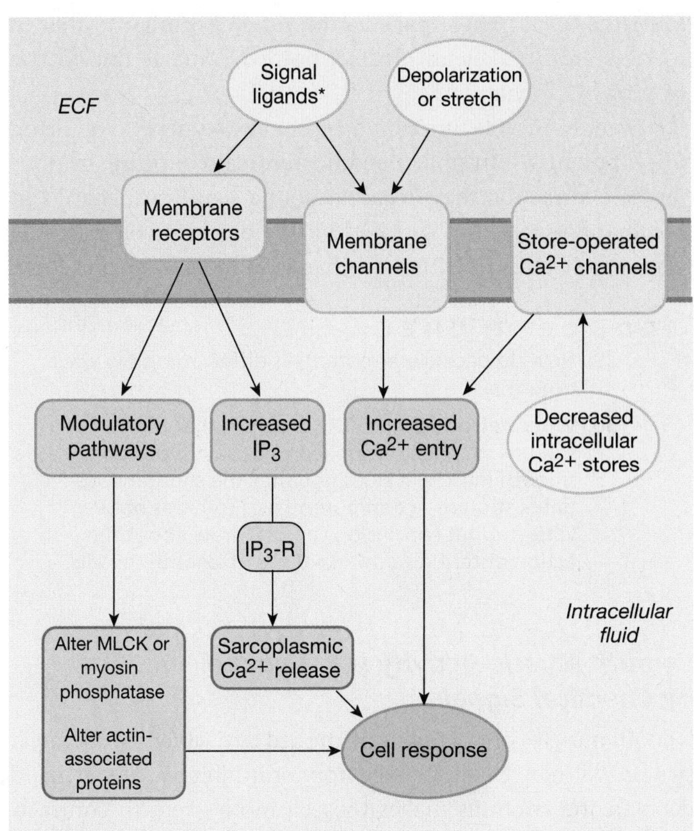

■ **FIGURE 12-30** *Control of smooth muscle contraction*

in smooth muscle are limited, sustained contractions depend on continued influx of Ca^{2+} from the extracellular fluid. The entry of variable amounts of Ca^{2+} into the muscle fiber creates contractions whose force is graded according to the strength of the Ca^{2+} signal.

Recall from the introduction to this section that smooth muscle contraction can be initiated by neurotransmitters, hormones, or paracrines. This is where our model becomes complex. Figure 12-30 ■ is a generalized summary of the multiple pathways that can initiate or modulate contraction in smooth muscle.

Ca^{2+} enters a smooth muscle cell through membrane channels opened by depolarization, membrane stretch, or chemical signals. One recently identified family of Ca^{2+} channels has been named **store-operated Ca^{2+} channels** because these channels open (by an as-yet-unidentified mechanism) in response to depleted intracellular stores of Ca^{2+}. Voltage-gated and stretch-activated channels are discussed in more detail below.

Sarcoplasmic reticulum Ca^{2+} release is mediated primarily by an IP_3-activated receptor-channel. The IP_3 receptor-channel opens as a result of signal transduction pathways begun by extracellular signal molecules.

The increase in cytosolic Ca^{2+} initiates contraction through the regulation of myosin ATPase as discussed in the previous section. In some types of smooth muscle, myosin regulation of crossbridge cycling is supplemented by regulation of actin. Several actin-associated regulatory proteins have been identified, including one called *caldesmon* and another called *calponin*. Second messengers that modulate contraction may act on myosin light chain kinase, on myosin phosphatase, or on the actin-associated regulatory proteins. The details of this modulation are still being worked out.

CONCEPT CHECK

28. Compare Ca^{2+} release channels in skeletal and smooth muscle sarcoplasmic reticulum. Answers: p. 434

Muscle Stretch Opens Ca^{2+} Channels

Smooth muscle cells contain stretch-activated Ca^{2+} channels that open when pressure or other force distorts the cell membrane. Because contraction in this instance originates from a property of the muscle fiber itself, it is known as a **myogenic contraction**. Myogenic contractions are common in blood vessels that maintain a certain amount of tone at all times.

Some smooth muscles adapt if the muscle cells are stretched for an extended period of time. As the stretch stimulus continues, the Ca^{2+} channels begin to close in a time-dependent fashion. Then, as Ca^{2+} is pumped out of the cell, the muscle relaxes. This adaptation response explains why the bladder develops tension as it fills, then relaxes as it adjusts to the increased volume. (There is a limit to the amount of stretch the muscle can endure, however, and once a critical volume is reached, the urination reflex empties the bladder.)

Some Smooth Muscles Have Unstable Membrane Potentials

A major route of Ca^{2+} influx for smooth muscle is entry through voltage-gated Ca^{2+} channels in the cell membrane. However, the role of membrane potentials in smooth muscle contraction is much more complex than in skeletal muscle, where contraction always begins in response to an action potential. In smooth muscle, an action potential is not required to open voltage-gated Ca^{2+} channels. Graded potentials open a few Ca^{2+} channels, allowing small amounts of Ca^{2+} into the cell. This ion entry depolarizes the cell and may open additional Ca^{2+} channels.

In addition, many types of smooth muscle display unstable resting membrane potentials that vary between −40 and −80 mV. Cells that exhibit cyclic depolarization and repolarization of their membrane potential are said to have **slow wave potentials** (Fig. 12-31a ■). Sometimes the cell simply cycles through a series of subthreshold slow waves. However, if the peak of the depolarization reaches threshold, action potentials fire, followed by contraction of the muscle.

(a) Slow wave potentials fire action potentials when they reach threshold.

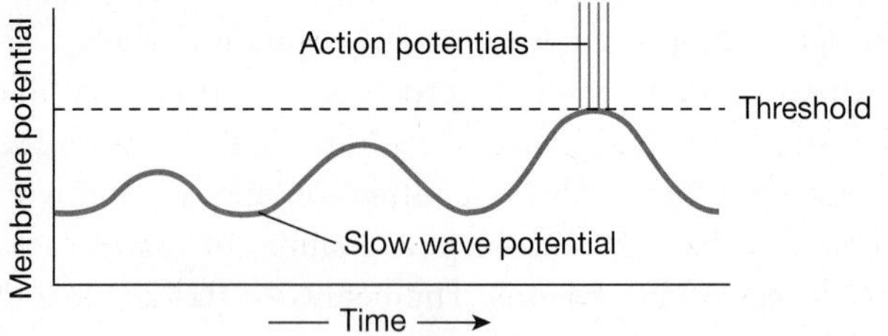

(b) Pacemaker potentials always depolarize to threshold.

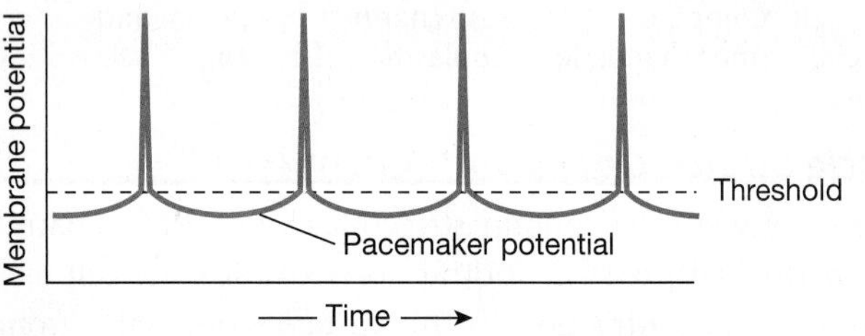

(c) Pharmacomechanical coupling occurs when chemical signals change muscle tension without a change in membrane potential.

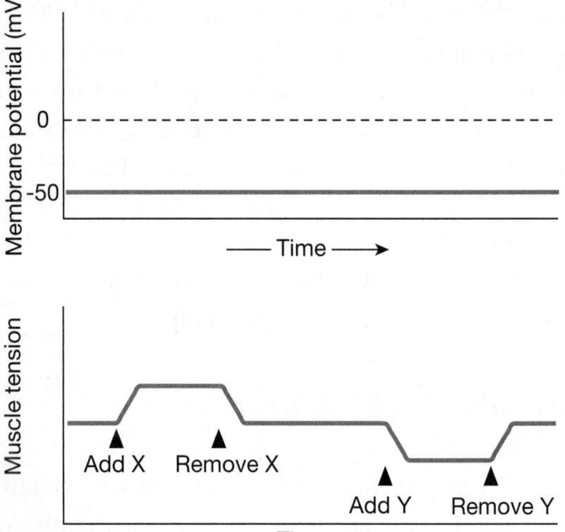

■ **FIGURE 12-31** ***Membrane potentials vary in smooth muscle***

Other types of smooth muscle with unstable membrane potentials have regular depolarizations that always reach threshold and fire an action potential (Fig. 12-31b). These depolarizations are called **pacemaker potentials** because they create regular rhythms of contraction. Pacemaker potentials are found in some cardiac muscles as well as in smooth muscle. Both slow wave and pacemaker potentials are due to ion channels in the cell membrane that spontaneously open and close.

Some smooth muscles have action potentials that look very much like action potentials in neurons. At the cellular level, however, smooth muscle action potentials are different from those in neurons and skeletal muscle because in smooth muscle, the depolarization phase is due to the entry of Ca^{2+} rather than Na^{+}. The repolarization phase is similar to that of neurons and in skeletal muscle, however, and is due to the opening of K^{+} channels.

Smooth muscle function does not always depend on firing action potentials. In **pharmacomechanical coupling**, smooth muscle contraction may occur without a significant change in membrane potential (Fig. 12-31c). Chemical signals may also relax muscle tension without a change in membrane potential.

CONCEPT CHECK

29. How do pacemaker potentials differ from slow wave potentials?
30. When tetrodotoxin (TTX), a poison that blocks sodium channels, is applied to certain types of smooth muscle, it does not alter the spontaneous generation of action potentials. From this observation, what conclusion can you draw about the action potentials of these types of smooth muscle?

Answers: p. 434

Smooth Muscle Activity Is Regulated by Chemical Signals

Smooth muscle contraction is controlled by a variety of chemical signals that may be either excitatory or inhibitory. In general, a depolarizing stimulus makes the cell more likely to contract. Hyperpolarization of the cell decreases the likelihood of contraction. Contraction can be modulated by second messenger action on myosin or by actin regulation.

Autonomic Neurotransmitters Many smooth muscles have dual innervation and are controlled by both sympathetic and parasympathetic neurons. However, other smooth muscles, such as those found in blood vessels, are controlled by only one of the two autonomic branches. In this type of *tonic control,* the response is graded by increasing or decreasing the amount of neurotransmitter released onto the muscle.

As we have seen, a neurotransmitter can have different effects in different tissues, depending on the receptors to which it binds. Thus, both the neurotransmitter and its receptor determine the response of a smooth muscle to nervous stimulation. Adrenergic and cholinergic muscarinic receptors act via IP_3 and cAMP second messenger systems. The exact response of the muscle depends on the adrenergic or cholinergic receptor subtype that is activated.

In addition to norepinephrine and acetylcholine, an amazing variety of other neurotransmitters are active in smooth muscle. In many instances we know how these chemicals affect smooth muscle contraction, but we do not understand the reflex pathways that trigger their release.

CONCEPT CHECK

31. How can a neuron alter the amount of neurotransmitter it releases? (*Hint:* see Fig. 8-13, p. 263)
32. Explain how hyperpolarization decreases the likelihood of contraction in smooth muscle.

Answers: p. 434

TABLE 12-3 Comparison of the Three Muscle Types

	SKELETAL	SMOOTH	CARDIAC
Appearance under light microscope	Striated	Smooth	Striated
Fiber arrangement	Sarcomeres	Oblique bundles	Sarcomeres
Fiber proteins	Actin, myosin; troponin and tropomyosin	Actin, myosin, tropomyosin	Actin, myosin; troponin and tropomyosin
Control	• Voluntary • Ca^{2+} and troponin • Fibers independent of one another	• Involuntary • Ca^{2+} and calmodulin • Fibers electrically linked via gap junctions	• Involuntary • Ca^{2+} and troponin • Fibers electrically linked via gap junctions
Nervous control	Somatic motor neuron	Autonomic neurons	Autonomic neurons
Hormonal influence	None	Multiple hormones	Epinephrine
Location	Attached to bones; a few sphincters close off hollow organs	Forms the walls of hollow organs and tubes; some sphincters	Heart muscle
Morphology	Multinucleate; large, cylindrical fibers	Uninucleate; small spindle-shaped fibers	Uninucleate; shorter branching fibers
Internal structure	T-tubule and sarcoplasmic reticulum	No t-tubules; sarcoplasmic reticulum reduced or absent	T-tubule and sarcoplasmic reticulum
Contraction speed	Fastest	Slowest	Intermediate
Contraction force of single fiber twitch	All-or-none	Graded	Graded
Initiation of contraction	Requires input from motor neuron	Can be autorhythmic	Autorhythmic

Hormones and Paracrines Hormones and paracrines also control smooth muscle contraction—unlike skeletal muscle, whose contraction is controlled only by the nervous system. Smooth muscles in the cardiovascular, gastrointestinal, urinary, respiratory, and reproductive systems respond either to blood-borne or to locally released chemicals. For example, asthma is a condition in which smooth muscle of the airways constricts in response to histamine release. This constriction can be reversed by the administration of epinephrine, a neurohormone that relaxes smooth muscle and dilates the airway. Note from this example that not all physiological responses are adaptive or favorable to the body: constriction of the airways triggered during an asthma attack, if left untreated, can be fatal.

Another important paracrine that affects smooth muscle contraction is *nitric oxide* [p. 187]. This gas is synthesized by the endothelial lining of blood vessels and relaxes adjacent smooth muscle that regulates the diameter of the blood vessels. For many years, the identity of this *endothelium-derived relaxing factor*, or EDRF, eluded scientists even though its presence could be demonstrated experimentally. We know now that EDRF is nitric oxide, an important paracrine in many systems of the body.

Although smooth muscles do not have nearly the mass of skeletal muscles, they play a critical role in the function of most organ systems. You will learn more about smooth muscle physiology in the chapters to come.

CARDIAC MUSCLE

Cardiac muscle, the specialized muscle of the heart, shares features with both smooth and skeletal muscle (Table 12-3 ■). Like skeletal muscle fibers, cardiac muscle fibers are striated and have a sarcomere structure. However, cardiac muscle fibers are shorter than skeletal muscle fibers, may be branched, and have a single nucleus (unlike multinucleate skeletal muscle fibers).

As in single-unit smooth muscle, cardiac muscle fibers are electrically linked to one another. The gap junctions are contained in specialized cell junctions known as *intercalated disks*. Some cardiac muscle, like some smooth muscle, exhibits pacemaker potentials. In addition, cardiac muscle is under sympathetic and parasympathetic control as well as hormonal control. In Chapter 14 you will learn more about cardiac muscle and how it functions within the heart.

RUNNING PROBLEM CONCLUSION

PERIODIC PARALYSIS

In this running problem, you were introduced to hyperkalemic periodic paralysis, a condition caused by a genetic defect in the Na^+ channels on muscle cell membranes. To learn more about hyperkalemic periodic paralysis, go to the web and search for Medlineplus, the illustrated medical encyclopedia of the U.S. National Library of Medicine. Once you read the information about periodic paralysis, compare the hyperkalemic and hypokalemic forms of the disease.

Now check your understanding of this running problem by comparing your answers with the information in the following summary table.

	QUESTION	FACTS	INTEGRATION AND ANALYSIS
1	What effect does the continuous influx of Na^+ have on the membrane potential of Paul's muscle fibers?	The resting membrane potential of cells is negative relative to the extracellular fluid.	The influx of positive charge will depolarize the membrane potential.
2	What ion is responsible for the repolarization phase of the muscle action potential, and in which direction does this ion move across the muscle fiber membrane?	Each muscle twitch results from an action potential in the muscle fiber. In the repolarization phase of the action potential, K^+ leaves the cell.	During the repeated contractions of exercise, K^+ leaves the muscle fiber and accumulates in the t-tubules. This increase in K^+ concentration in the t-tubules affects the Na^+ channels and triggers an attack.
3	Why does a Na^+ channel that will not inactivate cause paralysis?	During an attack, the Na^+ channels remain open and continuously admit Na^+, and the muscle fiber remains depolarized.	If the muscle fiber is unable to repolarize, it cannot fire additional action potentials. The first action potential causes a twitch, but the muscle then goes into a state of flaccid (uncontracted) paralysis.
4	Explain why oral glucose might help bring Paul out of his paralysis.	Muscle fibers use glucose to produce ATP to run the Na^+-K^+-ATPase. This transporter actively moves K^+ and Na^+ across the cell membrane.	Providing glucose to cells may increase the amount of ATP available to run the Na^+-K^+-ATPase, which removes K^+ from the extracellular fluid. Insulin, a hormone that enhances glucose uptake into cells, also helps relieve the paralysis.

397 410 412 419 423 430

12

CHAPTER SUMMARY

Muscles exhibit many of the physiological properties introduced in Chapter 1. They provide an excellent system for studying *structure-function* relationships at all levels, from actin, myosin, and sliding filaments in the cell to muscles pulling on bones and joints. *Mechanical properties* of muscles that influence contraction include elastic components, such as the protein titin and the series elastic elements of the intact muscle. *Compartmentation* is essential to muscle function, as demonstrated by the concentration of Ca^{2+} in the sarcoplasmic reticulum and the key role of Ca^{2+} signals in initiating contraction. The *law of mass action* is at work in the dynamics of Ca^{2+}-calmodulin and Ca^{2+}-troponin binding and unbinding. Muscles also show how *biological energy use* transforms stored energy in ATP's chemical bonds to the movement of motor proteins.

Muscles provide many examples of *communication* and *control* in the body. Communication occurs on a scale as small as electrical signals spreading among smooth muscle cells via gap junctions, or as large as a somatic motor neuron innervating multiple muscle fibers. Skeletal muscles are controlled only by somatic motor neurons, but smooth and cardiac muscle have complex regulation that ranges from neurotransmitters to hormones and paracrines.

1. Muscles generate motion, force, and heat. (p. 397)
2. The three types of muscle are **skeletal muscle**, **cardiac muscle**, and **smooth muscle**. Skeletal and cardiac muscles are **striated muscles**. (p. 397; Fig. 12-1)
3. Skeletal muscles are controlled by somatic motor neurons. Cardiac and smooth muscle are controlled by autonomic innervation, paracrines, and hormones. Some smooth and cardiac muscles are autorhythmic and contract spontaneously. (p. 397)

Skeletal Muscle

IP Muscular Physiology

4. Skeletal muscles are usually attached to bones by tendons. The **origin** is the end of the muscle attached closest to the trunk or to the more stationary bone. The **insertion** is the more distal or mobile attachment. (p. 398)
5. At a flexible joint, muscle contraction moves the skeleton. **Flexors** bring bones closer together; **extensors** move bones away from each other. Flexor-extensor pairs are examples of **antagonistic muscle groups**. (p. 398; Fig. 12-2)
6. A skeletal muscle is a collection of **muscle fibers**, large cells with many nuclei. (p. 398; Fig. 12-3, Tbl. 12-1)
7. **T-tubules** allow action potentials to move rapidly into the interior of the fiber and release calcium from the **sarcoplasmic reticulum**. (p. 398; Fig. 12-4)
8. **Myofibrils** are intracellular bundles of contractile and elastic proteins. **Thick filaments** are made of **myosin**. **Thin filaments** are made mostly of **actin**. **Titin** and **nebulin** hold thick and thin filaments in position. (pp. 399, 402; Figs. 12-3, 12-6)
9. Myosin binds to actin, creating **crossbridges** between the thick and thin filaments. (p. 399; Fig. 12-3)
10. One **sarcomere** is composed of two **Z disks** and the filaments between them. A sarcomere is divided into **I bands** (thin filaments only), an **A band** that runs the length of a thick filament, and a central **H zone** occupied by thick filaments only. The **M line** and Z disks represent attachment sites for myosin and actin, respectively. (p. 399; Fig. 12-5)
11. The force created by a contracting muscle is called **muscle tension**. The **load** is a weight or force that opposes contraction of a muscle. (p. 403)
12. The **sliding filament theory of contraction** states that during contraction, overlapping thick and thin filaments slide past each other in an energy-dependent manner as a result of actin-myosin crossbridge movement. (p. 403; Fig. 12-8)
13. Myosin converts energy from ATP into motion. **Myosin ATPase** hydrolyzes ATP to ADP and P_i. (p. 404; Fig. 12-9)
14. When myosin releases P_i, the myosin molecule moves in the **power stroke**. At the end of the power stroke, myosin releases ADP. The cycle ends in the **rigor state**, with myosin tightly bound to actin. (pp. 404–405; Fig. 12-9)
15. **Tropomyosin** blocks the myosin-binding site on actin. As contraction begins, **troponin** binds to Ca^{2+}. This unblocks the myosin-binding sites and allows myosin to complete its power stroke. (p. 406; Fig. 12-10)
16. During relaxation, the sarcoplasmic reticulum uses a **Ca^{2+} -ATPase** to pump Ca^{2+} back into its lumen. (p. 408)
17. In **excitation-contraction coupling**, a somatic motor neuron releases ACh, which initiates a skeletal muscle action potential that leads to contraction. (p. 407; Fig. 12-11a)
18. Voltage-sensing **DHP receptors** in the t-tubules open **Ca^{2+} release channels** in the sarcoplasmic reticulum. (p. 408; Fig. 12-11a)
19. A single contraction-relaxation cycle is known as a **twitch**. The **latent period** between the end of the muscle action potential and the beginning of muscle tension development represents the time required for Ca^{2+} release and binding to troponin. (p. 409; Fig. 12-12)
20. Muscle fibers store energy for contraction in **phosphocreatine**. Anaerobic metabolism of glucose is a rapid source of ATP but is not efficient. Aerobic metabolism is very efficient but requires an adequate supply of oxygen to the muscles. (p. 410; Fig. 12-13)
21. **Muscle fatigue** is a condition in which a muscle is no longer able to generate or sustain the expected power output. Fatigue has multiple causes. (p. 411; Fig. 12-14)
22. Skeletal muscle fibers can be classified on the basis of their speed of contraction and resistance to fatigue into **fast-twitch glycolytic fibers**, **fast-twitch oxidative-glycolytic fibers**, and **slow-twitch (oxidative) fibers**. Oxidative fibers are the most fatigue resistant. (p. 412–413; Fig. 12-15; Tbl. 12-2)
23. **Myoglobin** is an oxygen-binding pigment that transfers oxygen to the interior of the muscle fiber. (p. 412)
24. The tension of a skeletal muscle contraction is determined by the length of the sarcomeres before contraction begins. (p. 413; Fig. 12-16)
25. Increasing the stimulus frequency causes summation of twitches with an increase of tension. A state of maximal contraction is known as **tetanus**. (p. 415; Fig. 12-17)
26. A **motor unit** is composed of a group of muscle fibers and the somatic motor neuron that controls them. The number of muscle fibers in a motor unit varies, but all fibers in a single motor unit are of the same fiber type. (p. 415; Fig. 12-18)
27. The force of contraction within a skeletal muscle can be increased by **recruitment** of additional motor units. (p. 416)

Mechanics of Body Movement

28. An **isotonic contraction** creates force and moves a load. An **isometric contraction** creates force without moving a load. **Concentric actions** are shortening contractions. **Eccentric actions** are lengthening contractions. (p. 417; Fig. 12-19)
29. Isometric contractions occur because **series elastic elements** allow the fibers to maintain constant length even though the sarcomeres are shortening and creating tension. (p. 417; Fig. 12-20)
30. The body uses its bones and joints as **levers** and **fulcrums**. Most lever-fulcrum systems in the body maximize distance and speed but also require that muscles do more work. (p. 418; Figs. 12-21, 12-22)
31. Contraction speed is a function of muscle fiber type and load. Contraction is fastest when the load on the muscle is zero. (p. 419; Fig. 12-23)

Smooth Muscle

32. Smooth muscle is slower than skeletal muscle but can sustain contractions for longer without fatiguing. (p. 421; Fig. 12-24)
33. **Single-unit smooth muscle** contracts as a single unit when depolarizations pass from cell to cell through gap junctions. In **multi-unit smooth muscle**, individual muscle fibers are stimulated independently. (pp. 422–423; Fig. 12-25)
34. Actin and myosin are arranged along the periphery of a smooth muscle cell. Smooth muscle actin lacks troponin. (p. 423; Fig. 12-27)
35. Smooth muscle has relatively little sarcoplasmic reticulum, and the primary Ca^{2+} release channel is an **IP_3-receptor channel.** (p. 423)
36. In smooth muscle contraction, Ca^{2+} binds to **calmodulin** and activates **myosin light chain kinase** (MLCK). (pp. 425–426; Fig. 12-28)
37. MLCK phosphorylates **myosin light protein chains**, which activates myosin ATPase. This allows crossbridge power strokes. (p. 426; Fig. 12-28)

38. During relaxation, Ca^{2+} is pumped out of the cytosol, and myosin light chains are dephosphorylated by **myosin phosphatase**. (p. 426; Fig. 12-29)
39. Ca^{2+} for contraction enters the cell through Ca^{2+} channels in the cell membrane. Additional Ca^{2+} is released from the sarcoplasmic reticulum. (p. 426; Fig. 12-30)
40. In **myogenic contraction**, stretch opens membrane Ca^{2+} channels. (p. 427)
41. Unstable membrane potentials in smooth muscle take the form of either **slow wave potentials** or **pacemaker potentials**. (pp. 427–428; Fig. 12-31a, b)
42. The rising phase of smooth muscle action potentials is due to Ca^{2+} entry rather than Na^+ entry. (p. 428)
43. In **pharmacomechanical coupling**, Ca^{2+} entry causes smooth muscle contraction without a significant change in membrane potential. (p. 428; Fig. 12-31c)
44. Smooth muscle is controlled by sympathetic and parasympathetic neurons and a variety of chemical signals. (p. 428)

Cardiac Muscle

45. Cardiac muscle fibers are striated, have a single nucleus, and are electrically linked through gap junctions. Cardiac muscle shares features with both skeletal and smooth muscle. (p. 429; Tbl. 12-3)

QUESTIONS

(Answers to the Review Questions begin on page A1.)

THE PHYSIOLOGY PLACE

Access more review material online at **The Physiology Place** website. There you'll find review questions, problem-solving activities, case studies, flashcards, and direct links to both *InterActive Physiology®* and PhysioEx™. To access the site, go to *www.physiologyplace.com* and select Human Physiology, Fourth Edition.

12

LEVEL ONE REVIEWING FACTS AND TERMS

1. The three types of muscle tissue found in the human body are __________, __________, and __________. Which type is attached to the bones, enabling it to control body movement?
2. Which two muscle types are striated?
3. Which type of muscle tissue is controlled only by somatic motor neurons?
4. Which of the following statement(s) is(are) true about skeletal muscles?
   (a) They constitute about 60% of a person's total body weight.
   (b) They position and move the skeleton.
   (c) The insertion of the muscle is more distal or mobile than the origin.
   (d) They are often paired into antagonistic muscle groups called flexors and extensors.
5. Arrange the following skeletal muscle components in order, from outermost to innermost: sarcolemma, connective tissue sheath, thick and thin filaments, myofibrils.
6. The modified endoplasmic reticulum of skeletal muscle is called the __________. Its role is to sequester __________ ions.
7. T-tubules allow __________ to move to the interior of the muscle fiber.
8. List six proteins that make up the myofibrils. Which protein creates the power stroke for contraction?
9. List the letters used to label the elements of a sarcomere. Which band has a Z disk in the middle? Which is the darkest band? Why? Which element forms the boundaries of a sarcomere? Name the line that divides the A band in half. What is the function of this line?
10. Briefly explain the functions of titin and nebulin.
11. During contraction, the __________ band remains a constant length. This band is composed primarily of __________ molecules. Which components approach each other during contraction?
12. Explain the sliding filament theory.
13. Match the following characteristics with the appropriate type(s) of muscle.

(a) has the largest diameter	1. fast-twitch glycolytic fibers
(b) uses anaerobic metabolism, thus fatigues quickly	2. fast-twitch oxidative-glycolytic fibers
(c) has the most blood vessels	3. slow-twitch oxidative fibers
(d) has some myoglobin	
(e) is used for quick, fine movements	
(f) is also called red muscle	
(g) uses a combination of oxidative and glycolytic metabolism	
(h) has the most mitochondria	

14. Explain the roles of troponin, tropomyosin, and Ca^{2+} in skeletal muscle contraction.
15. Which neurotransmitter is released by somatic motor neurons?
16. What is the motor end plate, and what kinds of receptors are found there? Explain how neurotransmitter binding to these receptors creates an action potential.
17. A single contraction-relaxation cycle in a skeletal muscle fiber is known as a __________.
18. List the steps of skeletal muscle contraction that require ATP.
19. The basic unit of contraction in an intact skeletal muscle is the __________. The force of contraction within a skeletal muscle is increased by __________ additional motor units.
20. The two functional types of smooth muscle are __________ and __________.

LEVEL TWO REVIEWING CONCEPTS

21. Make a map of muscle fiber structure using the following terms. Add additional terms if you like (continued page 433).

actin	myosin
Ca^{2+}	nucleus
cell	regulatory protein
cell membrane	sarcolemma

contractile protein
crossbridges
cytoplasm
elastic protein
glycogen
mitochondria
muscle fiber
sarcoplasm
sarcoplasmic reticulum
titin
tropomyosin
troponin
t-tubule

22. Arrange the following terms to create a map of skeletal muscle excitation, contraction, and relaxation. Terms may be used more than once. Add any additional terms you like.

acetylcholine
ACh receptor
actin
action potential
ADP
ATP
axon terminal
Ca^{2+}
Ca^{2+}-ATPase
calcium-release channels
contraction
crossbridge
DHP receptor
end-plate potential
exocytosis
motor end plate
myosin
Na^+
neuromuscular junction
P_i
power stroke
relaxation
rigor state
sarcoplasmic reticulum
somatic motor neuron
tropomyosin
troponin
t-tubules
voltage-gated Ca^{2+} channels

23. How does an action potential in a muscle fiber trigger a Ca^{2+} signal inside the fiber?
24. Muscle fibers depend on a continuous supply of ATP. How do the fibers in the different types of muscle generate ATP? What is used for a backup energy source?
25. Define muscle fatigue. Summarize factors that could play a role in its development. How can muscle fibers adapt to resist fatigue?
26. Explain how you vary the strength and effort made by your muscles in picking up a pencil versus picking up a full gallon container of milk.
27. Compare and contrast the cellular anatomy and neural and chemical control of contraction in skeletal and smooth muscle.
28. What is the role of the sarcoplasmic reticulum in muscular contraction? How can smooth muscle contract when it has so little sarcoplasmic reticulum?
29. Compare and contrast:
    (a) fast-twitch oxidative-glycolytic, fast-twitch glycolytic, and slow-twitch muscle fibers
    (b) a twitch and tetanus
    (c) action potentials in motor neurons and action potentials in skeletal muscles
    (d) temporal summation in motor neurons and summation in skeletal muscles
    (e) isotonic contraction, isometric contraction, concentric action, and eccentric action
    (f) slow-wave and pacemaker potentials
    (g) the source and role of Ca^{2+} in skeletal and smooth muscle contraction
30. Explain the different factors that influence Ca^{2+} entry and release in smooth muscle fibers.

LEVEL THREE PROBLEM SOLVING

31. One way that scientists study muscles is to put them into a state of rigor by removing ATP. In this condition, actin and myosin are strongly linked but unable to move. On the basis of what you know about muscle contraction, predict what would happen to these muscles in a state of rigor if you (a) added ATP but no free calcium ions; (b) added ATP with a substantial concentration of calcium ions.
32. When curare, a South American Indian arrow poison, is placed on a nerve-muscle preparation, the muscle will not contract when the nerve is stimulated, even though neurotransmitter is still being released from the nerve. Give all possible explanations for the action of curare that you can think of.
33. On the basis of what you have learned about muscle fiber types and metabolism, predict what variations in structure you would find among these athletes:
    (a) a 7 foot, 2 inch tall, 325-pound basketball player
    (b) a 5 foot, 10 inch tall, 180-pound steer wrestler
    (c) a 5 foot, 7 inch tall, 130-pound female figure skater
    (d) a 4 foot, 11 inch tall, 89-pound female gymnast

LEVEL FOUR QUANTITATIVE PROBLEMS

34. Look at the following graph, created from data published in "Effect of ambient temperature on human skeletal muscle metabolism during fatiguing submaximal exercise," *Journal of Applied Physiology* 86(3):902–908, 1999. What hypotheses might you develop about the cause(s) of muscle fatigue based on these data?

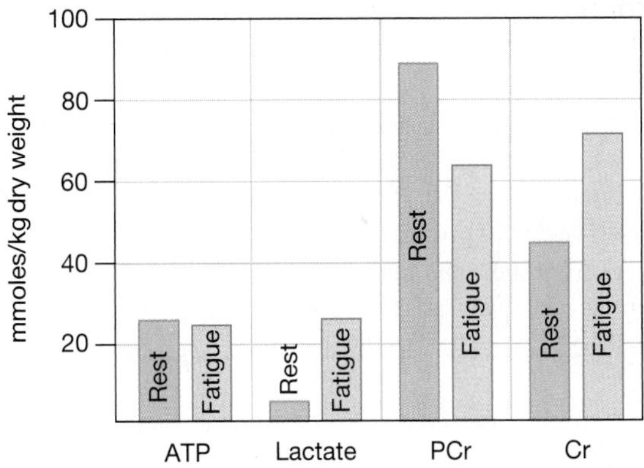

Muscle metabolites in resting muscle and after cycling exercise to fatigue

35. Use the arm in Figure 12-21b to answer the following questions.
    (a) How much force would a biceps muscle inserted 4 cm from the fulcrum need to exert to hold the arm stationary at a 90° angle? How does this force compare with the force needed when the insertion point is 5 cm from the fulcrum?
    (b) If a 7-kg weight band is placed around the wrist 20 cm from the fulcrum, how much force does the biceps inserted 5 cm from the fulcrum need to exert to hold the arm stationary at a 90° angle? How does this force compare with the force needed to keep the arm horizontal in the situation shown in Figure 12.21c, with the same weight in the hand (25 cm from the fulcrum)?

12

ANSWERS

Answers to Concept Check Questions

Page 398

1. Some examples are biceps/triceps in the upper arm; hamstring (flexor)/quadriceps (extensor) in the upper leg; tibialis anterior (flexor)/gastrocnemius (extensor) for foot movement at the ankle.

Page 402

2. Ends of the A bands are darkest because they are where the thick and thin filaments overlap.
3. T-tubules allow action potentials to travel from the surface of the muscle fiber to its interior.
4. The banding pattern of organized filaments in the sarcomere forms striations in the muscle.

Page 403

5. A neuromuscular junction consists of axon terminals from one somatic motor neuron, the synaptic cleft, and the motor end plate on the muscle fiber.
6. The chemical signal at a neuromuscular junction is acetylcholine.

Page 406

7. Each myosin molecule has binding sites for ATP and actin.
8. F-actin is a polymer filament of actin made from globular G-actin molecules.

Page 407

9. Titin is an elastic fiber in the sarcomere.
10. The crossbridges do not all unlink at one time, so while some myosin heads are free and swiveling, others are still tightly bound.

Page 409

11. The release of myosin heads from actin requires ATP binding. Energy from ATP is required for the power stroke. Relaxation does not directly require ATP, but relaxation will not occur unless Ca^{2+} is pumped back into the sarcoplasmic reticulum using a Ca^{2+}-ATPase.
12. The events of the latent period include creation of the muscle action potential, release of Ca^{2+} from the sarcoplasmic reticulum, and diffusion of Ca^{2+} to the contractile filaments.

Page 411

13. *Creatine* is the substrate, and *kinase* tells you that this enzyme phosphorylates the substrate.
14. Because creatine kinase catalyzes the reaction in both directions, the relative concentrations of the reactants and products determine the direction of the reaction. The reaction obeys the law of mass action and goes to equilibrium.

Page 412

15. Increasing extracellular K^+ will cause the cell to depolarize and become less negative.

Page 415

16. Tension.
17. Strength of the graded potential.

Page 416

18. A marathoner probably has more slow-twitch muscle fibers, whereas a sprinter probably has more fast-twitch muscle fibers.

Page 417

19. Increased motor neuron firing rate causes summation in a muscle fiber, which increases the force of contraction.
20. The nervous system increases the force of contraction by recruiting additional motor units.

Page 420

21. If the muscle insertion point is farther from the joint, the leverage is better and a contraction creates more rotational force.

Page 423

22. Multi-unit smooth muscle increases force by recruiting additional muscle fibers; single-unit smooth muscle increases force by increasing Ca^{2+} entry.

Page 425

23. Dense bodies are analogous to Z disks.
24. Smooth muscle myosin is longer, has heads the entire length of the filament, and has slower ATPase activity.
25. Smooth muscle actin is longer than skeletal muscle actin, and it lacks troponin.

Page 425

26. Item 1: In skeletal muscles, all Ca^{2+} comes from the sarcoplasmic reticulum (④ in Fig. 12-11). Item 3: Ca^{2+} binds directly to troponin in skeletal muscle. Item 4: Phosphorylation does not regulate skeletal muscle myosin. Item 5: The primary control point in skeletal muscle is Ca^{2+} binding to troponin.

Page 426

27. Without ECF Ca^{2+}, contraction either decreases or stops altogether because little or no Ca^{2+} is available to initiate the process.

Page 427

28. Skeletal muscle Ca^{2+} release channels are linked to DHP receptors and open upon depolarization. Smooth muscle Ca^{2+} release channels are activated by IP_3.

Page 428

29. Pacemaker potentials always reach threshold and create regular rhythms of contraction. Slow wave potentials are variable in magnitude and may not reach threshold each time.
30. The depolarization phase of the action potentials must not be due to Na^+ entry.

Page 428

31. More action potentials in the neuron increase neurotransmitter release.
32. Many Ca^{2+} channels open with depolarization; therefore, hyperpolarization decreases the likelihood that these channels open. The presence of Ca^{2+} is necessary for contraction.

Answers to Figure and Graph Questions

Page 409

Fig. 12-12: (a) Muscle V_m is −90 mV, and neuron V_m is −70 mV. This illustrates the fact that V_m is not the same in all cells. (b) Muscle action potential is due to Na^+ entering the fiber during depolarization, and K^+ leaving during repolarization.

Page 420

Fig. 12-21: Biceps force × 5 cm = 7 kg × 25 cm = 35 kg (additional force).

Page 421

Fig. 12-22: The hand moves upward at a speed of 5 cm/sec.

Page 421

Fig. 12-23: Contraction is isometric at B because at this point muscle does not shorten. Maximum velocity is at A, where the load on the muscle is zero.

14

Only in the 17th century did the brain displace the heart as the controller of our actions.

—Mary A. B. Brazier, ***A History of Neurophysiology in the 19th Century,*** ***1988***

Immunofluorescent staining of actin (pink) and nebulin (green) in cultured cardiac muscle cells.

Cardiovascular Physiology

BACKGROUND BASICS

Diffusion: **133** Striated muscle: **397** Desmosomes: **71** Excitation-contraction coupling: **403** Length-tension relationship in muscle: **413** Tetanus in skeletal muscle: **415** Muscle contraction: **407** Gap junctions: **175** Catecholamines: **222** Vagus nerve: **381** Isometric contraction: **417**

RUNNING PROBLEM

MYOCARDIAL INFARCTION

At 9: 06 A.M., the blood clot that had silently formed in Walter Parker's left coronary artery made its sinister presence known. The 53-year-old advertising executive had arrived at the Dallas Convention Center feeling fine, but suddenly a dull ache started in the center of his chest, and he became nauseated. At first he brushed it off as the aftereffects of the convention banquet the night before. When the ache persisted, however, he made his way to the Aid Station. "I'm not feeling very well," he told the medic. "I think it may be indigestion." The medic, on hearing Walter's symptoms and seeing his pale, sweaty face, immediately thought of a heart attack. "Let's get you over to the hospital and get this checked out."

In the classic movie *Indiana Jones and the Temple of Doom,* the evil priest reaches into the chest of a sacrificial victim and pulls out his heart, still beating. This act was not dreamed up by some Hollywood scriptwriter—it was taken from rituals of the ancient Mayans, who documented this grisly practice in their carvings and paintings. The heart has been an object of fascination for centuries, but how can this workhorse muscle, which pumps 7200 liters of blood a day, keep beating outside the body? Before we can answer that question, we must first consider the role of hearts in cardiovascular systems.

As life evolved, simple one-celled organisms began to band together, first into cooperative colonies and then into multicelled organisms. In most multicellular animals, only the surface layer of cells is in direct contact with the environment. This body plan presents a problem because diffusion slows as distance increases [p. 133]. For example, oxygen consumption in the interior cells of larger animals exceeds the rate at which oxygen can diffuse from the body surface.

One solution to overcome slow diffusion was the evolutionary development of circulatory systems that move fluid between the body's surface and its deepest parts. In simple animals, muscular activity creates fluid flow when the animal moves. More complex animals have muscular pumps called hearts to circulate internal fluid.

In the most efficient circulatory systems, the heart pumps blood through a closed system of vessels. This one-way circuit steers the blood along a specific route and ensures systematic distribution of gases, nutrients, signal molecules, and wastes. A circulatory system comprising a heart, blood vessels, and blood is known as a **cardiovascular system** [*kardia,* heart + *vasculum,* little vessel].

Although the idea of a closed cardiovascular system that cycles blood in an endless loop seems intuitive to us today, it has not always been so. **Capillaries**, the microscopic vessels in which blood exchanges material with the interstitial fluid, were not discovered until Marcello Malpighi, an Italian anatomist, observed them through a microscope in the middle of the seventeenth century. At that time European medicine was still heavily influenced by the ancient belief that the cardiovascular system distributed both blood and air.

Blood was thought to be made in the liver and distributed throughout the body in the veins. Air went from the lungs to the heart, where it was digested and picked up "vital spirits." From the heart, air was distributed to the tissues through vessels called arteries. Anomalies—such as the fact that a cut artery squirted blood rather than air—were ingeniously explained by unseen links between arteries and veins that opened upon injury.

According to this model of the circulatory system, the tissues consumed all blood delivered to them, and the liver had to synthesize new blood continuously. It took the calculations of William Harvey (1578–1657), court physician to King Charles I of England, to show that the weight of blood pumped by the heart in a single hour exceeds the weight of the entire body! Once it became obvious that the liver could not make blood as rapidly as the heart pumped it, Harvey looked for an anatomical route that would allow the blood to recirculate rather than be consumed in the tissues. He showed that valves in the heart and veins created a one-way flow of blood, and that veins carried blood back to the heart, not out to the limbs. He also showed that blood entering the right side of the heart had to go to the lungs before it could go to the left side of the heart.

The results of these studies created a furor among Harvey's contemporaries, leading Harvey to say in a huff that no one under the age of 40 could understand his conclusions. Ultimately, Harvey's work became the foundation of modern cardiovascular physiology. Today, we understand the structure of the cardiovascular system at microscopic and molecular levels that Harvey never dreamed existed. Yet some things have not changed. Even now, with our sophisticated technology, we are searching for "spirits" in the blood, although today we call them by such names as *hormone* and *cytokine*.

OVERVIEW OF THE CARDIOVASCULAR SYSTEM

In the simplest terms, a cardiovascular system is a series of tubes (the blood vessels) filled with fluid (blood) and connected to a pump (the heart). Pressure generated in the heart propels blood through the system continuously. The blood picks up oxygen at the lungs and nutrients in the intestine and then delivers these substances to the body's cells while simultaneously removing cellular wastes for excretion. In addition, the cardiovascular system plays an important role in cell-to-cell communication and in defending the body against foreign invaders. This chapter focuses on an overview of the cardiovascular system and on the heart as a pump. We will examine the properties of the blood vessels and the homeostatic controls that regulate blood flow and blood pressure in Chapter 15.

The Cardiovascular System Transports Materials Throughout the Body

The primary function of the cardiovascular system is the transport of materials to and from all parts of the body. Substances transported by the cardiovascular system can be divided into (1) nutrients, water, and gases that enter the body from the external environment, (2) materials that move from cell to cell within the body, and (3) wastes that the cells eliminate (Table 14-1 ■).

Oxygen enters the body at the exchange surface of the lungs. Nutrients and water are absorbed across the intestinal epithelium. Once in the blood, all these materials are distributed by the circulation. A steady supply of oxygen for the cells is particularly important because many cells deprived of oxygen become irreparably damaged within a short period of time. For example, about 5–10 seconds after blood flow to the brain is stopped, a person loses consciousness. If oxygen delivery stops for 5–10 minutes, permanent brain damage results. Neurons of the brain have a very high rate of oxygen consumption and are unable to meet their metabolic need for ATP by using anaerobic pathways, which have low yields of ATP/glucose [p. 106]. Because of the brain's sensitivity to *hypoxia* [*hypo-*, low + *-oxia*, oxygen], homeostatic controls do everything possible to maintain cerebral blood flow, even if it means depriving other cells of oxygen.

Cell-to-cell communication is a key function of the cardiovascular system. For example, hormones secreted by endocrine glands are carried in the blood to their targets. Nutrients, such as glucose from the liver and fatty acids from adipose tissue, are transported to metabolically active cells. Finally, the defense team of white blood cells and antibodies patrols the circulation to intercept foreign invaders.

The cardiovascular system also picks up carbon dioxide and metabolic wastes released by cells and transports them to the lungs and kidneys for excretion. Some waste products are transported to the liver for processing before they are excreted in the urine or feces. Heat also circulates through the blood, moving from the body core to the surface, where it dissipates.

The Cardiovascular System Consists of the Heart, Blood Vessels, and Blood

The cardiovascular system is composed of the heart, the blood vessels (also known as the *vasculature*), and the cells and plasma of the blood. Blood vessels that carry blood away from the heart are called **arteries**. Blood vessels that return blood to the heart are called **veins**.

TABLE 14-1 Transport in the Cardiovascular System

SUBSTANCE MOVED	FROM	TO
Materials entering the body		
Oxygen	Lungs	All cells
Nutrients and water	Intestinal tract	All cells
Materials moved from cell to cell		
Wastes	Some cells	Liver for processing
Immune cells, antibodies, clotting proteins	Present in blood continuously	Available for any cell that needs them
Hormones	Endocrine cells	Target cells
Stored nutrients	Liver and adipose tissue	All cells
Materials leaving the body		
Metabolic wastes	All cells	Kidneys
Heat	All cells	Skin
Carbon dioxide	All cells	Lungs

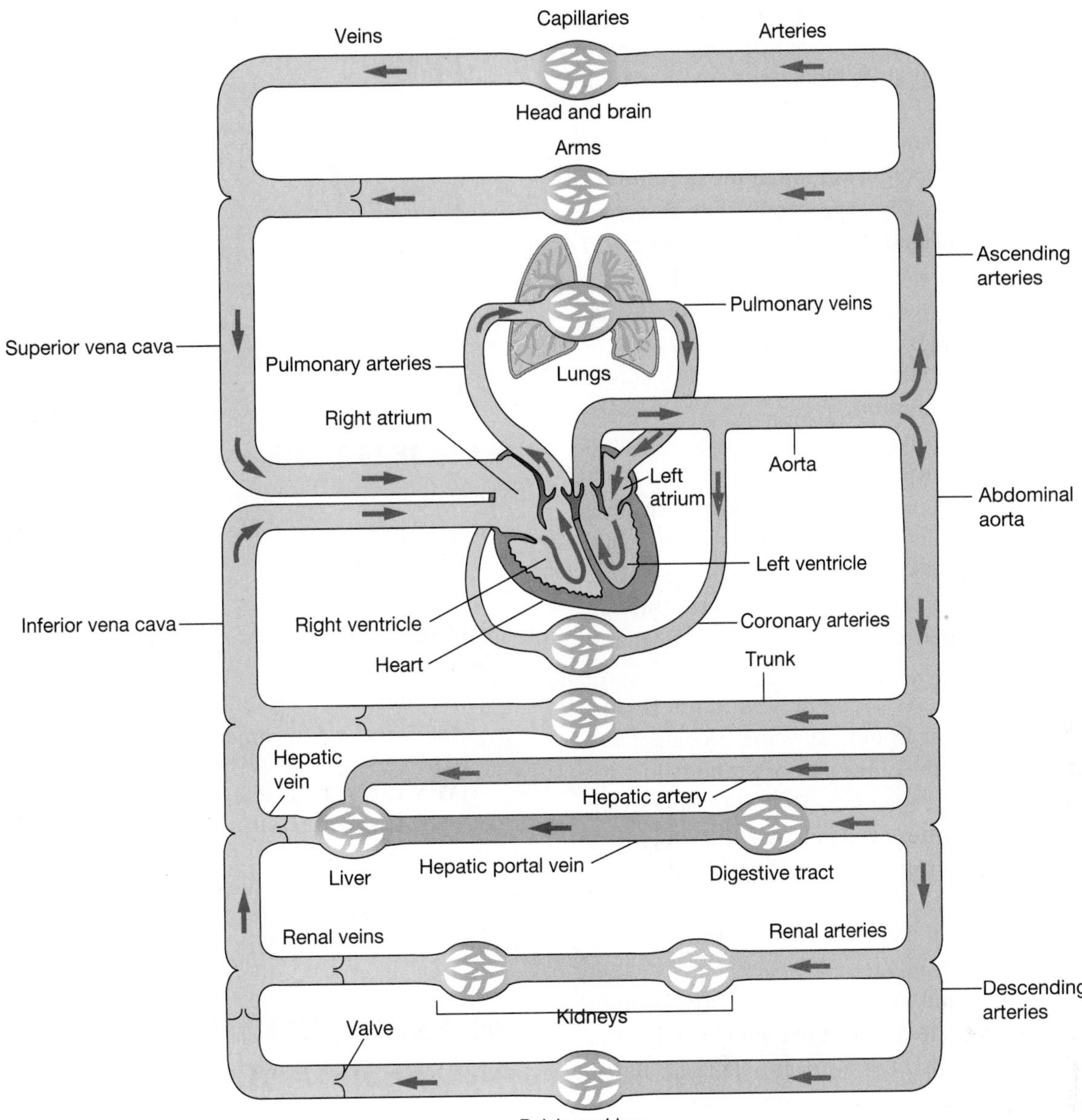

■ **FIGURE 14-1** ***Overview of cardiovascular system anatomy***

As blood moves through the cardiovascular system, a system of valves in the heart and veins ensures that the blood flows in one direction only. Like the turnstiles at an amusement park, the valves keep the blood from reversing its direction of flow. Figure 14-1 ■ is a schematic diagram that shows these components and the route that blood follows through the body. Notice in this illustration, as well as in most other diagrams of the heart, that the right side of the heart is on the left side of the page; that is, the heart is labeled as if you were viewing the heart of a person facing you.

The heart is divided by a central wall, or **septum**, into left and right halves. Each half functions as an independent pump that consists of an **atrium** [*atrium*, central room; plural *atria*] and a **ventricle** [*ventriculus*, belly]. The atrium receives blood returning to the heart from the blood vessels; the ventricle pumps blood out into the blood vessels. The right side of the heart receives blood from the tissues and sends it to the lungs for oxygenation. The left side of the heart receives newly oxygenated blood from the lungs and pumps it to tissues throughout the body.

Starting in the right atrium in Figure 14-1, trace the path taken by blood as it flows through the cardiovascular system. Note that blood in the right side of the heart is colored blue. This is a convention used to show blood from which the tissues have extracted oxygen. Although this blood is often described as *deoxygenated*, it is not completely devoid of oxygen. It simply has less oxygen than blood going from the lungs to the tissues.

In living people, well-oxygenated blood is bright red, and low-oxygen blood is a darker red. Under some conditions, low-oxygen blood can impart a bluish color to certain areas of the skin, such as around the mouth and under the fingernails. This condition, known as *cyanosis* [*kyanos,* dark blue], is the reason blue is used in drawings to indicate blood with lower oxygen content.

From the right atrium, blood flows into the right ventricle of the heart. From there it is pumped through the **pulmonary arteries** to the lungs, where it is oxygenated. Note the color change from blue to red in Figure 14-1, indicating higher oxygen content after the blood leaves the lungs. From the lungs, blood travels to the left side of the heart through the **pulmonary veins.** The blood vessels that go from the right ventricle to the lungs and back to the left atrium are known collectively as the **pulmonary circulation.**

Blood from the lungs enters the heart at the left atrium and passes into the left ventricle. Blood pumped out of the left ventricle enters the large artery known as the **aorta**. The aorta branches into a series of smaller and smaller arteries that finally lead into networks of capillaries. Notice at the top of Figure 14-1 the color change from red to blue as the blood passes through the capillaries, indicating that oxygen has left the blood and diffused into the tissues.

After leaving the capillaries, blood flows into the venous side of the circulation, moving from small veins into larger and larger veins. The veins from the upper part of the body join together to form the **superior vena cava**. Those from the lower part of the body form the **inferior vena cava**. The two *venae cavae* empty into the right atrium. The blood vessels that carry blood from the left side of the heart to the tissues and back to the right side of the heart are collectively known as the **systemic circulation**.

Return to Figure 14-1 and follow the divisions of the aorta after it leaves the left ventricle. The first branch represents the *coronary arteries,* which nourish the heart muscle itself. Blood from these arteries flows into capillaries, then into the *coronary veins,* which empty directly into the right atrium at the *coronary sinus*. Ascending branches of the aorta go to the arms, head, and brain. The abdominal aorta supplies blood to the trunk, the legs, and the internal organs such as the kidneys (*renal arteries*), liver (*hepatic artery*), and digestive tract.

Notice two special arrangements of the circulation. One is the blood supply to the digestive tract and liver. Both regions receive well-oxygenated blood through their own arteries, but, in addition, blood leaving the digestive tract goes directly to the liver by means of the *hepatic portal vein*. The liver is an important site for nutrient processing and plays a major role in the detoxification of foreign substances. Most nutrients absorbed in the intestine are routed directly to the liver, allowing that organ to process material before it is released into the general circulation. The two capillary beds of the digestive tract and liver, joined by the hepatic portal vein, are examples of a *portal system*.

A second portal system occurs in the kidneys, where two capillary beds are connected in series. You will learn more about this special vascular arrangement in Chapter 19. A third portal system, discussed earlier but not shown here, is the hypothalamic-hypophyseal portal system, which connects the hypothalamus and the anterior pituitary [p. 229].

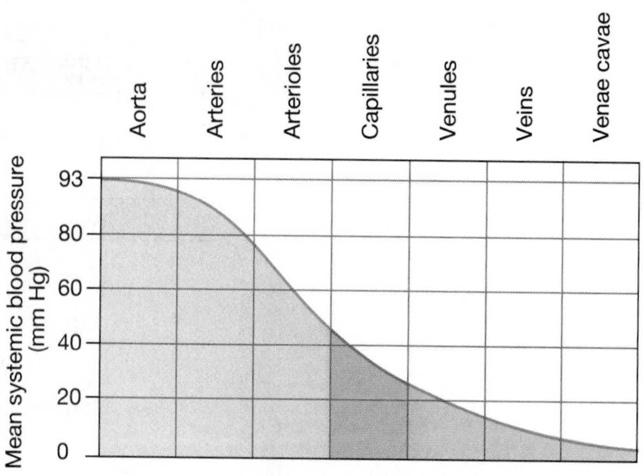

■ **FIGURE 14-2** ***Pressure gradient in the blood vessels***

The mean blood pressure of the systemic circulation ranges from a high of 93 mm Hg (millimeters of mercury) in the aorta to a low of a few mm Hg in the venae cavae.

CONCEPT CHECK

1. A cardiovascular system has what three major components?
2. What is the difference between (a) the pulmonary and systemic circulations, (b) an artery and a vein, (c) an atrium and a ventricle?

Answers: p. 498

PRESSURE, VOLUME, FLOW, AND RESISTANCE

If you ask people why blood flows through the cardiovascular system, many of them respond, "So that oxygen and nutrients can get to all parts of the body." Although this is true, it is a teleological answer, one that describes the purpose of blood flow. In physiology, we are also concerned with how blood flows—in other words, with the mechanisms or forces that create blood flow.

A simple mechanistic answer to "Why does blood flow?" is that liquids and gases flow down **pressure gradients** (**ΔP**) from regions of higher pressure to regions of lower pressure. Therefore, blood can flow in the cardiovascular system only if one region develops higher pressure than other regions.

In humans, high pressure is created in the chambers of the heart when it contracts. Blood flows out of the heart (the region of highest pressure) into the closed loop of blood vessels (a region of lower pressure). As blood moves through the system, pressure is lost because of friction between the fluid and the blood vessel walls. Consequently, pressure falls continuously as blood moves farther from the heart (Fig. 14-2 ■). The highest

(a)

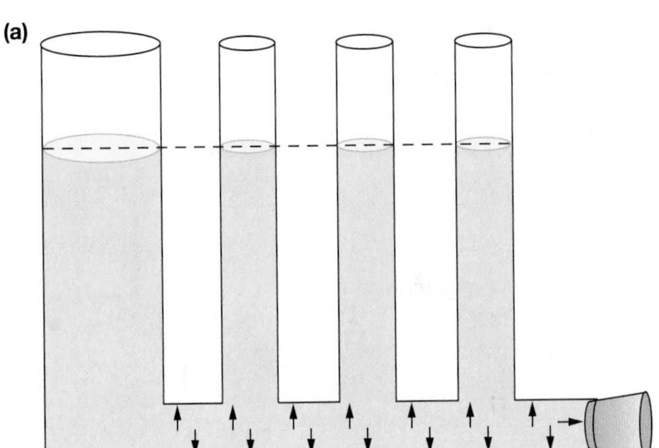

Hydrostatic pressure is the pressure exerted on the walls of the container by the fluid within the container. Hydrostatic pressure is proportional to the height of the water column.

(b)

Once fluid begins to flow through the system, pressure falls with distance as energy is lost because of friction. This is the situation in the cardiovascular system.

■ **FIGURE 14-3** ***Pressure differences in static and flowing fluids***

pressure in the vessels of the cardiovascular system is found in the aorta and systemic arteries as they receive blood from the left ventricle. The lowest pressure is in the venae cavae, just before they empty into the right atrium.

In this section we review the laws of physics that explain the interaction of pressure, volume, flow, and resistance in the cardiovascular system. Many of these principles apply broadly to the flow of all types of liquids and gases, including the flow of air in the respiratory system. However, in this chapter we will focus on the flow of blood and its relevance to the function of the heart.

The Pressure of Fluid in Motion Decreases over Distance

Pressure in a fluid is the force exerted by the fluid on its container. If the fluid is not moving, the pressure it exerts is called **hydrostatic pressure** (Fig. 14-3a ■), and force is exerted equally in all directions. For example, a column of fluid in a tube exerts hydrostatic pressure on the floor and sides of the tube. In the heart and blood vessels, pressure is commonly measured in millimeters of mercury (mm Hg).* One millimeter of mercury is equivalent to the hydrostatic pressure exerted by a 1-mm-high column of mercury on an area of 1 cm^2.

In a system in which fluid is flowing, pressure falls over distance as energy is lost because of friction (Fig. 14-3b). In addition, the pressure exerted by moving fluid has two components: a dynamic, flowing component that represents the kinetic energy of the system, and a lateral component that represents the hydrostatic pressure (potential energy) exerted on the walls of the system. Pressure within our cardiovascular system is usually called hydrostatic pressure even though it is a

RUNNING PROBLEM

When people speak of a "heart attack," they are referring to a clot that stops the blood supply to part of the heart, creating a condition known as *ischemia* [*ischien,* to suppress + *-emia,* blood]. In medical terms, a heart attack is called a *myocardial infarction,* referring to an area of heart muscle that is dying because of a lack of blood supply. The clot in Walter's coronary artery had restricted blood flow to his heart, and its cells were beginning to die from lack of oxygen. When someone has a heart attack, immediate medical intervention is critical. While waiting for the ambulance, the medic gave Walter oxygen, hooked him to a heart monitor, and started an intravenous (IV) injection of normal (isotonic) saline. With an intravenous injection line in place, other drugs could be given rapidly if Walter's condition should suddenly worsen.

Question 1:
Why did the medic give Walter oxygen?

Question 2:
What effect would the injection of isotonic saline have on Walter's extracellular fluid volume? On his intracellular fluid volume? On his total body osmolarity? [Hint: p. 157]

*Some physiological literature reports pressures in torr (1 torr = 1 mm Hg) or in centimeters of water: 1 cm H_2O = 0.74 mm Hg.

system in which fluid is in motion. Some textbooks are beginning to replace the term *hydrostatic pressure* with the term *hydraulic pressure*. Hydraulics is the study of fluid in motion.

Pressure Changes in Liquids Without a Change in Volume

If the walls of a fluid-filled container contract, the pressure exerted on the fluid in the container increases. You can demonstrate this principle by filling a balloon with water and squeezing the water balloon in your hand. Water is minimally compressible, and so the pressure you apply to the balloon is transmitted throughout the fluid. As you squeeze, higher pressure in the fluid causes parts of the balloon to bulge. If the pressure becomes high enough, the stress on the balloon will cause it to pop. The water volume inside the balloon did not change, but the pressure in the fluid increased.

In the human heart, contraction of the blood-filled ventricles is similar to squeezing a water balloon: pressure created by the contracting muscle is transferred to the blood. This high-pressure blood then flows out of the ventricle and into the blood vessels, displacing lower-pressure blood already in the vessels. The pressure created in the ventricles is called the **driving pressure** because it is the force that drives blood through the blood vessels.

When the walls of a fluid-filled container expand, the pressure exerted on the fluid decreases. Thus, when the heart relaxes and expands, pressure in the fluid-filled chambers falls.

Pressure changes can also take place in the blood vessels. If blood vessels dilate, blood pressure inside them falls. If blood vessels constrict, blood pressure increases. Volume changes of the blood vessels and heart are major factors that influence blood pressure in the cardiovascular system.

Blood Flows from an Area of Higher Pressure to One of Lower Pressure

As stated earlier, blood flow through the cardiovascular system requires a pressure gradient. This pressure gradient is analogous to the difference in pressure between two ends of a tube through which fluid flows (Fig. 14-4a ■). Flow through the tube is directly proportional to (∝) the pressure gradient (ΔP):

$$\text{Flow} \propto \Delta P \quad (1)$$

where $\Delta P = P_1 - P_2$. This relationship says that the higher the pressure gradient, the greater the fluid flow.

A pressure gradient is not the same thing as the absolute pressure in the system. For example, the tube in Figure 14-4b has an absolute pressure of 100 mm Hg at each end. However, because there is no pressure gradient between the two ends of the tube, there is no flow through the tube.

On the other hand, two identical tubes can have very different absolute pressures but the same flow. The top tube in Figure 14-4c has a hydrostatic pressure of 100 mm Hg at one end and 75 mm Hg at the other end, which means that the pressure gradient between the ends of the tube equals 25 mm Hg. The identical bottom tube has a hydrostatic pressure of 40 mm Hg at one end and 15 mm Hg at the other end. This tube has lower absolute pressure all along its length but the same pressure gradient as the top tube—25 mm Hg. Because the pressure difference in the two tubes is identical, the fluid flow through the tubes is the same.

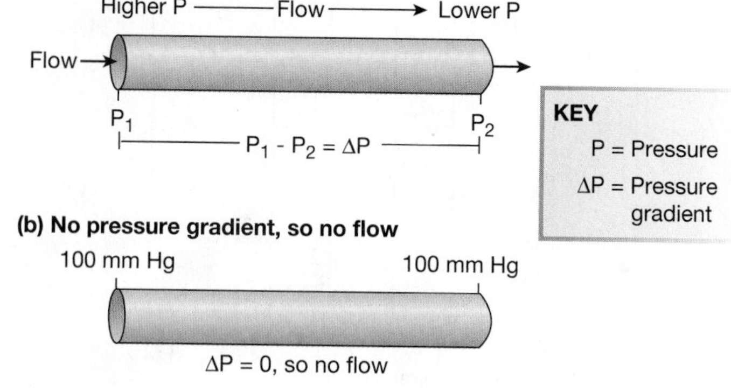

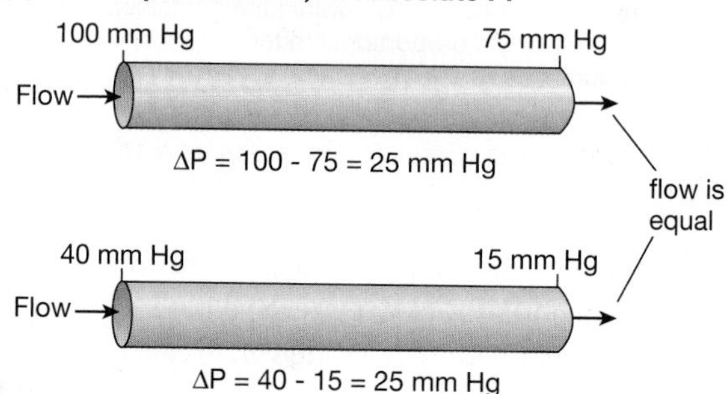

■ **FIGURE 14-4** ***Fluid flow through a tube***

Resistance Opposes Flow

In an ideal system, a substance in motion would remain in motion. However, no system is ideal because all movement creates friction. Just as a ball rolled across the ground loses energy to friction, blood flowing through blood vessels encounters friction from the walls of the vessels and from cells within the blood rubbing against one another as they flow.

The tendency of the cardiovascular system to oppose blood flow is called the system's **resistance** to flow. Resistance (R) is a term that most of us understand from everyday life. We speak of people being resistant to change or taking the path of least resistance. This concept translates well to the cardiovascular system because blood flow also takes the path of least resistance. An increase in the resistance of a blood vessel results in a decrease in the flow through that vessel. We can express that relationship as

$$\text{Flow} \propto 1/R \quad (2)$$

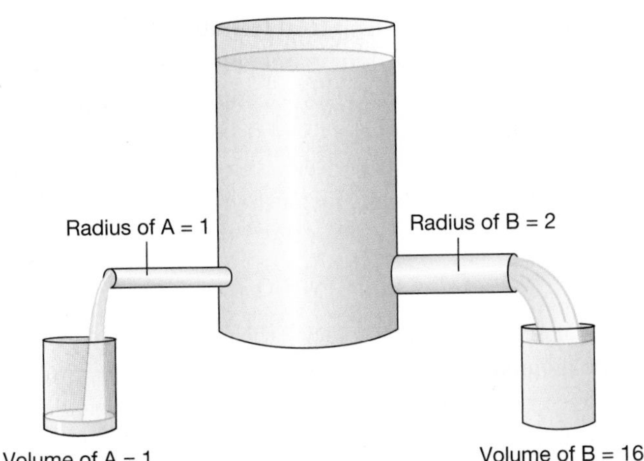

Resistance $\propto \frac{1}{\text{radius}^4}$	
Tube A	Tube B
$R \propto \frac{1}{1^4}$ $R \propto 1$	$R \propto \frac{1}{2^4}$ $R \propto \frac{1}{16}$

Flow $\propto \frac{1}{\text{resistance}}$	
Tube A	Tube B
Flow $\propto \frac{1}{1}$ Flow $\propto 1$	Flow $\propto \frac{1}{\frac{1}{16}}$ Flow $\propto 16$

■ **FIGURE 14-5** ***The role of radius in determining resistance to flow***

This expression says that flow is inversely proportional to resistance: if resistance increases, flow decreases; if resistance decreases, flow increases.

What parameters determine resistance? For fluid flowing through a tube, resistance is influenced by three components: the radius of the tube (r), the length of the tube (L), and the **viscosity** (thickness) of the fluid (η, the Greek letter eta). The following equation, derived by the French physician Jean Leonard Marie Poiseuille and known as **Poiseuille's law**, shows the relationship of these factors:

$$R = 8L\eta/\pi r^4 \qquad (3)$$

Because the value of $8/\pi$ is a constant, this factor can be removed from the equation, and the relationship can be rewritten as

$$R \propto L\eta/r^4 \qquad (4)$$

This expression says that (1) the resistance to fluid flow offered by a tube increases as the length of the tube increases, (2) resistance increases as the viscosity of the fluid increases, but (3) resistance decreases as the tube's radius increases.

To remember these relationships, think of drinking through a straw. You do not need to suck as hard on a short straw as on a long one (the resistance offered by the straw increases with length). Drinking water through a straw is easier than drinking a thick milkshake (resistance increases with viscosity). And drinking the milkshake through a big fat straw is much easier than through a skinny cocktail straw (resistance increases as radius decreases).

How significant are tube length, fluid viscosity, and tube radius to blood flow in a normal individual? The length of the systemic circulation is determined by the anatomy of the system and is essentially constant. Blood viscosity is determined by the ratio of red blood cells to plasma and by how much protein is in the plasma. Normally, viscosity is constant, and small changes in either length or viscosity have little effect on resistance. This leaves changes in the radius of the blood vessels as the main variable that affects resistance in the systemic circulation.

Let's return to the example of the straw and the milkshake to illustrate how changes in radius affect resistance. If we assume that the length of the straw and the viscosity of the milkshake do not change, this system is similar to the cardiovascular system—the radius of the tube has the greatest effect on resistance. If we consider only resistance (R) and radius (r) from equation 4, the relationship between resistance and radius can be expressed as

$$R \propto 1/r^4 \qquad (5)$$

If the skinny straw has a radius of 1, its resistance is proportional to $1/1^4$, or 1. If the fat straw has a radius of 2, the resistance it offers is $1/2^4$, or 1/16th, that of the skinny straw (Fig. 14-5 ■). Because flow is inversely proportional to resistance, flow increases 16-fold when the radius doubles.

As you can see from this example, a small change in the radius of a tube has a large effect on the flow of a fluid through that tube. Thus a small change in the radius of a blood vessel will have a large effect on the resistance to blood flow offered by that vessel. A decrease in blood vessel diameter is known as **vasoconstriction** [*vas*, a vessel or duct]. An increase in blood vessel diameter is called **vasodilation**. Vasoconstriction decreases blood flow through a vessel; vasodilation increases blood flow through a vessel.

In summary, by combining equations 1 and 2, we get the equation

$$\text{Flow} \propto \Delta P/R \qquad (6)$$

which, translated into words, says that the flow of blood in the cardiovascular system is directly proportional to the pressure gradient in the system, and inversely proportional to the resistance of the system to flow. If the pressure gradient remains constant, then flow will vary inversely with resistance.

CONCEPT CHECK

3. Which is more important for determining flow through a tube: absolute pressure or the pressure gradient?
4. The following two identical tubes have the pressures shown at each end. Which tube has the greater flow? Defend your choice.

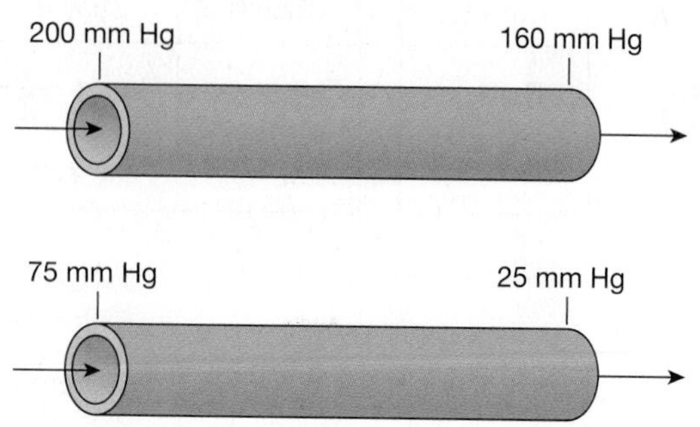

5. The following four tubes have the same driving pressure. Which tube has the highest flow? Which has the lowest flow? Defend your choices.

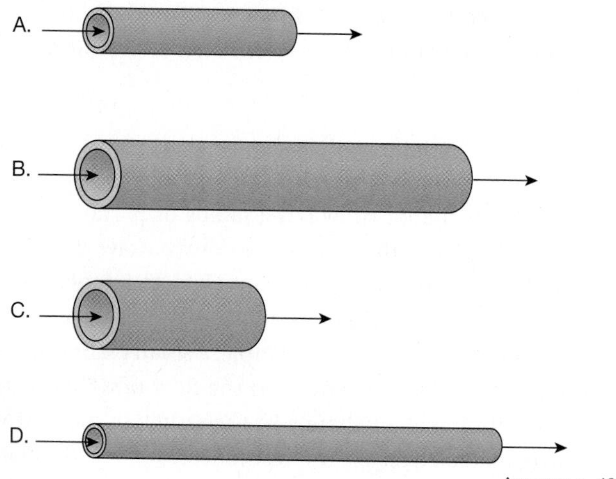

Answers: p. 498

14

Velocity of Flow Depends on the Flow Rate and the Cross-Sectional Area

The word *flow* is sometimes used imprecisely in cardiovascular physiology, leading to confusion. Flow usually means **flow rate**, the volume of blood that passes a given point in the system per unit time. In the circulation, flow is expressed in either liters per minute (L/min) or milliliters per minute (mL/min). For instance, blood flow through the aorta of a 70-kg man at rest is about 5 L/min.

Flow rate should not be confused with **velocity of flow**, the distance a fixed volume of blood travels in a given period of time. Velocity of flow is a measure of *how fast* blood flows past a point. Flow rate measures *how much* (volume) blood flows past a point in a given period of time. For example, look through the open door at the hallway outside your classroom. The number of people passing the door in one minute is the flow rate of people through the hallway. How quickly those people are walking past the door is their velocity of flow.

The relationship between velocity of flow (v), flow rate (Q), and cross-sectional area of the tube (A) is expressed by the equation

$$v = Q/A \qquad (7)$$

which shows that the velocity through a tube equals the flow rate divided by the tube's cross-sectional area. In a tube of fixed diameter (and thus fixed cross-sectional area), velocity of flow is directly related to flow rate. In a tube of variable diameter, if the flow rate is constant, velocity of flow varies inversely with the diameter. In other words, velocity is faster in narrow sections, and slower in wider sections.

Figure 14-6 ■ shows how the velocity of flow varies as the cross-sectional area of the tube changes. The vessel in the figure has two widths: narrow, with a cross-sectional area of 1 cm^2, and wide, with a cross-sectional area of 12 cm^2. The flow rate is identical in both parts of the vessel: 12 cm^3 per minute.* This flow rate means that in one minute, 12 cm^3 of fluid flows past point X in the narrow section, and 12 cm^3 of fluid flows past point Y in the wide section.

But *how fast* does the fluid need to flow to accomplish that rate? According to equation 7, the velocity of flow at point X is 12 cm/min, but at point Y it is only 1 cm/min. Thus, fluid flows more rapidly through narrow sections of a tube than through wide sections.

To see this principle in action, watch a leaf as it floats down a stream. Where the stream is narrow, the leaf moves rapidly, carried by the fast velocity of the water. In sections where the stream widens into a pool, the velocity of the water decreases and the leaf meanders more slowly.

In this chapter and the next, we will apply the physics of fluid flow to the cardiovascular system. The heart generates pressure when it contracts and pumps blood into the arterial side of the circulation. Arteries act as a pressure reservoir during the heart's relaxation phase, maintaining the *mean arterial pressure* (MAP) that is the primary driving force for blood flow. Mean arterial pressure is influenced by two parameters: *cardiac output* (the volume of blood the heart pumps per minute) and *peripheral resistance* (the resistance of the blood vessels to blood flow through them):

$$\text{Mean arterial pressure} \propto \text{cardiac output} \times \text{peripheral resistance}$$

Chapter 15 discusses peripheral resistance and blood flow. The remainder of this chapter examines heart function and the parameters that influence cardiac output.

---

*1 cm^3 = 1 cubic centimeter (cc) = 1 mL.

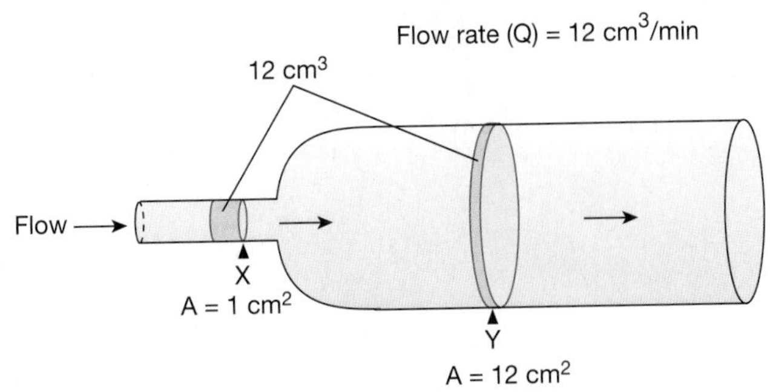

The narrower the vessel, the faster the velocity of flow.

Velocity (v) = $\frac{\text{Flow rate (Q)}}{\text{Cross-sectional area (A)}}$	
At point X	**At point Y**
$v = \frac{12\ cm^3/min}{1\ cm^2}$	$v = \frac{12\ cm^3/min}{12\ cm^2}$
v = 12 cm/min	v = 1 cm/min

■ **FIGURE 14-6** ***Flow rate versus velocity of flow***

CONCEPT CHECK

6. Two canals in Amsterdam are identical in size, but the water flows faster through one than through the other. Which canal has the higher flow rate? Answers: p. 498

CARDIAC MUSCLE AND THE HEART

To ancient civilizations, the heart was more than a pump—it was *the seat of the mind.* When ancient Egyptians mummified their dead, they removed most of the viscera but left the heart in place so that the gods could weigh it as an indicator of the owner's worthiness. Aristotle characterized the heart as the most important organ of the body, as well as *the seat of intelligence.* We can still find evidence of these ancient beliefs in modern expressions such as "heartfelt emotions." The link between the heart and mind is one that is still explored today.

The heart is the workhorse of the body, a muscle that contracts continually, resting only in the milliseconds-long pause between beats. By one estimate, in one minute the heart performs work equivalent to lifting a 5-pound weight up 1 foot. The energy demands of this work require a continuous supply of nutrients and oxygen to the heart muscle.

The Heart Has Four Chambers

The heart is a muscular organ, about the size of a fist, that lies in the center of the *thoracic cavity* (see Anatomy Summary, Fig. 14-7a, b, d ■). The pointed *apex* of the heart angles down to the left side of the body, while the broader *base* lies just behind the breastbone, or *sternum.* Because we usually associate the word *base* with the bottom, remember that the base of a cone is the broad end, and the apex is the pointed end. The heart can be thought of as an inverted cone with apex down and base up. Within the thoracic cavity, the heart lies on the ventral side, sandwiched between the two lungs, with its apex resting on the diaphragm (Fig. 14-7b).

The heart is encased in a tough membranous sac, the **pericardium** [*peri,* around + *kardia,* heart] (Fig. 14-7d, e). A thin layer of clear pericardial fluid inside the pericardium lubricates the external surface of the heart as it beats within the sac. Inflammation of the pericardium (*pericarditis*) may reduce this lubrication to the point that the heart rubs against the pericardium, creating a sound known as a *friction rub.*

The heart itself is composed mostly of cardiac muscle, or **myocardium** [*myo,* muscle + *kardia,* heart], covered by thin outer and inner layers of epithelium and connective tissue. Seen from the outside, the bulk of the heart is the thick muscular walls of the ventricles, the two lower chambers (Fig. 14-7f). The thinner-walled atria lie above the ventricles.

The major blood vessels all emerge from the base of the heart. The aorta and *pulmonary trunk* (artery) direct blood from the heart to the tissues and lungs, respectively. The venae cavae and pulmonary veins return blood to the heart (Table 14-2 ■). When the heart is viewed from the front (anterior view), as in Figure 14-7f, the pulmonary veins are hidden behind the other major blood vessels. Running across the surface of the ventricles are shallow grooves containing the **coronary arteries** and **coronary veins**, which supply blood to the heart muscle.

The relationship between the atria and ventricles can be seen in a cross-sectional view of the heart (Fig. 14-7g). As noted earlier, the left and right sides of the heart are separated by the interventricular septum, so that blood on one side does not mix with blood on the other side. Although blood flow in the left heart is separated from flow in the right heart, the two sides contract in a coordinated fashion. First the atria contract together, then the ventricles contract together.

Blood flows from veins into the atria and from there through one-way valves into the ventricles, the pumping chambers. Blood leaves the heart via the pulmonary trunk from the right ventricle and via the aorta from the left ventricle. A second set of valves guards the exits of the ventricles so that blood cannot flow back into the heart once it has been ejected.

Notice in Figure 14-7g that blood enters each ventricle at the top of the chamber but also leaves at the top. This is because during development, the tubular embryonic heart twists back on itself (Fig. 14-8b ■). This twisting puts the arteries (through which blood leaves) close to the top of the ventricles. Functionally, this

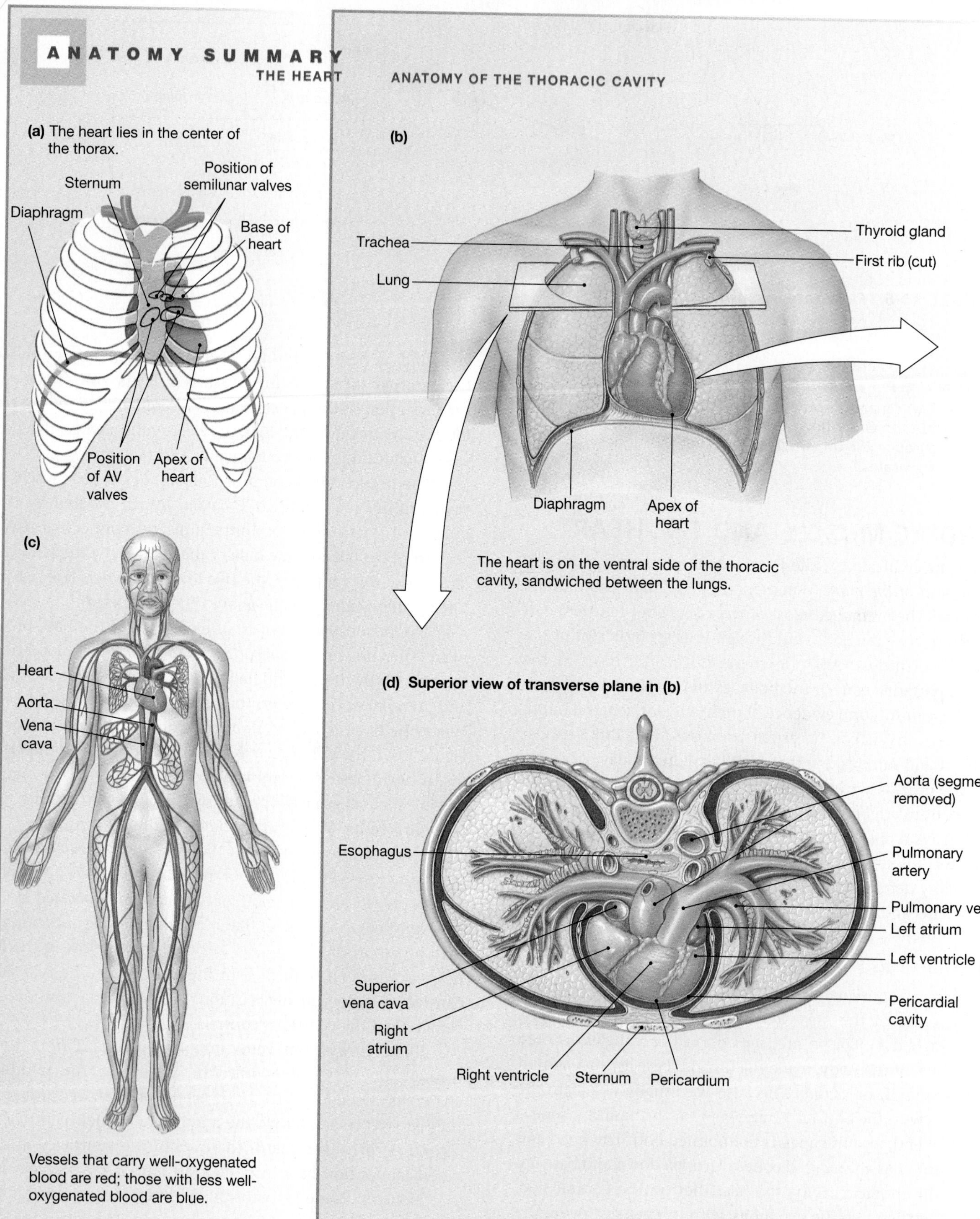
ANATOMY SUMMARY
THE HEART
(a) The heart lies in the center of the thorax.
Sternum
Position of semilunar valves
Diaphragm
Base of heart
Position of AV valves
Apex of heart
(c)
Heart
Aorta
Vena cava
Vessels that carry well-oxygenated blood are red; those with less well-oxygenated blood are blue.
ANATOMY OF THE THORACIC CAVITY
(b)
Trachea
Lung
Thyroid gland
First rib (cut)
Diaphragm
Apex of heart
The heart is on the ventral side of the thoracic cavity, sandwiched between the lungs.
(d) Superior view of transverse plane in (b)
Esophagus
Superior vena cava
Right atrium
Right ventricle
Sternum
Pericardium
Aorta (segment removed)
Pulmonary artery
Pulmonary vein
Left atrium
Left ventricle
Pericardial cavity

FIGURE 14-7

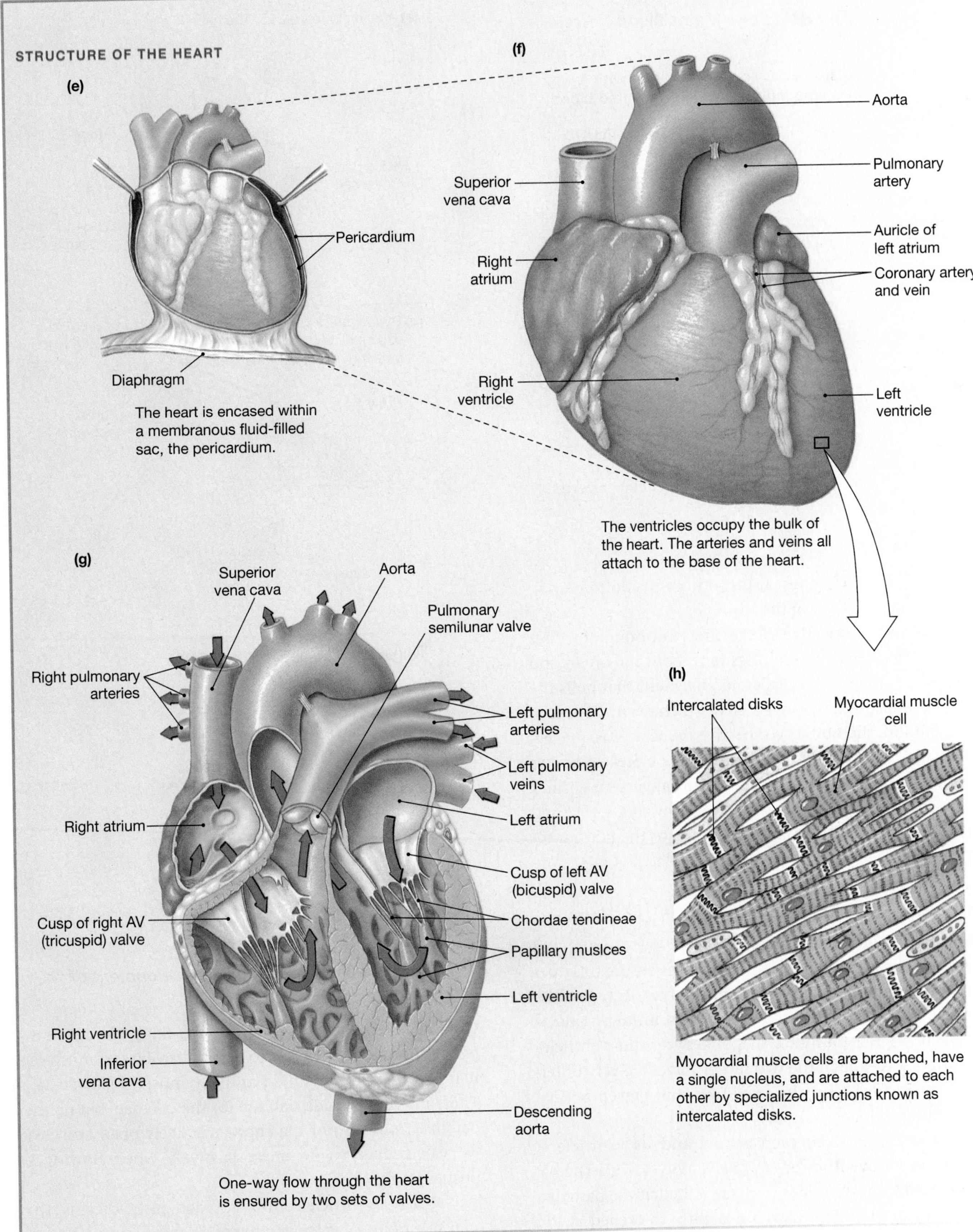
STRUCTURE OF THE HEART
(e)
Pericardium
Diaphragm
The heart is encased within a membranous fluid-filled sac, the pericardium.
(f)
Aorta
Superior vena cava
Pulmonary artery
Auricle of left atrium
Right atrium
Coronary artery and vein
Right ventricle
Left ventricle
The ventricles occupy the bulk of the heart. The arteries and veins all attach to the base of the heart.
(g)
Superior vena cava
Aorta
Pulmonary semilunar valve
Right pulmonary arteries
Left pulmonary arteries
Left pulmonary veins
Right atrium
Left atrium
Cusp of left AV (bicuspid) valve
Chordae tendineae
Cusp of right AV (tricuspid) valve
Papillary muslces
Left ventricle
Right ventricle
Inferior vena cava
Descending aorta
One-way flow through the heart is ensured by two sets of valves.
(h)
Intercalated disks
Myocardial muscle cell
Myocardial muscle cells are branched, have a single nucleus, and are attached to each other by specialized junctions known as intercalated disks.

FIGURE 14-7 *(continued)*

TABLE 14-2 The Heart and Major Blood Vessels

Blue type indicates structures containing blood with lower oxygen content; red type indicates well-oxygenated blood.

	RECEIVES BLOOD FROM	SENDS BLOOD TO
Heart		
Right atrium	Venae cavae	Right ventricle
Right ventricle	Right atrium	Lungs
Left atrium	Pulmonary veins	Left ventricle
Left ventricle	Left atrium	Body except for lungs
Vessels		
Venae cavae	Systemic veins	Right atrium
Pulmonary trunk (artery)	Right ventricle	Lungs
Pulmonary vein	Veins of the lungs	Left atrium
Aorta	Left ventricle	Systemic arteries

means that the ventricles must contract from the bottom up so that blood is squeezed out of the top.

Four fibrous connective tissue rings surround the four heart valves (Fig. 14-9a). These rings form both the origin and insertion for the cardiac muscle, an arrangement that pulls the apex and base of the heart together when the ventricles contract. In addition, the fibrous connective tissue acts as an electrical insulator, blocking most transmission of electrical signals between the atria and the ventricles. This arrangement ensures that the electrical signals can be directed through a specialized conduction system to the apex of the heart for the bottom-to-top contraction.

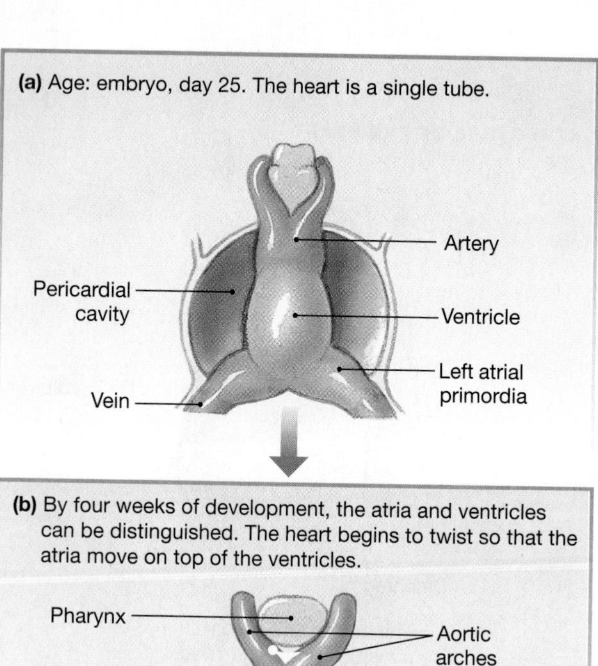
(a) Age: embryo, day 25. The heart is a single tube.
Artery
Pericardial cavity
Ventricle
Left atrial primordia
Vein

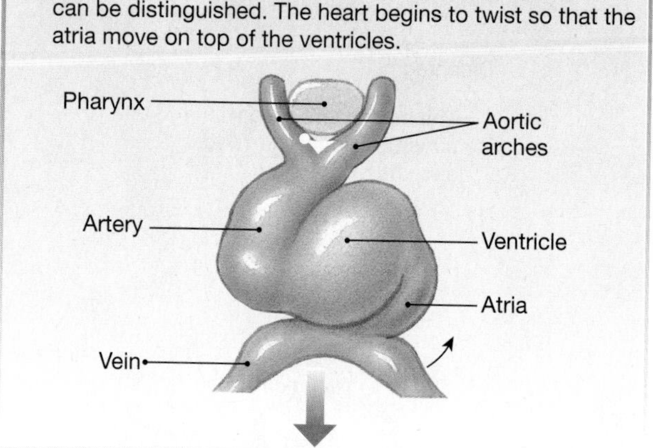
(b) By four weeks of development, the atria and ventricles can be distinguished. The heart begins to twist so that the atria move on top of the ventricles.
Pharynx
Aortic arches
Artery
Ventricle
Atria
Vein

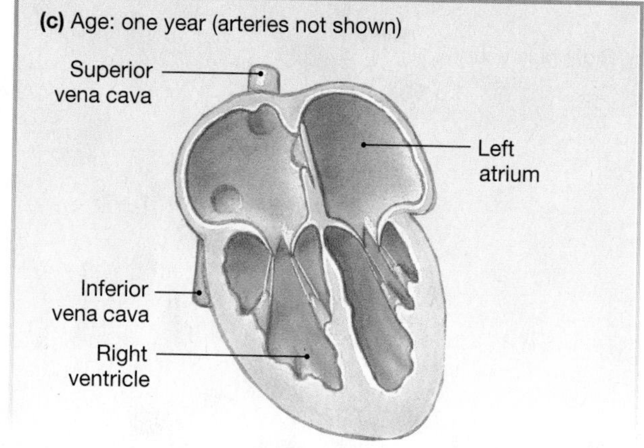
(c) Age: one year (arteries not shown)
Superior vena cava
Left atrium
Inferior vena cava
Right ventricle

■ **FIGURE 14-8** ***Embryological development of the heart***

Heart Valves Ensure One-Way Flow in the Heart

As the arrows in Figure 14-7g indicate, blood flows through the heart in one direction. Two sets of heart valves ensure this one-way flow: one set (the **atrioventricular valves**) between the atria and ventricles, and the second set (the **semilunar valves**, named for their crescent-moon shape) between the ventricles and the arteries. Although the two sets of valves are very different in structure, they serve the same function: preventing the backward flow of blood.

The opening between each atrium and its ventricle is guarded by an atrioventricular (AV) valve (Fig. 14-7g). The AV valve is formed from thin flaps of tissue joined at the base to a connective tissue ring. The flaps are slightly thickened at the edge and connect on the ventricular side to collagenous tendons, the **chordae tendineae** (Fig. 14-9b, d ■). Most of the chordae fasten to the edges of the valve flaps. The opposite ends of the chordae are tethered to moundlike extensions of ventricular muscle known as the **papillary muscles** [*papilla,* nipple]. These muscles provide stability for the chordae, but neither the papillary muscles nor the chordae actively open and close the AV valves. The valves move passively when flowing blood pushes on them.

When a ventricle contracts, blood pushes against the bottom side of its AV valve and forces it upward into a closed position (Fig. 14-9b). The chordae tendineae prevent the valve from being pushed back into the atrium, just as the struts on an

VENTRICULAR CONTRACTION

(a) Transverse section

Tricuspid (right AV) valve
Fibrous skeleton
Mitral (left A V), or bicuspid, valve
Aortic semilunar valve (open)
Pulmonary semilunar valve (open)

During ventricular contraction, the **AV valves** remain closed to prevent blood flow backward into the atria.

(b) Frontal section

Aorta
Aortic semilunar valve (open)
Left atrium
Mitral valve
Chordae tendineae (tense)
Papillary muscles (tense)
Left ventricle (contracted)

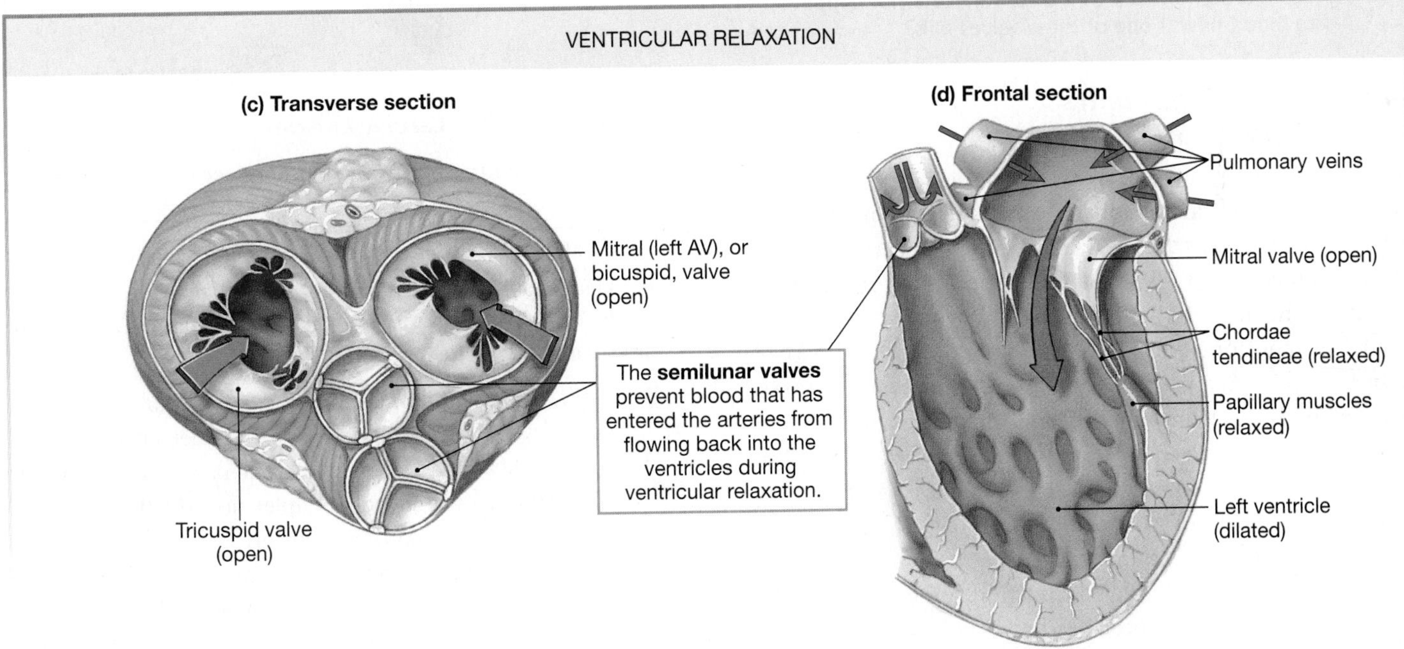

■ **FIGURE 14-9** ***Heart valves***

Views **(a)** and **(c)** show the AV valves as viewed from the atria and the semilunar valves as viewed from inside the arteries.

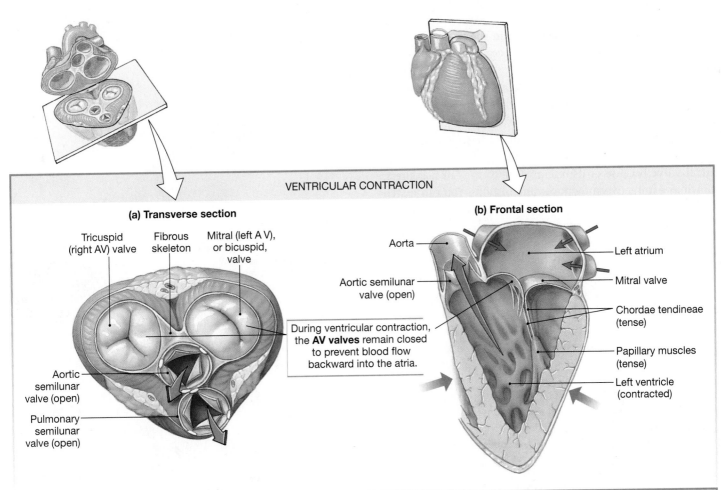

umbrella keep the umbrella from turning inside out in a high wind. Occasionally, the chordae fail, and the valve is pushed back into the atrium during ventricular contraction, an abnormal condition known as *prolapse*.

The two AV valves are not identical. The valve that separates the right atrium and right ventricle has three flaps and is called the **tricuspid valve** [*cuspis*, point] (Fig. 14-9a). The valve between the left atrium and left ventricle has only two flaps and is called the **bicuspid valve**. The bicuspid is also called the **mitral valve** because of its resemblance to the tall headdress, known as a miter, worn by popes and bishops. You can match AV valves to the proper side of the heart by remembering that the Right Side has the Tricuspid (R-S-T).

The semilunar valves separate the ventricles from the major arteries. The **aortic valve** is between the left ventricle and the aorta, and the **pulmonary valve** lies between the right ventricle and the pulmonary trunk. Both semilunar valves have three cuplike leaflets that snap closed when blood attempting to flow back into the ventricles fills them (Fig. 14-9c, d). Because of their shape, the semilunar valves do not need connective tendons as the AV valves do.

CONCEPT CHECK

7. What prevents electrical signals from passing through the connective tissue in the heart?
8. Trace a drop of blood from the superior vena cava to the aorta, naming all structures the drop encounters along its route.
9. What is the function of the AV valves? What happens to blood flow if one of these valves fails? Answers: p. 498

Cardiac Muscle Cells Contract Without Nervous Stimulation

The bulk of the heart is composed of cardiac muscle cells, or myocardium. Most cardiac muscle is contractile, but about 1% of the myocardial cells are specialized to generate action potentials spontaneously. These cells are responsible for a unique property of the heart: its ability to contract without any outside signal. As mentioned in the introduction to this chapter, records tell us of Spanish explorers in the New World witnessing human sacrifices in which hearts torn from the chests of living victims continued to beat for minutes. The heart can contract without a connection to other parts of the body because the signal for contraction is *myogenic*, originating within the heart muscle itself.

The signal for myocardial contraction comes not from the nervous system but from specialized myocardial cells known as **autorhythmic cells**. The autorhythmic cells are also called **pacemakers** because they set the rate of the heartbeat. Myocardial autorhythmic cells are anatomically distinct from contractile cells: autorhythmic cells are smaller and contain few contractile fibers. Because they do not have organized sarcomeres, autorhythmic cells do not contribute to the contractile force of the heart.

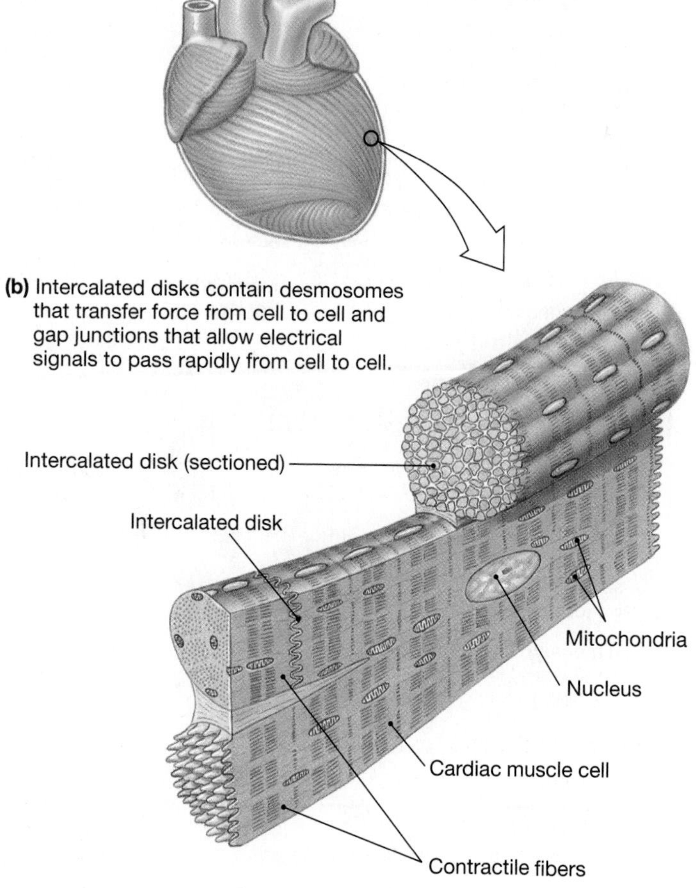

(a) The spiral arrangement of ventricular muscle allows ventricular contraction to squeeze the blood upward from the apex of the heart.
(b) Intercalated disks contain desmosomes that transfer force from cell to cell and gap junctions that allow electrical signals to pass rapidly from cell to cell.
Intercalated disk (sectioned)
Intercalated disk
Mitochondria
Nucleus
Cardiac muscle cell
Contractile fibers

■ **FIGURE 14-10** ***Cardiac muscle***

For an electron micrograph of gap junctions, see Figure 3-21c on p. 70.

Contractile cells are typical striated muscle, however, with contractile fibers organized into sarcomeres [p. 399]. Cardiac muscle differs in significant ways from skeletal muscle and shares some properties with smooth muscle:

1. Cardiac muscle fibers are much smaller than skeletal muscle fibers and usually have a single nucleus per fiber.
2. Individual cardiac muscle cells branch and join neighboring cells end-to-end to create a complex network (Fig. 14-10b ■). The cell junctions, known as **intercalated disks** [*inter-*, between + *calare*, to proclaim], consist of interdigitated membranes. Intercalated disks have two components: *desmosomes* [p. 71] and gap junctions [p. 175]. Desmosomes are strong connections that tie adjacent cells together, thereby allowing force created in one cell to be transferred to the adjacent cell.
3. *Gap junctions* in the intercalated disks electrically connect cardiac muscle cells to one another. Waves of depolarization thus can spread rapidly from cell to cell, allowing all

the heart muscle cells to contract almost simultaneously. In this respect, cardiac muscle resembles single-unit smooth muscle.

4. The t-tubules of myocardial cells are larger than those of skeletal muscle, and they branch inside the myocardial cells.
5. Myocardial sarcoplasmic reticulum is smaller than that of skeletal muscle, reflecting the fact that cardiac muscle depends in part on extracellular Ca^{2+} to initiate contraction. In this respect, cardiac muscle resembles smooth muscle.
6. Mitochondria occupy about one-third the cell volume of a cardiac contractile fiber, a reflection of the high energy demand of these cells. By one estimate, cardiac muscle consumes 70–80% of the oxygen delivered to it by the blood, more than twice the amount extracted by other cells in the body.

During periods of increased activity, the heart uses almost all the oxygen brought to it by the coronary arteries. Thus, the only way to get more oxygen to exercising heart muscle is to increase the blood flow. Reduced myocardial blood flow from narrowing of a coronary vessel by a clot or fatty deposit can damage or even kill myocardial cells.

See Table 12-3, p. 429, for a summary comparison of the three muscle types.

RUNNING PROBLEM

When Walter arrived at the University of Texas Southwestern Medical Center emergency room, one of the first tasks was to determine whether he had actually had a heart attack. Walter's vital signs (pulse and breathing rates, blood pressure, and temperature) were taken. He was given aspirin and heparin to decrease blood clotting, and nitroglycerin to dilate coronary blood vessels. A technician drew blood for enzyme assays to determine the level of cardiac creatine kinase in Walter's blood. When heart muscle cells die, they release various enzymes that serve as markers of a heart attack. A second tube of blood was sent for an assay of its troponin I level. Troponin I is a good indicator of heart damage following a heart attack.

Question 3:
A related form of creatine kinase is found in skeletal muscle. What are related forms of an enzyme called? [Hint: p. 96]

Question 4:
What is troponin, and why would elevated blood levels of troponin indicate heart damage? [Hint: p. 407]

Cardiac EC Coupling Combines Features of Skeletal and Smooth Muscle

In Chapters 11 and 12 you learned how acetylcholine from a somatic motor neuron causes a skeletal muscle action potential to begin excitation-contraction coupling (EC coupling) [p. 403]. In cardiac muscle, an action potential also initiates EC coupling, but the action potential originates spontaneously in the heart's pacemaker cells and spreads into the contractile cells through gap junctions. (Neurotransmitters modulate the pacemaker rate, as you will learn later in this chapter.)

An action potential that enters a contractile cell moves across the sarcolemma and into the t-tubules, where it opens voltage-gated Ca^{2+} channels in the cell membrane. Ca^{2+} enters the cell and opens *ryanodine receptor-channels (RyR)* in the sarcoplasmic reticulum (Fig. 14-11 ■). Note that these ryanodine receptors are operated by Ca^{2+} binding, not by mechanical linkage as the RyR channels in skeletal muscle are.

The ryanodine receptors are Ca^{2+} channels, and opening them causes **Ca^{2+}-induced Ca^{2+} release**. Stored Ca^{2+} flows out of the sarcoplasmic reticulum and into the cytosol, creating a Ca^{2+} "spark" that can be seen using special biochemical methods [p. 188]. Multiple sparks from different RyR channels sum to create a Ca^{2+} signal.

Calcium released from the sarcoplasmic reticulum provides about 90% of the Ca^{2+} needed for muscle contraction. Calcium diffuses through the cytosol to the contractile elements, where the ions bind to troponin and initiate the cycle of crossbridge formation and movement. Contraction takes place by the same type of sliding filament movement that occurs in skeletal muscle [p. 403].

Relaxation in cardiac muscle is generally similar to that in skeletal muscle. As cytoplasmic Ca^{2+} concentrations decrease, Ca^{2+} unbinds from troponin, myosin releases actin, and the contractile filaments slide back to their relaxed position. As in skeletal muscle, Ca^{2+} is transported back into the sarcoplasmic reticulum with the help of a Ca^{2+}-ATPase. However, in cardiac muscle Ca^{2+} is also removed from the cell in exchange for Na^+ via a Na^+-Ca^{2+} antiport protein. Each Ca^{2+} moves out of the cell against its electrochemical gradient in exchange for 3 Na^+ entering the cell down their electrochemical gradient. Sodium that enters the cell during this transfer is removed by the Na^+-K^+-ATPase.

CONCEPT CHECK

10. If a myocardial contractile cell is placed in interstitial fluid and depolarized, the cell will contract. If Ca^{2+} is removed from the fluid surrounding the myocardial cell and the cell is depolarized, it will not contract. If the experiment is repeated with a skeletal muscle fiber, the skeletal muscle will contract when depolarized, whether or not Ca^{2+} is present in the surrounding fluid. What conclusion can you draw from the results of this experiment?

Answers: p. 498

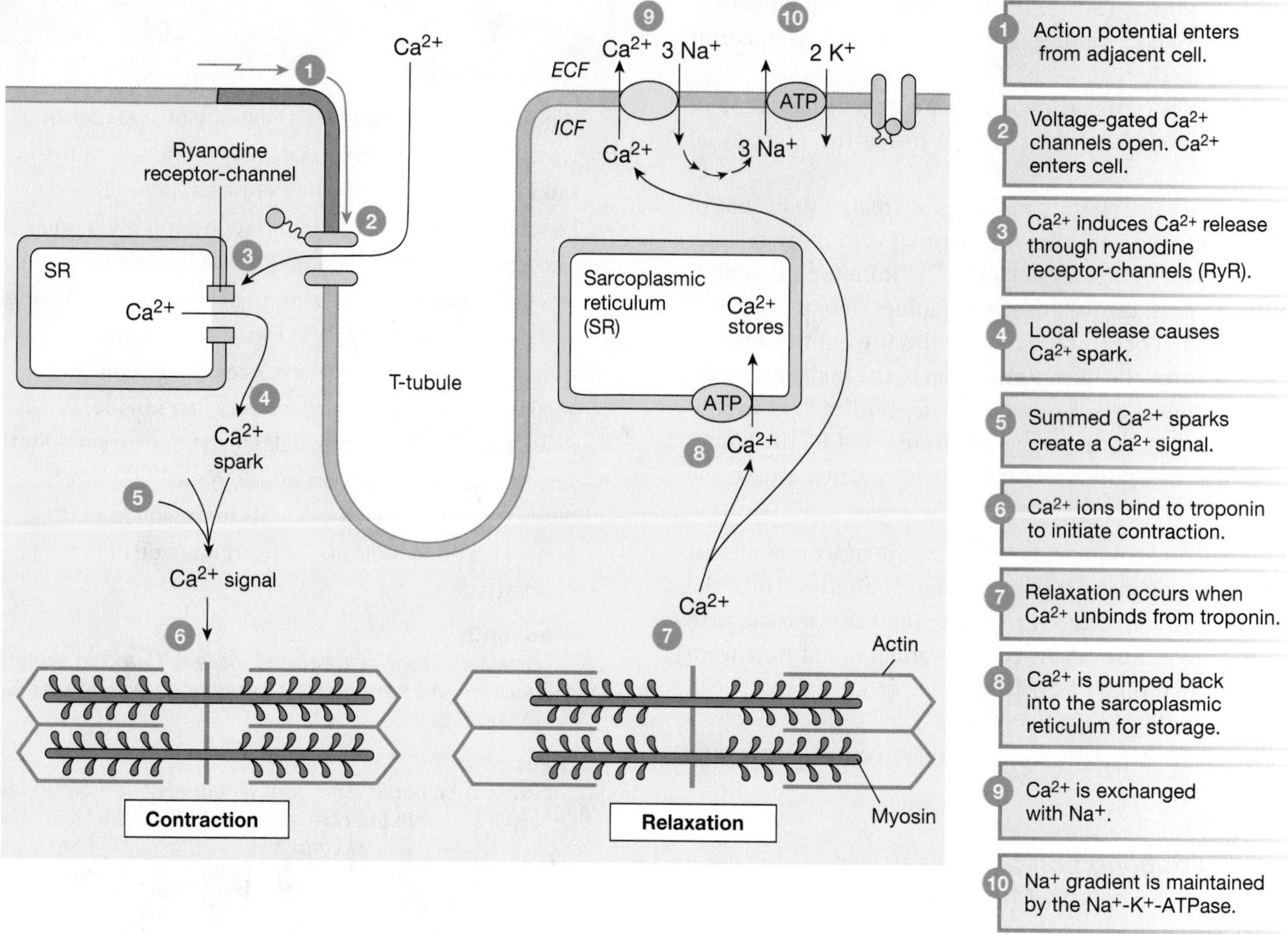

Ca2+
ECF
ICF
Ryanodine receptor-channel
SR
Ca2+
Ca2+ spark
Ca2+ signal
T-tubule
Ca2+ 3 Na+
2 K+
ATP
Ca2+
3 Na+
Sarcoplasmic reticulum (SR)
Ca2+ stores
ATP
Ca2+
Ca2+
Actin
Myosin
Contraction
Relaxation
1 Action potential enters from adjacent cell.
2 Voltage-gated Ca2+ channels open. Ca2+ enters cell.
3 Ca2+ induces Ca2+ release through ryanodine receptor-channels (RyR).
4 Local release causes Ca2+ spark.
5 Summed Ca2+ sparks create a Ca2+ signal.
6 Ca2+ ions bind to troponin to initiate contraction.
7 Relaxation occurs when Ca2+ unbinds from troponin.
8 Ca2+ is pumped back into the sarcoplasmic reticulum for storage.
9 Ca2+ is exchanged with Na+.
10 Na+ gradient is maintained by the Na+-K+-ATPase.

■ **FIGURE 14-11** ***Excitation-contraction coupling and relaxation in cardiac muscle***

Cardiac Muscle Contraction Can Be Graded

A key property of cardiac muscle cells is the ability of a single muscle fiber to execute *graded contractions,* in which the fiber varies the amount of force it generates. (Recall that in skeletal muscle, contraction in a single fiber is all-or-none at any given fiber length.) The force generated by cardiac muscle is proportional to the number of crossbridges that are active. The number of active crossbridges is determined by how much Ca^{2+} is bound to troponin.

If cytosolic Ca^{2+} concentrations are low, some crossbridges will not be activated and contraction force will be small. If additional Ca^{2+} enters the cell from the extracellular fluid, more Ca^{2+} is released from the sarcoplasmic reticulum. This additional Ca^{2+} binds to troponin, enhancing the ability of myosin to form crossbridges with actin and creating additional force.

When Cardiac Muscle Is Stretched, It Contracts More Forcefully

Another factor that affects the force of contraction in cardiac muscle is the sarcomere length at the beginning of contraction. For both cardiac and skeletal muscle, the tension generated is directly proportional to the initial length of the muscle fiber [p. 413]. As muscle fiber length and sarcomere length increase, tension increases, up to a maximum (Fig. 14-12 ■).

In the intact heart, stretch on the individual fibers is a function of how much blood is in the chambers of the heart. The relationship between force and ventricular volume is an important property of cardiac function and is discussed in detail later in this chapter.

CONCEPT CHECK

11. A drug that blocks all Ca^{2+} channels in the myocardial cell membrane is placed in the solution around the cell. What will happen to the force of contraction in that cell?

Answers: p. 499

Action Potentials in Myocardial Cells Vary According to Cell Type

Cardiac muscle, like skeletal muscle and neurons, is an excitable tissue with the ability to generate action potentials. Each of the two types of cardiac muscle cells has a distinctive action potential. In both types, Ca^{2+} plays an important role in the action potential, in contrast to the action potentials of skeletal muscle and neurons.

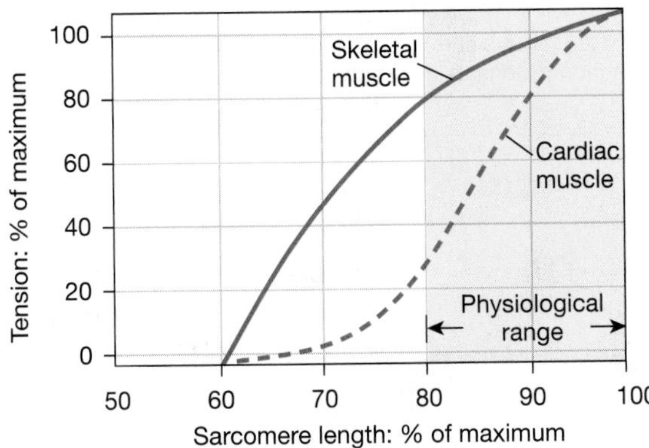

■ **FIGURE 14-12** ***Length-tension relationships in skeletal and cardiac muscle***

These data represent tension developed during isometric contraction. The physiological range is the sarcomere length in which the muscle normally functions.

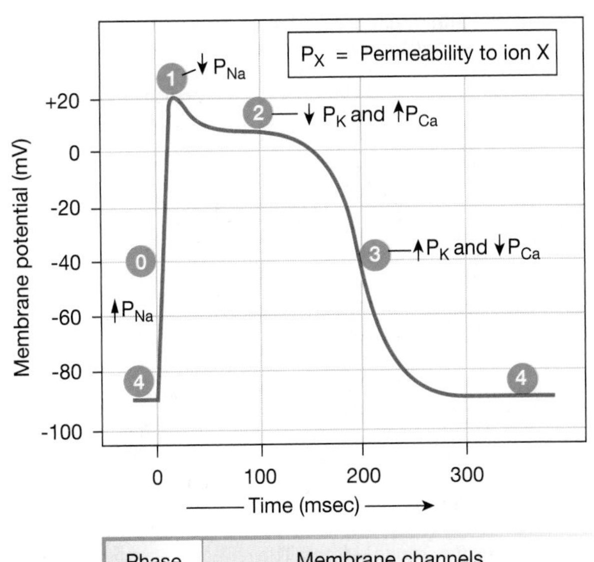

Phase	Membrane channels
0	Na^+ channels open
1	Na^+ channels close
2	Ca^{2+} channels open; fast K^+ channels close
3	Ca^{2+} channels close; slow K^+ channels open
4	Resting potential

■ **FIGURE 14-13** ***Action potential of a cardiac contractile cell***

The phase numbers are a convention.

Myocardial Contractile Cells The action potentials of myocardial contractile cells are similar in several ways to those of neurons and skeletal muscle [p. 257]. The rapid depolarization phase of the action potential is the result of Na^+ entry, and the steep repolarization phase is due to K^+ leaving the cell. The main difference between the action potential of the myocardial contractile cell and that of a skeletal muscle fiber or a neuron is that in the myocardial cell, there is a lengthening of the action potential caused by Ca^{2+} entry. Let's take a look at these longer action potentials (Fig. 14-13 ■).

Phase 4: resting membrane potential. Myocardial contractile cells have a stable resting potential of about –90 mV.

Phase 0: depolarization. When a wave of depolarization moves into a contractile cell through gap junctions, the membrane potential becomes more positive. Voltage-gated Na^+ channels open, allowing Na^+ to enter the cell and rapidly depolarize it. The membrane potential reaches about +20 mV before the Na^+ channels close. These are double-gated Na^+ channels, similar to the voltage-gated Na^+ channels of the axon [p. 260].

Phase 1: initial repolarization. When the Na^+ channels close, the cell begins to repolarize as K^+ leaves through open K^+ channels.

Phase 2: the plateau. The initial repolarization is very brief. The action potential then flattens into a plateau as the result of two events: a decrease in K^+ permeability and an increase in Ca^{2+} permeability. Voltage-gated Ca^{2+} channels activated by depolarization have been slowly opening during phases 0 and 1. When they finally open, Ca^{2+} enters the cell. At the same time, some K^+ channels close. The combination of Ca^{2+} influx and decreased K^+ efflux causes the action potential to flatten out into a plateau.

Phase 3: rapid repolarization. The plateau ends when Ca^{2+} channels close and K^+ permeability increases once more. The K^+ channels responsible for this phase are similar to those in the neuron: they are activated by depolarization but are slow to open. When the delayed K^+ channels open, K^+ exits rapidly, returning the cell to its resting potential (phase 4).

The influx of Ca^{2+} during phase 2 lengthens the total duration of a myocardial action potential. A typical action potential in a neuron or skeletal muscle fiber lasts between 1 and 5 msec. In a contractile myocardial cell, the action potential typically lasts 200 msec or more. The longer myocardial action potential helps prevent the sustained contraction called tetanus. Prevention of tetanus in the heart is important because cardiac muscles must relax between contractions so the ventricles can fill with blood.

To understand why a longer action potential prevents tetanus, compare the relationship between action potentials and contraction in skeletal and cardiac muscle cells (Fig. 14-14 ■). As you may recall from Chapter 12, the skeletal muscle action potential (red curve) is ending as contraction (blue curve) begins. Thus, a second action potential fired immediately after the refractory period will cause summation of the contractions. If a series of action potentials occurs in rapid succession, the sustained

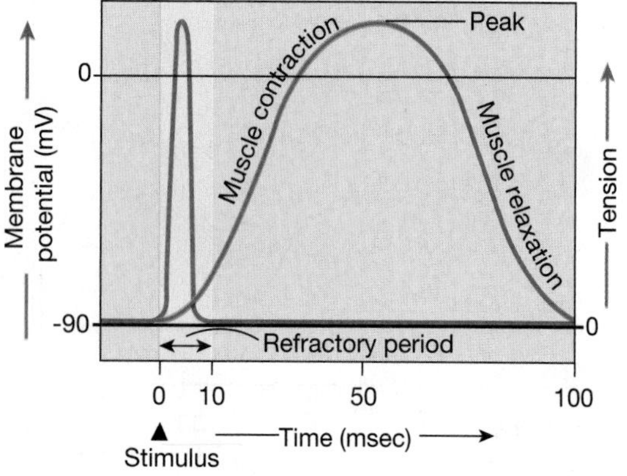

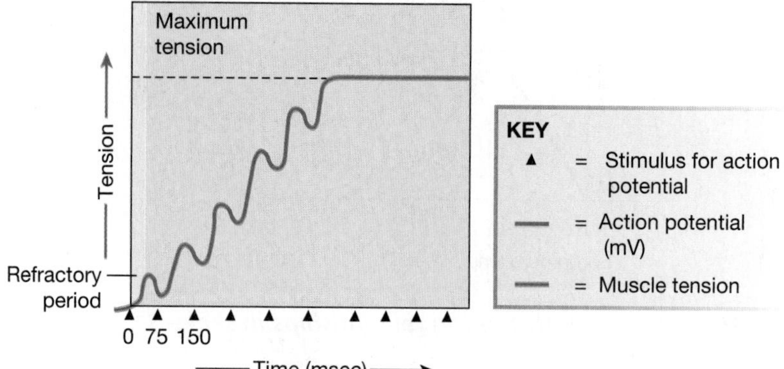

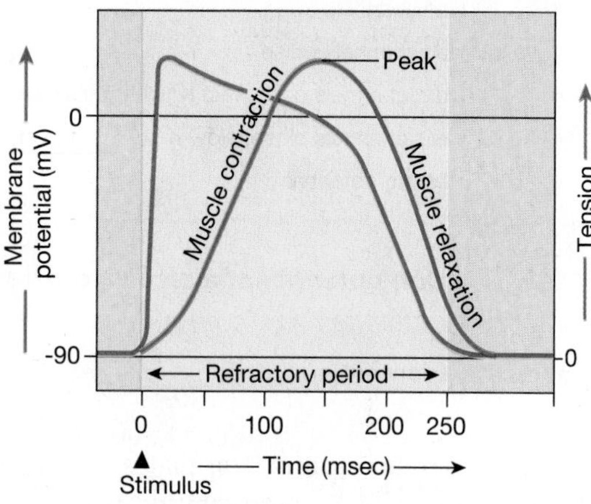

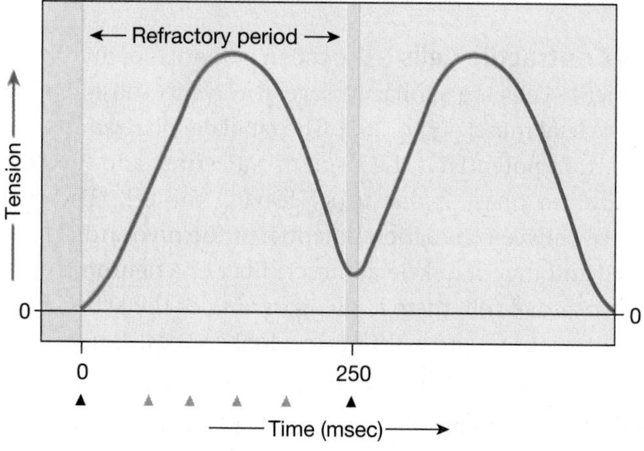

■ **FIGURE 14-14** ***Refractory periods and summation in skeletal and cardiac muscle***

contraction known as tetanus results (Fig. 14-14b). Tetanus cannot occur in cardiac muscle because the longer action potential means the refractory period and the contraction end almost simultaneously (Fig. 14-14c). By the time a second action potential takes place, the myocardial cell has almost completely relaxed. Consequently, no summation occurs (Fig. 14-14d).

CONCEPT CHECK

12. Which ions moving in what directions cause the depolarization and repolarization phases of a neuronal action potential?
13. At the molecular level, what is happening during the refractory period in neurons and muscle fibers?
14. Lidocaine is a molecule that blocks the action of voltage-gated cardiac Na^+ channels. What will happen to the action potential of a myocardial contractile cell if lidocaine is applied to the cell? Answers: p. 499

Myocardial Autorhythmic Cells What gives myocardial autorhythmic cells their unique ability to generate action potentials spontaneously in the absence of input from the nervous system? This property results from their unstable membrane potential, which starts at −60 mV and slowly drifts upward toward threshold (Fig. 14-15a ■). Because the membrane potential never "rests" at a constant value, it is called a **pacemaker potential** rather than a resting membrane potential. Whenever the pacemaker potential depolarizes to threshold, the autorhythmic cell fires an action potential.

What causes the membrane potential of these cells to be unstable? Our current understanding is that the autorhythmic cells contain channels that are different from the channels of other excitable tissues. When the cell membrane potential is −60 mV, $\mathbf{I_f}$ **channels** that are permeable to both K^+ and Na^+ open (Fig. 14-15c). These channels are called I_f channels because they allow current (I) to flow and because of their unusual properties. The researchers who first described the ion current through these channels initially did not understand its behavior and named it *funny* current—hence the subscript *f*.

When I_f channels open at negative membrane potentials, Na^+ influx exceeds K^+ efflux (Fig. 14-15b). (This is similar to

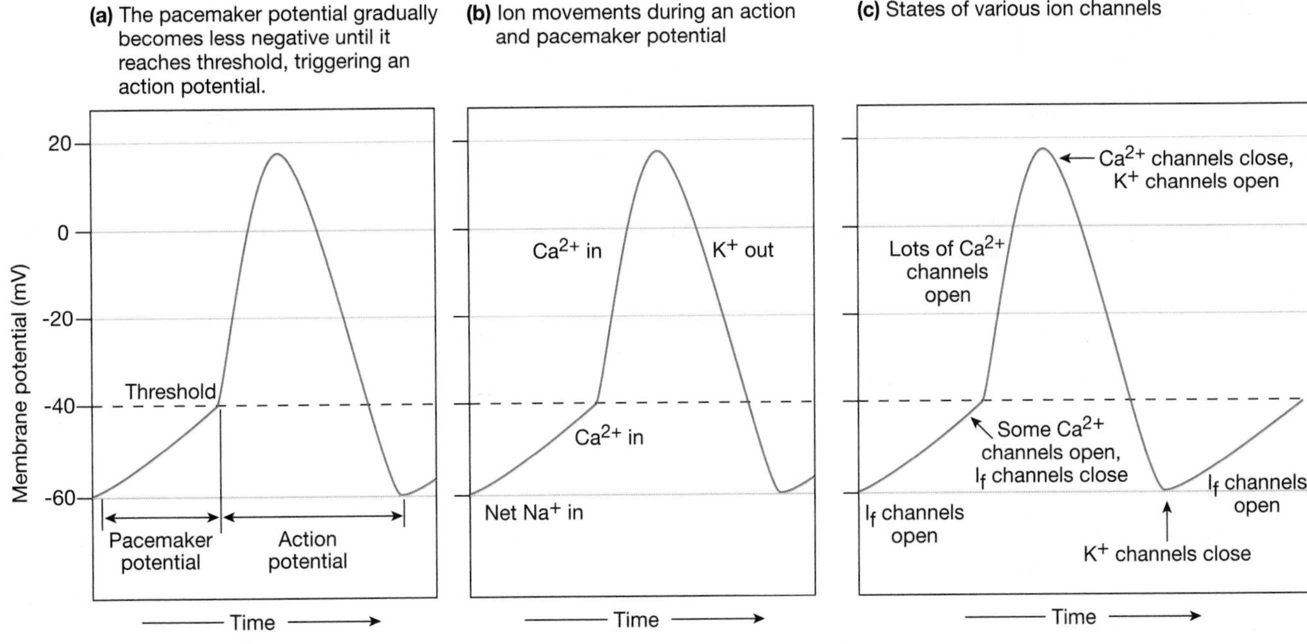

GRAPH QUESTION

Match the appropriate phases of the myocardial contractile cell action potential (Fig.14-13) to the pacemaker action potential above.

■ **FIGURE 14-15** *Action potentials in cardiac autorhythmic cells*

what happens at the neuromuscular junction when nonspecific cation channels open [p. 390].) The net influx of positive charge slowly depolarizes the autorhythmic cell. As the membrane potential becomes more positive, the I_f channels gradually close and some Ca^{2+} channels open. The subsequent influx of Ca^{2+} continues the depolarization, and the membrane potential moves steadily toward threshold.

When the membrane potential reaches threshold, additional Ca^{2+} channels open. Calcium rushes into the cell, creating the steep depolarization phase of the action potential. Note that this process is different from that in other excitable cells, in which the depolarization phase is due to the opening of voltage-gated Na^+ channels.

When the Ca^{2+} channels close at the peak of the action potential, slow K^+ channels have opened. The repolarization phase of the autorhythmic action potential is due to the resultant efflux of K^+. This phase is similar to repolarization in other types of excitable cells.

Autonomic Neurotransmitters Modulate Heart Rate

The speed with which pacemaker cells depolarize determines the rate at which the heart contracts (the heart rate). The interval between action potentials can be modified by altering the permeability of the autorhythmic cells to different ions. Increased permeability to Na^+ and Ca^{2+} during the pacemaker potential phase speeds up depolarization and heart rate. Decreased Ca^{2+} permeability or increased K^+ permeability slows depolarization and thus slows the heart rate.

CONCEPT CHECK

15. What would increasing K^+ permeability do to the membrane potential of the cell? Answers: p. 499

Sympathetic stimulation of pacemaker cells speeds up heart rate. The catecholamines norepinephrine (from sympathetic neurons) and epinephrine (from the adrenal medulla) increase ion flow through both I_f and Ca^{2+} channels. More rapid cation entry speeds up the rate of the pacemaker depolarization, causing the cell to reach threshold faster and increasing the rate of action potential firing (Fig. 14-16a ■). When the pacemaker fires action potentials more rapidly, heart rate increases.

Catecholamines exert their effect by binding to and activating β_1-adrenergic receptors on the autorhythmic cells. The β_1-receptors use a cAMP second messenger system to alter the transport properties of the ion channels. In the case of the I_f channels, cAMP itself is the messenger. When cAMP binds to open I_f channels, they remain open longer. The I_f channels

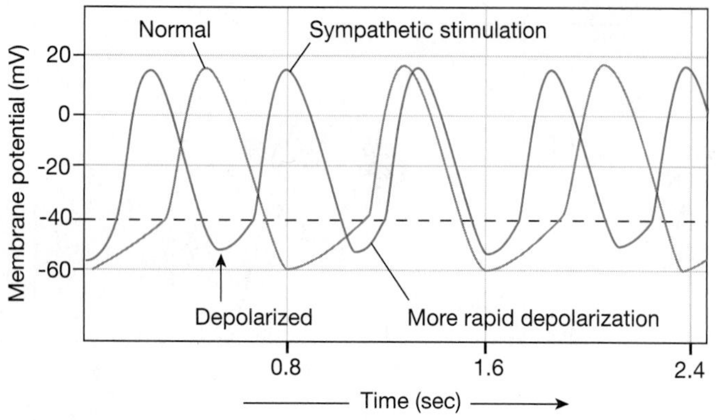
(a) Sympathetic stimulation and epinephrine depolarize the autorhythmic cell and speed up the depolarization rate, increasing the heart rate.
Normal
Sympathetic stimulation
Membrane potential (mV)
20
0
-20
-40
-60
Depolarized
More rapid depolarization
0.8
1.6
2.4
Time (sec)

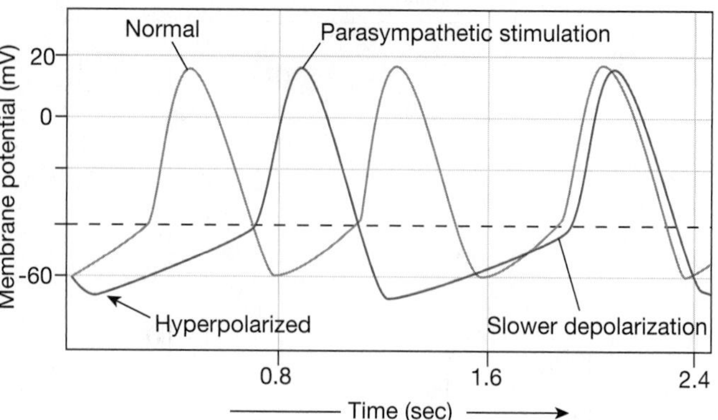
(b) Parasympathetic stimulation hyperpolarizes the membrane potential of the autorhythmic cell and slows depolarization, decreasing the heart rate.
Normal
Parasympathetic stimulation
Membrane potential (mV)
20
0
-60
Hyperpolarized
Slower depolarization
0.8
1.6
2.4
Time (sec)

■ **FIGURE 14-16** ***Modulation of heart rate by the nervous system***

belong to a family called the *HCN channels*, or *hyperpolarization-activated cyclic nucleotide-gated channels*. Other members of the HCN family are found in neurons.

The parasympathetic neurotransmitter acetylcholine (ACh) slows heart rate. Acetylcholine activates muscarinic cholinergic receptors that influence K^+ and Ca^{2+} channels in the pacemaker cell. Potassium permeability increases, hyperpolarizing the cell so that the pacemaker potential begins at a more negative value (Fig. 14-16b). At the same time, Ca^{2+} permeability of the pacemaker decreases. Decreased Ca^{2+} permeability slows the rate at which the pacemaker potential depolarizes. The combination of the two effects causes the cell to take longer to reach threshold, delaying the onset of the action potential in the pacemaker and slowing the heart rate.

Table 14-3 ■ compares action potentials of the two types of myocardial muscle with those of skeletal muscle. Next we will see how action potentials of autorhythmic cells spread throughout the heart to coordinate contraction.

14

TABLE 14-3 Comparison of Action Potentials in Cardiac and Skeletal Muscle

	SKELETAL MUSCLE	CONTRACTILE MYOCARDIUM	AUTORHYTHMIC MYOCARDIUM
Membrane potential	Stable at −70 mV	Stable at −90 mV	Unstable pacemaker potential; usually starts at −60 mV
Events leading to threshold potential	Net Na^+ entry through ACh-operated channels	Depolarization enters via gap junctions	Net Na^+ entry through I_f channels; reinforced by Ca^{2+} entry
Rising phase of action potential	Na^+ entry	Na^+ entry	Ca^{2+} entry
Repolarization phase	Rapid; caused by K^+ efflux	Extended plateau caused by Ca^{2+} entry; rapid phase caused by K^+ efflux	Rapid; caused by K^+ efflux
Hyperpolarization	Due to excessive K^+ efflux at high K^+ permeability when K^+ channels close; leak of K^+ and Na^+ restores potential to resting state	None; resting potential is −90 mV, the equilibrium potential for K^+	None; when repolarization hits −60 mV, the I_f channels open again
Duration of action potential	Short: 1–2 msec	Extended: 200+ msec	Variable; generally 150+ msec
Refractory period	Generally brief	Long because resetting of Na^+ channel gates delayed until end of action potential	None

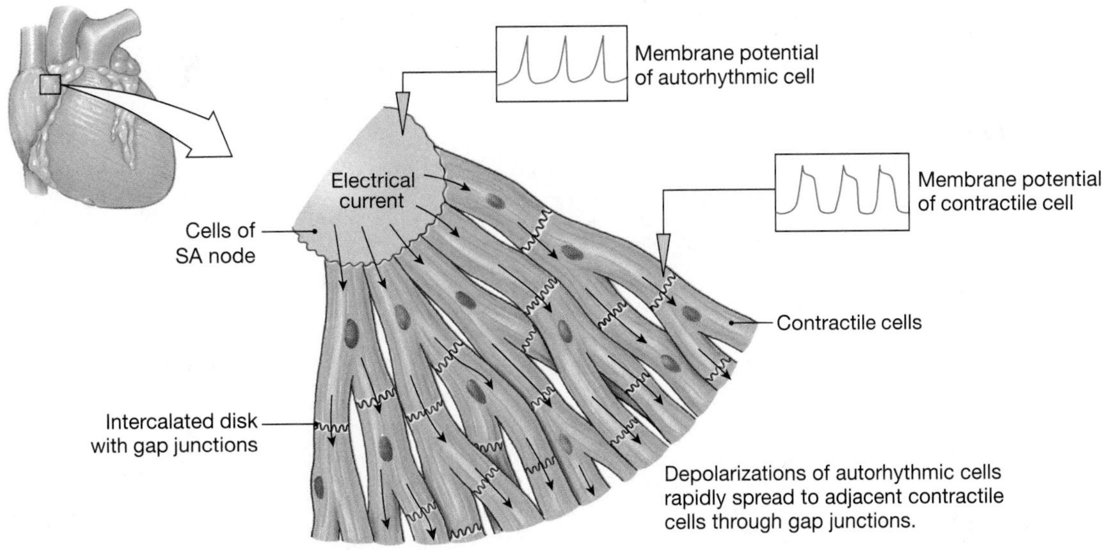

Membrane potential of autorhythmic cell

Electrical current

Cells of SA node

Membrane potential of contractile cell

Contractile cells

Intercalated disk with gap junctions

Depolarizations of autorhythmic cells rapidly spread to adjacent contractile cells through gap junctions.

■ **FIGURE 14-17** *Electrical conduction in myocardial cells*

CONCEPT CHECK

16. Do you think that the Ca^{2+} channels in autorhythmic cells are the same as the Ca^{2+} channels in contractile cells? Defend your answer.
17. What will happen to the action potential of a myocardial autorhythmic cell if tetrodotoxin, which blocks voltage-gated Na^+ channels, is applied to the cell?
18. In an experiment, the vagus nerve [p. 381] to the heart was cut. The investigators noticed that heart rate increased. What can you conclude about the vagal neurons that innervate the heart? Answers: p. 499

THE HEART AS A PUMP

We now turn from single myocardial cells to the intact heart. How can one tiny noncontractile autorhythmic cell cause the entire heart to beat? And why do those doctors on TV shows shock patients with electric paddles when their hearts malfunction? You're about to learn the answers to these questions.

Electrical Conduction in the Heart Coordinates Contraction

The heart is like a group of people around a stalled car. One person can push on the car, but it's not likely to move very far unless everyone pushes together. In the same way, individual myocardial cells must depolarize and contract in a coordinated fashion if the heart is to create enough force to circulate the blood.

Electrical communication in the heart begins with an action potential in an autorhythmic cell. The depolarization spreads rapidly to adjacent cells through gap junctions in the intercalated disks (Fig. 14-17 ■). The depolarization wave is followed by a wave of contraction that passes across the atria, then moves into the ventricles.

The depolarization begins in the **sinoatrial node (SA node)**, autorhythmic cells in the right atrium that serve as the main pacemaker of the heart (Fig. 14-18 ■). The depolarization wave then spreads rapidly through a specialized conducting system of noncontractile autorhythmic fibers. A branched **internodal pathway** connects the SA node to the **atrioventricular node (AV node)**, a group of autorhythmic cells near the floor of the right atrium. From the AV node, the depolarization moves into **Purkinje fibers** in the **atrioventricular bundle (AV bundle)*** in the septum between the ventricles. (Purkinje fibers are specialized conducting cells that transmit electrical signals very rapidly.) A short way down the septum, the AV bundle fibers divide into left and right **bundle branches**. The bundle branch fibers continue downward to the apex of the heart, where they divide into smaller Purkinje fibers that spread outward among the contractile cells.

The electrical signal for contraction begins when the SA node fires an action potential and the depolarization spreads to adjacent cells through gap junctions (Fig. 14-18, ①). Electrical conduction is rapid through the internodal conducting pathways ② but slower through the contractile cells of the atria ③.

As action potentials spread across the atria, they encounter the fibrous skeleton of the heart at the junction of the atria and ventricles. This barricade prevents the transfer of electrical signals from the atria to the ventricles. Consequently, the AV node is the only pathway through which action potentials can reach the contractile fibers of the ventricles.

The electrical signal passes from the AV node through the AV bundle and bundle branches to the apex of the heart (Fig. 14-18, ④). The Purkinje fibers transmit impulses very

*The AV bundle is also called the **bundle of His** ("hiss").

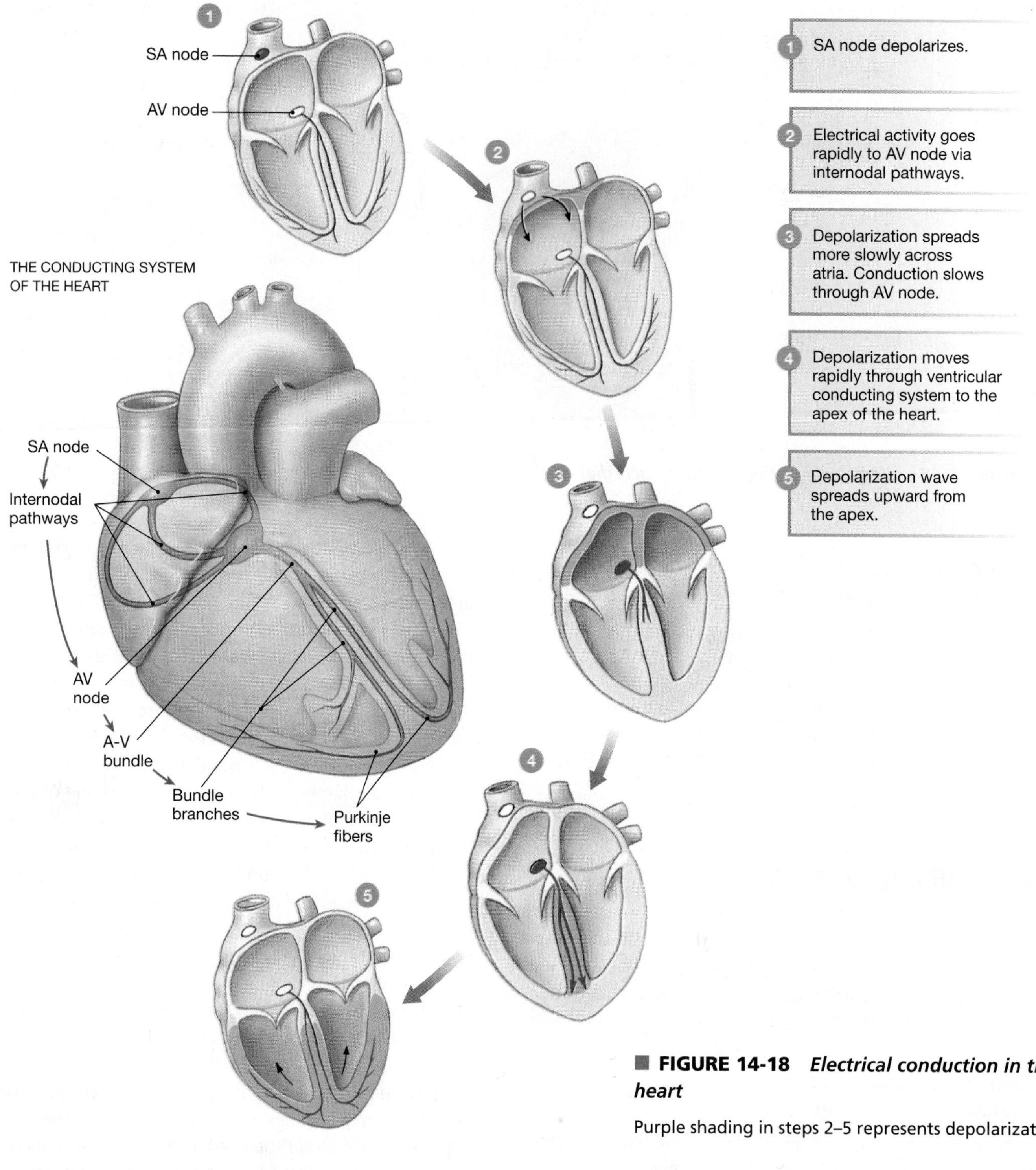

THE CONDUCTING SYSTEM OF THE HEART

SA node → Internodal pathways → AV node → A-V bundle → Bundle branches → Purkinje fibers

1. SA node depolarizes.
2. Electrical activity goes rapidly to AV node via internodal pathways.
3. Depolarization spreads more slowly across atria. Conduction slows through AV node.
4. Depolarization moves rapidly through ventricular conducting system to the apex of the heart.
5. Depolarization wave spreads upward from the apex.

■ **FIGURE 14-18** ***Electrical conduction in the heart***

Purple shading in steps 2–5 represents depolarization.

rapidly, with speeds up to 4 m/sec, so that all contractile cells in the apex contract nearly simultaneously ⑤.

Why is it necessary to direct the electrical signals through the AV node? Why not allow them to spread downward from the atria? The answer lies in the fact that blood is pumped out of the ventricles through openings at the top of the chambers (see Fig. 14-9b). If electrical signals from the atria were conducted directly into the ventricles, the ventricles would start contracting at the top. Then blood would be squeezed downward and would become trapped in the bottom of the ventricles (think of squeezing a toothpaste tube at the top). The apex-to-base contraction squeezes blood toward the arterial openings at the base of the heart.

The ejection of blood from the ventricles is aided by the spiral arrangement of the muscles in the walls (see Fig. 14-10a). As these muscles contract, they pull the apex and base of the heart closer together, squeezing blood out the openings at the top of the ventricles.

A second function of the AV node is to delay the transmission of action potentials slightly, allowing the atria to complete

RUNNING PROBLEM

The results of the creatine kinase and troponin I assays do not come back for several hours. If a coronary artery were blocked, damage to the heart muscle could be severe by that time. In Walter's case, an electrocardiogram (ECG) showed an abnormal pattern of electrical activity. "He's definitely had an MI," said the ER physician, referring to a myocardial infarction, or heart attack. "Let's start him on a beta-blocker and t-PA." t-PA (short for *tissue plasminogen activator*) activates plasminogen, a substance that is produced in the body and dissolves blood clots. Given within 1–3 hours of a heart attack, t-PA can help dissolve blood clots that are blocking blood flow to the heart muscle. This will help limit the extent of ischemic damage.

Question 5:
How do electrical signals move from cell to cell in the myocardium?

Question 6:
What happens to contraction in a myocardial contractile cell if a wave of depolarization passing through the heart bypasses it?

Question 7:
A beta-blocker is an antagonist to β_1-adrenergic receptors. What will this drug do to Walter's heart rate? Why is that response helpful following a heart attack?

their contraction before ventricular contraction begins. The **AV node delay** is accomplished by slowing conduction through the nodal cells. Action potentials here move at only 1/20 the rate of action potentials in the atrial internodal pathway.

Pacemakers Set the Heart Rate

The cells of the SA node set the pace of the heartbeat. Other cells in the conducting system, such as the AV node and the Purkinje fibers, have unstable resting potentials and can also act as pacemakers under some conditions. However, because their rhythm is slower than that of the SA node, they do not usually have a chance to set the heartbeat. The Purkinje fibers, for example, can spontaneously fire action potentials, but their firing rate is very slow, between 25 and 40 beats per minute.

Why does the fastest pacemaker determine the pace of the heartbeat? Consider the following analogy. A group of people are playing "follow the leader" as they walk. Initially, everyone is walking at a different pace—some fast, some slow. When the game starts, everyone must match his or her pace to the pace of the person who is walking the fastest. The fastest person in the group is the SA node, walking at 70 steps per minute. Everyone else in the group (autorhythmic and contractile cells) sees that the SA node is fastest, and so they pick up their pace and follow the leader. In the heart, the cue to follow the leader is the electrical signal sent from the SA node to the other cells.

Now suppose the SA node gets tired and drops out of the group. The role of leader defaults to the next fastest person, the AV node, who is walking at a rate of 50 steps per minute. The group slows to match the pace of the AV node, but everyone is still following the fastest walker.

What happens if the group divides? Suppose that when they reach a corner, the AV node leader goes left but a renegade Purkinje fiber decides to go right. Those people who follow the AV node continue to walk at 50 steps per minute, but the people who follow the Purkinje fiber slow down to match his pace of 35 steps per minute. Now there are two leaders, each walking at a different pace.

In the heart, the SA node is the fastest pacemaker and normally sets the heart rate. If this node is damaged and cannot function, one of the slower pacemakers in the heart takes over. Heart rate then matches the rate of the new pacemaker. It is even possible for different parts of the heart to follow different pacemakers, just as the walking group split at the corner.

CLINICAL FOCUS

FIBRILLATION

Coordination of myocardial contraction is essential for normal cardiac function. In extreme cases in which the myocardial cells contract in a disorganized manner, a condition known as *fibrillation* results. Ventricular fibrillation is a life-threatening emergency because without coordinated contraction of the muscle fibers, the ventricles cannot pump enough blood to supply adequate oxygen to the brain. One way to correct this problem is to administer an electrical shock to the heart. The shock creates a depolarization that triggers action potentials in all cells simultaneously, coordinating them again. You have probably seen this procedure on television hospital shows, when a doctor places flat paddles on the patient's chest and tells everyone to stand back ("Clear!") while the paddles pass an electrical current through the body.

In a condition known as *complete heart block,* the conduction of electrical signals from the atria to the ventricles through the AV node is disrupted. The SA node fires at its rate of 70 beats per minute, but those signals never reach the ventricles. So the ventricles coordinate with their fastest pacemaker. Because ventricular autorhythmic cells discharge only about 35 times a minute, the rate at which the ventricles contract is much slower than the rate at which the atria contract. If ventricular contraction is too slow to maintain adequate blood flow, it may be necessary for the heart's rhythm to be set artificially by a surgically implanted mechanical pacemaker. These battery-powered devices artificially stimulate the heart at a predetermined rate.

CONCEPT CHECK

19. Name two functions of the AV node. What is the purpose of AV node delay?
20. Where is the SA node located?
21. Occasionally an ectopic pacemaker [*ektopos*, out of place] will develop in part of the heart's conducting system. What happens to heart rate if an ectopic atrial pacemaker depolarizes at a rate of 120 times per minute?

Answers: p. 499

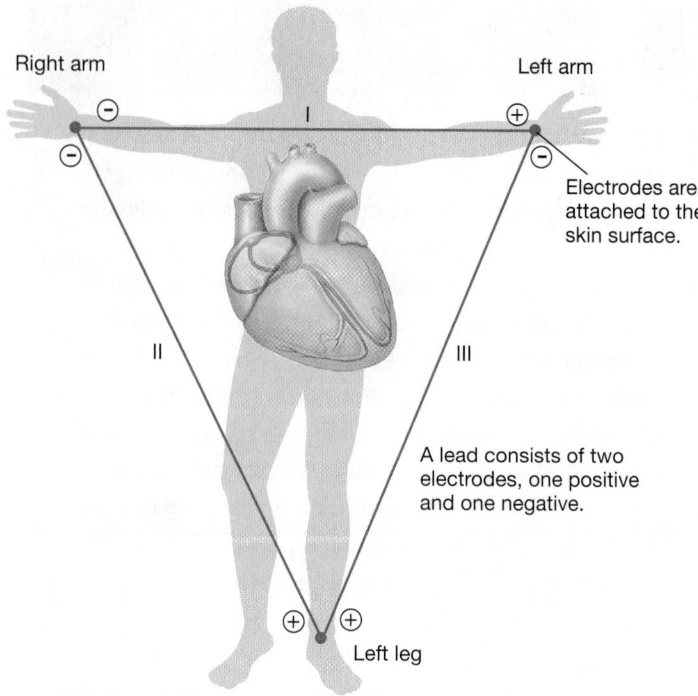

FIGURE 14-19 *Einthoven's triangle*

Electrodes attached to both arms and the left leg form a triangle. Two electrodes are active at any one time. Each two-electrode pair constitutes one *lead* (pronounced "leed"). Lead I, for instance, has the negative electrode attached to the right arm and the positive electrode attached to the left arm.

The Electrocardiogram Reflects the Electrical Activity of the Heart

At the end of the nineteenth century, physiologists discovered that they could place electrodes on the skin's surface and record the electrical activity of the heart. These recordings, called **electrocardiograms**, or ECGs,* provide indirect information about heart function. It is possible to use surface electrodes to record internal electrical activity because salt solutions, such as our NaCl-based extracellular fluid, are good conductors of electricity.

The first human electrocardiogram was recorded in 1887, but the procedure was not refined for clinical use until the first years of the twentieth century. The father of the modern ECG was a Dutch physiologist named Walter Einthoven. He named the parts of the ECG as we know them today and created "Einthoven's triangle," a hypothetical triangle created around the heart when electrodes are placed on both arms and the left leg (Fig. 14-19 ■). The sides of the triangle are numbered to correspond with the three leads, or pairs of electrodes, used for a recording. An ECG is recorded from one lead at a time. One electrode acts as the positive electrode of a lead and a second electrode acts as the negative electrode of the lead. (The third electrode is inactive.) For example, in lead I, the left arm electrode is designated as positive and the right arm electrode is designated as negative.

An ECG tracing shows the summed electrical potentials generated by all cells of the heart. Different components of the ECG reflect depolarization or repolarization of the atria and ventricles. Because depolarization initiates muscle contraction, these *electrical events* (waves) of an ECG can be associated with contraction or relaxation (collectively referred to as the *mechanical events* in the heart). Let's follow an ECG through a single contraction-relaxation cycle, otherwise known as a **cardiac cycle**.

There are two major components of an ECG: waves and segments. *Waves* appear as deflections above or below the baseline. *Segments* are sections of baseline between two waves. *Intervals* are combinations of waves and segments.

Three major waves can be seen on a normal ECG recorded from lead I (Fig. 14-20 ■). The first wave is the **P wave**, which corresponds to depolarization of the atria (Fig. 14-21 ■). The next trio of waves, the **QRS complex**, represents the progressive wave of ventricular depolarization. The final wave, the **T wave**, represents the repolarization of the ventricles. Atrial repolarization is not represented by a special wave but is incorporated into the QRS complex.

The mechanical events of the cardiac cycle lag slightly behind the electrical signals, just as the contraction of a single cardiac muscle cell follows its action potential (see Fig. 14-14c). Atrial contraction begins during the latter part of the P wave and continues during the PR segment. Ventricular contraction begins just after the Q wave and continues through the T wave.

One thing many people find confusing is that you cannot tell if an ECG recording represents depolarization or repolarization

*The abbreviation EKG—from the Greek word *kardia,* meaning *heart*—is sometimes used.

14

GRAPH QUESTION

If the chart speed is 25 mm /sec, what is the heart rate of the person? (1 little square = 1 mm)

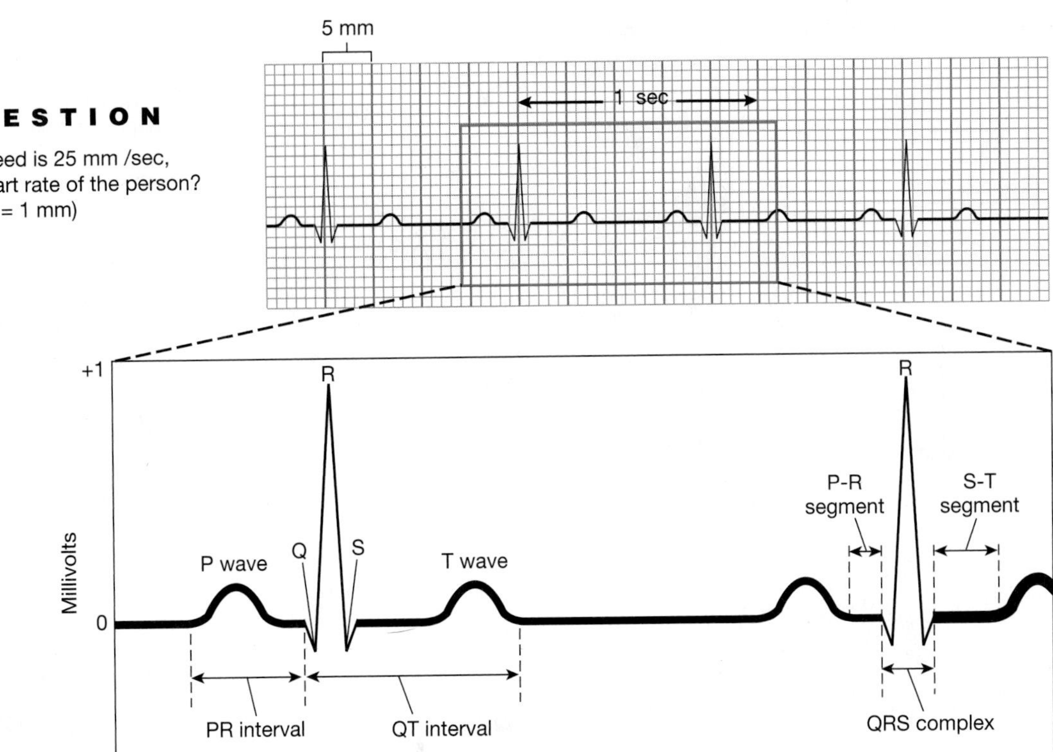

■ **FIGURE 14-20** ***The electrocardiogram***

An electrocardiogram is divided into waves (P, Q, R, S, and T), segments between the waves (the P-R and S-T segments, for example), and intervals consisting of a combination of waves and segments (such as the PR and QT intervals). This ECG tracing was recorded from lead I.

by looking at the shape of the waves relative to the baseline. For example, the P wave represents atrial depolarization and the T wave represents ventricular repolarization, but both the P wave and the T wave are deflections above the baseline. This is very different from the action potential recordings of neurons and muscle fibers, in which an upward deflection always represents depolarization [p. 257].

An ECG is not the same as a single action potential (Fig. 14-22 ■). An action potential is one electrical event in a single cell, recorded using an intracellular electrode. The ECG is an extracellular recording that represents the sum of multiple action potentials taking place in many heart muscle cells. When an electrical wave moving through the heart is directed toward the positive electrode, the ECG wave goes up from the baseline. If net charge movement through the heart is toward the negative electrode, the wave points downward. In addition, the amplitudes of action potential and ECG recordings are very different. A ventricular action potential has a voltage change of 110 mV, for example, but the ECG signal has an amplitude of only 1 mV by the time it reaches the surface of the body.

An important point to remember is that an ECG is an electrical "view" of a three-dimensional object. This is one reason we use multiple leads to assess heart function. Think of looking at an automobile. From the air, it looks like a rectangle, but from the side and front it has different shapes. Not everything that you see from the front of the car can be seen from its side, and vice versa. In the same way, the leads of an ECG provide different electrical "views" and give information about different regions of the heart. A 12-lead ECG (the three limb electrodes plus nine more electrodes placed on the chest and trunk) is the standard for clinical use. The additional leads provide detailed information about electrical conduction in the heart. Electrocardiograms are important diagnostic tools in medicine because they are quick, painless, and noninvasive (that is, do not puncture the skin).

An ECG provides information on heart rate and rhythm, conduction velocity, and even the condition of tissues in the heart. Thus, although obtaining an ECG is simple, interpreting some of its subtleties can be quite complicated. The interpretation of an ECG begins with the following questions (Fig. 14-23 ■).

1. What is the heart rate? Heart rate is normally timed either from the beginning of one P wave to the beginning of the next P wave or from the peak of one R wave to the peak of the next R wave. A normal resting heart rate is 60–100 beats per minute, although trained athletes often have slower heart rates at rest. A faster-than-normal rate is known as *tachycardia,* and a slower-than-normal rate is called *bradycardia* [*tachys,* swift; *bradys,* slow].

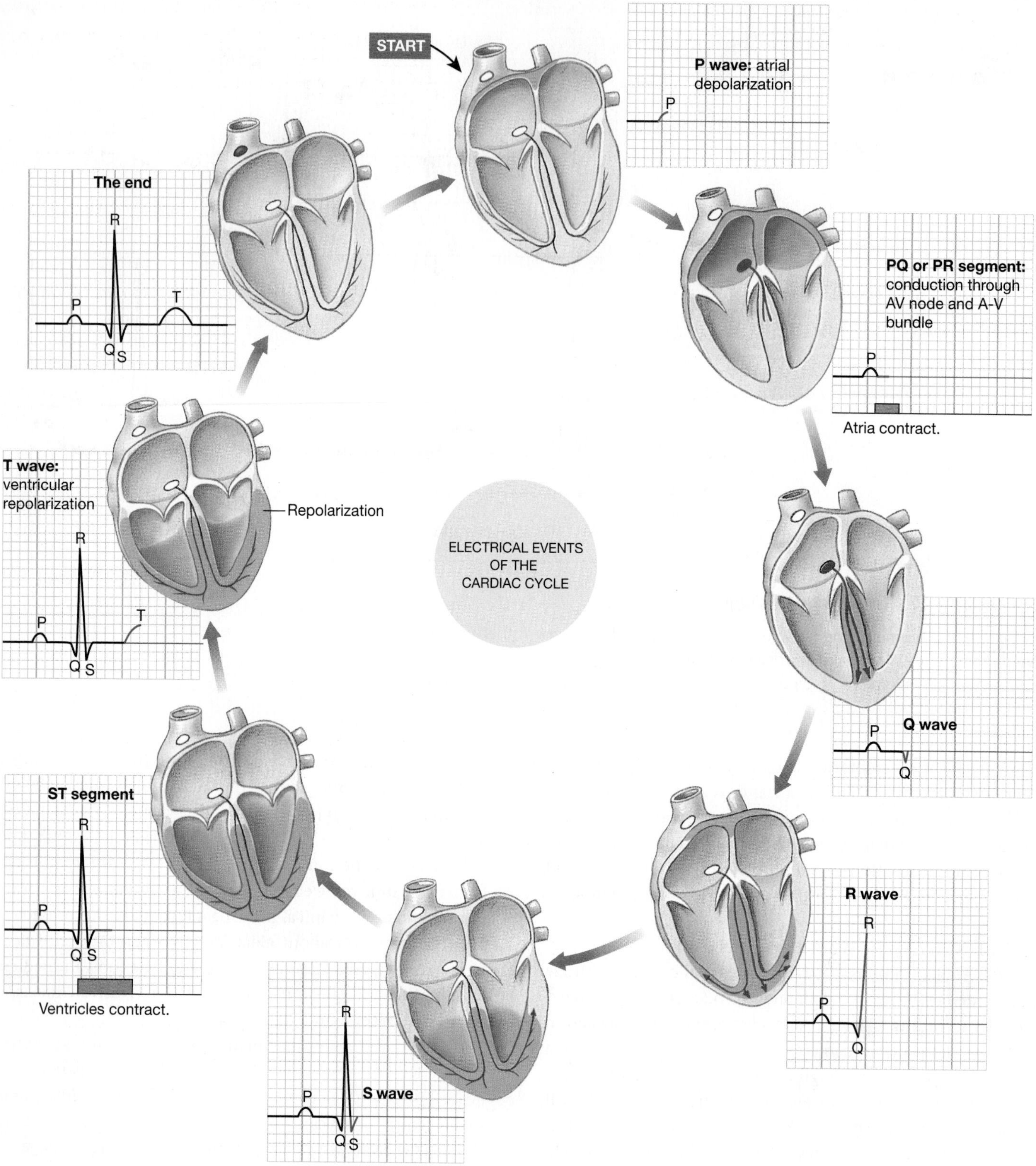

■ **FIGURE 14-21** ***Correlation between an ECG and electrical events in the heart***

The figure shows the correspondence between electrical events in the ECG and depolarizing (purple) and repolarizing (peach) regions of the heart.

2. Is the rhythm of the heartbeat regular (that is, occurs at regular intervals) or irregular? An irregular rhythm, or *arrhythmia* [*a-*, without + rhythm], can result from a benign extra beat or from more serious conditions such as atrial fibrillation, in which the SA node has lost control of the pacemaking.

   After determining heart rate and rhythm, the next step in analyzing an ECG is to look at the relationship of the various waves. To help your analysis, you might want to write the letters above the P, R, and T waves.

3. Does a QRS complex follow each P wave, and is the P-R segment constant in length? If not, a problem with conduction of signals through the AV node may exist. In heart block (the conduction problem mentioned earlier), action potentials from the SA node sometimes fail to be transmitted through the AV node to the ventricles. In these conditions, one or more P waves may occur without initiating a QRS complex. In the most severe form of heart block (third-degree), the atria depolarize regularly at one pace while the ventricles contract at a much slower pace (Fig. 14-23b).

The more difficult aspects of interpreting an ECG include looking for subtle changes, such as alterations in the shape or duration of various waves or segments. An experienced clinician can find signs pointing to changes in conduction velocity,

(a) The electrocardiogram represents the summed electrical activity of all cells recorded from the surface of the body.

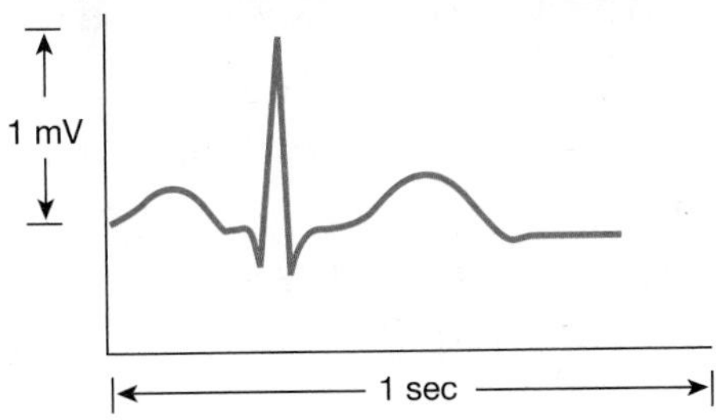

(b) The ventricular action potential is recorded from a single cell using an intracellular electrode. Notice that the voltage change is much greater when recorded intracellularly.

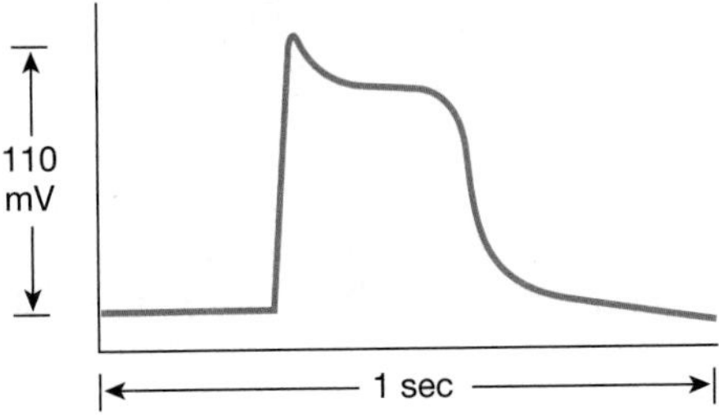

■ **FIGURE 14-22** ***Comparison of an ECG and a myocardial action potential***

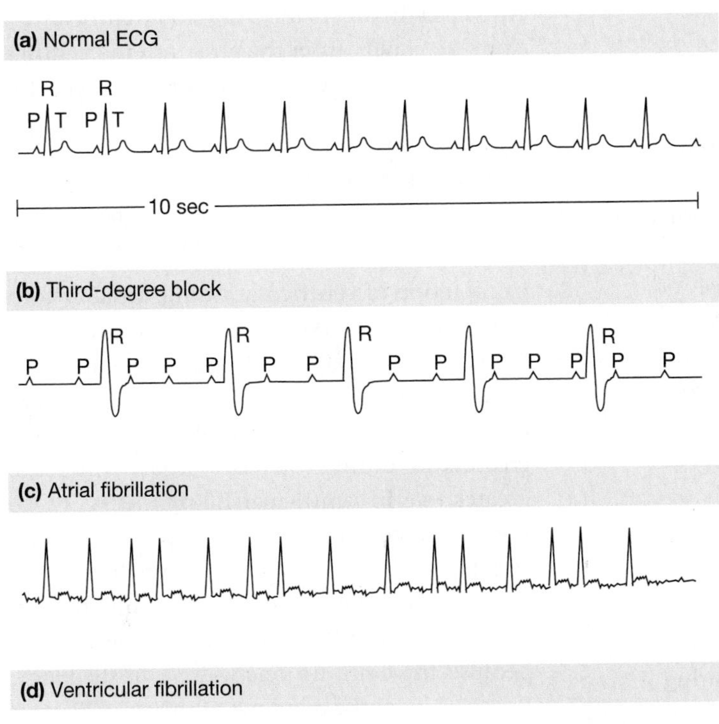

Questions to ask when analyzing ECG tracings:

1. What is the rate? Is it within the normal range of 60-100 beats per minute?
2. Is the rhythm regular?
3. Are all normal waves present in recognizable form?
4. Is there one QRS complex for each P wave? If yes, is the P-R segment constant in length?
5. If there is not one QRS complex for each P wave, count the heart rate using the P waves, then count it according to the R waves. Are the rates the same? Which wave would agree with the pulse felt at the wrist?

■ **FIGURE 14-23** ***Normal and abnormal electrocardiograms***

All tracings represent 10-sec recordings.

enlargement of the heart, or tissue damage resulting from periods of ischemia. An amazing number of conclusions can be drawn about heart function simply by looking at alterations in the heart's electrical activity as recorded on an ECG.

CONCEPT CHECK

22. Three abnormal ECGs are shown in Figure 14-23b–d. Study them and see if you can relate the ECG changes to disruption of the normal electrical conduction pattern in the heart.
23. Identify the waves on the following 10-second ECG recording. Look at the pattern of their occurrence and describe what has happened to electrical conduction in the heart. Answers: p. 499

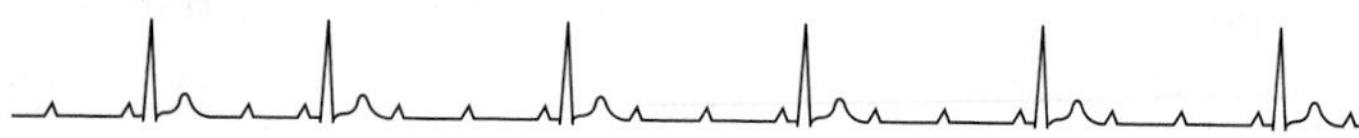

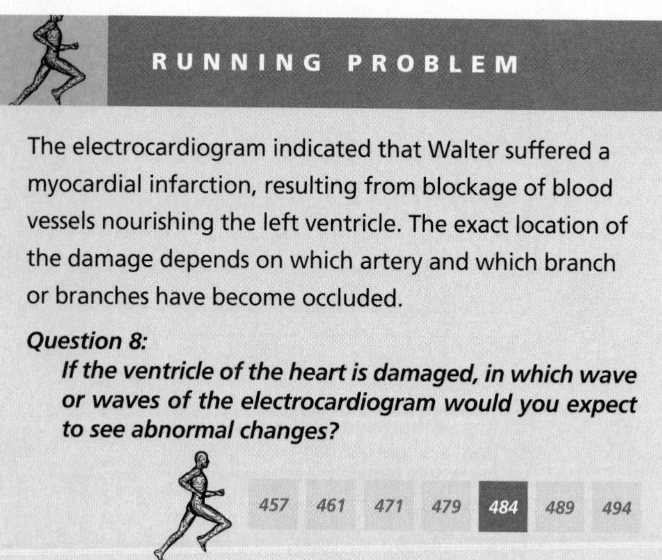

RUNNING PROBLEM

The electrocardiogram indicated that Walter suffered a myocardial infarction, resulting from blockage of blood vessels nourishing the left ventricle. The exact location of the damage depends on which artery and which branch or branches have become occluded.

Question 8:

If the ventricle of the heart is damaged, in which wave or waves of the electrocardiogram would you expect to see abnormal changes?

457 461 471 479 **484** 489 494

Cardiac arrhythmias are a family of cardiac pathologies that range from benign to those with potentially fatal consequences. Arrhythmias are electrical problems that arise during the generation or conduction of action potentials through the heart, and they can usually be seen on an ECG. Some arrhythmias are "dropped beats" that result when the ventricles do not get their usual signal to contract. Other arrhythmias, such as *premature ventricular contractions* (PVCs), are extra beats that occur when an autorhythmic cell other than the SA node jumps in and fires an action potential out of sequence.

One interesting heart condition that can be observed on an ECG is *long QT syndrome* (LQTS), named for the change in the QT interval. LQTS has several forms. Some are inherited channelopathies, in which mutations occur in myocardial Na^+ or K^+ channels [p. 254]. In another form of LQTS, the ion channels are normal but the protein *ankyrin-B* that anchors the channels to the cell membrane is defective. *Iatrogenic* (physician-caused) forms of LQTS can occur as a side effect of taking certain medications. One well-publicized incident occurred in the 1990s when patients took a non-sedating antihistamine called terfenadine (Seldane®) that binds to K^+ repolarization channels. After at least eight deaths were attributed to the drug, the U.S. Food and Drug Administration removed Seldane from the market.

The Heart Contracts and Relaxes Once During a Cardiac Cycle

Each cardiac cycle has two phases: **diastole**, the time during which cardiac muscle relaxes, and **systole**, the time during which the muscle is contracting [*diastole*, dilation; *systole*, contraction]. Because the atria and ventricles do not contract and relax at the same time, we will discuss atrial and ventricular events separately.

In thinking about blood flow during the cardiac cycle, remember that blood flows from an area of higher pressure to one of lower pressure, and that contraction increases pressure while relaxation decreases pressure. In this discussion, we divide the cardiac cycle into the five phases shown in Figure 14-24 ■:

1. **The heart at rest: atrial and ventricular diastole.** We enter the cardiac cycle at the brief moment during which both the atria and the ventricles are relaxing. The atria are filling with blood from the veins, and the ventricles have just completed a contraction. As the ventricles relax, the AV valves between the atria and ventricles open. Blood flows by gravity from the atria into the ventricles. The relaxing ventricles expand to accommodate the entering blood.

CONCEPT CHECK

24. During atrial filling, is pressure in the atrium higher or lower than pressure in the venae cavae? Answers: p. 499

2. **Completion of ventricular filling: atrial systole.** Although most blood enters the ventricles while the atria are relaxed, the last 20% of filling is accomplished when the atria contract and push blood into the ventricles. (This applies to a normal person at rest. When heart rate increases, as during exercise, atrial contraction plays a greater role in ventricular filling.) Atrial systole, or contraction, begins following the wave of depolarization that sweeps across the atria. The pressure increase that accompanies contraction pushes blood into the ventricles. A small amount of blood is forced backward into the veins because there are no one-way valves to block backward flow, although the openings of the veins do narrow during contraction. This retrograde movement of blood back into the veins may be observed as a pulse in the jugular vein of a normal person who is lying with the head and chest elevated about 30°. (Look in the hollow formed where the sternocleidomastoid muscle runs under the clavicle.) An

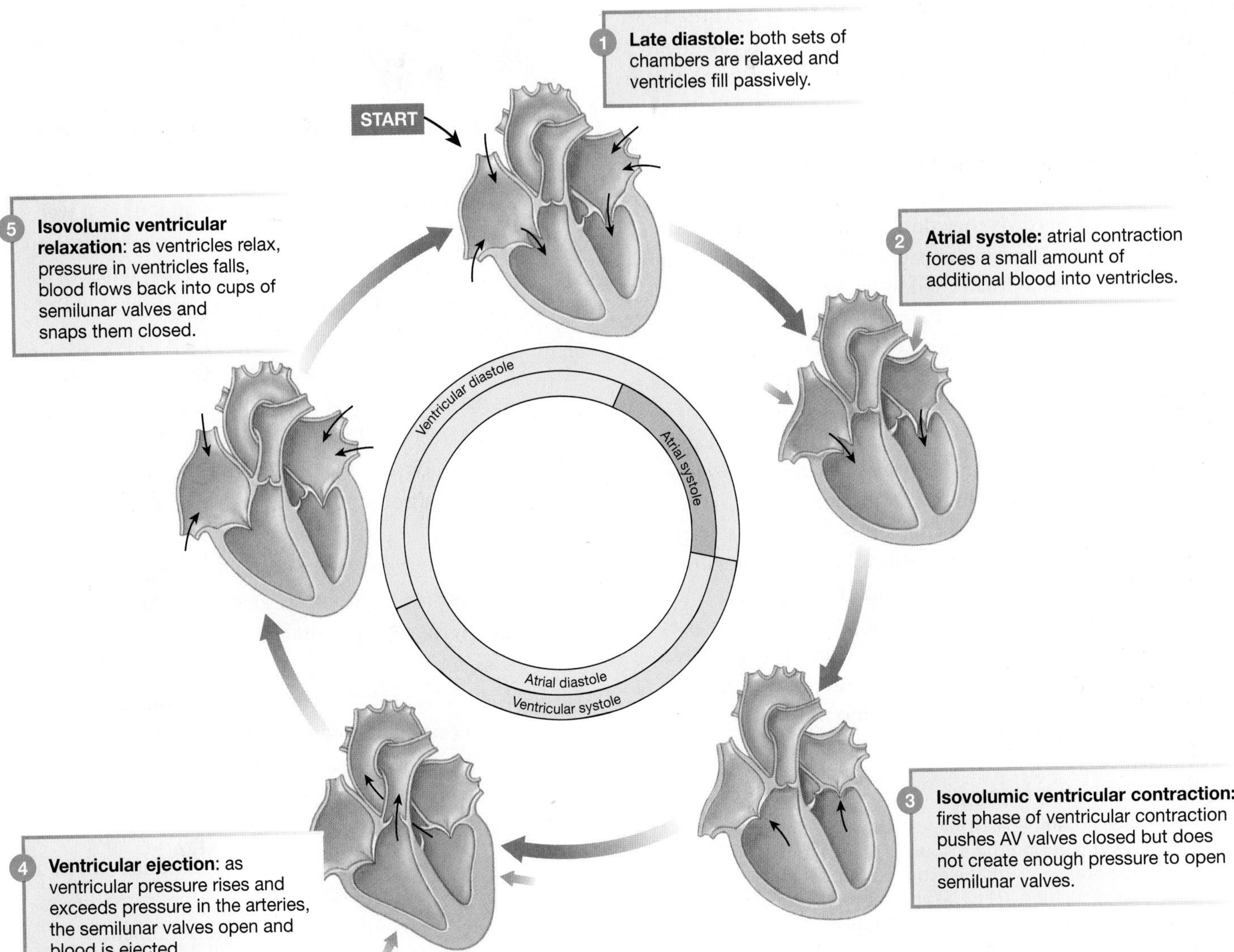

1 Late diastole: both sets of chambers are relaxed and ventricles fill passively.
START
2 Atrial systole: atrial contraction forces a small amount of additional blood into ventricles.
3 Isovolumic ventricular contraction: first phase of ventricular contraction pushes AV valves closed but does not create enough pressure to open semilunar valves.
4 Ventricular ejection: as ventricular pressure rises and exceeds pressure in the arteries, the semilunar valves open and blood is ejected.
5 Isovolumic ventricular relaxation: as ventricles relax, pressure in ventricles falls, blood flows back into cups of semilunar valves and snaps them closed.
Ventricular diastole
Atrial systole
Atrial diastole
Ventricular systole

FIGURE 14-24 ***Mechanical events of the cardiac cycle***

observable jugular pulse higher on the neck of a person sitting upright is a sign that pressure in the right atrium is higher than normal.

3. **Early ventricular contraction and the first heart sound.** As the atria are contracting, the depolarization wave is moving slowly through the conducting cells of the AV node, then rapidly down the Purkinje fibers to the apex of the heart. Ventricular systole begins there as spiral bands of muscle squeeze the blood upward toward the base. Blood pushing against the underside of the AV valves forces them closed so that blood cannot flow back into the atria. Vibrations following closure of the AV valves create the **first heart sound,** S_1, the "lub" of "lub-dup."

   With both sets of AV and semilunar valves closed, blood in the ventricles has nowhere to go. Nevertheless, the ventricles continue to contract, squeezing on the blood in the same way that you might squeeze a water balloon in your hand. This is similar to an isometric contraction, in which muscle fibers create force without movement [p. 417]. To return to the toothpaste tube analogy, it is like squeezing the tube with the cap on: high pressure develops within the tube, but the toothpaste has nowhere to go. This phase is called **isovolumic ventricular contraction** [*iso-*, equal], to underscore the fact that the volume of blood in the ventricle is not changing.

   While the ventricles begin to contract, the atrial muscle fibers are repolarizing and relaxing. When atrial pressure falls below that in the veins, blood flows from the veins into the atria again. Closure of the AV valves isolates the upper and lower cardiac chambers, meaning that atrial filling is independent of events taking place in the ventricles.

4. **The heart pumps: ventricular ejection.** As the ventricles contract, they generate enough pressure to open the semilunar valves and push blood into the arteries. The pressure created by ventricular contraction becomes the driving

force for blood flow. High-pressure blood is forced into the arteries, displacing the low-pressure blood that fills them and pushing it farther into the vasculature. During this phase, the AV valves remain closed and the atria continue to fill.

5. **Ventricular relaxation and the second heart sound.** At the end of ventricular ejection, the ventricles begin to repolarize and relax. As they do so, ventricular pressure decreases. Once ventricular pressure falls below the pressure in the arteries, blood starts to flow backward into the heart. This backflow of blood fills the cuplike cusps of the semilunar valves, forcing them together into the closed position. The vibrations created by semilunar valve closure are the **second heart sound,** S_2, the "dup" of "lub-dup."

   Once the semilunar valves close, the ventricles again become sealed chambers. The AV valves remain closed because ventricular pressure, although falling, is still higher than atrial pressure. This period is called **isovolumic ventricular relaxation** because the volume of blood in the ventricles is not changing.

   When ventricular relaxation causes ventricular pressure to become less than atrial pressure, the AV valves open. Blood that has been accumulating in the atria during ventricular contraction rushes into the ventricles. The cardiac cycle has begun again.

CONCEPT CHECK

25. Which chamber—atrium or ventricle—has higher pressure during the following phases of the cardiac cycle? (a) ventricular ejection, (b) isovolumic ventricular relaxation, (c) atrial and ventricular diastole, (d) isovolumic ventricular contraction
26. *Murmurs* are abnormal heart sounds caused either by blood forced through a narrowed valve opening or by backward flow (regurgitation) through a valve that has not closed completely. *Valvular stenosis* [*stenos*, narrow] may be an inherited condition or may result from inflammation or other disease processes. At which step(s) in the cardiac cycle (Fig. 14-24) would you expect to hear a murmur caused by the following pathologies? (a) aortic valvular stenosis, (b) mitral valve regurgitation, (c) aortic valve regurgitation

Answers: p. 499

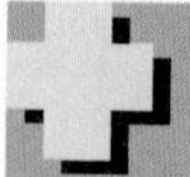

CLINICAL FOCUS

GALLOPS, CLICKS, AND MURMURS

The simplest direct assessment of heart function consists of listening to the heart through the chest wall, a process known as **auscultation** [*auscultare,* to listen to] that has been practiced since ancient times. In its simplest form, auscultation is done by placing an ear against the chest. Today, however, it is usually performed by listening through a stethoscope placed against the chest and the back. Normally, there are two audible heart sounds. The first ("lub") is associated with closure of the AV valves. The second ("dup") is associated with closure of the semilunar valves.

Two additional heart sounds can be recorded with very sensitive electronic stethoscopes. The third heart sound is caused by turbulent blood flow into the ventricles during ventricular filling, and the fourth sound is associated with turbulence during atrial contraction. In certain abnormal conditions, these latter two sounds may become audible through a regular stethoscope. They are called gallops because their timing puts them close to one of the normal heart sounds: "lub—dup-dup," or "lub-lub—dup." Other abnormal heart sounds include clicking, caused by abnormal movement of one of the valves, and murmurs, caused by the "whoosh" of blood leaking through an incompletely closed or excessively narrowed (*stenosed*) valve.

Pressure-Volume Curves Represent One Cardiac Cycle

Another way to describe the cardiac cycle is with a pressure-volume graph, shown in Figure 14-25 ■. This figure represents the changes in volume (*x*-axis) and pressure (*y*-axis) that occur during one cardiac cycle. The flow of blood through the heart is governed by the same principle that governs the flow of all liquids and gases: flow proceeds from areas of higher pressure to areas of lower pressure. When the heart contracts, the pressure increases and blood flows out of the heart into areas of lower pressure. Figure 14-25 represents pressure and volume changes in the left ventricle, which sends blood into the systemic circulation. The left side of the heart creates higher pressures than the right side, which sends blood through the shorter pulmonary circuit.

The cycle begins at point A. The ventricle has completed a contraction and contains the minimum amount of blood that it will hold during the cycle. It has relaxed, and its pressure is also at its minimum value. Blood is flowing into the atrium from the pulmonary veins.

Once pressure in the atrium exceeds pressure in the ventricle, the mitral valve between the atrium and ventricle opens (Fig. 14-25, point A). Atrial blood now flows into the ventricle, increasing its volume (point A to point B). As blood flows in, the relaxing ventricle expands to accommodate the entering blood. Consequently, the volume of the ventricle increases but the pressure in the ventricle goes up very little.

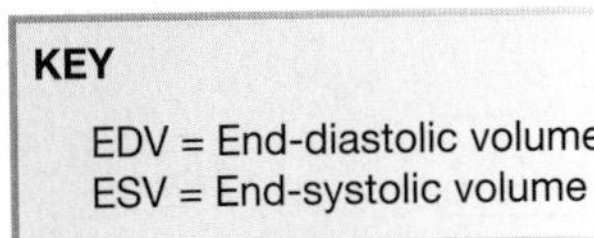

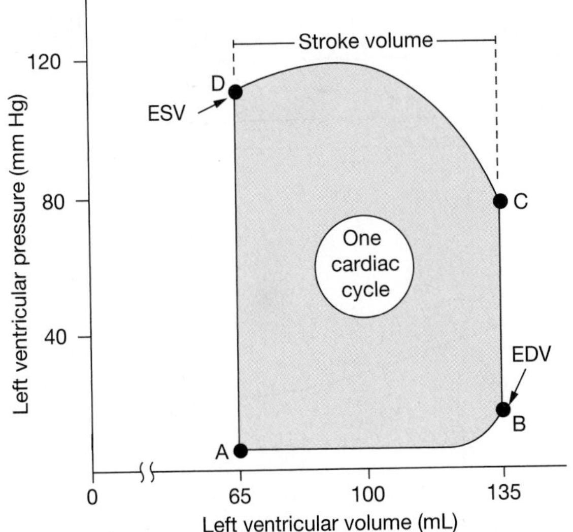

GRAPH QUESTIONS

Match the following segments to the corresponding ventricular events:

A → B: (a) Ejection of blood into aorta
B → C: (b) Isovolumic contraction
C → D: (c) Isovolumic relaxation
D → A: (d) Passive filling and atrial contraction

Match the following events to points A – D:
(a) aortic valve opens
(b) mitral valve opens
(c) aortic valve closes
(d) mitral valve closes

■ **FIGURE 14-25** ***Left ventricular pressure-volume changes during one cardiac cycle***

The last portion of ventricular filling is completed by atrial contraction. The ventricle now contains the maximum volume of blood that it will hold during this cardiac cycle (point B). Because maximum filling occurs at the end of ventricular relaxation (diastole), this volume is called the **end-diastolic volume (EDV)**. In a 70-kg man at rest, end-diastolic volume is about 135 mL, but this value will vary under different conditions. During periods of very high heart rate, for instance, when the ventricle does not have time to fill completely between beats, the end-diastolic value may be less than 135 mL.

When ventricular contraction begins, the mitral valve closes. With both the AV valve and the semilunar valve closed, blood in the ventricle has nowhere to go. Nevertheless, the ventricle continues to contract, causing the pressure in this chamber to increase rapidly during isovolumic contraction (B → C in Fig. 14-25). Once ventricular pressure exceeds the pressure in the aorta, the aortic valve opens (point C). Pressure continues to increase as the ventricle contracts further, but ventricular volume decreases as blood is pushed out into the aorta (C → D).

The heart does not empty itself completely of blood each time the ventricle contracts. The amount of blood left in the ventricle at the end of contraction is known as the **end-systolic volume (ESV)**. The ESV (point D) is the minimum amount of blood the ventricle will contain during one cycle. An average ESV value in a person at rest is 65 mL, meaning that nearly half of the 135 mL that was in the ventricle at the start of the contraction is still there at the end of the contraction.

At the end of each ventricular contraction, the ventricle begins to relax. As it does so, ventricular pressure decreases. Once pressure in the ventricle falls below aortic pressure, the semilunar valve closes, and the ventricle again becomes a sealed chamber. The remainder of relaxation occurs without a change in blood volume, and so this phase is called *isovolumic relaxation* (Fig. 14-25, D → A). When ventricular pressure finally falls to the point at which atrial pressure exceeds ventricular pressure, the mitral valve opens and the cycle begins again.

The electrical and mechanical events of the cardiac cycle are summarized together in Figure 14-26 ■, known as a Wiggers diagram after the physiologist who first created it.

CONCEPT CHECK

27. In Figure 14-24, at what points in the cycle do EDV and ESV occur?
28. On the Wiggers diagram in Figure 14-26, match the following events to the lettered boxes: (a) end diastolic volume, (b) aortic valve opens, (c) mitral valve opens, (d) aortic valve closes, (e) mitral valve closes, (f) end systolic volume
29. Why does atrial pressure increase just to the right of point C in Figure 14-26? Why does it decrease during the initial part of ventricular systole, then increase? Why does it decrease to the right of point D?
30. Why does ventricular pressure shoot up suddenly at point C in Figure 14-26?

Answers: p. 499

Stroke Volume Is the Volume of Blood Pumped by One Ventricle in One Contraction

What is the purpose of blood remaining in the ventricles at the end of each contraction? For one thing, the resting end-systolic volume of 65 mL provides a safety margin. With a more forceful contraction, the heart can decrease its ESV, sending additional blood to the tissues. Like many organs of the body, the heart does not usually work "all out."

The amount of blood pumped by one ventricle during a contraction is known as the **stroke volume**. It is measured in milliliters per beat and can be calculated as follows:

$$\text{Volume of blood before contraction} - \text{Volume of blood after contraction} = \text{stroke volume}$$

$$\text{EDV} - \text{ESV} = \text{stroke volume}$$

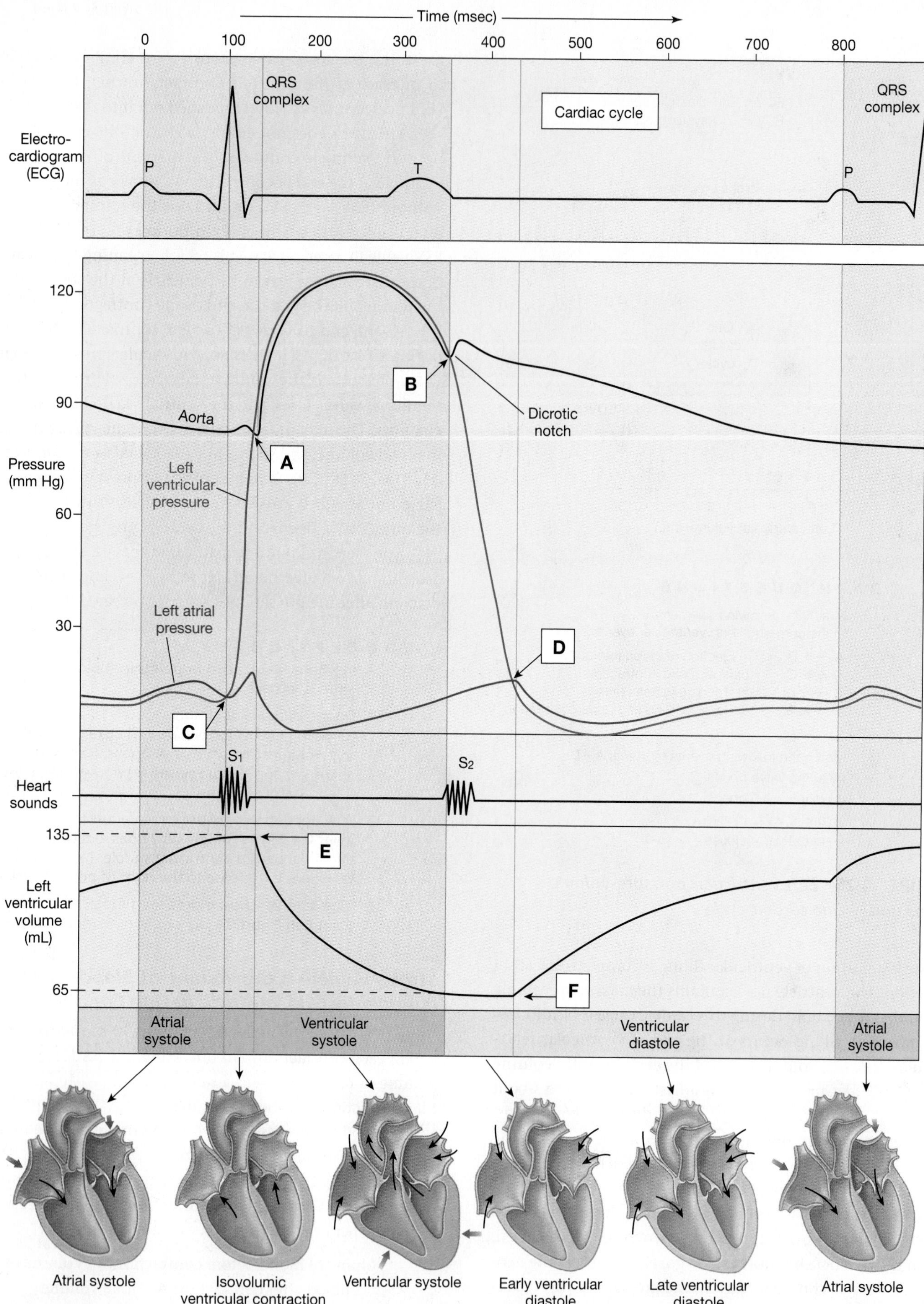

■ **FIGURE 14-26** ***The Wiggers diagram***

The boxed letters refer to Concept Checks 28–30.

For the average contraction in a person at rest:

$$135 \text{ mL} - 65 \text{ mL} = 70 \text{ mL, the normal stroke volume}$$

Stroke volume is not constant and can increase to as much as 100 mL during exercise. Stroke volume, like heart rate, is homeostatically regulated by mechanisms discussed later in this chapter.

Cardiac Output Is a Measure of Cardiac Performance

How can we assess the effectiveness of the heart as a pump? One way is to measure **cardiac output**, the volume of blood pumped by one ventricle in a given period of time. Because all blood that leaves the heart flows through the tissues, cardiac output is an indicator of total blood flow through the body. However, cardiac output does not tell us how blood is distributed to various tissues. That aspect of blood flow is regulated at the tissue level.

Cardiac output (CO) can be calculated by multiplying heart rate (beats per minute) by stroke volume (mL per beat, or per contraction):

$$\text{cardiac output} = \text{heart rate} \times \text{stroke volume}$$

For an average resting heart rate of 72 beats per minute and a stroke volume of 70 mL per beat, we have

$$\begin{aligned} \text{CO} &= 72 \text{ beats/min} \times 70 \text{ mL/beat} \\ &= 5040 \text{ mL/min} \quad \text{(or approx. 5 L/min)} \end{aligned}$$

Average total blood volume is about 5 liters. This means that, at rest, one side of the heart pumps all the blood in the body through it in only one minute!

Normally, cardiac output is the same for both ventricles. However, if one side of the heart begins to fail for some reason and is unable to pump efficiently, cardiac output becomes mismatched. In that situation, blood will pool in the circulation behind the weaker side of the heart.

During exercise, cardiac output may increase to 30–35 L/min. Homeostatic changes in cardiac output are accomplished by varying the heart rate, the stroke volume, or both. Both local and reflex mechanisms can alter cardiac output, as we will see in the sections that follow.

CONCEPT CHECK

31. If the stroke volume of the left ventricle is 250 mL/beat and the stroke volume of the right ventricle is 251 mL/beat, what will happen to the relative distribution of blood between the systemic and pulmonary circulation after 10 beats? Answers: p. 499

Heart Rate Is Modulated by Autonomic Neurons and Catecholamines

An average resting heart rate in an adult is about 70 beats/minute (bpm). The normal range is highly variable, however. Trained athletes may have resting heart rates of 50 bpm or less, while someone who is excited or anxious may have a rate of 125 bpm or higher. Children have higher average heart rates than adults. Although heart rate is initiated by autorhythmic cells in the SA node, it is modulated by neural and hormonal input.

The sympathetic and parasympathetic branches of the autonomic division influence heart rate through antagonistic control (Fig. 14-27 ■) [Fig. 6-21, p. 194]. Parasympathetic activity slows heart rate, while sympathetic activity speeds it up. Normally, tonic control of heart rate is dominated by the parasympathetic branch. This can be shown experimentally by blocking all autonomic input to the heart. When all sympathetic and parasympathetic input is blocked, the spontaneous depolarization rate of the SA node is 90–100 times per minute. To achieve a resting heart rate of 70 beats per minute, tonic parasympathetic activity must slow the intrinsic rate down from 90 beats per minute.

An increase in heart rate can be achieved in two ways. The simplest method for increasing rate is to decrease parasympathetic activity. As parasympathetic influence is withdrawn from the autorhythmic cells, they resume their intrinsic rate of depolarization, and heart rate increases to 90–100 beats per minute. Alternatively, sympathetic input is required to increase heart rate above the intrinsic rate. As you learned earlier, norepinephrine (or epinephrine) on β_1-receptors speeds up the

RUNNING PROBLEM

Walter was in the cardiac care unit by 1 P.M., where the cardiologist visited him. "We need to keep an eye on you here for the next week. There is a good chance the damage from your heart attack could cause an irregular heartbeat." Once Walter was stable, he would have a coronary angiogram, a procedure in which an opaque dye visible on X-rays shows where coronary artery lumens have narrowed from atherosclerotic plaques. Depending on the results of that test, the physician might recommend either balloon angioplasty, in which a tube passed into the coronary artery is inflated to open up the blockage, or coronary bypass surgery, in which veins from other parts of the body are grafted onto the heart arteries to provide bypass channels around blocked regions.

Question 9:

If Walter's heart attack has damaged the muscle of his left ventricle, what do you predict will happen to his left cardiac output?

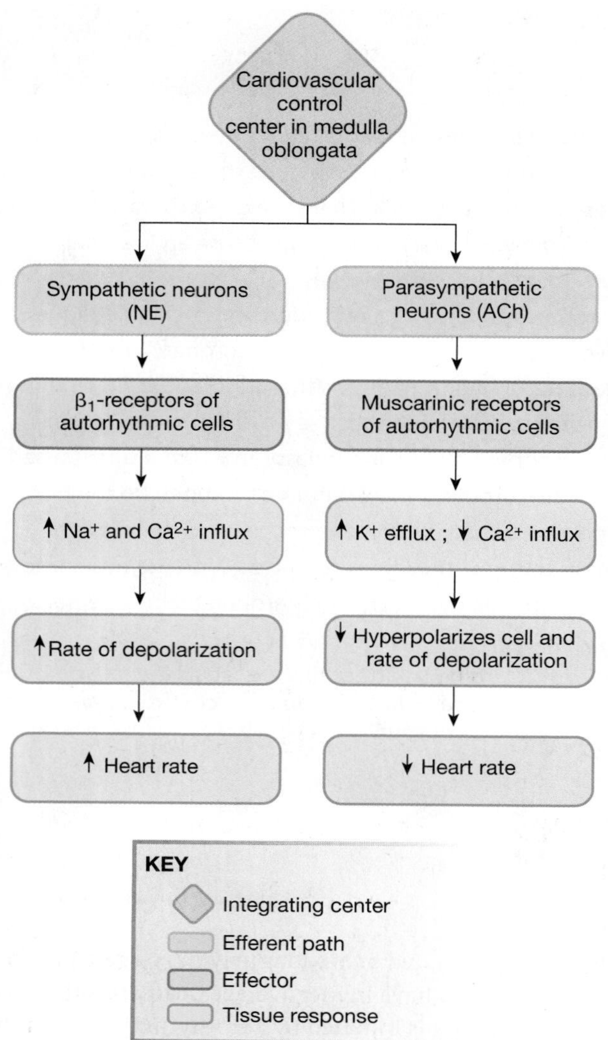

■ **FIGURE 14-27** ***Reflex control of heart rate***

depolarization rate of the autorhythmic cells and increases heart rate.

Both autonomic branches also alter the rate of conduction through the AV node. Acetylcholine secreted by parasympathetic neurons slows the conduction of action potentials through the AV node, thereby increasing AV node delay. In contrast, the catecholamines epinephrine and norepinephrine enhance conduction of action potentials through the AV node and through the conducting system.

Multiple Factors Influence Stroke Volume

Stroke volume, the volume of blood pumped per ventricle per contraction, is directly related to the force generated by cardiac muscle during a contraction. Normally, the greater the force of contraction, the greater the stroke volume. In the isolated heart, the force of ventricular contraction is affected by two parameters: the length of muscle fibers at the beginning of contraction and the contractility of the heart. The volume of blood in the

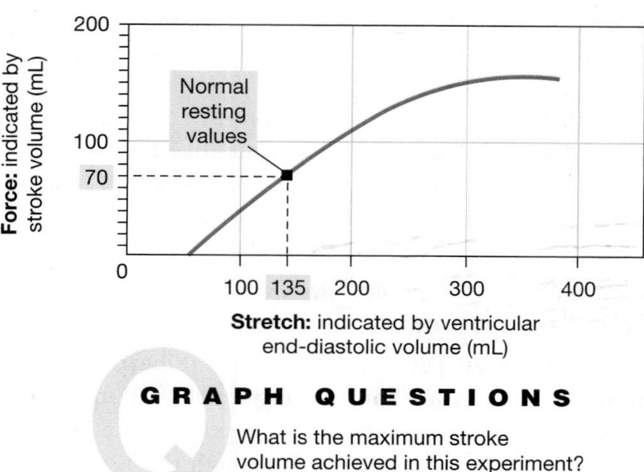

GRAPH QUESTIONS

What is the maximum stroke volume achieved in this experiment? At what end-diastolic volume is maximum stroke volume first achieved?

■ **FIGURE 14-28** ***Length-force relationships in the intact heart: a Starling curve***

In the intact heart, stroke volume is used as an indicator of contractile force.

ventricle at the beginning of contraction (the end-diastolic volume) determines the length of the muscle. **Contractility** is the intrinsic ability of a cardiac muscle fiber to contract at any given fiber length and is a function of Ca^{2+} interaction with the contractile filaments.

Length-Tension Relationships and the Frank-Starling Law of the Heart As you learned earlier in this chapter, the force created by a myocardial muscle fiber is directly related to the length of the sarcomere. As sarcomere length increases (up to an optimum length), contraction force increases. In the intact heart, as stretch of the ventricular wall increases, so does the stroke volume. If additional blood flows into the ventricles, the muscle fibers stretch, then contract more forcefully, ejecting more blood. The degree of myocardial stretch before contraction begins is called the **preload** on the heart because this stretch represents the load placed on cardiac muscles before they contract.

This relationship between stretch and force in the intact heart was first described by a German physiologist, Otto Frank. A British physiologist, Ernest Starling, then expanded on Frank's work. Starling attached an isolated heart-lung preparation from a dog to a reservoir so that he could regulate the amount of blood returning to the heart. He found that in the absence of any nervous or hormonal control, the heart pumped all the blood that returned to it.

The relationship between stretch and force in the intact heart is plotted on a *Starling curve* (Fig. 14-28 ■). The *x*-axis represents the end-diastolic volume. This volume is a measure of stretch in the ventricles, which in turn determines sarcomere length. The *y*-axis of the Starling curve represents the stroke volume and is an indicator of the force of contraction.

The graph shows that stroke volume is proportional to EDV. As additional blood enters the heart, the heart contracts more forcefully and ejects more blood. This relationship is known as the **Frank-Starling law of the heart**. It means that within physiological limits, the heart pumps all the blood that returns to it.

Stroke Volume and Venous Return According to the Frank-Starling law, stroke volume increases as end-diastolic volume increases. End-diastolic volume is normally determined by **venous return**, the amount of blood that enters the heart from the venous circulation. Three factors affect venous return: (1) contraction or compression of veins returning blood to the heart (the skeletal muscle pump), (2) pressure changes in the abdomen and thorax during breathing (the respiratory pump), and (3) sympathetic innervation of veins.

Skeletal muscle pump is the name given to skeletal muscle contractions that squeeze veins (particularly in the legs), compressing them and pushing blood toward the heart. During exercise that involves the lower extremities, the skeletal muscle pump helps return blood to the heart. During periods of sitting or standing motionless, the skeletal muscle pump does not assist venous return.

The **respiratory pump** is created by movement of the thorax during inspiration (breathing in). As the chest expands and the diaphragm moves toward the abdomen, the thoracic cavity enlarges and develops a subatmospheric pressure. This low pressure decreases pressure in the inferior vena cava as it passes through the thorax, which helps draw more blood into the vena cava from veins in the abdomen. The respiratory pump is aided by the higher pressure placed on the outside of abdominal veins when the abdominal contents are compressed during inspiration. The combination of increased pressure in the abdominal veins and decreased pressure in thoracic veins enhances venous return during inspiration.

Constriction of veins by sympathetic activity is the third factor that affects venous return. When the veins constrict, their volume decreases, squeezing more blood out of them and into the heart. With a larger ventricular volume at the beginning of the next contraction, the ventricle contracts more forcefully, sending the blood out into the arterial side of the circulation. In this manner, sympathetic innervation of veins allows the body to redistribute some venous blood to the arterial side of the circulation.

Contractility Is Controlled by the Nervous and Endocrine Systems

Any chemical that affects contractility is called an **inotropic agent** [*ino,* fiber], and its influence is called an **inotropic effect.** If a chemical increases the force of contraction, it is said to have a positive inotropic effect. For example, the catecholamines epinephrine and norepinephrine and drugs such as digitalis enhance contractility and are therefore considered to have a positive inotropic effect. Chemicals with negative inotropic effects decrease contractility.

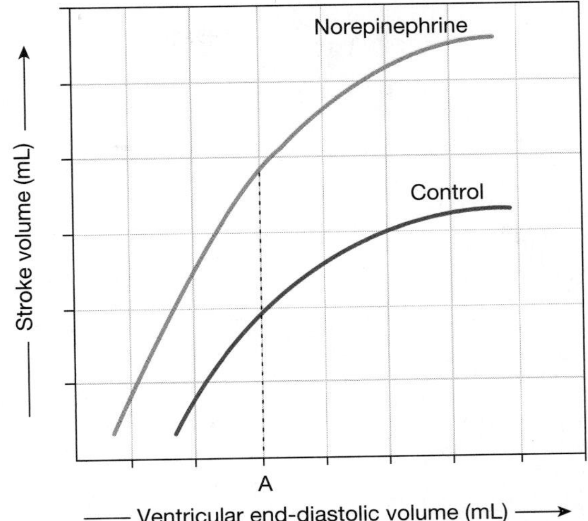

GRAPH QUESTION

At the end-diastolic volume indicated by point A, which heart will create more force: the control heart or the heart under the influence of norepinephrine?

FIGURE 14-29 ***The effect of norepinephrine on contractility of the heart***

Norepinephrine is a positive inotropic agent.

Figure 14-29 shows a normal Starling curve (the control curve) along with a curve showing how the stroke volume changes with increased contractility due to norepinephrine. Note that contractility is distinct from the length-tension relationship. A muscle can remain at one length (for example, the end-diastolic volume marked A in Figure 14-29) but show increased contractility. Contractility increases as the amount of calcium available for contraction increases. Contractility was once considered to be distinct from changes in force resulting from variations in muscle (sarcomere) length. However, it now appears that increasing sarcomere length also makes cardiac muscle more sensitive to Ca^{2+}, thus linking contractility to muscle length.

The mechanism by which catecholamines increase Ca^{2+} entry and storage and exert their positive inotropic effect is mapped in Figure 14-30. The signal molecules bind to and activate β_1-adrenergic receptors [p. 270] on the contractile myocardial cell membrane. Activated β_1-receptors use a cyclic AMP second messenger system to phosphorylate specific intracellular proteins [p. 183]. Phosphorylation of voltage-gated Ca^{2+}

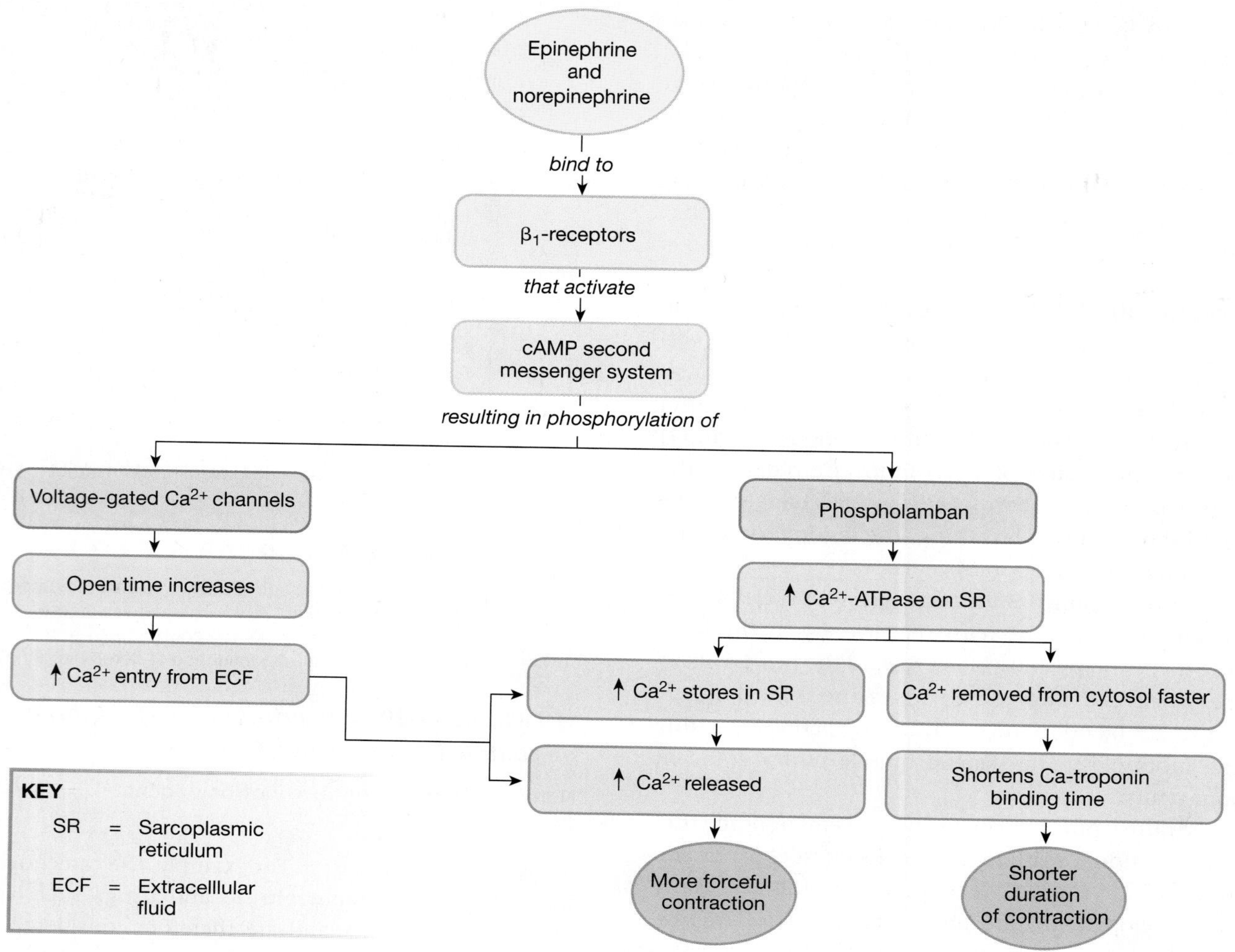

■ **FIGURE 14-30** ***Modulation of cardiac contraction by catecholamines***

channels increases the probability that they will open. More open channels allow more Ca^{2+} to enter the cell.

The catecholamines increase Ca^{2+} storage through the use of a regulatory protein called **phospholamban** (Fig. 14-30). Phosphorylation of phospholamban enhances Ca^{2+}-ATPase activity in the sarcoplasmic reticulum. The ATPase concentrates Ca^{2+} in the sarcoplasmic reticulum, making more Ca^{2+} available for calcium-induced calcium release. Because more cytosolic Ca^{2+} means more active crossbridges, and because the force of contraction is proportional to the number of active crossbridges, the net result of catecholamine stimulation is a stronger contraction.

In addition to increasing the force of cardiac contraction, catecholamines also shorten the duration of contraction. The enhanced Ca^{2+}-ATPase speeds up removal of Ca^{2+} from the cytosol. This in turn shortens the time that Ca^{2+} is bound to troponin and decreases the active time of the myosin crossbridges. The muscle twitch is therefore briefer.

A different mechanism that enhances contractility can be triggered by the administration of cardiac glycosides, a class of molecules first discovered in the plant *Digitalis purpurea* (purple foxglove). Cardiac glycosides include digitoxin and the related compound *ouabain,* a molecule used to inhibit sodium transport in research studies. Glycosides increase contractility by slowing Ca^{2+} removal from the cytosol (in contrast to the catecholamines just discussed, which speed up Ca^{2+} removal). This mechanism is a pharmacological effect and does not occur in the absence of the drug.

Cardiac glycosides have been used since the eighteenth century as a remedy for *heart failure,* a pathological condition in which the heart is unable to contract forcefully. These highly toxic drugs depress Na^+-K^+-ATPase activity in all cells, not just those of the heart. With depressed Na^+-K^+-ATPase activity, Na^+ builds up in the cytosol, and the concentration gradient for Na^+ across the cell membrane diminishes. This in turn decreases the potential energy available for indirect active transport [p. 144]. In the myocardial cell, cardiac glycosides decrease the cell's ability to remove Ca^{2+} by means of the Na^+-Ca^{2+} exchanger. The resultant increase in cytosolic Ca^{2+} causes more forceful myocardial contractions.

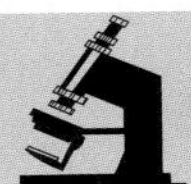

EMERGING CONCEPTS

STEM CELLS FOR HEART DISEASE

One of the interesting (and scary) aspects of translating basic scientific research into medicine is that sometimes therapies work but no one knows why. An example is the use of bone marrow stem cells to treat heart disease. After a heart attack, portions of the myocardium may be so damaged from lack of oxygen that they can no longer contract and contribute to cardiac function. A therapy that could replace dead and damaged cells and restore function would be a dream come true. In 2001 a group of researchers reported that bone marrow stem cells injected into mice with damaged hearts differentiated into new myocardial cells. This dramatic result prompted rapid translation of the basic research into human clinical trials. By 2004 there were more than 12 trials in which bone marrow cells were being injected into patients with impaired cardiac function. Early results indicated that some patients were exhibiting functional improvement. At the same time, however, scientists were reporting that they had been unable to duplicate the 2001 findings that bone marrow stem cells differentiate into myocardial cells. The reason for the discrepancy between the clinical improvement of patients injected with stem cells and the apparent failure of stem cells to form new myocardial cells remains unclear. One possible explanation is that the bone marrow extracts contain growth factors that promoted endogenous myocardial cell repair. Both basic research and clinical trials on this subject are continuing.

CONCEPT CHECK

32. Using the myocardial cell in Figure 14-11 as a model, draw a contractile cell and show how catecholamines increase myocardial contractility. Answers: p. 499

EDV and Arterial Blood Pressure Determine Afterload

Many of the experiments that uncovered the relationship between myocardial stretch and contractile force were conducted using isolated hearts. In the intact animal, ventricular force must be used to overcome the resistance created by blood filling the arterial system. The combined load of EDV and arterial resistance during ventricular contraction is known as **afterload**.

As an analogy, think of waiters carrying trays of food through a swinging door. A tray is a load equivalent to blood in the ventricles at the beginning of contraction. The door is an additional load that the waiter must push against to leave the kitchen. Normally this additional load is relatively minor. If someone decides to play a prank, however, and piles furniture against the dining room side of the door (increased afterload), the waiter must expend considerably more force to push through the door. Similarly, ventricular contraction must push a load of blood through a semilunar valve and out into the blood-filled arteries.

Increased afterload is found in several pathological situations, including elevated arterial blood pressure and loss of stretchability (compliance) in the aorta. To maintain constant stroke volume when afterload increases, the ventricle must increase its force of contraction, which then increases the muscle's need for oxygen and ATP production. If increased afterload becomes a chronic situation, the myocardial cells hypertrophy, resulting in increased thickness of the ventricular wall.

Clinically, arterial blood pressure is often used as an indirect indicator of afterload. Other aspects of ventricular function can be assessed noninvasively by echocardiography, an ultrasound procedure in which sound waves are reflected off heart tissue. A common functional index derived from this procedure is the **ejection fraction**, or percentage of EDV ejected with one contraction (stroke volume/EDV). Using our standard values for the 70-kg man, ejection fraction at rest is 70 mL/135 mL, or 52%. If stroke volume increases to 100 mL with exercise, the ejection fraction increases to 74%.

CONCEPT CHECK

33. A person's aortic valve opening has become constricted, creating a condition known as *aortic stenosis*. Which ventricle is affected by this change? What happens to the afterload on this ventricle? Answers: p. 499

The factors that determine cardiac output are summarized in Figure 14-31 ■. Cardiac output varies with both heart rate and stroke volume. Heart rate is modulated by the autonomic division of the nervous system and by epinephrine. The determination of stroke volume is more complex because stroke volume is a function of an intrinsic myocardial response to stretch (the length-tension relationship of the Frank-Starling law) interacting with adrenergically mediated changes in contractility. Venous return is a major determinant of end-diastolic volume and stretch.

The heart is a complex organ with many parts that can malfunction. In the next chapter we will examine how cardiac output plays a key role in blood flow through the circulation. You will learn about high blood pressure and atherosclerosis, and how these conditions can cause the heart to fail in its role as a pump.

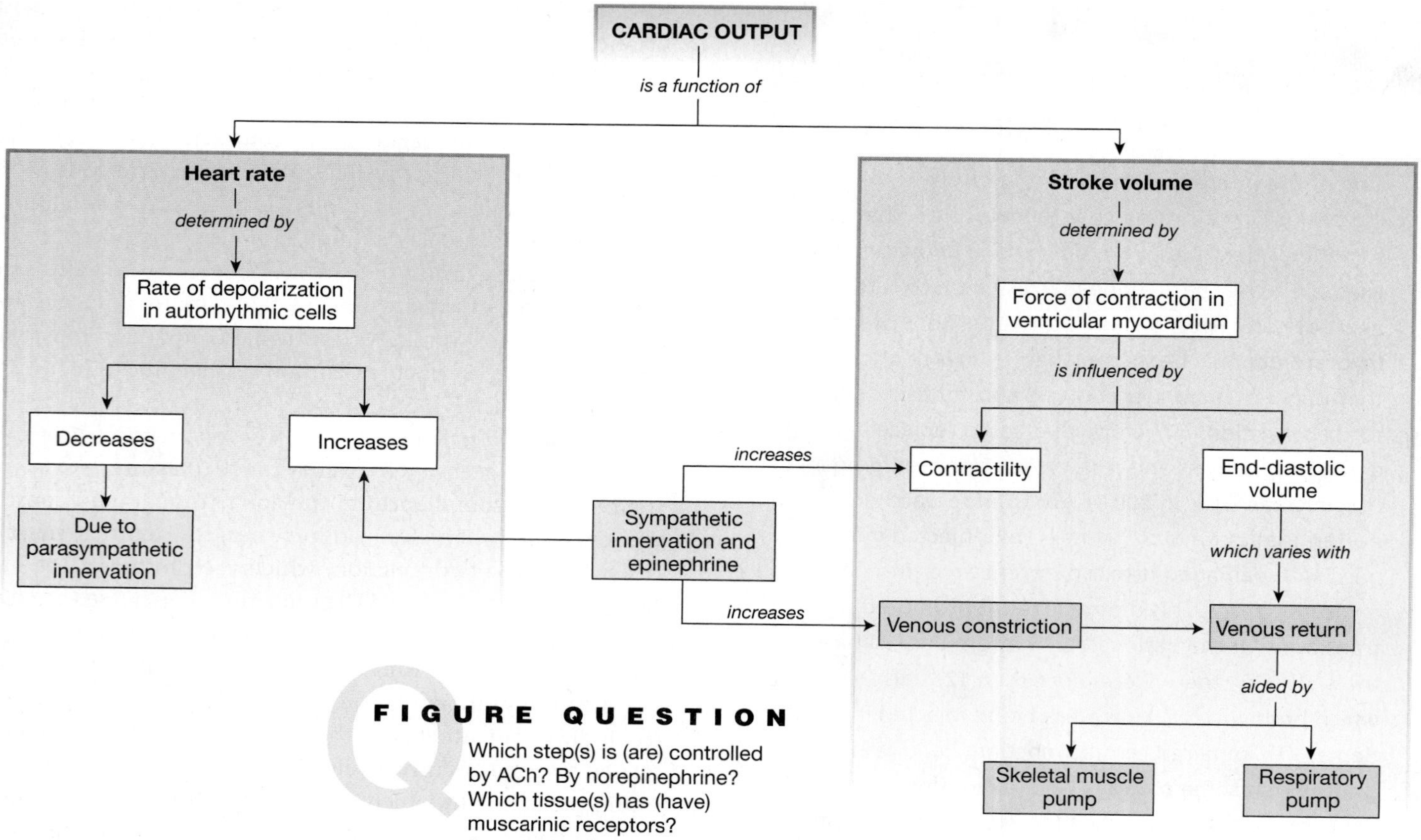

CARDIAC OUTPUT
is a function of

Heart rate
determined by
Rate of depolarization in autorhythmic cells
Decreases
Due to parasympathetic innervation
Increases

Stroke volume
determined by
Force of contraction in ventricular myocardium
is influenced by
Contractility
End-diastolic volume
which varies with
Venous return
aided by
Skeletal muscle pump
Respiratory pump

Sympathetic innervation and epinephrine
increases
Contractility
increases
Venous constriction

FIGURE QUESTION

Which step(s) is (are) controlled by ACh? By norepinephrine? Which tissue(s) has (have) muscarinic receptors? β_1-receptors?

■ **FIGURE 14-31** ***Factors that affect cardiac output***

RUNNING PROBLEM CONCLUSION

MYOCARDIAL INFARCTION

Walter's angiogram showed two blocked arteries, which were opened by balloon angioplasty. He returned home with instructions from his doctor for modifying his lifestyle to include a better diet, regular exercise, and no cigarette smoking. As part of his follow-up, Walter had a *myocardial perfusion imaging* test, in which he was administered radioactive thallium. The distribution of thallium throughout the heart is an indicator of blood flow to the heart muscle.

In this running problem, you learned about some current techniques for diagnosing and treating heart attacks. You also learned that many of these treatments depend on speed to work effectively. Check your understanding of the physiology covered in this problem by comparing your answers with the information in the summary table.

	QUESTION	FACTS	INTEGRATION AND ANALYSIS
1	Why did the medic give Walter oxygen?	The medic suspects that Walter has had a heart attack. Blood flow and oxygen supply to the heart muscle may be blocked.	If the heart is not pumping effectively, the brain may not receive adequate oxygen. Administration of oxygen will raise the amount of oxygen that reaches both the heart and the brain.
2	What effect would the injection of isotonic saline have on Walter's extracellular fluid volume? On his intracellular fluid volume? On his total body osmolarity?	An isotonic solution is one that does not change cell volume [p. 157]. Isotonic saline (NaCl) is isosmotic to the body.	The extracellular volume will increase because all of the saline administered will remain in that compartment. Intracellular volume and total body osmolarity will not change.

	QUESTION	FACTS	INTEGRATION AND ANALYSIS
3	A related form of creatine kinase is found in skeletal muscle. What are related forms of an enzyme called?	Related forms of an enzyme are called isozymes [p. 96].	Although isozymes are variants of the same enzymes, their activity may vary under different conditions, and their structures are slightly different. Cardiac and skeletal muscle isozymes can be distinguished by their different structures.
4	What is troponin, and why would elevated blood levels of troponin indicate heart damage?	Troponin is the regulatory protein bound to tropomyosin [p. 407]. Ca^{2+} binding to troponin uncovers the myosin-binding site of actin to allow contraction.	Troponin is part of the contractile apparatus of the muscle cell. If troponin escapes from the cell and enters the blood, this is an indication that the cell either has been damaged or is dead.
5	How do electrical signals move from cell to cell in the myocardium?	Electrical signals pass through gap junctions in intercalated disks [p. 175].	The cells of the heart are electrically linked by gap junctions.
6	What happens to contraction in a myocardial contractile cell if a wave of depolarization passing through the heart bypasses it?	Depolarization in a muscle cell is the signal for contraction.	If a myocardial cell is not depolarized, it will not contract. Failure to contract creates a nonfunctioning region of heart muscle and impairs the pumping function of the heart.
7	What will a beta-blocker do to Walter's heart rate? Why is that response helpful following a heart attack?	A beta-blocker is an antagonist to β_1-adrenergic receptors. Activation of β_1-receptors increases heart rate.	A beta-blocker therefore decreases heart rate and lowers oxygen demand. Cells that need less oxygen are less likely to die if their blood supply is diminished.
8	If the ventricle of the heart is damaged, in which wave or waves of the electrocardiogram would you expect to see abnormal changes?	The P wave represents atrial depolarization. The QRS complex and T wave represent ventricular depolarization and repolarization, respectively.	The QRS complex and the T wave are most likely to show changes after a heart attack. Changes indicative of myocardial damage include enlargement of the Q wave, shifting of the S-T segment off the base-line (elevated or depressed), and inversion of the T wave.
9	If Walter's heart attack has damaged the muscle of his left ventricle, what do you predict will happen to his left cardiac output?	Cardiac output equals stroke volume times heart rate.	If the ventricular myocardium has been weakened, stroke volume may decrease. Decreased stroke volume will in turn decrease cardiac output.

457 461 471 479 484 489 494

CHAPTER SUMMARY

The cardiovascular system exemplifies many of the basic themes in physiology. Blood flows through vessels as a result of high pressure created during ventricular contraction (*mass flow*). The circulation of blood provides an essential route for *cell-to-cell communication,* particularly for hormones and other chemical signals. Myocardial contraction, like contraction in skeletal and smooth muscle, demonstrates the importance of *molecular interactions, biological energy use,* and the *mechanical properties* of cells and tissues. This chapter also introduced the *control systems* for cardiovascular physiology, a theme that will be expanded in the next chapter.

Overview of the Cardiovascular System

IP Cardiovascular—Anatomy Review: The Heart

1. The human **cardiovascular system** consists of a **heart** that pumps **blood** through a closed system of **blood vessels**. (p. 457; Fig. 14-1)
2. The primary function of the cardiovascular system is the transport of nutrients, water, gases, wastes, and chemical signals to and from all parts of the body. (p. 458; Tbl. 14-1)
3. Blood vessels that carry blood away from the heart are called **arteries**. Blood vessels that return blood to the heart are called **veins**. **Valves** in the heart and veins ensure unidirectional blood flow. (p. 458; Fig. 14-1)
4. The heart is divided into two **atria** and two **ventricles**. (p. 459; Fig. 14-1)
5. The **pulmonary circulation** goes from the right side of the heart to the lungs and back to the heart. The **systemic circulation** goes from the left side of the heart to the tissues and back to the heart. (p. 460; Fig. 14-1)

Pressure, Volume, Flow, and Resistance

6. Blood flows down a **pressure gradient** (ΔP), from the highest pressure in the **aorta** and arteries to the lowest pressure in the **venae cavae** and **pulmonary veins**. (p. 460; Fig. 14-2)
7. In a system in which fluid is flowing, pressure decreases over distance. (p. 461; Fig. 14-3)
8. The pressure created when the ventricles contract is called the **driving pressure** for blood flow. (p. 462)
9. **Resistance** of a fluid flowing through a tube increases as the length of the tube and the **viscosity** (thickness) of the fluid increase, and as the radius of the tube decreases. Of these three factors, radius has the greatest effect on resistance. (pp. 462–463)
10. If resistance increases, flow rate decreases. If resistance decreases, flow rate increases. (p. 462; Fig. 14-5)
11. Fluid flow through a tube is proportional to the pressure gradient (ΔP). A pressure gradient is not the same thing as the absolute pressure in the system. (p. 462; Fig. 14-4)
12. **Flow rate** is the volume of blood that passes one point in the system per unit time. (p. 464)
13. **Velocity of flow** is the distance a volume of blood travels in a given period of time. At a constant flow rate, the velocity of flow through a small tube is faster than the velocity of flow through a larger tube. (p. 464; Fig. 14-6)

Cardiac Muscle and the Heart

IP Cardiovascular—Cardiac Action Potential

14. The heart is composed mostly of cardiac muscle, or **myocardium**. Most cardiac muscle is typical striated muscle. (p. 465; Fig. 14-7h)
15. The signal for contraction originates in **autorhythmic cells** in the heart. Autorhythmic cells are noncontractile myocardium. (p. 470)
16. Myocardial cells are linked to one another by **intercalated disks** that contain gap junctions. The junctions allow depolarization to spread rapidly from cell to cell. (p. 470; Fig. 14-10)
17. In contractile cell excitation-contraction coupling, an action potential opens Ca^{2+} channels. Ca^{2+} entry into the cell triggers the release of additional Ca^{2+} from the sarcoplasmic reticulum through **calcium-induced calcium release**. (p. 471; Fig. 14-11)
18. The force of cardiac muscle contraction can be graded according to how much Ca^{2+} enters the cell. (p. 471)
19. As initial muscle fiber length increases, force of contraction increases. (p. 472; Fig. 14-12)
20. The action potentials of myocardial contractile cells have a rapid depolarization phase created by Na^+ influx, and a steep repolarization phase due to K^+ efflux. The action potential also has a plateau phase created by Ca^{2+} influx. (p. 473; Fig. 14-13)
21. Autorhythmic myocardial cells have an unstable membrane potential called a **pacemaker potential**. The pacemaker potential is due to $\mathbf{I_f}$ **channels** that allow net influx of positive charge. (p. 474; Fig. 14-15)
22. The steep depolarization phase of the autorhythmic cell action potential is caused by Ca^{2+} influx. The repolarization phase is due to K^+ efflux. (p. 474; Fig. 14-15)
23. Norepinephrine and epinephrine act on β_1-receptors to speed up the rate of the pacemaker depolarization and increase heart rate. Acetylcholine activates muscarinic receptors and slows down heart rate. (p. 475; Fig. 14-16)

The Heart as a Pump

IP Cardiovascular—Intrinsic Conduction System

24. Action potentials originate at the **sinoatrial node** (SA node) and spread rapidly from cell to cell in the heart. Action potentials are followed by a wave of contraction. (p. 477; Fig. 14-17)
25. The electrical signal moves from the SA node through the **internodal pathway** to the **atrioventricular node** (AV node), then into the **AV bundle**, **bundle branches**, terminal **Purkinje fibers**, and myocardial contractile cells. (p. 477; Fig. 14-18)
26. The SA node sets the pace of the heartbeat. If the SA node malfunctions, other autorhythmic cells in the AV node or ventricles will take control of heart rate. (p. 479)
27. An **electrocardiogram** (ECG) is a surface recording of the electrical activity of the heart. The **P wave** represents atrial depolarization. The **QRS complex** represents ventricular depolarization. The **T wave** represents ventricular repolarization. Atrial repolarization is incorporated in the QRS complex. (p. 480; Figs. 14-20, 14-21)
28. An ECG provides information on heart rate and rhythm, conduction velocity, and the condition of cardiac tissues. (p. 481)

IP Cardiovascular—The Cardiac Cycle

29. One **cardiac cycle** includes one cycle of contraction and relaxation. **Systole** is the contraction phase; **diastole** is the relaxation phase. (p. 484; Fig. 14-24)
30. Most blood enters the ventricles while the atria are relaxed. Only 20% of ventricular filling at rest is due to atrial contraction. (p. 484)
31. The **AV valves** prevent backflow of blood into the atria. Vibrations following closure of the AV valves create the **first heart sound**. (p. 485; Figs. 14-9, 14-24)
32. During **isovolumic ventricular contraction**, the ventricular blood volume does not change, but pressure rises. When ventricular pressure exceeds arterial pressure, the **semilunar valves** open, and blood is ejected into the arteries. (pp. 485–486; Figs. 14-9, 14-24)
33. When the ventricles relax and ventricular pressure falls, the semilunar valves close, creating the **second heart sound**. (p. 486; Fig. 14-9, 14-24)
34. The amount of blood pumped by one ventricle during one contraction is known as the **stroke volume**. (p. 487; Fig. 14-25)

IP Cardiovascular—Cardiac Output

35. **Cardiac output** is the volume of blood pumped per ventricle per unit time. It is equal to heart rate times stroke volume. The average cardiac output at rest is 5 L/min. (p. 489)

36. Homeostatic changes in cardiac output are accomplished by varying heart rate, stroke volume, or both. (p. 493; Fig. 14-31)
37. Parasympathetic activity slows heart rate; sympathetic activity speeds it up. (p. 489; Fig. 14-27)
38. The **Frank-Starling law of the heart** says that an increase in **end-diastolic volume** results in a greater stroke volume. (p. 491; Fig. 14-28)
39. Epinephrine and norepinephrine increase the force of myocardial contraction when they bind to β_1-adrenergic receptors. They also shorten the duration of cardiac contraction. (p. 491; Fig. 14-30)
40. End-diastolic volume and **preload** are determined by **venous return**. Venous return is affected by skeletal muscle contractions, the respiratory pump, and constriction of veins by sympathetic activity. (p. 491)
41. **Contractility** of the heart is enhanced by catecholamines and certain drugs. Chemicals that alter contractility are said to have an **inotropic effect**. (p. 491; Fig. 14-29)
42. **Afterload** is the load placed on the ventricle as it contracts. Afterload reflects the preload and the effort required to push the blood out into the arterial system. Mean arterial pressure is a clinical indicator of afterload. (p. 493)
43. **Ejection fraction**, the percent of EDV ejected with one contraction (stroke volume/EDV), is one measure for evaluating ventricular function. (p. 493)

QUESTIONS

(Answers to the Review Questions begin on page A1.)

THE PHYSIOLOGY PLACE

Access more review material online at **The Physiology Place** website. There you'll find review questions, problem-solving activities, case studies, flashcards, and direct links to both *InterActive Physiology®* and PhysioEx™. To access the site, go to *www.physiologyplace.com* and select Human Physiology, Fourth Edition.

LEVEL ONE REVIEWING FACTS AND TERMS

1. What contributions to understanding the cardiovascular system did each of the following people make?
   (a) William Harvey
   (b) Otto Frank and Ernest Starling
   (c) Marcello Malpighi
2. List three functions of the cardiovascular system.
3. Put the following structures in the order in which blood passes through them, starting and ending with the left ventricle:
   (a) left ventricle
   (b) systemic veins
   (c) pulmonary circulation
   (d) systemic arteries
   (e) aorta
   (f) right ventricle
4. The primary factor causing blood to flow through the body is a __________ gradient. In humans, the value of this gradient is highest at the __________ and in the __________. It is lowest in the __________. In a system in which fluid is flowing, pressure decreases over distance because __________.
5. If vasodilation occurs in a blood vessel, pressure (increases/decreases).
6. The specialized cell junctions between myocardial cells are called __________. These areas contain __________ that allow rapid conduction of electrical signals.
7. Trace an action potential from the SA node through the conducting system of the heart.
8. Distinguish between the two members of each of the following pairs:
   (a) end-systolic volume and end-diastolic volume
   (b) sympathetic and parasympathetic control of heart rate
   (c) diastole and systole
   (d) systemic and pulmonary circulation
   (e) AV node and SA node
9. Match the descriptions with the correct anatomic terms. Not all terms are used. Give a definition for the unused terms.
   (a) tough membranous sac that encases the heart
   (b) valves between ventricles and the main arteries
   (c) a vessel that carries blood away from the heart
   (d) lower chamber of the heart
   (e) valve between left atrium and left ventricle
   (f) primary artery of the systemic circulation
   (g) muscular layer of the heart
   (h) narrow end of the heart; points downward
   (i) valve with papillary muscles
   (j) the upper chambers of the heart

   1. aorta
   2. apex
   3. artery
   4. atria
   5. atrium
   6. AV valve
   7. base
   8. bicuspid valve
   9. endothelium
   10. myocardium
   11. pericardium
   12. semilunar valve
   13. tricuspid valve
   14. ventricle
10. What events cause the two principal heart sounds?
11. What is the proper term for each of the following?
   (a) number of heart contractions per minute
   (b) volume of blood in the ventricle before the heart contracts
   (c) volume of blood that enters the aorta with each contraction
   (d) volume of blood that leaves the heart in one minute
   (e) volume of blood in the entire body

LEVEL TWO REVIEWING CONCEPTS

12. Concept maps:
   (a) Create a map showing blood flow through the heart and body. Label as many structures as you can.
   (b) Create a map for control of cardiac output using the following terms. You may add additional terms.

ACh	heart rate
adrenal medulla	length-tension relationship
autorhythmic cells	muscarinic receptor
β_1-receptor	norepinephrine
Ca^{2+}	parasympathetic neurons
Ca^{2+}-induced Ca^{2+} release	respiratory pump
cardiac output	skeletal muscle pump
contractile myocardium	stroke volume
contractility	sympathetic neurons
force of contraction	venous return
13. List the events of the cardiac cycle in sequence, beginning with atrial and ventricular diastole. Note when valves open and close. Describe what happens to pressure and blood flow in each chamber at each step of the cycle.

14. Compare and contrast the structure of a cardiac muscle cell with that of a skeletal muscle cell. What unique properties of cardiac muscle are essential to its function?
15. Explain why contractions in cardiac muscle cannot sum or exhibit tetanus.
16. Correlate the waves of an ECG with mechanical events in the atria and ventricles. Why are there only three electrical events but four mechanical events?
17. Match the following ion movements with the appropriate phrase. More than one ion movement may apply to a single phrase. Some choices may not be used.

(a) slow rising phase of autorhythmic cells
(b) plateau phase of contractile cells
(c) rapid rising phase of contractile cells
(d) rapid rising phase of autorhythmic cells
(e) rapid falling phase of contractile cells
(f) falling phase of autorhythmic cells
(g) cardiac muscle contraction
(h) cardiac muscle relaxation

1. K^+ from ECF to ICF
2. K^+ from ICF to ECF
3. Na^+ from ECF to ICF
4. Na^+ from ICF to ECF
5. Ca^{2+} from ECF to ICF
6. Ca^{2+} from ICF to ECF

18. List and briefly explain four types of information that an ECG provides about the heart.
19. Define inotropic effect. Name two drugs that have a positive inotropic effect on the heart.

LEVEL THREE PROBLEM SOLVING

20. Two drugs used to reduce cardiac output are calcium channel blockers and beta (receptor) blockers. What effect do these drugs have on the heart that explains how they decrease cardiac output?
21. Police Captain Jeffers has suffered a myocardial infarction.
    (a) Explain to his (nonmedically oriented) family what has happened to his heart.
    (b) When you analyzed his ECG, you referred to several different leads, such as lead I and lead III. What are leads?
    (c) Why is it possible to record an ECG on the body surface without direct access to the heart?
22. What might cause a longer-than-normal PR interval in an ECG?
23. The following paragraph is a summary of a newspaper article:

    A new treatment for atrial fibrillation due to an excessively rapid rate at the SA node involves a high-voltage electrical pulse administered to the AV node to destroy its autorhythmic cells. A ventricular pacemaker is then implanted in the patient.

    Briefly explain the physiological rationale for this treatment. Why is a rapid atrial depolarization rate dangerous? Why is the AV node destroyed in this procedure? Why must a pacemaker be implanted?

LEVEL FOUR QUANTITATIVE PROBLEMS

24. Police Captain Jeffers in question 21 has an ejection fraction (SV divided by EDV) of only 25%. His stroke volume is 40 mL/beat, and his heart rate is 100 beats/min. What are his EDV, ESV, and CO? Show your calculations.
25. If 1 cm water = 0.74 mm Hg:
    (a) Convert a pressure of 120 mm Hg to cm H_2O.
    (b) Convert a pressure of 90 cm H_2O to mm Hg.
26. Calculate cardiac output if stroke volume is 65 mL/beat and heart rate is 80 beats/min.
27. Calculate end-systolic volume if end-diastolic volume is 150 mL and stroke volume is 65 mL/beat.
28. A person has a total blood volume of 5 L. Of this total, assume that 4 L is contained in the systemic circulation and 1 L is in the pulmonary circulation. If the person has a cardiac output of 5 L/min, how long will it take (a) for a drop of blood leaving the left ventricle to return to the left ventricle and (b) for a drop of blood to go from the right ventricle to the left ventricle?

ANSWERS

Answers to Concept Check Questions

Page 460

1. A cardiovascular system has tubes (vessels), fluid (blood), and a pump (heart).
2. (a) The pulmonary circulation takes blood to and from the lungs; the systemic circulation takes blood to and from the rest of the body. (b) An artery carries blood away from the heart; a vein carries blood to the heart. (c) An atrium is an upper heart chamber that receives blood entering the heart; a ventricle is a lower heart chamber that pumps blood out of the heart.

Page 464

3. The pressure gradient is more important.
4. The bottom tube has the greater flow because it has the larger pressure gradient (50 mm Hg versus 40 mm Hg for the top tube).
5. Tube C has the highest flow because it has the largest radius of the four tubes (less resistance) and the shorter length (less resistance). (Tube B has the same radius as tube C but a longer length and therefore offers greater resistance to flow.) Tube D, with the greatest resistance due to longer length and narrow radius, has the lowest flow.

Page 465

6. If the canals are identical in size and therefore in cross-sectional area A, the canal with the higher velocity of flow v has the higher flow rate Q. (From equation 7, $Q = v \times A$.)

Page 470

7. Connective tissue is not excitable and is therefore unable to conduct action potentials.
8. Superior vena cava → right atrium → tricuspid (right AV) valve → right ventricle → pulmonary (right semilunar) valve → pulmonary trunk → pulmonary vein → left atrium → mitral (bicuspid, left AV) valve → left ventricle → aortic (left semilunar) valve → aorta
9. The AV valves prevent backward flow of blood. If one fails, blood leaks back into the atrium.

Page 471

10. From this experiment, it is possible to conclude that myocardial cells require extracellular calcium for contraction but skeletal muscle cells do not.

Page 472

11. If all calcium channels in the muscle cell membrane are blocked, there will be no contraction. If only some are blocked, the force of contraction will be smaller than the force created with all channels open.

Page 474

12. Na^+ influx causes neuronal depolarization, and K^+ efflux causes neuronal repolarization.
13. The refractory period represents the time required for the Na^+ channel gates to reset (activation gate closes, inactivation gate opens).
14. If cardiac Na^+ channels are blocked with lidocaine, the cell will not depolarize and therefore will not contract.

Page 475

15. Increasing K^+ permeability hyperpolarizes the membrane potential.

Page 477

16. The Ca^{2+} channels in autorhythmic cells are not the same as those in contractile cells. Autorhythmic Ca^{2+} channels open rapidly when the membrane potential reaches about −50 mV and close when it reaches about +20 mV. The Ca^{2+} channels in contractile cells are slower and do not open until the membrane has depolarized fully.
17. If tetrodotoxin is applied to a myocardial autorhythmic cell, nothing will happen because there are no voltage-gated Na^+ channels in the cell.
18. Cutting the vagus nerve caused heart rate to increase, so the nerve must contain parasympathetic fibers that slow heart rate.

Page 480

19. The AV node conducts action potentials from atria to ventricles. It also slows down the speed at which those action potentials are conducted, allowing atrial contraction to end before ventricular contraction begins.
20. The SA node is in the upper right atrium.
21. The fastest pacemaker sets the heart rate, so the heart rate increases to 120 beats/min.

Page 484

22. In Figure 14-23b, notice that there is no regular association between the P waves and the QRS complexes (the P-R segment varies in length). Notice also that not every P wave has an associated QRS complex. Both P waves and QRS complexes appear at regular intervals, but the atrial rate (P waves) is faster than the ventricular rate (QRS complexes). In (c), there are identifiable R waves but no P waves. In (d), there are no recognizable waves at all, indicating that the depolarizations are not following the normal conduction path.
23. Starting at left, the waves are P, P, QRS, T, P, P, QRS, T, P, P, P, and so on. Each P wave that is not followed by a QRS wave suggests an intermittent conduction block at the AV node. See also Figure 14-23b.

Page 484

24. The atrium has lower pressure than the venae cavae.

Page 486

25. (a) ventricle, (b) ventricle, (c) atrium, (d) ventricle
26. (a) ventricular ejection, (b) isovolumic ventricular contraction and ventricular ejection (c) from isovolumic ventricular relaxation until ventricular contraction begins again

Page 487

27. EDV occurs in step 3, and ESV occurs in step 5.
28. (a) E, (b) A, (c) D, (d) B, (e) C, (f) F
29. Atrial pressure increases because pressure on the mitral valve pushes the valve back into the atrium, decreasing atrial volume. Atrial pressure decreases during the initial part of ventricular systole as the atrium relaxes. The pressure then increases as the atrium fills with blood. Atrial pressure begins to decrease at point D, when the mitral valve opens and blood flows down into the ventricles.
30. Ventricular pressure shoots up when the ventricles contract on a fixed volume of blood.

Page 489

31. After 10 beats, the pulmonary circulation will have gained 10 mL of blood and the systemic circulation will have lost 10 mL.

Page 493

32. Your drawing should show a β_1-receptor on the cell membrane activating intracellular cAMP, which should have an arrow drawn to Ca^{2+} channels on the sarcoplasmic reticulum. Open channels should be shown as increasing cytoplasmic Ca^{2+}. A second arrow should go from cAMP to Ca^{2+}-ATPase on the SR and the cell membrane, showing increased uptake in the SR and increased removal of Ca^{2+} from the cell.

Page 493

33. The aortic valve is found in the left ventricle. A stenotic aortic valve would increase the afterload on the ventricle.

Answers to Figure and Graph Questions

Page 475

Figure 14-15: Phase 2 (the plateau) of the contractile cell action potential has no equivalent in the autorhythmic cell action potential. Phase 4 is approximately equivalent to the pacemaker potential. Both action potentials have rising phases, peaks, and falling phases.

Page 481

Figure 14-20: The heart rate is either 75 beats/min or 80 beats/min, depending on how you calculate it. If you use the data from one R peak to the next, the time interval between the two peaks is 0.8 sec; therefore,

$$\frac{1 \text{ beat}}{0.8 \text{ sec}} \times \frac{60 \text{ sec}}{1 \text{ min}} = 75 \text{ beats/min}$$

However, it is more accurate to estimate rate by using several seconds of the ECG tracing rather than one RR interval because beat-to-beat intervals may vary. If you start counting at the first R wave on the top graph and go right for 3 sec, there are 4 beats in that time period, which means

$$\frac{4 \text{ beats}}{3 \text{ sec}} \times \frac{60 \text{ sec}}{1 \text{ min}} = 80 \text{ beats/min}$$

Page 487

Figure 14-25: Match segments to events: (a) C → D, (b) B → C, (c) D → A, (d) A → B. Match events to points: (a) C, (b) A, (c) D, (d) B.

Page 490

Figure 14-28: Maximum stroke volume is about 160 mL/beat, first achieved when end-diastolic volume is about 330 mL.

Page 491

Fig. 14-29: At point A, the heart under the influence of norepinephrine has a larger stroke volume and is therefore creating more force.

Page 494

Fig. 14-31: Heart rate is the only parameter controlled by ACh. Heart rate and contractility are both controlled by norepinephrine. The SA node has muscarinic receptors. The SA node and contractile myocardium have β_1-receptors.

15

Since 1900, CVD (cardiovascular disease) has been the No. 1 killer in the United States every year but 1918.

—American Heart Association, *Heart Disease and Stroke Statistics—2003 Update*

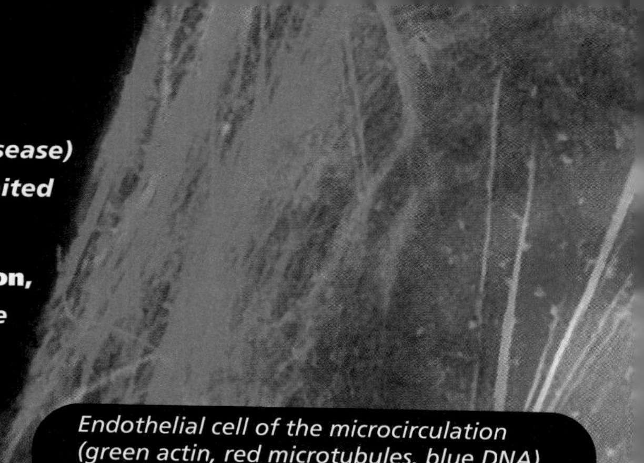

Endothelial cell of the microcirculation (green actin, red microtubules, blue DNA).

Blood Flow and the Control of Blood Pressure

BACKGROUND BASICS

Basement membrane: **72** Nitric oxide: **187** Transcytosis: **153** Fight-or-flight response: **377**
Exchange epithelium: **73** Catecholamines and receptors: **276** Caveolae: **149** Diffusion: **133** Tonic control: **192**

RUNNING PROBLEM

ESSENTIAL HYPERTENSION

"Doc, I'm as healthy as a horse," says Kurt English, age 56, during his annual physical examination. "I don't want to waste your time. Let's get this over with." But to Dr. Arthur Cortez, Kurt does not appear to be the picture of health: he is about 30 pounds overweight. When Dr. Cortez asks about his diet, Kurt replies, "Well, I like to eat." Exercise? "Who has the time? " replies Kurt. Dr. Cortez wraps a blood pressure cuff around Kurt's arm and takes a reading. "Your blood pressure is 164 over 100," says Dr. Cortez. "We'll take it again in 15 minutes. If it's still high, we'll need to discuss it further." Kurt stares at his doctor, flabbergasted. "But how can my blood pressure be too high? I feel fine!" he protests.

Anthony was sure he was going to be a physician, until the day in physiology laboratory they studied blood types. When the lancet pierced his fingertip and he saw the drop of bright red blood well up, the room started to spin, then everything went black. He awoke, much embarrassed, to the sight of his classmates and the teacher bending over him.

Anthony suffered an attack of *vasovagal syncope* (fainting), a benign and common emotional reaction to blood, hypodermic needles, or other upsetting sights. Normally, homeostatic regulation of the cardiovascular system maintains adequate blood flow (*perfusion*) to the heart and brain. In vasovagal syncope, signals from the nervous system cause a sudden drop in blood pressure, and the individual faints from lack of oxygen to the brain. In this chapter you will learn how the heart and blood vessels work together most of the time to prevent such problems.

A simplified model of the cardiovascular system (Fig. 15-1 ■) illustrates the key points we will discuss in this chapter. This model shows the heart as two separate pumps that work in series (one after the other), with the right heart pumping blood first to the lungs and then to the left heart. The left heart then pumps blood through the rest of the body and back to the right heart.

Blood leaving the left heart enters systemic arteries, shown here as an expandable, elastic region. Pressure produced by

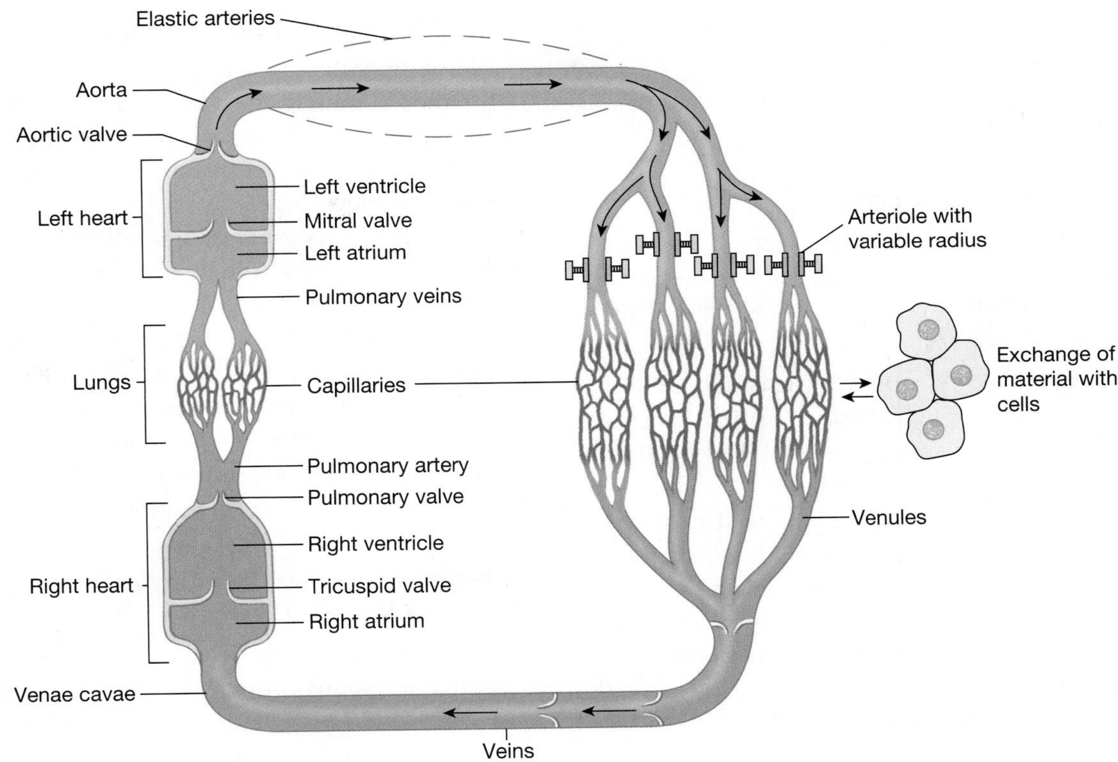

■ **FIGURE 15-1** ***Functional model of the cardiovascular system***

The heart functions as two pumps working in series. The systemic arteries are a pressure reservoir that maintains blood flow during ventricular relaxation. The arterioles, shown with adjustable screws representing variable radii, are the site of variable resistance. Exchange between the blood and cells takes place only at the capillaries.

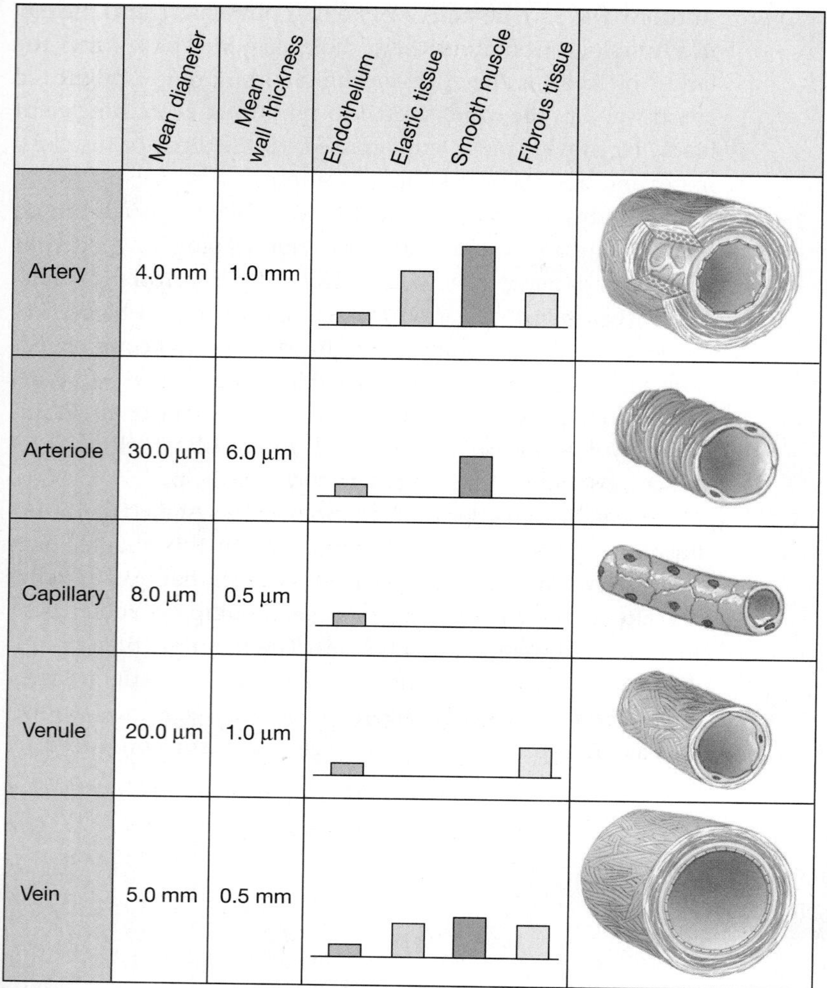

Mean diameter
Mean wall thickness
Endothelium
Elastic tissue
Smooth muscle
Fibrous tissue
Artery
4.0 mm
1.0 mm
Arteriole
30.0 μm
6.0 μm
Capillary
8.0 μm
0.5 μm
Venule
20.0 μm
1.0 μm
Vein
5.0 mm
0.5 mm

■ **FIGURE 15-2** ***Blood vessel structure***

The walls of blood vessels vary in diameter and composition. The endothelium and its underlying elastic tissue together form the tunica intima. (Adapted from A. C. Burton, *Physiol. Rev.* 34:619–642, 1954.)

contraction of the left ventricle is stored in the elastic walls of arteries and slowly released through *elastic recoil*. This mechanism maintains a continuous driving pressure for blood flow during the time when the ventricles are relaxing.

Downstream from the arteries, small vessels called **arterioles** create a high-resistance outlet for arterial blood flow. Arterioles direct distribution of blood flow to individual tissues by selectively constricting and dilating. Arteriolar diameter is regulated both by local factors, such as tissue oxygen concentrations, and by homeostatic control.

Once blood flows into the capillaries, a leaky epithelium allows exchange of materials between the plasma, the interstitial fluid, and the cells of the body. At the distal end of the capillaries, blood flows into the venous side of the circulation and from there back to the right heart.

Total blood flow through any level of the circulation is equal to cardiac output. For example, if cardiac output is 5 L/min, blood flow through all the systemic capillaries is 5 L/min. In the same manner, blood flow through the pulmonary side of the circulation is equal to blood flow through the systemic circulation.

THE BLOOD VESSELS

The walls of blood vessels are composed of layers of smooth muscle, elastic connective tissue, and fibrous connective tissue (Fig. 15-2 ■). The inner lining of all blood vessels is a thin layer of **endothelium**, a type of epithelium. For years, the endothelium was thought to be simply a passive barrier. However, we now know that endothelial cells secrete many paracrines and play important roles in the regulation of blood pressure, blood vessel growth, and absorption of materials.

Surrounding the endothelium are layers of connective tissue and smooth muscle. The endothelium and its adjacent elastic connective tissue together make up the *tunica intima*, usually called simply the *intima*. The layers of smooth muscle and connective tissue surrounding the intima vary in thickness in different vessels. The descriptions that follow apply to the vessels of the systemic circulation, although those of the pulmonary circulation are generally similar.

Blood Vessels Contain Vascular Smooth Muscle

The smooth muscle of blood vessels is known as **vascular smooth muscle**. Most blood vessels contain smooth muscle, arranged in either circular or spiral layers. *Vasoconstriction* narrows the diameter of the vessel lumen, whereas *vasodilation* widens it.

In most blood vessels, smooth muscle cells maintain a state of partial contraction at all times, creating the condition known as *muscle tone* [p. 440]. Contraction of smooth muscle, like that of cardiac muscle, depends on the entry of Ca^{2+} from the extracellular fluid through Ca^{2+} channels [p. 426]. A variety of chemicals influences vascular smooth muscle tone, including neurotransmitters, hormones, and paracrines. Many vasoactive paracrines are secreted either by endothelial cells lining blood vessels or by tissues surrounding the vessels.

Arteries and Arterioles Carry Blood Away from the Heart

The aorta and major arteries are characterized by walls that are both stiff and springy. Arteries have a thick smooth muscle layer and large amounts of elastic and fibrous connective tissue (Fig. 15-2). Because of the stiffness of the fibrous tissue, substantial amounts of energy are required to stretch the walls of an artery outward. This energy comes in the form of high-pressure blood ejected from the left ventricle. Once the artery is distended with blood, energy stored by stretched elastic fibers is released through elastic recoil.

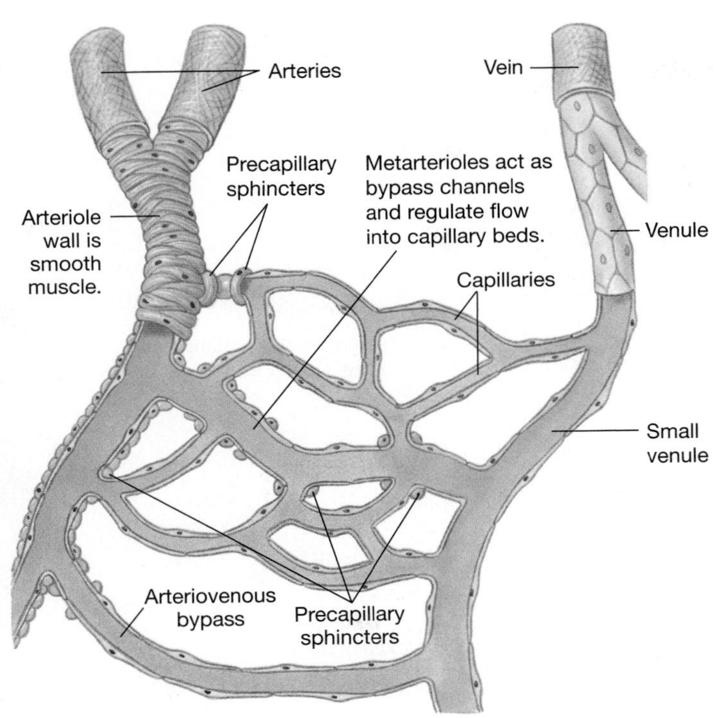

■ **FIGURE 15-3** ***Metarterioles***

The arteries and arterioles are characterized by a divergent [*divergere,* bend apart] pattern of blood flow. As major arteries divide into smaller and smaller arteries, the character of the wall changes, becoming less elastic and more muscular. The walls of arterioles contain several layers of smooth muscle that contract and relax under the influence of various chemical signals.

Some arterioles branch into vessels known as **metarterioles** [*meta-,* beyond] (Fig. 15-3 ■). Blood flowing through metarterioles can either be directed into adjoining capillary beds or can bypass the capillaries and go directly to the venous circulation if muscle rings called **precapillary sphincters** [*sphingein,* to hold tight] are contracted. True arterioles have a continuous smooth muscle layer, but only part of the wall of metarterioles is surrounded by smooth muscle.

In addition to regulating blood flow through the capillaries, metarterioles allow white blood cells to go directly from the arterial to the venous circulation. Capillaries are barely large enough to let red blood cells through, much less white blood cells, which are twice as large.

Arterioles, along with capillaries and small postcapillary vessels called venules, form the *microcirculation.* Regulation of blood flow through the microcirculation is an active area of physiological research.

Exchange Between the Blood and Interstitial Fluid Takes Place in the Capillaries

Capillaries are the smallest vessels in the cardiovascular system. They and the postcapillary venules are the site of exchange between the blood and the interstitial fluid. To facilitate exchange of materials, capillaries lack smooth muscle and elastic or fibrous tissue reinforcement (Fig. 15-2). Instead, their walls consist of a flat layer of endothelium, one cell thick, supported on an acellular matrix called the *basal lamina* (basement membrane) [p. 72].

Many capillaries are closely associated with cells known as **pericytes** [*peri-,* around]. These highly branched contractile cells surround the capillaries, forming a meshlike outer layer between the capillary endothelium and the interstitial fluid. Pericytes contribute to the "tightness" of capillary permeability: the more pericytes, the less leaky the capillary endothelium. Cerebral capillaries, for example, are surrounded by pericytes and glial cells and have tight junctions that create the *blood-brain barrier* [p. 299].

Pericytes secrete factors that influence capillary growth, and they can differentiate to become new endothelial or smooth muscle cells. Loss of pericytes around capillaries of the retina is a hallmark of the disease *diabetic retinopathy,* a leading cause of blindness. Scientists are now trying to determine whether pericyte loss is a cause or consequence of the retinopathy.

Blood Flow Converges in the Venules and Veins

Blood flows from the capillaries into small vessels called venules. The very smallest venules are similar to capillaries, with a thin exchange epithelium and little connective tissue (Fig. 15-2). They are distinguished from capillaries by their convergent pattern of flow.

Smooth muscle begins to appear in the walls of larger venules. From venules, blood flows into veins that become larger in diameter as they travel toward the heart. Finally, the largest veins, the venae cavae, empty into the right atrium.

Veins are more numerous than arteries and have a larger diameter. As a result of their large volume, the veins hold more than half of the blood in the circulatory system. Veins lie closer to the surface of the body than arteries, forming the bluish blood vessels that you see running just under the skin. Veins have thinner walls than arteries, with less elastic tissue. As a result, they expand easily when they fill with blood.

When you have blood drawn from your arm (*venipuncture*), the technician uses a tourniquet to exert pressure on the blood vessels. Blood flow into the arm through deep high-pressure arteries is not affected, but pressure exerted by the tourniquet stops outflow through the low-pressure veins. As a result, blood collects in the surface veins, making them stand out against the underlying muscle tissue.

Angiogenesis Creates New Blood Vessels

One topic of tremendous interest to researchers is **angiogenesis,** [*angeion,* vessel + *gignesthai,* to beget], the process by which new blood vessels develop, especially after birth. In children, blood vessel growth is necessary for normal development. In adults, angiogenesis takes place as wounds heal and as the uterine

(a) Ventricular contraction

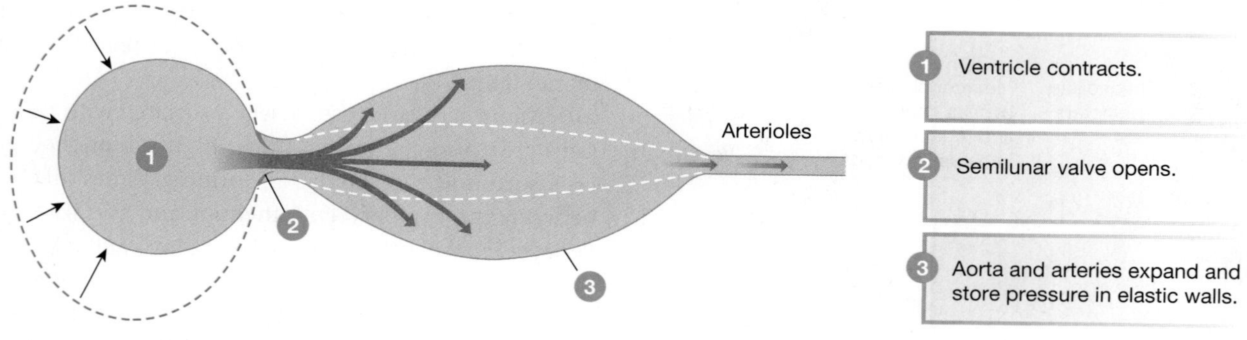
Arterioles
1 Ventricle contracts.
2 Semilunar valve opens.
3 Aorta and arteries expand and store pressure in elastic walls.

(b) Ventricular relaxation

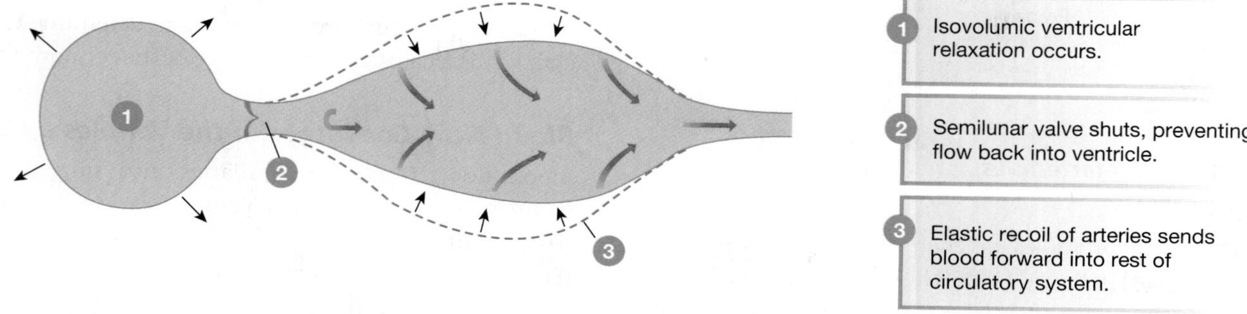
1 Isovolumic ventricular relaxation occurs.
2 Semilunar valve shuts, preventing flow back into ventricle.
3 Elastic recoil of arteries sends blood forward into rest of circulatory system.

■ **FIGURE 15-4** ***Elastic recoil in the arteries***

The arteries maintain driving pressure when the ventricles are in diastole.

lining grows after menstruation. Angiogenesis also occurs with endurance exercise training, enhancing blood flow to the heart muscle and to skeletal muscles.

From studies of normal blood vessels and tumor cells, scientists learned that angiogenesis is controlled by a balance of angiogenic and antiangiogenic cytokines. A number of related growth factors, including *vascular endothelial growth factor* (VEGF) and *fibroblast growth factor* (FGF), promote angiogenesis. These growth factors are *mitogens,* meaning they promote mitosis, or cell division. They are normally produced by smooth muscle cells and pericytes.

Cytokines that inhibit angiogenesis include *angiostatin,* made from the blood protein plasminogen, and *endostatin* [*stasis,* a state of standing still]. Scientists are currently using these cytokines to develop new treatments for two major illnesses: cancer and coronary heart disease. As cancer cells invade tissues and multiply, they instruct the host tissue to develop new blood vessels to feed the growing tumor. Without these new vessels, the interior cells of a cancerous mass would be unable to get adequate oxygen and nutrients, and would die. Angiostatin and endostatin are being used in clinical trials to see if they can block angiogenesis and literally starve tumors to death.

In contrast, **coronary heart disease,** also known as *coronary artery disease,* is a condition in which we would like to be able to selectively induce angiogenesis. In coronary heart disease, blood flow to the myocardium is decreased by fatty deposits that narrow the lumen of the coronary arteries. In some individuals, new blood vessels develop spontaneously and form *collateral circulation* that supplements flow through the partially blocked artery. Researchers are looking for a way to duplicate this natural process and induce angiogenesis to replace occluded vessels [*occludere,* to close up].

BLOOD PRESSURE

The pressure created by ventricular contraction is the driving force for blood flow through the cardiovascular system. As blood is ejected from the left ventricle, the aorta and arteries expand to accommodate it (Fig. 15-4 ■). When the ventricle relaxes and the semilunar valve closes, the elastic arterial walls recoil, propelling the blood forward into smaller arteries and

TABLE 15-1 Pressure, Flow, and Resistance in the Cardiovascular System

Flow ∝ ΔP/R
1. Blood flows if a pressure gradient (ΔP) is present.
2. Blood flows from areas of higher pressure to areas of lower pressure.
3. Blood flow is opposed by the resistance R of the system.
4. Three factors affecting resistance are radius of the blood vessels, viscosity of the blood, and length of the system [p. 462].
5. Flow is usually expressed in either liters or milliliters per minute (L/min or mL/min).
6. Velocity of flow is usually expressed in either centimeters per minute (cm/min) or millimeters per second (mm/sec).
7. The primary determinant of velocity of flow (when flow rate is constant) is the total cross-sectional area of the vessel(s).

arterioles (Fig. 15-4b). By sustaining the driving pressure for blood flow during ventricular relaxation, the arteries create continuous blood flow through the blood vessels.

Blood flow obeys the rules of fluid flow that were introduced in Chapter 14 [p. 462]. Flow is directly proportional to the pressure gradient between any two points, and inversely proportional to the resistance of the vessels to flow (Table 15-1 ■). Unless otherwise noted, the discussion that follows is restricted to the events that take place in the systemic circuit. Pulmonary blood flow will be discussed in Chapter 17.

Systemic Blood Pressure Is Highest in Arteries and Lowest in Veins

Blood pressure is highest in the arteries and decreases continuously as blood flows through the circulatory system (Fig. 15-5 ■). The decrease in pressure occurs because energy is lost as a result of the resistance to flow offered by the vessels. Resistance to blood flow also results from friction between the blood cells.

In the systemic circulation, the highest pressure occurs in the aorta and reflects pressure created by the left ventricle. Aortic pressure reaches an average high of 120 mm Hg during ventricular systole (**systolic pressure**), then falls steadily to a low of 80 mm Hg during ventricular diastole (**diastolic pressure**). Notice that although pressure in the ventricle falls to nearly 0 mm Hg as the ventricle relaxes, diastolic pressure in the large arteries remains relatively high. The high diastolic pressure in arteries reflects the ability of those vessels to capture and store energy in their elastic walls.

The rapid pressure increase that occurs when the left ventricle pushes blood into the aorta can be felt as a **pulse**, or pressure wave, transmitted through the fluid-filled arteries. The pressure wave travels about 10 times faster than the blood itself. Even so, a pulse felt in the arm is occurring slightly after the ventricular contraction that created the wave.

The amplitude of the pressure wave decreases over distance because of friction, and the wave finally disappears at the capillaries (Fig. 15-5). **Pulse pressure**, a measure of the strength of the pressure wave, is defined as systolic pressure minus diastolic pressure:

$$\text{Systolic pressure} - \text{diastolic pressure} = \text{pulse pressure}$$

For example, in the aorta:

$$120 \text{ mm Hg} - 80 \text{ mm Hg} = 40 \text{ mm Hg pulse pressure}$$

By the time blood reaches the veins, pressure has fallen because of friction, and a pressure wave no longer exists. Low-pressure blood in veins below the heart must flow "uphill," or against gravity, to return to the heart. Try holding your arm straight down without moving for several minutes and notice how the veins in the back of your hand begin to stand out as they fill with blood. (This effect may be more evident in older people, whose subcutaneous connective tissue has lost elasticity.)

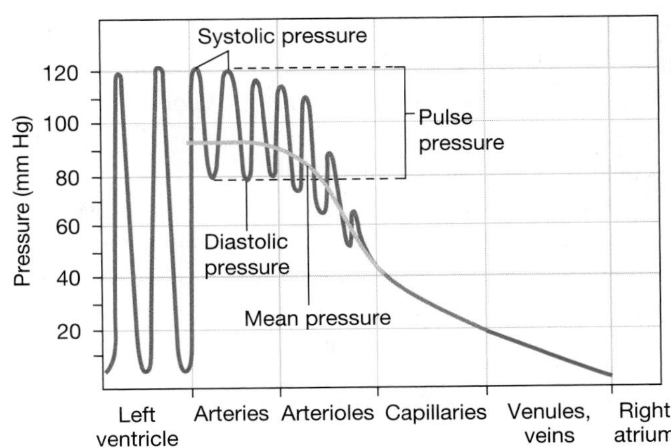

■ **FIGURE 15-5** ***Pressure throughout the systemic circulation***

Pressure waves created by ventricular contraction are reflected into the blood vessels. They diminish in amplitude with distance and disappear at the capillaries.

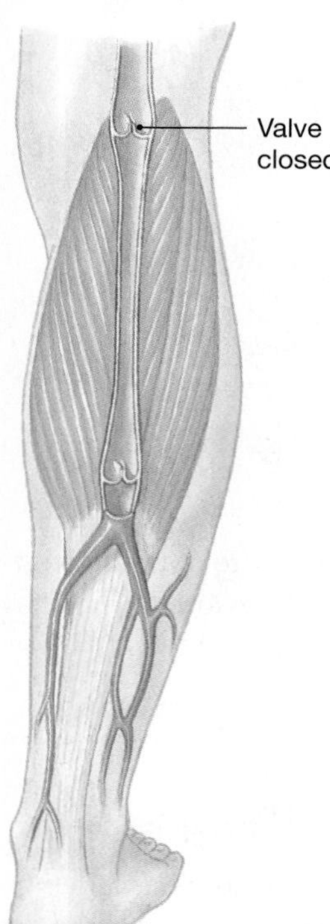
Valves in the veins prevent backflow of blood.
Valve closed

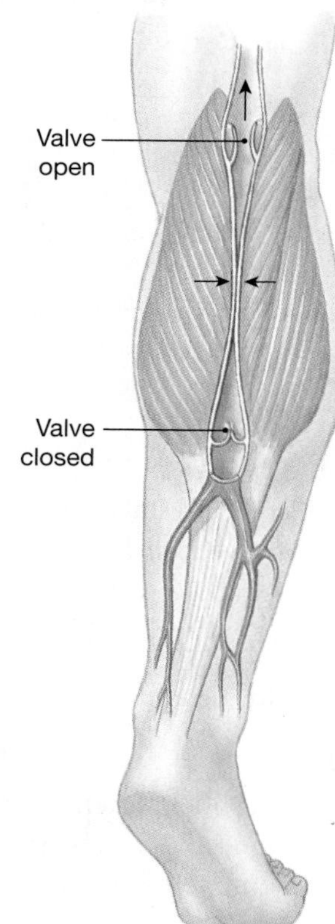
When the skeletal muscles compress the veins, they force blood toward the heart (the skeletal muscle pump).
Valve open
Valve closed

■ **FIGURE 15-6** ***Valves ensure one-way flow in veins***

Then raise your hand so that gravity assists the venous flow and watch the bulging veins disappear.

To assist venous flow, some veins have internal one-way valves (Fig. 15-6 ■). These valves, like those in the heart, ensure that blood passing the valve cannot flow backward. Once blood reaches the vena cava, there are no valves. Venous blood flow is steady rather than pulsatile, pushed along by the continuous movement of blood out of the capillaries.

Venous return to the heart is aided by the *skeletal muscle pump* and the *respiratory pump* [p. 491]. When muscles such as those in the calf of the leg contract, they compress the veins, forcing the blood upward past the valves. While your hand is hanging down, try clenching and unclenching your fist to see the effect muscle contraction has on distention of the veins.

CONCEPT CHECK

1. Would you expect to find valves in the veins leading from the brain to the heart? Defend your answer.
2. If you checked the pulse in a person's carotid artery and left wrist at the same time, would the pressure waves occur simultaneously? Explain.
3. Who has the higher pulse pressure, someone with blood pressure of 90/60 or someone with blood pressure of 130/95?

Answers: p. 533

Arterial Blood Pressure Reflects the Driving Pressure for Blood Flow

Arterial blood pressure, or simply "blood pressure," reflects the driving pressure created by the pumping action of the heart. Because ventricular pressure is difficult to measure, it is customary to assume that arterial blood pressure reflects ventricular pressure. Because arterial pressure is pulsatile, we use a single value—the **mean arterial pressure** (MAP)—to represent driving pressure. Mean arterial pressure is estimated as diastolic pressure plus one-third of pulse pressure:

$$\text{MAP} = \text{diastolic P} + 1/3\ (\text{systolic P} - \text{diastolic P})$$

For a person whose systolic pressure is 120 and diastolic pressure is 80:

$$\text{MAP} = 80 \text{ mm Hg} + 1/3\ (120 - 80 \text{ mm Hg})$$

$$\text{MAP} = 93 \text{ mm Hg}$$

Mean arterial pressure is closer to diastolic pressure than to systolic pressure because diastole lasts twice as long as systole.

Abnormally high or low arterial blood pressure can be indicative of a problem in the cardiovascular system. If blood pressure falls too low (*hypotension*), the driving force for blood flow will be unable to overcome opposition by gravity. In this instance, blood flow and oxygen supply to the brain are impaired, and the subject may become dizzy or faint.

On the other hand, if blood pressure is chronically elevated (a condition known as *hypertension,* or high blood pressure), high pressure on the walls of blood vessels may cause weakened areas to rupture and bleed into the tissues. If a rupture occurs in the brain, it is called a *cerebral hemorrhage* and may cause the loss of neurological function commonly called a *stroke.* If a weakened area ruptures in a major artery, such as the descending aorta, rapid blood loss into the abdominal cavity will cause blood pressure to fall below the critical minimum. Without prompt treatment, rupture of a major artery is fatal.

CONCEPT CHECK

4. The formula given for calculating MAP applies to a typical resting heart rate of 60–80 beats/min. If heart rate increases, would the contribution of systolic pressure to mean arterial pressure decrease or increase, and would MAP decrease or increase?
5. Peter's systolic pressure is 112 mm Hg, and his diastolic pressure is 68 mm Hg (written 112/68). What is his pulse pressure? His mean arterial pressure?

Answers: p. 533

Blood Pressure Is Estimated by Sphygmomanometry

We estimate arterial blood pressure in the radial artery of the arm using a *sphygmomanometer,* an instrument consisting of an inflatable cuff and a pressure gauge [*sphygmus,* pulse + *manometer,* an instrument for measuring pressure of a fluid]. The cuff encircles the upper arm and is inflated until it exerts

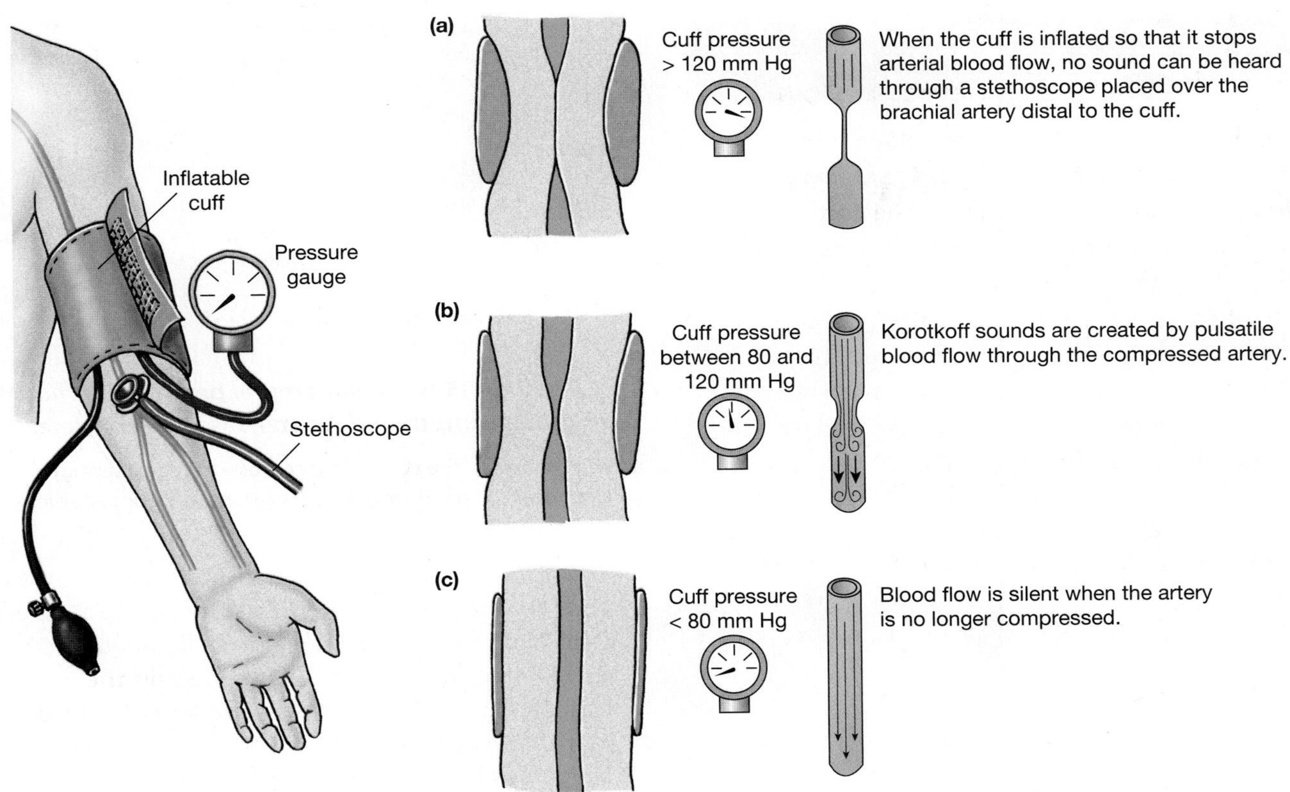

(a)
Cuff pressure
> 120 mm Hg
When the cuff is inflated so that it stops arterial blood flow, no sound can be heard through a stethoscope placed over the brachial artery distal to the cuff.
Inflatable cuff
Pressure gauge
(b)
Cuff pressure between 80 and 120 mm Hg
Korotkoff sounds are created by pulsatile blood flow through the compressed artery.
Stethoscope
(c)
Cuff pressure
< 80 mm Hg
Blood flow is silent when the artery is no longer compressed.

■ **FIGURE 15-7** ***Measurement of arterial blood pressure***

Arterial blood pressure is measured with a sphygmomanometer (an inflatable cuff plus a pressure gauge) and a stethoscope. The inflation pressure shown is for a person whose blood pressure is 120/80.

pressure higher than the systolic pressure driving arterial blood. When cuff pressure exceeds arterial pressure, blood flow into the lower arm stops (Fig. 15-7a ■).

Now pressure on the cuff is gradually released. When cuff pressure falls below systolic arterial blood pressure, blood begins to flow again. As blood squeezes through the still-compressed artery, a thumping noise called a **Korotkoff sound** can be heard with each pressure wave (Fig. 15-7b). Once the cuff pressure no longer compresses the artery, the sounds disappear (Fig. 15-7c).

The pressure at which a Korotkoff sound is first heard represents the highest pressure in the artery and is recorded as the systolic pressure. The point at which the Korotkoff sounds disappear is the lowest pressure in the artery and is recorded as the diastolic pressure. By convention, blood pressure is written as systolic pressure over diastolic pressure.

For years the "average" value for blood pressure has been stated as 120/80. Like many average physiological values, however, these numbers are subject to wide variability, both from one person to another and within a single individual from moment to moment. A systolic pressure that is consistently over 140 mm Hg at rest, or a diastolic pressure that is chronically over 90 mm Hg, is considered a sign of hypertension in an otherwise healthy person. Furthermore, the guidelines published in the 2003 JNC 7 Report* recommend that individuals maintain their blood pressure *below* 120/80. Persons whose systolic pressure is consistently in the range of 120–139 or whose diastolic pressure is in the range of 80–89 now are considered to be prehypertensive and should be counseled on lifestyle modification strategies to reduce their blood pressure.

Cardiac Output and Peripheral Resistance Determine Mean Arterial Pressure

Mean arterial pressure is the driving force for blood flow, but what determines mean arterial pressure? Arterial pressure is a balance between blood flow into the arteries and blood flow out of the arteries. If flow in exceeds flow out, blood collects in the arteries, and mean arterial pressure increases. If flow out exceeds flow in, mean arterial pressure falls.

Blood flow into the aorta is equal to the cardiac output of the left ventricle. Blood flow out of the arteries is influenced primarily by **peripheral resistance**, defined as the resistance to

*Seventh Report of the Joint National Committee on Prevention, Detection, Evaluation, and Treatment of High Blood Pressure, National Institutes of Health. *www.nhlbi.nih.gov/guidelines/hypertension*

RUNNING PROBLEM

Kurt's second blood pressure reading is 158/98. Dr. Cortez asks him to take his blood pressure at home daily for two weeks and then return to the doctor's office. When Kurt comes back with his diary, the story is the same: his blood pressure continues to average 160/100. After running some tests, Dr. Cortez concludes that Kurt is one of approximately 50 million adult Americans with high blood pressure, also called hypertension. If not controlled, hypertension can lead to heart failure, stroke, and kidney failure.

Question 1:
Why are people with high blood pressure at greater risk for having a hemorrhagic (or bleeding) stroke?

501 508 510 513 521 529

flow offered by the arterioles (Fig. 15-8 ■). We can express the relationship between cardiac output, peripheral resistance, and mean arterial pressure as

$$\text{Mean arterial pressure} \propto \text{cardiac output} \times \text{resistance of arterioles}$$

$$\text{MAP} \propto \text{CO} \times R_{\text{arterioles}}$$

Let's consider how this works. If cardiac output increases, the heart pumps more blood into the arteries per unit time. If resistance to blood flow out of the arteries does not change, flow into the arteries is greater than flow out, blood volume in the arteries increases, and arterial blood pressure increases.

In another example, suppose cardiac output remains unchanged but peripheral resistance increases. Flow in is unchanged, but flow out is less. Blood again accumulates in the arteries, and the arterial pressure again increases. Most cases of hypertension are believed to be caused by increased peripheral resistance without changes in cardiac output.

Two additional factors can influence arterial blood pressure: total blood volume and the distribution of blood in the systemic circulation.

Changes in Blood Volume Affect Blood Pressure

Although the volume of the blood in the circulation is usually relatively constant, changes in blood volume can affect arterial blood pressure. If blood volume increases, blood pressure increases. When blood volume decreases, blood pressure decreases.

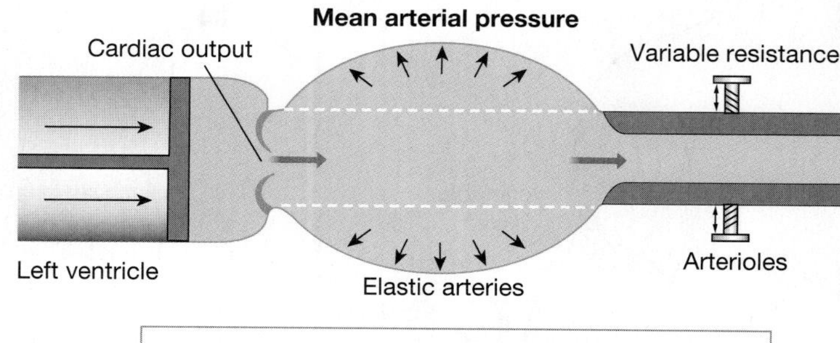

■ **FIGURE 15-8** ***Mean arterial pressure is a function of cardiac output and resistance in the arterioles***

In this model, the ventricle is represented by a syringe. The variable diameter of the arterioles is represented by adjustable screws.

To understand the relationship between blood volume and pressure, think of the circulatory system as an elastic balloon filled with water. If only a small amount of water is in the balloon, little pressure is exerted on the walls, and the balloon is soft and flabby. As more water is added to the balloon, more pressure is exerted on the elastic walls. If you fill a balloon close to the bursting point, you risk popping the balloon. The best way to reduce this pressure is to remove some of the water.

Small increases in blood volume occur throughout the day due to ingestion of food and liquids, but these increases usually do not create long-lasting changes in blood pressure because of homeostatic compensations. Adjustments for increased blood volume are primarily the responsibility of the kidneys. If blood volume increases, the kidneys restore normal volume by excreting excess water in the urine (Fig. 15-9 ■).

Compensation for decreased blood volume is more difficult and requires an integrated response from the kidneys and the cardiovascular system. If blood volume decreases, *the kidneys cannot restore the lost fluid.* The kidneys can only conserve blood volume and thereby prevent further decreases in blood pressure. The only way to restore lost fluid volume is through drinking or intravenous infusions. This is an example of mass balance: volume lost to the external environment must be replaced from the external environment.

Cardiovascular compensation for decreased blood volume includes vasoconstriction and increased sympathetic stimulation of the heart [Fig. 14-31, p. 494]. However, there are limits to the effectiveness of cardiovascular compensation, and if the fluid loss is too great, adequate blood pressure cannot be maintained. Typical events that might cause significant changes in blood volume include dehydration, hemorrhage, and ingestion of a large quantity of fluid. The integrated compensation for these events will be discussed in Chapter 20.

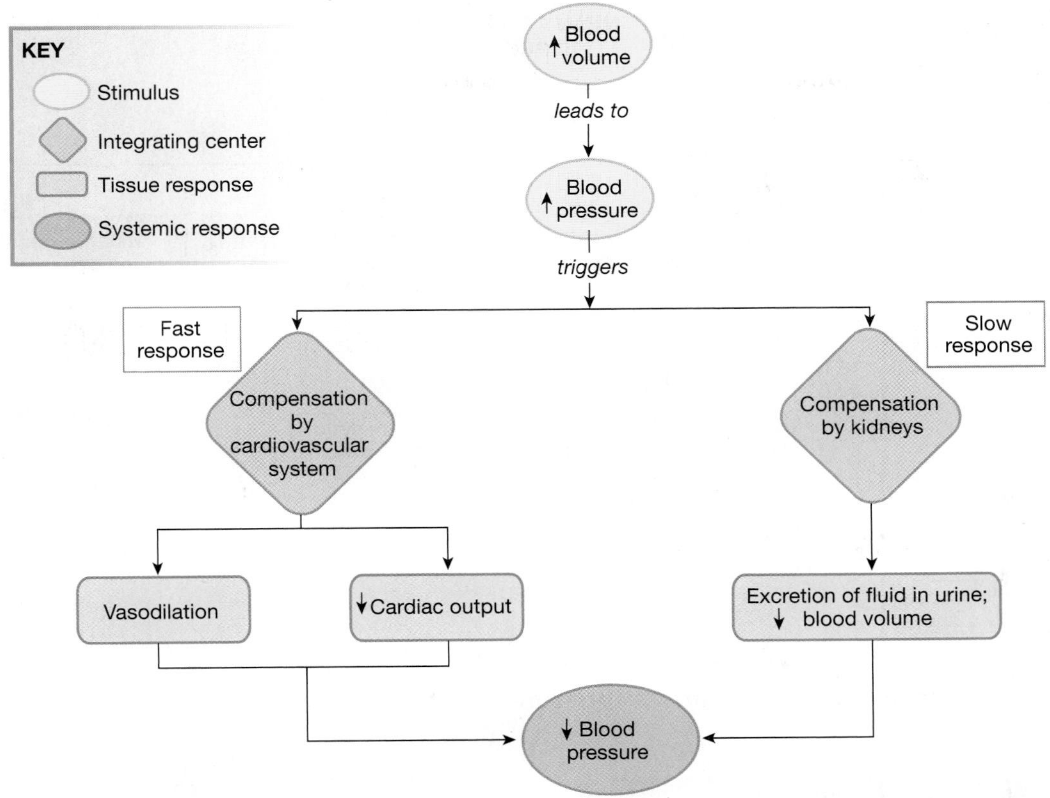

■ **FIGURE 15-9** ***Blood pressure control involves both the cardiovascular system and the renal system***

The cardiovascular system carries out rapid responses, while the renal response is slower.

In addition to the absolute volume of blood in the cardiovascular system, the relative distribution of blood between the arterial and venous sides of the circulation can be an important factor in maintaining arterial blood pressure. Arteries are low-volume vessels that usually contain only about 11% of total blood volume at any one time. Veins, in contrast, are high-volume vessels that hold about 60% of the circulating blood volume at any one time. The veins act as a volume reservoir, holding blood that can be redistributed to the arteries if needed. When arterial blood pressure falls, increased sympathetic activity constricts veins, decreasing their holding capacity and redistributing blood to the arterial side of the circulation. Figure. 15-10 ■ summarizes the four key factors that influence mean arterial blood pressure.

RESISTANCE IN THE ARTERIOLES

As we saw in Chapter 14 [p. 462], resistance to blood flow (R) is directly proportional to the length of the tubing through which the fluid flows (L) and to the viscosity (η) of the fluid, and inversely proportional to the fourth power of the tubing radius (r):

$$R \propto L\eta/r^4$$

Normally the length of the systemic circulation and the blood's viscosity are relatively constant. That leaves only the radius of the blood vessels as the primary resistance to blood flow:

$$R \propto 1/r^4$$

The arterioles are the main site of variable resistance in the systemic circulation and contribute more than 60% of the total resistance to flow in the system. Resistance in arterioles is variable because of the large amounts of smooth muscle in the arteriolar walls. When the smooth muscle contracts and relaxes, the radius of the arterioles changes.

Arteriolar resistance is influenced by both systemic and local control mechanisms:

1. *Sympathetic reflexes* mediated by the central nervous system maintain mean arterial pressure and govern blood distribution for certain homeostatic needs, such as temperature regulation.
2. *Local control of arteriolar resistance* matches tissue blood flow to the metabolic needs of the tissue. In the heart and skeletal muscle, these local controls take precedence over reflex control by the central nervous system.
3. *Hormones*—particularly those that regulate salt and water excretion by the kidneys—influence blood pressure by acting directly on the arterioles and by altering autonomic reflex control.

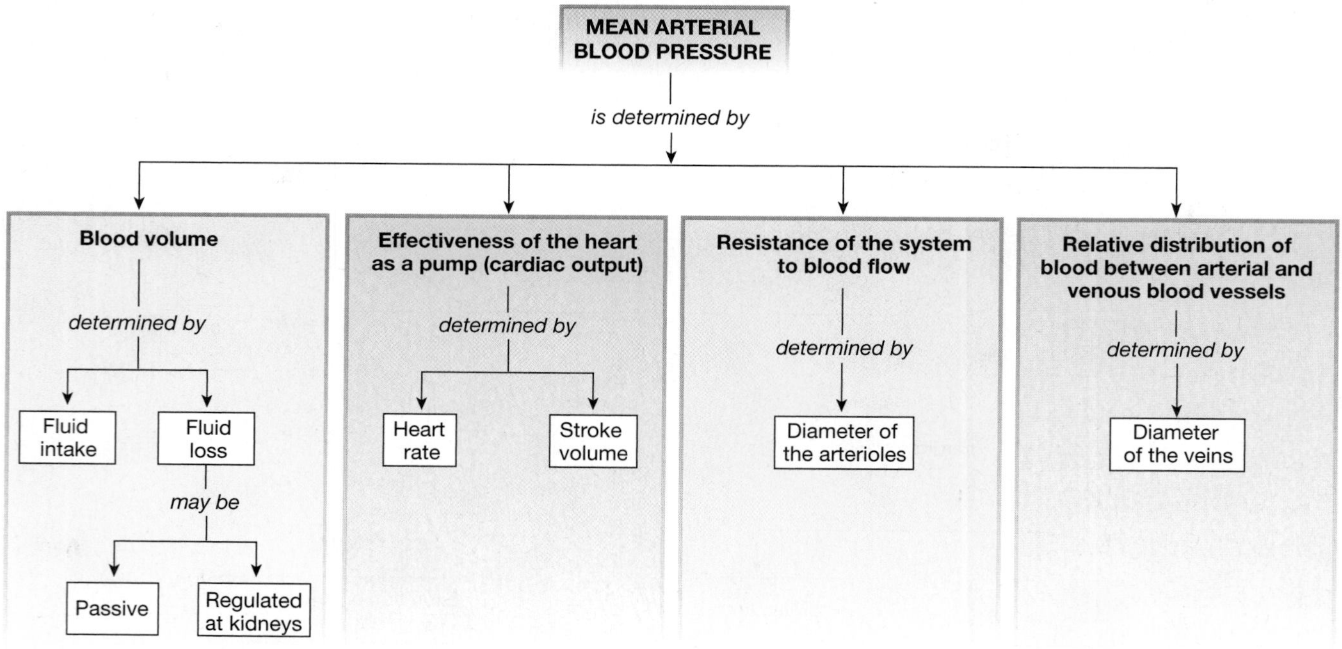

FIGURE 15-10 ***Factors that influence mean arterial pressure***

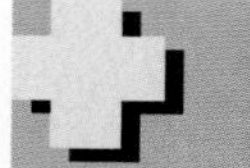

CLINICAL FOCUS

SHOCK

Shock is a broad term that refers to generalized, severe circulatory failure. Shock can arise from multiple causes: failure of the heart to maintain normal cardiac output (*cardiogenic shock*), decreased circulating blood volume (*hypovolemic shock*), bacterial toxins (*septic shock*), and miscellaneous causes, such as the massive immune reactions that cause *anaphylactic shock*. No matter what the cause, the results are similar: low cardiac output and falling peripheral blood pressure. When tissue perfusion can no longer keep up with tissue oxygen demand, the cells begin to sustain damage from inadequate oxygen and from the buildup of metabolic wastes. Once this damage occurs, a positive feedback cycle begins. The shock becomes progressively worse until it becomes irreversible, and the patient dies. The management of shock includes administration of oxygen, fluids, and norepinephrine, which stimulates vasoconstriction and increases cardiac output. If the shock arises from a cause that is treatable, such as a bacterial infection, measures must also be taken to remove the precipitating cause.

Table 15-2 ■ lists the chemicals that mediate arteriolar resistance by producing vasoconstriction or vasodilation. The following sections look at the factors that influence blood flow at the tissue level.

Myogenic Autoregulation Automatically Adjusts Blood Flow

Vascular smooth muscle has the ability to regulate its own state of contraction, a process called **myogenic autoregulation**. In the absence of autoregulation, an increase in blood pressure increases

RUNNING PROBLEM

Most hypertension is *essential hypertension,* which means high blood pressure that cannot be attributed to any particular cause. "Since your blood pressure is only mildly elevated," Dr. Cortez tells Kurt, "let's see if we can control it with lifestyle changes. You need to reduce salt and fat in your diet, get some exercise, and lose some weight." "Looks like you're asking me to turn over a whole new leaf," says Kurt.

Question 2:
What is the rationale for reducing salt intake to control hypertension? (Hint: salt causes water retention.)

501 508 510 513 521 529

TABLE 15-2 Chemicals Mediating Vasoconstriction and Vasodilation

CHEMICAL	PHYSIOLOGICAL ROLE	SOURCE	TYPE
Vasoconstriction			
Norepinephrine (α-receptors)	Baroreceptor reflex	Sympathetic neurons	Neurotransmitter
Serotonin	Platelet aggregation, smooth muscle contraction	Neurons, digestive tract, platelets	Paracrine, neurotransmitter
Substance P	Pain, increase capillary permeability	Neurons, digestive tract	Paracrine, neurotransmitter
Endothelin	Paracrine mediator	Vascular endothelium	Paracrine
Vasopressin	Increase blood pressure in hemorrhage	Posterior pituitary	Neurohormone
Angiotensin II	Increase blood pressure	Plasma hormone	Hormone
Vasodilation			
Epinephrine (β_2-receptors)	Increase blood flow to skeletal muscle, heart, liver	Adrenal medulla	Neurohormone
Acetylcholine (via NO)	Erection of clitoris or penis	Parasympathetic neurons	Neurotransmitter
Vasoactive intestinal peptide	Digestive secretion, relax smooth muscle	Neurons	Neurotransmitter, neurohormone
Nitric oxide (NO)	Paracrine mediator	Endothelium	Paracrine
Bradykinin (via NO)	Increase blood flow	Multiple tissues	Paracrine
Adenosine	Increase blood flow to match metabolism	Hypoxic cells	Paracrine
$\downarrow O_2$, $\uparrow CO_2$, $\uparrow H^+$, $\uparrow K^+$	Increase blood flow to match metabolism	Cell metabolism	Paracrine
Histamine	Increase blood flow	Mast cells	Paracrine
Natriuretic peptides (example—ANP)	Reduce blood pressure	Atrial myocardium, brain	Hormone, neurotransmitter

blood flow through an arteriole. However, when smooth muscle fibers in the wall of the arteriole stretch because of increased blood pressure, the arteriole constricts. This vasoconstriction increases the resistance offered by the arteriole, automatically decreasing blood flow through the vessel. With this simple and direct response to pressure, arterioles regulate their own blood flow.

The mechanism responsible for the intrinsic response of vascular smooth muscle is stretch that opens mechanically gated Ca^{2+} channels in the muscle membrane. Calcium entering the smooth muscle cell combines with calmodulin and activates myosin light chain kinase, which in turn increases myosin ATPase activity and crossbridge activity [p. 426].

Paracrines Alter Vascular Smooth Muscle Contraction

Local control of arteriolar resistance is an important method by which individual tissues regulate their own blood supply. Local regulation is accomplished by paracrines (including the gases O_2, CO_2, and NO) secreted by the vascular endothelium or by cells to which the arterioles are supplying blood (Table 15-2).

The concentrations of many paracrines change as cells become more or less metabolically active. For example, if aerobic metabolism increases, tissue O_2 levels decrease while CO_2 production goes up. Both low O_2 and high CO_2 dilate arterioles. This vasodilation increases blood flow into the tissue, bringing additional O_2 to meet the increased metabolic demand and removing waste CO_2 (Fig. 15-11a ■). The process in which an increase in blood flow accompanies an increase in metabolic activity is known as **active hyperemia** [*hyper-*, above normal + *(h)aimia*, blood].

If blood flow to a tissue is occluded [*occludere*, to close up] for a few seconds to a few minutes, O_2 levels fall and metabolically produced paracrines such as CO_2 and H^+ accumulate in the interstitial fluid. Local *hypoxia* [*hypo-*, low + *oxia*, oxygen]

(a) Active hyperemia

↑ Tissue metabolism

↑ Release of metabolic vasodilators into ECF

Arterioles dilate.

↓ Resistance

↑ Blood flow

Blood flow matches metabolism.

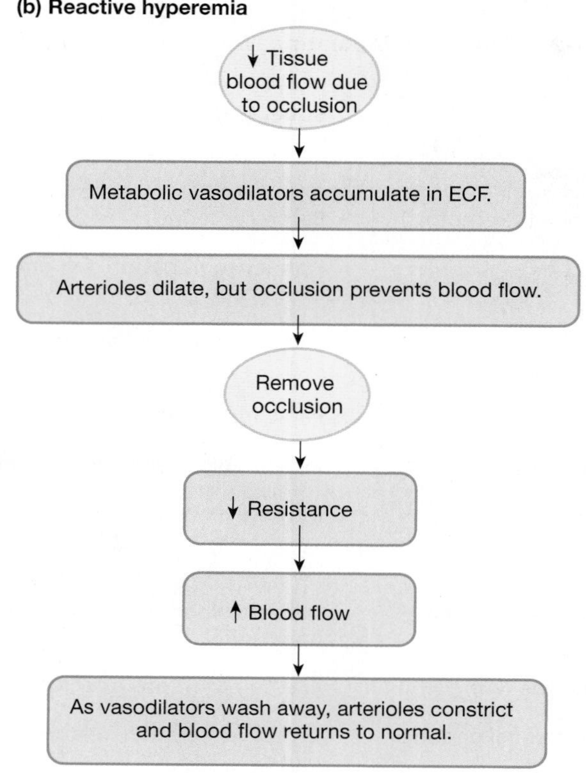
(b) Reactive hyperemia
↓ Tissue blood flow due to occlusion
Metabolic vasodilators accumulate in ECF.
Arterioles dilate, but occlusion prevents blood flow.
Remove occlusion
↓ Resistance
↑ Blood flow
As vasodilators wash away, arterioles constrict and blood flow returns to normal.

■ **FIGURE 15-11** ***Hyperemia***

causes endothelial cells to synthesize the vasodilator nitric oxide. When blood flow to the tissue resumes, the increased concentrations of NO, CO_2, and other paracrines immediately trigger significant vasodilation. As the vasodilators are metabolized or washed away by the restored tissue blood flow, the radius of the arteriole gradually returns to normal. An increase in tissue blood flow following a period of low perfusion is known as **reactive hyperemia** (Fig. 15-11b).

Our knowledge concerning the importance of nitric oxide as a vasodilator is growing as additional research studies are published. NO plays an important physiological role in the male erection reflex (see Chapter 26), and drugs used to treat erectile dysfunction prolong NO activity. Decreases in endogenous NO activity are suspected to play a role in several significant conditions, including hypertension and the elevated blood pressure that sometimes occurs during pregnancy.

Another vasodilator paracrine is the nucleotide **adenosine**. If oxygen consumption in heart muscle exceeds the rate at which oxygen is supplied by the blood, myocardial hypoxia results. In response to low tissue oxygen, the myocardial cells release adenosine. Adenosine dilates coronary arterioles in an attempt to bring additional blood flow into the muscle.

Not all vasoactive paracrines reflect changes in metabolism. For example, *kinins* and *histamine* are potent vasodilators that play a role in inflammation. *Serotonin* (5-HT), previously mentioned as a CNS neurotransmitter [p. 274], is also a vasoconstricting paracrine released by activated platelets. When damaged blood vessels activate platelets, the subsequent serotonin-mediated vasoconstriction helps slow blood loss. Serotonin agonists called triptans (for example, *sumatriptan*) are drugs that bind to 5-HT_1 receptors and cause vasoconstriction. These drugs are used to treat migraine headaches, which are caused by inappropriate cerebral vasodilation.

CONCEPT CHECK

6. Resistance to blood flow is determined *primarily* by (a) blood viscosity, (b) blood volume, (c) cardiac output, (d) blood vessel diameter, or (e) blood pressure gradient (ΔP).
7. The extracellular fluid concentration of K^+ increases in exercising skeletal muscles. What effect will this increase in K^+ have on blood flow in the muscles?

Answers: p. 533

The Sympathetic Branch Controls Most Vascular Smooth Muscle

Smooth muscle contraction in arterioles is regulated by neural and hormonal signals in addition to locally produced paracrines. Among the hormones with significant vasoactive properties are *atrial natriuretic peptide* and *angiotensin II*. These hormones also have significant effects on the kidney's excretion of ions and water, as you will learn in Chapter 20.

Most systemic arterioles are innervated by sympathetic neurons. A notable exception is arterioles involved in the erection reflex of the penis and clitoris. They are controlled

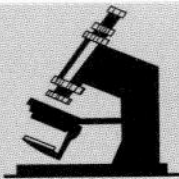

EMERGING CONCEPTS

FROM DYNAMITE TO VASODILATION

In 1998 the Nobel prize in physiology and medicine was awarded to Robert Furchgott, Louis Ignarro, and Ferid Murad for their research on the role of nitric oxide as a signal molecule in the cardiovascular system (*www.nobel.se/medicine*). Who would have thought that this component of smog and derivative of dynamite would turn out to be a biological messenger? Certainly not the referees who initially rejected Louis Ignarro's attempts to publish his research findings on the elusive gas. However, the ability of nitrate-containing compounds to relax blood vessels has been known for more than 100 years, ever since workers in Alfred Nobel's dynamite factory complained of headaches caused by nitrate-induced vasodilation. Ever since the 1860s, physicians have used nitroglycerin to relieve *angina*—heart pain that results from constricted blood vessels—and even today heart patients carry little nitroglycerin tablets to slide under their tongues when angina strikes. Still, it took years of work to isolate the short-lived gas that is the biologically active molecule derived from nitroglycerin. Despite all our twenty-first-century technology, direct research on NO is still difficult, and many studies investigate its influence indirectly by studying the location and activity of nitric oxide synthase (NOS), the enzyme that produces NO.

indirectly by parasympathetic innervation that causes paracrine release of nitric oxide, resulting in vasodilation.

Tonic discharge of norepinephrine from sympathetic neurons helps maintain myogenic tone of arterioles (Fig. 15-12 ■). Norepinephrine binding to α-receptors on vascular smooth muscle causes vasoconstriction. If sympathetic release of norepinephrine decreases, the arterioles dilate. If sympathetic stimulation increases, the arterioles constrict.

Epinephrine from the adrenal medulla travels through the blood and binds with α-receptors, reinforcing vasoconstriction. However, α-receptors have a lower affinity for epinephrine and do not respond as strongly to it as they do to norepinephrine [p. 276].

Epinephrine also binds to β_2-receptors, found on vascular smooth muscle of heart, liver, and skeletal muscle arterioles.

RUNNING PROBLEM

After a month, Kurt returns to the doctor's office for a checkup. He has lost five pounds and is walking at least a mile daily, but his blood pressure has not changed. "I swear, I'm trying to do better," says Kurt, "but it's difficult." Because lifestyle changes alone have not lowered Kurt's blood pressure, Dr. Cortez prescribes an antihypertensive drug. "This drug, called an ACE inhibitor, blocks production of a chemical called angiotensin II, a powerful vasoconstrictor. This medication should bring your blood pressure back to a normal value."

Question 3:
Why would blocking the action of a vasoconstrictor lower blood pressure?

501 508 510 513 521 529

These receptors are not innervated and therefore respond primarily to circulating epinephrine [p. 276]. Activation of vascular β_2-receptors by epinephrine causes vasodilation.

One way to remember which arterioles have β_2-receptors is to think of a fight-or-flight response to a stressful event [p. 377]. This response includes a generalized increase in sympathetic activity, along with the release of epinephrine. Blood vessels that have β_2-receptors respond to epinephrine by vasodilating. Such β_2-mediated vasodilation enhances blood flow to the heart, skeletal muscles, and liver, tissues that are active during the fight-or-flight response. (The liver produces glucose for muscle contraction.)

During fight or flight, increased sympathetic activity at arteriolar α-receptors causes vasoconstriction. The increase in resistance diverts blood from nonessential organs, such as the gastrointestinal tract, to the skeletal muscles, liver, and heart. The nervous system's ability to selectively alter blood flow to organs is an important aspect of cardiovascular regulation.

CONCEPT CHECK

8. What happens when epinephrine combines with β_1-receptors in the heart? With β_2-receptors in the heart? (*Hint:* "in the heart" is vague. The heart has multiple tissue types. Which heart tissues possess the different types of β-receptors? [p. 491])
9. Skeletal muscle arterioles have both α- and β-receptors on their smooth muscle. Epinephrine can bind to both. Will the arterioles constrict or dilate in response to epinephrine? Explain.

Answers: p. 533

■ **FIGURE 15-12** ***Tonic control of arteriolar diameter***

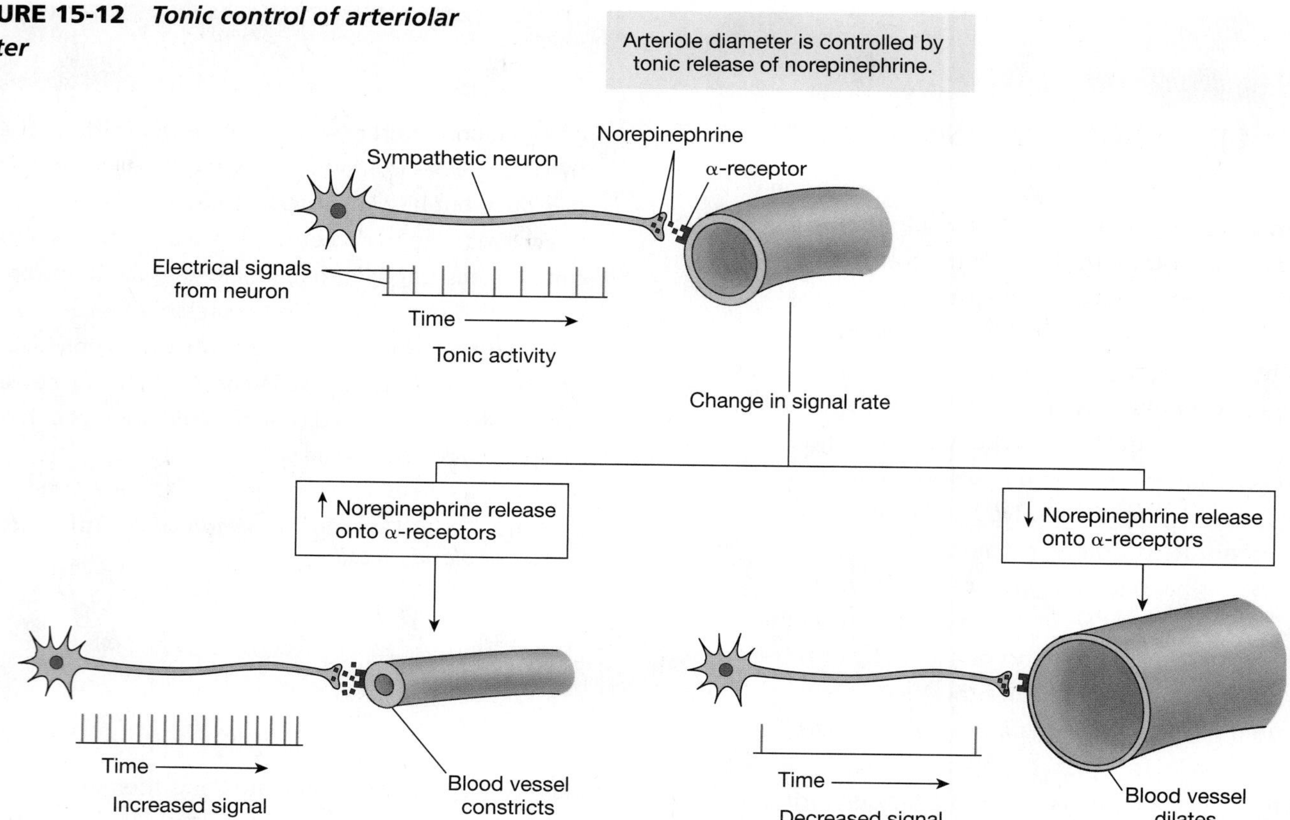

DISTRIBUTION OF BLOOD TO THE TISSUES

The distribution of systemic blood varies according to the metabolic needs of individual organs. Distribution is governed by a combination of local control mechanisms and homeostatic reflexes. For example, skeletal muscles at rest receive about 20% of cardiac output. During exercise, when the muscles use more oxygen and nutrients, they receive as much as 85%.

Blood flow to individual organs is set to some degree by the number and size of arteries feeding the organ. Figure 15-13 ■ shows how blood is distributed to various organs when the body is at rest. Usually, more than two-thirds of the cardiac output is routed to the digestive tract, liver, muscles, and kidneys.

Variations in blood flow to individual tissues are possible because the arterioles in the body are arranged in parallel. That is, all arterioles receive blood at the same time from the aorta (Fig. 15-1). Total blood flow through *all* the arterioles of the body always equals the cardiac output.

However, the flow through individual arterioles depends on their resistance. The higher the resistance in the arteriole, the lower the blood flow through it. If an arteriole constricts and resistance goes up, blood flow through that arteriole goes down (Fig. 15-14 ■):

$$\text{Flow}_{\text{arteriole}} \propto 1/\text{resistance}_{\text{arteriole}}$$

In other words, blood is diverted from high-resistance arterioles to lower-resistance arterioles. You might say that blood traveling through the arterioles takes the path of least resistance.

In a tissue, blood flow into individual capillaries can be regulated by the precapillary sphincters described earlier in the chapter. When these small bands of smooth muscle at metarteriole-capillary junctions constrict, they restrict blood flow into the capillaries (Fig. 15-15 ■). When the sphincters dilate, blood flow into the capillaries increases. This mechanism provides an additional site for local control of blood flow.

CONCEPT CHECK

10. Use Figure 15-13 to answer these questions. (a) Which tissue has the highest blood flow per unit weight? (b) Which tissue has the least blood flow, regardless of weight?

Answers: p. 533

EXCHANGE AT THE CAPILLARIES

The transport of materials around the body is only part of the function of the cardiovascular system. Once blood reaches the capillaries, the plasma and the cells exchange materials across the thin capillary walls. Most cells are located within 0.1 mm of the nearest capillary, and diffusion over this short distance proceeds rapidly.

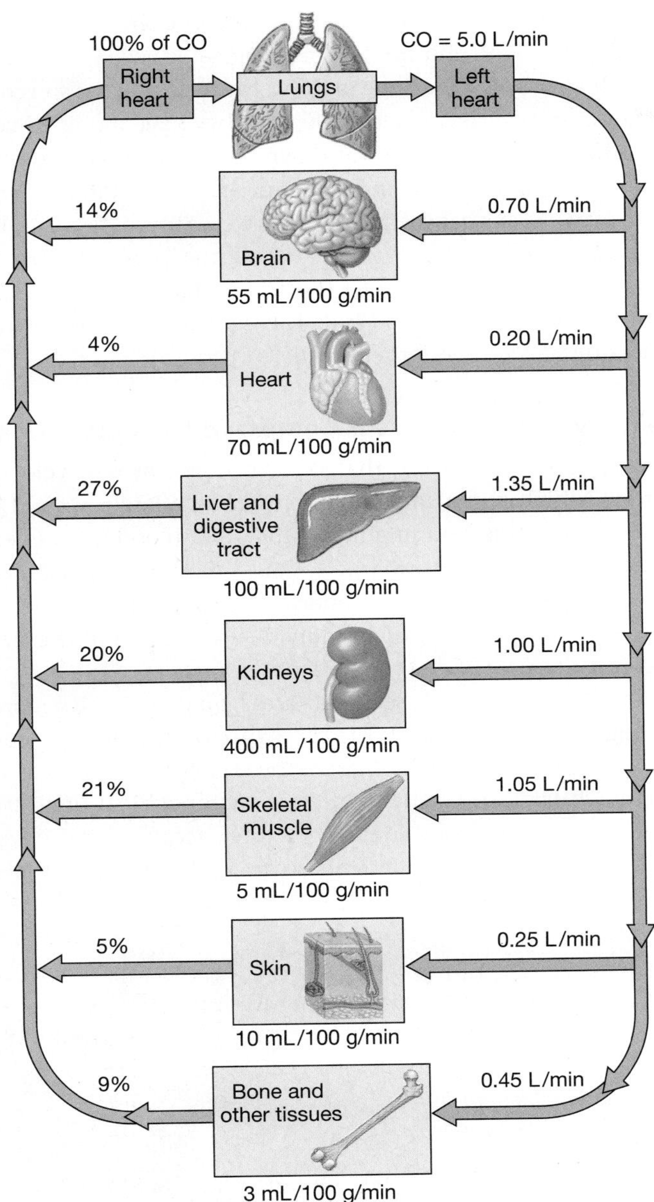

FIGURE QUESTION

What is the rate of blood flow through the lungs?

■ **FIGURE 15-13** ***Distribution of blood in the body at rest***

Blood flow to the major organs is represented in three ways: as a percentage of total flow, as volume per 100 grams of tissue per minute, and as an absolute rate of flow (in L/min).

The capillary density in any given tissue is directly related to the metabolic activity of the tissue's cells. Tissues with a higher metabolic rate require more oxygen and nutrients. Those tissues have more capillaries per unit area. Subcutaneous tissue and cartilage have the lowest capillary density. Muscles and glands have the highest. By one estimate, the adult human body has about 50,000 miles of capillaries, with a total exchange surface area of more than 6300 m^2, nearly the surface area of two football fields.

(a) Blood flow through four identical vessels (A–D) is equal. Total flow into vessels equals total flow out.

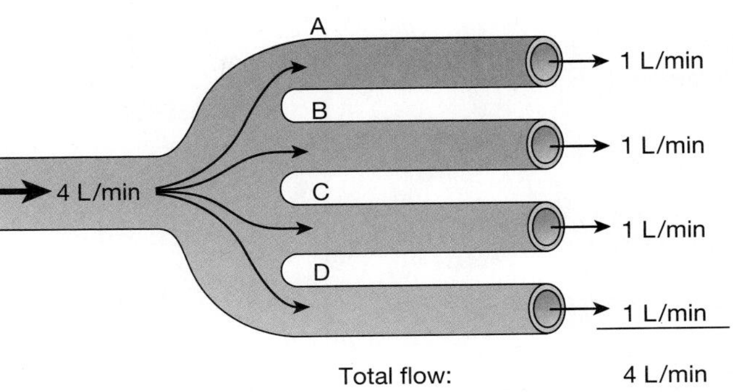

(b) When vessel B constricts, resistance of B increases and flow through B decreases. Flow diverted from B is divided among the lower-resistance vessels A, C, and D.

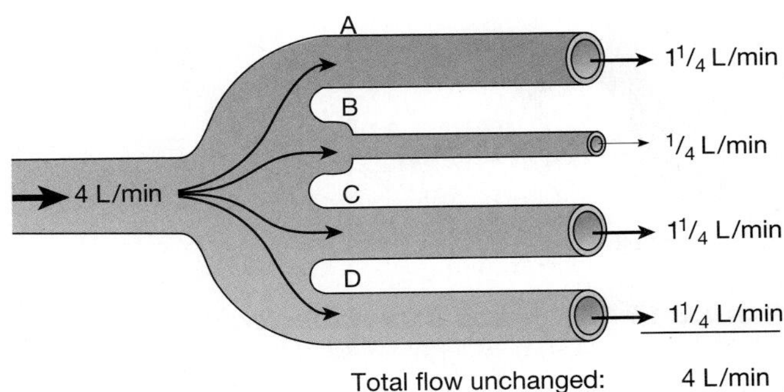

■ **FIGURE 15-14** ***Blood flow through individual blood vessels is determined by the vessel's resistance to flow***

Capillaries have the thinnest walls of all the blood vessels, composed of a single layer of flattened endothelial cells supported on a basal lamina (Figure 15-2). The diameter of a capillary is just larger than that of a red blood cell, forcing the blood cells to pass through single file. Cell junctions between the endothelial cells vary from tissue to tissue and help determine the "leakiness" of the capillary.

Capillaries can be divided into two types based on structure. The most common capillaries are **continuous capillaries,** whose endothelial cells are joined to one another with leaky junctions (Fig. 15-16a ■). These capillaries are found in muscle, connective tissue, and neural tissue. The continuous capillaries of the brain have evolved to form the blood-brain barrier, with tight junctions that protect neural tissue from toxins that may be present in the bloodstream [p. 299].

Fenestrated capillaries [*fenestra,* window] have large pores (*fenestrae*) that allow high volumes of fluid to pass rapidly between the plasma and interstitial fluid (Fig. 15-16b). These capillaries

(a) When precapillary sphincters are relaxed, blood flows through all capillaries in the bed.

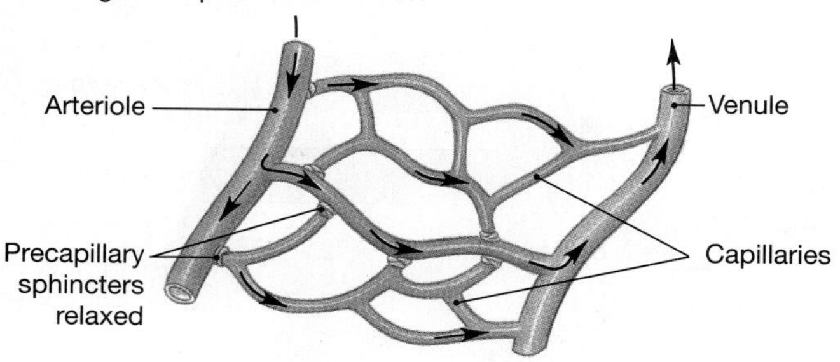

(b) If precapillary sphincters constrict, blood flow bypasses capillaries completely and flows through metarterioles.

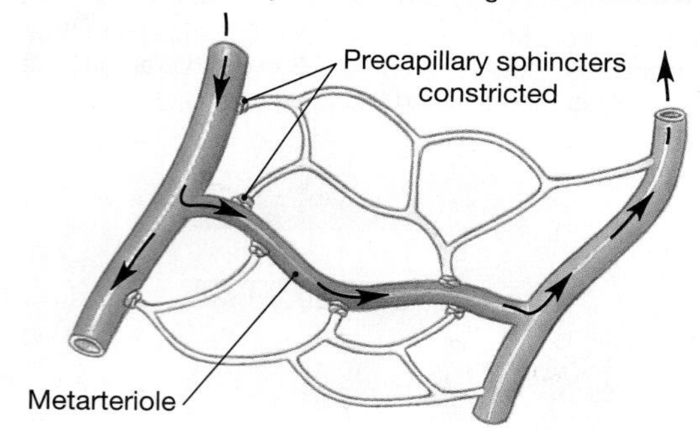

■ **FIGURE 15-15** ***Precapillary sphincters***

are found primarily in the kidney and the intestine, where they are associated with absorptive transporting epithelia.

Three tissues—the bone marrow, the liver, and the spleen—do not have typical capillaries. Instead they have modified vessels called **sinusoids** that are as much as five times wider than a capillary. The sinusoid endothelium has fenestrations, and there may be gaps between the cells as well. Sinusoids are found in locations where blood cells and plasma proteins need to cross the endothelium to enter the blood. Figure 16-5, Focus on Bone Marrow, shows blood cells leaving the bone marrow by squeezing between endothelial cells.

Velocity of Blood Flow is Lowest in the Capillaries

In Chapter 14 you learned that at a constant flow rate, velocity of flow is higher in a smaller vessel than in a larger vessel [p. 464]. From this, you might conclude that blood moves very rapidly through the capillaries because they are the smallest blood vessels. However, the primary determinant for velocity of flow is not the diameter of an individual capillary but the *total cross-sectional area* of *all* the capillaries.

What is total cross-sectional area? Imagine circles representing cross sections of all the capillaries placed edge to edge, and you have it. For the capillaries, those circles would cover an area much larger than the total cross-sectional areas of all the arteries and veins combined. Therefore, because total cross-sectional area of the capillaries is so large, the velocity of flow through them is low.

(a) Continuous capillaries have leaky junctions.

Basement membrane
Endothelial cell
Nucleus
Endothelial cell junctions allow water and small dissolved solutes to pass.
Basement membrane
Transcytosis vesicles

(b) Fenestrated capillaries have large pores.

Pores
Basement membrane (cut)
Transcytosis vesicles
Fenestrations or pores
Endothelial cell junction
Basement membrane
Transcytosis brings proteins and macromolecules across endothelium.
Some vesicles may fuse to create temporary channels.

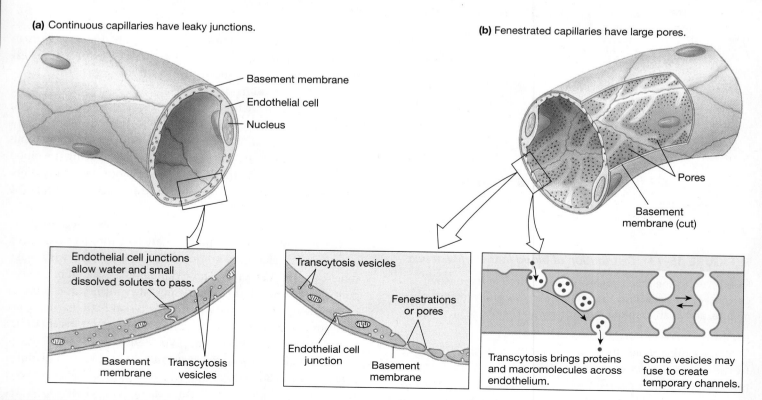

■ **FIGURE 15-16** ***The two types of capillaries***

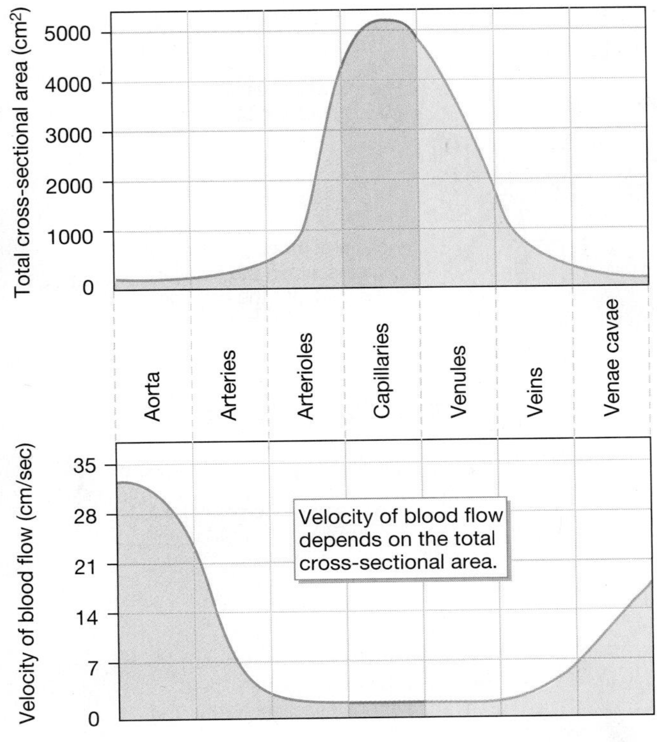

GRAPH QUESTION

(a) Is velocity of flow directly proportional to or inversely proportional to cross-sectional area?
(b) What effect does changing only the cross-sectional area have on flow rate?

■ **FIGURE 15-17** ***Velocity of flow depends on total cross-sectional area of the vessels***

Figure 15-17 ■ compares cross-sectional areas of different parts of the systemic circulation with the velocity of blood flow in each part. The fastest flow is in the relatively small-diameter arterial system. The slowest flow is in the capillaries and venules, which collectively have the largest cross-sectional area. The low velocity of flow through capillaries is a useful characteristic that allows diffusion enough time to go to equilibrium [p. 133].

Most Capillary Exchange Takes Place by Diffusion and Transcytosis

Exchange between the plasma and interstitial fluid takes place either by movement between endothelial cells (the *paracellular pathway*) or by movement through the cells (*transendothelial transport*). Smaller dissolved solutes and gases move by diffusion between or through the cells, depending on their lipid solubility [p. 24]. Larger solutes and proteins move mostly by vesicular transport [p. 148].

The diffusion rate for dissolved solutes is determined primarily by the concentration gradient between the plasma and the interstitial fluid. Oxygen and carbon dioxide diffuse freely across the thin endothelium. Their concentrations reach equilibrium with the interstitial fluid and cells by the time blood reaches the venous end of the capillary. In capillaries with leaky cell junctions, most small dissolved solutes can diffuse freely between the cells or through the fenestrae.

Blood cells and most plasma proteins are unable to pass through the junctions between capillary endothelial cells. However, we know that proteins do move from plasma to interstitial fluid and vice versa. In most capillaries, larger molecules (including selected proteins) are transported across the endothelium by *transcytosis* [p. 153]. The endothelial cell surface appears dotted with numerous *caveolae* and noncoated pits that become vesicles for transcytosis. It appears that in some capillaries, chains of vesicles fuse to create open channels that extend across the endothelial cell (Fig. 15-16b).

Capillary Filtration and Absorption Take Place by Bulk Flow

A third form of capillary exchange is bulk flow into and out of the capillary. **Bulk flow** refers to the mass movement of fluid between the blood and the interstitial fluid as the result of hydrostatic or osmotic pressure gradients. If the direction of bulk flow is into the capillary, the fluid movement is called **absorption**. If the direction of flow is out of the capillary, the fluid movement is known as **filtration**. Capillary filtration is caused by hydrostatic pressure that forces fluid out of the capillary through leaky cell junctions. As an analogy, think of garden "soaker" hoses whose perforated walls allow water to ooze out.

Most capillaries show a transition from net filtration at the arterial end to net absorption at the venous end. There are some exceptions to this rule, though. Capillaries in part of the kidney filter fluid along their entire length, for instance, and some capillaries in the intestine are only absorptive, picking up digested nutrients that have been transported into the interstitial fluid from the lumen of the intestine.

Two forces regulate bulk flow in the capillaries. One is hydrostatic pressure, the lateral pressure component of blood flow that pushes fluid out through the capillary pores [p. 461], and the other is osmotic pressure [p. 155]. These forces are sometimes called *Starling forces,* after the English physiologist E. H. Starling, who first described them (the same Starling as in the Frank-Starling law of the heart).

Osmotic pressure is determined by solute concentration of a compartment. The main solute difference between plasma and interstitial fluid is due to proteins, which are present in the plasma but mostly absent from interstitial fluid. The osmotic pressure created by the presence of these proteins is known as **colloid osmotic pressure** (π). Note that colloid osmotic pressure is *not* equivalent to the total osmotic pressure in a capillary.

(a) Filtration in systemic capillaries

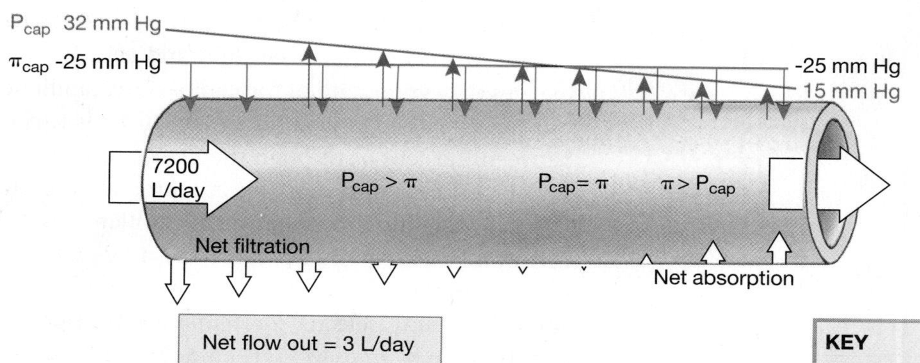

(b) Relationship between capillaries and lymph vessels

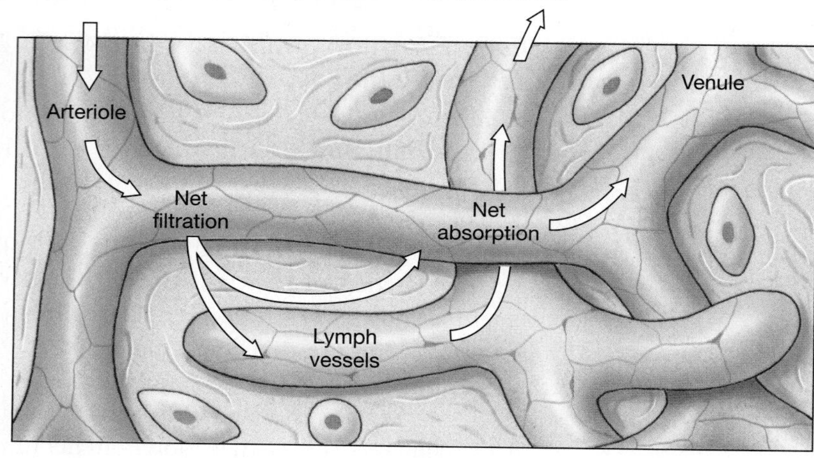

Arteriole
Venule
Net filtration
Net absorption
Lymph vessels
The excess water and solutes that filter out of the capillary are picked up by the lymph vessels and returned to the circulation.

■ **FIGURE 15-18** ***Fluid exchange at a capillary***

A net average of 3 L/day of fluid filters out of the capillaries.

It is simply a measure of the osmotic pressure created by proteins. Because the capillary endothelium is freely permeable to ions and other solutes in the plasma and interstitial fluid, these other solutes do not contribute to the osmotic gradient.

Colloid osmotic pressure is higher in the plasma (π_{cap} = 25mm Hg) than in the interstitial fluid (π_{IF} = 0 mm Hg). Therefore, the osmotic gradient favors water movement by osmosis from the interstitial fluid into the plasma, represented by the red vertical arrows in Figure 15-18a ■. For the purposes of our discussion, we will consider colloid osmotic pressure to be constant along the length of the capillary, at π_{cap} = 25 mm Hg.

Capillary hydrostatic pressure (P_{cap}), on the other hand, decreases along the length of the capillary as energy is lost to friction. Average values for capillary hydrostatic pressure, shown in Figure 15-18a, are 32 mm Hg at the arterial end of a capillary and 15 mm Hg at the venous end. The hydrostatic pressure of the interstitial fluid (P_{IF}) is very low, and so we will consider it to be essentially zero. This means that water movement due to hydrostatic pressure will always be directed out of the capillary, as denoted by the blue vertical arrows in Figure 15-18a, with the pressure gradient decreasing from the arterial end to the venous end.

Net fluid flow across the capillary is determined by the difference between the hydrostatic pressure gradient favoring filtration and the colloid osmotic pressure favoring absorption:

$$\text{Filtration } (P_{out}) = \text{hydrostatic pressure gradient} = P_{cap} - P_{IF}$$

$$\text{Absorption } (\pi_{in}) = \text{colloid osmotic pressure gradient} = \pi_{IF} - \pi_{cap}$$

$$\text{Net pressure} = \text{hydrostatic pressure gradient} + \text{colloid osmotic pressure gradient} = P_{out} + \pi_{in}$$

If we assume that the interstitial hydrostatic and colloid osmotic pressures are zero, as discussed above, then we get the following values at the arterial end of a capillary:

$$\text{Net pressure}_{\text{arterial end}} = (32 \text{ mm Hg} - 0) + (0 - 25 \text{ mm Hg}) = 32 - 25 \text{ mm Hg} = 7 \text{ mm Hg}$$

Because at the arterial end P_{out} is greater than π_{in}, the net pressure is 7 mm Hg of filtration pressure. At the venous end, where capillary hydrostatic pressure is less:

$$\text{Net } P_{\text{venous end}} = (15 \text{ mm Hg} - 0) + (0 - 25 \text{ mm Hg}) = 15 - 25 \text{ mm Hg} = -10 \text{ mm Hg}$$

Here π_{in} is greater than P_{out}, and therefore the net pressure is 10 mm Hg favoring absorption. (A negative net pressure indicates absorption.)

Fluid movement down the length of a capillary is shown in Figure 15-18a. At the arterial end there is net filtration, and at the venous end there is net absorption. If the point at which filtration equals absorption occurred in the middle of the capillary, there would be no net movement of fluid. All volume that was filtered at the arterial end would be absorbed at the venous end. However, filtration is usually greater than absorption, resulting in bulk flow of fluid out of the capillary into the interstitial space. By most estimates, that bulk flow amounts to about 3 liters per day, which is the equivalent of the entire plasma volume! Unless this filtered fluid is returned to the plasma, the blood will turn into a sludge of blood cells and proteins. Restoring fluid lost from the capillaries to the circulatory system is one of the functions of the lymphatic system, which we discuss next.

CONCEPT CHECK

11. Suppose that the hydrostatic pressure P_{cap} at the arterial end of a capillary increases from the 32 mm Hg shown in Figure 15-18a to 35 mm Hg. If P_{cap} remains 15 mm Hg at the venous end, will net filtration in this capillary decrease, increase, or stay the same?
12. A person with liver disease may lose the ability to synthesize plasma proteins. What will happen to the colloid osmotic pressure of his blood? What will happen to the balance between filtration and absorption in his capillaries?
13. Why did this discussion refer to the osmotic pressure of the plasma rather than the osmolarity of the plasma?

Answers: p. 533

THE LYMPHATIC SYSTEM

The vessels of the lymphatic system interact with three other physiological systems: the cardiovascular system, the digestive system, and the immune system. Functions of the lymphatic system include (1) returning fluid and proteins filtered out of the capillaries to the circulatory system, (2) picking up fat absorbed at the small intestine and transferring it to the circulatory system, and (3) serving as a filter to help capture and destroy foreign pathogens. In this discussion we focus on the role of the lymphatic system in fluid transport. The other two functions will be discussed in connection with digestion (Chapter 21) and immunity (Chapter 24).

The lymphatic system is designed for the one-way movement of interstitial fluid from the tissues into the circulation. Blind-end lymph vessels (*lymph capillaries*) lie close to all blood capillaries except those in the kidney and central nervous system (Fig. 15-18b). The smallest lymph vessels are composed of a single layer of flattened endothelium that is even thinner than the capillary endothelium.

The walls of these tiny lymph vessels are anchored to the surrounding connective tissue by fibers that hold the thin-walled vessels open. Large gaps between cells allow fluid, interstitial proteins, and particulate matter such as bacteria to be swept into the lymph vessels by bulk flow. Once inside the lymphatics, this clear fluid is called simply **lymph**.

Lymph vessels in the tissues join one another to form larger lymphatic vessels that progressively increase in size (Fig. 15-19 ■). These vessels have a system of semilunar valves, similar to valves in the venous circulation. The largest lymph ducts empty into the venous circulation just under the collarbones, where the left and right subclavian veins join the internal jugular veins. At intervals along the way, vessels enter **lymph nodes,** bean-shaped nodules of tissue with a fibrous outer capsule and an internal collection of immunologically active cells, including lymphocytes and macrophages.

The lymphatic system has no single pump like the heart. Lymph flow depends primarily on waves of contraction of smooth muscle in the walls of the larger lymph vessels. Flow is aided by contractile fibers in the endothelial cells, by the one-way valves, and by external compression created by skeletal muscles.

The skeletal muscle pump plays a significant role in lymph flow, as you know if you have ever injured a wrist or ankle. An immobilized limb frequently swells from the accumulation of fluid in the interstitial space, a condition known as **edema** [*oidema,* swelling]. Patients with edema in an injured limb are told to elevate the limb above the level of the heart so gravity will assist lymph flow back to the blood.

An important reason for returning filtered fluid to the circulation is the recycling of plasma proteins. The body must maintain a low protein concentration in the interstitial fluid because colloid osmotic pressure is the only significant force that opposes capillary hydrostatic pressure. If proteins move from the plasma to the interstitial fluid, the osmotic pressure gradient that opposes filtration decreases. With less opposition to capillary hydrostatic pressure, additional fluid moves into the interstitial space.

Inflammation is an example of a situation in which the balance of colloid osmotic and hydrostatic pressures is disrupted.

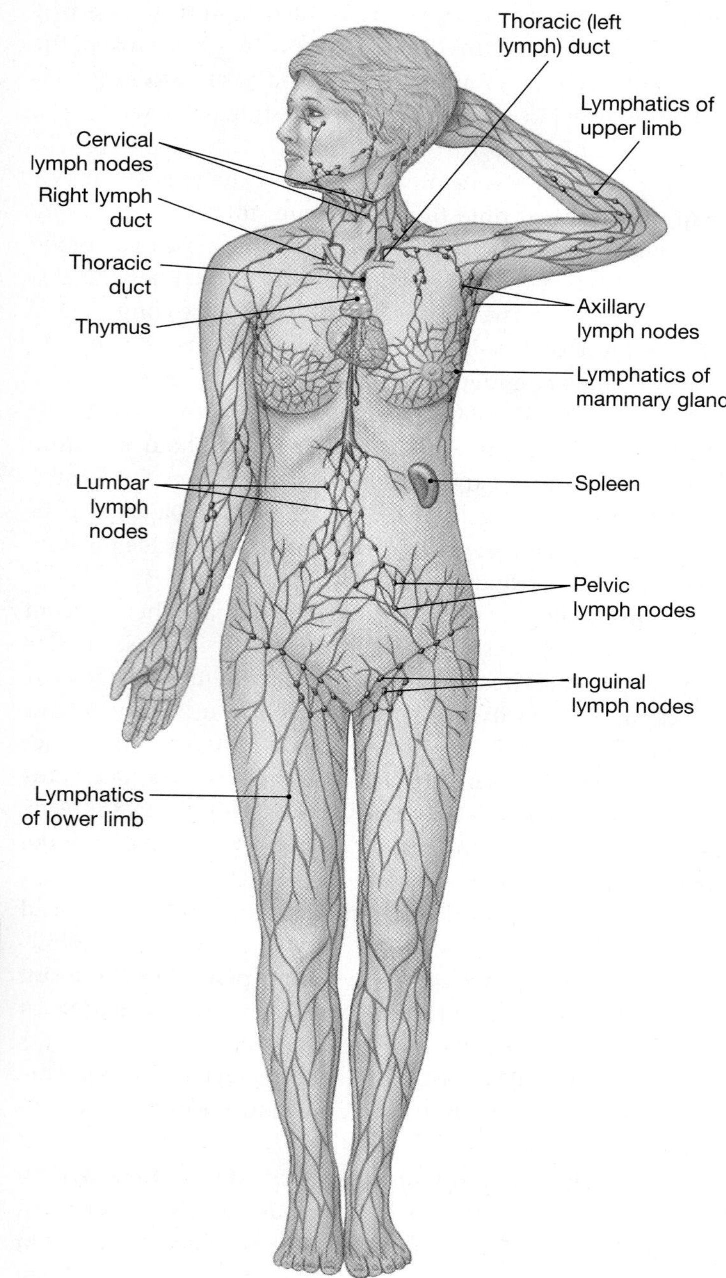

■ **FIGURE 15-19** ***The lymphatic system***

Blind-end lymph vessels in the tissues remove fluid and filtered proteins.

Histamine released in the inflammatory response makes capillary walls leakier and allows proteins to escape from the plasma into the interstitial fluid. Thus, the local swelling that accompanies a region of inflammation is an example of edema caused by redistribution of proteins from the plasma to the interstitial fluid.

Edema Is the Result of Alterations in Capillary Exchange

Edema is a sign that normal exchange between the circulatory system and the lymphatics has been disrupted. Edema usually arises from one of two causes: (1) inadequate drainage of lymph or (2) blood capillary filtration that greatly exceeds capillary absorption.

Inadequate lymph drainage occurs with obstruction of the lymphatic system, particularly at the lymph nodes. Parasites, cancer, or fibrotic tissue growth caused by therapeutic radiation can block the movement of lymph through the system. For example, *elephantiasis* is a chronic condition marked by gross enlargement of the legs and lower appendages when parasites block the lymph vessels. Lymph drainage may also be impaired if lymph nodes are removed during surgery, a common procedure in the diagnosis and treatment of cancer.

Factors that disrupt the normal balance between capillary filtration and absorption include:

1. *An increase in capillary hydrostatic pressure.* Increased hydrostatic pressure is usually indicative of elevated venous pressure. An increase in arterial pressure is generally not noticeable at the capillaries because of autoregulation of pressure in the arterioles.

   One common cause of increased venous pressure is *heart failure,* a condition in which one ventricle loses pumping power and can no longer pump all the blood sent to it by the other ventricle (see Ch. 14 Concept Check #31 on p. 489). For example, if the right ventricle begins to fail but the left ventricle maintains its cardiac output, blood accumulates in the systemic circulation. Blood pressure rises first in the right atrium, then in the veins and capillaries draining into the right side of the heart. When capillary hydrostatic pressure increases, filtration greatly exceeds absorption, leading to edema.
2. *A decrease in plasma protein concentration.* Plasma protein concentrations may decrease as a result of severe malnutrition or liver failure. The liver is the main site for plasma protein synthesis.
3. *An increase in interstitial proteins.* As discussed earlier, excessive leakage of proteins out of the blood will decrease plasma colloid osmotic pressure and will increase net capillary filtration.

On occasion, changes in the balance between filtration and absorption help the body maintain homeostasis. For example, if arterial blood pressure falls, capillary hydrostatic pressure also decreases. This change increases fluid absorption. If blood pressure falls low enough, there will be net absorption in the capillaries rather than net filtration. This passive mechanism helps maintain blood volume in situations in which blood pressure is very low, such as hemorrhage or severe dehydration.

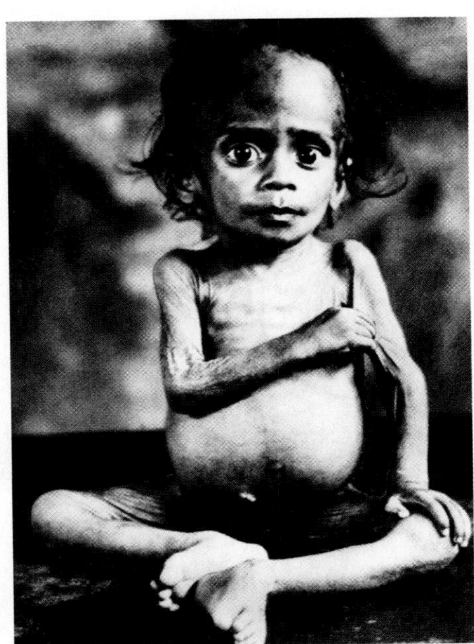

■ **FIGURE 15-20** ***Ascites (abdominal edema) in a child with protein malnutrition***

The African word for protein malnutrition is *kwashiorkor*.

RUNNING PROBLEM

Another few weeks go by, and Kurt again returns to Dr. Cortez for a checkup. Kurt's blood pressure is finally closer to the normal range and has been averaging 135/87. "But, Doc, can you give me something for this dry, hacking cough I've been having? I don't feel bad, but it's driving me nuts." Dr. Cortez explains that a dry cough is an occasional side effect of taking ACE inhibitors. "It is more of a nuisance than anything else, but let's change your medicine. I'd like to try you on a calcium channel blocker this time."

Question 4:

How do calcium channel blockers lower blood pressure?

501 508 510 513 521 529

CONCEPT CHECK

14. If the left ventricle fails to pump normally, blood will back up into what set of blood vessels? Where would you expect edema to occur?
15. Malnourished children who have inadequate protein in their diet often have grotesquely swollen bellies; this condition, which can be described as edema of the abdomen, is called *ascites* (Fig. 15-20 ■). Use the information you have just learned about capillary filtration to explain why malnutrition causes ascites.

Answers: p. 533

REGULATION OF BLOOD PRESSURE

The central nervous system coordinates the reflex control of blood pressure. The main integrating center is in the medulla oblongata. Because of the difficulty of studying neural networks in the brain, however, we still know relatively little about the nuclei, neurotransmitters, and interneurons of the **medullary cardiovascular control centers**.

The Baroreceptor Reflex Is the Primary Homeostatic Control for Blood Pressure

The primary function of the cardiovascular control center is to maintain adequate blood flow to the brain and heart. Sensory input to this integrating center comes from a variety of peripheral sensory receptors. Stretch-sensitive mechanoreceptors known as **baroreceptors** are located in the walls of the carotid arteries and aorta (Fig. 15-21 ■), where they monitor the pressure of blood flowing to the brain (carotid baroreceptors) and to the body (aortic baroreceptors). The carotid and aortic baroreceptors are tonically active stretch receptors that fire action potentials continuously at normal blood pressures.

The primary reflex pathway for homeostatic control of blood pressure is the **baroreceptor reflex**. When increased blood pressure in the arteries stretches the baroreceptor membrane, firing rate of the receptor increases. If blood pressure falls, the firing rate of the receptor decreases.

Action potentials from the baroreceptors travel to the medullary cardiovascular control center via sensory neurons. The cardiovascular control center integrates the sensory input and initiates an appropriate response. The response of the baroreceptor reflex is quite rapid: changes in cardiac output and peripheral resistance occur within two heartbeats of the stimulus.

Efferent output from the cardiovascular control center is carried via both sympathetic and parasympathetic autonomic neurons. Peripheral resistance is under tonic sympathetic control, with increased sympathetic discharge causing vasoconstriction.

Heart function is regulated by antagonistic control. Increased sympathetic activity increases heart rate at the SA node, shortens conduction time through the AV node, and enhances the force of myocardial contraction. Increased parasympathetic activity slows heart rate but has only a small effect on ventricular contraction.

The baroreceptor reflex is summarized in Figure 15-22 ■. Baroreceptors increase their firing rate as blood pressure increases, activating the medullary cardiovascular control center.

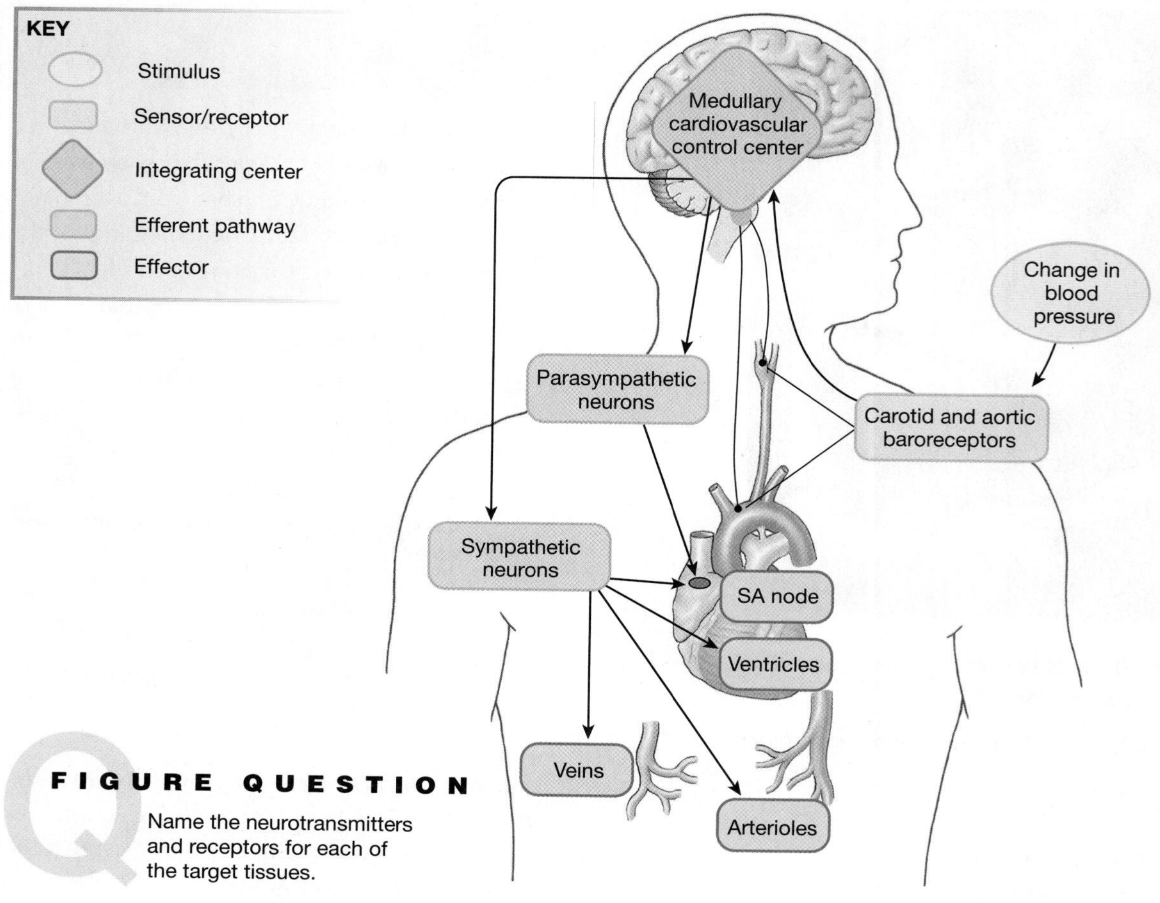

■ **FIGURE 15-21** ***Components of the baroreceptor reflex***

In response, the cardiovascular control center increases parasympathetic activity and decreases sympathetic activity to slow down the heart. When heart rate falls, cardiac output falls. In the circulation, decreased sympathetic activity causes dilation of the arterioles, allowing more blood to flow out of the arteries. The combination of reduced cardiac output and decreased peripheral resistance lowers the mean arterial blood pressure.

Cardiovascular function can be modulated by input from peripheral receptors other than the baroreceptors. For example, arterial chemoreceptors activated by low blood oxygen levels increase cardiac output. The cardiovascular control center also has reciprocal communication with centers in the medulla that control breathing.

The integration of function between the respiratory and circulatory systems is adaptive. If tissues require more oxygen, it is supplied by the cardiovascular system working in tandem with the respiratory system. Consequently, increases in breathing rate are usually accompanied by increases in cardiac output.

Blood pressure is also subject to modulation by higher brain centers, such as the hypothalamus and cerebral cortex. The hypothalamus is responsible for vascular responses involved in body temperature regulation (see Chapter 22) and for the fight-or-flight response. Learned and emotional responses may originate in the cerebral cortex and be expressed by cardiovascular responses such as blushing and fainting.

One such reflex is the *vasovagal response,* which may be triggered in some people by the sight of blood or a hypodermic needle. (Recall Anthony's experience at the beginning of this chapter.) In this pathway, increased parasympathetic activity and decreased sympathetic activity slow heart rate and cause widespread vasodilation. Cardiac output and peripheral resistance both fall, triggering a precipitous fall in blood pressure. With insufficient blood to the brain, the individual faints.

Regulation of blood pressure in the cardiovascular system is closely tied to regulation of body fluid balance by the kidneys. Thus, certain hormones secreted from the heart act on the kidneys, while hormones secreted from the kidneys act on the heart and blood vessels. Together, the heart and kidneys play a major role in maintaining homeostasis of body fluids, the subject of Chapter 20. The overlap of these systems is an excellent example of the integration of organ system function.

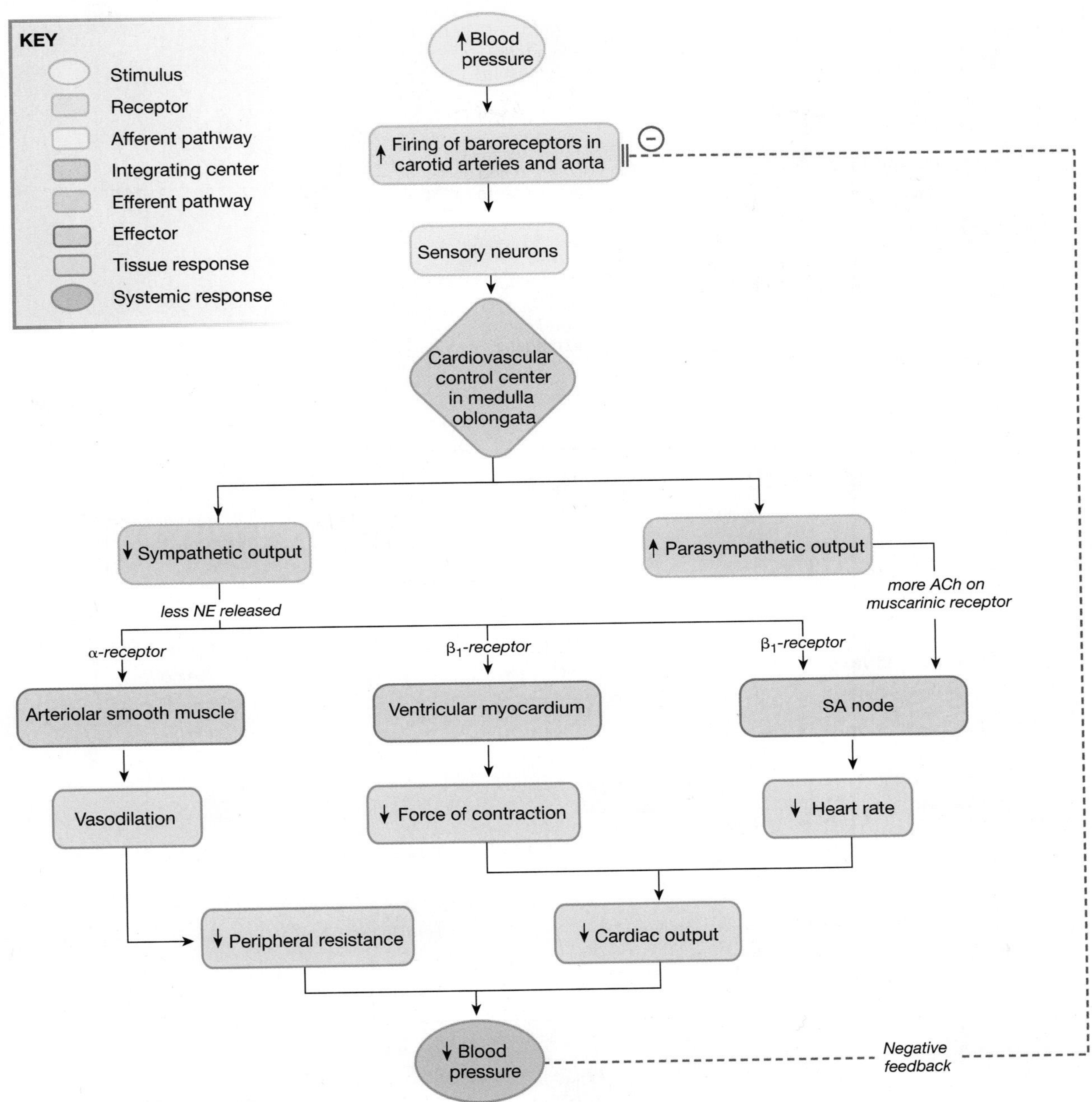

■ **FIGURE 15-22** ***The baroreceptor reflex: the response to increased blood pressure***

CONCEPT CHECK

16. Baroreceptors have stretch-sensitive ion channels in their cell membrane. Increased pressure stretches the receptor cell membrane, opens the channels, and initiates action potentials. What ion probably flows through these channels and in which direction (into or out of the cell)? Answers: p. 533

Orthostatic Hypotension Triggers the Baroreceptor Reflex

The baroreceptor reflex functions every morning when you get out of bed. When you are lying flat, gravitational forces are distributed evenly up and down the length of your body, and blood is distributed evenly throughout the circulation. When you stand up, gravity causes blood to pool in the lower extremities. This pooling creates an instantaneous decrease in venous return. As a result, less blood is in the ventricles at the beginning of the next contraction. Cardiac output falls from 5 L/min to 3 L/min, causing arterial blood pressure to decrease. This decrease in blood pressure upon standing is known as *orthostatic hypotension* [*orthos*, upright + *statikos*, to stand].

Orthostatic hypotension in a normal person triggers the baroreceptor reflex. The carotid and aortic baroreceptors respond to the fall in arterial blood pressure by decreasing their firing rate (Fig. 15-23■). Diminished sensory input into the cardiovascular control center increases sympathetic activity and

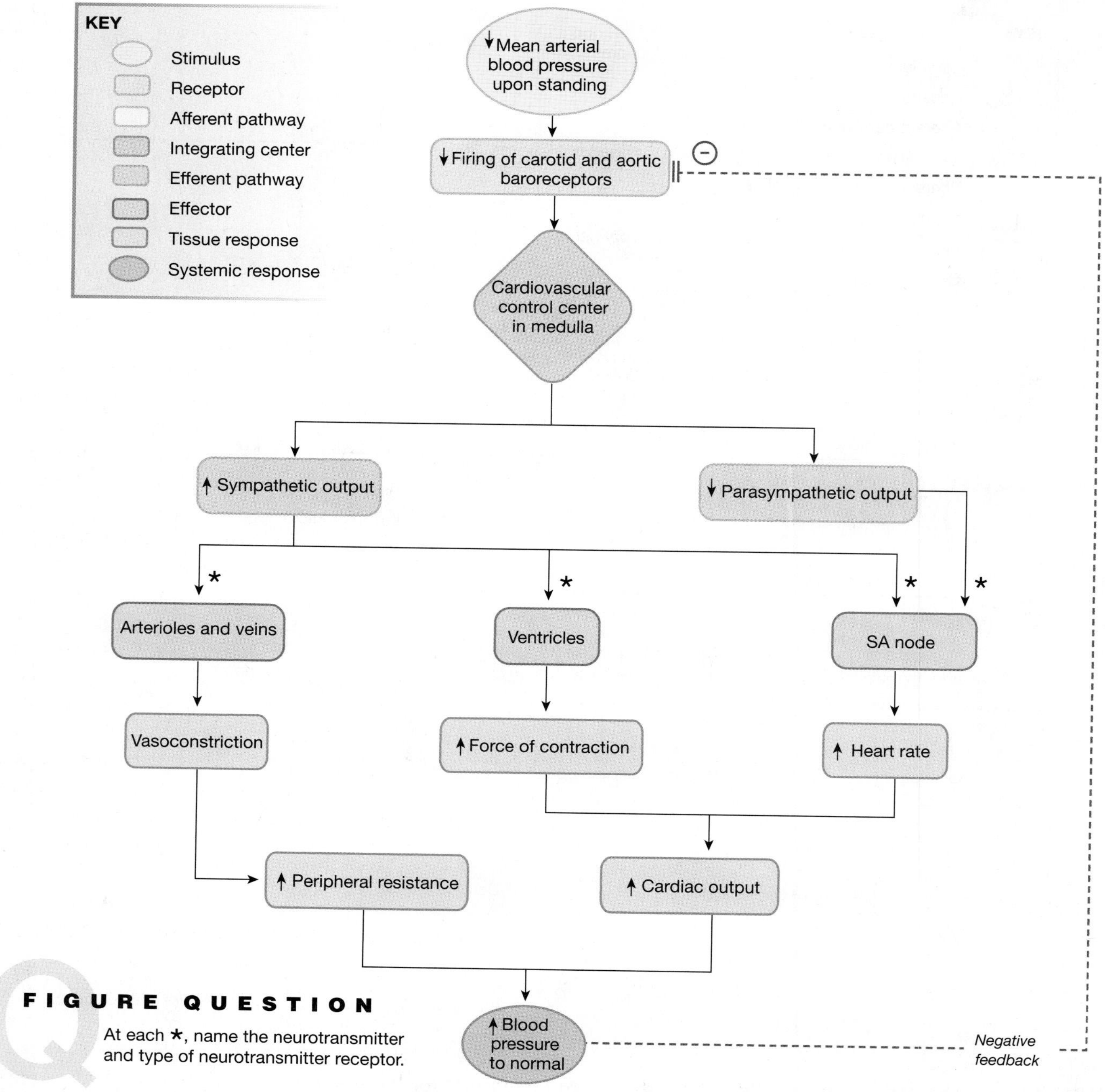

■ **FIGURE 15-23** ***The baroreceptor reflex: the response to orthostatic hypotension***

decreases parasympathetic activity. As a result of autonomic changes, heart rate and force of contraction increase while arterioles and veins constrict. The combination of increased cardiac output and increased peripheral resistance increases mean arterial pressure and restores it to normal within two heartbeats. The skeletal muscle pump also contributes to the recovery by enhancing venous return when abdominal and leg muscles contract to maintain an upright position.

The baroreceptor reflex is not always effective, however. For example, during extended bed rest or in the zero-gravity conditions of space flights, blood from the lower extremities is distributed evenly throughout the body rather than pooling in the lower extremities. This even distribution raises arterial pressure, triggering the kidneys to excrete what is perceived as excess fluid. Over the course of three days, excretion of water leads to a 12% decrease in blood volume. When the person finally gets out of bed or returns to earth, gravity again causes blood to pool in the legs. Orthostatic hypotension occurs, and the baroreceptors attempt to compensate. In this instance, however, the cardiovascular system is unable to restore normal pressure because of the loss of blood volume. As a result, the subject may become dizzy or even faint from reduced delivery of oxygen to the brain.

CONCEPT CHECK

17. In the movie *Jurassic Park,* Dr. Ian Malcolm must flee from the *T. rex*. Draw a reflex map showing the cardiovascular response to his fight-or-flight situation. (*Hints:* what is the stimulus? Fear is integrated in the limbic system.) Answers: p. 533

CARDIOVASCULAR DISEASE

Diseases of the heart and blood vessels, such as heart attacks and strokes, play a role in more than half of all deaths in the United States. According to the American Heart Association, in 2005 cardiovascular diseases will cost people in the United States more than $393 billion in medical expenses and lost wages. The prevalence of cardiovascular disease is reflected in the tremendous amount of research being done worldwide. The scientific investigations range from large-scale clinical studies that track cardiovascular disease in thousands of people, such as the Framingham (Massachusetts) Heart Study, to experiments at the cellular and molecular levels.

Much of the research at the cellular and molecular levels is designed to expand our understanding of both normal and abnormal function in the heart and blood vessels. Scientists are studying a virtual alphabet soup of transporters and regulators. Some of these molecules, such as adenosine, endothelin, vascular endothelial growth factor (VEGF), phospholamban, and nitric oxide, you have studied here and in Chapter 14.

As we increase our knowledge of cardiovascular function, we also begin to understand the actions of drugs that have been used for centuries. A classic example is the cardiac glycoside *digitalis* [p. 492], whose mechanism of action was explained when scientists discovered the role of Na^+-K^+-ATPase. It is a sobering thought to realize that for many therapeutic drugs, we know *what* they do without fully understanding *how* they do it.

Risk Factors for Cardiovascular Disease Include Smoking, Obesity, and Inheritable Factors

As you learned in Chapter 1, conducting and interpreting research on humans is a complicated endeavor in part because of the difficulty of designing well-controlled experiments [p. 10]. The economic and social importance of cardiovascular disease (CVD) make it the focus of many studies each year as researchers try to improve treatments and prediction algorithms. (An *algorithm* is a set of rules or a sequence of steps used to solve a problem.) We can predict the likelihood that a person will develop cardiovascular disease during his or her lifetime by examining the various risk factors that the person possesses. The list of risk factors described here is the result of following the medical histories of thousands of people for many years in studies such as the Framingham Heart Study. As more data become available, additional risk factors may be added.

Risk factors are generally divided into those over which the person has no control and those that can be controlled. Medical intervention is aimed at reducing risk from the controllable factors. The risk factors that cannot be controlled include gender, age, and a family history of early cardiovascular disease. As noted earlier in the chapter, *coronary heart disease* (CHD) is a form of cardiovascular disease in which the coronary arteries become blocked by cholesterol deposits and blood clots. Up until middle age, men have a 3–4 times higher risk of developing CHD than do women. After age 55, when most women have entered menopause, the death rate from CHD equalizes in men and women. In general, the risk of coronary heart disease increases as people age. Heredity also plays an important role. If a person has one or more close relatives with this condition, his or her risk is elevated.

Risk factors that can be controlled include cigarette smoking, obesity, sedentary lifestyle, and untreated hypertension. In the United States, smoking-related illnesses are the primary preventable cause of death, followed by conditions related to overweight and obesity. Physical inactivity and obesity have been steadily increasing in the United States since 1991, and currently 70% of U.S. adults are either overweight or obese.

Two risk factors for cardiovascular disease—blood lipids and diabetes mellitus—have both an uncontrollable genetic component and a modifiable lifestyle component. Diabetes mellitus is a metabolic disorder that puts a person at risk for developing coronary heart disease by contributing to the development of **atherosclerosis** ("hardening of the arteries"), in which fatty deposits form inside arterial blood vessels. Elevated serum cholesterol and triglycerides also lead to atherosclerosis. (Lipid metabolism is discussed in more detail in Chapter 22.)

The increasing prevalence of these risk factors has created an epidemic in the United States, with more than 1.4 million deaths in 2002 attributed to all forms of cardiovascular disease.

Atherosclerosis Is an Inflammatory Process

Coronary heart disease accounts for the majority of cardiovascular disease deaths and is the single largest killer of Americans. Let's look at the underlying cause of this disease: atherosclerosis.

The role of elevated blood cholesterol in the development of atherosclerosis is well established. Cholesterol, like other lipids, is not very soluble in aqueous solutions, such as the plasma. Therefore, when cholesterol in the diet is absorbed from the digestive tract, it combines with lipoproteins to make it more soluble. (The details of cholesterol digestion, absorption, and metabolism are discussed in Chapters 21 and 22.) Multiple lipoproteins associate with cholesterol, but clinicians generally are concerned with two: those found in **high-density lipoprotein-cholesterol (HDL-C)** complexes and those found in **low-density lipoprotein-cholesterol (LDL-C)** complexes. HDL-C is the more desirable form of blood cholesterol because high levels of HDL are associated with lower risk of heart attacks. (Memory aid: let the "H" in HDL stand for "healthy.")

LDL-C is sometimes called "bad" cholesterol because elevated plasma LDL-C levels are associated with coronary heart

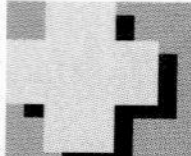

CLINICAL FOCUS

DIABETES AND CARDIOVASCULAR DISEASE

Having diabetes is one of the major risk factors for developing cardiovascular disease, and almost two-thirds of people with diabetes will die from cardiovascular problems. In diabetes, cells that cannot use glucose turn to fats and proteins for their energy. The body breaks down fat into fatty acids [p. 112] and dumps them into the blood. Plasma cholesterol levels are also elevated. When LDL-C remains in the blood, the excess is ingested by macrophages, starting a series of events that lead to atherosclerosis. Because of the pivotal role that LDL-C plays in atherosclerosis, many forms of therapy, ranging from dietary modification and exercise to drugs, are aimed at lowering LDL-C levels. Left untreated, blockage of small and medium-sized blood vessels in the lower extremities can lead to loss of sensation and *gangrene* (tissue death) in the feet. Atherosclerosis in larger vessels causes heart attacks and strokes. To learn more about diabetes and the increased risk of cardiovascular disease, visit the websites of the American Diabetes Association (*www.diabetes.org)* and the American Heart Association (*www.americanheart.org*).

disease. (Remember this by associating "L" with "lethal.") Normal levels of LDL-C are not bad, however, because LDL is necessary for cholesterol transport into cells. LDL-C's binding site—a protein called **apoB**—combines with an LDL receptor found in clathrin-coated pits on the cell membrane, and the receptor-LDL-C complex is brought into the cell by endocytosis [Fig. 5-24, p. 149]. The LDL receptor recycles to the cell membrane, and the endosome fuses with a lysosome. LDL-C's proteins are digested to amino acids, and the freed cholesterol is used to make cell membranes or steroid hormones.

Although LDL is needed for cellular uptake of cholesterol, excess levels of plasma LDL-C lead to atherosclerosis. Endothelial cells lining the arteries transport LDL-C into the extracellular space so that it accumulates just under the intima. There, macrophages ingest cholesterol and other lipids to become lipid-filled *foam cells* (Fig. 15-24b ■). Cytokines released by the macrophages promote smooth muscle cell division. This early-stage *lesion* [*laesio*, injury] is called a *fatty streak*. As the condition progresses, the lipid core grows, and smooth muscle cells reproduce, forming bulging *plaques* that protrude into the lumen of the artery. In the advanced stages of atherosclerosis, the plaques develop hard, calcified regions and fibrous collagen caps (Fig. 15-24c). The mechanism by which calcium carbonate is deposited is still being investigated.

We once believed that the occlusion (blockage) of coronary blood vessels by large plaques was the primary cause of heart attacks, but that model has been revised. The new model indicates that blood clot formation on plaques is more dependent on the structure of a plaque than on its size. *Vulnerable plaques* have thin fibrous caps that are more likely to rupture, exposing collagen and activating platelets that initiate blood clots (*thrombi*) (Fig. 15-24d). *Stable plaques* have thick fibrous caps that separate the lipid core from the blood and do not activate platelets. Atherosclerosis is now considered to be an inflammatory process in which macrophages release enzymes that convert stable plaques to vulnerable plaques.

EMERGING CONCEPTS

INFLAMMATORY MARKERS FOR CARDIOVASCULAR DISEASE

In clinical studies, it is sometimes difficult to determine whether a factor that has a positive correlation with a disease functions in a cause-effect relationship or represents a simple association. For example, two factors associated with higher incidence of heart disease are C-reactive protein and homocysteine. *C-reactive protein* (CRP) is a molecule involved in the body's response to inflammation, and in one study, women who had elevated blood CRP levels were more than twice as likely to have a serious cardiovascular problem as women with low CRP. Does that mean that CRP is causing cardiovascular disease? Or could it simply be a marker that can be used clinically to predict who is more likely to develop cardiovascular complications, such as a heart attack or stroke?

Similarly, elevated homocysteine levels are associated with an increased incidence of CVD. (*Homocysteine* is an amino acid that takes part in a complicated metabolic pathway that also requires folate and vitamin B_{12} as cofactors.) Should physicians routinely measure homocysteine along with cholesterol? Currently there is little clinical evidence to show that reducing either CRP or homocysteine decreases a person's risk of developing CVD. If these two markers are not indicators for *modifiable* risk factors, should a patient's insurance be asked to pay for the tests used to detect them?

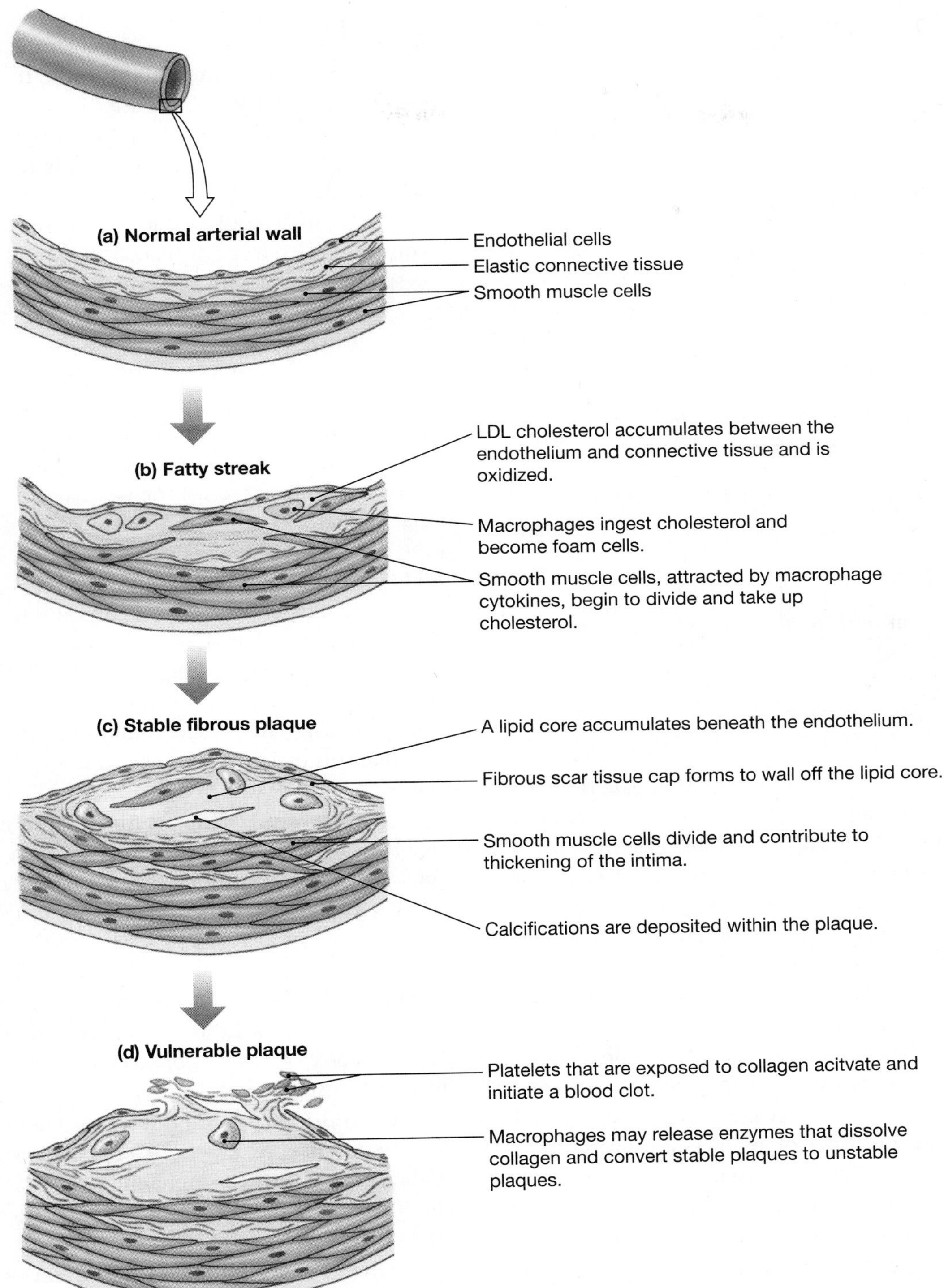

(a) Normal arterial wall
Endothelial cells
Elastic connective tissue
Smooth muscle cells
(b) Fatty streak
LDL cholesterol accumulates between the endothelium and connective tissue and is oxidized.
Macrophages ingest cholesterol and become foam cells.
Smooth muscle cells, attracted by macrophage cytokines, begin to divide and take up cholesterol.
(c) Stable fibrous plaque
A lipid core accumulates beneath the endothelium.
Fibrous scar tissue cap forms to wall off the lipid core.
Smooth muscle cells divide and contribute to thickening of the intima.
Calcifications are deposited within the plaque.
(d) Vulnerable plaque
Platelets that are exposed to collagen acitvate and initiate a blood clot.
Macrophages may release enzymes that dissolve collagen and convert stable plaques to unstable plaques.

FIGURE 15-24 ***The development of atherosclerotic plaques***

If a clot blocks blood flow to the heart muscle, a heart attack (*myocardial infarction*) results. Blocked blood flow in a coronary artery cuts off the oxygen supply to myocardial cells supplied by that artery. The oxygen-starved cells must then rely on anaerobic metabolism [p. 106], which produces lactic acid (H^+). As ATP production declines, the contractile cells are unable to pump Ca^{2+} out of the cell. The combination of unusually high Ca^{2+} and H^+ concentrations in the cytosol closes gap junctions in the damaged cells. Closure electrically isolates the damaged cells so that they no longer contract, and it forces action potentials to find an alternate route from cell to cell. If the damaged area of myocardium is large, the disruption can lead

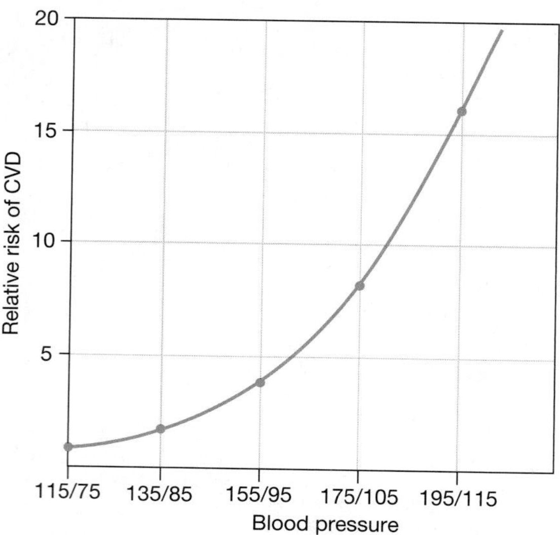

FIGURE 15-25 ***The relationship between increasing blood pressure and the risk of developing cardiovascular disease***

to an irregular heartbeat (*arrhythmia*) and potentially result in cardiac arrest and/or death.

Hypertension Represents a Failure of Homeostasis

One controllable risk factor for cardiovascular disease is hypertension—chronically elevated blood pressure, with systolic pressures greater than 140 mm Hg or diastolic pressures greater than 90 mm Hg. Hypertension is a common disease in the United States and is one of the most common reasons for visits to physicians and for the use of prescription drugs. High blood pressure is associated with increasing risk of CVD: the risk doubles for each 20/10 mm Hg increase in blood pressure over a baseline value of 115/75 (Fig. 15-25 ■).

More than 90% of all patients with hypertension are considered to have *essential* (or *primary*) *hypertension,* with no clear-cut cause other than heredity. Cardiac output is usually normal in these people, and their elevated blood pressure appears to be associated with increased peripheral resistance. Some investigators have speculated that the increased resistance may be due to a lack of nitric oxide, the locally produced vasodilator formed by endothelial cells in the arterioles. In the remaining 5–10% of hypertensive cases, the cause is known, and the hypertension is considered to be secondary to an underlying pathology. For instance, the cause might be an endocrine disorder that causes fluid retention.

A key feature of hypertension from all causes is adaptation of the carotid and aortic baroreceptors to higher pressure, with subsequent down-regulation of their activity. Without input from the baroreceptors, the cardiovascular control center interprets the high blood pressure as "normal," and no reflex reduction of pressure occurs.

Hypertension is a risk factor for atherosclerosis because high pressure in the arteries damages the endothelial lining of the vessels and promotes the formation of atherosclerotic plaques. In addition, high arterial blood pressure puts additional strain on the heart by increasing afterload [p. 493]. When resistance in the arterioles is high, the myocardium must work harder to push the blood into the arteries.

Amazingly, stroke volume in hypertensive patients remains constant up to a mean blood pressure of about 200 mm Hg, despite the increasing amount of work that the ventricle must perform as blood pressure increases. The cardiac muscle of the left ventricle responds to chronic high systemic resistance in the same way that skeletal muscle responds to a weight-lifting routine. The heart muscle *hypertrophies,* increasing the size and strength of the muscle fibers.

However, if resistance remains high over time, the heart muscle is unable to meet the work load and begins to fail: cardiac output by the left ventricle decreases. If cardiac output of the right heart remains normal while the output from the left side decreases, fluid collects in the lungs, creating *pulmonary edema.* At this point, a detrimental positive feedback loop begins. Oxygen exchange in the lungs diminishes because of the pulmonary edema, leading to less oxygen in the blood. Lack of oxygen for aerobic metabolism further weakens the heart, and its pumping effectiveness diminishes even more. Unless treated, this condition, known as *congestive heart failure,* eventually leads to death.

Many of the treatments for hypertension have their basis in the cardiovascular physiology you have learned. For example, calcium entry into vascular smooth muscle and cardiac muscle can be decreased by a class of drugs known as *calcium channel blockers.* These drugs bind to Ca^{2+} channel proteins, making it less likely that the channels will open in response to depolarization. With less Ca^{2+} entry, vascular smooth muscle dilates, while in the heart the depolarization rate of the SA node and the force of contraction decrease. Vascular smooth muscle is more sensitive than cardiac muscle to certain classes of calcium channel blockers, and it is possible to get vasodilation at drug doses that are low enough to have no effect on heart rate. Other tissues with Ca^{2+} channels, such as neurons, are only minimally affected by calcium channel blockers because their Ca^{2+} channels are of a different subtype.

Other drugs used to treat hypertension include diuretics, which decrease blood volume, and beta-blocking drugs that target β_1-receptors and decrease catecholamine stimulation of cardiac output. Two other groups of antihypertensive drugs, the ACE inhibitors and the angiotensin receptor blockers, act by decreasing the activity of angiotensin, a powerful vasoconstrictor substance. You will learn more about angiotensin later in the book, when you study the integrated control of blood pressure by the cardiovascular and renal systems. In the future, we may be seeing new treatments for hypertension that are based on the molecular physiology of the heart and blood vessels.

RUNNING PROBLEM CONCLUSION

ESSENTIAL HYPERTENSION

Kurt remained on the calcium channel blocker, and after several months his blood pressure stabilized at 130/85—a significant improvement. Kurt's new diet also brought his total blood cholesterol down below 200 mg/dL plasma. By improving two of his controllable risk factors, Kurt decreased his chances of having a heart attack. To learn more about hypertension and some of the therapies currently used to treat it, visit the website of the American Heart Association (*www.americanheart.org*).

Check your understanding of this running problem by comparing your answers with the information in the summary table.

	QUESTION	FACTS	INTEGRATION AND ANALYSIS
1	Why are people with high blood pressure at greater risk for having a hemorrhagic (or bleeding) stroke?	High blood pressure exerts force on the walls of the blood vessels.	If an area of blood vessel wall is weakened or damaged, high blood pressure may cause that area to rupture, allowing blood to leak out of the vessel into the surrounding tissues.
2	What is the rationale for reducing salt intake to control hypertension?	Salt causes water retention.	Blood pressure will increase if the circulating blood volume increases. By restricting salt in the diet, a person can decrease retention of fluid in the extracellular compartment, which includes the plasma.
3	Why would blocking the action of a vasoconstrictor lower blood pressure?	Peripheral blood pressure is determined by cardiac output and peripheral resistance.	Resistance is inversely proportional to the radius of the blood vessels. Therefore, if blood vessels dilate as a result of blocking a vasoconstrictor, resistance and blood pressure will decrease.
4	How do calcium channel blockers lower blood pressure?	Calcium entry from the extracellular fluid plays an important role in both smooth muscle and cardiac muscle contraction.	Blocking Ca^{2+} entry through Ca^{2+} channels will decrease the force of cardiac contraction and decrease the contractility of vascular smooth muscle. Both of these effects will lower blood pressure.

501 508 510 513 521 529

CHAPTER SUMMARY

Blood flow through the cardiovascular system is an excellent example of *mass flow* in the body. Cardiac contraction creates high pressure in the ventricles, and this pressure drives blood through the vessels of the systemic and pulmonary circuits, speeding up cell-to-cell *communication*. Resistance to flow is regulated by *local and reflex control mechanisms* that act on arteriolar smooth muscle and help match tissue perfusion to tissue needs. The *homeostatic* baroreceptor reflex monitors arterial pressure to ensure adequate perfusion of the brain and heart. Capillary *exchange of material* between the plasma and interstitial fluid *compartments* uses several transport mechanisms, including diffusion, transcytosis, and bulk flow.

1. Homeostatic regulation of the cardiovascular system is aimed at maintaining adequate blood flow to the brain and heart. (p. 501)
2. Total blood flow at any level of the circulation is equal to the cardiac output. (p. 502)

The Blood Vessels

IP Cardiovascular—Anatomy Review: Blood Vessel Structure & Function

3. Blood vessels are composed of layers of smooth muscle, elastic and fibrous connective tissue, and **endothelium**. (p. 502; Fig. 15-2)

4. **Vascular smooth muscle** maintains a state of muscle tone. (p. 502)
5. The walls of the aorta and major arteries are both stiff and springy. This property allows them to absorb energy and release it through elastic recoil. (p. 502)
6. **Metarterioles** regulate blood flow through capillaries and allow white blood cells to go directly from arterioles to the venous circulation. (p. 503; Fig. 15-3)
7. Capillaries and postcapillary **venules** are the site of exchange between blood and interstitial fluid. (p. 503)
8. Veins hold more than half of the blood in the circulatory system. Veins have thinner walls with less elastic tissue than arteries, so veins expand easily when they fill with blood. (p. 503)
9. **Angiogenesis** is the process by which new blood vessels grow and develop, especially after birth. (p. 503)

Blood Pressure

IP Cardiovascular—Measuring Blood Pressure

10. The ventricles create high pressure that is the driving force for blood flow. The aorta and arteries act as a pressure reservoir during ventricular relaxation. (p. 504; Fig. 15-4)
11. Blood pressure is highest in the arteries and decreases as blood flows through the circulatory system. At rest, average **systolic pressure** is 120 mm Hg, and average **diastolic pressure** is 80 mm Hg. (p. 505; Fig. 15-5)
12. Pressure created by the ventricles can be felt as a **pulse** in the arteries. **Pulse pressure** equals systolic pressure minus diastolic pressure. (p. 505)
13. Blood flow against gravity in the veins is assisted by one-way valves and by the respiratory and skeletal muscle pumps. (p. 505; Fig. 15-6)
14. Arterial blood pressure is indicative of the driving pressure for blood flow. **Mean arterial pressure** (MAP) is defined as diastolic pressure + 1/3 (systolic pressure−diastolic pressure). (p. 506)
15. Arterial blood pressure is usually measured with a sphygmomanometer. Blood squeezing through a compressed brachial artery makes **Korotkoff sounds**. (p. 507; Fig. 15-7)
16. Arterial pressure is a balance between cardiac output and the resistance to blood flow offered by the arterioles (**peripheral resistance**). (p. 507; Fig. 15-8)
17. If blood volume increases, blood pressure increases. If blood volume decreases, blood pressure decreases. (p. 508; Fig. 15-9)
18. Venous blood volume can be shifted to the arteries if arterial blood pressure falls. (p. 509; Fig. 15-10)

Resistance in the Arterioles

IP Cardiovascular—Factors that Affect Blood Pressure

19. The arterioles are the main site of variable resistance in the systemic circulation. A small change in the radius of an arteriole creates a large change in resistance: $R \propto 1/r^4$. (p. 509)
20. Arterioles regulate their own blood flow through **myogenic autoregulation**. Vasoconstriction increases the resistance offered by an arteriole and decreases the blood flow through the arteriole. (p. 510)
21. Arteriolar resistance is influenced by local control mechanisms that match tissue blood flow to the metabolic needs of the tissue. Vasodilator paracrines include nitric oxide, H^+, K^+, CO_2, prostaglandins, adenosine, and histamine. Low O_2 causes vasodilation. Endothelins are powerful vasoconstrictors. (p. 511; Tbl. 15-2)
22. **Active hyperemia** is a process in which increased blood flow accompanies increased metabolic activity. **Reactive hyperemia** is an increase in tissue blood flow following a period of low perfusion. (p. 511; Fig. 15-11)
23. Most systemic arterioles are under tonic sympathetic control. Norepinephrine causes vasoconstriction. Decreased sympathetic stimulation causes vasodilation. (p. 512)
24. Epinephrine binds to arteriolar α-receptors and causes vasoconstriction. Epinephrine on β_2-receptors, found in the arterioles of the heart, liver, and skeletal muscle, causes vasodilation. (p. 513)

Distribution of Blood to the Tissues

25. Changing the resistance of the arterioles affects mean arterial pressure and alters blood flow through the arteriole. (p. 514; Fig. 15-14)
26. The flow through individual arterioles depends on their resistance. The higher the resistance in an arteriole, the lower the blood flow in that arteriole: $Flow_{arteriole} \propto 1/R_{arteriole.}$ (p. 514)
27. Blood flow into individual capillaries can be regulated by **precapillary sphincters**. (p. 514; Fig. 15-15)

Exchange at the Capillaries

IP Cardiovascular—Autoregulation and Capillary Dynamics

28. Exchange of materials between the blood and the interstitial fluid occurs primarily by diffusion. (p. 514)
29. **Continuous capillaries** have leaky junctions between cells but also transport material using transcytosis. Continuous capillaries with tight junctions form the blood-brain barrier. (p. 515; Fig. 15-16)
30. **Fenestrated capillaries** have pores that allow large volumes of fluid to pass rapidly. (p. 515; Fig. 15-17)
31. The velocity of blood flow through the capillaries is slow, allowing diffusion to go to equilibrium. (p. 516; Fig. 15-17)
32. **Bulk flow** refers to the mass movement of fluid between the blood and the interstitial fluid. Fluid movement is called **filtration** if the direction of flow is out of the capillary, and **absorption** if the flow is directed into the capillary. (p. 517; Fig. 15-18)
33. The osmotic pressure difference between plasma and interstitial fluid due to the presence of plasma proteins is the **colloid osmotic pressure**. (p. 517)

The Lymphatic System

IP Fluids & Electrolytes—Electrolyte Homeostasis, Edema

34. About 3 liters of fluid filter out of the capillaries each day. The lymphatic system returns this fluid to the circulatory system. (p. 519; Fig. 15-19)
35. Lymph capillaries accumulate fluid, interstitial proteins, and particulate matter by bulk flow. Lymph flow depends on smooth muscle in vessel walls, one-way valves, and the skeletal muscle pump. (p. 519)
36. The condition in which excess fluid accumulates in the interstitial space is called **edema**. Factors that disrupt the normal balance between capillary filtration and absorption cause edema. (p. 519; Fig. 15-20)

Regulation of Blood Pressure

IP Cardiovascular—Blood Pressure Regulation

37. The reflex control of blood pressure resides in the medulla oblongata. **Baroreceptors** in the carotid artery and the aorta monitor

arterial blood pressure and trigger the **baroreceptor reflex.** (p. 521; Figs. 15-21, 15-22)

38. Efferent output from the medullary **cardiovascular control center** goes to the heart and arterioles. Increased sympathetic activity increases heart rate and force of contraction. Increased parasympathetic activity slows heart rate. Increased sympathetic discharge at the arterioles causes vasoconstriction. There is no significant parasympathetic control of arterioles. (p. 522)
39. Cardiovascular function can be modulated by input from higher brain centers and from the respiratory control center of the medulla. (p. 522)
40. The baroreceptor reflex functions each time a person stands up. The decrease in blood pressure upon standing is known as orthostatic hypotension. (p. 523; Fig. 15-23)

Cardiovascular Disease

41. **Cardiovascular disease** is the leading cause of death in the United States. Risk factors predict the likelihood that a person will develop cardiovascular disease during her or his lifetime. (p. 525)
42. **Atherosclerosis** is a condition in which fatty deposits called plaques develop in arteries. If plaques are unstable, they may block the arteries by triggering blood clots. (p. 525; Fig. 15-24)
44. Hypertension is a significant risk factor for the development of cardiovascular disease. (p. 528; Fig. 15-25)

QUESTIONS

(Answers to the Review Questions begin on page A1.)

THE PHYSIOLOGY PLACE

Access more review material online at **The Physiology Place** website. There you'll find review questions, problem-solving activities, case studies, flashcards, and direct links to both *InterActive Physiology®* and PhysioEx™ To access the site, go to *www.physiologyplace.com* and select Human Physiology, Fourth Edition.

LEVEL ONE REVIEWING FACTS AND TERMS

1. The first priority of blood pressure homeostasis is to maintain adequate perfusion to which two organs?
2. Match the types of blood vessels with the terms that describe them. Each vessel type may have more than one match, and matching items may be used more than once.

(a) arterioles	1. store pressure generated by the heart
(b) arteries	2. have walls that are both stiff and elastic
(c) capillaries	3. carry low-oxygen blood
(d) veins	4. have thin walls of exchange epithelium
(e) venules	5. act as a volume reservoir
	6. their diameter can be altered by neural input
	7. blood flow slowest through these vessels
	8. have lowest blood pressure
	9. are the main site of variable resistance

3. List the four tissue components of blood vessel walls, in order from inner lining to outer covering. Briefly describe the importance of each tissue.
4. Blood flow to individual tissues is regulated by selective vasoconstriction and vasodilation of which vessels?
5. Aortic pressure reaches a typical high value of __________ (give both numeric value and units) during __________, or contraction of the heart. As the heart relaxes during the event called __________, aortic pressure declines to a typical low value of __________. This blood pressure reading would be written as __________/__________.
6. The rapid pressure increase that occurs when the left ventricle pushes blood into the aorta can be felt as a pressure wave, or __________. What is the equation used to calculate the strength of this pressure wave?
7. List the factors that aid venous return to the heart.
8. What is hypertension, and why is it a threat to a person's health?
9. When measuring a person's blood pressure, at what point in the procedure are you likely to hear Korotkoff sounds?
10. List three paracrines that cause vasodilation. What is the source of each one? In addition to paracrines, list two other ways to control smooth muscle contraction in arterioles.
11. What is hyperemia? How does active hyperemia differ from reactive hyperemia?
12. Most systemic arterioles are innervated by the __________ branch of the nervous system. Increased sympathetic input will have what effect on arteriole diameter?
13. Match each event in the left column with all appropriate neurotransmitter(s) *and* receptor(s) from the list on the right.

(a) vasoconstriction of intestinal arterioles	1. norepinephrine
	2. epinephrine
(b) vasodilation of coronary arterioles	3. acetylcholine
	4. β_1-receptor
(c) increased heart rate	5. α-receptor
(d) decreased heart rate	6. β_2-receptor
(e) vasoconstriction of coronary arterioles	7. nicotinic receptor
	8. muscarinic receptor

14. Which organs receive more than two-thirds of the cardiac output at rest? Which organs have the highest flow of blood on a per unit weight basis?
15. By looking at the density of capillaries in a tissue, you can make assumptions about what property of the tissue? Which tissue has the lowest capillary density? Which tissue has the highest?
16. What type of transport is used to move each of the following substances across the capillary endothelium?
    (a) oxygen (c) glucose
    (b) proteins (d) water
17. With which three physiological systems do the vessels of the lymphatic system interact?
18. Define edema. List some ways in which it can arise.
19. Define the following terms and explain their significance to cardiovascular physiology.
    (a) perfusion (d) angiogenesis
    (b) colloid osmotic pressure (e) metarterioles
    (c) vasoconstriction (f) pericytes
20. The two major lipoprotein carriers of cholesterol are __________ and __________. Which type is bad when present in the body in elevated amounts?

LEVEL TWO REVIEWING CONCEPTS

21. **Concept map:** Map all the following factors that influence mean arterial pressure. You may add additional terms.

aorta	parasympathetic neuron
arteriole	peripheral resistance
baroreceptor	SA node
blood volume	sensory neuron
cardiac output	stroke volume
carotid artery	sympathetic neuron
contractility	vein
heart rate	venous return
medulla oblongata	ventricle

22. Compare and contrast the following sets of terms:
    (a) lymphatic capillaries and systemic capillaries
    (b) roles of the sympathetic and parasympathetic branches in blood pressure control
    (c) lymph and blood
    (d) continuous capillaries and fenestrated capillaries
    (e) hydrostatic pressure and colloid osmotic pressure in systemic capillaries
23. Calcium channel blockers prevent Ca^{2+} movement through Ca^{2+} channels. Explain two ways this action lowers blood pressure. Why are neurons and other cells unaffected by these drugs?
24. Define myogenic autoregulation. What mechanisms have been proposed to explain it?
25. Left ventricular failure may be accompanied by edema, shortness of breath, and increased venous pressure. Explain how these signs and symptoms develop.

LEVEL THREE PROBLEM SOLVING

26. Draw a reflex map that explains Anthony's vasovagal syncope at the sight of blood. Include all the steps of the reflex, and explain whether pathways are being stimulated or inhibited.
27. A physiologist placed a section of excised arteriole in a perfusion chamber containing saline. When the oxygen content of the saline perfusing (flowing through) the arteriole was reduced, the arteriole dilated. In a follow-up experiment, she used an isolated piece of arteriolar smooth muscle that had been stripped away from the other layers of the arteriole wall. When the oxygen content of the saline was reduced as in the first experiment, the isolated muscle showed no response. What do these two experiments suggest about how low oxygen exerts local control over arterioles?
28. Robert is a 52-year-old nonsmoker. He weighs 180 lbs and stands 5′9″ tall, and his blood pressure averaged 145/95 on three successive visits to his doctor's office. His father, grandfather, and uncle all had heart attacks in their early 50s, and his mother died of a stroke at the age of 71.
    (a) Identify Robert's risk factors for coronary heart disease.
    (b) Does Robert have hypertension? Explain.
    (c) Robert's doctor prescribes a drug called a beta blocker. Explain the mechanism by which a beta-receptor-blocking drug may help lower blood pressure.
29. The following figure is a schematic representation of the systemic circulation. Use it to help answer the following questions. (CO = cardiac output, MAP = mean arterial pressure.)
    (a) If resistance in vessels 1 and 2 increases because of the presence of local paracrines but cardiac output is unchanged, what happens to MAP? What happens to flow through vessels 1 and 2? Through vessels 3 and 4?
    (b) Homeostatic compensation occurs within seconds. Draw a reflex map to explain the compensation (stimulus, receptor, and so on).
    (c) When vessel 1 constricts, what happens to the filtration pressure in the capillaries downstream from that arteriole?

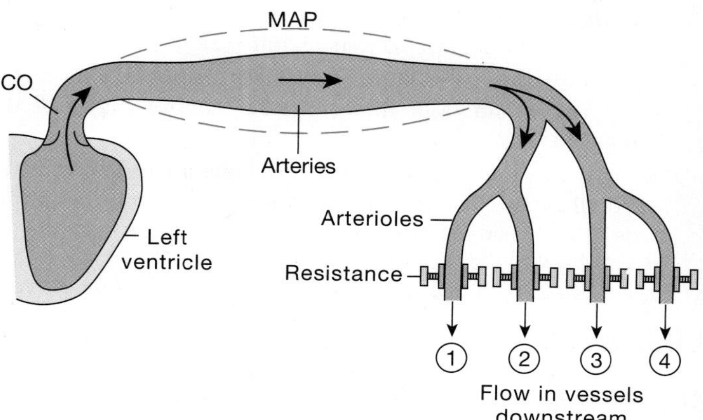

30. The following graphs are recordings of contractions in an isolated frog heart. The intact frog heart is innervated by sympathetic neurons that increase heart rate, and by parasympathetic neurons that decrease heart rate. Based on these four graphs, what conclusion can you draw about the mechanism of action of atropine? (Atropine does not cross the cell membrane.)

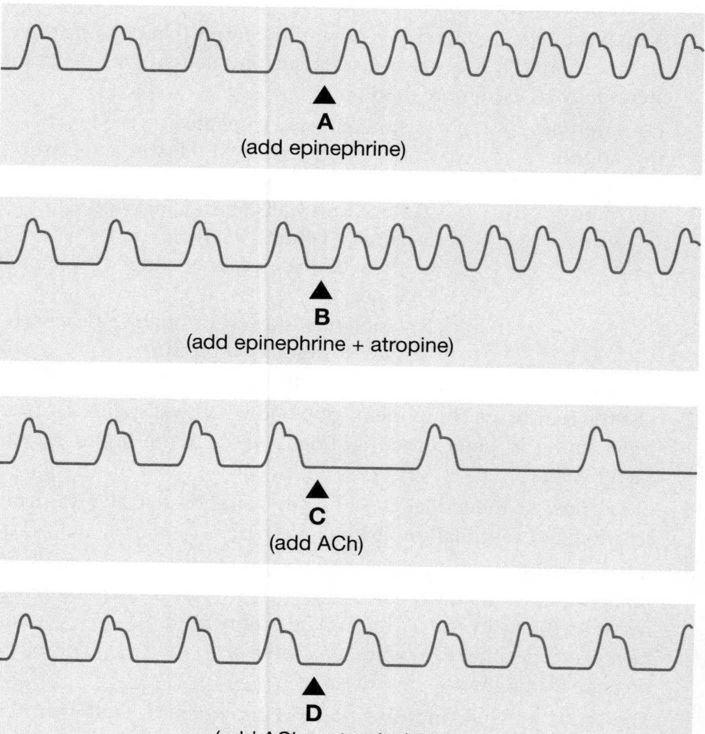

31. In advanced atherosclerosis, calcified plaques cause the normally elastic aorta and arteries to become stiff and noncompliant. (a) What effect does this change in the aorta have on afterload? (b) If cardiac output remains unchanged, what happens to peripheral resistance and mean arterial pressure?
32. During fetal development, most blood in the pulmonary artery bypasses the lungs and goes into the aorta by way of a channel called the *ductus arteriosus*. Normally this fetal bypass channel closes during the first day after birth, but each year about 4000 babies in the United States maintain a *patent* (open) ductus arteriosus and require surgery to close the channel.
    (a) Use this information to draw an anatomical diagram showing blood flow in an infant with a patent ductus arteriosus.
    (b) In the fetus, why does most blood bypass the lungs?
    (c) If the systemic side of the circulatory system is longer than the pulmonary side, which circuit has the greater resistance?
    (d) If flow is equal in the pulmonary and systemic circulations, which side of the heart must generate more pressure to overcome resistance?
    (e) Use your answer to (d) to figure out which way blood will flow through a patent ductus arteriosus.

LEVEL FOUR QUANTITATIVE PROBLEMS

33. Using the appropriate equation, mathematically explain what happens to blood flow if the *diameter* of a blood vessel increases from 2 mm to 4 mm.
34. Duplicate the calculations that led William Harvey to believe that blood circulated in a closed loop:
    (a) Take your resting pulse.
    (b) Assume that your heart at rest pumps 70 mL/beat, and that 1 mL of blood weighs one gram. Calculate how long it would take your heart to pump your weight in blood. (2.2 pounds = 1 kilogram)
35. Calculate the mean arterial pressure (MAP) and pulse pressure for a person with a blood pressure of 115/73.
36. According to the Fick principle, the oxygen consumption rate of an organ is equal to the blood flow through that organ times the amount of oxygen extracted from the blood as it flows through the organ:

$$\text{oxygen consumption rate} = \text{blood flow} \times (\text{arterial oxygen content} - \text{venous oxygen content})$$

$$\text{mL } O_2 \text{ consumed/min} = \text{mL blood/min} \times \text{mL } O_2\text{/mL blood}$$

A person has a total body oxygen consumption rate of 250 mL/min. The oxygen content of blood in his aorta is 200 mL O_2/L blood, the oxygen content of his pulmonary artery blood is 160 mL O_2/L blood. What is his cardiac output?

ANSWERS

Answers to Concept Check Questions

Page 506

1. Veins from the brain do not require valves because blood flow is aided by gravity.
2. The carotid wave would arrive slightly ahead of the wrist wave because the distance from heart to carotid artery is shorter.
3. Pressure of 130/95 has the higher pulse pressure (35 mm Hg).

Page 506

4. If heart rate increases, the relative time spent in diastole decreases. In that case, the contribution of systolic pressure to mean arterial pressure increases, and MAP increases.
5. Pulse pressure is 112 − 68 = 44 mm Hg. MAP is 68 + 1/3(44) = 82.7 mm Hg.

Page 512

6. (d)
7. Extracellular K^+ dilates arterioles, which increases blood flow.

Page 513

8. Epinephrine binding to myocardial β_1-receptors increases heart rate and force of contraction. Epinephrine binding to β_2-receptors on heart arterioles causes vasodilation.
9. α_1-Receptors have lower affinity for epinephrine than β_2-receptors, so the β_2-receptors dominate and arterioles dilate.

Page 514

10. (a) The kidney has the highest blood flow per unit weight. (b) The heart has the lowest total blood flow.

Pages 519

11. Net filtration will increase as a result of the increased hydrostatic pressure.
12. Loss of plasma proteins will decrease colloid osmotic pressure. As a result, hydrostatic pressure will have a greater effect in the filtration-absorption balance, and filtration will increase.
13. Using osmotic pressure rather than osmolarity allows a direct comparison between absorption pressure and filtration pressure, both of which are expressed in mm Hg.

Page 521

14. If the left ventricle fails, blood will back up into the left atrium and pulmonary veins, and then into lung capillaries. Edema in the lungs is known as *pulmonary edema*.
15. Low-protein diets result in a low concentration of plasma proteins. Capillary absorption is reduced while filtration remains constant resulting in edema and ascites.

Page 523

16. The most likely ion is Na^+ moving into the receptor cell.

Page 525

17. Stimulus: sight, sound, and smell of the *T. rex*. Receptors: eyes, ears, and nose. Integrating center: cerebral cortex, with descending pathways through the limbic system. Divergent pathways go to the cardiovascular control center, which increases sympathetic output to heart and arterioles. A second descending spinal pathway goes to the adrenal medulla, which releases epinephrine. Epinephrine on β_2-receptors of liver, heart, and skeletal muscle arterioles causes vasodilation of those arterioles. Norepinephrine onto α-receptors in other arterioles causes vasoconstriction. Both catecholamines increase heart rate and force of contraction.

Answers to Figure and Graph Questions

Page 515

Figure 15-13: Blood flow through the lungs is 5 L/min.

Page 517

Figure 15-17: (a) Velocity of flow is inversely proportional to area: as area increases, velocity decreases. (b) Changing only cross-sectional area has no effect on flow rate because flow rate is determined by cardiac output.

Page 522

Figure 15-21: SA node: muscarinic cholinergic receptors for ACh and β_1-receptors for catecholamines. Ventricles: β_1-receptors for catecholamines. Arterioles and veins: α-receptors for norepinephrine.

Page 524

Figure 15-23: Arterioles and veins: norepinephrine, α-receptors. Ventricles: norepinephrine, β_1-receptors. SA node: norepinephrine, β_1-receptors; and ACh, muscarinic receptors.

17

This being of mine, whatever it really is, consists of a little flesh, a little breath, and the part which governs.

—Marcus Aurelius Antoninus (A.D. 121–180)

Mouse fibroblasts secrete collagen-rich matrix.

Mechanics of Breathing

BACKGROUND BASICS

Ciliated and exchange epithelia: **72** Pressure, volume, flow, and resistance: **462** Pulmonary circulation: **460**
Hydrogen bonds and surface tension: **25** Autonomic and somatic motor neurons: **246** Velocity of flow: **464**

RUNNING PROBLEM

EMPHYSEMA

"Diagnosis: COPD (blue bloater)," reads Edna Wilson's patient chart. COPD—chronic obstructive pulmonary disease—is a name given to diseases in which air exchange is impaired by narrowing of the airways. Most people with COPD have emphysema or chronic bronchitis or a combination of the two. Individuals in whom chronic bronchitis predominates are nicknamed "blue bloaters," owing to the bluish tinge of their skin and a tendency to be overweight. "Pink puffers" suffer more from emphysema. They tend to be thin, have normal (pink) skin coloration, and breathe shallow, rapid breaths. Because COPD is usually caused by smoking, most people can avoid the disease simply by not smoking. Unfortunately, Edna has been a heavy smoker for 35 of her 47 years.

Imagine covering the playing surface of a racquetball court (about 75 m^2) with thin plastic wrap, then crumpling up the wrap and stuffing it into a 3-liter soft drink bottle. Impossible? Maybe so, if you use plastic wrap and a drink bottle. But the lungs of a 70-kg man have a gas exchange surface the size of that plastic wrap, compressed into a volume that is less than that of the bottle. This tremendous surface area for gas exchange is needed to supply the trillions of cells in the body with adequate amounts of oxygen.

Aerobic metabolism in cells depends on a steady supply of oxygen and nutrients from the environment, coupled with the removal of carbon dioxide. In very small aquatic animals, simple diffusion across the body surface meets these needs. Distance limits diffusion rate, however, so most multicelled animals require specialized respiratory organs associated with a circulatory system. Respiratory organs take a variety of forms, but all possess a large surface area compressed into a small space.

Besides needing a large exchange surface, humans and other terrestrial animals face an additional physiological challenge: dehydration. The exchange surface must be thin and moist to allow gases to pass from air into solution, and yet at the same time it must be protected from drying out as a result of exposure to air. Some terrestrial animals, such as the slug (a shell-less snail), meet the challenge of dehydration with behavioral adaptations that restrict them to humid environments and nighttime activities.

However, a more common solution is anatomical: an internalized respiratory epithelium. Human lungs are enclosed in the chest cavity to control their contact with the outside air. Internalization creates a humid environment for the exchange of gases with the blood and protects the delicate exchange surface from damage.

Internalized lungs create another problem, however: how to move air between the atmosphere and the exchange surface deep within the body. Air flow requires a muscular pump to create pressure gradients. Thus, in more complex body plans, the respiratory system consists of two separate components: a muscle-driven pump and a thin, moist exchange surface. In humans, the pump is the musculoskeletal structure of the thorax [p. 51]. The lungs themselves consist of the exchange epithelium and associated blood vessels.

The four primary functions of the respiratory system are:

1. **Exchange of gases between the atmosphere and the blood**. The body brings in O_2 for distribution to the tissues and eliminates CO_2 waste produced by metabolism.
2. **Homeostatic regulation of body pH**. The lungs can alter body pH by selectively retaining or excreting CO_2.
3. **Protection from inhaled pathogens and irritating substances**. Like all other epithelia that contact the external environment, the respiratory epithelium is well supplied with mechanisms that trap and destroy potentially harmful substances before they can enter the body.
4. **Vocalization**. Air moving across the vocal cords creates vibrations used for speech, singing, and other forms of communication.

In addition to serving these functions, the respiratory system is also a significant source of water loss and heat loss from the body. These losses must be balanced using homeostatic compensations.

In this chapter you will learn how the respiratory system carries out these functions by exchanging air between the environment and the interior air spaces of the lungs. This exchange is the *bulk flow* of air, and it follows many of the same principles that govern the bulk flow of blood through the cardiovascular system:

1. Flow takes place from regions of higher pressure to regions of lower pressure.
2. A muscular pump creates pressure gradients.
3. Resistance to air flow is influenced primarily by the diameter of the tubes through which the air is flowing.

The primary difference between air flow in the respiratory system and blood flow in the circulatory system is that air is a compressible mixture of gases while blood is a noncompressible liquid.

THE RESPIRATORY SYSTEM

The word *respiration* has several meanings in physiology (Fig. 17-1 ■). **Cellular respiration** refers to the intracellular reaction of oxygen with organic molecules to produce carbon dioxide,

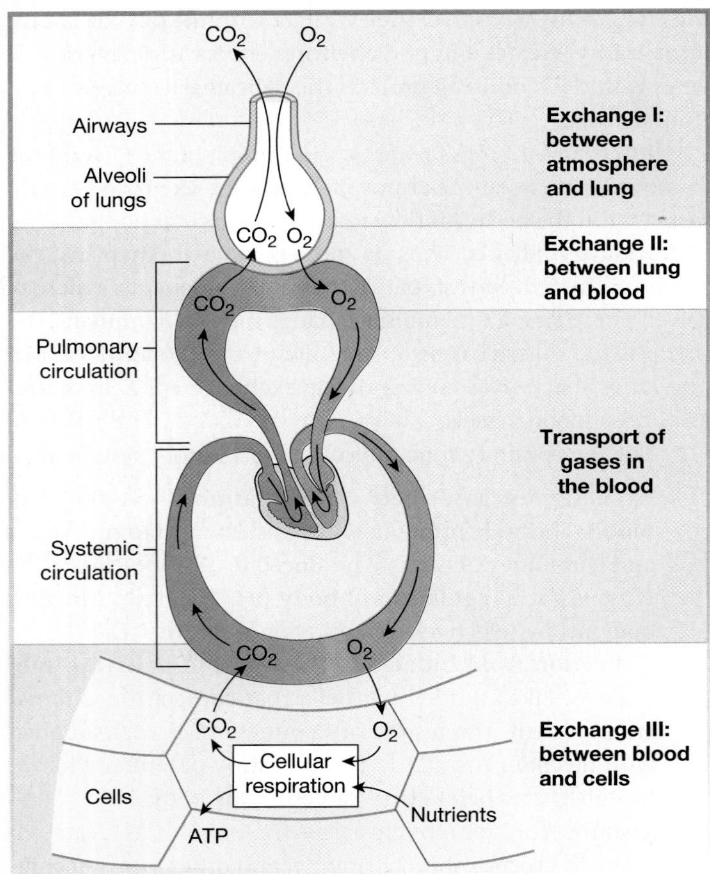

■ **FIGURE 17-1** ***Overview of external and cellular respiration***

water, and energy in the form of ATP [p. 107]. **External respiration**, the topic of this chapter and the next, is the movement of gases between the environment and the body's cells. External respiration can be subdivided into four integrated processes, illustrated in Figure 17-1:

1. *The exchange of air between the atmosphere and the lungs.* This process is known as **ventilation**, or breathing. **Inspiration** (inhalation) is the movement of air into the lungs. **Expiration** (exhalation) is the movement of air out of the lungs. The mechanisms by which ventilation takes place are collectively called the *mechanics of breathing.*
2. *The exchange of O_2 and CO_2 between the lungs and the blood.*
3. *The transport of O_2 and CO_2 by the blood.*
4. *The exchange of gases between blood and the cells.*

External respiration requires the coordinated functioning of the respiratory and cardiovascular systems. The **respiratory system** consists of structures involved in ventilation and gas exchange (Fig. 17-2 ■):

1. The **conducting system** of passages, or **airways**, that lead from the external environment to the exchange surface of the lungs.
2. The **alveoli** (singular **alveolus**) [*alveus,* a concave vessel], a series of interconnected sacs that collectively form the exchange surface, where oxygen moves from inhaled air to the blood, and carbon dioxide moves from the blood to air that is about to be exhaled.
3. The bones and muscles of the thorax (chest cavity) and abdomen that assist in ventilation.

The respiratory system can be divided into two parts. The **upper respiratory tract** consists of the mouth, nasal cavity, pharynx, and larynx. The **lower respiratory tract** consists of the trachea, two primary bronchi, their branches, and the lungs. The lower tract is also known as the *thoracic portion* of the respiratory system because it is enclosed in the thorax.

Bones and Muscles of the Thorax Surround the Lungs

The thorax is bounded by the bones of the spine and rib cage and their associated muscles. Together the bones and muscles are called the *thoracic cage.* The ribs and spine (the *chest wall*) form the sides and top of the cage. A dome-shaped sheet of skeletal muscle, the **diaphragm**, forms the floor (Fig. 17-2a).

Two sets of **intercostal muscles**, internal and external, connect the 12 pairs of ribs (Fig. 17-2b). Additional muscles, the **sternocleidomastoids** and the **scalenes**, run from the head and neck to the sternum and first two ribs.

Functionally, the thorax is a sealed container filled with three membranous bags, or sacs. One, the *pericardial sac,* contains the heart. The other two bags, the **pleural sacs**, contain the lungs [*pleura,* rib or side]. The esophagus and thoracic blood vessels and nerves pass between the pleural sacs (Fig. 17-2d).

Pleural Sacs Enclose the Lungs

The **lungs** (Fig. 17-2a, c) consist of light, spongy tissue whose volume is occupied mostly by air-filled spaces. These irregular cone-shaped organs nearly fill the thoracic cavity, with their bases resting on the curved diaphragm. Rigid conducting airways—the bronchi—connect the lungs to the main airway, the trachea.

Each lung is surrounded by a double-walled pleural sac whose membranes line the inside of the thorax and cover the outer surface of the lungs (Fig. 17-3 ■). Each *pleural membrane,* or **pleura**, contains several layers of elastic connective tissue and numerous capillaries. The opposing layers of pleural membrane are held together by a thin film of **pleural fluid** whose total volume is only a few milliliters. The result is similar to an air-filled balloon (the lung) surrounded by a water-filled balloon (the pleural sac). Most illustrations exaggerate the volume of the pleural fluid, but you can appreciate its thinness if you imagine spreading 3 mL of water evenly over the surface of a 3-liter soft drink bottle.

Pleural fluid serves several purposes. First, it creates a moist, slippery surface so that the opposing membranes can slide across one another as the lungs move within the thorax. Second, it holds the lungs tight against the thoracic wall. To visualize this arrangement, think of two panes of glass stuck together by a thin film of water. You can slide the panes back and forth across each other, but you cannot pull them apart because of the cohesiveness of the water [p. 25]. A similar fluid bond between the two pleural membranes makes the lungs "stick" to the thoracic cage and holds them stretched in a partially inflated state, even at rest.

Airways Connect Lungs to the External Environment

Air enters the upper respiratory tract through the mouth and nose and passes into the **pharynx**, a common passageway for food, liquids, and air [*pharynx,* throat]. From the pharynx, air flows through the **larynx** into the **trachea**, or windpipe (Fig. 17-2a). The larynx contains the **vocal cords**, connective tissue bands that tighten to create sound when air moves past them.

The trachea is a semiflexible tube held open by 15 to 20 C-shaped cartilage rings (Fig. 17-2e). It extends down into the thorax, where it branches (division 1) into a pair of **primary bronchi**, one *bronchus* to each lung. Within the lungs, the bronchi branch repeatedly (divisions 2–11) into progressively smaller bronchi (Fig. 17-2a, e). Like the trachea, the bronchi are semirigid tubes supported by cartilage.

In the lungs, the smallest bronchi branch to become **bronchioles**, small collapsible passageways with walls of smooth muscle. The bronchioles continue branching (divisions 12–23) until the *respiratory bronchioles* form a transition between the airways and the exchange epithelium of the lung.

The diameter of the airways becomes progressively smaller from the trachea to the bronchioles, but as the individual airways get narrower, their numbers increase (Fig. 17-4 ■). As a result, the total cross-sectional area increases with each division of the airways. Total cross-sectional area is lowest in the upper respiratory tract and greatest in the bronchioles, analogous to the increase in cross-sectional area that occurs from the aorta to the capillaries in the circulatory system [p. 517].

CONCEPT CHECK

1. What is the difference between cellular respiration and external respiration?
2. Name the components of the upper respiratory tract, and those of the lower respiratory tract.
3. Based on the total cross-sectional area of different airways, where is the velocity of air flow highest and lowest?
4. Give two functions of pleural fluid.
5. Name the components (including muscles) of the thoracic cage. List the contents of the thorax.
6. Which air passages of the respiratory system are collapsible?

Answers: p. 586

Alveoli Are the Site of Gas Exchange

The alveoli, clustered at the ends of terminal bronchioles, make up the bulk of lung tissue (Fig. 17-2f, g). Their primary function is the exchange of gases between themselves and the blood.

Each tiny alveolus is composed of a single layer of epithelium (Fig. 17-2g). Two types of epithelial cells are found in the alveoli, and they occur in roughly equal numbers. The smaller but thicker **type II alveolar cells** synthesize and secrete a chemical known as **surfactant.** Surfactant mixes with the thin fluid lining of the alveoli to aid lungs as they expand during breathing, as we will see later in this chapter. Type II cells also help minimize the amount of fluid present in the alveoli by transporting solutes, followed by water, out of the alveolar air space.

The larger **type I alveolar cells** are very thin so that gases can diffuse rapidly through them (Fig. 17-2h). In much of the exchange area, a layer of basement membrane fuses the alveolar epithelium to the capillary endothelium, and only a small amount of interstitial fluid is present.

The thin walls of the alveoli do not contain muscle because muscle fibers would block rapid gas exchange. As a result, lung tissue itself cannot contract. However, connective tissue between the alveolar epithelial cells contains many elastin fibers that create elastic recoil when lung tissue is stretched.

The close association of the alveoli with an extensive network of capillaries demonstrates the intimate link between the respiratory and cardiovascular systems. Blood vessels cover 80–90% of the alveolar surface, forming an almost continuous "sheet" of blood in close contact with the air-filled alveoli. The proximity of capillary blood to alveolar air is essential for the rapid exchange of gases.

The Pulmonary Circulation Is a High-Flow, Low-Pressure System

The pulmonary circulation begins with the pulmonary trunk, which receives low-oxygen blood from the right ventricle. The pulmonary trunk divides into two pulmonary arteries, one to each lung [Fig. 14-1, p. 459]. Oxygenated blood from the lungs returns to the left atrium via the pulmonary veins.

RUNNING PROBLEM

Patients with chronic bronchitis have excessive mucus production and general inflammation of the entire respiratory tract. The mucus narrows the airways and makes breathing difficult.

Question 1:
What does narrowing of the airways do to the resistance airways offer to air flow? (Hint: the relationship between radius and resistance is the same for air flow in the respiratory system as it is for blood flow in the circulatory system. [p. 509])

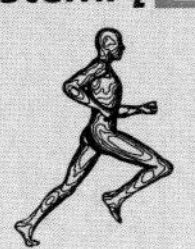

559 561 569 574 581 582

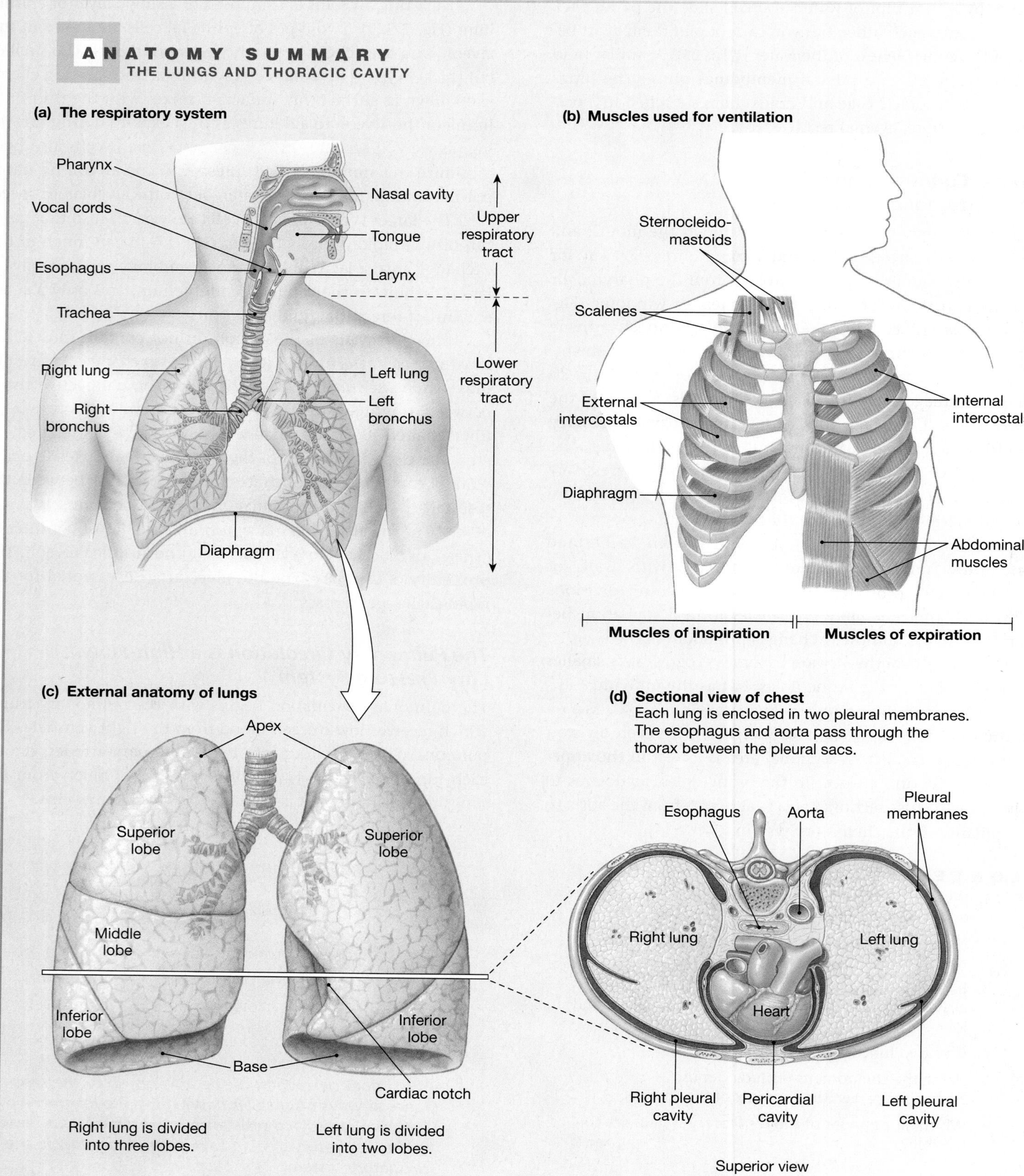
ANATOMY SUMMARY
THE LUNGS AND THORACIC CAVITY
(a) The respiratory system
Pharynx
Vocal cords
Esophagus
Trachea
Right lung
Right bronchus
Nasal cavity
Tongue
Larynx
Left lung
Left bronchus
Upper respiratory tract
Lower respiratory tract
Diaphragm
(b) Muscles used for ventilation
Sternocleido-mastoids
Scalenes
External intercostals
Diaphragm
Internal intercostals
Abdominal muscles
Muscles of inspiration
Muscles of expiration
(c) External anatomy of lungs
Apex
Superior lobe
Superior lobe
Middle lobe
Inferior lobe
Inferior lobe
Base
Cardiac notch
Right lung is divided into three lobes.
Left lung is divided into two lobes.
(d) Sectional view of chest
Each lung is enclosed in two pleural membranes. The esophagus and aorta pass through the thorax between the pleural sacs.
Esophagus
Aorta
Pleural membranes
Right lung
Left lung
Heart
Right pleural cavity
Pericardial cavity
Left pleural cavity
Superior view

■ **FIGURE 17-2**

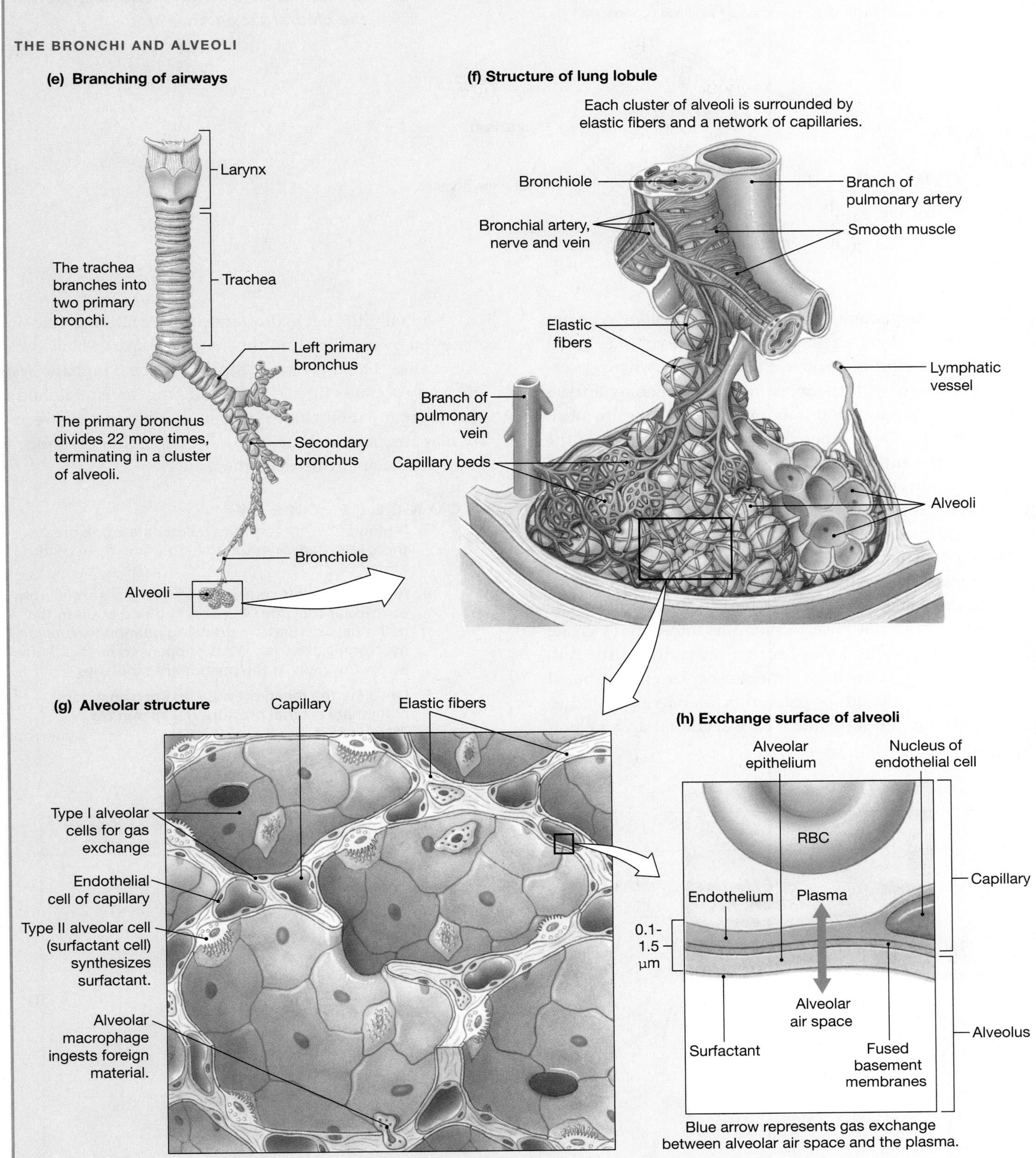
THE BRONCHI AND ALVEOLI
(e) Branching of airways
Larynx
Trachea
The trachea branches into two primary bronchi.
Left primary bronchus
The primary bronchus divides 22 more times, terminating in a cluster of alveoli.
Secondary bronchus
Bronchiole
Alveoli
(f) Structure of lung lobule
Each cluster of alveoli is surrounded by elastic fibers and a network of capillaries.
Bronchiole
Branch of pulmonary artery
Bronchial artery, nerve and vein
Smooth muscle
Elastic fibers
Lymphatic vessel
Branch of pulmonary vein
Capillary beds
Alveoli
(g) Alveolar structure
Capillary
Elastic fibers
Type I alveolar cells for gas exchange
Endothelial cell of capillary
Type II alveolar cell (surfactant cell) synthesizes surfactant.
Alveolar macrophage ingests foreign material.
(h) Exchange surface of alveoli
Alveolar epithelium
Nucleus of endothelial cell
RBC
Capillary
Endothelium
Plasma
0.1-1.5 µm
Alveolar air space
Alveolus
Surfactant
Fused basement membranes
Blue arrow represents gas exchange between alveolar air space and the plasma.

■ **FIGURE 17-2 (continued)**

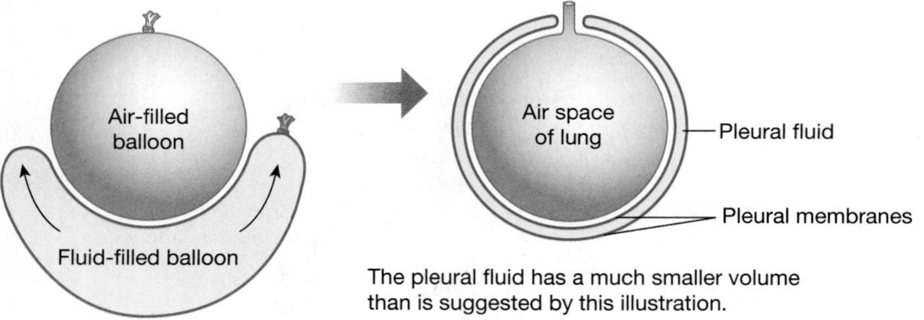

The pleural sac forms a double membrane surrounding the lung, similar to a fluid-filled balloon surrounding an air-filled balloon.
Air-filled balloon
Fluid-filled balloon
Air space of lung
Pleural fluid
Pleural membranes
The pleural fluid has a much smaller volume than is suggested by this illustration.

■ **FIGURE 17-3** ***The relationship between the pleural sac and the lung***

At any given moment, the pulmonary circulation contains about 0.5 liter of blood, or 10% of total blood volume. About 75 mL of this amount is found in the capillaries, where gas exchange takes place, with the remainder in pulmonary arteries and veins. The rate of blood flow through the lungs is much higher than the rate in other tissues [p. 515] because the lungs receive the entire cardiac output of the right ventricle: 5 L/min. This means that as much blood flows through the lungs in one minute as flows through the entire rest of the body in the same amount of time!

Despite the high flow rate, pulmonary blood pressure is low. Pulmonary arterial pressure averages 25/8 mm Hg, much lower than the average systemic pressure of 120/80 mm Hg. The right ventricle does not have to pump as forcefully to create blood flow through the lungs because resistance of the pulmonary circulation is low. This low resistance can be attributed to the shorter total length of pulmonary blood vessels and to the distensibility and large total cross-sectional area of pulmonary arterioles.

Normally, the net hydrostatic pressure filtering fluid out of a pulmonary capillary into the interstitial space is low because of low mean blood pressure [p. 518]. The lymphatic system efficiently removes filtered fluid, and lung interstitial fluid volume is usually minimal. As a result, the distance between the alveolar air space and the capillary endothelium is short, and gases diffuse rapidly between them.

CONCEPT CHECK

7. Is blood flow through the pulmonary trunk greater than, less than, or equal to blood flow through the aorta?
8. A person has left ventricular failure but normal right ventricular function. As a result, blood pools in the pulmonary circulation, doubling pulmonary capillary hydrostatic pressure. What happens to net fluid flow across the walls of the pulmonary capillaries?
9. Calculate the mean pressure in a person whose pulmonary arterial pressure is 25/8 mm Hg. [p. 506]

Answers: p. 586

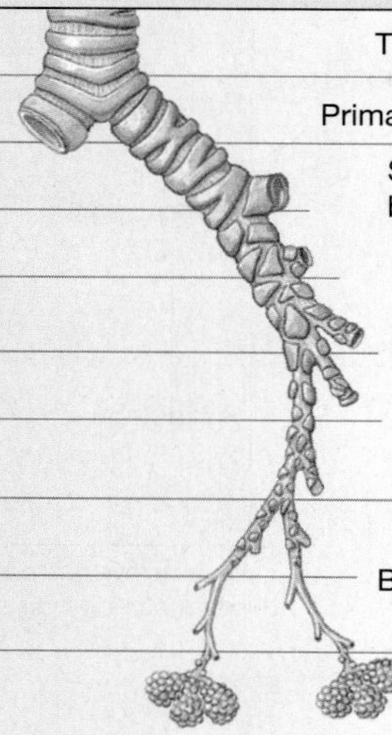

	Name	Division	Diameter (mm)	How many?	Cross-sectional area (cm^2)
Conducting system	Trachea	0	15–22	1	2.5
	Primary bronchi	1	10–15	2	↓
	Smaller bronchi ↓	2	1–10	4 ↓	
		3			
		4			
		5			
		6–11		1×10^4	
	Bronchioles	1–23	0.5–1	2×10^4 ↓ 8×10^7	100 ↓ 5×10^3
Exchange surface	Alveoli	24	0.3	$3–6 \times 10^8$	$>1 \times 10^6$

■ **FIGURE 17-4** ***Branching of the airways***

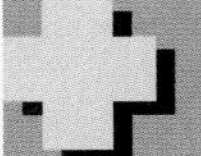

CLINICAL FOCUS

CONGESTIVE HEART FAILURE

When is a lung problem not a lung problem? The answer: when it's really a heart problem. Congestive heart failure (CHF) is an excellent example of the interrelationships among body systems, and of how disruptions in one system can have a domino effect in the others. The primary symptoms of heart failure are shortness of breath (*dyspnea*), wheezing during breathing, and sometimes a productive cough whose *phlegm* (pronounced "flem") may be pinkish due to the presence of blood. Congestive heart failure arises when the right heart is a more effective pump than the left heart (see Ch. 14, Concept Check 31, p. 489). When blood accumulates in the pulmonary circulation, increased volume increases pulmonary blood pressure and capillary hydrostatic pressure. Capillary filtration exceeds the ability of the lymph system to drain interstitial fluid, resulting in pulmonary edema. Treatment of CHF includes increasing urinary output of fluid, which brings yet another organ system into the picture. By current estimates, nearly 5 million Americans suffer from CHF. To learn more about this condition, visit the American Heart Association website (*www.americanheart.org*) or see the Health Information section for the National Heart, Lung, and Blood Institute of the National Institutes of Health (*www.nhlbi.nih.gov*).

GAS LAWS

Respiratory air flow is very similar in many respects to blood flow in the cardiovascular system, even though blood is a noncompressible liquid and air is a compressible mixture of gases. Blood pressure and environmental air pressure (**atmospheric pressure**) are both reported in millimeters of mercury (mm Hg).*

At sea level, normal atmospheric pressure is 760 mm Hg. However, in this book we will follow the convention of designating atmospheric pressure as 0 mm Hg. Because atmospheric pressure varies with altitude and because very few people live exactly at sea level, this convention allows us to compare pressure differences that occur during ventilation without correcting for altitude. Negative numbers designate subatmospheric pressures, and positive numbers denote higher-than-atmospheric pressures.

TABLE 17-1 Gas Laws

1. The total pressure of a mixture of gases is the sum of the pressures of the individual gases (Dalton's law).
2. Gases, singly or in a mixture, move from areas of higher pressure to areas of lower pressure.
3. If the volume of a container of gas changes, the pressure of the gas will change in an inverse manner (Boyle's law).

Table 17-1 ■ summarizes the rules that govern the behavior of gases in air. These rules provide the basis for the exchange of air between the external environment and the alveoli. Gas laws that govern the solubility of gases in solution will be considered in Chapter 18.

Air Is a Mixture of Gases

The atmosphere surrounding the earth is a mixture of gases and water vapor. **Dalton's law** states that the total pressure exerted by a mixture of gases is the sum of the pressures exerted by the individual gases. Thus, in dry air at an atmospheric pressure of 760 mm Hg, 78% of the total pressure is due to N_2, 21% to O_2, and so on (Table 17-2 ■).

In respiratory physiology, we are concerned not only with total atmospheric pressure but also with the individual pressures of oxygen and carbon dioxide. The pressure of a single gas in a mixture is known as its **partial pressure** (P_{gas}). To find the partial pressure of any one gas in a sample of air, multiply the atmospheric pressure (P_{atm}) by the gas's relative contribution (%) to P_{atm}:

$$\text{Partial pressure of an atmospheric gas} = P_{atm} \times \text{\% of gas in atmosphere}$$

$$\text{Partial pressure of oxygen} = 760 \text{ mm Hg} \times 21\%$$

$$P_{O_2} = 760 \times 0.21 = 160 \text{ mm Hg}$$

Thus, the partial pressure of oxygen (P_{O_2}) in dry air at sea level is 160 mm Hg. The pressure exerted by an individual gas is determined only by its relative abundance in the mixture and is independent of the molecular size or mass of the gas.

The partial pressures of gases in air vary slightly depending on how much water vapor is in the air because the pressure of water vapor "dilutes" the contribution of other gases to the total pressure. To calculate the partial pressure of a gas in humid air, you must first subtract the water vapor pressure from the total pressure. Table 17-2 compares the partial pressures of some gases in dry air and at 100% humidity.

*Respiratory physiologists sometimes report gas pressures in units of centimeters of water: 1 mm Hg = 1.36 cm H_2O.

TABLE 17-2 Partial Pressures (P_{gas}) of Atmospheric Gases at 760 mm Hg

GAS AND ITS PERCENTAGE IN AIR	P_{gas} IN DRY, 25° C AIR	P_{gas} IN 25° C AIR, 100% HUMIDITY	P_{gas} IN 37° C AIR, 100% HUMIDITY
Nitrogen (N_2) 78%	593 mm Hg	574 mm Hg	556 mm Hg
Oxygen (O_2) 21%	160 mm Hg	155 mm Hg	150 mm Hg
Carbon dioxide (CO_2) 0.033%	0.25 mm Hg	0.24 mm Hg	0.235 mm Hg
Water vapor	0 mm Hg	24 mm Hg	47 mm Hg

CONCEPT CHECK

10. If nitrogen is 78% of atmospheric air, what is the partial pressure of nitrogen (P_{N_2}) in a sample of dry air that has an atmospheric pressure of 720 mm Hg?

Answers: p. 586

Gases Move from Areas of Higher Pressure to Areas of Lower Pressure

Air flow occurs whenever there is a pressure gradient. Air flow, like blood flow, is directed from areas of higher pressure to areas of lower pressure. Meteorologists predict the weather by knowing that areas of high atmospheric pressure move in to replace areas of low pressure. In ventilation, bulk flow of air down pressure gradients explains how air exchanges between the external environment and the lungs. Movement of the thorax during breathing creates alternating conditions of high and low pressure in the lungs.

Movement down pressure gradients also applies to single gases. For example, oxygen moves from areas of higher oxygen partial pressure to areas of lower oxygen partial pressure. Diffusion of individual gases is important in the alveoli-blood and blood-cell gas exchanges discussed in Chapter 18.

Boyle's Law Describes Pressure-Volume Relationships of Gases

The pressure exerted by a gas or mixture of gases in a sealed container is created by the collisions of moving gas molecules with the walls of the container and with each other. If the size of the container is reduced, the collisions between the gas molecules and the walls become more frequent, and the pressure rises. This relationship can be expressed by the equation

$$P_1V_1 = P_2V_2$$

where P represents pressure and V represents volume.

For example, start with a 1-liter container (V_1) of a gas whose pressure is 100 mm Hg (P_1), as shown in Figure 17-5 ■. What happens to the pressure of the gas when the lid of the container moves in to decrease the volume to 0.5 L? According to our equation,

$$P_1V_1 = P_2V_2$$

$$100 \text{ mm Hg} \times 1 \text{ L} = P_2 \times 0.5 \text{ L}$$

$$P_2 = 200 \text{ mm Hg}$$

This calculation tells us that if the volume is reduced by one-half, the pressure doubles. If the volume were to double, the pressure would be reduced by one-half. This relationship between pressure and volume was first noted by Robert Boyle in the 1600s and has been called **Boyle's law** of gases.

In the respiratory system, changes in the volume of the chest cavity during ventilation cause pressure gradients that create air flow. When the chest volume increases, the alveolar pressure falls, and air flows into the respiratory system. When the chest volume decreases, the alveolar pressure rises, and air flows out into the atmosphere. This movement of air is bulk flow because the entire gas mixture is moving rather than merely one or two of the gas species contained in the air.

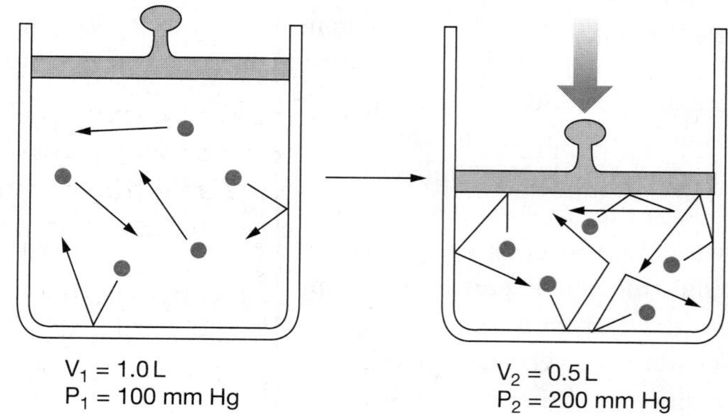

■ **FIGURE 17-5** ***Boyle's law***

Boyle's law ($P_1V_1 = P_2V_2$) assumes that temperature and the number of gas molecules remain constant.

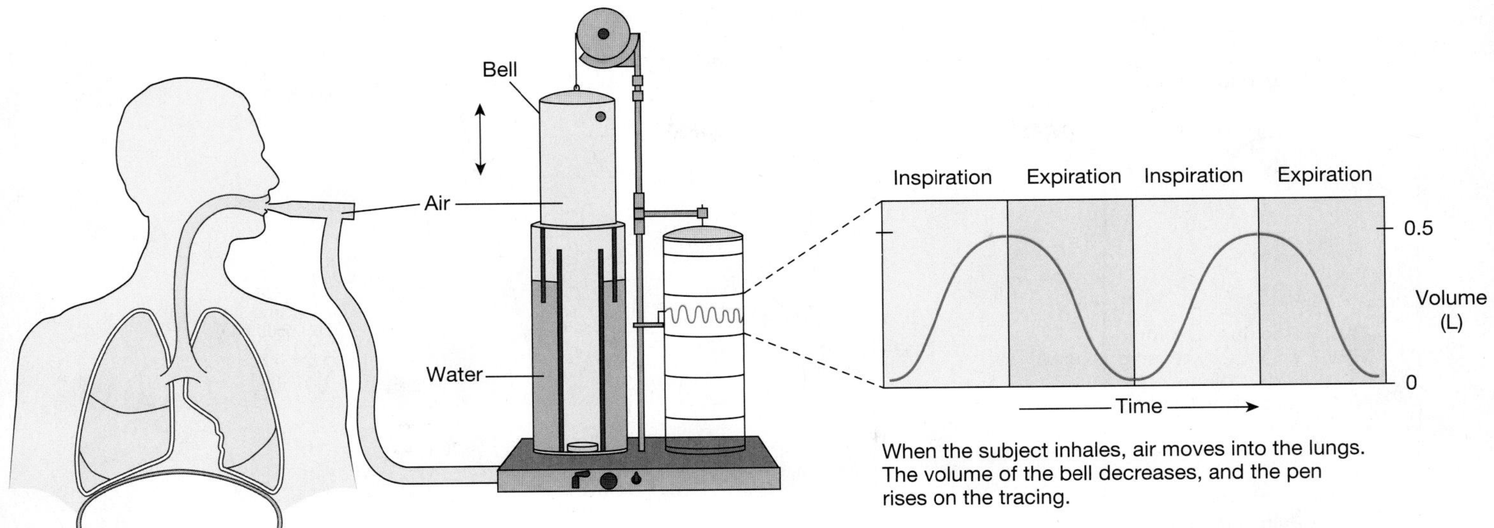
Bell
Air
Water
Inspiration
Expiration
Inspiration
Expiration
0.5
Volume (L)
0
Time
When the subject inhales, air moves into the lungs. The volume of the bell decreases, and the pen rises on the tracing.

■ **FIGURE 17-6** ***A spirometer***

The subject inserts a mouthpiece that is attached to an inverted bell filled with air or oxygen. The volume of the bell and the volume of the subject's respiratory tract create a closed system because the bell is suspended in water.

VENTILATION

The first exchange in respiratory physiology is ventilation, or breathing, the bulk flow exchange of air between the atmosphere and the alveoli (Fig. 17-1).

Lung Volumes Change During Ventilation

Physiologists and clinicians assess a person's pulmonary function by measuring how much air the person moves during quiet breathing, then with maximum effort. These **pulmonary function tests** use a **spirometer**, an instrument that measures the volume of air moved with each breath (Fig. 17-6 ■). (Most spirometers in clinical use today are small computerized machines rather than the traditional spirometer illustrated here.)

When a subject is attached to the traditional spirometer through a mouthpiece and the subject's nose is clipped closed, the subject's respiratory tract and the spirometer form a closed system. When the subject breathes in, air moves from the spirometer into the lungs, and the recording pen, which traces a graph on a rotating cylinder, moves up. When the subject exhales, air moves from the lungs back into the spirometer, and the pen moves down.

Lung Volumes The air moved during breathing can be divided into four lung volumes: (1) tidal volume, (2) inspiratory reserve volume, (3) expiratory reserve volume, and (4) residual volume. The numerical values given in Figure 17-7 ■ represent average volumes for a 70-kg man. The volumes for women are typically about 20–25% less. Lung volumes vary considerably with age, sex, and height. Each of the following paragraphs begins with the instructions you would be given if you were being tested for these volumes.

"Breathe quietly." The volume of air that moves during a single inspiration or expiration is known as the **tidal volume** (V_T). Average tidal volume during quiet breathing is about 500 mL.

"Now, at the end of a quiet inspiration, take in as much additional air as you possibly can." The additional volume you inspire above the tidal volume represents your **inspiratory reserve volume** (IRV). In a 70-kg man, this volume is about 3000 mL, a sixfold increase over the normal tidal volume.

"Now stop at the end of a normal exhalation, then exhale as much air as you possibly can." The amount of air forcefully exhaled after the end of a normal expiration is the **expiratory reserve volume** (ERV), which averages about 1100 mL.

The fourth volume cannot be measured directly. Even if you blow out as much air as you can, air still remains in the lungs and the airways. The volume of air in the respiratory system after maximal exhalation—about 1200 mL—is called the **residual volume** (RV). Most of this residual volume exists because the lungs are held stretched against the thoracic wall by the pleural fluid.

Lung Capacities The sum of two or more lung volumes is called a **capacity**. The **vital capacity** (VC) is the sum of the inspiratory reserve volume, expiratory reserve volume, and tidal volume. Vital capacity represents the maximum amount of air that can be voluntarily moved into or out of the respiratory system with one breath. To measure vital capacity, you would instruct the person to take in as much air as possible, then blow it all out. Vital capacity decreases with age.

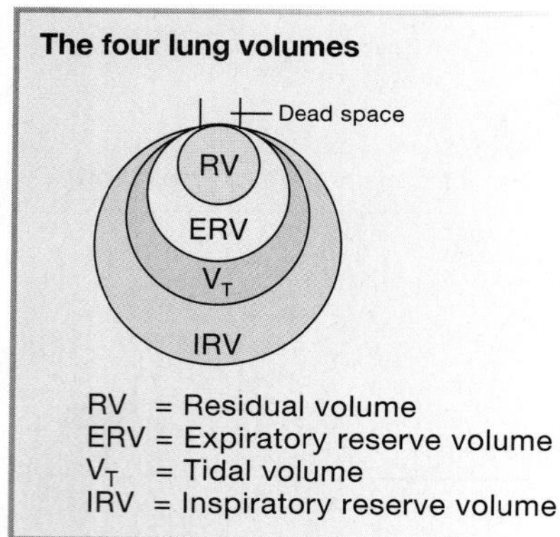

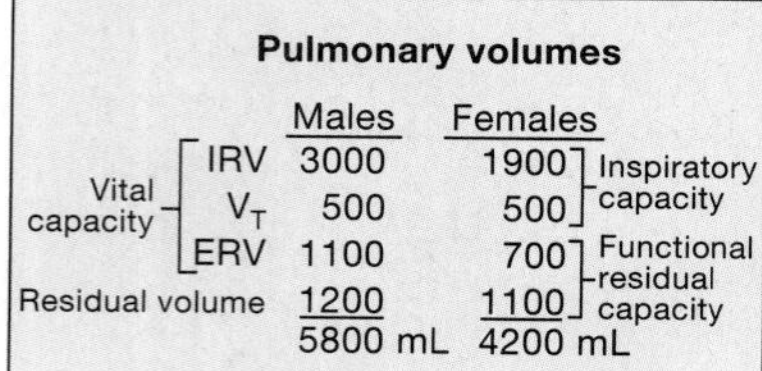

Pulmonary volumes

		Males	Females	
Vital capacity	IRV	3000	1900	Inspiratory capacity
	V_T	500	500	
	ERV	1100	700	Functional residual capacity
Residual volume		1200	1100	
		5800 mL	4200 mL	

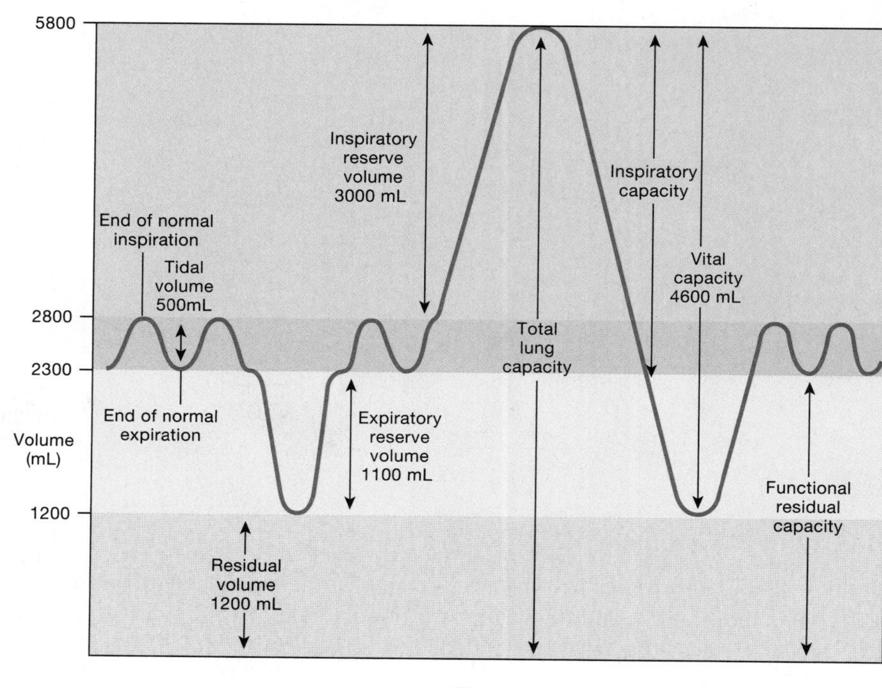

■ **FIGURE 17-7** ***Lung volumes and capacities***

The vital capacity plus the residual volume yields the **total lung capacity** (TLC). Other capacities of importance in pulmonary medicine include the **inspiratory capacity** (tidal volume + inspiratory reserve volume) and the **functional residual capacity** (expiratory reserve volume + residual volume).

CONCEPT CHECK

11. How are lung volumes related to lung capacities?
12. Which lung volume cannot be measured directly?
13. If vital capacity decreases with age but total lung capacity does not change, which lung volume must be changing? In which direction?

Answers: p. 586

The Airways Warm, Humidify, and Filter Inspired Air

During breathing, the upper airways and the bronchi do more than simply serve as passageways for air. They play an important role in conditioning air before it reaches the alveoli. Conditioning has three components:

1. *Warming* air to body temperature (37° C), so that core body temperature will not change and alveoli will not be damaged by cold air;
2. *Adding water vapor* until the air reaches 100% humidity, so that the moist exchange epithelium will not dry out; and
3. *Filtering out foreign material,* so that viruses, bacteria, and inorganic particles will not reach the alveoli.

Inhaled air is warmed by the body's heat and moistened by water evaporating from the mucosal lining of the airways. Under normal circumstances, by the time air reaches the trachea, it has been conditioned to 100% humidity and 37° C.

Breathing through the mouth is not nearly as effective at warming and moistening air as breathing through the nose. If you exercise outdoors in very cold weather, you may be familiar with the ache in your chest that results from breathing cold air through your mouth.

Filtration of air takes place both in the trachea and in the bronchi. These airways are lined with ciliated epithelium, that secretes both mucus and a dilute saline solution. The cilia are bathed in a watery saline layer (Fig. 17-8 ■). On top of them lies a sticky layer of mucus that traps most inhaled particles larger than 2 μm.

The mucus layer is secreted by *goblet cells* in the epithelium (Fig. 17-8). The cilia beat with an upward motion that moves the mucus continuously toward the pharynx, creating what is called the *mucociliary escalator.* Mucus contains *immunoglobulins* that can disable many pathogens, and once the mucus reaches the pharynx and is swallowed, stomach acid and enzymes destroy any remaining microorganisms.

Secretion of the watery saline layer beneath the mucus is essential for a functional mucociliary escalator. In the disease *cystic fibrosis,* for example, inadequate ion secretion decreases fluid movement in the airways. Without the saline layer, cilia

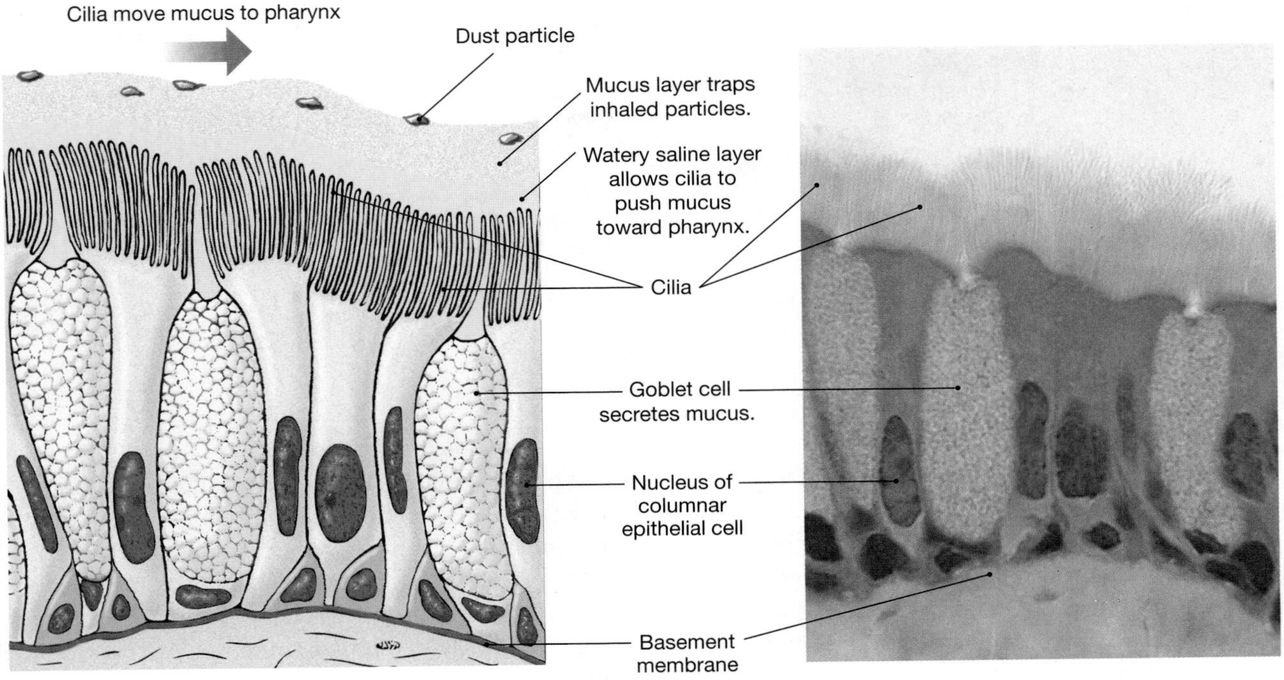

Cilia move mucus to pharynx

Dust particle

Mucus layer traps inhaled particles.

Watery saline layer allows cilia to push mucus toward pharynx.

Cilia

Goblet cell secretes mucus.

Nucleus of columnar epithelial cell

Basement membrane

Ciliated epithelium of the trachea

FIGURE 17-8 ***Ciliated respiratory epithelium***

Ciliary movement of the mucus layer toward the pharynx removes inhaled pathogens and particulate matter.

become trapped in thick, sticky mucus. Mucus cannot be cleared, and bacteria colonize the airways, resulting in recurrent lung infections.

CONCEPT CHECK

14. As inhaled air becomes humidified passing down the airways, what happens to the P_{O_2} of the air?
15. Cigarette smoking paralyzes cilia in the airways. Why would paralysis of the cilia cause smokers to develop a cough?

Answers: p. 586

During Ventilation, Air Flows Because of Pressure Gradients

Air flows into the lungs because of pressure gradients created by a pump, just as blood flows because of the pumping action of the heart. In the respiratory system, most lung tissue is thin exchange epithelium, so muscles of the thoracic cage and diaphragm must function as the pump. When these muscles contract, the lungs expand, held to the inside of the chest wall by the pleural fluid.

Breathing is an active process that uses muscle contraction to create a pressure gradient. The primary muscles involved in quiet breathing (breathing at rest) are the diaphragm, the external intercostals, and the scalenes. During forced breathing, other muscles of the chest and abdomen may be recruited to assist. Examples of physiological situations in which breathing is forced include exercise, playing a wind instrument, and blowing up a balloon.

As noted earlier in the chapter, air flow in the respiratory tract obeys the same rule as blood flow:

$$\text{Flow} \propto \Delta P/R$$

RUNNING PROBLEM

Smokers usually develop chronic bronchitis before they develop emphysema. Cigarette smoke paralyzes the cilia that sweep debris and mucus out of the airways. Without the action of cilia, mucus and debris pool in the airways, leading to a chronic cough. Eventually, breathing becomes difficult.

Question 2:

Why do people with chronic bronchitis have a higher-than-normal rate of respiratory infections?

559 561 569 574 581 582

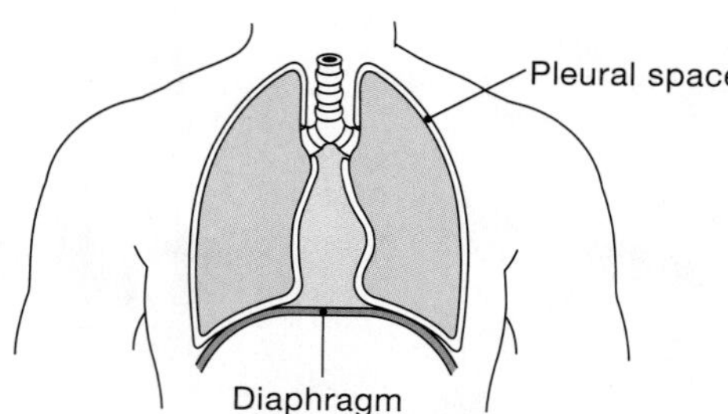
(a) At rest, diaphragm is relaxed.
Pleural space
Diaphragm

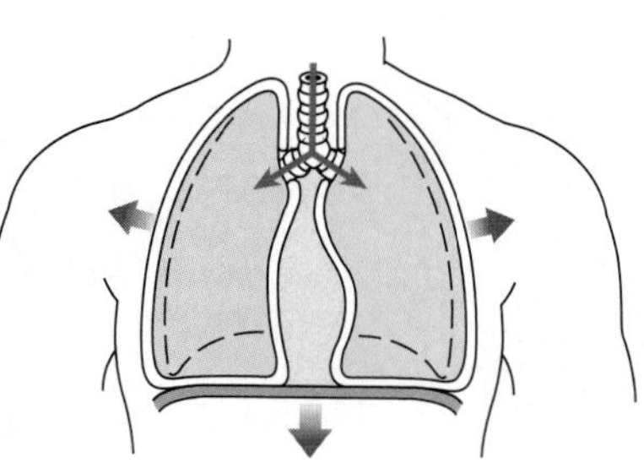
(b) Diaphragm contracts, thoracic volume increases.

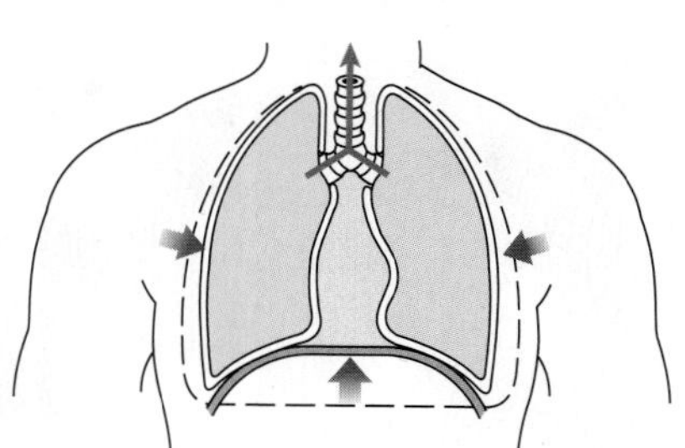
(c) Diaphragm relaxes, thoracic volume decreases.

■ **FIGURE 17-9** ***Movement of the diaphragm***

This equation means that (1) air flows in response to a pressure gradient (ΔP) and (2) flow decreases as the resistance (R) of the system to flow increases. Before we discuss resistance, we will consider how the respiratory system creates a pressure gradient.

Pressures in the respiratory system can be measured either in the air spaces of the lungs (**alveolar pressure**, P_A) or in the pleural fluid (**intrapleural pressure**). Because atmospheric pressure is relatively constant, pressure in the lungs must be higher or lower than atmospheric pressure for air to flow between the atmosphere and the alveoli.

Air moves into the lungs when you inhale and out of the lungs when you exhale. A single **respiratory cycle** consists of an inspiration followed by an expiration. Because the respiratory system ends in a dead end, the direction of air flow must reverse. The pressure-volume relationships of Boyle's law provide the basis for pulmonary ventilation.

CONCEPT CHECK

16. Compare the direction of air movement during one respiratory cycle with the direction of blood flow during one cardiac cycle.
17. Explain the relationship between the lungs, the pleural membranes, the pleural fluid, and the thoracic cage.

Answers: p. 586

Inspiration Occurs When Alveolar Pressure Decreases

For air to move into the lungs, pressure inside the lungs must become lower than atmospheric pressure. According to Boyle's law, an increase in volume will create a decrease in pressure. During inspiration, thoracic volume increases when certain skeletal muscles of the rib cage and diaphragm contract.

When the diaphragm contracts, it loses its dome shape and drops down toward the abdomen. In quiet breathing, the diaphragm moves about 1.5 cm. This movement increases thoracic volume by flattening its floor (Fig. 17-9 ■). Contraction of the diaphragm causes between 60% and 75% of the inspiratory volume change during normal quiet breathing.

Movement of the rib cage creates the remaining 25–40% of the volume change. During inhalation, the external intercostal and scalene muscles (see Fig. 17-2b) contract and pull the ribs upward and out. Rib movement during inspiration has been likened to a pump handle lifting up and away from the pump (the ribs moving up and away from the spine; Fig. 17-10a ■) and to the movement of a bucket handle as it lifts away from the side of a bucket (ribs moving outward in a lateral direction; Fig. 17-10b). The combination of these two movements broadens the rib cage in all directions. As thoracic volume increases, pressure decreases, and air flows into the lungs.

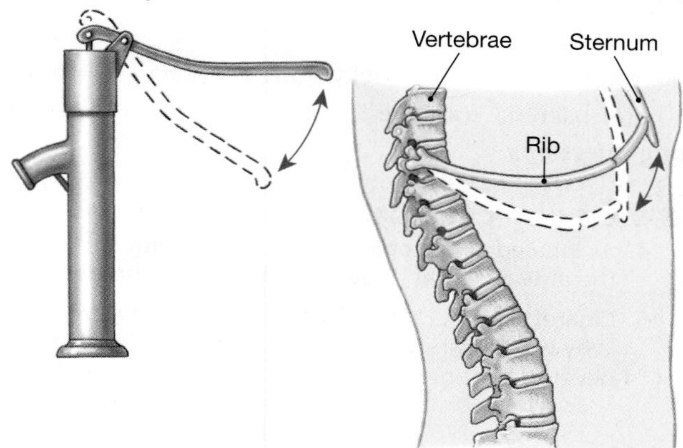
(a) "Pump handle" motion increases anterior-posterior dimension of rib cage.
Vertebrae
Sternum
Rib

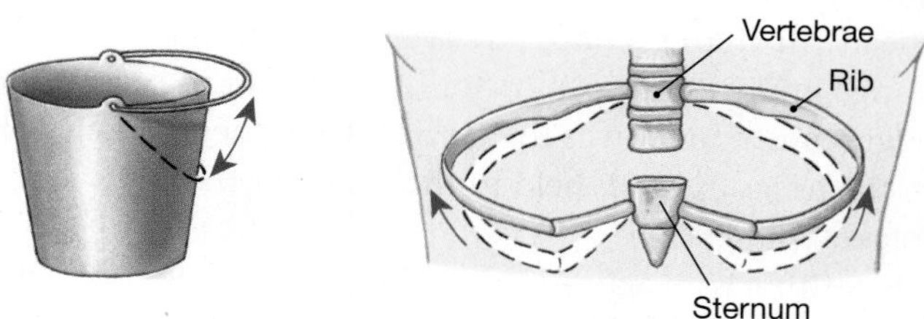
(b) "Bucket handle" motion increases lateral dimension of rib cage.
Vertebrae
Rib
Sternum

■ **FIGURE 17-10** ***Movement of the rib cage during inspiration***

Handles on a hand pump and a bucket serve as good models for rib movement during inspiration.

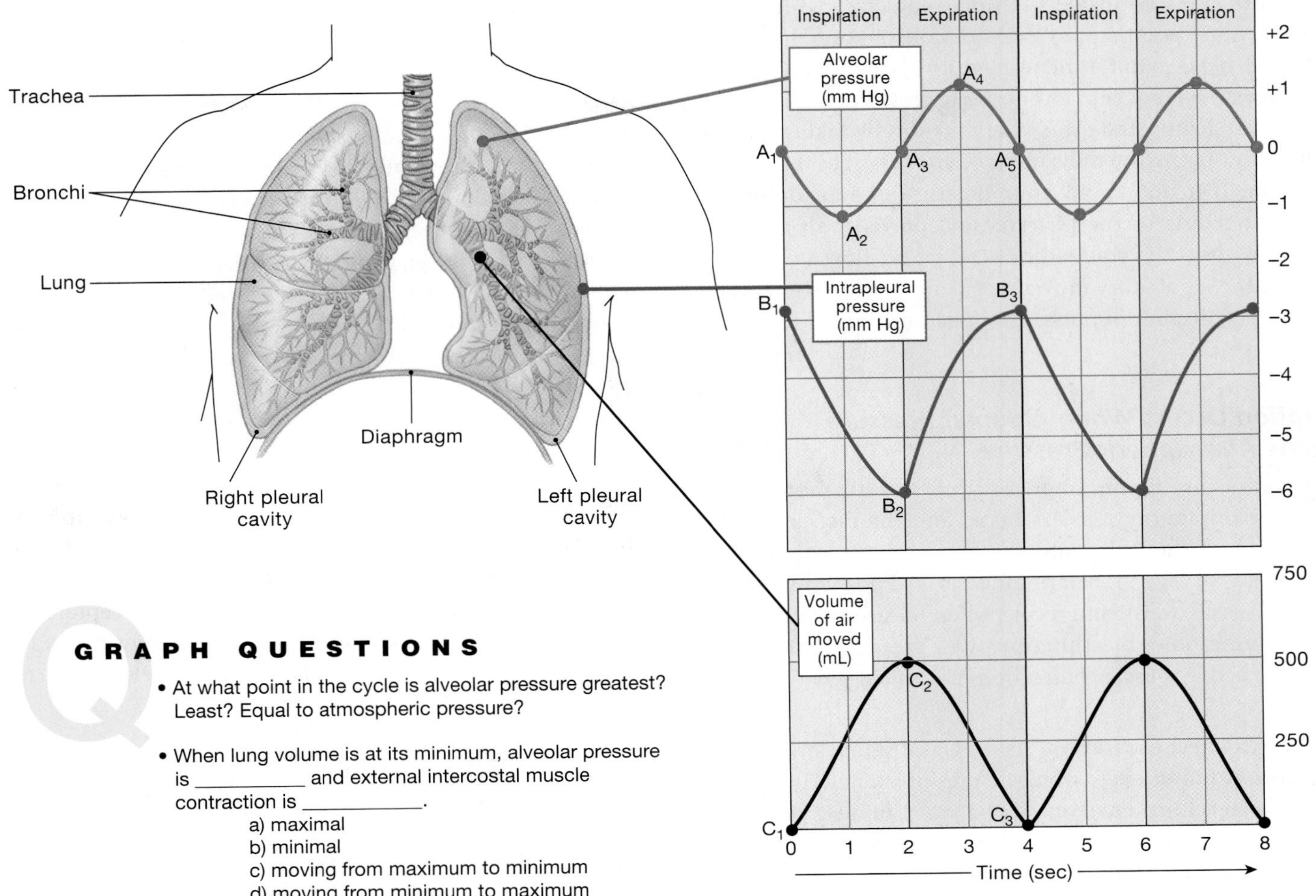

FIGURE 17-11 ***Pressure changes during quiet breathing***

For many years, quiet breathing was attributed solely to the action of the diaphragm and the external intercostal muscles. It was thought that the scalenes and sternocleidomastoid muscles were active only during deep breathing. In recent years, however, studies have changed our understanding of how these accessory muscles contribute to quiet breathing. If an individual's scalenes are paralyzed, inspiration is achieved primarily by contraction of the diaphragm. Observation of patients with neuromuscular disorders has revealed that although the contracting diaphragm increases thoracic volume by moving toward the abdominal cavity, it also tends to pull the lower ribs inward, working against inspiration. In normal individuals, we know that the lower ribs move up and out during inspiration rather than in. The fact that there is no up-and-out rib motion in patients with paralyzed scalenes tells us that normally the scalenes must be contributing to inspiration by lifting the sternum and upper ribs.

New evidence also downplays the role of the external intercostal muscles during quiet breathing. However, the external intercostals play an increasingly important role as respiratory activity increases. Because the exact contribution of external intercostals and scalenes varies depending on the type of breathing, we will group these muscles together and call them the *inspiratory muscles*.

Now let's see how alveolar pressure changes during a single inspiration. Follow the graphs in Figure 17-11 ■ as you read through the process.

Time 0. In the brief pause between breaths, alveolar pressure is equal to atmospheric pressure (0 mm Hg at point A_1). When pressures are equal, there is no air flow.

Time 0–2 sec: Inspiration. As inspiration begins, inspiratory muscles contract, and thoracic volume increases. With the increase in volume, alveolar pressure falls about 1 mm Hg below atmospheric pressure (−1 mm Hg, point A_2), and air flows into the alveoli (point C_1 to point C_2). Because the thoracic volume changes faster than air can flow, alveolar pressure reaches its lowest value about halfway through inspiration (point A_2).

As air continues to flow into the alveoli, pressure increases until the thoracic cage stops expanding, just before the end of inspiration. Air movement continues for a fraction of a second longer, until pressure inside the lungs equalizes with atmospheric pressure (point A_3). At the end of inspiration, lung volume is at its maximum for the respiratory cycle (point C_2), and alveolar pressure is equal to atmospheric pressure.

You can demonstrate this phenomenon by taking a deep breath and stopping the movement of your chest at the end of inspiration. (Do not "hold your breath" because doing so closes the opening of the pharynx and prevents air flow.) If you do this correctly, you will notice that air flow stops after you freeze the inspiratory movement. This exercise shows that at the end of inspiration, alveolar pressure is equal to atmospheric pressure.

Expiration Occurs When Alveolar Pressure Exceeds Atmospheric Pressure

At the end of inspiration, impulses from somatic motor neurons to the inspiratory muscles cease, and the muscles relax. Elastic recoil of the lungs and thoracic cage returns the diaphragm and rib cage to their original relaxed positions, just as a stretched elastic waistband recoils when released. Because expiration during quiet breathing involves passive elastic recoil rather than active muscle contraction, it is called **passive expiration**.

Time 2–4 sec: expiration. As lung and thoracic volumes decrease during expiration, air pressure in the lungs increases, reaching a maximum of about 1 mm Hg above atmospheric pressure (Fig. 17-11, point A_4). Alveolar pressure is now higher than atmospheric pressure, so air flow reverses and air moves out of the lungs.

Time 4 sec. At the end of expiration, air movement ceases when alveolar pressure is again equal to atmospheric pressure (point A_5). Lung volume reaches its minimum for the respiratory cycle (point C_3). At this point, the respiratory cycle has ended and is ready to begin again with the next breath.

The pressure differences shown in Figure 17-11 apply to quiet breathing. During exercise or forced heavy breathing, these values will become proportionately larger. **Active expiration** occurs during voluntary exhalations and when ventilation exceeds 30–40 breaths per minute. (Normal resting ventilation rate is 12–20 breaths per minute for an adult.) Active expiration uses the internal intercostal muscles and the abdominal muscles (see Fig. 17-2b), which are not used during inspiration. These muscles are collectively called the *expiratory muscles*.

The internal intercostal muscles line the inside of the rib cage. When they contract, they pull the ribs inward, reducing the volume of the thoracic cavity. To feel this action, place your hands on your rib cage. Forcefully blow as much air out of your lungs as you can, noting the movement of your hands as you do so.

The internal and external intercostals function as antagonistic muscle groups [p. 398] to alter the position and volume of the rib cage during ventilation. The diaphragm, however, has no antagonistic muscles. Instead, abdominal muscles contract during active expiration to supplement the activity of the internal intercostals. Abdominal contraction pulls the lower rib cage inward and decreases abdominal volume, actions that displace the intestines and liver upward. The displaced viscera push the diaphragm up into the thoracic cavity and passively decrease chest volume even more. The action of abdominal muscles during forced expiration is why aerobics instructors tell you to blow air out as you lift your head and shoulders during abdominal "crunches." The active process of blowing air out helps contract the abdominals, the very muscles you are trying to strengthen.

Any neuromuscular disease that weakens skeletal muscles or damages their motor neurons can adversely affect ventilation. With decreased ventilation, less fresh air enters the lungs. In addition, loss of the ability to cough increases the risk of pneumonia and other infections. Examples of diseases that affect the motor control of ventilation include *myasthenia gravis* [p. 274], an illness in which acetylcholine receptors of the motor end plates of skeletal muscles are destroyed, and *polio* (poliomyelitis), a viral illness that paralyzes skeletal muscles.

CONCEPT CHECK

18. Scarlett O'Hara is trying to squeeze herself into a corset with an 18-inch waist. Will she be more successful by taking a deep breath and holding it or by blowing all the air out of her lungs? Why?
19. Why would loss of the ability to cough increase the risk of respiratory infections? (*Hint:* what does coughing do to mucus in the airways?)

Answers: p. 586

Intrapleural Pressure Changes During Ventilation

Ventilation requires that the lungs, which are unable to expand and contract on their own, move in association with the contraction and relaxation of the thorax. As we noted earlier in this chapter, the lungs are "stuck" to the thoracic cage by cohesive forces exerted by the fluid between the two pleural membranes. Thus, if the thoracic cage moves, the lungs move with it.

The intrapleural pressure in the fluid between the pleural membranes is normally subatmospheric. This subatmospheric pressure arises during fetal development, when the thoracic cage with its associated pleural membrane grows more rapidly than the lung with its associated pleural membrane. The two pleural membranes are held together by the pleural fluid bond, so the elastic lungs are forced to stretch to conform to the larger volume of the thoracic cavity. At the same time, however, elastic recoil of the lungs creates an inwardly directed force that tends to pull the lungs away from the chest wall (Fig. 17-12a ■). The combination of the outward pull of the thoracic cage and inward recoil of the elastic lungs creates a subatmospheric intrapleural pressure of about −3 mm Hg.

You can create a similar situation by half-filling a syringe with water and capping it with a plugged-up needle. At this

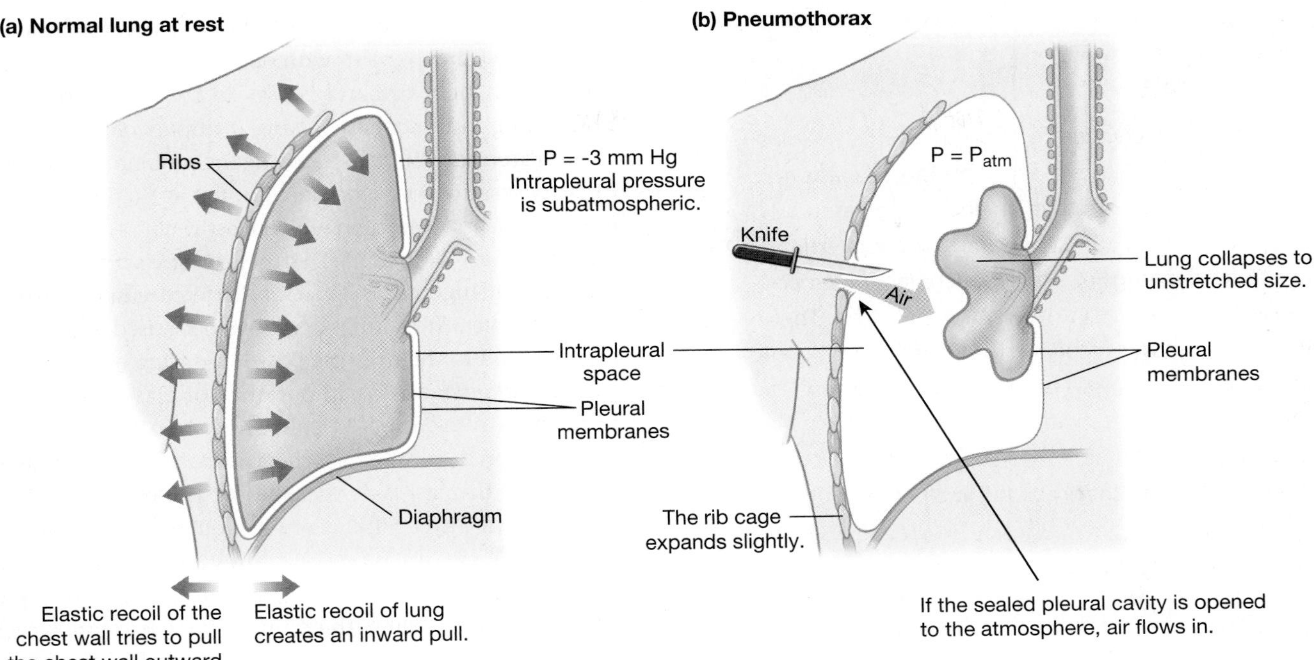

■ **FIGURE 17-12** ***Pressure in the pleural cavity***

point, the pressure inside the barrel is equal to atmospheric pressure. Now hold the syringe barrel (the chest wall) in one hand while you try to withdraw the plunger (the elastic lung pulling away from the chest wall). As you pull on the plunger, the volume inside the barrel increases slightly, but the cohesive forces between the water molecules cause the water to resist expansion. The pressure in the barrel, which was initially equal to atmospheric pressure, decreases slightly as you pull on the plunger. If you release the plunger, it snaps back to its resting position, restoring atmospheric pressure inside the syringe.

What happens to subatmospheric intrapleural pressure if an opening is made between the sealed pleural cavity and the atmosphere? A knife thrust between the ribs, a broken rib that punctures the pleural membrane, or any other event that opens the pleural cavity to the atmosphere will allow air to flow in down its pressure gradient, just as air enters when you break the seal on a vacuum-packed can.

Air in the pleural cavity breaks the fluid bond holding the lung to the chest wall. The chest wall expands outward while the elastic lung collapses to an unstretched state, like a deflated balloon (Fig. 17-12b). This condition, called **pneumothorax** [*pneuma,* air + *thorax,* chest], results in a collapsed lung that is unable to function normally. Pneumothorax can also occur spontaneously if a congenital *bleb* (or weakened section of lung tissue) ruptures, allowing air from inside the lung to enter the pleural cavity.

Correction of a pneumothorax has two components: removing as much air from the pleural cavity as possible with a suction pump, and sealing the hole to prevent more air from entering. Any air remaining in the cavity will gradually be absorbed into the blood, restoring the pleural fluid bond and reinflating the lung.

Pressures in the pleural fluid vary during a respiratory cycle. At the beginning of inspiration, intrapleural pressure is about −3 mm Hg (Fig. 17-11, point B_1). As inspiration proceeds, the pleural membranes and lungs follow the expanding thoracic cage because of the pleural fluid bond, but the elastic lung tissue resists being stretched. The lungs attempt to pull farther away from the chest wall, causing the intrapleural pressure to become even more negative (Fig. 17-11, point B_2).

Because this process is difficult to visualize, return to the analogy of the water-filled syringe with the plugged-up needle. You can pull the plunger out a small distance without much effort, but the cohesiveness of the water makes it difficult to pull the plunger out any farther. The increased amount of work you do trying to pull the plunger out is paralleled by the work your inspiratory muscles must do when they contract during inspiration. The bigger the breath, the more work is required to stretch the elastic lung.

By the end of a quiet inspiration, when the lungs are fully expanded, intrapleural pressure falls to around −6 mm Hg (Fig. 17-11, point B_2). During exercise or other powerful inspirations, intrapleural pressure may reach −8 mm Hg.

During expiration, the thoracic cage returns to its resting position. The lungs are released from their stretched position, and the intrapleural pressure returns to its normal value of about −3 mm Hg (point B_3). Notice that intrapleural pressure never equilibrates with atmospheric pressure because the pleural cavity is a closed compartment.

RUNNING PROBLEM

Emphysema is characterized by a loss of elastin, the elastic fibers that help the alveoli recoil during expiration. Elastin is destroyed by elastase, an enzyme released by cells of the immune system, which must work overtime in smokers to rid the lungs of irritants. People with emphysema have more difficulty exhaling than inhaling. Their alveoli have lost elastic recoil, which makes expiration—normally a passive process—require conscious effort. They literally must work to push air out of their lungs.

Question 3:

Name the muscles that patients with emphysema use to exhale actively.

Pressure gradients required for air flow are created by the work of skeletal muscle contraction. Normally, about 3–5% of the body's energy expenditure is used for quiet breathing. During exercise, the energy required for breathing increases substantially. The two factors that have the greatest influence on the amount of work needed for breathing are the stretchability of the lungs and the resistance of the airways to air flow.

CONCEPT CHECK

20. A person has periodic spastic contractions of the diaphragm, otherwise known as hiccups. What happens to intrapleural and alveolar pressures when a person hiccups?
21. A stabbing victim is brought to the emergency room with a knife wound between the ribs on the left side of his chest. What has probably happened to his left lung? To his right lung? Why does the left side of his rib cage seem larger than the right side? Answers: p. 586

Lung Compliance and Elastance May Change in Disease States

Adequate ventilation depends on the ability of the lungs to expand normally. Most of the work of breathing goes into overcoming the resistance of the elastic lungs and the thoracic cage to stretching. Clinically, the ability of the lung to stretch is called **compliance**. A high-compliance lung stretches easily, just as a compliant person is easy to persuade. A low-compliance lung requires more force from the inspiratory muscles to stretch it.

Compliance is different from **elastance** (elasticity). The fact that a lung stretches easily (high compliance) does not necessarily mean that it will return to its resting volume when the stretching force is released (elastance). You may have experienced something like this with old gym shorts. After many washings the elastic waistband is easy to stretch (high compliance) but lacking in elastance, making it impossible for the shorts to stay up around your waist. Analogous problems occur in the respiratory system. For example, as noted in the Running Problem, emphysema is a disease in which elastin fibers normally found in lung tissue are destroyed. Destruction of elastin results in lungs that exhibit high compliance and stretch easily during inspiration. However, these lungs also have decreased elastance, so they do not recoil to their resting position during expiration.

To understand the importance of elastic recoil to expiration, think of an inflated balloon and an inflated plastic bag. The balloon is similar to the normal lung. Its elastic walls squeeze on the air inside the balloon, thereby increasing the internal air pressure. When the neck of the balloon is opened to the atmosphere, elastic recoil causes air to flow out of the balloon. The inflated plastic bag, on the other hand, is like the lung of an individual with emphysema. It has high compliance and is easily inflated, but it has little elastic recoil. If the inflated plastic bag is opened to the atmosphere, most of the air remains inside the bag.

CLINICAL FOCUS

FIBROTIC LUNG DISEASE

One type of lung disease results from chronic inhalation of fine particulate matter that escapes the mucus lining the airways and reaches the exchange epithelium of the alveoli. The only protective mechanism in that region of the respiratory system is removal by wandering alveolar macrophages (see Fig. 17-2g). These phagocytic cells patrol the alveoli, engulfing any airborne particles that reach them. If the particles are organic, the macrophages digest them with lysosomal enzymes. However, if the particles cannot be digested or if they accumulate in large numbers, an inflammatory process ensues. Intracellular accumulation of particles causes the macrophage to secrete growth factors that stimulate fibroblasts in the lung's connective tissue. These fibroblasts produce collagen that forms inelastic, fibrous scar tissue. Large amounts of scar tissue reduce the compliance of the lung and result in **fibrotic lung disease**, or **fibrosis**. Particles that can trigger fibrosis include asbestos, coal dust, silicon, and even dust, paper particles, and industrial pollutants.

(a) Pressure is greater in the smaller bubble.

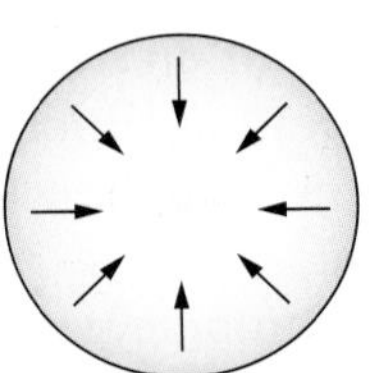

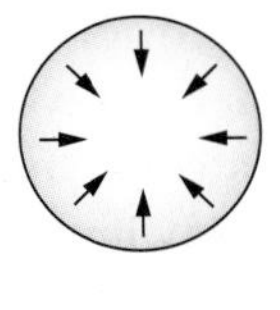

Law of LaPlace: P = 2T/r
P = pressure
T = surface tension
r = radius
According to the law of LaPlace, if two bubbles have the same surface tension, the smaller bubble will have higher pressure.

(b) Surfactant reduces surface tension (T). Pressure is equalized in the large and small bubbles.

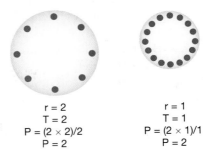

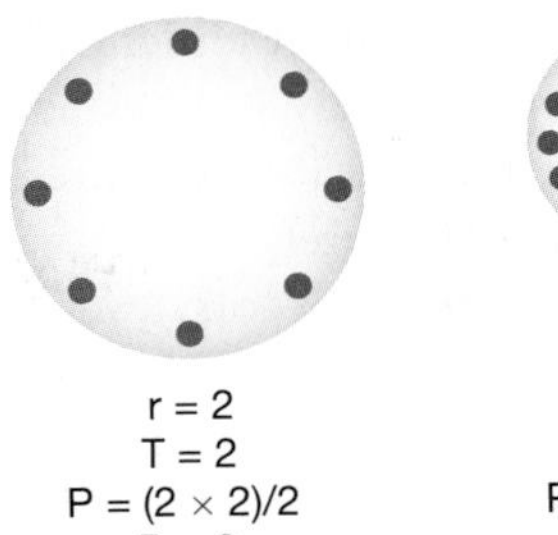

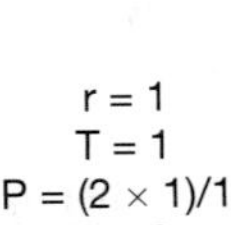

FIGURE 17-13 ***The law of LaPlace***

(a) Because r is in the denominator in the LaPlace equation, the pressure inside a bubble increases as bubble radius decreases. **(b)** The presence of surfactant lowers the surface tension in a film. In this way, surfactant helps equalize the interior pressure in bubbles of different sizes.

A decrease in lung compliance affects ventilation because more work must be expended to stretch a stiff lung. Pathological conditions in which compliance is reduced are called **restrictive lung diseases**. In these conditions, the energy expenditure required to stretch less-compliant lungs can far exceed the normal work of breathing. Two common causes of decreased compliance are inelastic scar tissue formed in *fibrotic lung diseases,* and inadequate alveolar production of surfactant, a chemical that facilitates lung expansion.

Surfactant Decreases the Work of Breathing

For years, physiologists assumed that elastin and other elastic fibers were the primary source of resistance to stretch in the lung. However, studies comparing the work required to expand air-filled and saline-filled lungs showed that air-filled lungs are much harder to inflate. From this result, researchers concluded that lung tissue itself contributes less to resistance than once thought. Some other property of the normal air-filled lung, a property not present in the saline-filled lung, must create most of the resistance to stretch.

This property is the surface tension [p. 25] created by the thin fluid layer between the alveolar cells and the air. At any air-fluid interface, the surface of the fluid is under tension, like a thin membrane being stretched. When the fluid is water, surface tension arises because of the hydrogen bonds between water molecules. The water molecules on the fluid's surface are attracted to other water molecules beside and beneath them but are not attracted to gases in the air at the air-fluid interface.

Alveolar surface tension is similar to that which exists in a spherical bubble. The surface tension created by the thin film of fluid is directed toward the center of the bubble and creates pressure in the interior (Fig. 17-13a ■). The **law of LaPlace** is an expression of this pressure. It states that the pressure (P) inside a bubble formed by a fluid film is a function of two factors: the surface tension of the fluid (T) and the radius of the bubble (r). This relationship is expressed by the equation

$$P = 2T/r$$

If two bubbles have different diameters but are formed by fluids that have the same surface tension, the pressure inside the smaller bubble is greater than that inside the larger bubble (Fig. 17-13a).

How does this apply to the lung? In physiology, we equate the bubble to a fluid-lined alveolus (although alveoli are not perfect spheres). The fluid lining all the alveoli creates surface tension. If the surface tension (T) of the fluid were the same in small and large alveoli, small alveoli would have higher inwardly-directed pressure than larger alveoli, and increased resistance to stretch. As a result, more work would be needed to expand smaller alveoli.

Normally, however, our lungs secrete a surfactant that reduces surface tension. Surfactants ("surface active agents") are molecules that disrupt cohesive forces between water molecules by substituting themselves for water at the surface. For example, that product you add to your dishwasher to aid in the rinse cycle is a surfactant that keeps the rinse water from beading up on the dishes (and forming "spots" when the water beads dry). In the lungs, surfactant decreases surface tension of the alveolar fluid and thereby decreases resistance of the lung to stretch.

Surfactant is more concentrated in smaller alveoli, making their surface tension less than that in larger alveoli (Fig. 17-13b). Lower surface tension helps equalize the pressure among alveoli of different sizes and makes it easier to inflate the smaller alveoli. With lower surface tension, the work needed to expand the alveoli with each breath is greatly reduced. Human surfactant is a mixture containing proteins and phospholipids, such as *dipalmitoylphosphatidylcholine*, which are secreted into the alveolar air space by type II alveolar cells (see Fig. 17-2g).

Normally, surfactant synthesis begins about the twenty-fifth week of fetal development under the influence of various hormones. Production usually reaches adequate levels by the thirty-fourth week (about six weeks before normal delivery). Babies who are born prematurely without adequate concentrations of surfactant in their alveoli develop *newborn respiratory distress syndrome (RDS)*. In addition to "stiff" (low-compliance) lungs, RDS babies also have alveoli that collapse each time they exhale. These infants must use a tremendous amount of energy to expand their collapsed lungs with each breath. Unless treatment is initiated rapidly, about 50% of these infants die. In the past, all physicians could do for RDS babies was administer oxygen. Today, however, the prognosis for RDS babies is much better. Amniotic fluid can be sampled to assess whether or not the fetal lungs are producing adequate amounts of surfactant. If they are not, and if delivery cannot be delayed, RDS babies can be treated with aerosol administration of artificial surfactant until the lungs mature enough to produce their own. The current treatment also includes artificial ventilation that forces air into the lungs and keeps the alveoli open.

Airway Diameter Is the Primary Determinant of Airway Resistance

The other factor besides compliance that influences the work of breathing is the resistance of the respiratory system to air flow. Resistance in the respiratory system is similar in many ways to resistance in the cardiovascular system [p. 462]. Three parameters contribute to resistance (R): the system's length (L), the viscosity of the substance flowing through the system (η), and the radius of the tubes in the system (r). As with flow in the cardiovascular system, Poiseuille's law relates these factors to one another:

$$R \propto L\eta/r^4$$

Because the length of the respiratory system is constant, we can ignore L in the equation. The viscosity of air is almost constant, although you may have noticed that it feels harder to breathe in a sauna filled with steam than in a room with normal humidity. Water droplets in the steam increase the viscosity of the steamy air, thereby increasing its resistance to flow. Viscosity also changes slightly with atmospheric pressure, decreasing as pressure decreases. A person at high altitude may feel less resistance to air flow than a person at sea level. Despite these exceptions, viscosity plays a very small role in resistance to air flow.

Because length and viscosity are essentially constant for the respiratory system, the radius (or diameter) of the airways becomes the primary determinant of airway resistance. Normally, however, the work needed to overcome resistance of the airways to air flow is much less than the work needed to overcome the resistance of the lungs and thoracic cage to stretch.

Nearly 90% of airway resistance normally can be attributed to the trachea and bronchi, rigid structures with the smallest total cross-sectional area. Because these structures are supported by cartilage and bone, their diameters normally do not change, and their resistance to air flow is constant. However, mucus accumulation from allergies or infections can dramatically increase resistance. If you have ever tried breathing through your nose when you have a cold, you can appreciate how the narrowing of an upper airway limits air flow!

The bronchioles normally do not contribute significantly to airway resistance because their total cross-sectional area is about 2000 times that of the trachea. Because the bronchioles are collapsible tubes, however, a decrease in their diameter can suddenly turn them into a significant source of airway resistance. **Bronchoconstriction** increases resistance to air flow and decreases the amount of fresh air that reaches the alveoli.

Bronchioles, like arterioles, are subject to reflex control by the nervous system and by hormones. However, most minute-to-minute changes in bronchiolar diameter occur in response to paracrines. Carbon dioxide in the airways is the primary paracrine that affects bronchiolar diameter. Increased CO_2 in expired air relaxes bronchiolar smooth muscle and causes **bronchodilation**.

Histamine is a paracrine that acts as a powerful bronchoconstrictor. This chemical is released by *mast cells* [p. 538] in response to either tissue damage or allergic reactions. In severe allergic reactions, large amounts of histamine may lead to widespread bronchoconstriction and difficult breathing. Immediate medical treatment in these patients is imperative.

The primary neural control of bronchioles comes from parasympathetic neurons that cause bronchoconstriction, a reflex designed to protect the lower respiratory tract from inhaled irritants. There is no significant sympathetic innervation of the bronchioles in humans. However, smooth muscle in the bronchioles is well supplied with β_2-receptors that respond to epinephrine. Stimulation of β_2-receptors relaxes airway smooth muscle and results in bronchodilation. This reflex is used therapeutically in the treatment of asthma and various allergic reactions characterized by histamine release and bronchoconstriction. Table 17-3 ■ summarizes the factors that alter airway resistance.

CONCEPT CHECK

22. In a normal person, which contributes more to the work of breathing: airway resistance or lung and chest wall compliance?
23. Coal miners who spend years inhaling fine coal dust have much of their alveolar surface area covered with scarlike tissue. What happens to their lung compliance as a result?
24. How does the work required for breathing change when surfactant is not present in the lungs?
25. A cancerous lung tumor has grown into the walls of a group of bronchioles, narrowing their lumens. What has happened to the resistance to air flow in these bronchioles?
26. Name the neurotransmitter and receptor for parasympathetic bronchoconstriction.

Answers: p. 586

TABLE 17-3	Factors That Affect Airway Resistance	
FACTOR	**AFFECTED BY**	**MEDIATED BY**
Length of the system	Constant; not a factor	
Viscosity of air	Usually constant; humidity and altitude may alter slightly	
Diameter of airways		
Upper airways	Physical obstruction	Mucus and other factors
Bronchioles	Bronchoconstriction	Parasympathetic neurons (muscarinic receptors), histamine, leukotrienes
	Bronchodilation	Carbon dioxide, epinephrine (β_2-receptors)

Rate and Depth of Breathing Determine the Efficiency of Breathing

You may recall that the efficiency of the heart is measured by the cardiac output, which is calculated by multiplying heart rate by stroke volume. Likewise, we can estimate the effectiveness of ventilation by calculating **total pulmonary ventilation**, the volume of air moved into and out of the lungs each minute. Total pulmonary ventilation, also known as the *minute volume*, is calculated as follows:

$$\text{total pulmonary ventilation} = \text{ventilation rate} \times \text{tidal volume}$$

The normal ventilation rate for an adult is 12–20 breaths per minute. Using the average tidal volume (500 mL) and the slowest ventilation rate, we get:

$$\text{total pulmonary ventilation} = 12 \text{ breaths/min} \times 500 \text{ mL/breath} = 6000 \text{ mL/min} = 6 \text{ L/min}$$

Total pulmonary ventilation represents the physical movement of air into and out of the respiratory tract, but is it a good indicator of how much fresh air reaches the alveolar exchange surface? Not necessarily.

Some air that enters the respiratory system does not reach the alveoli because part of every breath remains in the conducting airways, such as the trachea and bronchi. Because the conducting airways do not exchange gases with the blood, they are known as the **anatomic dead space**. Anatomic dead space averages about 150 mL.

To illustrate the difference between the total volume of air that enters the airways and the volume of fresh air that reaches the alveoli, let's consider a typical breath that moves 500 mL of air during a respiratory cycle (Fig. 17-14 ■).

1. At the end of an inspiration, lung volume is maximal, and fresh air fills the dead space.
2. The tidal volume of 500 mL is exhaled. However, the first portion of this 500 mL to exit the airways is the 150 mL of fresh air that had been in the dead space, followed by 350 mL of "stale" air from the alveoli. Thus even though 500 mL of air exited the alveoli, only 350 mL of that volume left the body. The remaining 150 mL of "stale" alveolar air stays in the dead space.
3. At the end of expiration, lung volume is at its minimum, and stale air from the most recent expiration fills the anatomic dead space.
4. With the next inspiration, 500 mL of fresh air enters the airways. The entering air returns the 150 mL of stale air in the anatomic dead space to the alveoli, followed by the first 350 mL of the fresh air. The last 150 mL of inspired fresh air again remains in the dead space and never reaches the alveoli.

Thus, although 500 mL of air entered the alveoli, only 350 mL of that volume was fresh air. The fresh air entering the alveoli equals the tidal volume minus the dead space volume.

Because a significant portion of inspired air never reaches an exchange surface, a more accurate indicator of ventilation efficiency is **alveolar ventilation**, the amount of fresh air that reaches the alveoli each minute. Alveolar ventilation is calculated by multiplying ventilation rate by the volume of fresh air that reaches the alveoli:

$$\text{alveolar ventilation} = \text{ventilation rate} \times (\text{tidal volume} - \text{dead space})$$

Using the same ventilation rate and tidal volume as before, and a dead space of 150 mL, then

$$\text{alveolar ventilation} = 12 \text{ breaths/min} \times (500 - 150 \text{ mL/breath}) = 4200 \text{ mL/min}$$

Thus, at 12 breaths per minute, the alveolar ventilation is 4.2 L/min. Although 6 L/min of fresh air enters the respiratory system, only 4.2 L reaches the alveoli.

Alveolar ventilation can be drastically affected by changes in the rate or depth of breathing. Table 17-4 ■ shows that three people can have the same total pulmonary ventilation but dramatically different alveolar ventilation. **Maximum voluntary ventilation**, which involves breathing as deeply and quickly as possible, may increase total pulmonary ventilation to as much as 170 L/min. Table 17-5 ■ describes various patterns of ventilation, and Table 17-6 ■ gives normal ventilation values.

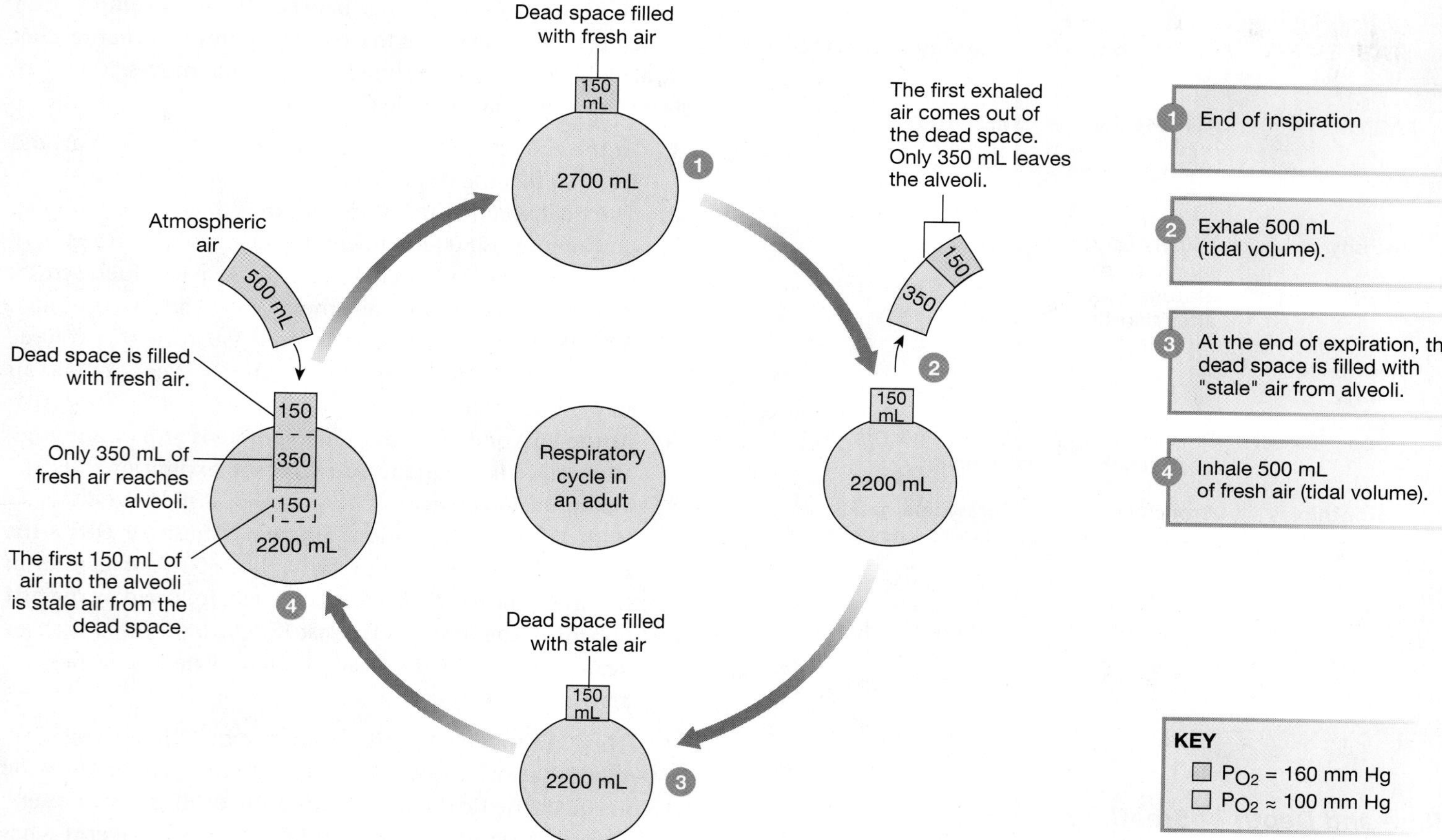

■ **FIGURE 17-14** ***Total pulmonary ventilation and alveolar ventilation***

In this example, total pulmonary ventilation is 500 mL/breath × ventilation rate but alveolar ventilation is only 350 mL/breath × ventilation rate.

Gas Composition in the Alveoli Varies Little During Normal Breathing

How much can a change in alveolar ventilation affect the amount of fresh air and oxygen that reach the alveoli? Fig. 17-15 ■ shows how the partial pressures P_{O_2} and P_{CO_2} in the alveoli vary with hyper- and hypoventilation. As alveolar ventilation increases above normal levels (**hyperventilation**), alveolar P_{O_2} rises to about 120 mm Hg, and alveolar P_{CO_2} falls to around 20 mm Hg. During **hypoventilation**, when less fresh air enters the alveoli, alveolar P_{O_2} decreases and alveolar P_{CO_2} increases.

Although a dramatic change in alveolar ventilation pattern will affect gas partial pressures in the alveoli, the P_{O_2} and

TABLE 17-4 **Effects of Breathing Pattern on Alveolar Ventilation**

TIDAL VOLUME (ML)	VENTILATION RATE (BREATHS/MIN)	TOTAL PULMONARY VENTILATION (ML/MIN)	FRESH AIR TO ALVEOLI (ML) (TIDAL VOLUME–DEAD SPACE VOLUME*)	ALVEOLAR VENTILATION (ML/MIN)
500 (normal)	12 (normal)	6000	350	4200
300 (shallow)	20 (rapid)	6000	150	3000
750 (deep)	8 (slow)	6000	600	4800

*Dead space volume is assumed to be 150 mL.

TABLE 17-5 Types and Patterns of Ventilation

NAME	DESCRIPTION	EXAMPLES
Eupnea	Normal quiet breathing	
Hyperpnea	Increased respiratory rate and/or volume in response to increased metabolism	Exercise
Hyperventilation	Increased respiratory rate and/or volume without increased metabolism	Emotional hyperventilation; blowing up a balloon
Hypoventilation	Decreased alveolar ventilation	Shallow breathing; asthma; restrictive lung disease
Tachypnea	Rapid breathing; usually increased respiratory rate with decreased depth	Panting
Dyspnea	Difficulty breathing (a subjective feeling sometimes described as "air hunger")	Various pathologies or hard exercise
Apnea	Cessation of breathing	Voluntary breath-holding; depression of CNS control centers

P_{CO_2} in the alveoli change surprisingly little during normal quiet breathing. Alveolar P_{O_2} is fairly constant at 100 mm Hg, and alveolar P_{CO_2} stays close to 40 mm Hg.

Intuitively, you might think that P_{O_2} would increase when fresh air first enters the alveoli, then decrease steadily as oxygen leaves to enter the blood. Instead, we find only very small swings in P_{O_2}. Why? The reasons are that (1) the amount of oxygen that enters the alveoli with each breath is roughly equal to the amount of oxygen that enters the blood, and (2) the amount of fresh air that enters the lungs with each breath is only a little more than 10% of the total lung volume at the end of inspiration.

CONCEPT CHECK

27. If a person increased his tidal volume, what would happen to his alveolar P_{O_2}?
28. If his breathing rate increased, what would happen to his alveolar P_{O_2}?

Answers: p. 586

TABLE 17-6 Normal Ventilation Values in Pulmonary Medicine

Total pulmonary ventilation	6 L/min
Total alveolar ventilation	4.2 L/min
Maximum voluntary ventilation	125–170 L/min
Respiration rate	12–20 breaths/min

Ventilation and Alveolar Blood Flow Are Matched

Moving oxygen from the atmosphere to the alveolar exchange surface is only the first step in external respiration. Next, gas exchange must occur across the alveolar-capillary interface.

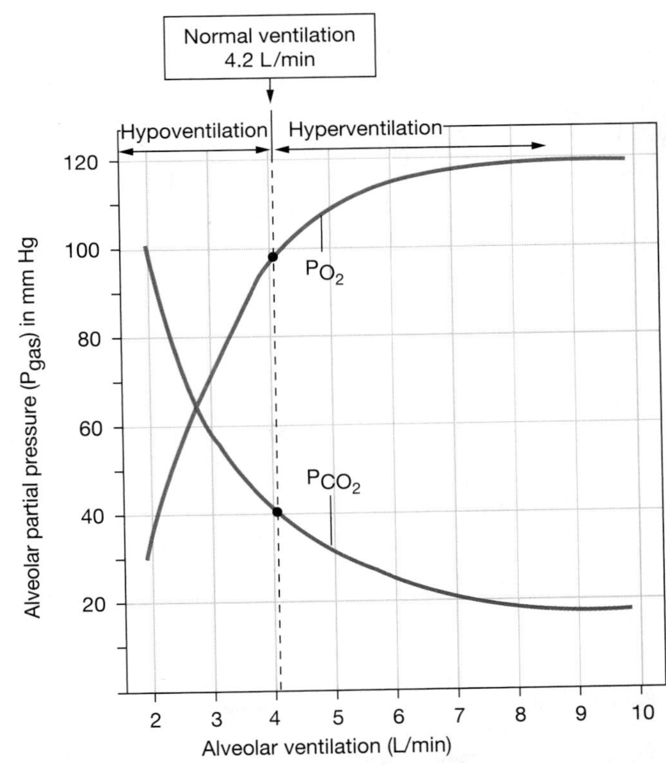

■ **FIGURE 17-15** ***Effect of changing alveolar ventilation on P_{O_2} and P_{CO_2} in the alveoli***

Finally, blood flow (*perfusion*) past the alveoli must be high enough to pick up the available oxygen. Matching the ventilation rate into groups of alveoli with blood flow past those alveoli is a two-part process involving local regulation of both air flow and blood flow.

Alterations in pulmonary blood flow depend almost exclusively on properties of the capillaries and on such local factors as the concentrations of oxygen and carbon dioxide in the lung tissue. Capillaries in the lungs are unusual because they are collapsible. If the pressure of blood flowing through the capillaries falls below a certain point, the capillaries close off, diverting blood to pulmonary capillary beds in which blood pressure is higher.

In a person at rest, some capillary beds in the apex (top) of the lung are closed off because of low hydrostatic pressure. Capillary beds at the base of the lung have higher hydrostatic pressure because of gravity and thus remain open. Consequently, blood flow is diverted toward the base of the lung. During exercise, when blood pressure rises, the closed apical capillary beds open, ensuring that the increased cardiac output will be fully oxygenated as it passes through the lungs. The ability of the lungs to recruit additional capillary beds during exercise is an example of the reserve capacity of the body.

At the local level, the body attempts to match air flow and blood flow in each section of the lung by regulating the diameters of the arterioles and bronchioles. Bronchiolar diameter is mediated primarily by CO_2 levels in exhaled air passing through them (Table 17-7 ■). An increase in the P_{CO_2} of expired air causes bronchioles to dilate. A decrease in the P_{CO_2} of expired air causes bronchioles to constrict.

Although there is some autonomic innervation of pulmonary arterioles, there is apparently little neural control of pulmonary blood flow. The resistance of pulmonary arterioles to blood flow is regulated primarily by the oxygen content of the interstitial fluid around the arteriole (Fig. 17-16 ■). If ventilation of alveoli in one area of the lung is diminished, the P_{O_2} in that area decreases, and the arterioles respond by constricting (Fig. 17-16c). This local vasoconstriction is adaptive because it diverts blood away from the underventilated region to better-ventilated parts of the lung.

On the other hand, if P_{O_2} in some region of the lung becomes higher than normal, the alveoli in that region are being overventilated relative to the blood flow past them. The arterioles supplying those alveoli dilate to bring in additional blood to pick up the extra oxygen.

Note that constriction of pulmonary arterioles in response to low P_{O_2} is the opposite of what occurs in the systemic circulation [p. 511]. In the systemic circulation, a decrease in the P_{O_2} of a tissue causes local arterioles to dilate, bringing more blood to those tissues that are consuming oxygen.

Another important point must be noted here. Local control mechanisms are not effective regulators of air and blood flow under all circumstances. If blood flow is blocked in one pulmonary artery, or if air flow is blocked at the level of the larger airways, local responses that shunt air or blood to other parts of the lung are ineffective because in these cases no part of the lung has normal ventilation or perfusion.

CONCEPT CHECK

29. If a lung tumor decreases blood flow in one small section of the lung to a minimum, what happens to P_{O_2} in the alveoli in that section and in the surrounding interstitial fluid? What happens to P_{CO_2} in that section? What is the compensatory response of the bronchioles in the affected section? Will the compensation bring ventilation in the affected section of the lung back to normal? Explain.

Answers: p. 586

Auscultation and Spirometry Assess Pulmonary Function

Most pulmonary function tests are relatively simple to perform. Auscultation of breath sounds is an important diagnostic technique in pulmonary medicine, just as auscultation of heart sounds is an important technique in cardiovascular diagnosis [p. 486]. Breath sounds are more complicated to interpret than heart sounds, however, because breath sounds have a wider range of normal variation.

TABLE 17-7 Local Control of Arterioles and Bronchioles by Oxygen and Carbon Dioxide

GAS COMPOSITION	BRONCHIOLES	PULMONARY ARTERIOLES	SYSTEMIC ARTERIOLES
P_{CO_2} increases	Dilate	(Constrict)*	Dilate
P_{CO_2} decreases	Constrict	(Dilate)	Constrict
P_{O_2} increases	(Constrict)	Dilate	Constrict
P_{O_2} decreases	(Dilate)	Constrict	Dilate

*Responses in parentheses indicate weak responses.

(a) Ventilation in alveoli is matched to perfusion through pulmonary capillaries.

Arteriole

Bronchiole

Low oxygen blood

Alveoli

Alveoli

(b) Ventilation-perfusion mismatch.

If ventilation decreases in a group of alveoli (blue), P_{CO_2} increases and P_{O_2} decreases. Blood flowing past those alveoli does not get oxygenated.

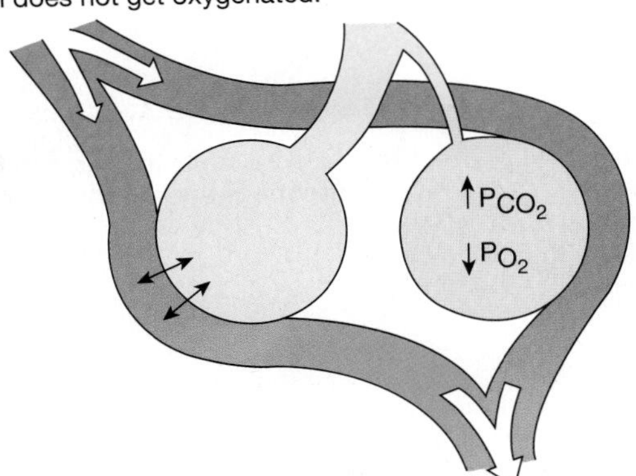
↑P_{CO_2}
↓P_{O_2}

(c) Local control mechanisms try to keep ventilation and perfusion matched.

Decreased tissue P_{O_2} around underventilated alveoli constricts their arterioles, diverting blood to better-ventilated alveoli.

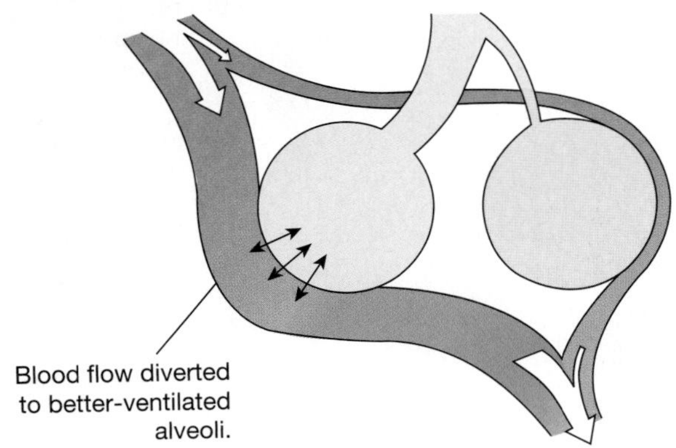
Blood flow diverted to better-ventilated alveoli.

■ **FIGURE 17-16** ***Local control matches ventilation and perfusion***

RUNNING PROBLEM

Edna has been admitted to the hospital for tests related to her COPD. One of the tests is a hematocrit, an indicator of the number of red blood cells in her blood. The results of this test show that Edna has higher-than-normal numbers of red blood cells.

Question 4:

Why does Edna have an increased hematocrit? (Hint: because of Edna's COPD, her arterial P_{O_2} is low.)

559 561 569 574 581 582

Normally, breath sounds are distributed evenly over the lungs and resemble a quiet "whoosh" made by flowing air. When air flow is reduced, such as in pneumothorax, breath sounds may be either diminished or absent. Abnormal sounds include various squeaks, pops, wheezes, and bubbling sounds caused by fluid and secretions in the airways or alveoli. Inflammation of the pleural membrane results in a crackling or grating sound known as a *friction rub*. It is caused by swollen, inflamed pleural membranes rubbing against each other, and it disappears when fluid again separates them.

Diseases in which air flow during expiration is diminished as a result of narrowing of the bronchioles are known as **obstructive lung diseases**. When patients with obstructive lung diseases are asked to exhale forcefully, air whistling through the narrowed lower airways creates a wheezing sound that can be heard even without a stethoscope. Depending on the severity of the disease, the bronchioles may even collapse and close off before a forced expiration is completed, reducing both the amount and rate of air flow as measured by a spirometer.

Obstructive lung diseases include asthma, emphysema, and chronic bronchitis. The latter two are sometimes called *chronic obstructive pulmonary disease* (COPD) because of their ongoing, or chronic, nature. Asthma is an inflammatory condition, often associated with allergies, that is characterized by bronchoconstriction and airway edema. Asthma can be triggered by exercise (exercise-induced asthma) and by rapid changes in the temperature or humidity of inspired air. Asthmatic patients complain of "air hunger" and difficulty breathing (dyspnea). The severity of asthma attacks ranges from mild to life threatening.

Studies of asthma at the cellular level show that a variety of chemical signals may be responsible for inducing asthmatic bronchoconstriction, including acetylcholine, histamine, substance P (a neuropeptide), and leukotrienes secreted by mast cells, macrophages, and eosinophils. *Leukotrienes* are lipid-like bronchoconstrictors that are released during the inflammatory response. Asthma is treated with inhaled and oral medications that include β_2-adrenergic agonists, anti-inflammatory drugs, and leukotriene antagonists.

CONCEPT CHECK

30. Restrictive lung diseases [p. 575] decrease lung compliance. How will inspiratory reserve volume change in patients with a restrictive lung disease?
31. Chronic obstructive lung disease causes patients to lose the ability to exhale fully. How does residual volume change in these patients? Answers: p. 586

This completes our discussion of the mechanics of ventilation. In the next chapter, we shift from bulk flow of air to the diffusion and transport of oxygen and carbon dioxide as they travel between the air spaces of the alveoli and the cells of the body.

RUNNING PROBLEM CONCLUSION

EMPHYSEMA

Edna is discharged from the hospital after three days and given prescriptions for bronchodilator and anti-inflammatory drugs to keep her airways as open as possible. Unfortunately, the lung changes that take place with COPD are not reversible, and she will require treatment for the rest of her life. According to the American Lung Association (*www.lungusa.org*), COPD is the fourth leading cause of death in the United States and costs more than $30 billion per year in direct medical costs and indirect costs such as lost wages.

In this running problem you learned about chronic obstructive pulmonary disease. Now check your understanding of the physiology in the problem by comparing your answers with those in the following table.

	QUESTION	FACTS	INTEGRATION AND ANALYSIS
1	What does narrowing of the airways do to the resistance airways offer to air flow?	The relationship between tube radius and resistance is the same for air flow as for blood flow: as radius decreases, resistance increases [p. 462].	When resistance increases, the body must use more energy to create air flow.
2	Why do people with chronic bronchitis have a higher-than-normal rate of respiratory infections?	Cigarette smoke paralyzes the cilia that sweep debris and mucus out of the airways. Without the action of cilia, mucus and trapped particles pool in the airways.	Bacteria trapped in the mucus can multiply and cause respiratory infections.
3	Name the muscles that patients with emphysema use to exhale actively.	Normal expiration depends on elastic recoil of muscles and elastic tissue in the lungs.	Forceful expiration involves the internal intercostal muscles and the abdominal muscles.
4	Why does Edna have an increased hematocrit?	Because of Edna's COPD, her arterial P_{O_2} is low. The major stimulus for red blood cell synthesis is hypoxia.	Low arterial oxygen levels trigger the synthesis of additional red blood cells. This provides more binding sites for oxygen transport.

559 561 569 574 581 582

CHAPTER SUMMARY

The process by which air flows into and out of the lungs is another example of the principle of *mass flow*. Like blood flow, air flow requires a pump to create a pressure gradient and encounters resistance primarily from changes in the diameter of the tubes through which it flows. The *mechanical properties* of the pleural sacs and elastic recoil in the chest wall and lung tissue are essential for normal ventilation.

1. Aerobic metabolism in living cells consumes oxygen and produces carbon dioxide. (p. 559)
2. Gas exchange requires a large, thin, moist exchange surface; a pump to move air; and a circulatory system to transport gases to the cells. (p. 559)
3. Respiratory system functions include gas exchange, pH regulation, vocalization, and protection from foreign substances. (p. 559)

Respiratory System

IP Respiratory System: Anatomy Review

4. **Cellular respiration** refers to cellular metabolism that consumes oxygen. **External respiration** is the exchange of gases between the atmosphere and cells of the body. It includes ventilation, gas exchange at the lung and cells, and transport of gases in the blood. **Ventilation** is the movement of air into and out of the lungs. (pp. 559–560; Fig. 17-1)
5. The **respiratory system** consists of anatomical structures involved in ventilation and gas exchange. (p. 560)
6. The **upper respiratory tract** includes the mouth, nasal cavity, **pharynx**, and **larynx**. The **lower respiratory tract** includes the **trachea**, **bronchi**, **bronchioles**, and exchange surfaces of the **alveoli**. (p. 560; Fig. 17-2a)
7. The thoracic cage is bounded by the ribs, spine, and **diaphragm**. Two sets of **intercostal muscles** connect the ribs. (p. 560; Fig. 17-2b)
8. Each **lung** is contained within a double-walled **pleural sac** that contains a small quantity of **pleural fluid**. (p. 560; Figs. 17-2d, 17-3)
9. The two **primary bronchi** enter the lungs. Each primary bronchus divides into progressively smaller bronchi and finally into collapsible **bronchioles**. (p. 561; Figs. 17-2e, 17-4)
10. The alveoli consist mostly of thin-walled **type I alveolar cells** for gas exchange. **Type II alveolar cells** produce surfactant. A network of capillaries surrounds each alveolus. (p. 561; Fig. 17-2f, g)
11. Blood flow through the lungs equals cardiac output. Resistance to blood flow in the pulmonary circulation is low. Pulmonary arterial pressure averages 25/8 mm Hg. (p. 564)

Gas Laws

IP Respiratory System: Pulmonary Ventilation

12. The total pressure of a mixture of gases is the sum of the pressures of the individual gases in the mixture (**Dalton's law**). **Partial pressure** is the pressure contributed by a single gas in a mixture. (p. 565; Tbls. 17-1, 17-2)
13. Bulk flow of air occurs down pressure gradients, as does the movement of any individual gas making up the air. (p. 566)
14. **Boyle's law** states that as the volume available to a gas increases, the gas pressure decreases. The body creates pressure gradients by changing thoracic volume. (p. 566; Fig. 17-5)

Ventilation

IP Respiratory System: Pulmonary Ventilation

15. **Tidal volume** is the amount of air taken in during a single normal inspiration. **Vital capacity** is tidal volume plus **expiratory** and **inspiratory reserve volumes**. Air volume in the lungs at the end of maximal expiration is the **residual volume**. (p. 567; Fig. 17-7)
16. The upper respiratory system filters, warms, and humidifies inhaled air. (p. 568)
17. Air flow in the respiratory system is directly proportional to the pressure gradient, and inversely related to the resistance to air flow offered by the airways. (p. 569)
18. A single **respiratory cycle** consists of an inspiration and an expiration. (p. 570)
19. During **inspiration**, **alveolar pressure** decreases, and air flows into the lungs. Inspiration requires contraction of the inspiratory muscles and the diaphragm. (p. 570; Fig. 17-9)
20. **Expiration** is usually passive, resulting from elastic recoil of the lungs. (p. 572)
21. **Active expiration** requires contraction of the internal intercostal and abdominal muscles. (p. 572)
22. **Intrapleural pressures** are always subatmospheric because the pleural cavity is a sealed compartment. (p. 572; Fig. 17-11)
23. **Compliance** is the ease with which the chest wall and lungs expand. Loss of compliance increases the work of breathing. **Elastance** is the ability of a stretched lung to return to its normal volume. (p. 574)
24. **Surfactant** decreases surface tension in the fluid lining the alveoli. This prevents smaller alveoli from collapsing. (p. 575; Fig. 17-13)
25. The diameter of the bronchioles determines how much resistance they offer to air flow. (p. 576)
26. Increased CO_2 in expired air dilates bronchioles. Parasympathetic neurons cause **bronchoconstriction** in response to irritant stimuli. There is no significant sympathetic innervation of bronchioles, but epinephrine causes **bronchodilation**. (p. 576; Tbl. 17-3)
27. **Total pulmonary ventilation** = tidal volume × ventilation rate. **Alveolar ventilation** = ventilation rate × (tidal volume − dead space volume). (p. 577; Fig. 17-14)
28. Alveolar gas composition changes very little during a normal respiratory cycle. **Hyperventilation** increases alveolar P_{O_2} and decreases alveolar P_{CO_2}. **Hypoventilation** has the opposite effect. (p. 578; Fig. 17-15)
29. Air flow is matched to blood flow around the alveoli by local mechanisms. Increased levels of CO_2 dilate bronchioles, and decreased O_2 constricts pulmonary arterioles. (p. 579; Fig. 17-16, Table 17-6)

QUESTIONS

(Answers to the Review Questions begin on page A1.)

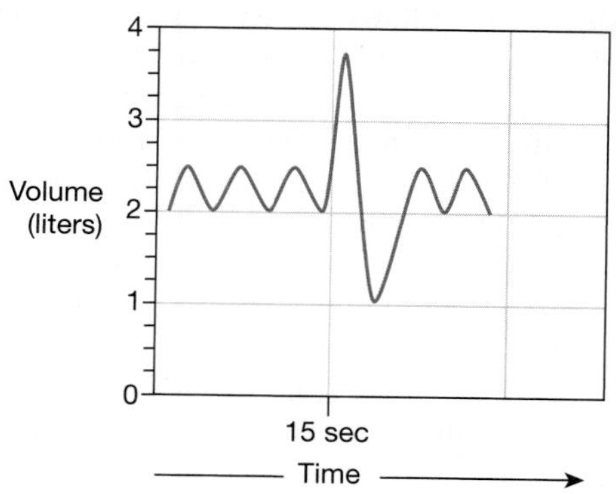

THE PHYSIOLOGY PLACE

Access more review material online at **The Physiology Place** website. There you'll find review questions, problem-solving activities, case studies, flashcards, and direct links to both *InterActive Physiology®* and PhysioEx™. To access the site, go to *www.physiologyplace.com* and select Human Physiology, Fourth Edition.

LEVEL ONE REVIEWING FACTS AND TERMS

1. List four functions of the respiratory system.
2. Give two definitions for the word *respiration.*
3. Which sets of muscles are used for normal quiet inspiration? For normal quiet expiration? For active expiration? What kind(s) of muscles are the different respiratory muscles (skeletal, cardiac, or smooth)?
4. What is the function of pleural fluid?
5. Name the anatomical structures that an oxygen molecule passes on its way from the atmosphere to the blood.
6. Diagram the structure of an alveolus, and state the function of each part. How are capillaries associated with an alveolus?
7. Trace the path of the pulmonary circulation. About how much blood is found here at any given moment? What is a typical arterial blood pressure for the pulmonary circuit, and how does this pressure compare with that of the systemic circulation?
8. What happens to inspired air as it is conditioned during its passage through the airways?
9. During inspiration, most of the thoracic volume change is the result of movement of the __________.
10. Describe the changes in alveolar and intrapleural pressure during one respiratory cycle.
11. What is the function of surfactants in general? In the respiratory system?
12. Of the three factors that contribute to the resistance of air flow through a tube, which plays the largest role in changing resistance in the human respiratory system?
13. Match the following items with their correct effect on the bronchioles:

(a) histamine	1. bronchoconstriction
(b) epinephrine	2. bronchodilation
(c) acetylcholine	3. no effect
(d) increased P_{CO_2}	

14. On the spirogram, label:
    (a) tidal volume (V_T), inspiratory and expiratory reserve volumes (IRV and ERV), residual volume (RV), vital capacity (VC), total lung capacity (TLC).
    (b) What is the value of each of the volumes and capacities you labeled?
    (c) What is this person's ventilation rate?

LEVEL TWO REVIEWING CONCEPTS

15. Compile the following terms into a map of ventilation. Use up arrows, down arrows, greater than symbols (>), and less than symbols (>) as modifiers. You may add additional terms.

abdominal muscles	inspiratory muscles
air flow	internal intercostals
contract	P_A
diaphragm	P_{atm}
expiratory muscles	$P_{intrapleural}$
external intercostals	quiet breathing
forced breathing	relax
in, out, from, to	scalenes

16. Compare and contrast the terms in each of the following sets:
    (a) compliance and elastance
    (b) inspiration, expiration, and ventilation
    (c) intrapleural pressure and alveolar pressure
    (d) total pulmonary ventilation and alveolar ventilation
    (e) type I and type II alveolar cells
    (f) pulmonary circulation and systemic circulation
17. List the major paracrines and neurotransmitters that cause bronchoconstriction and bronchodilation. What receptors do they act through? (muscarinic, nicotinic, α, β_1, β_2)
18. Decide whether each of the following parameters will increase, decrease, or not change in the situations given.
    (a) airway resistance with bronchodilation
    (b) intrapleural pressure during inspiration
    (c) air flow with bronchoconstriction
    (d) bronchiolar diameter with increased P_{CO_2}
    (e) tidal volume with decreased compliance
    (f) alveolar pressure during expiration
19. Define the following terms: pneumothorax, spirometer, auscultation, hypoventilation, bronchoconstriction, minute volume, partial pressure of a gas.
20. The cartoon coyote is blowing up a balloon as part of an attempt to once more catch the roadrunner. He first breathes in as much air as he can, then blows out all he can into the balloon.
    (a) The volume of air in the balloon is equal to the __________ __________ of the coyote's lungs. This volume can be measured directly by measuring the balloon volume or by adding which respiratory volumes together?

(b) In 10 years, when the coyote is still chasing the roadrunner, will he still be able to put as much air into the balloon in one breath? Explain.

21. Match the descriptions on the right to the appropriate phase(s) of ventilation:

(a) inspiration	____ usually depend(s) on elastic recoil
(b) expiration	____ is/are easier when lung compliance decreases
(c) both inspiration and expiration	____ is/are driven mainly by positive intrapleural pressure generated by muscular contraction
(d) neither	____ is usually an active process requiring smooth muscle contraction

22. Draw and label a graph showing the P_{O_2} of air in the primary bronchi during one respiratory cycle. (*Hint:* what parameter goes on each axis?)

23. Lung compliance decreases as we age. In the absence of other changes, would the following parameters increase, decrease, or not change as compliance decreases?
    (a) work required for breathing
    (b) ease with which lungs inflate
    (c) lung elastance
    (d) airway resistance during inspiration

24. Will pulmonary surfactant increase, decrease, or not change the following?
    (a) work required for breathing
    (b) lung compliance
    (c) surface tension in the alveoli

LEVEL THREE PROBLEM SOLVING

25. Assume a normal female has a resting tidal volume of 400 mL, a respiratory rate of 13 breaths/min, and an anatomic dead space of 125 mL. When she exercises, which of the following scenarios would be most efficient for increasing her oxygen delivery to the lungs?
    (a) increase respiratory rate to 20 breaths/min but have no change in tidal volume
    (b) increase tidal volume to 550 mL but have no change in respiratory rate
    (c) increase tidal volume to 500 mL and respiratory rate to 15 breaths/min

    Which of these scenarios is most likely to occur during exercise in real life?

26. A 30-year-old computer programmer has had asthma for 15 years. When she lies down at night, she has spells of wheezing and coughing. Over the years, she has found that she can breathe better if she sleeps sitting nearly upright. Upon examination, her doctor finds that she has an enlarged thorax. Her lungs are overinflated on X-ray. Here are the results of her examination and pulmonary function tests. Use the normal values and abbreviations in Figure 17-7 to help answer the questions.

Ventilation rate:	16 breaths/min
Tidal volume:	600 mL
ERV:	1000 mL
RV:	3500 mL
Inspiratory capacity:	1800 mL
Vital capacity:	2800 mL
Functional residual capacity:	4500 mL
TLC:	6300 mL

After she is given a bronchodilator, her vital capacity increased to 3650 mL.
    (a) What is her minute volume?
    (b) Explain the change in vital capacity with bronchodilators.
    (c) Which other values are abnormal? Can you explain why they might be, given her history and findings?

LEVEL FOUR QUANTITATIVE PROBLEMS

27. A container of gas with a movable piston has a volume of 500 mL and a pressure of 60 mm Hg. The piston is moved, and the new pressure is 150 mm Hg. What is the new volume of the container?

28. You have a mixture of gases in dry air, with an atmospheric pressure of 760 mm Hg. Calculate the partial pressure of each gas if the composition of the air is:
    (a) 21% oxygen, 78% nitrogen, 0.3% carbon dioxide
    (b) 40% oxygen, 13% nitrogen, 45% carbon dioxide, 2% hydrogen
    (c) 10% oxygen, 15% nitrogen, 1% argon, 25% carbon dioxide

29. Li is a tiny woman, with a tidal volume of 400 mL and a respiratory rate of 12 breaths per minute at rest. What is her total pulmonary ventilation? Just before a physiology exam, her ventilation increases to 18 breaths per minute from nervousness. Now what is her total pulmonary ventilation? Assuming her anatomic dead space is 120 mL, what is her alveolar ventilation in each case?

30. You collected the following data on your classmate Neelesh.

    Minute volume = 5004 mL/min
    Respiratory rate = 3 breaths/15 sec
    Vital capacity = 4800 mL
    Expiratory reserve volume = 1000 mL

    What are Neelesh's tidal volume and inspiratory reserve volume?

31. Use the illustrations below to help solve this problem. A spirometer with a volume of 1 liter (V_1) is filled with a mixture of oxygen and helium, with the helium concentration being 4 g/L (C_1). Helium does not move from the lungs into the blood or from the blood into the lungs. A subject is told to blow out all the air he possibly can. Once he finishes that exhalation, his lung volume is V_2. He then puts the spirometer tube in his mouth and breathes quietly for several breaths. At the end of that time, the helium is evenly dispersed in the spirometer and the subject's lungs. A measurement shows the new concentration of helium is 1.9 g/L. What was the subject's lung volume at the start of the experiment? (*Hint:* $C_1V_1 = C_2V_2$)

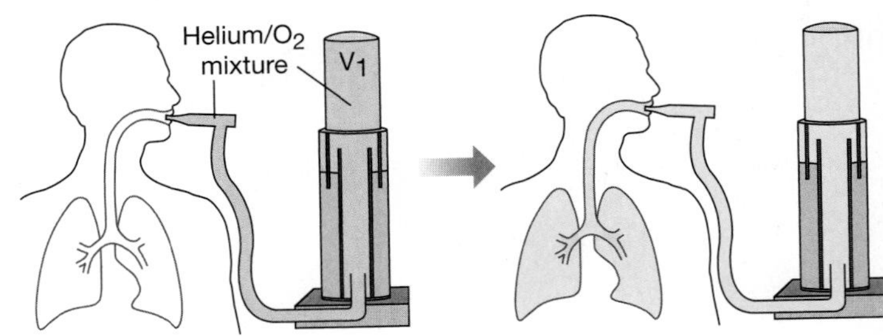

ANSWERS

Answers to Concept Check Questions

Page 561

1. Cellular respiration is intracellular and uses O_2 and organic substrates to produce ATP. External respiration is exchange and transport of gases between the atmosphere and cells.
2. Upper respiratory tract includes mouth, nasal cavity, pharynx, and larynx. Lower respiratory tract includes trachea, bronchi, bronchioles, and exchange surface of lungs.
3. Velocity is highest in the trachea and lowest in bronchioles.
4. Pleural fluid reduces friction and holds lungs tight against the chest wall.
5. The thoracic cage consists of rib cage with intercostal muscles, spinal (vertebral) column, and diaphragm. The thorax contains two lungs in pleural sacs, the heart and pericardial sac, esophagus, and major blood vessels.
6. The bronchioles are collapsible.

Page 564

7. Blood flow is equal in pulmonary trunk and aorta.
8. Increased hydrostatic pressure causes greater net filtration out of capillaries and may result in pulmonary edema.
9. Mean pressure = 8 mm Hg + 1/3(25 − 8) mm Hg = 8 + 17/3 mm Hg = 13.7 mm Hg.

Page 566

10. 720 mm Hg × 0.78 = 562 mm Hg

Page 568

11. Lung capacities are the sum of two or more lung volumes.
12. Residual volume cannot be measured directly.
13. If aging individuals have reduced vital capacity while total lung capacity does not change, then residual volume must increase.

Page 569

14. As air becomes humidified, the P_{O_2} decreases.
15. If cilia cannot move mucus, the collected mucus will trigger a cough reflex to clear the mucus out.

Page 570

16. Air flow reverses direction during a respiratory cycle, but blood flows in a loop and never reverses direction.
17. See Figures 17-2d and 17-3. The lungs are enclosed in a pleural sac. One pleural membrane attaches to the lung, and the other lines the thoracic cage. Pleural fluid fills the pleural sac.

Page 572

18. Scarlett will be more successful if she exhales deeply, as this will decrease her thoracic volume and will pull her lower rib cage inward.
19. Inability to cough decreases the ability to expel the potentially harmful material trapped in airway mucus.

Page 574

20. A hiccup causes a rapid decrease in both intrapleural pressure and alveolar pressure.
21. The knife wound would collapse the left lung if the knife punctured the pleural membrane. Loss of adhesion between the lung and chest wall would release the inward pressure exerted on the chest wall, and the rib cage would expand outward. The right side would be unaffected as the right lung is contained in its own pleural sac.

Page 576

22. Normally, lung and chest wall compliance contribute more to the work of breathing.
23. Scar tissue reduces lung compliance.
24. Without surfactant, the work of breathing increases.
25. When bronchiolar diameter decreases, resistance increases.
26. Neurotransmitter is acetylcholine, and receptor is muscarinic.

Page 579

27. Increased tidal volume increases alveolar P_{O_2}.
28. Increased breathing rate increases alveolar P_{O_2}. Increasing breathing rate or tidal volume increases alveolar ventilation.

Page 580

29. P_{O_2} in alveoli in the affected section will increase because O_2 is not leaving the alveoli. P_{CO_2} will decrease because new CO_2 is not entering the alveoli from the blood. Bronchioles constrict when P_{CO_2} decreases (see Table 17-6), shunting air to areas of the lung with better blood flow. This compensation cannot restore normal ventilation in this section of lung, and local control is insufficient to maintain homeostasis.

Page 582

30. Inspiratory reserve volume decreases.
31. Residual volume increases in patients who cannot fully exhale.

Answers to Graph Questions

Page 571

Fig. 17-11 Alveolar pressure is greatest in the middle of expiration and least in the middle of inspiration. It is equal to atmospheric pressure at the beginning and end of inspiration and expiration. When lung volume is at its minimum, alveolar pressure is (c) moving from maximum to minimum and external intercostal muscle contraction is (b) minimal.

18

The successful ascent of Everest without supplementary oxygen is one of the great sagas of the 20th century.

***—John B. West**, Climbing with O's, NOVA Online (www.pbs.org)*

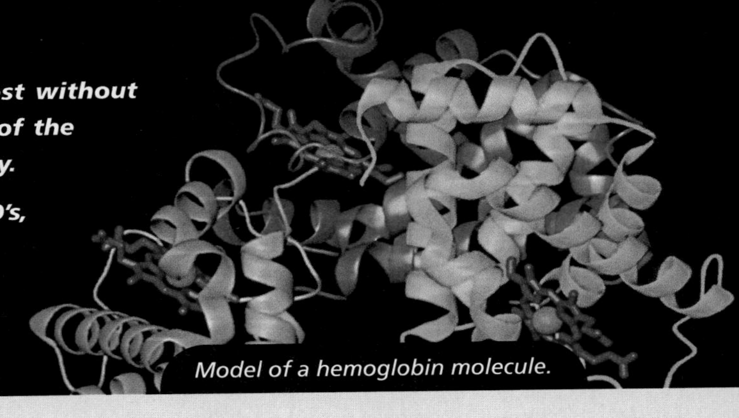

Model of a hemoglobin molecule.

Gas Exchange and Transport

BACKGROUND BASICS

Exchange epithelia: **73** pH and buffers: **38** Law of mass action: **39** Cerebrospinal fluid: **296** Simple diffusion: **133** Autonomic and somatic motor neurons: **379** Structure of the brain stem: **305** Red blood cells and hemoglobin: **542** Blood-brain barrier: **299**

RUNNING PROBLEM

HIGH ALTITUDE

In 1981 a group of 20 physiologists, physicians, and climbers, supported by 42 Sherpa assistants, formed the American Medical Research Expedition to Mt. Everest. The purpose of the expedition was to study human physiology at extreme altitudes, starting with the base camp at 5400 m (18,000 ft) and continuing on to the summit at 8850 m (over 29,000 ft). From the work of these scientists and others, we now have a good picture of the physiology of high-altitude acclimatization.

The book *Into Thin Air* by Jon Krakauer chronicles an ill-fated trek to the top of Mt. Everest. To reach the summit of Mt. Everest, climbers must pass through the "death zone" located at about 8000 meters (over 26,000 ft). Of the thousands of people who have attempted the summit, only about 2000 have been successful, and more than 185 have died. What are the physiological challenges of climbing Mt. Everest (8850 m or 29,035 ft), and why did it take so many years before humans successfully reached the top? The lack of oxygen at high altitude is part of the answer.

In the previous chapter we looked at the mechanics of breathing, the events that create the bulk flow of air into and out of the lungs. In this chapter we focus on the two gases that are most significant to physiology, oxygen and carbon dioxide, and look at how they move between alveolar air spaces and the cells of the body. The process can be divided into two components: the exchange of gases between compartments, which requires diffusion across cell membranes, and the transport of gases in the blood (Fig. 18-1 ■).

DIFFUSION AND SOLUBILITY OF GASES

The simple diffusion of oxygen and carbon dioxide across cell layers (between alveoli and pulmonary capillaries, or between systemic capillaries and cells) obeys the rules for simple diffusion across a membrane that are summarized in *Fick's law of diffusion* [p. 135]:

$$\text{diffusion rate} \propto \frac{\text{surface area} \times \text{concentration gradient} \times \text{membrane permeability}}{\text{membrane thickness}}$$

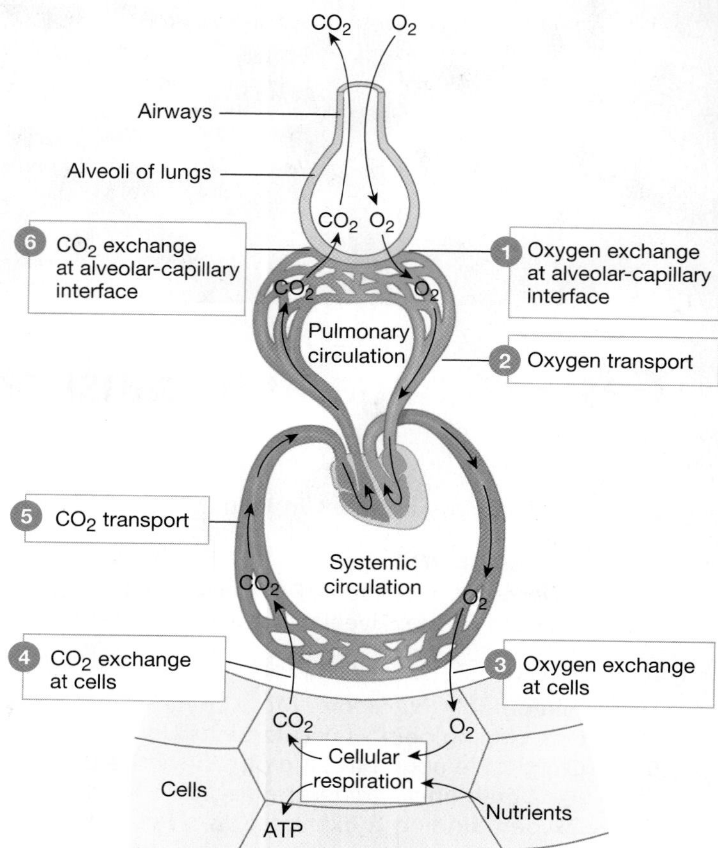

■ **FIGURE 18-1** ***Overview of oxygen and carbon dioxide exchange and transport***

Gases move into and out of the blood both at the pulmonary capillaries (steps 1 and 6) and at the systemic capillaries (steps 3 and 4).

If we assume that membrane permeability is constant, then three factors influence diffusion in the lungs:

1. *Surface area.* The rate of diffusion is directly proportional to the available surface area.
2. *Concentration gradient.* The rate of diffusion is directly proportional to the concentration gradient of the diffusing substance.
3. *Membrane thickness.* The rate of diffusion is inversely proportional to the thickness of the membrane.

From the general rules for diffusion, we can add a fourth influence: *diffusion distance*—diffusion is most rapid over short distances.

Under most circumstances, diffusion distance, surface area, and membrane thickness are constants in the body and are maximized to facilitate diffusion. Thus the most important factor for gas exchange in normal physiology is the concentration gradient.

When we think of concentrations in physiology, units such as moles per liter and milliosmoles per liter come to mind. However, respiratory physiologists commonly use *partial pressures* to express gas concentrations in solution. This measure allows direct comparison with partial pressures of the gases in air,

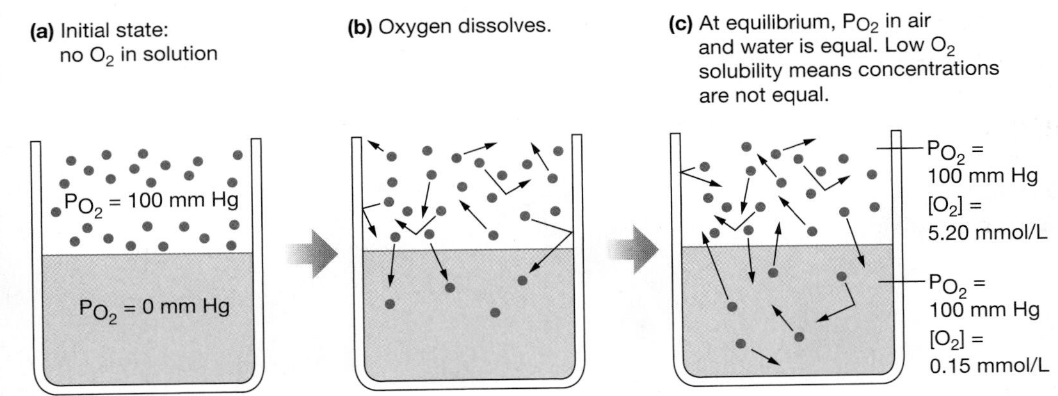

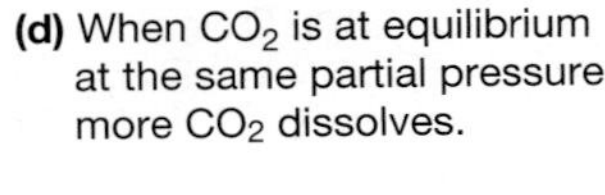

(d) When CO_2 is at equilibrium at the same partial pressure, more CO_2 dissolves.

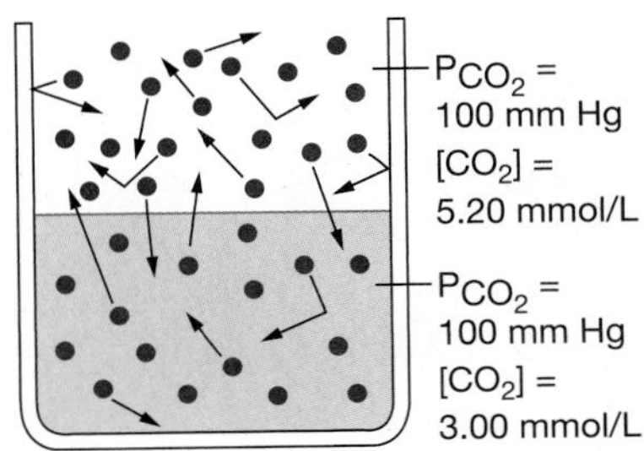

FIGURE 18-2 *Behavior of gases in solution*

When temperature remains constant, the amount of a gas that dissolves in a liquid depends on both the solubility of the gas in the liquid and the partial pressure of the gas.

which is important for establishing whether there is a concentration gradient between the alveoli and the blood.

The Solubility of Gases in Liquids Depends on Pressure, Solubility, and Temperature

When a gas is placed in contact with water and there is a pressure gradient, the gas molecules move from one phase to the other. If gas pressure is higher in the water than in the gaseous phase, then gas molecules will leave the water. If the gas pressure is higher in the gaseous phase than in the water, then the gas will dissolve into the water.

The movement of gas molecules from air into a liquid is directly proportional to three factors: (1) the pressure gradient of the gas, (2) the solubility of the gas in the liquid, and (3) temperature. Because temperature is relatively constant in mammals, we will ignore its contribution in this discussion.

The ease with which a gas dissolves in a liquid is the **solubility** of the gas in that liquid. If a gas is very soluble, large numbers of gas molecules will go into solution at a low gas partial pressure. With less soluble gases, even a high partial pressure may cause only a few molecules of the gas to dissolve in the liquid. For example, consider a container of water exposed to air with a P_{O_2} of 100 mm Hg (Fig. 18-2a ■). Initially, the water has no oxygen dissolved in it (water P_{O_2} = 0 mm Hg). As the air stays in contact with the water, some of the moving oxygen molecules in the air diffuse into the water and dissolve (Fig. 18-2b). This process continues until equilibrium is reached. At equilibrium (Fig. 18-2c), the movement of oxygen from the air into the water is equal to the movement of oxygen from the water back into the air.

We refer to the amount of oxygen that dissolves in the water at any given P_{O_2} as the *partial pressure of the gas in solution*. In our example, therefore, if the air has a P_{O_2} of 100 mm Hg, at equilibrium the water will also have a P_{O_2} of 100 mm Hg.

Note that this does *not* mean that the concentration of oxygen is the same in the air and in the water! The concentration of dissolved oxygen also depends on the *solubility* of oxygen in water. For example, when P_{O_2} is 100 mm Hg in both the air and the water, the oxygen concentration in the air is 5.2 mmol O_2/L air, but the oxygen concentration in the water is only 0.15 mmol O_2/L water (Fig. 18-2c). As you can see, oxygen is not very soluble in water and, by extension, in any aqueous solution. Its low solubility is one reason for the evolution of oxygen-carrying molecules in the aqueous solution we call blood.

Now compare oxygen solubility with CO_2 solubility (Fig. 18-2d). Carbon dioxide is 20 times as soluble in water as oxygen is. At a P_{CO_2} of 100 mm Hg, the CO_2 concentration in air is 5.2 mmol CO_2/L air, and its concentration in water is 3.0 mmol/L water. So although P_{O_2} and P_{CO_2} are both 100 mm Hg in the water, the amount of each gas that dissolves in the water is very different.

CONCEPT CHECK

1. A saline solution is exposed to a mixture of nitrogen gas and hydrogen gas in which $P_{H_2} = P_{N_2}$. What information do you need to predict whether equal amounts of H_2 and N_2 will dissolve in the solution?
2. If nitrogen is 78% of atmospheric air, what is the partial pressure of this gas when the dry atmospheric pressure is 720 mm Hg?
3. True or false? Plasma with a P_{O_2} of 40 mm Hg and a P_{CO_2} of 40 mm Hg has the same concentrations of oxygen and carbon dioxide.

Answers: p. 611

GAS EXCHANGE IN THE LUNGS AND TISSUES

The gas laws state that individual gases flow from regions of higher partial pressure to regions of lower partial pressure, and this rule governs the exchange of oxygen and carbon dioxide in the lungs and tissues.

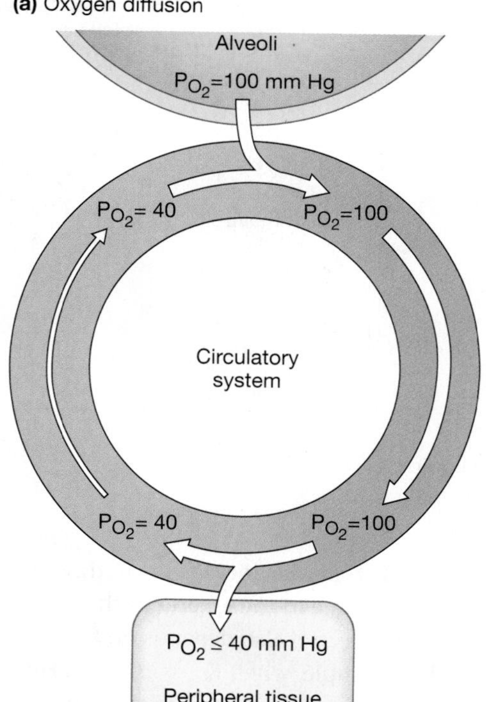

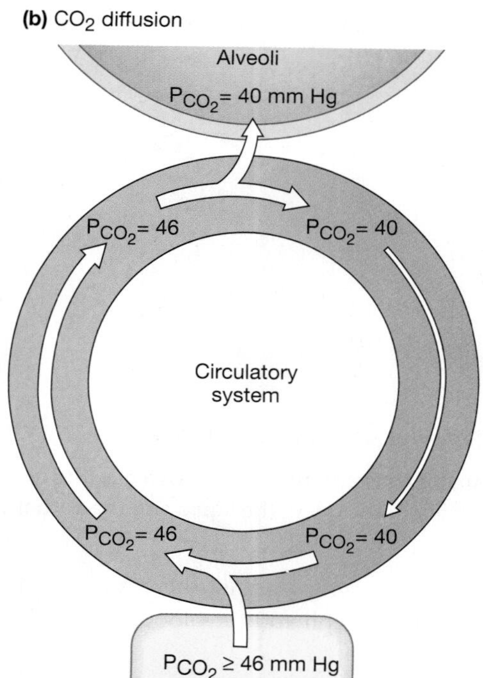

■ **FIGURE 18-3** ***Gas exchange at the alveoli and cells***

Gases diffuse down their partial pressure (concentration) gradient.

Normal alveolar P_{O_2} is about 100 mm Hg (Fig. 18-3a ■). The P_{O_2} of systemic venous blood arriving at the lungs is 40 mm Hg. Oxygen therefore moves down its partial pressure (concentration) gradient from the alveoli into the capillaries. Diffusion goes to equilibrium, and the P_{O_2} of arterial blood leaving the lungs is the same as in the alveoli: 100 mm Hg.

When arterial blood reaches tissue capillaries, the gradient is reversed. Cells are continuously using oxygen for oxidative phosphorylation. In the cells of a person at rest, intracellular P_{O_2} averages 40 mm Hg. Arterial blood arriving at the cells has a P_{O_2} of 100 mm Hg. Because P_{O_2} is lower in the cells, oxygen diffuses down its partial pressure gradient from plasma into cells. Once again, diffusion goes to equilibrium, and as a result venous blood has the same P_{O_2} as the cells it just passed.

Conversely, P_{CO_2} is higher in tissues than in systemic capillary blood because of CO_2 production during metabolism (Fig. 18-3b). Cellular P_{CO_2} in a person at rest is about 46 mm Hg, compared to an arterial plasma P_{CO_2} of 40 mm Hg. The gradient causes CO_2 to diffuse out of cells into the capillaries. Diffusion goes to equilibrium, and systemic venous blood averages a P_{CO_2} of 46 mm Hg.

At the pulmonary capillaries, the process reverses. Venous blood bringing waste CO_2 from the cells has a P_{CO_2} of 46 mm Hg. Alveolar P_{CO_2} is 40 mm Hg. Because P_{CO_2} is higher in the plasma, CO_2 moves from the capillaries into the alveoli. By the time blood leaves the alveoli, it has a P_{CO_2} of 40 mm Hg, identical to the P_{CO_2} of the alveoli (Fig. 18-3b). Table 18-1 ■ summarizes the arterial and venous partial pressures just discussed.

If the diffusion of gases between alveoli and blood is significantly impaired, *hypoxia* (a state of too little oxygen) results. Hypoxia frequently (but not always!) goes hand in hand with **hypercapnia**, elevated concentrations of carbon dioxide. These two conditions are clinical signs, not diseases, and clinicians must gather additional information to pinpoint their cause. Table 18-2 ■ lists several types of hypoxia and some typical causes.

Three categories of problems result in low arterial oxygen content: (1) inadequate oxygen reaching the alveoli, (2) problems with oxygen exchange between alveoli and pulmonary capillaries, and (3) inadequate transport of oxygen in the blood. We will consider these issues in the sections that follow.

TABLE 18-1 Normal Blood Values in Pulmonary Medicine

	ARTERIAL	VENOUS
P_{O_2}	95 mm Hg (85–100)	40 mm Hg
P_{CO_2}	40 mm Hg (35–45)	46 mm Hg
pH	7.4 (7.38–7.42)	7.37

TABLE 18-2 Classification of Hypoxias

TYPE	DEFINITION	TYPICAL CAUSES
Hypoxic hypoxia	Low arterial P_{O_2}	High altitude; alveolar hypoventilation; decreased lung diffusion capacity; abnormal ventilation-perfusion ratio
Anemic hypoxia	Decreased total amount of O_2 bound to hemoglobin	Blood loss; anemia (low [Hb] or altered HbO_2 binding); carbon monoxide poisoning
Ischemic hypoxia	Reduced blood flow	Heart failure (whole-body hypoxia); shock (peripheral hypoxia); thrombosis (hypoxia in a single organ)
Histotoxic hypoxia	Failure of cells to use O_2 because cells have been poisoned	Cyanide and other metabolic poisons

CONCEPT CHECK

4. Cellular metabolism review: which of the following three metabolic pathways—glycolysis, the citric acid cycle, and the electron transport system—is *directly* associated with (a) O_2 consumption and with (b) CO_2 production?
5. Why doesn't the movement of oxygen from the alveoli to the plasma decrease the P_{O_2} of the alveoli?

Answers: p. 611

A Decrease in Alveolar P_{O_2} Decreases Oxygen Uptake at the Lungs

The first requirement for adequate oxygen delivery to the tissues is adequate oxygen intake from the atmosphere, as reflected by the P_{O_2} of the alveoli. A decrease in alveolar P_{O_2} will result in less oxygen entering the blood. There are two possible causes of low alveolar P_{O_2}: either (1) the inspired air has abnormally low oxygen content or (2) alveolar ventilation is inadequate.

The main factor that affects the oxygen content of inspired air is altitude. The partial pressure of oxygen in air decreases along with total atmospheric pressure as you move from sea level (where normal atmospheric pressure is 760 mm Hg) to higher altitudes. For example, Denver, 1609 m above sea level, has an atmospheric pressure of about 628 mm Hg. The P_{O_2} of dry air in Denver is 132 mm Hg, down from 160 mm Hg at sea level.

Unless a person is traveling, however, altitude remains constant. If alveolar P_{O_2} is low but the composition of inspired air is normal, then the problem lies with alveolar ventilation. Low alveolar ventilation is also known as *hypoventilation* and is characterized by lower-than-normal volumes of fresh air entering the alveoli. Pathological factors that cause alveolar hypoventilation (Fig. 18-4 ■) include decreased lung compliance (fibrosis; Fig. 18-4c), increased airway resistance (asthma;

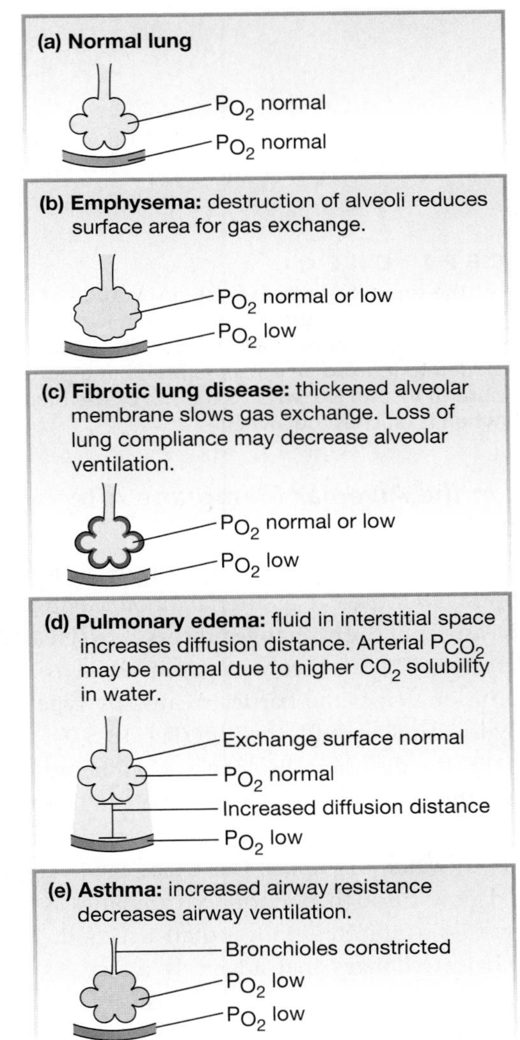
(a) Normal lung
P_{O_2} normal
P_{O_2} normal
(b) Emphysema: destruction of alveoli reduces surface area for gas exchange.
P_{O_2} normal or low
P_{O_2} low
(c) Fibrotic lung disease: thickened alveolar membrane slows gas exchange. Loss of lung compliance may decrease alveolar ventilation.
P_{O_2} normal or low
P_{O_2} low
(d) Pulmonary edema: fluid in interstitial space increases diffusion distance. Arterial P_{CO_2} may be normal due to higher CO_2 solubility in water.
Exchange surface normal
P_{O_2} normal
Increased diffusion distance
P_{O_2} low
(e) Asthma: increased airway resistance decreases airway ventilation.
Bronchioles constricted
P_{O_2} low
P_{O_2} low

■ **FIGURE 18-4** ***Pathological conditions that reduce alveolar ventilation and gas exchange***

RUNNING PROBLEM

Hypoxia is the primary problem that people experience when ascending to high altitude. High altitude is considered anything above 1500 m (5000 ft), but most pathological responses to altitude occur above 2500 m. By one estimate, 25% of people arriving at 2590 m will experience some form of altitude sickness.

Question 1:

If water vapor contributes 47 mm Hg to the pressure of fully humidified air, what is the P_{O_2} of inspired air reaching the alveoli at 2500 m, where dry atmospheric pressure is 542 mm Hg? How does this value for P_{O_2} compare with that of fully humidified air at sea level?

Fig. 18-4e), and overdoses of drugs (including alcohol) that depress the central nervous system and slow ventilation rate and depth.

CONCEPT CHECK

6. At the summit of Mt. Everest, an altitude of 8850 m, atmospheric pressure is only 250 mm Hg. What is the P_{O_2} of dry atmospheric air atop Everest? If water vapor added to inhaled air at the summit has a partial pressure of 47 mm Hg, what is the P_{O_2} of the inhaled air when it reaches the alveoli?

Answers: p. 611

Changes in the Alveolar Membrane Alter Gas Exchange

In situations in which the composition of the air reaching the alveoli is normal but the P_{O_2} of arterial blood leaving the lungs is low, some aspect of the exchange process between alveoli and blood is defective. The transfer of oxygen from alveoli to blood requires diffusion across the barrier created by type I alveolar cells and by the capillary endothelium (Fig. 18-5 ■).

Normally, the diffusion distance is small because the cells are thin and there is little or no interstitial fluid between the two cell layers. In addition, both oxygen and carbon dioxide are soluble in both water and lipids. Gas exchange in the lungs is rapid, blood flow through pulmonary capillaries is slow, and diffusion reaches equilibrium in less than 1 second.

Pathological changes that adversely affect gas exchange include (1) a decrease in the amount of alveolar surface area available for gas exchange, (2) an increase in the thickness of the alveolar membrane, and (3) an increase in the diffusion distance between the alveoli and the blood.

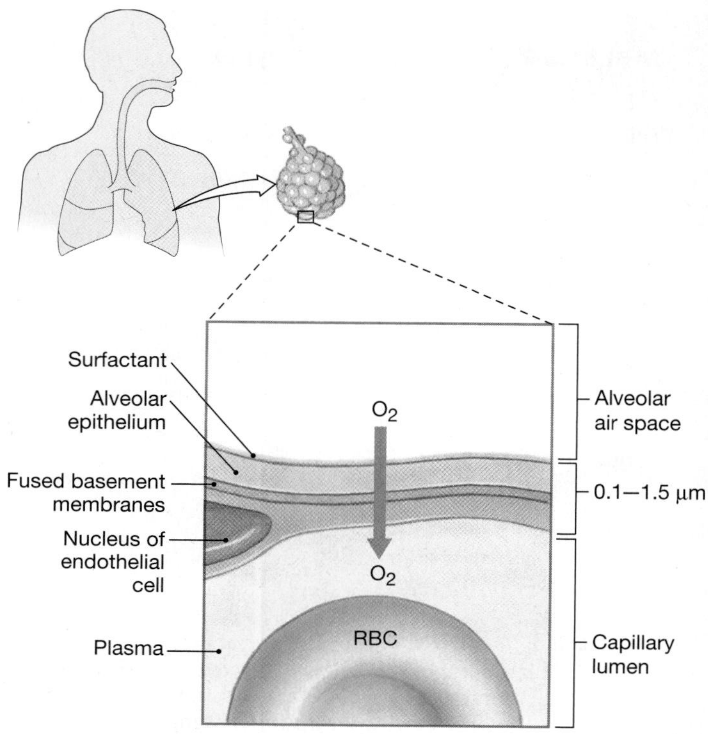

■ **FIGURE 18-5** ***Oxygen diffuses across alveolar epithelial cells and capillary endothelial cells to enter the plasma***

Physical loss of alveolar surface area is dramatic in *emphysema*, a degenerative lung disease most often caused by cigarette smoking (Fig. 18-4b). The irritating effect of smoke in the alveoli activates alveolar macrophages that release proteolytic enzymes. These enzymes destroy the elastic fibers of the lung [p. 77] and induce apoptosis of cells, breaking down the walls of the alveoli. The result is a high-compliance/low-elastic recoil lung with fewer and larger alveoli and less surface area for gas exchange.

Pathological changes in the alveolar membrane that alter its properties slow gas exchange. For example, in fibrotic lung diseases, deposition of scar tissue thickens the alveolar membrane (Fig. 18-4c). Diffusion of gases through this scar tissue is much slower than normal. However, because the lungs have a built-in reserve capacity, one-third of the exchange epithelium must be incapacitated before arterial P_{O_2} falls significantly.

One pathological condition in which the diffusion distance between alveoli and blood increases is **pulmonary edema**, characterized by excessive interstitial fluid volume in the lungs (Fig. 18-4d). Normally, only small amounts of interstitial fluid are present in the lungs, the result of low pulmonary blood pressure and effective lymph drainage. However, if pulmonary blood pressure rises for some reason, such as left ventricular failure or mitral valve dysfunction, the normal filtration/reabsorption balance at the capillary is disrupted [Fig. 15-18, p. 518]. When capillary hydrostatic pressure increases, more fluid filters out of the capillary. If filtration increases too much,

BIOTECHNOLOGY

THE PULSE OXIMETER

One important clinical indicator of the effectiveness of gas exchange in the lungs is the amount of oxygen in arterial blood. Obtaining an arterial blood sample is difficult and painful because it means finding an accessible artery. (Most blood is drawn from superficial veins rather than from arteries, which lie deeper within the body.) Over the years, however, scientists have developed instruments that quickly and painlessly measure blood oxygen levels through the surface of the skin on a finger or earlobe. One such instrument, the *pulse oximeter*, clips onto the skin and in seconds gives a digital reading of arterial hemoglobin saturation. The oximeter works by measuring light absorbance of the tissue at two wavelengths. Another instrument, the *transcutaneous oxygen sensor*, measures dissolved oxygen using a variant of traditional gas-measuring electrodes. Both methods have limitations but are popular because they provide a rapid, noninvasive means of estimating arterial oxygen concentration.

RUNNING PROBLEM

Acute mountain sickness is the mildest illness caused by altitude hypoxia. The primary symptom is a headache that may be accompanied by dizziness, nausea, fatigue, or confusion. More severe illnesses are *high-altitude pulmonary edema* (HAPE) and *high-altitude cerebral edema*. HAPE is the major cause of death from altitude sickness. It is characterized by high pulmonary arterial pressure, extreme shortness of breath, and sometimes a productive cough yielding a pink, frothy fluid. Treatment is immediate relocation to lower altitude and administration of oxygen.

Question 2:
Why would someone with HAPE be short of breath?

Question 3:
Based on what you learned about the mechanisms for matching ventilation and perfusion in the lung [p. 579], can you explain why patients with HAPE have elevated pulmonary arterial blood pressure?

588 592  593 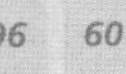 596  601  606 608

the lymphatics are unable to remove all the fluid, and excess accumulates in the pulmonary interstitial space, creating pulmonary edema. In severe cases, fluid even leaks across the alveolar membrane, collecting inside the alveoli.

Oxygen has low solubility in body fluids and takes longer to cross the increased diffusion distance present in pulmonary edema, resulting in decreased arterial P_{O_2}. Carbon dioxide, in contrast, is relatively soluble in body fluids, so the increased diffusion distance may not significantly affect carbon dioxide exchange. In some cases of pulmonary edema, arterial P_{O_2} is low but arterial P_{CO_2} is normal because of the different solubilities of the two gases.

CONCEPT CHECK

7. Why does left ventricular failure or mitral valve dysfunction cause elevated pulmonary blood pressure?
8. If alveolar ventilation increases, what will happen to arterial P_{O_2}? To arterial P_{CO_2}? To venous P_{O_2} and P_{CO_2}? Explain your answers.

Answers: p. 611

GAS TRANSPORT IN THE BLOOD

Now that we have described gas exchange, we turn our attention to how oxygen and carbon dioxide are transported in the blood. The *law of mass action* [p. 39] plays an important role in this process. Changes in oxygen or CO_2 concentration disturb the equilibrium of reactions, shifting the balance between substrates and products.

Hemoglobin Transports Most Oxygen to the Tissues

Oxygen is transported two ways in the blood: dissolved in the plasma and bound to hemoglobin (Hb). This fact can be summarized as follows:

$$\text{Total blood oxygen content} = \text{amount dissolved in plasma} + \text{amount bound to hemoglobin}$$

Hemoglobin, the oxygen-binding protein in red blood cells, binds reversibly to oxygen, as summarized in the equation

$$Hb + O_2 \rightleftharpoons HbO_2$$

In the pulmonary capillaries, where plasma P_{O_2} increases as oxygen diffuses in from the alveoli, hemoglobin binds oxygen. At the cells, where oxygen is being used and plasma P_{O_2} falls, hemoglobin gives up its oxygen. Because oxygen is only slightly soluble in aqueous solutions, we must have adequate amounts of hemoglobin in our blood to survive.

The importance of hemoglobin in oxygen transport is summarized in Figure 18-6 ■. More than 98% of the oxygen in a given volume of blood is bound to hemoglobin and transported inside red blood cells. The balance remains dissolved in plasma.

To understand just how low the solubility of oxygen is, consider the following example. In a situation in which blood has no hemoglobin, only 3 mL of O_2 will dissolve in the plasma

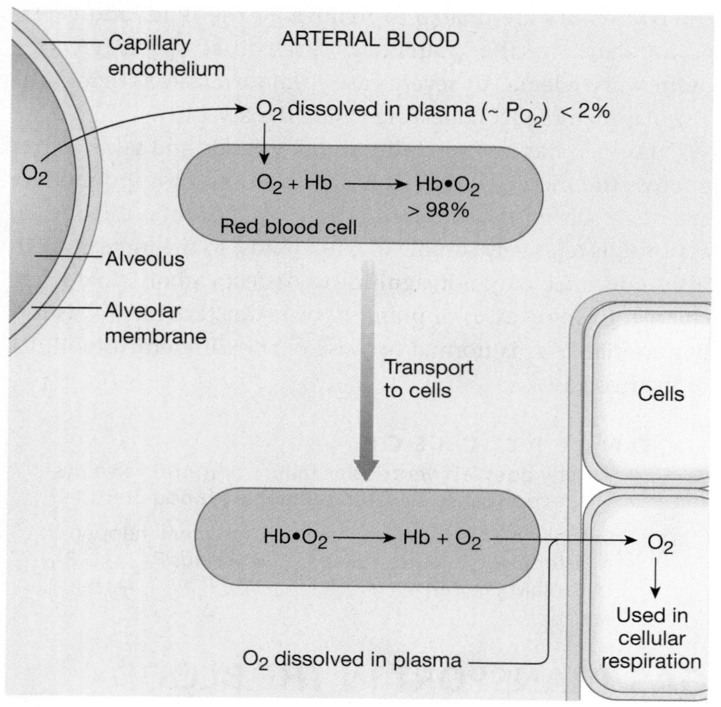

FIGURE QUESTION

How many cell membranes will O_2 cross in its passage between the airspace of the alveolus and binding to hemoglobin?

■ **FIGURE 18-6** ***Summary of oxygen transport in the blood***

More than 98% of the oxygen in blood is bound to hemoglobin in red blood cells; less than 2% is dissolved in plasma.

fraction of 1 liter of arterial blood (Fig. 18-7a ■). Thus, with a typical cardiac output of 5 L blood/min, about 15 mL of dissolved oxygen reaches the systemic tissues each minute. This small amount cannot begin to meet the needs of the tissues, because oxygen consumption at rest is about 250 mL O_2 per minute, and that figure increases dramatically with exercise. Thus the oxygen brought to cells dissolved in plasma provides less than 10% of what the cells consume, so the body is heavily dependent on oxygen carried by hemoglobin.

At normal hemoglobin levels, red blood cells carry about 197 mL O_2/L blood (Fig. 18-7b). Thus:

$$\text{total arterial } O_2 \text{ carrying capacity} = 3 \text{ mL dissolved } O_2\text{/L blood} + 197 \text{ mL } HbO_2\text{/L blood} = 200 \text{ mL } O_2\text{/L blood}$$

If cardiac output remains 5 L/min, hemoglobin-assisted oxygen delivery to cells is almost 1000 mL/min, four times the oxygen consumption needed by the tissues at rest.

The amount of oxygen that binds to hemoglobin depends on two factors: (1) the P_{O_2} in the plasma surrounding the red blood cells and (2) the number of potential binding sites available in the red blood cells.

Plasma P_{O_2} is the primary factor determining how many of the available hemoglobin binding sites are occupied by oxygen. Figure 18-7c shows what happens to oxygen transport when alveolar and arterial P_{O_2} decrease. As you learned in previous sections, arterial P_{O_2} is established by (1) the composition of inspired air, (2) the alveolar ventilation rate, and (3) the efficiency of gas exchange from alveoli to blood.

The total number of oxygen-binding sites depends on the number of hemoglobin molecules in red blood cells. Clinically, this number can be estimated either by counting the red blood cells and quantifying the amount of hemoglobin per red blood cell (*mean corpuscular hemoglobin*) or by determining the blood hemoglobin content (g Hb/dL whole blood). Any pathological condition that decreases the amount of hemoglobin in the cells or the number of red blood cells will adversely affect the blood's oxygen-transporting capacity.

People who have lost large amounts of blood need to replace hemoglobin for oxygen transport. A blood transfusion is the ideal replacement for blood loss, but in emergencies this is

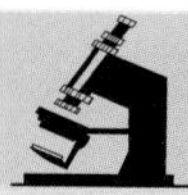

EMERGING CONCEPTS

BLOOD SUBSTITUTES

Physiologists have been attempting to find a substitute for blood ever since 1878, when an intrepid physician named T. Gaillard Thomas transfused a patient with whole milk in place of blood. Although milk seems an unlikely replacement for blood, it has two important properties: proteins to provide colloid osmotic pressure and molecules (emulsified lipids) capable of binding to oxygen. In the development of hemoglobin substitutes, oxygen transport is the most difficult property to mimic. A hemoglobin solution would seem to be the obvious answer, but hemoglobin that is not compartmentalized in red blood cells behaves differently than hemoglobin that is compartmentalized. Investigators are making progress by polymerizing hemoglobin into larger, more stable molecules and loading these hemoglobin polymers into phospholipid liposomes [p. 55]. Perfluorocarbon emulsions are also being tested as oxygen carriers. To learn more about this research, read "Physiological properties of blood substitutes," in *News in Physiological Sciences* 16(1):38–41, 2001 Feb. (*http://nips.physiology.org*).

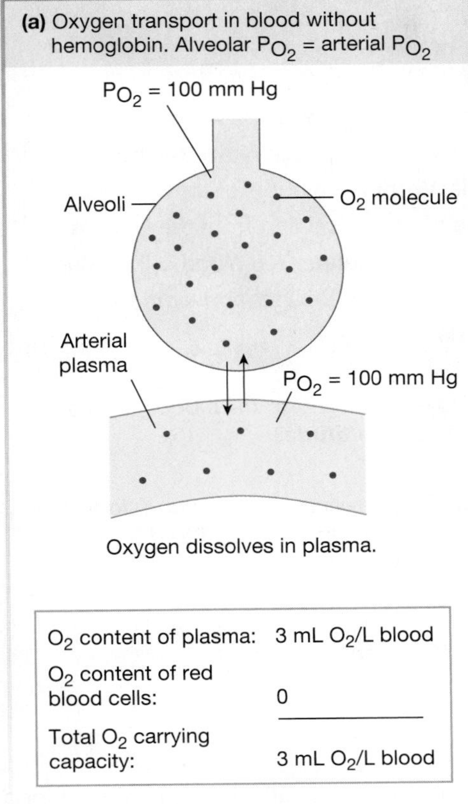
(a) Oxygen transport in blood without hemoglobin. Alveolar P_{O_2} = arterial P_{O_2}
P_{O_2} = 100 mm Hg
Alveoli
O_2 molecule
Arterial plasma
P_{O_2} = 100 mm Hg
Oxygen dissolves in plasma.
O_2 content of plasma: 3 mL O_2/L blood
O_2 content of red blood cells: 0
Total O_2 carrying capacity: 3 mL O_2/L blood

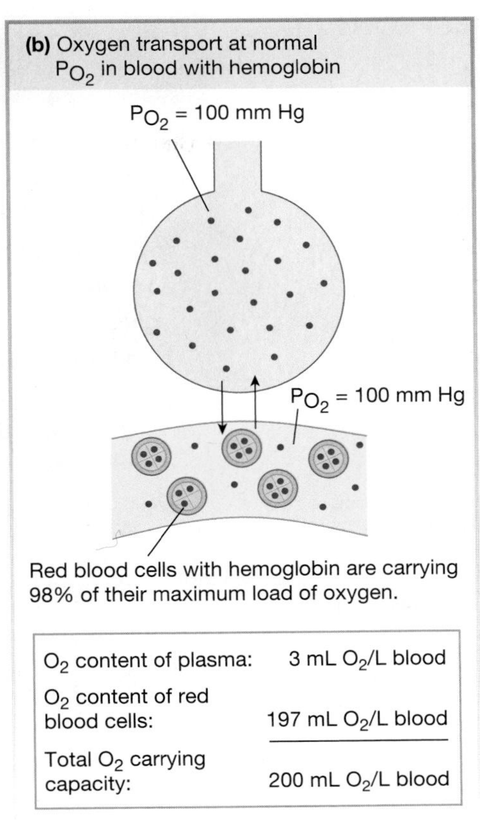
(b) Oxygen transport at normal P_{O_2} in blood with hemoglobin
P_{O_2} = 100 mm Hg
P_{O_2} = 100 mm Hg
Red blood cells with hemoglobin are carrying 98% of their maximum load of oxygen.
O_2 content of plasma: 3 mL O_2/L blood
O_2 content of red blood cells: 197 mL O_2/L blood
Total O_2 carrying capacity: 200 mL O_2/L blood

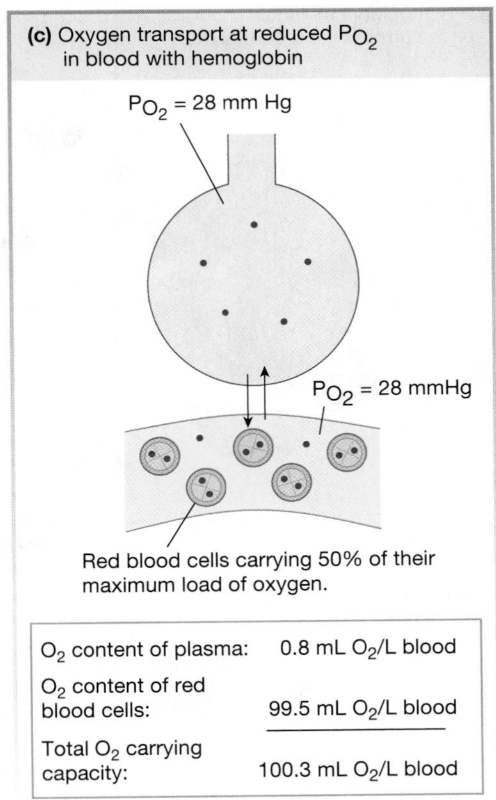
(c) Oxygen transport at reduced P_{O_2} in blood with hemoglobin
P_{O_2} = 28 mm Hg
P_{O_2} = 28 mmHg
Red blood cells carrying 50% of their maximum load of oxygen.
O_2 content of plasma: 0.8 mL O_2/L blood
O_2 content of red blood cells: 99.5 mL O_2/L blood
Total O_2 carrying capacity: 100.3 mL O_2/L blood

■ **FIGURE 18-7** ***The role of hemoglobin in oxygen transport***

not always possible. Saline infusions can replace lost blood volume, but saline (like plasma) cannot transport sufficient quantities of oxygen to support cellular respiration. Faced with this problem, researchers are currently testing artificial oxygen carriers to replace hemoglobin. In times of large-scale disasters, these hemoglobin substitutes would eliminate the need to identify a patient's blood type before giving transfusions.

One Hemoglobin Molecule Binds Up to Four Oxygen Molecules

Why is hemoglobin an effective oxygen carrier? The answer lies in its molecular structure. Hemoglobin is a large, complex protein whose quaternary structure has four globular protein chains, each of which is wrapped around an iron-containing **heme group** (Fig. 18-8a ■). The four heme groups in a hemoglobin molecule are identical. Each consists of a carbon-hydrogen-nitrogen *porphyrin ring* with an iron atom (Fe) in the center. About 70% of the iron in the body is found in the heme groups of hemoglobin.

The central iron atom of each heme group can bind reversibly with one oxygen molecule. Because there are four iron atoms per hemoglobin, each hemoglobin molecule has the potential to bind four oxygen molecules. The iron-oxygen interaction is a weak bond that can be easily broken without altering either the hemoglobin or the oxygen.

There are several forms of **globin** protein chains in hemoglobin. The most common forms are designated *alpha* (α), *beta* (β), *gamma* (γ), and *delta* (δ), depending on the structure of the chain. Most adult hemoglobin (designated *HbA*) has two alpha chains and two beta chains. However, a small portion of adult hemoglobin (about 2.5%) has two alpha chains and two delta chains (HbA_2).

The human fetus has a different isoform of hemoglobin that is adapted to attract oxygen from maternal blood in the placenta. *Fetal hemoglobin* (*HbF*) has two gamma chains in place of the two beta chains found in adult hemoglobin. Shortly after birth, fetal hemoglobin is replaced with the adult form as new red blood cells are made. The different binding properties of adult and fetal hemoglobin are discussed in the sections that follow.

Oxygen-Hemoglobin Binding Obeys the Law of Mass Action

Hemoglobin bound to oxygen is known as **oxyhemoglobin**, abbreviated HbO_2. (It would be more accurate to show the number of oxygen molecules carried on each hemoglobin molecule—$Hb(O_2)_{1-4}$—but we will use the simpler abbreviation because the number of bound oxygen molecules varies from one hemoglobin molecule to another.)

(a) A hemoglobin molecule is composed of four protein globin chains, each surrounding a central heme group.

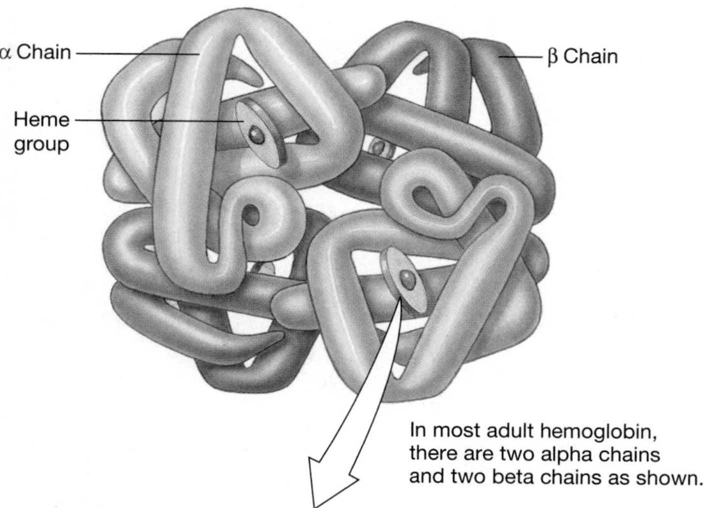

(b) Each heme group consists of a porphyrin ring with an iron atom in the center.

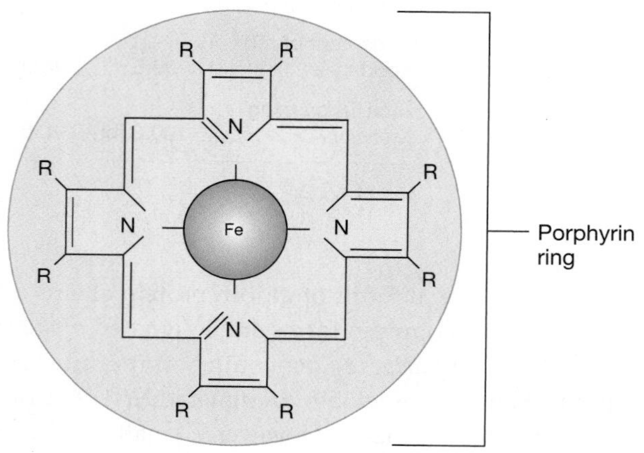

■ **FIGURE 18-8** ***The hemoglobin molecule***

Oxygen-hemoglobin binding obeys the law of mass action:

$$Hb + O_2 \rightleftharpoons HbO_2$$

If oxygen concentration increases, this *oxygen-hemoglobin binding reaction* shifts to the right and more oxygen binds to hemoglobin. If the concentration of oxygen decreases, the reaction shifts to the left and hemoglobin releases some of its bound oxygen.

P_{O_2} Determines Oxygen-Hemoglobin Binding

Because of the law of mass action, the amount of oxygen bound to hemoglobin depends primarily on the P_{O_2} of plasma surrounding the red blood cells (Fig. 18-6). In the pulmonary capillaries, O_2 dissolved in the plasma diffuses into red blood cells, where it binds to hemoglobin. This removes dissolved O_2 from the plasma, causing more oxygen to diffuse in from the alveoli.

RUNNING PROBLEM

In most people arriving at high altitude, normal physiological responses kick in to help acclimatize the body to the chronic hypoxia. Within two hours of arrival, hypoxia triggers the release of erythropoietin from the kidneys and liver. This hormone stimulates red blood cell production, and as a result, new erythrocytes appear in the blood within four days.

Question 4:
How does adding erythrocytes to the blood help a person acclimatize to high altitude?

Question 5:
What does adding erythrocytes to the blood do to the viscosity of the blood? What effect will that change in viscosity have on blood flow?

588 592 593 596 601 606 608

The transfer of oxygen from alveolar air to plasma to red blood cells and onto hemoglobin occurs so rapidly that blood in the pulmonary capillaries normally picks up as much oxygen as the P_{O_2} of the plasma and the number of red blood cells permit.

Once arterial blood reaches the tissues, the exchange process that took place in the lungs reverses. Dissolved oxygen diffuses out of systemic capillaries into cells, and the resultant decrease in plasma P_{O_2} disturbs the equilibrium of the oxygen-hemoglobin binding reaction by removing oxygen from the left side of the equation. The equilibrium shifts to the left according to the law of mass action, and the hemoglobin molecules release their oxygen stores, as represented in the bottom half of Figure 18-6.

Like oxygen loading at the lungs, this process of transferring oxygen to the body's cells takes place very rapidly and goes to equilibrium. The P_{O_2} of the cells determines how much oxygen unloads from hemoglobin. As cells increase their metabolic activity, their P_{O_2} decreases, and hemoglobin releases more oxygen to them.

Oxygen Binding Is Expressed as a Percentage

The amount of oxygen bound to hemoglobin at any given P_{O_2} is expressed as a percentage:

$$(\text{amount of } O_2 \text{ bound/maximum that could be bound}) \times 100 = \text{percent saturation of hemoglobin}$$

The **percent saturation of hemoglobin** refers to the percentage of available binding sites that are bound to oxygen. If all binding sites of all hemoglobin molecules are occupied by oxygen molecules, the blood is 100% oxygenated, or *saturated* with oxygen. If half the available binding sites are carrying oxygen, the hemoglobin is 50% saturated, and so on.

The relationship between plasma P_{O_2} and percent saturation of hemoglobin can be explained with the following analogy. The hemoglobin molecules carrying oxygen are like students moving books from an old library to a new one. Each student (a hemoglobin molecule) can carry a maximum of four books (100% saturation). The librarian in charge controls how many books (O_2 molecules) each student will carry, just as plasma P_{O_2} determines the amount of oxygen that binds to hemoglobin.

At the same time, the total number of books being carried depends on the number of available students, just as the amount of oxygen delivered to the tissues depends on the number of available hemoglobin molecules. For example, if there are 100 students, and the librarian gives each of them four books (100% saturation), then 400 books will be carried to the new library. If the librarian gives out only three books to each student (decreased plasma P_{O_2}), then only 300 books will go to the new library, even though each student could carry four. (Students carrying only three out of a possible four books corresponds to 75% saturation of hemoglobin). If the librarian is handing out four books per student but only 50 students show up (fewer hemoglobin molecules), then only 200 books will get to the new library, even though the students will be carrying the maximum number of books they can carry.

The physical relationship between P_{O_2} and how much oxygen binds to hemoglobin can be studied *in vitro*. Researchers expose samples of hemoglobin to various P_{O_2} levels and quantitatively determine the amount of oxygen that binds. **Oxyhemoglobin dissociation curves**, such as the one shown in Figure 18-9 ■, are the result of these *in vitro* binding studies.

The shape of the HbO_2 dissociation curve reflects the properties of the hemoglobin molecule and its affinity for oxygen. If you look at the curve, you find that at normal alveolar and arterial P_{O_2} (100 mm Hg), 98% of the hemoglobin is bound to oxygen. In other words, as blood passes through the lungs under normal conditions, hemoglobin picks up nearly the maximum amount of oxygen that it can carry.

Notice that the curve is nearly flat at P_{O_2} levels higher than 100 mm Hg (that is, the slope approaches zero). At P_{O_2} above 100 mm Hg, even large changes in P_{O_2} cause only minor changes in percent saturation. In fact, hemoglobin will not be 100% saturated until the P_{O_2} reaches nearly 650 mm Hg, a partial pressure far higher than anything we encounter in everyday life.

The flattening of the dissociation curve at higher P_{O_2} also means that alveolar P_{O_2} can fall a good bit below 100 mm Hg without significantly lowering hemoglobin saturation. As long as P_{O_2} in the alveoli (and thus in the pulmonary capillaries) stays above 60 mm Hg, hemoglobin will be more than 90% saturated and will maintain near-normal levels of oxygen

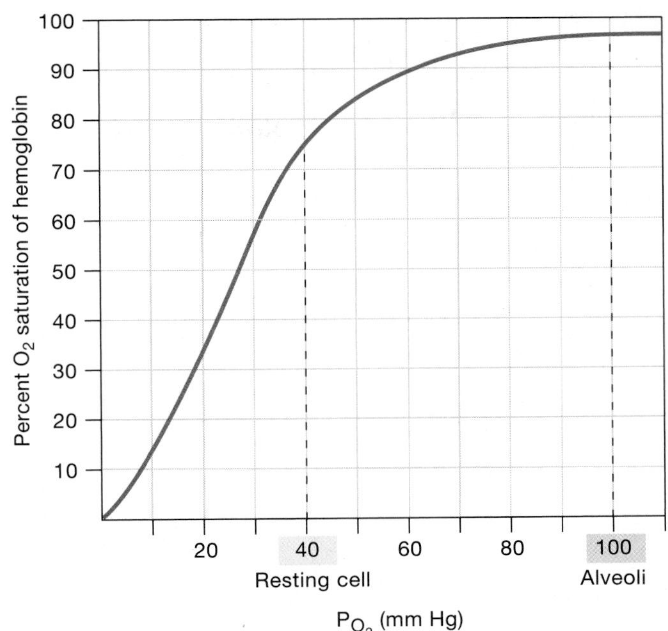

GRAPH QUESTION

(a) When the P_{O_2} is 20 mm Hg, what is the percent O_2 saturation of hemoglobin?
(b) At what P_{O_2} is hemoglobin 50% saturated with O_2?

■ **FIGURE 18-9** ***An oxygen-hemoglobin dissociation curve***

transport. However, once P_{O_2} falls below 60 mm Hg, the curve becomes steeper. The steep slope means that a small decrease in P_{O_2} causes a relatively large release of oxygen.

For example, if P_{O_2} falls from 100 mm Hg to 60 mm Hg, the percent saturation of hemoglobin goes from 98% to about 90%, a decrease of 8%. This is equivalent to a saturation change of 2% for each 10 mm Hg change. If P_{O_2} falls further, from 60 to 40 mm Hg, the percent saturation goes from 90% to 75%, a decrease of 7.5% for each 10 mm Hg. In the 40–20 mm Hg range, the curve is even steeper. Hemoglobin saturation declines from 75% to 35%, a change of 20% for each 10 mm Hg change.

What is the physiological significance of the shape of the dissociation curve? In blood leaving systemic capillaries with a P_{O_2} of 40 mm Hg (the normal partial pressure of resting cells), hemoglobin is still 75% saturated, which means that at the cells it released only one-fourth of the oxygen it is capable of carrying. The oxygen that remains bound serves as a reservoir that cells can draw on if metabolism increases.

When metabolically active tissues use additional oxygen, their cellular P_{O_2} decreases, and additional oxygen is released by hemoglobin at the cells. At a P_{O_2} of 20 mm Hg (an average value for exercising muscle), hemoglobin saturation falls to about 35%. With this 20 mm Hg decrease in P_{O_2} (40 mm Hg to 20 mm Hg), hemoglobin releases an additional 40% of the

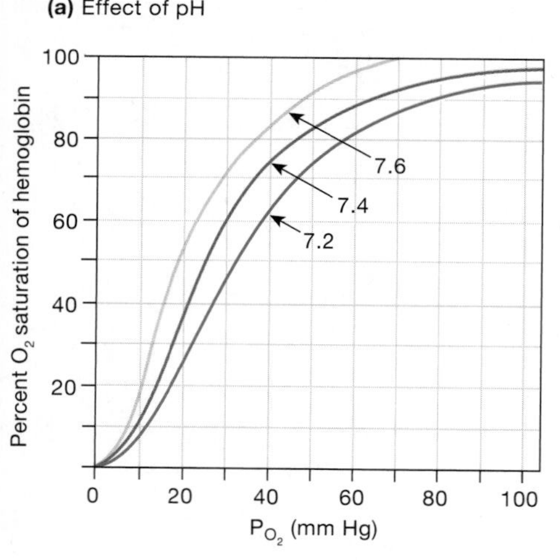

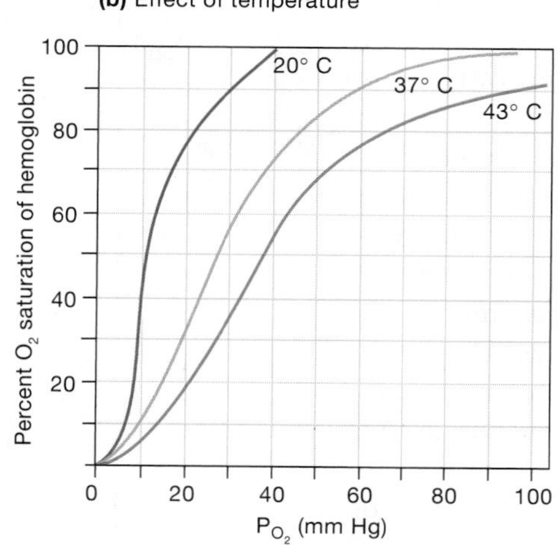

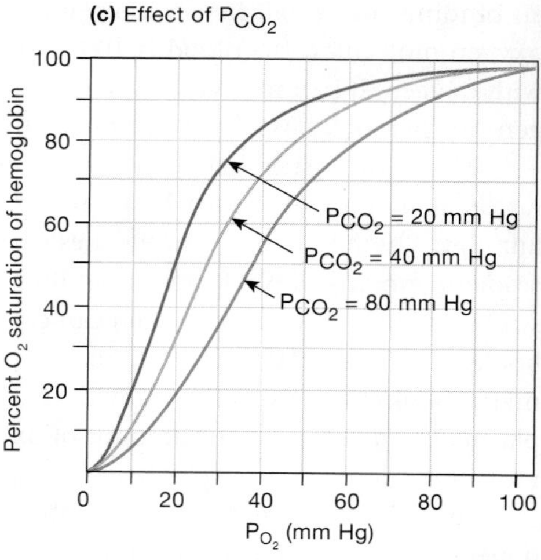

GRAPH QUESTIONS

(a) At a P_{O_2} of 20 mm Hg, how much more oxygen is released at an exercising muscle cell whose pH is 7.2 than by a cell with a pH of 7.4?

(b) What happens to oxygen release when the exercising muscle cell warms up?

FIGURE 18-10 ***Physical factors alter hemoglobin's affinity for oxygen***

oxygen it is capable of carrying. This is another example of the built-in reserve capacity of the body.

CONCEPT CHECK

9. Can a person breathing 100% oxygen at sea level achieve 100% saturation of her hemoglobin?
10. What effect does hyperventilation have on the percent saturation of arterial hemoglobin? (*Hint:* see Fig. 17-15.)

Answers: p. 611

Temperature, pH, and Metabolites Affect Oxygen-Hemoglobin Binding

Any factor that changes the conformation of the hemoglobin protein may affect its ability to bind oxygen. In humans, physiological changes in plasma pH, P_{CO_2}, and temperature all alter the oxygen-binding affinity of hemoglobin. Changes in binding affinity are reflected by changes in the shape of the HbO_2 dissociation curve.

Increased temperature, increased P_{CO_2}, or decreased pH will decrease the affinity of hemoglobin for oxygen and shift the oxygen-hemoglobin dissociation curve to the right (Fig. 18-10 ■). When these factors change in the opposite direction, binding affinity increases, and the curve shifts to the left. Notice that when the curve shifts in either direction, the changes are much more pronounced in the steep part of the curve. Physiologically, this means that oxygen binding at the lungs (in the 90–100 mm Hg P_{O_2} range) is not greatly affected, but oxygen delivery at the tissues (in the 20–40 mm Hg range) will be significantly altered.

Let's examine one example, the affinity shift that takes place when pH decreases from 7.4 (normal) to 7.2 (more acidic). (The normal range for blood pH is 7.38–7.42, but a pH of 7.2 is compatible with life.) Look at the graph in Figure 18-10a. At a P_{O_2} of 40 mm Hg (equivalent to a resting cell) and pH of 7.4, hemoglobin is about 75% saturated. At the same P_{O_2}, if the pH falls to 7.2, the percent saturation decreases to about 62%. This means that hemoglobin molecules release 13% more oxygen at pH 7.2 than they do at pH 7.4.

When does the body undergo shifts in blood pH? One situation is with maximal exertion that pushes cells into anaerobic metabolism. Anaerobic metabolism in exercising muscle fibers produces lactic acid, which in turn releases H^+ into the cytoplasm and extracellular fluid. As H^+ concentrations increase, pH falls, the affinity of hemoglobin for oxygen decreases, and the HbO_2 dissociation curve shifts to the right. More oxygen is released at the tissues as the blood becomes more acidic (pH decreases). A shift in the hemoglobin saturation curve that results from a change in pH is called the **Bohr effect**.

An additional factor that affects oxygen-hemoglobin binding is **2,3-diphosphoglycerate** (2,3-DPG; also called *2,3-bisphosphoglycerate* or 2,3-BPG), a compound made from an intermediate of the glycolysis pathway. **Chronic hypoxia** (extended periods of low oxygen) triggers an increase in 2,3-DPG

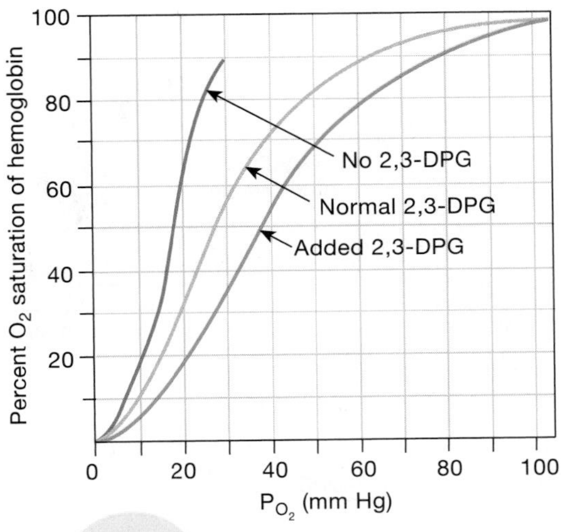

GRAPH QUESTION

Blood stored in blood banks loses its normal content of 2,3-DPG. Is this good or bad? Explain.

■ **FIGURE 18-11** ***2,3-DPG alters hemoglobin's affinity for oxygen***

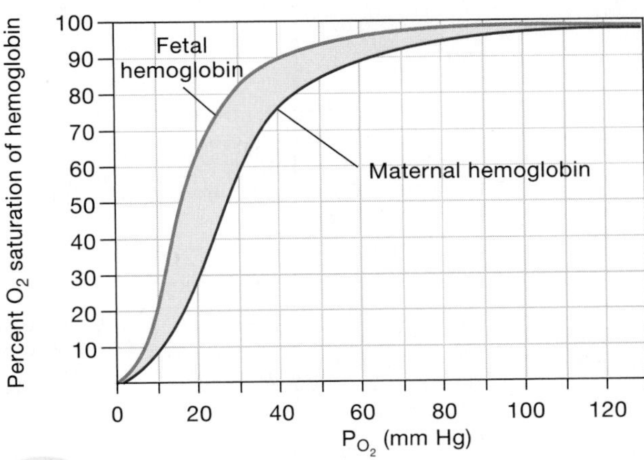

GRAPH QUESTIONS

(a) Because of incomplete gas exchange across the thick membranes of the placenta, hemoglobin in fetal blood leaving the placenta is 80% saturated with oxygen. What is the P_{O_2} of that placental blood?

(b) Blood in the vena cava of the fetus has a P_{O_2} around 10 mm Hg. What is the percent O_2 saturation of maternal hemoglobin at the same P_{O_2}?

■ **FIGURE 18-12** ***Differences in the oxygen-binding properties of maternal and fetal hemoglobin***

production in red blood cells. Increased levels of 2,3-DPG lower the binding affinity of hemoglobin and shift the HbO_2 dissociation curve to the right (Fig. 18-11 ■). Ascent to high altitude and anemia are two situations that increase 2,3-DPG production.

Changes in hemoglobin's structure also change its oxygen-binding affinity. For example, fetal hemoglobin has gamma chain isoforms for two of its subunits. The presence of gamma chains enhances the ability of fetal hemoglobin to bind oxygen in the low-oxygen environment of the placenta. The altered binding affinity is reflected by the shape of the fetal HbO_2 dissociation curve, which differs from the shape of the adult curve (Fig. 18-12 ■).

Figure 18-13 ■ summarizes the factors that influence the total oxygen content of arterial blood.

CONCEPT CHECK

11. A muscle that is actively contracting may have a cellular P_{O_2} of 25 mm Hg. What happens to oxygen binding to hemoglobin at this low P_{O_2}? What is the P_{O_2} of the venous blood leaving the active muscle?

Answers: p. 611

Carbon Dioxide Is Transported in Three Ways

Gas transport in the blood includes carbon dioxide removal from the cells as well as oxygen delivery to cells. The hemoglobin molecule, as we will see, also plays an important role in CO_2 transport. Carbon dioxide is a by-product of cellular respiration [p. 107]. It is more soluble in body fluids than oxygen is, but the cells produce far more CO_2 than can dissolve in the plasma.

Only about 7% of the CO_2 carried by venous blood is dissolved in the blood. The remaining 93% diffuses into red blood cells, where 70% is converted to bicarbonate ion, as explained below, and 23% binds to hemoglobin (Hb–CO_2). Figure 18-14 ■ summarizes these three mechanisms of carbon dioxide transport in the blood.

Why is removing CO_2 from the body so important? The reason is that elevated P_{CO_2} (*hypercapnia*) causes the pH disturbance known as *acidosis*. Extremes of pH interfere with hydrogen bonding of molecules and can denature proteins [p. 37]. Abnormally high P_{CO_2} levels also depress central nervous system function, causing confusion, coma, or even death. Thus, CO_2 is a potentially toxic waste product that must be removed by the lungs.

CO_2 and Bicarbonate Ions As just noted, about 70% of the CO_2 that enters the blood is transported to the lungs as bicarbonate ions (HCO_3^-) dissolved in the plasma. The conversion of CO_2 to HCO_3^- serves two purposes: (1) it provides an additional means by which CO_2 can be transported from cells to lungs, and (2) HCO_3^- is available to act as a buffer for metabolic acids [p. 38], thereby helping stabilize the body's pH.

How does CO_2 turn into HCO_3^-? The rapid conversion depends on the presence of **carbonic anhydrase** (CA), an enzyme found concentrated in red blood cells. Let's see how this happens. Dissolved CO_2 in the plasma diffuses into red blood cells, where it may react with water in the presence of carbonic

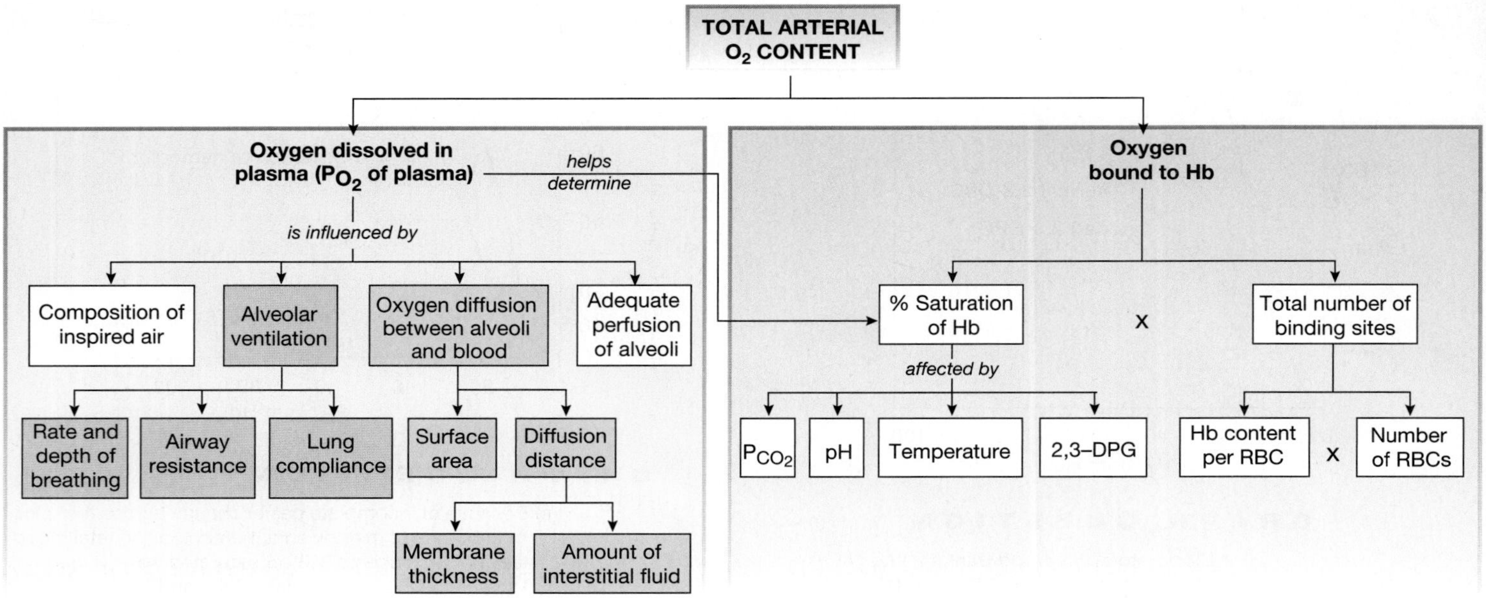

TOTAL ARTERIAL O_2 CONTENT
Oxygen dissolved in plasma (P_{O_2} of plasma)
helps determine
Oxygen bound to Hb
is influenced by
Composition of inspired air
Alveolar ventilation
Oxygen diffusion between alveoli and blood
Adequate perfusion of alveoli
Rate and depth of breathing
Airway resistance
Lung compliance
Surface area
Diffusion distance
Membrane thickness
Amount of interstitial fluid
% Saturation of Hb
x
Total number of binding sites
affected by
P_{CO_2}
pH
Temperature
2,3–DPG
Hb content per RBC
x
Number of RBCs

■ **FIGURE 18-13** ***Factors contributing to the total oxygen content of arterial blood***

anhydrase to form *carbonic acid* (top portion of Fig. 18-14). Carbonic acid then dissociates into a hydrogen ion and a bicarbonate ion:

$$CO_2 + H_2O \underset{}{\overset{\text{carbonic anhydrase}}{\rightleftharpoons}} \underset{\text{carbonic acid}}{H_2CO_3} \rightleftharpoons H^+ + HCO_3^-$$

Because the carbonic acid dissociates readily, we sometimes ignore the intermediate step and summarize the reaction as:

$$CO_2 + H_2O \rightleftharpoons H^+ + HCO_3^-$$

This reaction is reversible. The rate in either direction depends on the relative concentrations of the substrates and obeys the law of mass action.

18

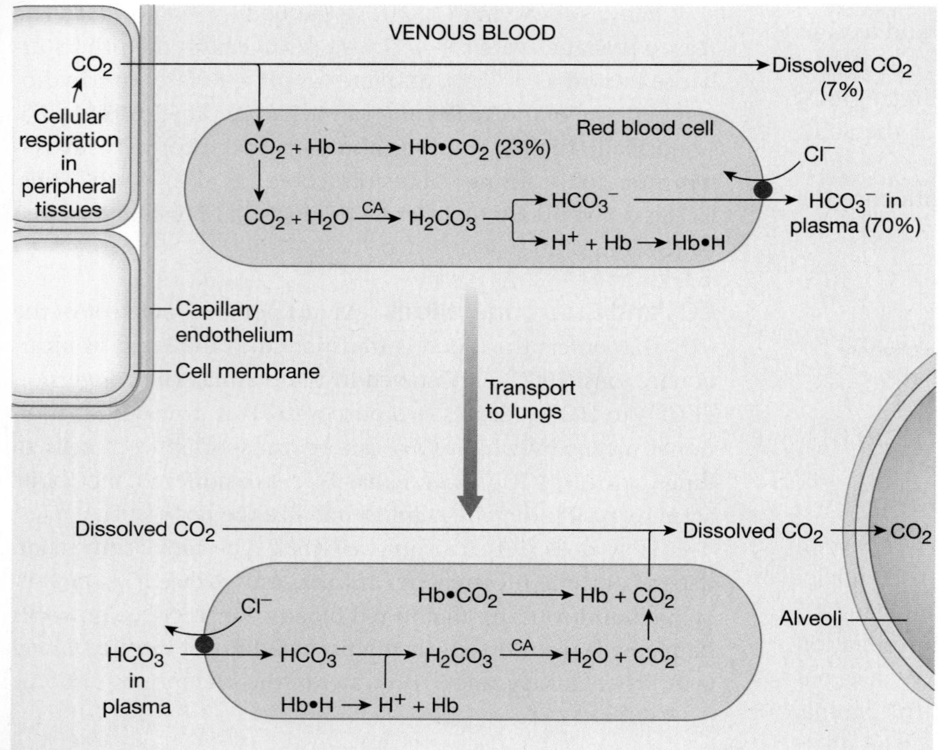

■ **FIGURE 18-14** ***Carbon dioxide transport in the blood***

CA = carbonic anhydrase.

RUNNING PROBLEM

The usual homeostatic response to high-altitude hypoxia is hyperventilation, which begins on arrival. Hyperventilation enhances alveolar ventilation, but this may not help elevate arterial P_{O_2} levels significantly when atmospheric P_{O_2} is low. However, hyperventilation does lower plasma P_{CO_2}.

Question 6:
What happens to plasma pH during hyperventilation? (Hint: apply the law of mass action to figure out what happens to the balance between CO_2 and $H^+ + HCO_3^-$.)

Question 7:
How does this change in pH affect oxygen binding at the lungs when P_{O_2} is decreased? How does it affect unloading of oxygen at the cells?

The conversion of carbon dioxide to H^+ and HCO_3^- will continue until equilibrium is reached. (Water is always in excess in the body, so water concentration plays no role in the dynamic equilibrium of this reaction.) To keep the reaction going, the products (H^+ and HCO_3^-) must be removed from the cytoplasm of the red blood cell. If the product concentrations are kept low, the reaction cannot reach equilibrium. Carbon dioxide continues to move out of plasma into the red blood cells, which in turn allows more CO_2 to diffuse out of tissues into the blood.

Two separate mechanisms remove free H^+ and HCO_3^-. In the first, bicarbonate leaves the red blood cell on an antiport protein [p. 139]. This transport process, known as the **chloride shift**, exchanges one HCO_3^- for one Cl^-. The one-for-one exchange maintains electrical neutrality so that the cell's membrane potential is not affected. The transfer of HCO_3^- into the plasma makes this buffer [p. 38] available to moderate pH changes caused by the production of metabolic acids. Bicarbonate is the most important extracellular buffer in the body.

Hemoglobin and H⁺ The second mechanism removes free H^+ from the red blood cell cytoplasm. Hemoglobin within the red blood cell acts as a buffer and binds hydrogen ions in the reaction

$$H^+ + Hb \rightarrow Hb \cdot H$$

Hemoglobin's buffering of H^+ is an important step that prevents large changes in the body's pH. If blood P_{CO_2} is elevated much above normal, the hemoglobin buffer cannot soak up all the H^+ produced from the reaction of CO_2 and water. In those cases, excess H^+ accumulates in the plasma, causing the condition known as **respiratory acidosis**. Further information on the role of the respiratory system in maintaining pH homeostasis is found in Chapter 20.

Hemoglobin and CO₂ Although most carbon dioxide that enters red blood cells is converted to bicarbonate ions, about 23% of the CO_2 in venous blood binds directly to hemoglobin. When oxygen leaves its binding sites on the hemoglobin molecule, CO_2 binds with free hemoglobin at exposed amino groups ($-NH_2$), forming **carbaminohemoglobin:**

$$CO_2 + Hb \rightleftharpoons Hb \cdot CO_2 \text{ (carbaminohemoglobin)}$$

The formation of carbaminohemoglobin is facilitated by the presence of CO_2 and H^+ because both these factors decrease hemoglobin's binding affinity for oxygen (see Fig. 18-10).

CO₂ Removal at the Lungs When venous blood reaches the lungs, the processes that took place in the systemic capillaries reverse (bottom portion of Fig. 18-14). The P_{CO_2} of the alveoli is lower than that of venous blood in the pulmonary capillaries. Therefore, CO_2 diffuses down its pressure gradient—in other words, out of plasma into the alveoli—and the plasma P_{CO_2} begins to fall.

The decrease in plasma P_{CO_2} allows dissolved CO_2 to diffuse out of the red blood cells. As CO_2 levels in the red blood cells decrease, the equilibrium of the CO_2-HCO_3^- reaction is disturbed, shifting toward production of more CO_2. Removal of CO_2 causes H^+ to leave the hemoglobin molecules, and the chloride shift reverses: Cl^- returns to the plasma in exchange for HCO_3^- moving back into the red blood cells. The HCO_3^- and newly released H^+ re-form into carbonic acid, which is then converted into water and CO_2. This CO_2 is then free to diffuse out of the red blood cell and into the alveoli.

Figure 18-15 ■ shows the combined transport of CO_2 and O_2 in the blood. At the alveoli, O_2 diffuses down its pressure gradient, moving from the alveoli into the plasma and then from the plasma into the red blood cells. Hemoglobin binds to O_2, increasing the amount of oxygen that can be transported to the cells.

At the cells, the process reverses. Because P_{O_2} is lower in cells than in the arterial blood, O_2 diffuses from the plasma into the cells. The decrease in plasma P_{O_2} causes hemoglobin to release O_2, making additional oxygen available to enter cells.

Carbon dioxide from aerobic metabolism simultaneously leaves cells and enters the blood, dissolving in the plasma. From there, CO_2 enters red blood cells, where most is converted to HCO_3^- and H^+. The HCO_3^- is returned to the plasma in exchange for a Cl^- while the H^+ binds to hemoglobin. A fraction of the CO_2 that enters red blood cells also binds directly to hemoglobin. At the lungs, the process reverses as CO_2 diffuses out of the pulmonary capillaries and into the alveoli.

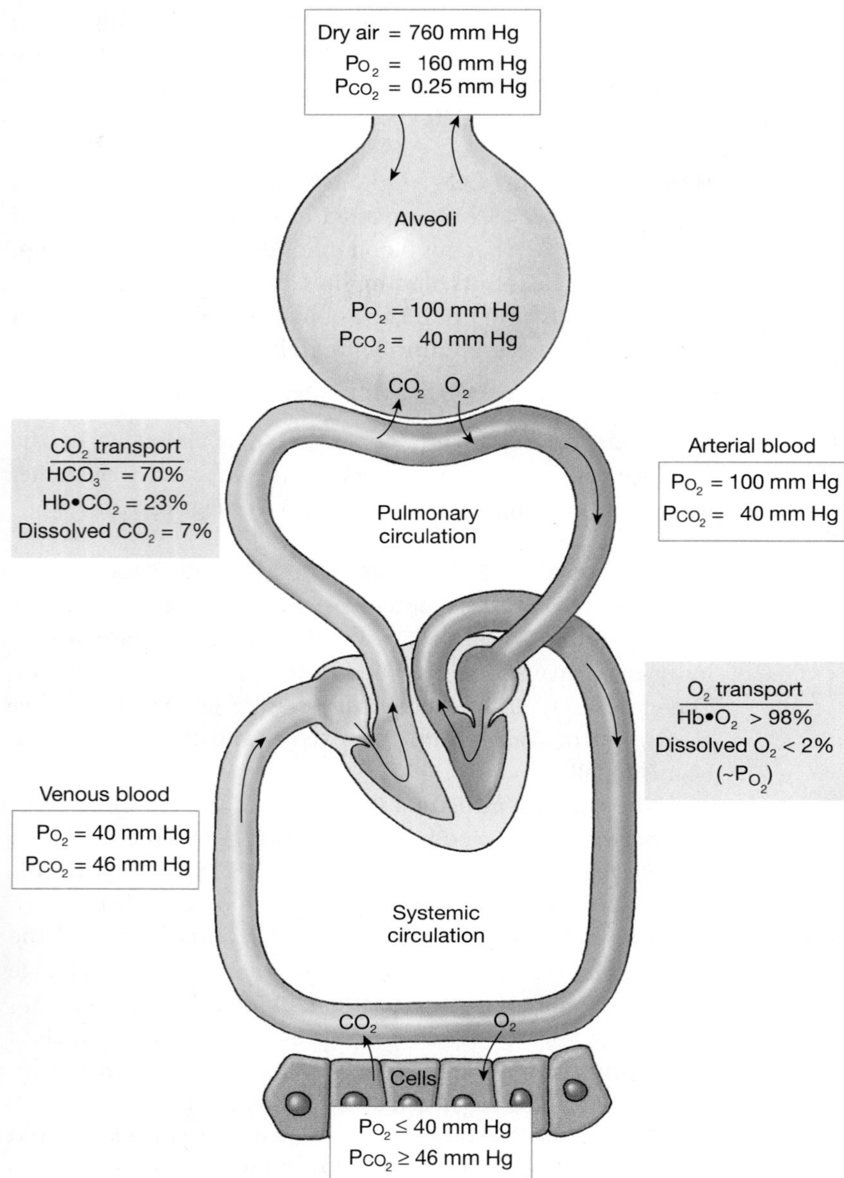

FIGURE 18-15 ***Summary of gas transport***

To understand fully how the respiratory system coordinates delivery of oxygen to the lungs with transport of oxygen in the circulation, we will now consider the central nervous system control of ventilation.

CONCEPT CHECK

12. How would an obstruction of the airways affect alveolar ventilation, arterial P_{CO_2}, and the body's pH?

Answers: p. 611

REGULATION OF VENTILATION

Breathing is a rhythmic process that usually occurs without conscious thought or awareness. In that respect, it resembles the rhythmic beating of the heart. However, skeletal muscles, unlike autorhythmic cardiac muscles, are not able to contract spontaneously. Instead, skeletal muscle contraction must be initiated by somatic motor neurons, which in turn are controlled by the central nervous system. The intrinsic rhythmicity of ventilation is subject to modulation by a variety of influences, including chemoreceptor reflexes, interaction with the cardiovascular control center, emotions, and conscious and unconscious control by higher brain centers.

In the respiratory system, contraction of the diaphragm and intercostals is initiated by groups of neurons in the pons and medulla of the brain stem (Fig. 18-16 ■). These neurons take the form of a network with a **central pattern generator** that has intrinsic rhythmic activity [p. 445]. Research suggests the rhythmic activity arises from pacemaker neurons that have unstable membrane potentials.

Direct study of the brain centers controlling ventilation is difficult because of the complexity of the neuronal network and its anatomical location. Consequently, some of our understanding of how ventilation is controlled has come from observing patients with brain damage. Other information has come from animal experiments in which the neural connections between major parts of the brain stem were severed.

From these observations and the hypotheses formed from them, the following model for the control of ventilation has been proposed. Although some parts of the model are well supported with experimental evidence, other aspects are still under investigation. The model states that:

1. Respiratory neurons in the medulla control inspiration and expiration.
2. Neurons in the pons modulate ventilation.
3. The rhythmic pattern of breathing arises from a network of spontaneously discharging neurons.
4. Ventilation is subject to modulation by various chemoreceptor-linked reflexes and by higher brain centers.

Neurons in the Medulla Control Breathing

Classic descriptions of how the brain controls ventilation divided groups of neurons into various control centers. More recent descriptions, however, are less specific about assigning function to particular centers and simply refer to the network of neurons in the brain stem as the central pattern generator.

The central pattern generator functions automatically throughout a person's life but can also be controlled voluntarily, up to a point. Complicated synaptic interactions between neurons in the network create the rhythmic cycles of inspiration and expiration, influenced continuously by sensory input from chemoreceptors for CO_2, O_2, and H^+. Ventilation pattern depends in large part on the levels of these three substances in the extracellular fluid.

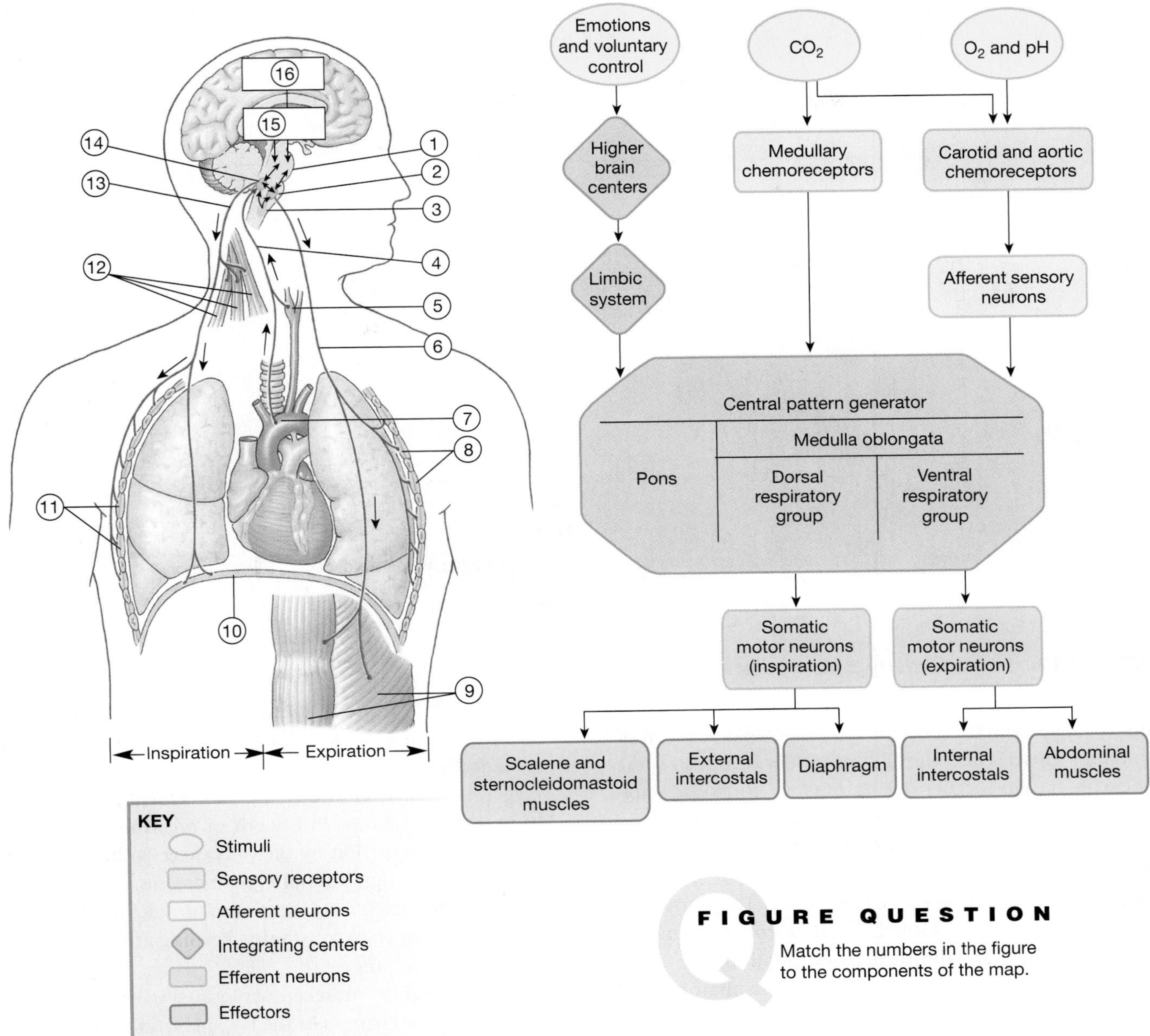

FIGURE QUESTION

Match the numbers in the figure to the components of the map.

■ **FIGURE 18-16** ***Reflex control of ventilation***

Chemoreceptors monitor blood gases and pH. Control centers in the brain stem regulate activity in somatic motor neurons leading to respiratory muscles.

Although there is still much to be learned about the central pattern generator, we do know that respiratory neurons are concentrated in two centers in the medulla oblongata. The **dorsal respiratory group** (DRG) of neurons contains mostly *inspiratory neurons* that control the diaphragm (Fig. 18-16). The **ventral respiratory group** (VRG) of neurons controls muscles used for active expiration and some inspiratory muscles, particularly those active during greater-than-normal inspiration, such as occurs during vigorous exercise. Fibers from the VRG also innervate muscles of the larynx, pharynx, and tongue to keep the upper airways open during breathing.

During quiet respiration at 12 breaths/min, the inspiratory neurons gradually increase stimulation of the inspiratory muscles for 2 seconds. This increase is sometimes called *ramping* because of the shape of the graph of inspiratory neuron activity (Fig. 18-17 ■). A few inspiratory neurons fire to begin the ramp. The firing of these neurons recruits other inspiratory neurons to fire in an apparent positive feedback loop. As more neurons fire, more skeletal muscle fibers are recruited. The rib cage expands smoothly as the diaphragm contracts.

At the end of 2 seconds, the inspiratory neurons abruptly stop firing, and the respiratory muscles relax. Over the next

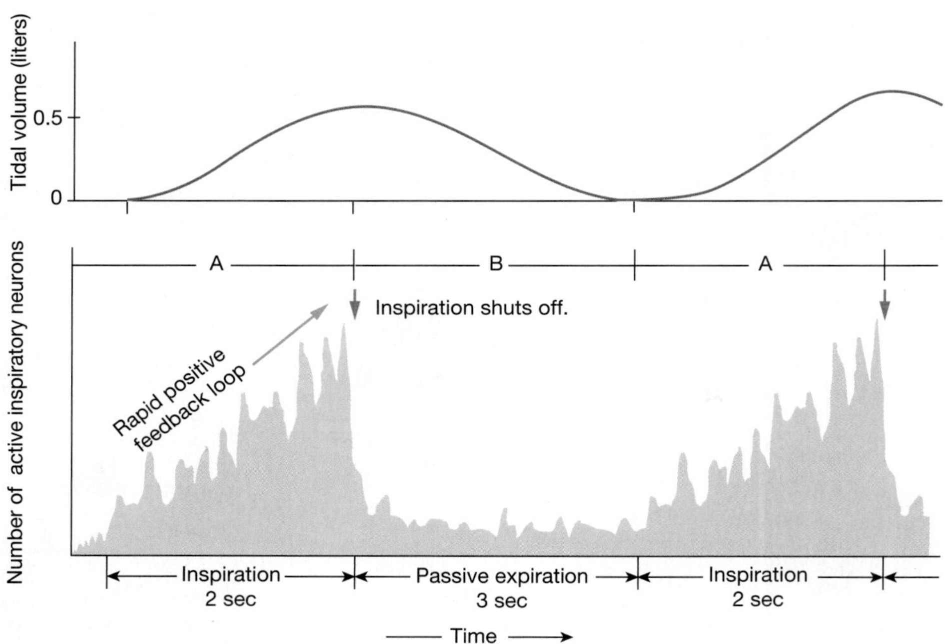
Tidal volume (liters)
0.5
0
Number of active inspiratory neurons
A
B
A
Inspiration shuts off.
Rapid positive feedback loop
Inspiration 2 sec
Passive expiration 3 sec
Inspiration 2 sec
Time
During inspiration, the activity of inspiratory neurons increases steadily, apparently through a positive feedback mechanism. At the end of inspiration, the activity shuts off abruptly and expiration takes place through recoil of elastic lung tissue.

■ **FIGURE 18-17** ***Neural activity during quiet breathing***

3 seconds, passive expiration occurs because of elastic recoil of the inspiratory muscles and elastic lung tissue. However, some motor neuron activity occurs during passive expiration, suggesting that perhaps muscles in the upper airways contract to slow the flow of air out of the respiratory system.

The expiratory neurons of the ventral respiratory group remain mostly inactive during quiet respiration. They function primarily during forced breathing, when inspiratory movements are exaggerated, and during active expiration.

In forced breathing, increased activity of inspiratory neurons stimulates accessory inspiratory muscles, such as the sternocleidomastoids. Contraction of the accessory inspiratory muscles enhances expansion of the thorax by raising the sternum and upper ribs.

With active expiration, expiratory neurons from the ventral respiratory group activate the internal intercostal and abdominal muscles. There seems to be some reciprocal inhibition between inspiratory and expiratory neurons, as inspiratory neurons are inhibited during active expiration.

Carbon Dioxide, Oxygen, and pH Influence Ventilation

Sensory input from central and peripheral chemoreceptors [p. 330] modifies the rhythmicity of the central pattern generator. Carbon dioxide is the primary stimulus for changes in ventilation. Oxygen and plasma pH play lesser roles.

The chemoreceptors for oxygen and carbon dioxide are strategically associated with the arterial circulation. If too little oxygen is present in arterial blood destined for the brain and other tissues, the rate and depth of breathing increase. If the rate of CO_2 production by the cells exceeds the rate of CO_2 removal by the lungs, arterial P_{CO_2} increases, and ventilation is intensified to match CO_2 removal to production. These homeostatic reflexes operate constantly, keeping arterial P_{O_2} and P_{CO_2} within a narrow range.

Peripheral chemoreceptors located in the carotid and aortic arteries sense changes in the P_{O_2}, pH, and P_{CO_2} of the plasma (Fig. 18-16). These **carotid** and **aortic bodies** are close to the locations of the baroreceptors involved in reflex control of blood pressure [p. 521]. **Central chemoreceptors** in the brain respond to changes in the concentration of CO_2 in the cerebrospinal fluid. These central receptors lie on the ventral surface of the medulla, close to neurons involved in respiratory control.

Peripheral Chemoreceptors When specialized **glomus cells** [*glomus,* a ball-shaped mass] in the carotid and aortic bodies are activated by a decrease in P_{O_2} or pH or by an increase in P_{CO_2}, they trigger a reflex increase in ventilation. The details of glomus cell function remain to be worked out, but the basic mechanism by which these chemoreceptors respond to low oxygen is similar to the mechanism you learned for insulin release by pancreatic beta cells [p. 166] or taste transduction in taste buds [p. 345].

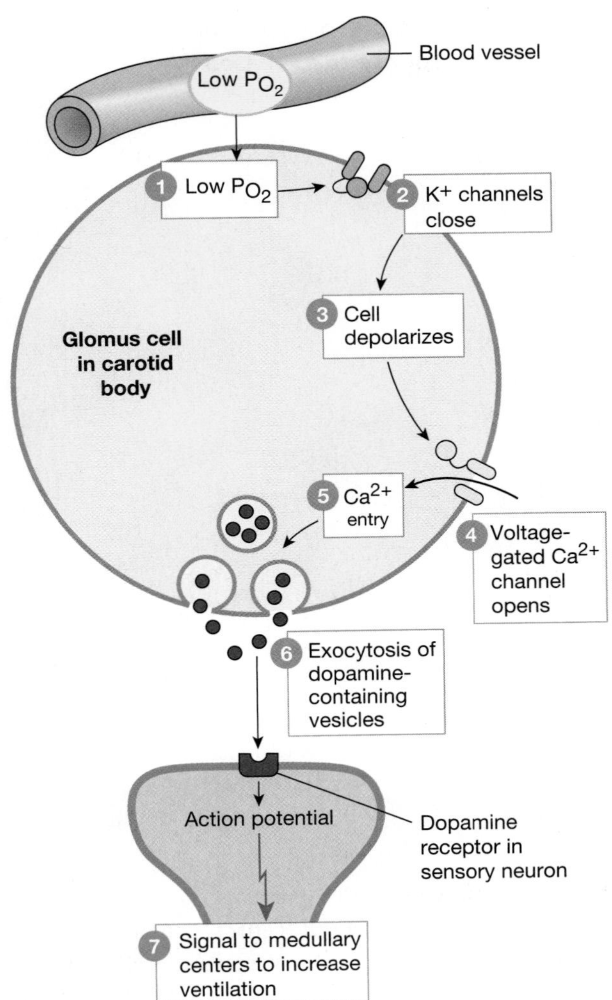

■ **FIGURE 18-18** ***Carotid body oxygen sensor releases neurotransmitter when P_{O_2} decreases***

In all three examples, a stimulus inactivates K^+ channels, causing the receptor cell to depolarize (Fig. 18-18 ■). Depolarization opens voltage-gated Ca^{2+} channels, and Ca^{2+} entry causes exocytosis of neurotransmitter (probably dopamine in glomus cells) onto the sensory neuron. In the carotid and aortic bodies, dopamine initiates action potentials in sensory neurons leading to the brain stem respiratory centers, signaling them to increase ventilation.

Under most circumstances, oxygen is not an important factor in modulating ventilation because arterial P_{O_2} must fall to less than 60 mm Hg before ventilation is stimulated. This large decrease in P_{O_2} is equivalent to ascending to an altitude of 3000 m. (For reference, Denver is located at an altitude of 1609 m.)

Because the peripheral chemoreceptors respond only to dramatic changes in arterial P_{O_2}, they do not play a role in the everyday regulation of ventilation. However, unusual physiological conditions, such as ascending to high altitude, and pathological conditions, such as chronic obstructive pulmonary disease (COPD), can reduce arterial P_{O_2} to levels that are low enough to activate the peripheral chemoreceptors.

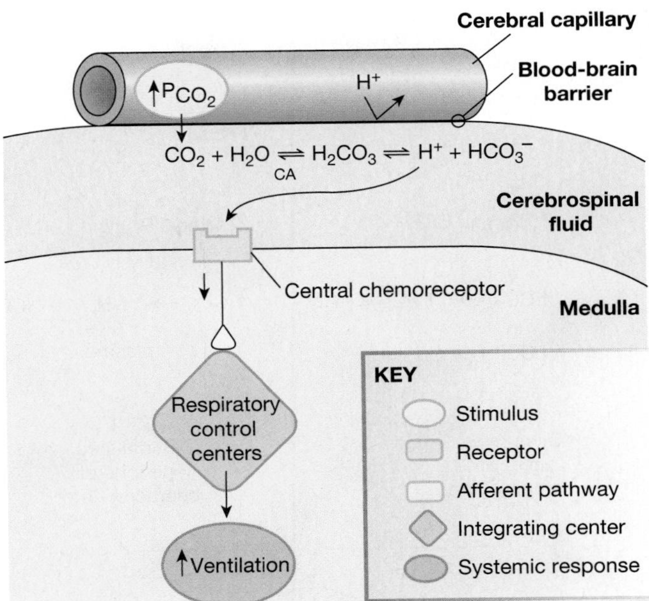

■ **FIGURE 18-19** ***Central chemoreceptors monitor CO_2 in cerebrospinal fluid***

CA = carbonic anhydrase.

The peripheral chemoreceptors in the carotid and aortic bodies are more responsive to changes in P_{O_2} than to changes in plasma pH and P_{CO_2}. However, any condition that reduces plasma pH or increases P_{CO_2} stimulates ventilation by way of the peripheral chemoreceptors.

Central Chemoreceptors The most important chemical controller of ventilation is carbon dioxide, mediated through central chemoreceptors located in the medulla (Fig. 18-19 ■). These receptors set the respiratory pace, providing continuous input into the central pattern generator. When arterial P_{CO_2} increases, CO_2 crosses the blood-brain barrier quite rapidly and activates the central chemoreceptors. These receptors signal the central pattern generator to increase the rate and depth of ventilation, thereby increasing alveolar ventilation and removing CO_2 from the blood (Fig. 18-20 ■).

Although we say that the central chemoreceptors monitor CO_2, they actually respond to pH changes in the cerebrospinal fluid. Carbon dioxide that diffuses across the blood-brain barrier into the cerebrospinal fluid is converted to bicarbonate and H^+:

$$CO_2 + H_2O \rightleftharpoons H_2CO_3^- \rightleftharpoons H^+ + HCO_3^-$$

Experiments indicate that the H^+ produced by this reaction is what actually initiates the chemoreceptor reflex, rather than the increased level of CO_2.

Note, however, that pH changes in the plasma *do not* usually influence the central chemoreceptors directly. Free H^+ in

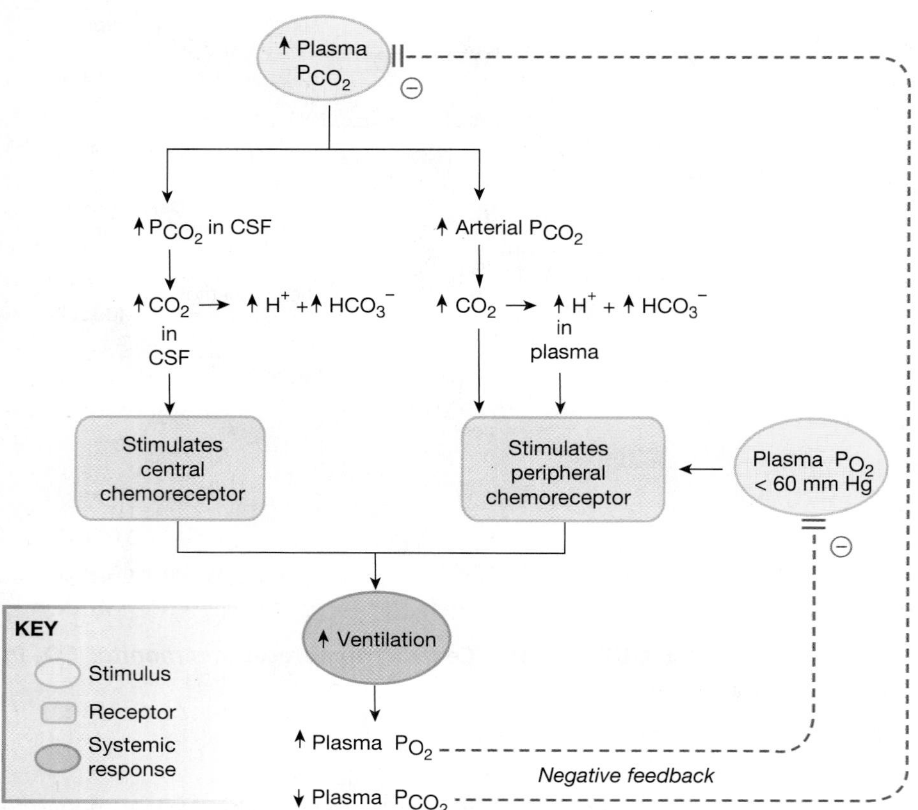

■ **FIGURE 18-20** ***Chemoreceptor response to increased*** P_{CO_2}

18

the plasma crosses the blood-brain barrier very slowly and therefore has little effect on the central chemoreceptors.

When plasma P_{CO_2} increases, the central chemoreceptors initially respond strongly by increasing ventilation. However, if P_{CO_2} remains elevated for several days, ventilation falls back toward normal rates as the chemoreceptors adapt. This adaptation occurs because over time the choroid plexus begins to transport HCO_3^- into the cerebrospinal fluid. These ions act as a buffer, removing H^+ from the cerebrospinal fluid and decreasing H^+ stimulation of the central pattern generator.

Fortunately for people with chronic lung diseases, the response of peripheral chemoreceptors to low arterial P_{O_2} remains intact over time, even though central chemoreceptors adapt to high P_{CO_2}. In some situations, low P_{O_2} becomes the primary chemical stimulus for ventilation. For example, patients with severe chronic lung disease, such as emphysema, have chronic hypercapnia and hypoxia. Their arterial P_{CO_2} may rise to 50–55 mm Hg (normal is 35–45) while their P_{O_2} falls to 45–50 mm Hg (normal 75–100). Because these levels are chronic, the central chemoreceptors adapt to the elevated P_{CO_2}. Most of the chemical stimulus for ventilation in this situation then comes from low P_{O_2}, sensed by the carotid and aortic chemoreceptors. If these patients are given too much oxygen, they may stop breathing because their chemical stimulus for ventilation is eliminated.

The central chemoreceptors respond to decreased arterial P_{CO_2} as well as to increased P_{CO_2}. If alveolar P_{CO_2} falls, as it might during hyperventilation, plasma P_{CO_2} and cerebrospinal fluid P_{CO_2} follow suit. As a result, central chemoreceptor activity declines, and the central pattern generator slows the ventilation rate. When ventilation decreases, carbon dioxide begins to accumulate in alveoli and the plasma. Eventually, the arterial P_{CO_2} rises above the threshold level for the chemoreceptors. At that point, the receptors fire, and the central pattern generator again increases ventilation.

RUNNING PROBLEM

The hyperventilation response to hypoxia creates a peculiar breathing pattern called *periodic breathing*, in which the person goes through a 10–15-second period of breath-holding followed by a short period of hyperventilation. Periodic breathing occurs most often during sleep.

Question 8:

Based on your understanding of how the body controls ventilation, why do you think periodic breathing occurs most often during sleep?

588 592 593 596 601 606 608

Protective Reflexes Guard the Lungs

In addition to the chemoreceptor reflexes that help regulate ventilation, the body has protective reflexes that respond to physical injury or irritation of the respiratory tract and to over-inflation of the lungs. The major protective reflex is *broncho-constriction,* mediated through parasympathetic neurons that innervate bronchiolar smooth muscle. Inhaled particles or noxious gases stimulate **irritant receptors** in the airway mucosa. The irritant receptors send signals through sensory neurons to control centers in the central nervous system that trigger bronchoconstriction. Protective reflex responses also include coughing and sneezing.

The **Hering-Breuer inflation reflex** prevents overexpansion of the lungs during strenuous exercise. If tidal volume exceeds 1 liter, stretch receptors in the lung signal the brain stem to terminate inspiration. However, because normal tidal volume is only 500 mL, this reflex does not operate during quiet breathing and mild exertion.

Higher Brain Centers Affect Patterns of Ventilation

Conscious and unconscious thought processes also affect respiratory activities. Higher centers in the hypothalamus and cerebrum can alter the activity of the central pattern generator and change ventilation rate and depth. Voluntary control of ventilation falls into this category. Higher brain center control is not a *requirement* for ventilation, however. Even if the brain stem above the pons is severely damaged, essentially normal respiratory cycles continue.

Respiration can also be affected by stimulation of portions of the limbic system. As a result, emotional and autonomic activities such as fear and excitement may affect the pace and depth of respiration. In some of these situations, the neural pathway goes directly to the somatic motor neurons, bypassing the central pattern generator in the brain stem.

Although we can temporarily alter our respiratory performance, we cannot override the chemoreceptor reflexes. Holding your breath is a good example. You can hold your breath voluntarily only until elevated P_{CO_2} in the blood and cerebrospinal fluid activates the chemoreceptor reflex, forcing you to inhale.

Small children having temper tantrums sometimes attempt to manipulate parents by threatening to hold their breath until they die. However, the chemoreceptor reflexes make it impossible for the children to carry out that threat. Extremely strong-willed children can continue holding their breath until they turn blue and pass out from hypoxia, but once they are unconscious, normal breathing automatically resumes.

Breathing is intimately linked to cardiovascular function. The integrating centers for both functions are located in the brain stem, and interneurons project between the two centers, allowing signaling back and forth. In Chapter 20 we will examine the integration of cardiovascular, respiratory, and renal function as the three systems work together to maintain fluid and acid-base homeostasis. First, however, we examine the physiology of the kidneys in Chapter 19.

RUNNING PROBLEM CONCLUSION

HIGH ALTITUDE

On May 29, 1953, Edmund Hillary and Tenzing Norgay of the British Everest Expedition were the first humans to reach the summit of Mt. Everest. They carried supplemental oxygen with them, as it was believed that this feat was impossible without it. In 1978, however, Reinhold Messner and Peter Hebeler achieved the "impossible." On May 8, they struggled to the summit using sheer willpower and no extra oxygen. In Messner's words, "I am nothing more than a single narrow gasping lung, floating over the mists and summits." Learn more about these Everest expeditions by doing a Google search for *Hillary Everest* or *Messner Everest*.

To learn more about different types of mountain sickness, see "All about altitude illness," *www.high-altitude-medicine.com;* "High altitude medicine," *American Family Physician* 1998 Apr. 15, *www.aafp.org/afp/980415ap/harris.html;* and "High-altitude pulmonary edema," *New England Journal of Medicine* 346(21):1606–1607, 2002 May 23, *www.nejm.org.*

In this running problem you learned about normal and abnormal responses to high altitude. Check your understanding of the physiology behind this respiratory challenge by comparing your answers with the information in the following table.

	QUESTION	FACTS	INTEGRATION AND ANALYSIS
1	What is the P_{O_2} of inspired air reaching the alveoli at 2500 m, where dry atmospheric pressure is 542 mm Hg? How does this value for P_{O_2} compare with the P_{O_2} value for fully-humidified air at sea level?	Water vapor contributes a partial pressure of 47 mm Hg to fully humidified air. Oxygen is 21% of dry air. Normal atmospheric pressure at sea level is 760 mm Hg.	Correction for water vapor: $542 - 47 = 495$ mm Hg $\times$ 21% $= P_{O_2} =$ 104 mm Hg. In humidified air at sea level, $P_{O_2} = 150$ mm Hg.
2	Why would someone with HAPE be short of breath?	Pulmonary edema increases the diffusion distance for oxygen.	The increased diffusion distance worsens the normal hypoxia of altitude.
3	Based on what you learned about mechanisms for matching ventilation and perfusion in the lung, can you explain why patients with HAPE have elevated pulmonary arterial blood pressure?	Low oxygen levels constrict pulmonary arterioles.	Constriction of pulmonary arterioles causes blood to collect in the pulmonary arteries behind the constriction. This increases arterial blood pressure.
4	How does adding erythrocytes to the blood help a person acclimatize to high altitude?	98% of arterial oxygen is carried bound to hemoglobin.	Additional hemoglobin increases the oxygen-carrying capacity of the blood.
5	What does adding erythrocytes to the blood do to the viscosity of the blood? What effect will that change in viscosity have on blood flow?	Adding cells increases blood viscosity.	According to Poiseuille's law, increased viscosity increases resistance to flow, so blood flow will decrease.
6	What happens to plasma pH during hyperventilation?	Apply the law of mass action to the equation $CO_2 + H_2O \rightleftharpoons H^+ + HCO_3^-$.	The amount of CO_2 in the plasma decreases during hyperventilation, which means the equation shifts to the left. This shift decreases H^+, which increases pH (alkalosis).
7	How does this change in pH affect oxygen binding at the lungs when P_{O_2} is decreased? How does it affect unloading of oxygen at the cells?	See Figure 18-10a.	The left shift of the curve means that, at any given P_{O_2}, more O_2 binds to hemoglobin. Less O_2 will unbind at the tissues for a given P_{O_2}, but P_{O_2} in the cells is probably lower than normal, and consequently there may be no change in unloading.
8	Why do you think periodic breathing occurs most often during sleep?	Periodic breathing alternates periods of breath-holding (apnea) and hyperventilation.	An awake person is more likely to make a conscious effort to breathe during the breath-holding spells, eliminating the cycle of periodic breathing.

588 592 593 596 601 606 608

CHAPTER SUMMARY

In this chapter, you learned why climbing Mt. Everest is such a respiratory challenge for the human body, and why people with emphysema experience the same respiratory challenges at sea level. The exchange and transport of oxygen and carbon dioxide in the body illustrate the *mass flow* of gases along concentration gradients. The *homeostatic balance* of these blood gases demonstrates *mass balance*: the concentration in the blood varies according to what enters or leaves at the lungs and tissues. The *law of mass action* governs the chemical reactions through which hemoglobin binds oxygen, and carbonic anhydrase catalyzes the conversion of CO_2 and water to carbonic acid.

Diffusion and Solubility of Gases

1. Diffusion of oxygen and CO_2 is influenced by partial pressure gradients, surface area, membrane thickness, and diffusion distance. (p. 588)
2. The amount of a gas that dissolves in a liquid is proportional to the partial pressure of the gas and to the **solubility** of the gas in the liquid. Carbon dioxide is 20 times more soluble in aqueous solutions than oxygen is. (p. 589; Fig. 18-2)

Gas Exchange in the Lungs and Tissues

IP Respiratory System: Gas Exchange

3. Normal alveolar and arterial P_{O_2} is about 100 mm Hg. Normal arterial P_{CO_2} is about 40 mm Hg. (p. 590; Fig. 18-3)
4. Normal venous P_{O_2} is 40 mm Hg, and normal venous P_{CO_2} is 46 mm Hg. (p. 590; Fig. 18-3)
5. Both the composition of inspired air and the effectiveness of alveolar ventilation affect alveolar P_{O_2}. (p. 591)
6. Changes in alveolar surface area, in alveolar membrane thickness, and in interstitial distance between alveoli and pulmonary capillaries all affect gas exchange efficiency and arterial P_{O_2}. (p. 592; Fig. 18-4)

Gas Transport in the Blood

IP Respiratory System: Gas Transport

7. Oxygen is transported either dissolved in plasma (<2%) or bound to hemoglobin (>98%). (p. 593; Fig. 18-6)
8. The P_{O_2} of plasma determines how much oxygen will bind to hemoglobin. (p. 596; Fig. 18-9)
9. Oxygen-hemoglobin binding is influenced by pH, temperature, and **2,3-diphosphoglycerate**. (p. 598; Figs. 18-10, 18-11)
10. Venous blood carries 7% of its carbon dioxide dissolved in plasma, 23% as **carbaminohemoglobin**, and 70% as bicarbonate ion in the plasma. (p. 601; Fig. 18-14)
11. **Carbonic anhydrase** in red blood cells converts CO_2 to carbonic acid, which dissociates into H^+ and HCO_3^-. The H^+ then binds to hemoglobin, and HCO_3^- enters the plasma using the **chloride shift**. (p. 599)

Regulation of Ventilation

IP Respiratory System: Control of Respiration

12. Respiratory control resides in a **central pattern generator**, a network of neurons in the brain stem. (p. 602)
13. The medullary **dorsal respiratory group** contains inspiratory neurons that control somatic motor neurons to the diaphragm. The **ventral respiratory group** of neurons assists in inspiration and active expiration. (p. 603; Fig. 18-16)
14. **Peripheral chemoreceptors** in the carotid and aortic bodies monitor P_{O_2}, P_{CO_2}, and pH. Ventilation increases when P_{O_2} falls below 60 mm Hg. (p. 604; Fig. 18-18)
15. Carbon dioxide is the primary stimulus for changes in ventilation. **Central chemoreceptors** in the medulla respond to changes in P_{CO_2}. (p. 604; Fig. 18-19)
16. Protective reflexes monitored by peripheral receptors prevent injury to the lungs from overinflation or irritants. (p. 607)
17. Conscious and unconscious thought processes can affect respiratory activity. (p. 607)

18

QUESTIONS

(Answers to the Review Questions begin on page A1.)

THE PHYSIOLOGY PLACE

Access more review material online at **The Physiology Place** website. There you'll find review questions, problem-solving activities, case studies, flashcards, and direct links to both *InterActive Physiology®* and PhysioEx™. To access the site, go to *www.physiologyplace.com* and select Human Physiology, Fourth Edition.

LEVEL ONE REVIEWING FACTS AND TERMS

1. List five factors that influence the diffusion of gases between alveolus to blood.
2. More than __________% of the oxygen in arterial blood is transported bound to hemoglobin. How is the remaining oxygen transported to the cells?
3. Name four factors that influence the amount of oxygen that binds to hemoglobin. Which of these four factors is the most important?
4. Describe the structure of a hemoglobin molecule. What chemical element is essential for hemoglobin synthesis?
5. The centers for control of ventilation are found in the __________ and __________ of the brain. What do the dorsal and ventral respiratory groups of neurons control? What is a central pattern generator?

6. Name the chemoreceptors that influence ventilation, and explain how they do so. What chemical is the most important controller of ventilation?
7. Describe the protective reflexes of the respiratory system. What does the Hering-Breuer reflex prevent? How is this reflex initiated?
8. What causes the exchange of oxygen and carbon dioxide between alveoli and blood or between blood and cells?
9. List five possible physical changes that could result in less oxygen reaching the arterial blood.

LEVEL TWO REVIEWING CONCEPTS

10. **Concept map**: Construct a map of gas transport using the following terms. You may add additional terms.

P_{CO_2}	carbonic anhydrase
P_{O_2}	chloride shift
alveoli	dissolved CO_2
arterial blood	dissolved O_2
carbaminohemoglobin	hemoglobin
hemoglobin saturation	pressure gradient
oxyhemoglobin	red blood cell
plasma	venous blood

11. In respiratory physiology, it is customary to talk of the P_{O_2} of the plasma. Why is this not the most accurate way to describe the oxygen content of blood?
12. Compare and contrast the concepts in the following pairs:
    (a) transport of oxygen and of carbon dioxide in arterial blood
    (b) partial pressure and concentration of a gas dissolved in a liquid
13. Will HbO_2 binding increase, decrease, or not change with decreased pH?
14. Define hypoxia, COPD, and hypercapnia.
15. Why did oxygen-transporting pigments need to evolve in animals?
16. Draw and label the following graphs:
    (a) The effect of ventilation on arterial P_{O_2}
    (b) The effect of arterial P_{CO_2} on ventilation
17. As the P_{O_2} of plasma increases:
    (a) what happens to the amount of oxygen that dissolves in plasma?
    (b) what happens to the amount of oxygen that binds to hemoglobin?
18. If a person is anemic and has a lower-than-normal level of hemoglobin in her red blood cells, what will her arterial P_{O_2} be compared to normal?
19. Create reflex pathways (stimulus, receptor, afferent path, and so on) for the chemical control of ventilation, starting with the following stimuli:
    (a) Increased arterial P_{CO_2}
    (b) Arterial P_{O_2} = 55 mm Hg

    Be as specific as possible regarding anatomical locations. Where known, include neurotransmitters and their receptors.

LEVEL THREE PROBLEM SOLVING

20. Marco tries to hide at the bottom of a swimming hole by breathing in and out through a garden hose, which greatly increases his anatomic dead space. What happens to the following parameters in his arterial blood, and why?
    (a) P_{CO_2} (b) P_{O_2}
    (c) bicarbonate ion (d) pH
21. Which person will carry more oxygen in his blood:
    (a) one with a normal hemoglobin level of 15 g/dL and an arterial P_{O_2} of 80 mm Hg
    (b) one with a reduced hemoglobin level of 12 g/dL and a normal arterial P_{O_2} of 100 mm Hg
22. What would happen to each of the following parameters in a person suffering from an acute asthma attack (bronchoconstriction)?
    (a) arterial P_{O_2}
    (b) arterial hemoglobin saturation
    (c) alveolar ventilation
23. In early research on the control of rhythmic breathing, scientists made the following observations. What hypotheses might the researchers have formulated from each observation?
    (a) *Observation.* If the brain stem is severed below the medulla, all respiratory movement ceases.
    (b) *Observation.* If the brain stem is severed above the level of the pons, ventilation is normal.
    (c) *Observation.* If the medulla is completely separated from the pons and higher brain centers, ventilation becomes gasping but the respiratory rhythm remains.
24. A hospitalized patient with severe chronic obstructive lung disease has a P_{CO_2} of 55 mm Hg and a P_{O_2} of 50 mm Hg. To elevate his blood oxygen, he is given pure oxygen through a nasal tube. The patient immediately stops breathing. Explain why this might occur.
25. You are a physiologist on a space flight to a distant planet. You find intelligent humanoid creatures inhabiting the planet, and they willingly submit to your tests. Some of the data you have collected are described below. The first graph shows the oxygen dissociation curve for the oxygen-carrying pigment in the blood of the humanoid named Bzork. Bzork's normal alveolar P_{O_2} is 85 mm Hg. His normal cell P_{O_2} is 20 mm Hg, but it drops to 10 mm Hg with exercise.

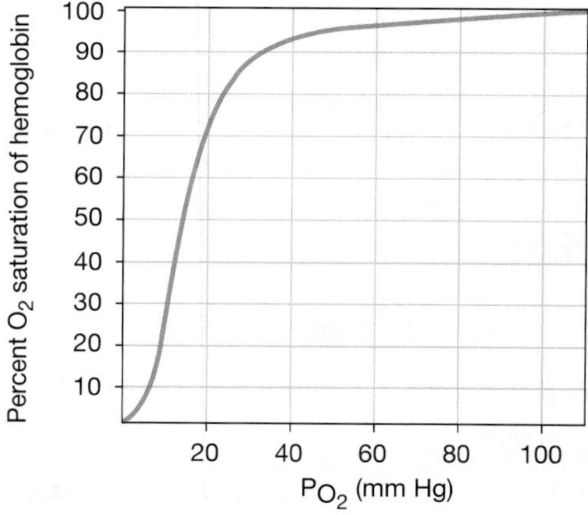

    (a) What is the percent saturation for Bzork's oxygen-carrying pigment in blood at the alveoli? In blood at an exercising cell?
    (b) Based on the graph, what conclusions can you draw about Bzork's oxygen requirements during normal activity and during exercise?

26. The next experiment on Bzork involves his ventilatory response to different conditions. The data from that experiment are graphed below. Interpret the results of experiments A and C.

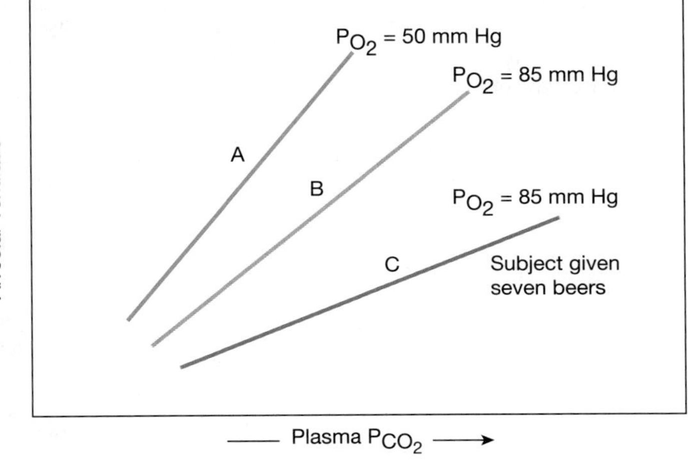

LEVEL FOUR QUANTITATIVE PROBLEMS

27. You are given the following information on a patient.

    Blood volume = 5.2 liters

    Hematocrit = 47%

    Hemoglobin concentration = 12 g/dL whole blood

    Total amount of oxygen carried in blood = 1015 mL

    Arterial plasma P_{O_2} = 100 mm Hg

    You know that at a plasma P_{O_2} of 100 mm Hg, plasma contains 0.3 mL oxygen/dL, and that hemoglobin is 98% saturated. Each hemoglobin molecule can bind to a maximum of four molecules of oxygen. Using this information, calculate the maximum oxygen-carrying capacity of hemoglobin (100% saturated). Units will be mL oxygen/g hemoglobin.

28. Adolph Fick, the nineteenth-century physiologist who derived Fick's law of diffusion, also developed the Fick equation that relates oxygen consumption, cardiac output, and blood P_{O_2}:

    $$O_2 \text{ consumption} = \text{cardiac output} \times (\text{arterial } O_2 \text{ content} - \text{venous } O_2 \text{ content})$$

    A person has a cardiac output of 4.5 L/min, an arterial oxygen content of 105 mL O_2/L blood, and a vena cava oxygen content of 60 mL O_2/L blood. What is this person's oxygen consumption?

29. Describe what happens to the oxygen-hemoglobin dissociation curve in Figure 18-9 when blood hemoglobin falls from 15 g/dL blood to 10 g/dL blood.

ANSWERS

Answers to Concept Check Questions

Page 589

1. The other factor that affects how much of each gas will dissolve in the saline solution is the solubility of the gas in that solution.
2. 720 mm Hg × 0.78 N_2 = 561.6 mm Hg
3. False. Plasma is essentially water, and Figure 18-2 shows that CO_2 is more soluble in water than O_2.

Page 591

4. (a) electron transport system (b) citric acid cycle
5. The P_{O_2} of the alveoli does not decrease because it is constantly being replenished by fresh air being inhaled from the external environment. [p. 578]

Page 592

6. Air is 21% oxygen. Therefore, for dry air on Everest, P_{O_2} = 0.21 × 250 mm Hg = 53 mm Hg. Correction for P_{H_2O}: P_{O_2} = (250 mm Hg − 47 mm Hg) × 21% = (203 mm Hg) × 0.21 = 43 mm Hg.

Page 593

7. These pathological conditions cause blood to pool in the lungs because the left heart is unable to pump all the blood coming into it from the pulmonary circulation. Increased blood volume in the lungs increases pulmonary blood pressure.
8. When alveolar ventilation increases, arterial P_{O_2} increases because more fresh air is entering the alveoli. Arterial P_{CO_2} decreases because the low P_{CO_2} of fresh air dilutes alveolar P_{CO_2} below its normal value (40 mm Hg). The CO_2 pressure gradient between the venous blood (46 mm Hg) and the alveoli increases, causing more CO_2 to leave the blood. Venous P_{O_2} and P_{CO_2} do not change because these pressures are determined by levels of oxygen consumption and CO_2 production in the cells.

Page 598

9. Yes. Hemoglobin reaches 100% saturation at 650 mm Hg. At sea level, atmospheric pressure is 760 mm Hg, and if the "atmosphere" is 100% oxygen, then P_{O_2} is 760 mm Hg.
10. The flatness at the top of the P_{O_2} curve in Figure 17-15 tells you that hyperventilation causes only a minimal increase in percent saturation of arterial hemoglobin.

Page 599

11. As the P_{O_2} of the exercising muscle falls, more oxygen is released by hemoglobin. The P_{O_2} of the venous blood leaving the muscle will be 25 mm Hg, the same as the P_{O_2} of the muscle.

Page 602

12. An airway obstruction would decrease alveolar ventilation and increase arterial P_{CO_2}. Elevated arterial P_{CO_2} would increase the H^+ concentration in the arterial blood and decrease pH.

Answers to Figure and Graph Questions

Page 594

Fig. 18-6: O_2 will cross five cell membranes: two of the alveolar cell, two of the capillary endothelium, and one of the red blood cell.

Page 597

Fig. 18-9: (a) When P_{O_2} is 20 mm Hg, hemoglobin is about 34% saturated with oxygen. (b) Hemoglobin is 50% saturated with oxygen at a P_{O_2} of 28 mm Hg.

Page 598

Fig. 18-10: (a) When pH falls from 7.4 to 7.2, hemoglobin saturation decreases by 13%, from about 37% saturation to 24%. (b) When an exercising muscle cell warms up, it releases more oxygen at any given P_{O_2}.

Page 599

Fig. 18-11: Loss of 2,3-DPG is not good because then hemoglobin binds more tightly to oxygen at the P_{O_2} values found in cells.

Page 599

Fig. 18-12: (a) The P_{O_2} of placental blood is about 28 mm Hg. (b) At a P_{O_2} of 10 mm Hg, maternal blood is only about 8% saturated with oxygen.

Page 603

Fig. 18-16: 1. pons; 2. ventral respiratory group; 3. medullary chemoreceptor; 4. sensory neuron; 5. carotid chemoreceptor; 6. somatic motor neuron (expiration); 7. aortic chemoreceptor; 8. internal intercostals; 9. abdominal muscles; 10. diaphragm; 11. external intercostals; 12. scalenes and sternocleiodmastoids; 13. somatic motor neuron (inspiration); 14. dorsal respiratory group; 15. limbic system; 16. higher brain centers (emotions and voluntary control)

19

Plasma undergoes modification to urine in the nephron.

*—**Arthur Grollman**, in Clinical Physiology: The Functional Pathology of Disease, 1957*

Glomerular capillaries (green) of a living rat.

The Kidneys

BACKGROUND BASICS

Transepithelial transport: **150** Mass balance: **129** Osmolarity and tonicity: **155** Filtration in capillaries: **517** Transcytosis: **153** Saturation: **43** Autoregulation of vascular resistance: **510** Transport across membranes: **137** pH and buffers: **37** Transporting epithelium: **73** Fenestrated capillaries: **515** Phosphocreatine: **410** Competition: **146**

RUNNING PROBLEM

GOUT

Michael Moustakakis, 43, has spent the last two days on the sofa, suffering from a relentless throbbing pain in his left big toe. When the pain began, Michael thought he had a mild sprain or perhaps the beginnings of arthritis. Then the pain intensified, and the toe joint became hot and red. Michael finally hobbled into his doctor's office, feeling a little silly about his problem. On hearing his symptoms, the doctor seems to know instantly what is wrong. "Sounds to me like you have gout," says Dr. Garcia.

About A.D. 100, Aretaeus the Cappadocian wrote, "Diabetes is a wonderful affection, not very frequent among men, being a melting down of the flesh and limbs into urine. . . . The patients never stop making water [urinating], but the flow is incessant, as if from the opening of aqueducts." Physicians have known for centuries that **urine**, the fluid waste produced by the kidneys, reflects the functioning of the body. To aid them in their diagnosis of illness, they even carried special flasks for the collection and inspection of patients' urine.

The first step in examining a urine sample was to determine its color. Was it dark yellow (concentrated), pale straw (dilute), red (indicating the presence of blood), or black (indicating the presence of hemoglobin metabolites)? One form of malaria was called *blackwater fever* because metabolized hemoglobin from the abnormal breakdown of red blood cells turned victims' urine black or dark red.

Physicians also inspected urine samples for clarity, froth (indicating abnormal presence of proteins), smell, and even taste. Physicians who did not want to taste the urine themselves would allow their students the "privilege" of tasting it for them. A physician without students might expose insects to the urine and study their reaction.

Probably the most famous example of using urine for diagnosis was the taste test for diabetes mellitus, historically known as the *honey-urine disease*. Diabetes is an endocrine disorder characterized by the presence of glucose in the urine. The urine of diabetics tasted sweet and attracted insects, making the diagnosis clear.

Although today we have much more sophisticated tests for glucose in the urine, the first step of a *urinalysis* is still to examine the color, clarity, and odor of the urine. In this chapter you will learn why we can tell so much about how the body is functioning by what is present in the urine.

FUNCTIONS OF THE KIDNEYS

If you asked people on the street, "What is the most important function of the kidney?" they would probably say, "The removal of wastes." Actually, the most important function of the kidney is the homeostatic regulation of the water and ion content of the blood, also called *salt and water balance* or *fluid and electrolyte balance*. Waste removal is important, but disturbances in blood volume or ion levels will cause serious medical problems before the accumulation of metabolic wastes reaches toxic levels.

The kidneys maintain normal blood concentrations of ions and water by balancing intake of those substances with their excretion in the urine, obeying the principle of mass balance [p. 129]. We can divide kidney function into six general areas:

1. **Regulation of extracellular fluid volume and blood pressure.** When extracellular fluid volume decreases, blood pressure also decreases [p. 508]. If ECF volume and blood pressure fall too low, the body cannot maintain adequate blood flow to the brain and other essential organs. The kidneys work in an integrated fashion with the cardiovascular system to ensure that blood pressure and tissue perfusion remain within an acceptable range.
2. **Regulation of osmolarity.** The body integrates kidney function with behavioral drives, such as thirst, to maintain blood osmolarity at a value close to 290 mOsM. We will examine the reflex pathways for regulation of ECF volume and osmolarity in Chapter 20.
3. **Maintenance of ion balance.** The kidneys keep concentrations of key ions within a normal range by balancing dietary intake with urinary loss. Sodium (Na^+) is the major ion involved in the regulation of extracellular fluid volume and osmolarity. Potassium (K^+) and calcium (Ca^{2+}) concentrations are also closely regulated. We will discuss renal control of sodium and potassium balance in Chapter 20 but defer the discussion of calcium until Chapter 22, when we look at all aspects of calcium homeostasis.
4. **Homeostatic regulation of pH.** The pH of plasma is normally kept within a narrow range [p. 37]. If extracellular fluid becomes too acidic, the kidneys remove H^+ and conserve bicarbonate ions (HCO_3^-), which act as a buffer [p. 38]. Conversely, when extracellular fluid becomes too alkaline, the kidneys remove HCO_3^- and conserve H^+. The kidneys play a significant role in pH homeostasis, but they do not correct pH disturbances as rapidly as the lungs do, as you will learn in Chapter 20.
5. **Excretion of wastes.** The kidneys remove metabolic waste products and foreign substances, such as drugs and environmental toxins. Metabolic wastes include creatinine from muscle metabolism [p. 410] and the nitrogenous wastes *urea* [p. 111] and *uric acid*. A metabolite of hemoglobin called *urobilinogen* gives urine its characteristic yellow color. Hormones are another endogenous substance the kidneys clear from the blood.

Examples of foreign substances that the kidneys actively remove include the artificial sweetener *saccharin* and the anion *benzoate,* part of the preservative *potassium benzoate* that you ingest each time you drink a diet soft drink.

6. **Production of hormones.** Although the kidneys are not endocrine glands, they play important roles in three endocrine pathways. Kidney cells synthesize *erythropoietin,* the cytokine/hormone that regulates red blood cell synthesis [p. 541]. They also release *renin,* an enzyme that regulates the production of hormones involved in sodium balance and blood pressure homeostasis. Renal enzymes help convert vitamin D_3 into a hormone that regulates Ca^{2+} balance.

The kidneys, like many other organs in the body, have a tremendous reserve capacity. By most estimates, you must lose nearly three-fourths of your kidney function before homeostasis begins to be affected. Many people function perfectly normally with only one kidney, including the one person in 1000 born with only one kidney (the other fails to develop during gestation) or those people who donate a kidney for transplantation.

CONCEPT CHECK

1. Ion regulation is a key feature of kidney function. What happens to the resting membrane potential of a neuron if extracellular K^+ levels decrease? [p. 269]
2. What happens to the force of cardiac contraction if plasma Ca^{2+} levels decrease substantially? [p. 471]

Answers: p. 639

ANATOMY OF THE URINARY SYSTEM

The **urinary system** is composed of the kidneys and accessory structures (Fig. 19-1a ■). The study of kidney function is called **renal physiology**, from the Latin word *renes,* meaning "kidneys."

The Urinary System Consists of Kidneys, Ureters, Bladder, and Urethra

Let's begin by following the route a drop of water takes on its way from plasma to excretion in the urine. In the first step of urine production, water and solutes move from plasma into the hollow tubules (*nephrons*) that make up the bulk of the paired **kidneys**. These tubules modify the composition of the fluid as it passes through. The modified fluid leaves the kidney and passes into a hollow tube called a **ureter**. There are two ureters, one leading from each kidney to the **urinary bladder**. The bladder expands and fills with urine until, by reflex action, it contracts and expels urine through a single tube, the **urethra**.

The urethra in males exits the body through the shaft of the penis. In females, the urethral opening is found anterior to the openings of the vagina and anus. *Micturition,* or urination, is the process by which urine is excreted.

The kidneys are the site of urine formation. They lie on either side of the spine at the level of the eleventh and twelfth ribs, just above the waist (Fig. 19-1b). Although they are below the diaphragm, they are technically outside the abdominal cavity, sandwiched between the membranous **peritoneum**, which lines the abdomen, and the bones and muscles of the back. Because of their location behind the peritoneal cavity, the kidneys are sometimes described as being *retroperitoneal* [*retro-,* behind].

The concave surface of each kidney faces the spine. The renal blood vessels, nerves, lymphatics, and ureters all emerge from this surface. **Renal arteries**, which branch off the abdominal aorta, supply blood to the kidneys. **Renal veins** carry blood from the kidneys to the inferior vena cava.

At any given time, the kidneys receive 20–25% of the cardiac output, even though they constitute only 0.4% of total body weight (4.5–6 ounces each). This high rate of blood flow through the kidneys is critical to renal function.

The Nephron Is the Functional Unit of the Kidney

A cross section through a kidney shows that the interior is arranged in two layers: an outer **cortex** and inner **medulla** (Fig. 19-1c). The layers are formed by the organized arrangement of microscopic tubules called **nephrons**. About 80% of the nephrons in a kidney are almost completely contained within the cortex (*cortical* nephrons), but the other 20%—called *juxtamedullary* nephrons [*juxta-,* beside]—dip down into the medulla (Fig. 19-1i).

The nephron is the functional unit of the kidney. (A *functional unit* is the smallest structure that can perform all the functions of an organ.) Each of the 1 million nephrons in a kidney is divided into sections (Fig. 19-1j), and each section is closely associated with specialized blood vessels (Fig. 19-1g, h).

CLINICAL FOCUS

URINARY TRACT INFECTIONS

Because of the shorter length of the female urethra and its proximity to bacteria leaving the large intestine, women are more prone than men to develop bacterial infections of the bladder and kidneys, or **urinary tract infections** (UTIs). The most common cause of UTIs is the bacterium *Escherichia coli,* a normal inhabitant of the human large intestine. *E. coli* is not harmful while restricted to the lumen of the large intestine, but it is pathogenic [*patho-,* disease + *-genic,* causing] if it gets into the urethra. The most common symptoms of a UTI are pain or burning during urination and increased frequency of urination. A urine sample from a patient with a UTI often contains many red and white blood cells, neither of which is commonly found in normal urine. UTIs are treated with antibiotics.

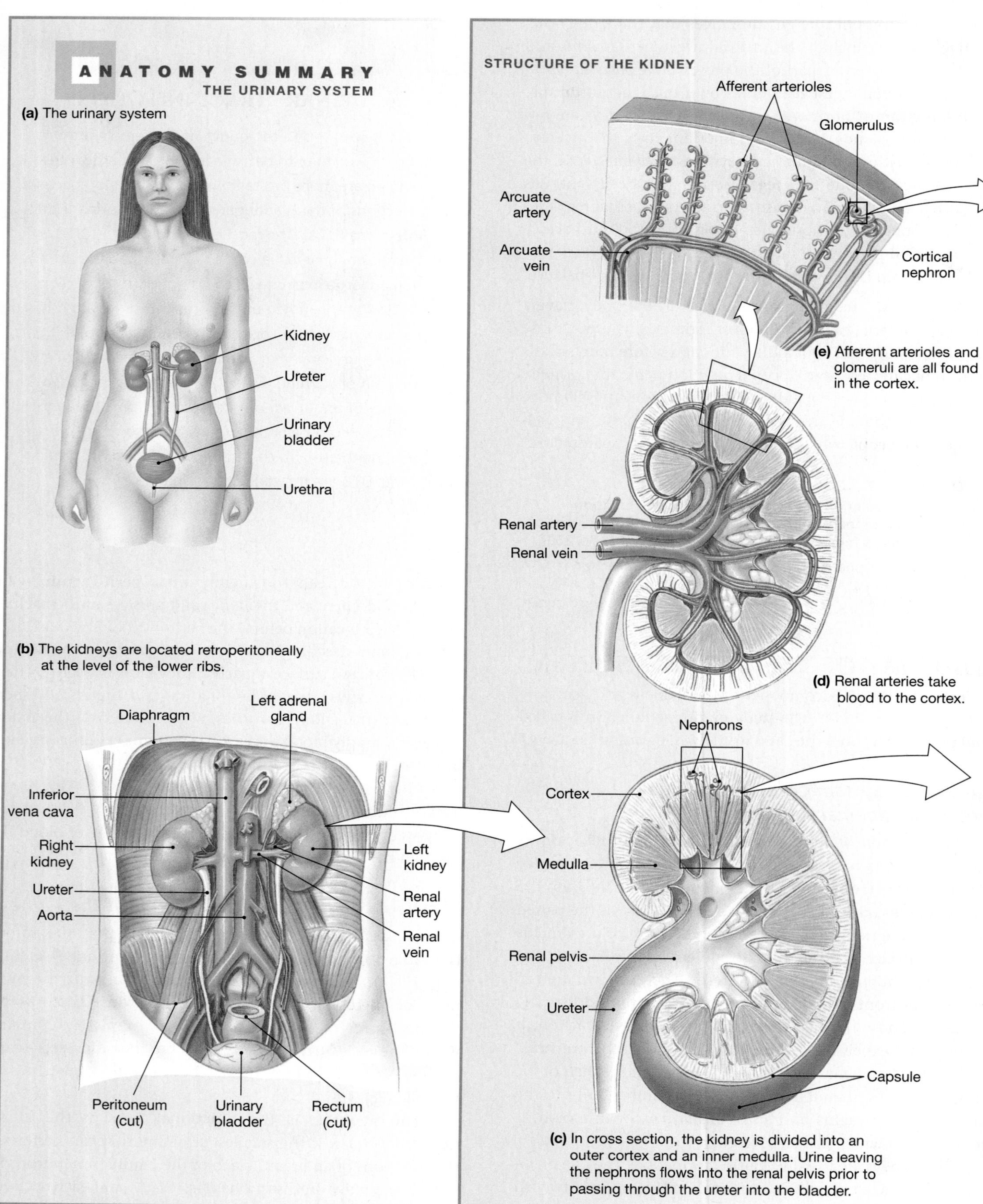
ANATOMY SUMMARY
THE URINARY SYSTEM
(a) The urinary system
Kidney
Ureter
Urinary bladder
Urethra
(b) The kidneys are located retroperitoneally at the level of the lower ribs.
Diaphragm
Left adrenal gland
Inferior vena cava
Right kidney
Ureter
Aorta
Left kidney
Renal artery
Renal vein
Peritoneum (cut)
Urinary bladder
Rectum (cut)
STRUCTURE OF THE KIDNEY
Afferent arterioles
Glomerulus
Arcuate artery
Arcuate vein
Cortical nephron
(e) Afferent arterioles and glomeruli are all found in the cortex.
Renal artery
Renal vein
(d) Renal arteries take blood to the cortex.
Nephrons
Cortex
Medulla
Renal pelvis
Ureter
Capsule
(c) In cross section, the kidney is divided into an outer cortex and an inner medulla. Urine leaving the nephrons flows into the renal pelvis prior to passing through the ureter into the bladder.
19

FIGURE 19-1

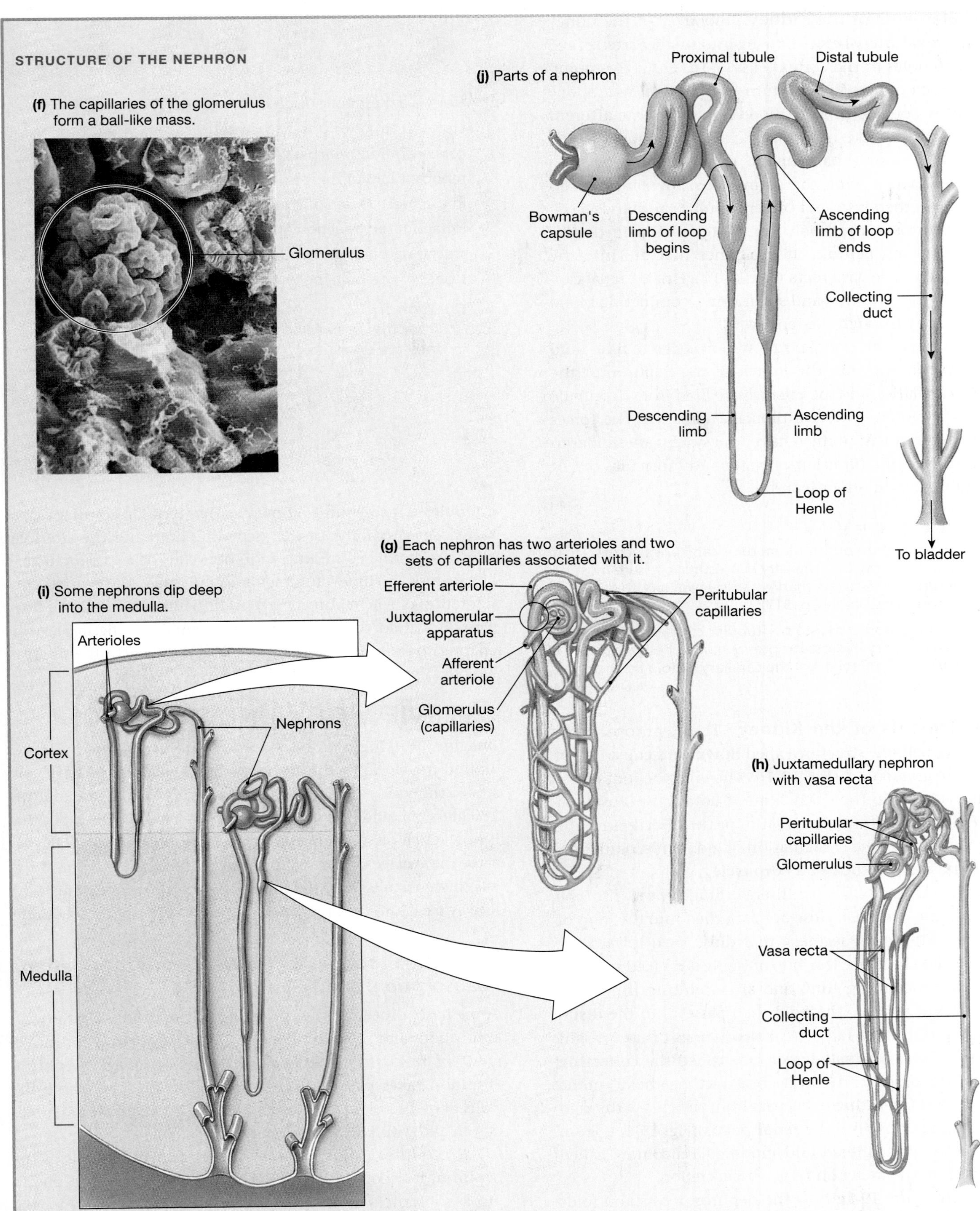
STRUCTURE OF THE NEPHRON
(f) The capillaries of the glomerulus form a ball-like mass.
Glomerulus
(j) Parts of a nephron
Proximal tubule
Distal tubule
Bowman's capsule
Descending limb of loop begins
Ascending limb of loop ends
Collecting duct
Descending limb
Ascending limb
Loop of Henle
To bladder
(g) Each nephron has two arterioles and two sets of capillaries associated with it.
Efferent arteriole
Juxtaglomerular apparatus
Afferent arteriole
Glomerulus (capillaries)
Peritubular capillaries
(i) Some nephrons dip deep into the medulla.
Arterioles
Nephrons
Cortex
Medulla
(h) Juxtamedullary nephron with vasa recta
Peritubular capillaries
Glomerulus
Vasa recta
Collecting duct
Loop of Henle

■ **FIGURE 19-1** ***(continued)***

Vascular Elements of the Kidney Blood enters the kidney through the renal artery before flowing into smaller arteries and then into arterioles in the cortex (Fig. 19-1d, e). At this point, the arrangement of blood vessels turns into a *portal system,* one of three in the body [p. 229]. Blood flows from the **afferent arteriole** into a ball-like network of capillaries known as the **glomerulus** [*glomus,* a ball-shaped mass; plural *glomeruli*] (Fig. 19-1f). Blood leaving the glomerulus flows into an **efferent arteriole**, then into a set of **peritubular capillaries** [*peri-,* around] that surround the tubule (Fig. 19-1g). In juxtamedullary nephrons, the long peritubular capillaries that dip into the medulla are called the **vasa recta** (Fig. 19-1h). Finally, renal capillaries join to form venules and small veins, conducting blood out of the kidney through the renal vein.

The function of the renal portal system is first to filter fluid out of the blood and into the lumen of the nephron at the glomerular capillaries, and then to *reabsorb* fluid from the tubule back into the blood at the peritubular capillaries. The forces behind fluid movement in the renal portal system are similar to those that govern the filtration of water and molecules out of systemic capillaries in other tissues.

CONCEPT CHECK

3. If net filtration out of glomerular capillaries occurs, then you know that capillary hydrostatic pressure must be (*greater than/less than/equal to*) capillary colloid osmotic pressure. [p. 517]
4. If net reabsorption into peritubular capillaries occurs, then capillary hydrostatic pressure must be (*greater than/less than/equal to*) the capillary colloid osmotic pressure.

Answers: p. 639

19

Tubular Elements of the Kidney The nephron begins with a hollow, ball-like structure called **Bowman's capsule** that surrounds the glomerulus (Fig. 19-1j). The endothelium of the glomerulus is fused to the epithelium of Bowman's capsule so that fluid filtering out of the capillaries passes directly into the lumen of the tubule. The combination of glomerulus and Bowman's capsule is called the **renal corpuscle.**

From Bowman's capsule, filtered fluid flows into the **proximal tubule** [*proximal,* close or near], then into the **loop of Henle**, a hairpin-shaped segment that dips down toward the medulla and then back up. The loop of Henle is divided into two limbs, a thin **descending limb** and an **ascending limb** with thin and thick segments. The fluid then passes into the **distal tubule** [*distal,* distant or far]. The distal tubules of up to eight nephrons drain into a single larger tube called the **collecting duct.** (The distal tubule and its collecting duct together form the **distal nephron.**) Collecting ducts pass from the cortex through the medulla and drain into the **renal pelvis** (Fig. 19-1c). From the renal pelvis, the filtered and modified fluid, now called **urine**, flows into the ureter on its way to excretion.

Notice in Figure 19-1g how the nephron twists and folds back on itself so that the final part of the ascending limb of the loop of Henle passes between the afferent and efferent arterioles. This region is known as the **juxtaglomerular apparatus.** The proximity of the ascending limb and the arterioles allows paracrine communication between the two structures, a key feature of kidney autoregulation. Because the twisted configuration of the nephron makes it difficult to follow fluid flow, we will unfold the nephron in the remaining figures in this chapter so that fluid flows from left to right across the figure.

RUNNING PROBLEM

Gout is a metabolic disease characterized by high blood concentrations of uric acid (*hyperuricemia*). If uric acid concentrations reach a critical level (7.5 mg/dL), crystals of monosodium urate form in peripheral joints, particularly in the feet, ankles, and knees. These crystals trigger an inflammatory reaction and cause periodic attacks of excruciating pain. Uric acid crystals may also form kidney stones in the renal pelvis.

Question 1:

Trace the route followed by these kidney stones when they are excreted.

OVERVIEW OF KIDNEY FUNCTION

Imagine drinking a 12-ounce soft drink every three minutes around the clock: by the end of 24 hours, you would have consumed the equivalent of 90 2-liter bottles. The thought of putting 180 liters of liquid into your intestinal tract is staggering, but that is how much plasma moves into the nephrons every day! But because the average volume of urine leaving the kidneys is only 1.5 L/day, more than 99% of the fluid that enters nephrons must find its way back into the blood, or the body would rapidly dehydrate.

The Three Processes of the Nephron Are Filtration, Reabsorption, and Secretion

Three basic processes take place in the nephron: filtration, reabsorption, and secretion (Fig. 19-2 ■). **Filtration** is the movement of fluid from blood into the lumen of the nephron. Filtration takes place only in the renal corpuscle, where the walls of glomerular capillaries and Bowman's capsule are modified to allow bulk flow of fluid.

Once filtered fluid (*filtrate*) passes into the lumen of the nephron, it becomes part of the body's external environment, just as substances in the lumen of the intestinal tract are part of the external environment [Figure 1-2, p. 4]. Thus, anything that filters into the nephron is destined for removal in the urine unless it is reabsorbed into the body.

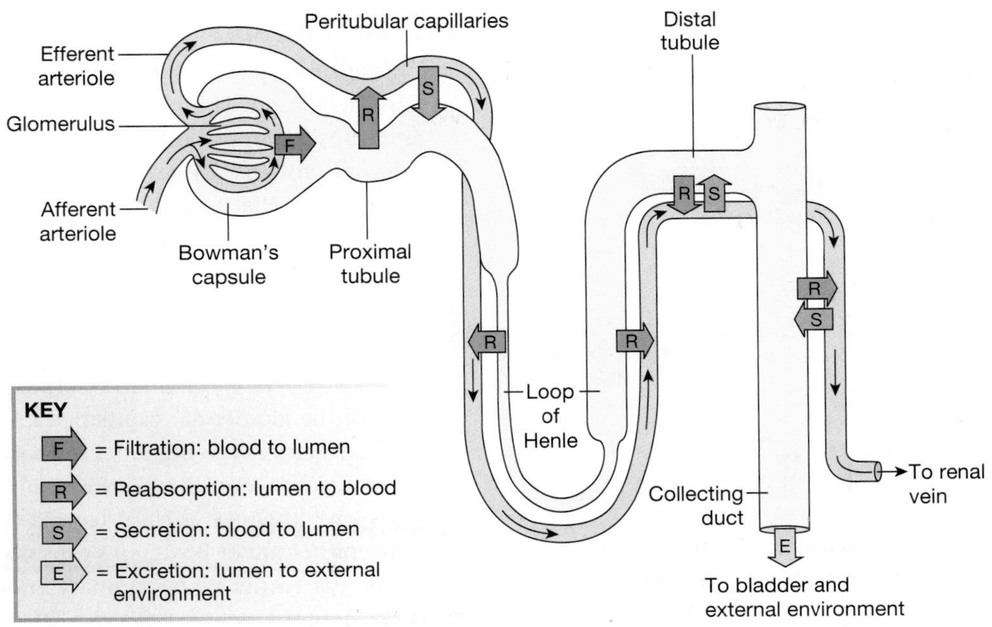

■ **FIGURE 19-2** ***Filtration, reabsorption, secretion, and excretion***

After filtrate leaves Bowman's capsule, it is modified by reabsorption and secretion. **Reabsorption** is the process of moving substances in the filtrate from the lumen of the tubule back into the blood flowing through peritubular capillaries. **Secretion** removes selected molecules from the blood and adds them to the filtrate in the tubule lumen. Although secretion and glomerular filtration both move substances from blood into the tubule, secretion is a more selective process that usually uses membrane proteins to move molecules across the tubule epithelium.

Volume and Osmolarity Change as Fluid Flows Through the Nephron

Now let's follow some filtrate through the nephron to learn what happens to it in the various segments (Table 19-1 ■). The 180 liters of fluid that filters into Bowman's capsule each day are almost identical in composition to plasma and nearly isosmotic—about 300 mOsM [p. 155]. As this filtrate flows through the proximal tubule, about 70% of its volume is reabsorbed, leaving 54 liters in the lumen. Reabsorption occurs when proximal tubule cells transport solutes out of the lumen, and water follows by osmosis. Filtrate leaving the proximal tubule has the same osmolarity as filtrate that entered. Thus, we say that the primary function of the proximal tubule is the *bulk reabsorption of isosmotic fluid.*

TABLE 19-1 Changes in Filtrate Volume and Osmolarity Along the Nephron

LOCATION IN NEPHRON	VOLUME OF FLUID	OSMOLARITY OF FLUID
Bowman's capsule	180 L/day	300 mOsM
End of proximal tubule	54 L/day	300 mOsM
End of loop of Henle	18 L/day	100 mOsM
End of collecting duct (final urine)	1.5 L/day (average)	50–1200 mOsM

After leaving the proximal tubule, filtrate passes into the loop of Henle, the primary site for creating dilute urine. As the filtrate passes through the loop, proportionately more solute is reabsorbed than water, and the filtrate becomes hyposmotic relative to the plasma. By the time filtrate flows out of the loop, it averages 100 mOsM, and its volume has fallen from 54 L/day to about 18 L/day. Now 90% of the volume originally filtered into Bowman's capsule has been reabsorbed into the capillaries.

From the loop of Henle, filtrate passes into the distal tubule and the collecting duct. In these two segments, the fine regulation of salt and water balance takes place under the control of several hormones. Reabsorption and (to a lesser extent) secretion determine the final composition of the filtrate. By the end of the collecting duct, the filtrate has a volume of 1.5 L/day and an osmolarity that can range from 50 mOsM to 1200 mOsM. The final volume and osmolarity of urine depend on the body's need to conserve or excrete water and solute.

A word of caution here: it is very easy to confuse *secretion* with *excretion*. Try to remember the origins of the two prefixes. *Se-* means *apart,* as in to separate something from its source. In the nephron, secreted solutes are moved from plasma to tubule lumen. *Ex-* means *out,* or *away,* as in out of or away from the body. Excretion refers to the removal of a substance from the body.

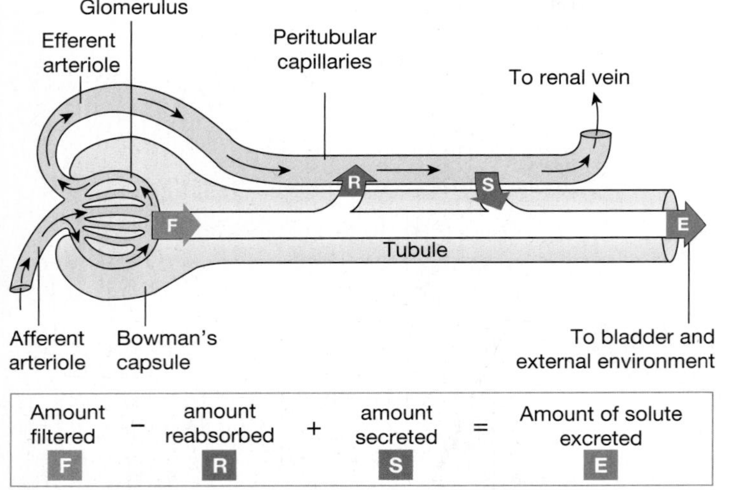

Amount filtered F	−	amount reabsorbed R	+	amount secreted S	=	Amount of solute excreted E

■ **FIGURE 19-3** ***The urinary excretion of a substance depends on its filtration, reabsorption, and secretion***

Besides the kidneys, other organs that carry out excretory processes include the lungs (CO_2) and intestines (undigested food, bilirubin).

Figure 19-2 summarizes filtration, reabsorption, secretion, and excretion. Filtration takes place in the renal corpuscle as fluid moves from the capillaries of the glomerulus into Bowman's capsule. Reabsorption and secretion occur along the remainder of the tubule, transferring materials between the lumen and the peritubular capillaries. The quantity and composition of the substances being reabsorbed and secreted vary in different segments of the nephron. Filtrate that remains in the lumen at the end of the nephron is excreted as urine.

19

The amount of any substance excreted in the urine reflects how that substance was handled during its passage through the nephron (Fig. 19-3 ■). The amount excreted is equal to the amount filtered into the tubule, minus the amount reabsorbed into the blood, plus the amount secreted into the tubule lumen:

$$\text{amount excreted} = \text{amount filtered} - \text{amount reabsorbed} + \text{amount secreted}$$

This equation is a useful way to think about renal handling of solutes. In the following sections, we will look in more detail at the important processes of filtration, reabsorption, secretion, and excretion.

CONCEPT CHECK

5. Name one way in which filtration and secretion are alike. Name one way in which they differ.
6. A water molecule enters the renal corpuscle from the blood and ends up in the urine. Name all the anatomical structures that the molecule passes through on its trip to the outside world.
7. What would happen to the body if filtration continued at a normal rate but reabsorption dropped to half the normal rate?

Answers: p. 639

FILTRATION

The filtration of plasma into the kidney tubule is the first step in urine formation. This relatively nonspecific process creates a filtrate whose composition is like that of plasma minus most of the plasma proteins. Under normal conditions, blood cells remain in the capillary, so that the filtrate is composed only of water and dissolved solutes.

The Renal Corpuscle Contains Three Filtration Barriers

Filtration takes place in the renal corpuscle (Fig. 19-4 ■), which consists of the glomerular capillaries surrounded by Bowman's capsule. Substances leaving the plasma must pass through three *filtration barriers* before entering the tubule lumen: the glomerular capillary endothelium, a basal lamina (basement membrane), and the epithelium of Bowman's capsule (Fig. 19-4d).

The first barrier is the capillary endothelium. Glomerular capillaries are *fenestrated capillaries* [p. 515] with large pores that allow most components of the plasma to filter through the endothelium. The pores are small enough, however, to prevent blood cells from leaving the capillary. The negatively charged proteins on the pore surfaces also help repel negatively charged plasma proteins.

Glomerular **mesangial cells** lie between and around the glomerular capillaries (Fig. 19-4c). Mesangial cells have cytoplasmic bundles of actin-like filaments that enable them to contract and alter blood flow through the capillaries. In addition, mesangial cells secrete cytokines associated with immune and inflammatory processes. Disruptions of mesangial cell function have been linked to several disease processes in the kidney.

The second filtration barrier is an acellular layer of extracellular matrix called the **basal lamina**, which separates the capillary endothelium from the epithelial lining of Bowman's capsule (Fig. 19-4d). The basal lamina consists of negatively charged glycoproteins and a collagen-like material that act like a coarse sieve, excluding most plasma proteins from the fluid that filters through it.

The third filtration barrier is the epithelium of Bowman's capsule. The portion of the capsule epithelium that surrounds each glomerular capillary consists of specialized cells called **podocytes** [*podos,* foot] (Fig. 19-4c). Podocytes have long cytoplasmic extensions called **foot processes** that extend from the main cell body (Fig. 19-4a, b). These processes wrap around the glomerular capillaries and interlace with one another, leaving narrow **filtration slits** closed by a membrane. Podocytes, like mesangial cells, contain contractile fibers. These are connected to the basal lamina by integrins.

When you visualize plasma filtering out of the glomerular capillaries, it is easy to imagine that all the plasma in the capillary moves into Bowman's capsule. However, filtration of all the plasma would leave behind a sludge of blood cells and proteins that could not flow out of the glomerulus. Instead, only about one-fifth of the plasma that flows through the kidneys filters into

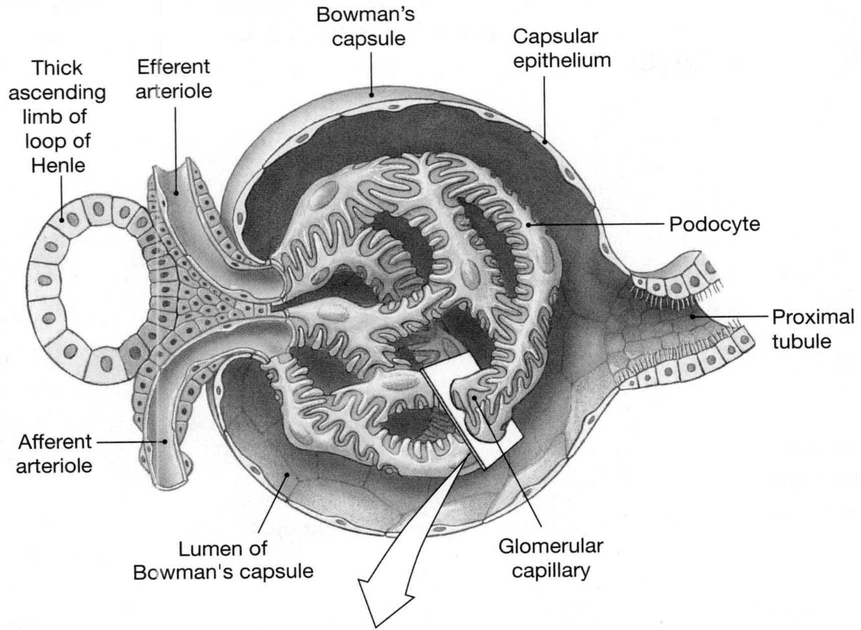

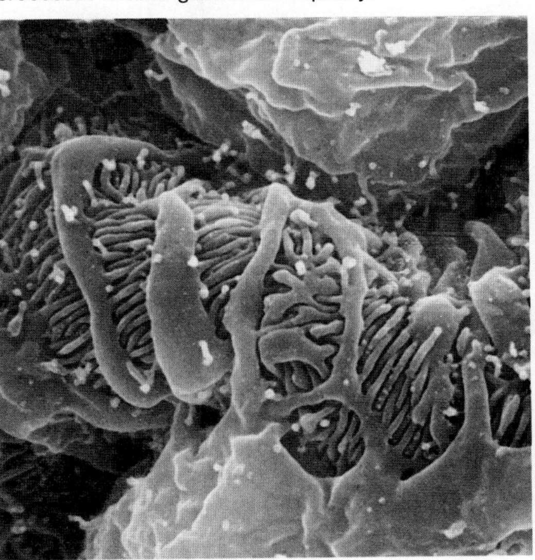

(b) Micrograph showing podocyte foot processes around glomerular capillary.

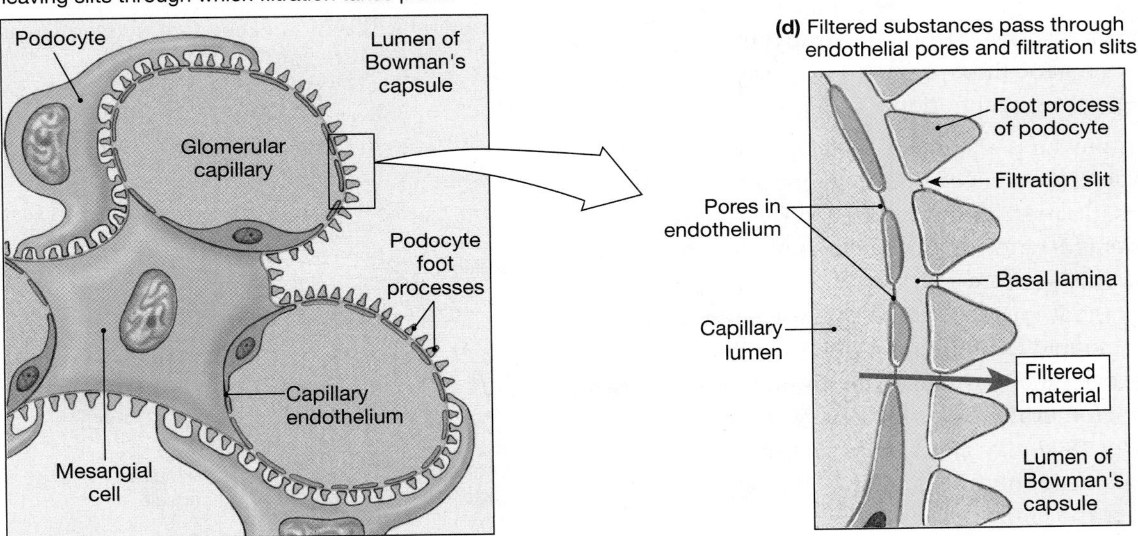

FIGURE 19-4 ***The renal corpuscle***

The glomerular capillary endothelium, basal lamina, and Bowman's capsule epithelium create a three-layer filtration barrier.

the nephrons. The remaining four-fifths of the plasma, along with most plasma proteins and blood cells, flows into the peritubular capillaries (Fig. 19-5 ■). The percentage of total plasma volume that filters into the tubule is called the **filtration fraction**.

Filtration Occurs Because of Hydrostatic Pressure in the Capillaries

What drives filtration across the walls of the glomerular capillaries? The process is similar in many ways to filtration of fluid out of systemic capillaries [p. 517] and is influenced by the following forces:

1. The *hydrostatic pressure* (P_H) of blood flowing through the glomerular capillaries forces fluid through the leaky endothelium. Capillary blood pressure averages 55 mm Hg and favors filtration into Bowman's capsule. Although pressure declines along the length of the capillaries, it remains higher than the opposing pressures. Consequently, filtration takes place along nearly the entire length of the glomerular capillaries.

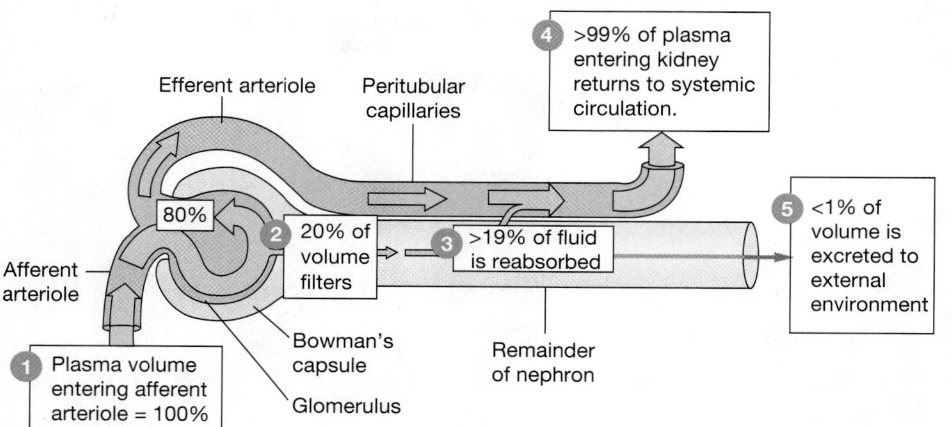

FIGURE 19-5 ***The filtration fraction***

Only 20% of the plasma that passes through the glomerulus is filtered. Less than 1% of filtered fluid is eventually excreted.

2. The *colloid osmotic pressure* (π) inside glomerular capillaries is higher than that of the fluid in Bowman's capsule. This pressure gradient is due to the presence of proteins in the plasma. The osmotic pressure gradient averages 30 mm Hg and favors fluid movement back into the capillaries.
3. Bowman's capsule is an enclosed space (unlike the interstitial fluid), and so the presence of fluid in the capsule creates a hydrostatic *fluid pressure* (P_{fluid}) that opposes fluid movement into the capsule. Fluid filtering out of the capillaries must displace the fluid already in the capsule lumen. Hydrostatic fluid pressure in the capsule averages 15 mm Hg, opposing filtration.

The three pressures—capillary blood pressure, capillary colloid osmotic pressure, and capsule fluid pressure—that influence glomerular filtration are summarized in Figure 19-6 ■. The net driving force is 10 mm Hg in the direction favoring filtration. Although this pressure may not seem very high, when combined with the very leaky nature of the fenestrated capillaries, it results in rapid fluid filtration into the tubules.

19

The volume of fluid that filters into Bowman's capsule per unit time is the **glomerular filtration rate (GFR)**. Average GFR is 125 mL/min, or 180 L/day, an incredible rate considering that total plasma volume is only about 3 liters. This rate means that the kidneys filter the entire plasma volume 60 times a day, or 2.5 times every hour. If most of the filtrate were not reabsorbed during its passage through the nephron, we would run out of plasma in only 24 minutes of filtration!

GFR is influenced by two factors: the net filtration pressure just described and the filtration coefficient. Filtration pressure is determined primarily by renal blood flow and blood pressure. The **filtration coefficient** has two components: the surface area of the glomerular capillaries available for filtration and the permeability of the capillary-Bowman's capsule interface. In this respect, glomerular filtration is similar to gas exchange at the alveoli, where the rate of gas exchange depends on partial pressure differences, the surface area of the alveoli, and the permeability of the alveolar membrane.

CONCEPT CHECK

8. Why is the osmotic pressure of plasma in efferent arterioles higher than that in afferent arterioles?

Answers: p. 640

Blood Pressure and Renal Blood Flow Influence GFR

Blood pressure provides the hydrostatic pressure that drives glomerular filtration. Therefore, it seems reasonable to assume

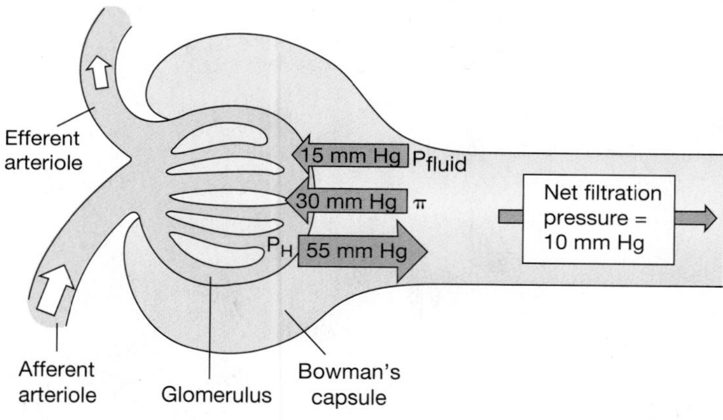

$$P_H - \pi - P_{fluid} = \text{net filtration pressure}$$
$$55 \text{ mm Hg} - 30 \text{ mm Hg} - 15 \text{ mm Hg} = 10 \text{ mm Hg}$$

KEY

P_H = Hydrostatic pressure (blood pressure)
π = Colloid osmotic pressure gradient due to proteins in plasma but not in Bowman's capsule
P_{fluid} = Fluid pressure created by fluid in Bowman's capsule

FIGURE 19-6 ***Filtration pressure in the renal corpuscle depends on hydrostatic pressure, colloid osmotic pressure, and fluid pressure***

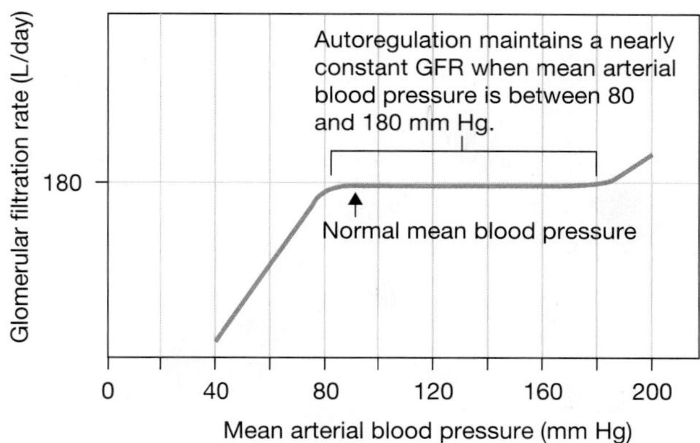

FIGURE 19-7 ***Autoregulation of glomerular filtration rate takes place over a wide range of blood pressures***

that if blood pressure increases, GFR goes up, and if blood pressure falls, GFR goes down. That is not usually the case, however. Instead, GFR is remarkably constant over a wide range of blood pressures. As long as mean arterial blood pressure remains between 80 mm Hg and 180 mm Hg, GFR averages 180 L/day (Fig. 19-7 ■).

GFR is controlled primarily by regulation of blood flow through the renal arterioles (Fig. 19-8 ■). If the overall resistance of the renal arterioles increases, renal blood flow decreases, and

EMERGING CONCEPTS

DIABETES

DIABETIC NEPHROPATHY

End-stage renal failure, in which kidney function has deteriorated beyond recovery, is a life-threatening complication in 30–40% of people with type 1 diabetes and in 10–20% of those with type 2 diabetes. As with many other complications of diabetes, the exact causes of renal failure are not clear. Diabetic nephropathy usually begins with an increase in glomerular filtration. This is followed by the appearance of proteins in the urine (*proteinuria*), an indication that the normal filtration barrier has been altered. In later stages, filtration rates decline. This stage is associated with thickening of the glomerular basal lamina and changes in both podocytes and mesangial cells. Abnormal proliferation of mesangial cells compresses the glomerular capillaries and impedes blood flow, contributing to the decrease in glomerular filtration. At this point, patients must have their kidney function supplemented by dialysis, and eventually they may need a kidney transplant.

(a) Renal blood flow and GFR change if resistance in the arterioles changes.

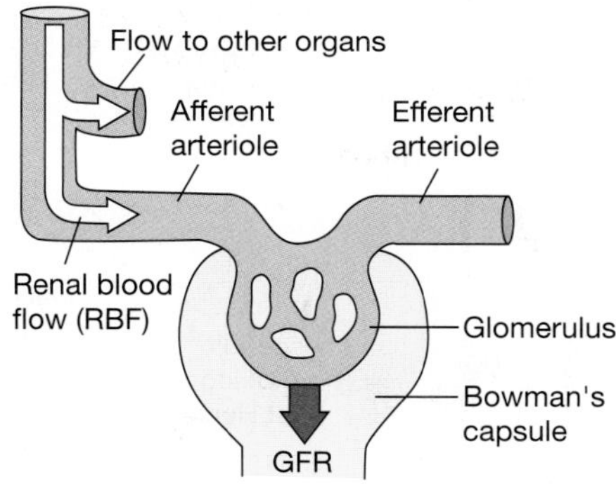

(b) Vasoconstriction of the afferent arteriole increases resistance and decreases renal blood flow, capillary blood pressure (P_H), and GFR.

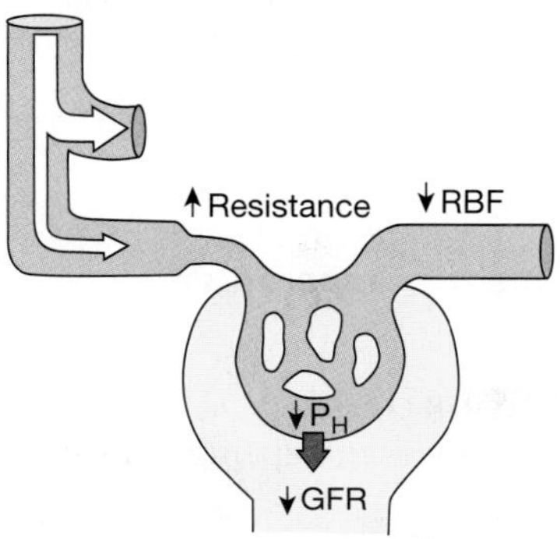

(c) Increased resistance of efferent arteriole decreases renal blood flow but increases P_H and GFR.

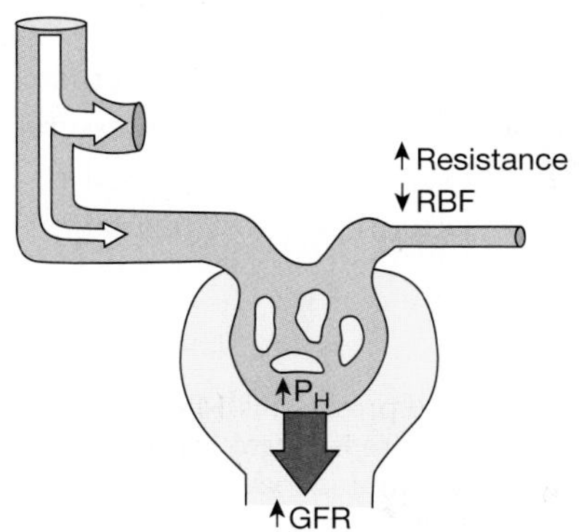

(d)

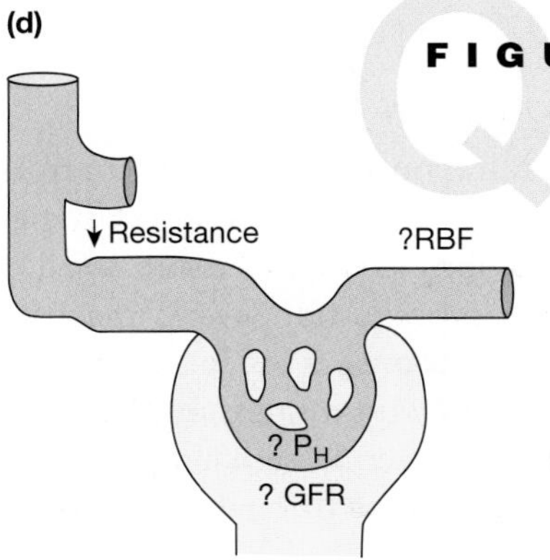

FIGURE QUESTION

What happens to capillary blood pressure, GFR, and RBF when the afferent arteriole dilates?

FIGURE 19-8 ***Resistance changes in renal arterioles alter GFR and renal blood flow***

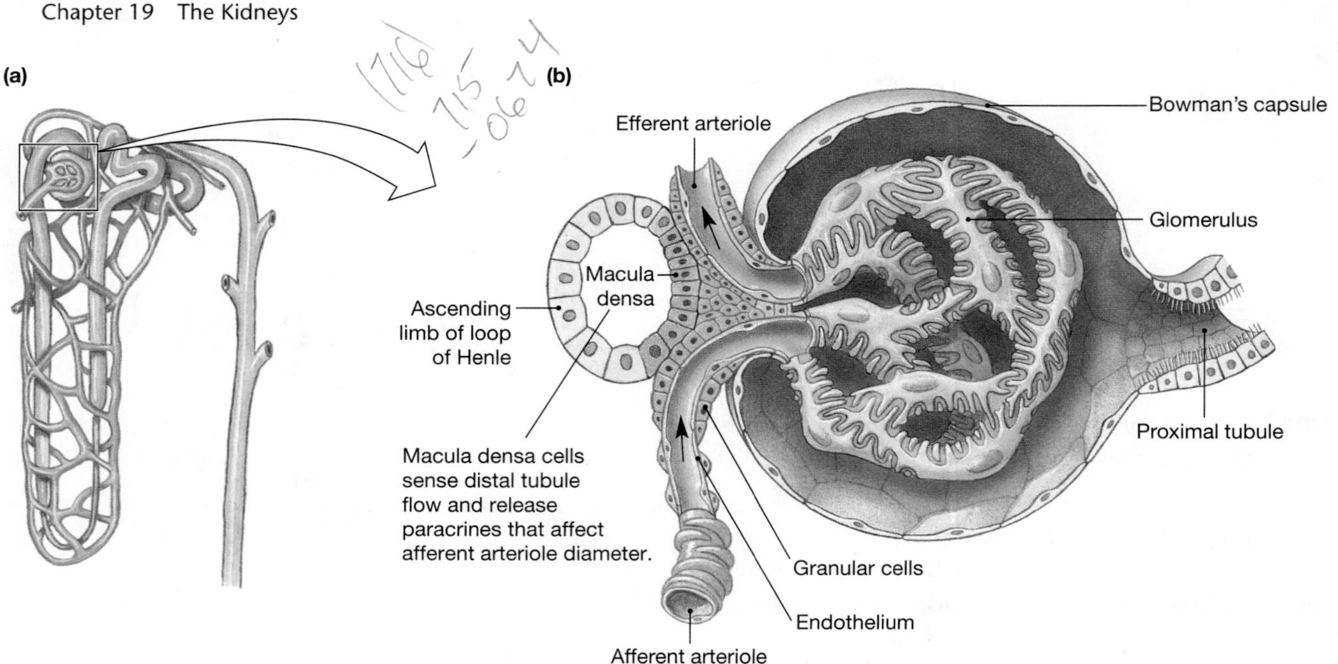

■ **FIGURE 19-9** ***The juxtaglomerular apparatus***

blood is diverted to other organs [Fig. 15-14, p. 515]. The effect of increased resistance on GFR, however, depends on *where* the resistance change takes place.

If resistance increases in the *afferent* arteriole (Fig. 19-8b), hydrostatic pressure decreases on the glomerular side of the constriction. This translates into a decrease in GFR. If resistance increases in the *efferent* arteriole, blood "dams up" in front of the constriction, and hydrostatic pressure in the glomerular capillaries increases (Fig. 19-8c). Increased glomerular pressure increases GFR. The opposite changes occur with decreased resistance in the afferent or efferent arterioles. Most regulation occurs at the afferent arteriole.

CONCEPT CHECK

9. If a hypertensive person's blood pressure is 143/107 mm Hg and mean arterial pressure is diastolic pressure + 1/3 the pulse pressure, what is this person's mean arterial pressure? What is this person's GFR according to Figure 19-7? Answers: p. 640

GFR Is Subject to Autoregulation

Autoregulation of glomerular filtration rate is a local control process in which the kidney maintains a relatively constant GFR in the face of normal fluctuations in blood pressure. We do not completely understand the process, but several mechanisms are at work. The **myogenic response** is the intrinsic ability of vascular smooth muscle to respond to pressure changes. **Tubuloglomerular feedback** is a paracrine signaling mechanism through which changes in fluid flow through the loop of Henle influence GFR.

Myogenic Response The myogenic response of afferent arterioles is similar to autoregulation in other systemic arterioles. When smooth muscle in the arteriole wall stretches because of increased blood pressure, stretch-sensitive ion channels open, and the muscle cells first depolarize, then contract [p. 472]. Vasoconstriction increases resistance to flow, and so blood flow through the arteriole diminishes. The decrease in blood flow decreases filtration pressure in the glomerulus.

If blood pressure decreases, the tonic level of arteriolar contraction disappears, and the arteriole becomes maximally dilated. However, vasodilation is not as effective at maintaining GFR as vasoconstriction because normally the afferent arteriole is fairly relaxed. Consequently, when mean blood pressure drops below 80 mm Hg, GFR decreases. This decrease is adaptive in the sense that if less plasma is filtered, the potential for fluid loss in the urine is decreased. In other words, a decrease in GFR helps the body conserve blood volume.

Tubuloglomerular Feedback Tubuloglomerular feedback is a local control pathway in which fluid flow through the tubule influences GFR. The twisted configuration of the nephron causes the final portion of the ascending limb of the loop of Henle to pass between the afferent and efferent arterioles (Fig. 19-9a ■). The tubule and arteriolar walls are modified in the regions where they contact each other and together form the *juxtaglomerular apparatus*.

The modified portion of the tubule epithelium is a plaque of cells called the **macula densa** (Fig. 19-9b). The adjacent wall of the afferent arteriole has specialized smooth muscle cells called **granular cells** (also known as *juxtaglomerular cells* or *JG cells*). The granular cells secrete *renin*, an enzyme involved in salt and water balance. When NaCl delivery past the macula densa increases as a result of increased GFR, the macula densa cells send a paracrine message to the neighboring afferent arteriole

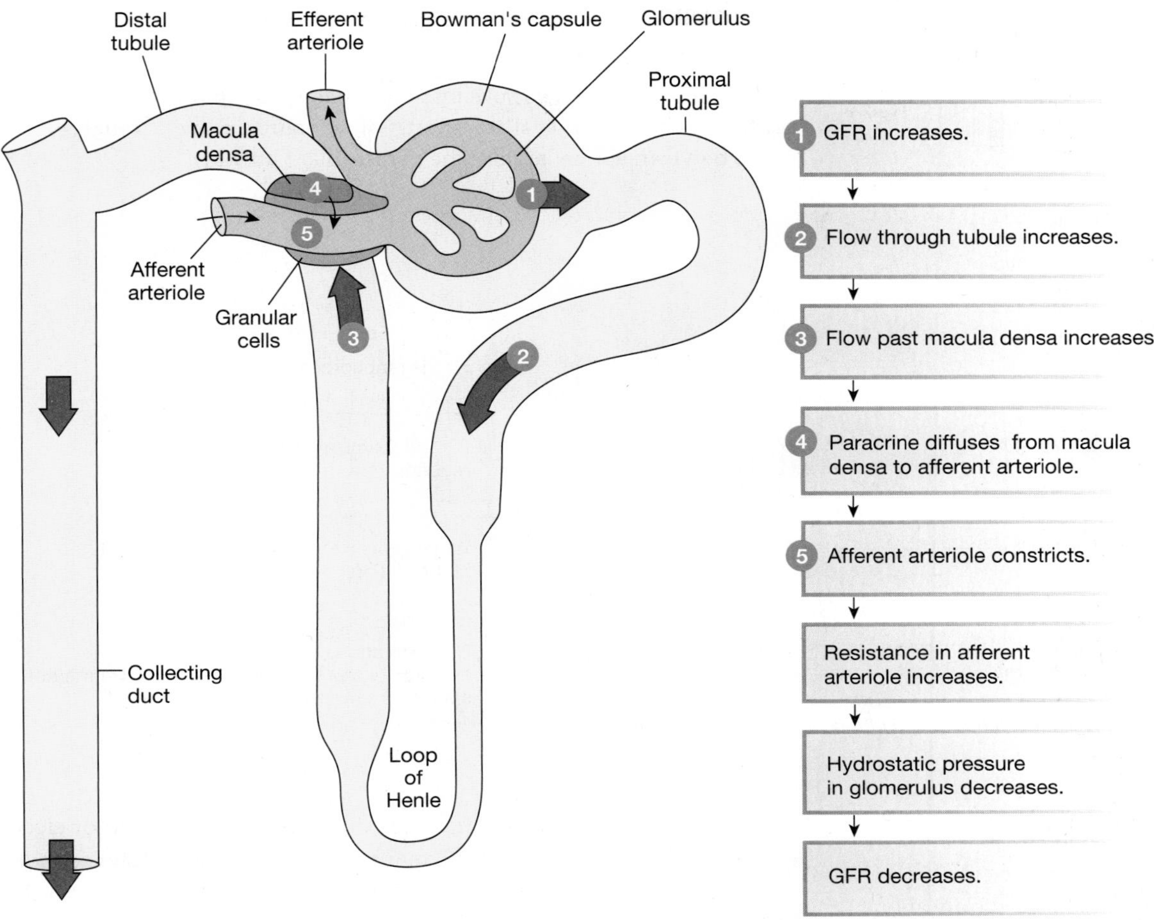

■ **FIGURE 19-10** ***Tubuloglomerular feedback***

(Fig. 19-10 ■). The afferent arteriole constricts, increasing resistance and decreasing GFR.

Experimental evidence indicates that the macula densa cells transport NaCl, and that changes in salt transport initiate tubuloglomerular feedback. The paracrine signaling between the macula densa and the afferent arteriole is complex, and the details are not clear. Experiments show that several paracrine signals, including ATP, adenosine, and nitric oxide, pass from the macula densa to the arteriole.

Hormones and Autonomic Neurons Also Influence GFR

One of the major functions of the kidneys is the integrated control of systemic blood pressure. Consequently, integrating centers outside the kidney may use hormones and the autonomic nervous system to alter glomerular filtration rate. These neural and hormonal signals work in two ways: by changing resistance in the arterioles and by altering the filtration coefficient.

Neural control of GFR is mediated by sympathetic neurons that innervate both the afferent and efferent arterioles. Sympathetic innervation of α-receptors on vascular smooth muscle causes vasoconstriction [p. 512]. If sympathetic activity is moderate, there is little effect on GFR. If systemic blood pressure drops sharply, however, as occurs with hemorrhage or severe dehydration, sympathetically induced vasoconstriction of the arterioles decreases GFR and renal blood flow. This is an adaptive response that helps conserve fluid volume.

A variety of hormones also influence arteriolar resistance. Among the most important are *angiotensin II,* a potent vasoconstrictor, and prostaglandins, which act as vasodilators. These same hormones may affect the filtration coefficient by acting on podocytes or mesangial cells. Podocytes change the size of the glomerular filtration slits. If the slits widen, more surface area is available for filtration, and GFR increases. Contraction of mesangial cells apparently changes the glomerular capillary surface area available for filtration. We still have much to learn about these processes, and physiologists are actively investigating them.

CONCEPT CHECK

10. If systemic blood pressure remains constant but the afferent arteriole of a nephron constricts, what happens to renal blood flow and GFR in that nephron?
11. A person with cirrhosis of the liver has lower-than-normal levels of plasma proteins and consequently a higher-than-normal GFR. Explain why a decrease in plasma protein concentration causes an increase in GFR.

Answers: p. 640

19

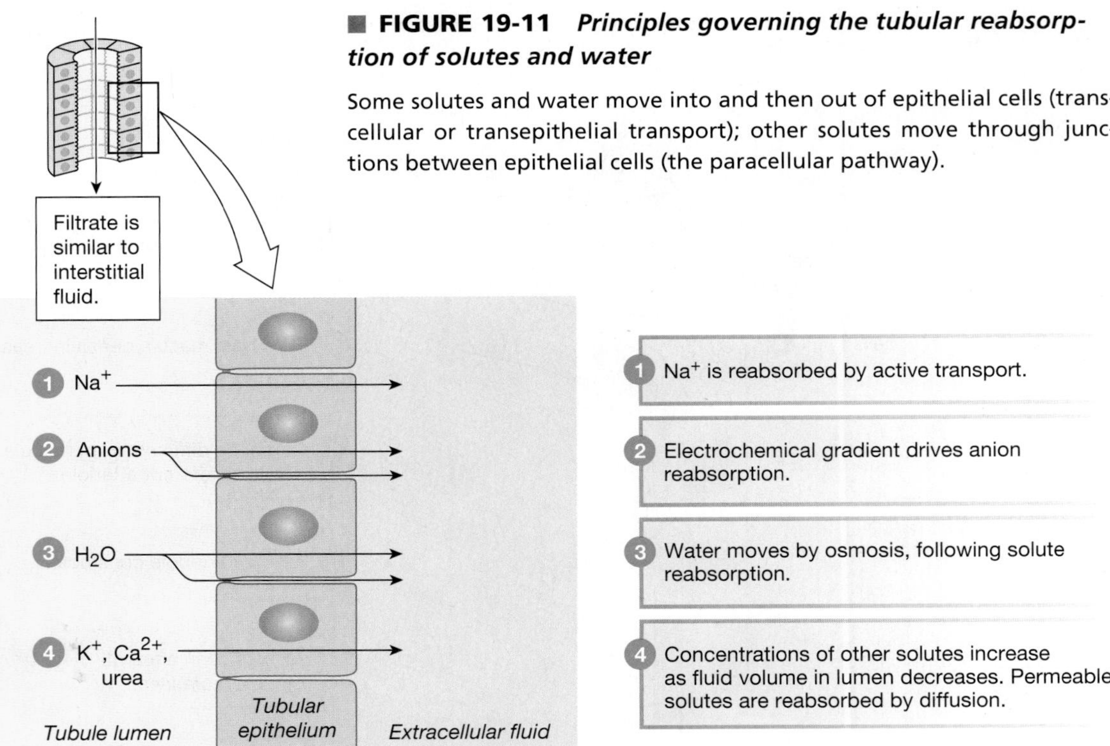
Filtrate is similar to interstitial fluid.
1 Na+
2 Anions
3 H2O
4 K+, Ca2+, urea
Tubule lumen
Tubular epithelium
Extracellular fluid
1 Na+ is reabsorbed by active transport.
2 Electrochemical gradient drives anion reabsorption.
3 Water moves by osmosis, following solute reabsorption.
4 Concentrations of other solutes increase as fluid volume in lumen decreases. Permeable solutes are reabsorbed by diffusion.

■ **FIGURE 19-11** ***Principles governing the tubular reabsorption of solutes and water***

Some solutes and water move into and then out of epithelial cells (transcellular or transepithelial transport); other solutes move through junctions between epithelial cells (the paracellular pathway).

REABSORPTION

Each day, 180 liters of filtered fluid pass from the glomerular capillaries into the tubules, yet only about 1.5 liters are excreted in the urine. Thus more than 99% of the fluid entering the tubules must be reabsorbed into the blood as filtrate moves through the nephrons. Most of this reabsorption takes place in the proximal tubule, with a smaller amount of reabsorption in the distal segments of the nephrons. Regulated reabsorption in the distal nephron allows the kidneys to return ions and water to the plasma selectively—as needed to maintain homeostasis.

19

One question you might be asking is, "Why bother to filter 180 L/day and then reabsorb 99% of it? Why not simply filter and excrete the 1% that needs to be eliminated?" There are two reasons. First, many foreign substances are filtered into the tubule but not reabsorbed into the blood. The high daily filtration rate helps clear such substances from the plasma very rapidly.

Second, filtering ions and water into the tubule simplifies their regulation. If a portion of filtrate that reaches the distal nephron is not needed to maintain homeostasis, it passes into the urine. With a high GFR, this excretion can occur quite rapidly. However, if the ions and water are needed, they are reabsorbed.

Reabsorption May Be Active or Passive

Reabsorption of water and solutes from the tubule lumen to the extracellular fluid depends on active transport. The filtrate flowing out of Bowman's capsule into the proximal tubule has the same solute concentrations as extracellular fluid. To move solute out of the lumen, the tubule cells must therefore use active transport to create concentration or electrochemical gradients. Water osmotically follows solutes as they are reabsorbed.

Figure 19-11 ■ is a general overview of reabsorption. Active transport of Na^+ from the tubule lumen to the extracellular fluid creates a transepithelial electrical gradient in which the lumen is more negative than the ECF. Anions then follow the positively charged Na^+ out of the lumen. The net movement of Na^+ and anions from lumen to extracellular fluid causes water to follow by osmosis. The loss of volume from the lumen increases the concentration of solutes (including K^+, Ca^{2+}, and urea) left behind in the filtrate: an unchanged amount of solute in a smaller volume produces an increased concentration. Once luminal solute concentrations are higher than solute concentrations in the extracellular fluid, the solutes are free to diffuse out of the lumen if the epithelium of the tubule is permeable to them.

Reabsorption involves both **transepithelial transport** (also called *transcellular transport*), in which substances cross both the apical and basolateral membranes of the tubule epithelial cell [p. 150], and the **paracellular pathway**, in which substances pass through the junction between two adjacent cells. Which route a solute takes depends on the permeability of the epithelial junctions and on the electrochemical gradient for the solute. For solutes that move through the epithelial cells, their concentration gradients determine their transport mechanisms. Solutes moving down their concentration (or electrochemical) gradient use open leak channels or facilitated diffusion carriers to cross the cell membrane. Molecules that need to be pushed against their concentration gradient are moved by either primary or secondary active transport. Sodium is directly or indirectly involved in many instances of both passive and active transport.

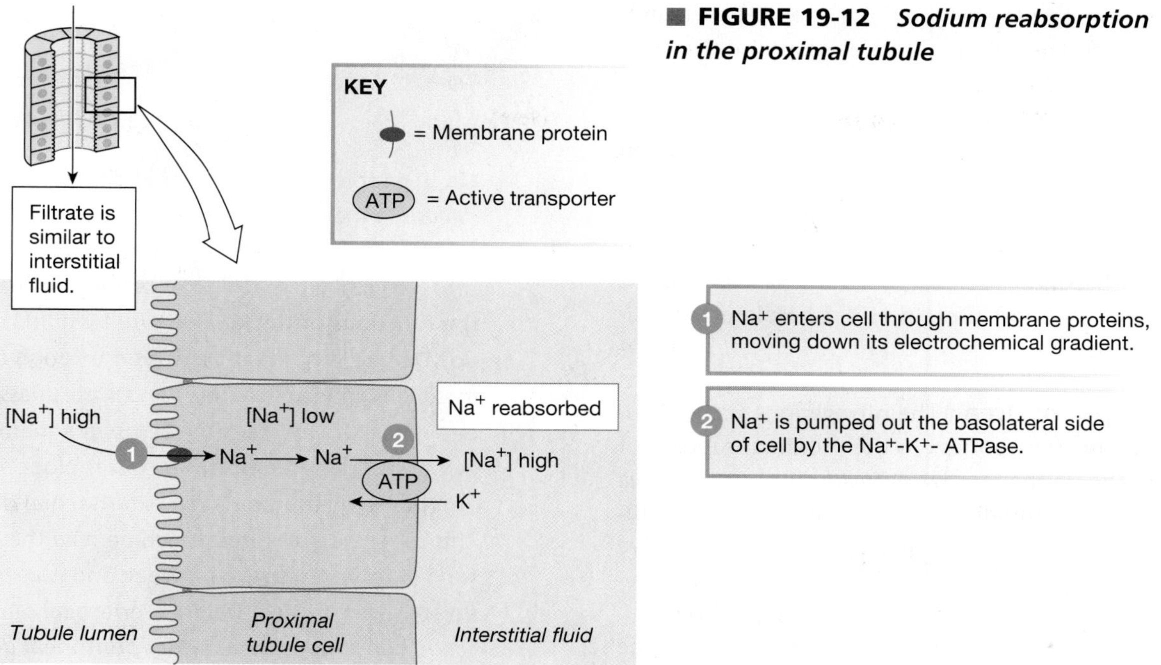

■ **FIGURE 19-12** ***Sodium reabsorption in the proximal tubule***

Active Transport of Sodium The active transport of Na^+ is the primary driving force for most renal reabsorption. As noted earlier, filtrate entering the proximal tubule is similar in ion composition to plasma, with a higher Na^+ concentration than is found in cells. Thus Na^+ in the filtrate can enter tubule cells passively by moving down its electrochemical gradient (Fig. 19-12 ■). Apical movement of Na^+ uses a variety of symport and antiport transport proteins [p. 139] or open leak channels. In the proximal tubule, a **Na^+-H^+ antiporter** plays a major role in Na^+ reabsorption. Once inside a tubule cell, Na^+ is actively transported out across the basolateral membrane by the Na^+-K^+-ATPase. The end result is Na^+ reabsorption across the tubule epithelium.

Secondary Active Transport: Symport with Sodium Sodium-linked secondary active transport in the nephron is responsible for the reabsorption of many substances, including glucose, amino acids, ions, and various organic metabolites. Figure 19-13 ■ shows one example: Na^+-dependent

19

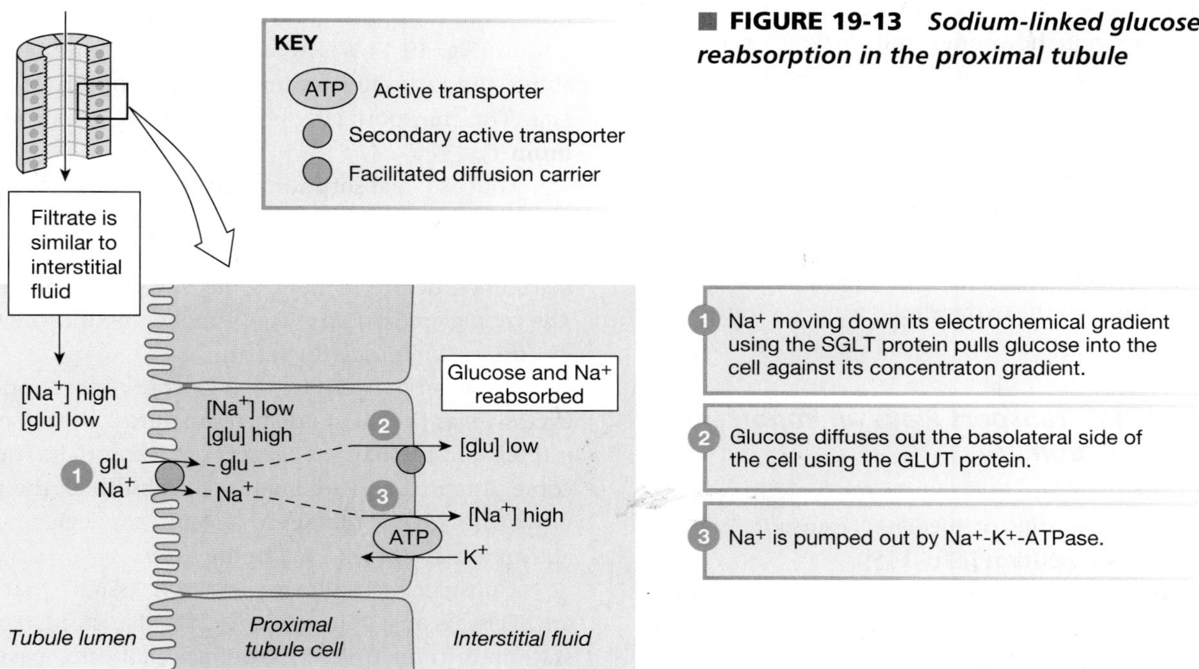

■ **FIGURE 19-13** ***Sodium-linked glucose reabsorption in the proximal tubule***

glucose reabsorption across the proximal tubule epithelium [, Fig. 5-26, p. 152]. The apical membrane contains the Na^+-glucose co-transporter (SGLT) that brings glucose into the cytoplasm against its concentration gradient by harnessing the energy of Na^+ moving down its electrochemical gradient. On the basolateral side of the cell, Na^+ is pumped out by the Na^+-K^+-ATPase while glucose diffuses out with the aid of a facilitated diffusion GLUT transporter. The same basic pattern holds for many other molecules absorbed by Na^+-dependent transport: an apical symport protein and a basolateral facilitated diffusion carrier.

Passive Reabsorption: Urea The nitrogenous waste product urea has no active transporters in the proximal tubule but will move across the epithelium by diffusion if there is a urea concentration gradient. Initially, urea concentrations in the filtrate and extracellular fluid are equal. However, the active transport of Na^+ and other solutes in the proximal tubule creates a urea concentration gradient by the following process.

When Na^+ and other solutes are reabsorbed from the proximal tubule, the transfer of osmotically active particles makes the extracellular fluid more concentrated than the filtrate remaining in the lumen (see Fig. 19-11). In response to the osmotic gradient, water moves by osmosis across the epithelium. Up to this point, no urea molecules have moved out of the lumen because there has been no urea concentration gradient. Now, however, when water leaves the lumen, the filtrate concentration of urea increases because the same amount of urea is contained in a smaller volume. Once a concentration gradient for urea exists, urea diffuses out of the lumen into the extracellular fluid.

Transcytosis: Plasma Proteins Filtration of plasma at the glomerulus normally leaves most plasma proteins in the blood, but some smaller protein hormones and enzymes can pass through the filtration barrier. Most filtered proteins are reabsorbed in the proximal tubule, with the result that normally only trace amounts of protein appear in urine.

Small as they are, filtered proteins are too large to be reabsorbed by carriers or through channels. Instead they enter proximal tubule cells by endocytosis at the apical membrane. Once in the cells, the proteins may be digested and released as amino acids or delivered intact to the extracellular fluid via transcytosis [p. 153].

Saturation of Renal Transport Plays an Important Role in Kidney Function

Most transport in the nephron uses membrane proteins and exhibits the three characteristics of mediated transport: saturation, specificity, and competition [p. 145].

Saturation refers to the maximum rate of transport that occurs when all available carriers are occupied by (are saturated with) substrate. At substrate concentrations below the saturation point, transport rate is directly related to substrate concentration (Fig. 19-14 ■). At substrate concentrations equal to or above the saturation point, transport occurs at a maximum rate. The transport rate at saturation is the **transport maximum T_m** [p. 147].

Glucose reabsorption in the nephron is an excellent example of the consequences of saturation. At normal plasma glucose concentrations, all glucose that enters the nephron is reabsorbed before it reaches the end of the proximal tubule. The tubule epithelium is well supplied with carriers to capture glucose as the filtrate flows past.

But what happens if blood glucose concentrations become excessive, as they do in diabetes mellitus? In that case, glucose is filtered faster than the carriers can reabsorb it. The carriers become saturated and are unable to reabsorb all the glucose that flows through the tubule. As a result, some glucose escapes reabsorption and is excreted in the urine.

Consider the following analogy. Assume that the carriers are like seats on a train at Disney World. Instead of boarding the stationary train from a stationary platform, passengers step

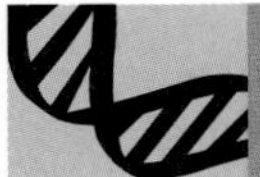

BIOTECHNOLOGY

ARTIFICIAL KIDNEYS

Many people with severe renal disease depend on *dialysis*, a medical procedure that either supplements or completely replaces their kidney function. Imagine trying to make a machine or procedure that performs the functions of the kidney. What would it have to do? Dialysis is based on diffusion through a semipermeable membrane. Solutes and water pass from a patient's extracellular fluid across the membrane into a dialysis fluid. *Hemodialysis* routes blood from the arm past a membrane in an external dialysis machine. This technique requires attachment to the machine for 3–5 hours three days a week and is used for more severe cases of renal failure. *Peritoneal dialysis* is also called *continuous ambulatory peritoneal dialysis* (CAPD) because it takes place while the patient moves about during daily activities. In CAPD, dialysis fluid is injected into the peritoneal cavity, where it accumulates waste products from the blood for 4–6 hours before being drained out. For more information about dialysis, see the website for the National Institute of Diabetes and Digestive and Kidney Diseases (*www.niddk.nih.gov*) and look under Health Information: Kidney.

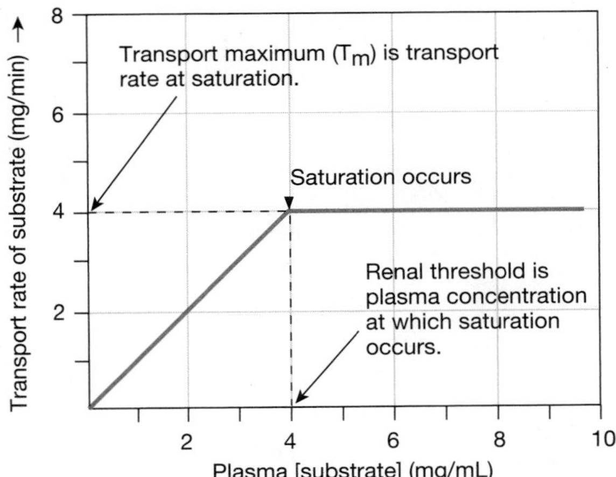

GRAPH QUESTION

What is the transport rate at the following plasma substrate concentrations: 3 mg/mL, 5 mg/mL, 8 mg/mL? At what plasma substrate concentration is the transport rate 4 mg/min?

FIGURE 19-14 ***Saturation of mediated transport***

The transport rate of a substance is proportional to the plasma concentration of the substance, up to the point at which transporters become saturated. Once saturation occurs, transport rate reaches a maximum, known as the transport maximum. The plasma concentration of substrate at which the transport maximum occurs is called the renal threshold.

onto a moving sidewalk that rolls them past the train. As the passengers see an open seat, they grab it. However, if more people are allowed onto the moving sidewalk than there are seats in the train, some people will not find seats. And because the sidewalk is moving people past the train toward an exit, they cannot wait for the next train. Instead, they end up being transported out the exit.

In the same fashion, glucose molecules entering Bowman's capsule in the filtrate are like passengers stepping onto the moving sidewalk. In order to be reabsorbed, each glucose molecule must bind to a transporter as the filtrate flows through the proximal tubule. If only a few glucose molecules enter the tubule at a time, each one will find a free transporter and be reabsorbed, just as a small number of people on the moving sidewalk all find seats on the train. However, if glucose molecules filter into the tubule faster than the glucose carriers can transport them, some glucose remains in the lumen and is excreted in the urine.

Figure 19-15 ■ is a graphic representation of glucose handling by the kidney. Figure 19-15a shows that the filtration rate of glucose from plasma into Bowman's capsule is proportional to the plasma concentration of glucose. Because filtration does not exhibit saturation, the graph continues infinitely in a straight line: the filtrate glucose concentration is always equal to the plasma glucose concentration.

Figure 19-15b plots the reabsorption rate of glucose in the proximal tubule against the plasma concentration of glucose. Reabsorption exhibits a maximum transport rate (T_m) when the carriers reach saturation.

Figure 19-15c plots the excretion rate of glucose in relation to the plasma concentration of glucose. When plasma glucose concentrations are low enough that 100% of the filtered glucose is reabsorbed, no glucose is excreted. Once the carriers reach saturation, glucose excretion begins. The plasma concentration at which glucose first appears in the urine is called the **renal threshold** for glucose.

Figure 19-15d is a composite graph that compares filtration, reabsorption, and excretion of glucose. Recall from our earlier discussion that

$$\text{amount excreted} = \text{amount filtered} - \text{amount reabsorbed} + \text{amount secreted}$$

For glucose, which is not secreted, the equation can be rewritten as

$$\text{glucose excreted} = \text{glucose filtered} - \text{glucose reabsorbed}$$

Under normal conditions, all filtered glucose is reabsorbed. In other words, filtration is equal to reabsorption.

Notice in Figure 19-15d that the lines representing filtration and reabsorption are identical up to the plasma glucose concentration that equals the renal threshold. If filtration equals reabsorption, the algebraic difference between the two is zero, and there is no excretion. Once the renal threshold is reached, filtration begins to exceed reabsorption. Notice on the graph that the filtration and reabsorption lines diverge at this point. The difference between the filtration line and the reabsorption line represents the excretion rate:

$$\text{excretion} = \underset{\text{(increasing)}}{\text{filtration}} - \underset{\text{(constant)}}{\text{reabsorption}}$$

Excretion of glucose in the urine is called **glucosuria** or **glycosuria** [*-uria,* in the urine] and usually indicates an elevated blood glucose concentration. Rarely, glucose appears in the urine even though the blood glucose concentrations are normal. This situation is due to a genetic disorder in which the nephron does not make enough carriers.

Peritubular Capillary Pressures Favor Reabsorption

The reabsorption we have just discussed refers to the movement of solutes and water from the tubule lumen to the interstitial fluid. How does that reabsorbed fluid then get into the capillary? The answer is that the driving force for reabsorption from the interstitial fluid into the capillaries is the low hydrostatic pressure that exists along the entire length of the peritubular capillaries. This low pressure favors reabsorption.

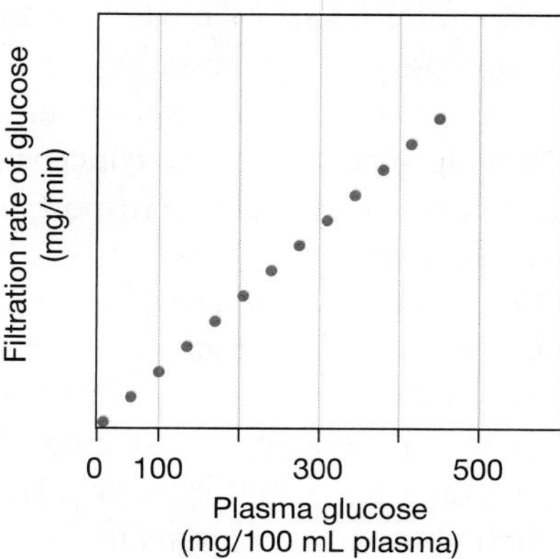

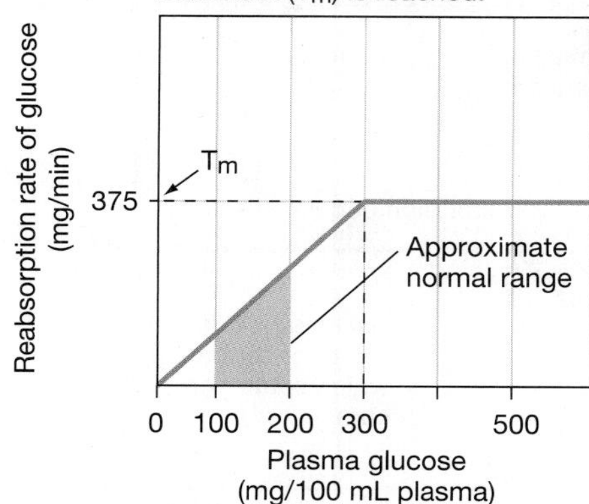

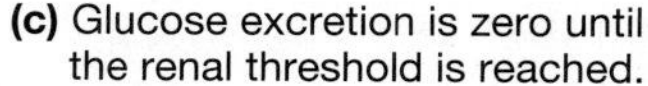

(c) Glucose excretion is zero until the renal threshold is reached.

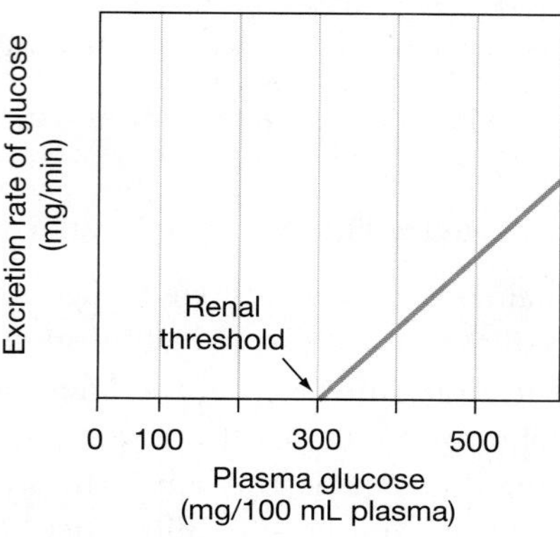

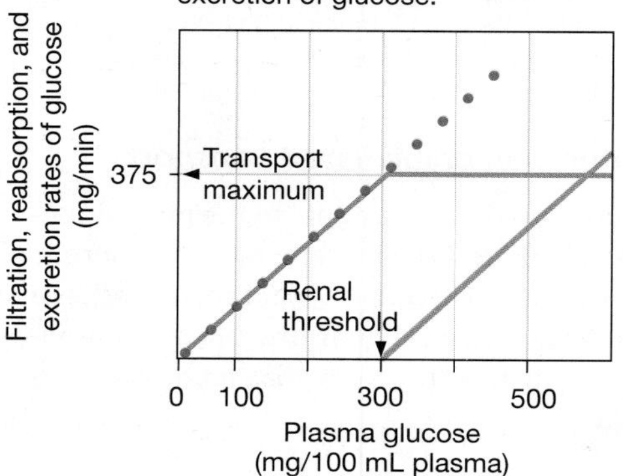

■ **FIGURE 19-15** ***Glucose handling by the nephron***

RUNNING PROBLEM

Uric acid, the molecule that causes gout, is a normal product of purine metabolism. Increased uric acid production may be associated with cell and tissue breakdown, or it may occur as a result of inherited enzyme defects. Uric acid in the blood filters freely into Bowman's capsule but is almost totally reabsorbed in the proximal tubule. Some uric acid is secreted into the proximal tubule.

Question 2:

Why would uric acid levels in the blood go up when cell breakdown increases? (Hint: purines are part of which category of biomolecules?)

Question 3:

Based on what you have learned about uric acid, predict two ways a person may develop hyperuricemia.

The peritubular capillaries have an average hydrostatic pressure of 10 mm Hg (in contrast to the glomerular capillaries, where hydrostatic pressure averages 55 mm Hg). Colloid osmotic pressure, which favors movement of fluid into the capillaries, is 30 mm Hg. As a result, the pressure gradient in peritubular capillaries is 20 mm Hg, favoring the absorption of fluid into the capillaries. Fluid that is reabsorbed passes from the capillaries to the venous circulation and returns to the heart.

SECRETION

Secretion is the transfer of molecules from extracellular fluid into the lumen of the nephron (see Fig. 19-2). Secretion, like reabsorption, depends mostly on membrane transport systems. The secretion of K^+ and H^+ by the nephron is important in the homeostatic regulation of those ions (see Chapter 20). In addition, many organic compounds are secreted. These compounds include both metabolites produced in the body and substances brought into the body.

Secretion enables the nephron to enhance excretion of a substance. If a substance is filtered and not reabsorbed, it will be excreted very effectively. If, however, the substance is filtered into the tubule, not reabsorbed, *and* then more of it is secreted into the tubule from the peritubular capillaries, excretion will be even more effective.

Secretion is an active process because it requires moving substrates against their concentration gradients. Most organic compounds are transported across the tubule epithelium into the lumen by secondary active transport.

Competition Decreases Penicillin Secretion

An interesting and important example of an organic molecule secreted by the nephron is the antibiotic *penicillin*. Many people today take antibiotics for granted, but until the early decades of the twentieth century, infections were a leading cause of death.

In 1928, Alexander Fleming discovered a substance in the bread mold *Penicillium* that retarded the growth of bacteria. But the antibiotic was difficult to isolate, so it did not become available for clinical use until the late 1930s. During World War II, penicillin made a major difference in the number of deaths and amputations caused by infected wounds. The only means of producing penicillin, however, was to isolate it from bread mold, and supplies were limited.

Demand for the drug was heightened by the fact that kidney tubules secrete penicillin. Renal secretion is so efficient at clearing foreign molecules from the blood that within three to four hours after a dose of penicillin has been administered, about 80% has been excreted in the urine. During the war, the drug was in such short supply that it was common procedure to collect the urine from patients being treated with penicillin so that the antibiotic could be isolated and reused.

This was not a satisfactory solution, however, and so researchers looked for a way to slow penicillin secretion. They hoped to find a molecule that could compete with penicillin for the organic anion transporter responsible for secretion [p. 146]. That way, when presented with both drugs, the carrier would bind preferentially to the competitor and secrete it, leaving penicillin behind in the blood. A synthetic compound named *probenecid* was the answer. When probenecid is administered concurrently with penicillin, the transporter removes probenecid preferentially, prolonging the activity of penicillin in the body. Once mass-produced synthetic penicillin became available and supply was no longer a problem, the medical use of probenecid declined.

RUNNING PROBLEM

Michael finds it amazing that a metabolic problem could lead to pain in his big toe. "There's a way to treat gout, right?" he asks. Dr. Garcia explains that the treatment includes anti-inflammatory agents, lots of water, and avoidance of alcohol, which can trigger gout attacks. "In addition, I would like to put you on a *uricosuric agent*, like probenecid, which will enhance renal excretion of uric acid," replies Dr. Garcia. "By enhancing excretion, we can reduce uric acid levels in your blood and thus provide relief." Michael agrees to try these measures and on his way home stops off at a convenience store for a case of his favorite bottled water.

Question 4:
Uric acid is reabsorbed from the proximal tubule on a membrane transporter. Uricosuric agents are organic acids. Given these two facts, explain how uricosuric agents might enhance excretion of uric acid.

EXCRETION

Urine output is the result of all the processes that take place in the kidney. By the time fluid reaches the end of the nephron, it bears little resemblance to the filtrate that started in Bowman's capsule. Glucose, amino acids, and useful metabolites are gone, having been reabsorbed into the blood, and organic wastes are more concentrated. The concentrations of ions and water in the urine are highly variable, depending on the state of the body.

Although excretion tells us what the body is eliminating, excretion by itself cannot tell us the details of renal function. Recall that for any substance,

$$\text{excretion} = \text{filtration} - \text{reabsorption} + \text{secretion}$$

Thus simply looking at the excretion rate of a substance tells us nothing about how the kidney handled that substance. The excretion rate of a substance depends on (1) its filtration rate and (2) whether the substance is reabsorbed, secreted, or both as it passes through the tubule.

Renal handling of a substance and GFR are often of clinical interest. For example, clinicians use information about a person's glomerular filtration rate as an indicator of overall kidney function. And pharmaceutical companies developing drugs must provide the Food and Drug Administration with complete information on how the human kidney handles each new compound.

But how can investigators dealing with living humans assess filtration, reabsorption, and secretion at the level of the individual nephron? They have no way to do this directly because the kidneys are not easily accessible and the nephrons are microscopic. Scientists therefore had to develop a technique that would allow them to assess renal function using only analysis of the urine and blood. From their work came the concept of clearance.

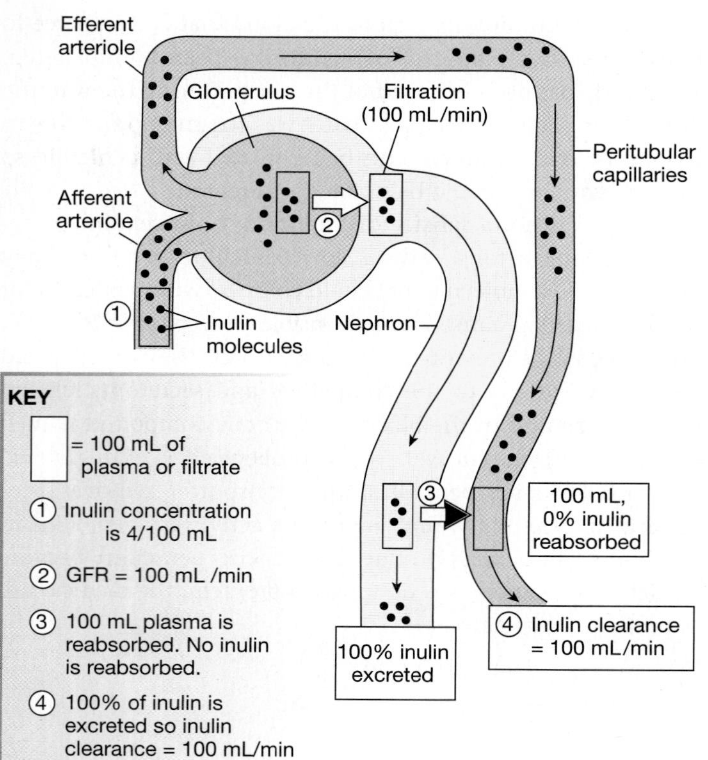
Efferent arteriole
Glomerulus
Filtration (100 mL/min)
Peritubular capillaries
Afferent arteriole
Inulin molecules
Nephron
KEY
= 100 mL of plasma or filtrate
1 Inulin concentration is 4/100 mL
2 GFR = 100 mL /min
3 100 mL plasma is reabsorbed. No inulin is reabsorbed.
4 100% of inulin is excreted so inulin clearance = 100 mL/min
100 mL, 0% inulin reabsorbed
100% inulin excreted
4 Inulin clearance = 100 mL/min

■ **FIGURE 19-16** ***Inulin clearance***

Clearance Is a Noninvasive Way to Measure GFR

Clearance of a solute is the rate at which that solute disappears from the body by excretion or by metabolism [p. 130]. For any solute that is cleared only by renal excretion, clearance is expressed as the volume of plasma passing through the kidneys that has been totally cleared of that solute in a given period of time. Because this is such an indirect way to think of excretion (how much blood has been cleared of X rather than how much X has been excreted), clearance is often a very difficult concept for students.

Before we jump into the mathematical expression of clearance, let's look at an example that shows how clearance relates to kidney function. For our example, we will use **inulin**, a polysaccharide isolated from the tuberous roots of a variety of plants. (Inulin is not the same as *insulin,* the protein hormone that regulates glucose metabolism.) Scientists discovered from experiments with isolated nephrons that inulin injected into the plasma filters freely into the nephron. As it passes through the kidney tubule, inulin is neither reabsorbed nor secreted. Thus, 100% of the inulin that filters into the tubule is excreted.

How does this relate to clearance? To answer this question, take a look at Figure 19-16 ■, which assumes that 100% of a filtered volume of plasma is reabsorbed. (This is not too far off the actual value, which is more than 99%.) Inulin has been injected so that its plasma concentration is 4 inulin molecules per 100 mL plasma. If GFR is 100 mL plasma filtered per minute, we can calculate the filtration rate, or *filtered load,* of inulin using the equation

$$\text{filtered load of X} = [\text{X}]_{\text{plasma}} \times \text{GFR}$$

$$\begin{aligned}\text{filtered load of inulin} &= (4 \text{ inulin}/100 \text{ mL plasma}) \\ &\quad \times 100 \text{ mL plasma filtered/min} \\ &= 4 \text{ inulin/min}\end{aligned}$$

As the filtered inulin and the filtered plasma pass along the nephron, all the plasma is reabsorbed but all the inulin remains in the tubule. The reabsorbed plasma contains no inulin, so we say it has been totally *cleared* of inulin. The *inulin clearance* therefore is 100 mL of plasma cleared/min. At the same time, the excretion rate of inulin is 4 inulin molecules excreted per minute.

What good is this information? For one thing, we can use it to calculate the glomerular filtration rate. Notice from Figure 19-16 that inulin clearance (100 mL plasma cleared/min) is equal to the GFR (100 mL plasma filtered/min). Thus, *for any substance that is freely filtered but neither reabsorbed nor secreted, its clearance is equal to GFR.*

Now let's show mathematically that inulin clearance is equal to GFR. We already know that

$$\text{filtered load of inulin} = [\text{inulin}]_{\text{plasma}} \times \text{GFR} \qquad (1)$$

We also know that 100% of the inulin that filters into the tubule is excreted. In other words:

$$\text{filtered load of inulin} = \text{excretion rate of inulin} \qquad (2)$$

Because of this equality, we can substitute excretion rate for filtered load in equation (1) by using algebra (if A = B and A = C, then B = C):

$$\text{excretion rate of inulin} = [\text{inulin}]_{\text{plasma}} \times \text{GFR} \qquad (3)$$

This equation can be rearranged to read

$$\text{GFR} = \frac{\text{excretion rate of inulin}}{[\text{inulin}]_{\text{plasma}}} \qquad (4)$$

It turns out that the right side of this equation is identical to the clearance equation for inulin. Thus the general equation for the clearance of any substance X (mL plasma cleared/min) is

$$\text{clearance of X} = \frac{\text{excretion rate of X (mg/min)}}{[\text{X}]_{\text{plasma}} \text{ (mg/mL plasma)}} \qquad (5)$$

For inulin:

$$\text{inulin clearance} = \frac{\text{excretion rate of inulin}}{[\text{inulin}]_{\text{plasma}}} \qquad (6)$$

The right sides of equations (4) and (6) are identical, so by using algebra again, we can say that:

$$\text{GFR} = \text{inulin clearance} \qquad (7)$$

So why is this important? For one thing, you have just learned how we can measure GFR in a living human by taking only blood and urine samples. Try the example in Concept Check 12 to see if you understand the preceding discussion.

Inulin is not practical for routine clinical applications because it does not occur naturally in the body and must be administered by continuous intravenous infusion. As a result, inulin use is restricted to research. Unfortunately, no substance that occurs naturally in the human body is handled by the kidney exactly the way inulin is handled.

In clinical settings, physicians use creatinine to estimate GFR. **Creatinine** is a breakdown product of phosphocreatine, an energy-storage compound found primarily in muscles [p. 410]. It is constantly produced by the body and need not be administered. Normally, the production and breakdown rates of phosphocreatine are relatively constant, and the plasma concentration of creatinine does not vary much.

Although creatinine is always present in the plasma and is easy to measure, it is not the perfect molecule for estimating GFR because a small amount is secreted into the urine. However, the amount secreted is small enough that, in most people, *creatinine clearance* is routinely used to estimate GFR.

CONCEPT CHECK

12. If plasma creatinine = 1.8 mg/100 mL plasma, urine creatinine = 1.5 mg/mL urine, and urine volume is 1100 mL in 24 hours, what is the creatinine clearance? What is GFR?

Answers: p. 640

RUNNING PROBLEM

Three weeks later, Michael is back in Dr. Garcia's office. The anti-inflammatory drugs and probenecid had eliminated the pain in his toe, but last night he had gone to the hospital with a very painful kidney stone. "We'll have to wait until the analysis comes back," says Dr. Garcia, "but I will guess that it is a uric acid stone. Did you drink as much water as I told you to?" Sheepishly, Michael admits that he had good intentions but could never find the time at work to get out his bottled water. "You have to drink enough water while on this drug to produce 3000 milliliters or more of urine a day. That's more than three quarts. Otherwise, you may end up with another uric acid kidney stone." Michael agrees that this time, he will follow instructions to the letter.

Question 5:
Explain why not drinking enough water while taking uricosuric agents may cause uric acid stones to form in the urinary tract.

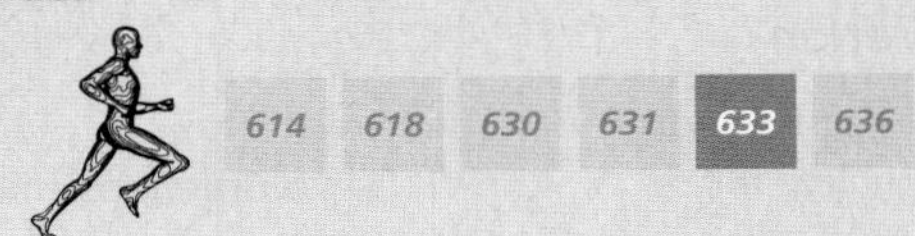

Clearance and GFR Help Us Determine Renal Handling of Solutes

Once we know a person's GFR, we can determine how the kidney handles any solute by measuring the solute's plasma concentration and its excretion rate. If we assume that the solute is freely filtered at the glomerulus, we know from equation (1) that

$$\text{Filtered load of X} = [\text{X}]_{\text{plasma}} \times \text{GFR}$$

By comparing the filtered load of the solute with its excretion rate, we can tell how the nephron handled that substance (Table 19-2 ■). For example, if less of the substance appears in the urine than was filtered, net reabsorption occurred (excreted = filtered − reabsorbed). If more of the substance appears in the urine than was filtered, there must have been net secretion of the substance into the lumen (excreted = filtered + secreted). If the same amount of the substance is filtered and excreted, then the substance is handled like inulin—neither reabsorbed nor secreted.

TABLE 19-2 Renal Handling of Solutes

For any molecule X that is freely filtered at the glomerulus:	
If filtration rate is greater than excretion rate,	there is net reabsorption of X.
If excretion rate is greater than filtration rate,	there is net secretion of X.
If filtration and excretion rate are the same,	X passes through the nephron without net reabsorption or secretion.
If the clearance of X is less than inulin clearance,	there is net reabsorption of X.
If the clearance of X is equal to inulin clearance,	X is neither reabsorbed nor secreted.
If the clearance of X is greater than inulin clearance,	there is net secretion of X.

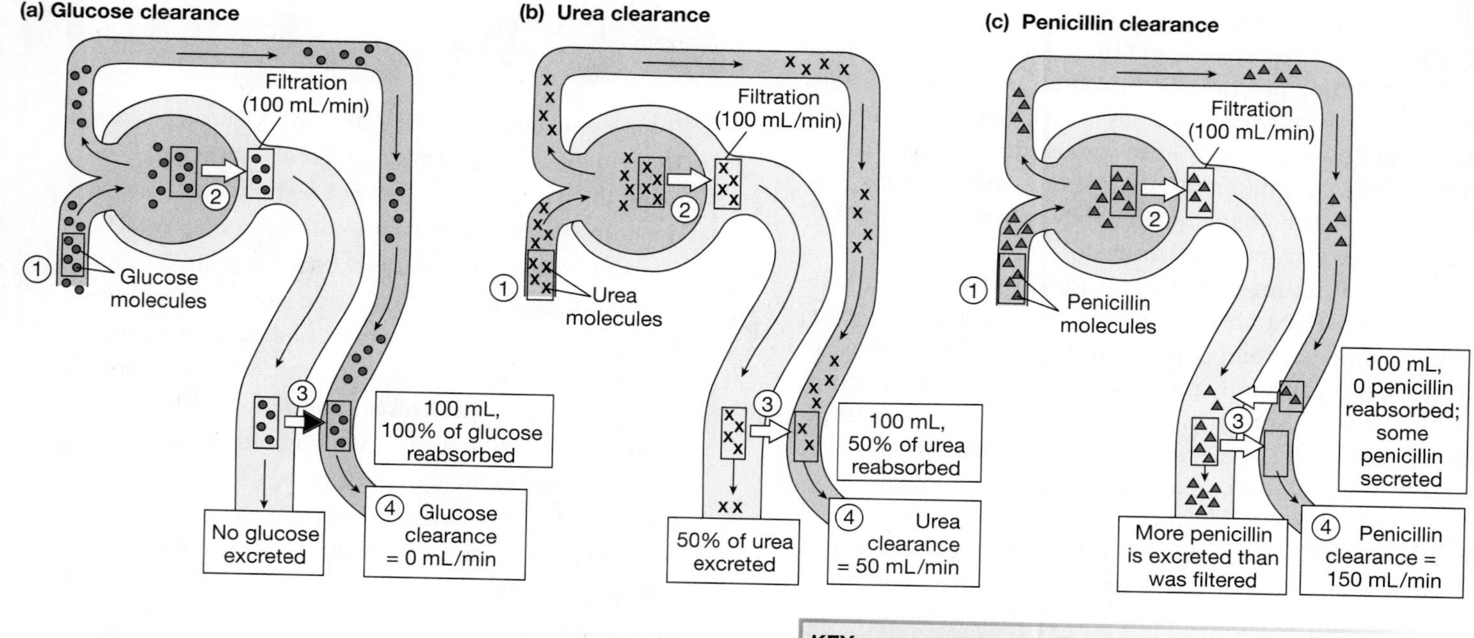

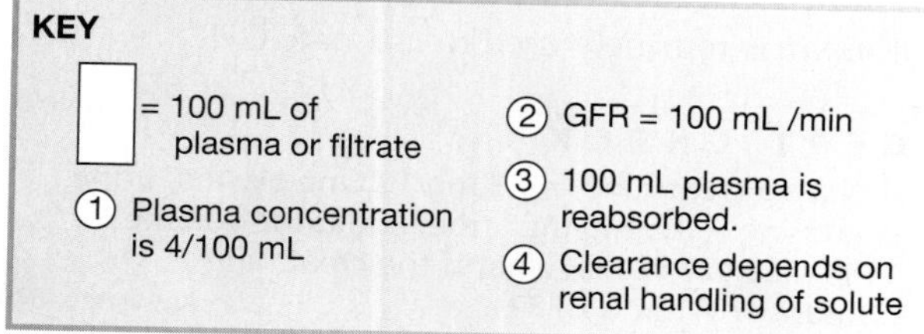

KEY
= 100 mL of plasma or filtrate
1 Plasma concentration is 4/100 mL
2 GFR = 100 mL /min
3 100 mL plasma is reabsorbed.
4 Clearance depends on renal handling of solute

■ **FIGURE 19-17** ***The relationship between clearance and excretion***

The figure represents the events taking place in one minute. For simplicity, 100% of the filtered volume is assumed to be reabsorbed.

19

Suppose that glucose is present in the plasma at 100 mg glucose/dL plasma, and GFR is calculated from creatinine clearance to be 125 mL plasma/min. For these values, equation (1) tells us that

$$\text{Filtered load of glucose} = (100 \text{ mg glucose}/100 \text{ mL plasma}) \times 125 \text{ mL plasma/min}$$

$$\text{Filtered load of glucose} = 125 \text{ mg glucose/min}$$

There is no glucose in this person's urine, however: glucose excretion is zero. Because glucose was filtered at a rate of 125 mg/min but excreted at a rate of 0 mg/min, it must have been totally reabsorbed.

Clearance values can also be used to determine how the nephron handles a filtered solute. In this method, researchers calculate creatinine or inulin clearance, then compare the clearance of the solute being investigated with the creatinine or inulin clearance (Table 19-2). If clearance of the solute is less than the inulin clearance, the solute has been reabsorbed. If the clearance of the solute is higher than the inulin clearance, additional solute has been secreted into the urine. More plasma was cleared of the solute than was filtered, so the additional solute must have been removed from the plasma by secretion.

Figure 19-17 ■ shows clearance of three molecules: glucose, urea, and penicillin. All solutes have the same concentration in the blood entering the glomerulus: 4 molecules/100 mL plasma. GFR is 100 mL/min, and we assume for simplicity that the entire 100 mL of plasma filtered into the tubule is reabsorbed.

For any solute, its clearance reflects how the kidney tubule handles it. For example, 100% of the glucose that filters is reabsorbed, and glucose clearance is zero (Fig. 19-17a). Urea is partially reabsorbed; four molecules filter, but only two are reabsorbed (Fig. 19-17b, ③). Consequently, urea clearance is 50 mL plasma per minute. Urea and glucose clearance are both less than the inulin clearance of 100 mL/min, which tells you that urea and glucose have been reabsorbed.

Penicillin (Fig. 19-17c) is filtered but not reabsorbed, and additional penicillin molecules are secreted from plasma in the peritubular capillaries. In this example, an extra 50 mL of plasma have been cleared of penicillin in addition to the original 100 mL that filtered. The penicillin clearance therefore is 150 mL plasma per minute. Penicillin clearance is greater than the inulin clearance of 100 mL/min, which tells you that net secretion of penicillin occurs.

Note that a comparison of clearance values tells you only the *net* handling of the solute. It does not tell you if a molecule is both reabsorbed and secreted. For example, nearly all K^+ filtered is reabsorbed in the proximal tubule and loop of Henle, and then a small amount is secreted back into the tubule lumen at the distal nephron. On the basis of K^+ clearance, it appears that only reabsorption occurred.

Clearance calculations are relatively simple because all you need to know are the urine excretion rates and the plasma concentrations for any solute of interest; both values are easily

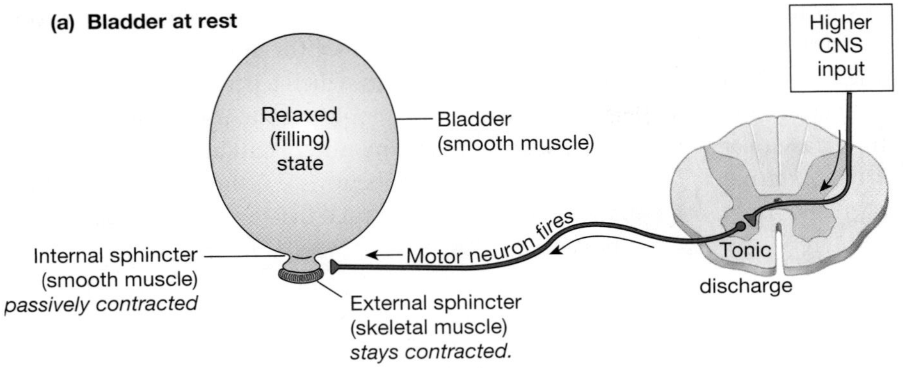

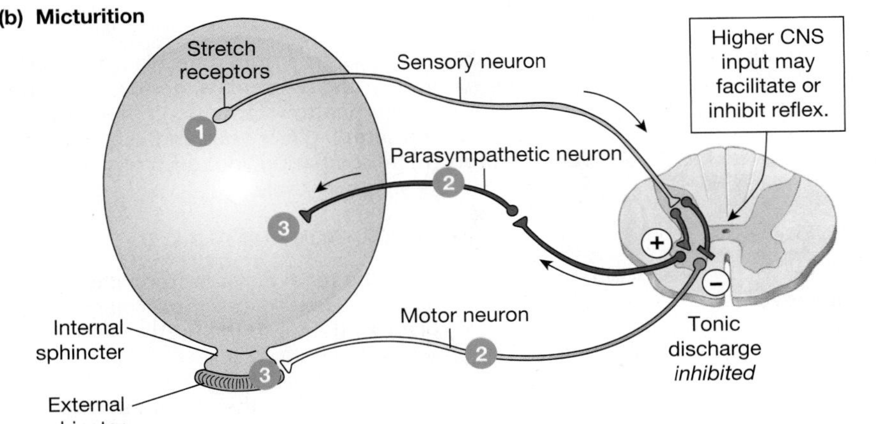

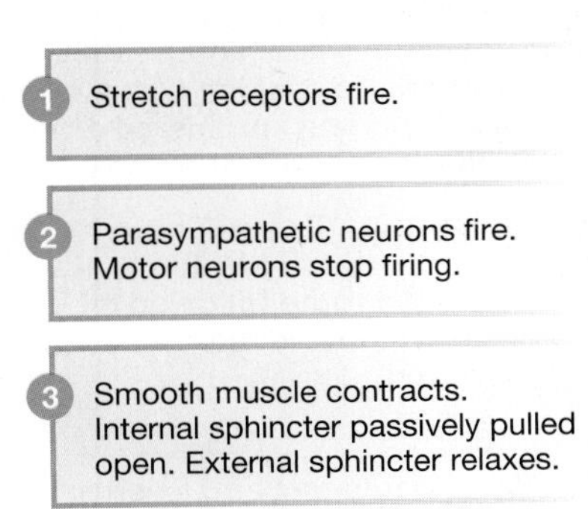

1 Stretch receptors fire.
2 Parasympathetic neurons fire. Motor neurons stop firing.
3 Smooth muscle contracts. Internal sphincter passively pulled open. External sphincter relaxes.

■ **FIGURE 19-18** ***The storage of urine and the micturition reflex***

obtained. If you also know either inulin or creatinine clearance, then you can determine the renal handling of any compound.

MICTURITION

Once filtrate leaves the collecting ducts, it can no longer be modified, and its composition does not change. The filtrate, now called urine, flows into the renal pelvis and then down the *ureter* to the bladder with the help of rhythmic smooth muscle contractions. The bladder is a hollow organ whose walls contain well-developed layers of smooth muscle. In the bladder, urine is stored until released in the process known as urination, voiding, or more formally, **micturition** [*micturire*, to desire to urinate].

The bladder can expand to hold a volume of about 500 mL. The neck of the bladder is continuous with the *urethra,* a single tube through which urine passes to reach the external environment. The opening between the bladder and urethra is closed by two rings of muscle called *sphincters* (Fig. 19-18a ■).

The **internal sphincter** is a continuation of the bladder wall and consists of smooth muscle. Its normal tone keeps it contracted. The **external sphincter** is a ring of skeletal muscle controlled by somatic motor neurons. Tonic stimulation from the central nervous system maintains contraction of the external sphincter except during urination.

Micturition is a simple spinal reflex that is subject to both conscious and unconscious control from higher brain centers. As the bladder fills with urine and its walls expand, stretch receptors send signals via sensory neurons to the spinal cord (Fig. 19-18b). There the information is integrated and transferred to two sets of neurons. The stimulus of a full bladder excites parasympathetic neurons leading to the smooth muscle in the bladder wall. The smooth muscle contracts, increasing the pressure on the bladder contents. Simultaneously, somatic motor neurons leading to the external sphincter are inhibited.

Contraction of the bladder occurs in a wave that pushes urine downward toward the urethra. Pressure exerted by the urine forces the internal sphincter open while the external sphincter relaxes. Urine passes into the urethra and out of the body, aided by gravity.

This simple micturition reflex occurs primarily in infants who have not yet been toilet trained. A person who has been toilet trained acquires a learned reflex that keeps the micturition reflex inhibited until she or he consciously desires to urinate. The learned reflex involves additional sensory fibers in the bladder that signal the degree of fullness. Centers in the brain stem and cerebral cortex receive that information and override the basic micturition reflex by directly inhibiting the parasympathetic fibers and by reinforcing contraction of the external sphincter. When an appropriate time to urinate arrives, those same centers remove the inhibition and facilitate the reflex by inhibiting the external sphincter.

In addition to conscious control of urination, various subconscious factors can affect the micturition reflex. "Bashful bladder" is a condition in which a person is unable to urinate in the presence of other people despite the conscious intent to do so. The sound of running water facilitates micturition and is often used to help patients urinate if the urethra is irritated from insertion of a *catheter,* a tube inserted into the bladder to drain it passively.

RUNNING PROBLEM CONCLUSION

GOUT

In this running problem, you learned that gout, which often presents as a debilitating pain in the big toe, is a metabolic problem whose cause and treatment may be linked to kidney function. Gout is one of the oldest known diseases and for many years was considered a "rich man's" disease caused by too much rich food and drink. Thomas Jefferson and Benjamin Franklin both suffered from gout. To learn more about its causes, symptoms, and treatments, go to the U.S. National Library of Medicine's Health Information page (*http://www.nlm.nih.gov/hinfo.html*). Check your understanding of this running problem by comparing your answers against the information in the summary table.

	QUESTION	FACTS	INTEGRATION AND ANALYSIS
1	Trace the route followed by kidney stones when they are excreted.	Kidney stones often form in the renal pelvis.	From the renal pelvis, a stone passes down the ureter, into the urinary bladder, then into the urethra and out of the body.
2	Why would uric acid levels in the blood go up when cell breakdown increases?	Purines include adenine and guanine, which are components of DNA, RNA, and ATP [p. 32].	When a cell dies, the nucleus and other components are broken down into biomolecules. Degradation of the cell's DNA, RNA, and ATP increases purine production, which in turn increases uric acid production.
3	Based on what you have learned about uric acid, predict two ways a person may develop hyperuricemia.	Hyperuricemia is a condition of elevated uric acid levels in the blood. Uric acid is made from purines. It is filtered, reabsorbed, and secreted in the kidneys.	Hyperuricemia results either from overproduction of uric acid or from failure of the kidneys to excrete uric acid. Because uric acid normally gets into the urine by secretion, a defect in the renal secretory mechanism would lead to hyperuricemia.
4	Uric acid is reabsorbed on a membrane transporter. Uricosuric agents are organic acids. Given these two facts, explain how uricosuric agents might enhance excretion of uric acid.	Mediated transport exhibits competition, in which related molecules compete for one transporter. Usually, one molecule binds preferentially and therefore inhibits transport of the second molecule.	Uricosuric agents may compete with uric acid for the proximal tubule transporter. Preferential binding of the uricosuric agents would block uric acid access to the transporter, leaving it in the lumen and increasing the amount of it excreted.
5	Explain why not drinking enough water while taking uricosuric agents may cause uric acid stones to form in the urinary tract.	Uric acid stones form when uric acid concentrations exceed a critical level.	If a person drinks large volumes of water, the excess water will be excreted by the kidneys. Large amounts of water dilute the urine, thereby preventing the high concentrations of uric acid needed for stone formation.

614 618 630 631 633 636

19

CHAPTER SUMMARY

The urinary system, like the lungs, uses the principle of *mass balance* to maintain homeostasis. The components of urine are constantly changing and reflect the kidney's functions of regulating ions and water and removing wastes.

One of the body's three *portal systems*—each of which includes two capillary beds—is found in the kidney. Filtration occurs in the first capillary bed, and reabsorption in the second. The *pressure-flow-resistance* relationship you encountered in the cardiovascular and pulmonary systems also plays a role in glomerular filtration and urinary excretion.

Compartmentation is illustrated by the movement of water and solutes between the internal and external environments as filtrate is modified along the nephron. Reabsorption and secretion of solutes depend on *molecular interactions* and on the *movement of molecules across membranes* of the tubule cells.

Functions of the Kidneys

1. The kidneys regulate extracellular fluid volume, blood pressure, and osmolarity; maintain ion balance; regulate pH; excrete wastes and foreign substances; and participate in endocrine pathways. (p. 614)

Anatomy of the Urinary System

IP Urinary System: Glomerular Filtration

2. The **urinary system** is composed of two kidneys, two ureters, a bladder, and a urethra. (p. 615; Fig. 19-1a)
3. Each **kidney** has about 1 million **nephrons**. In cross-section, a kidney is arranged into an outer **cortex** and inner **medulla**. (p. 615; Fig. 19-1c)
4. Renal blood flow goes from **afferent arteriole** to **glomerulus** to **efferent arteriole** to **peritubular capillaries**. The **vasa recta** capillaries dip into the medulla. (p. 618; Fig. 19-1h, i)
5. Fluid filters from the glomerulus into **Bowman's capsule**. From there, it flows through the **proximal tubule, loop of Henle, distal tubule**, and **collecting duct**, then drains into the **renal pelvis**. **Urine** flows through the **ureter** to the **urinary bladder**. (p. 618; Fig. 19-1c, j)

Overview of Kidney Function

6. **Filtration** is the movement of fluid from plasma into Bowman's capsule. **Reabsorption** is the movement of filtered materials from tubule to blood. **Secretion** is the movement of selected molecules from blood to tubule. (pp. 618–619; Fig. 19-2)
7. Average urine volume is 1.5 L/day. Osmolarity varies between 50 and 1200 mOsM. (p. 619; Tbl. 19-1)
8. The amount of a solute excreted equals the amount filtered minus the amount reabsorbed plus the amount secreted. (p. 620; Fig. 19-3)

Filtration

IP Urinary System: Glomerular Filtration

9. Filtered solutes must pass first through glomerular capillary endothelium, then through a **basal lamina**, and finally through Bowman's capsule epithelium before reaching the lumen of Bowman's capsule. (p. 620; Fig. 19-4)
10. Filtration allows most components of plasma to enter the tubule but excludes blood cells and most plasma proteins. (p. 620)
11. The Bowman's capsule epithelium has specialized cells called **podocytes** that wrap around the glomerular capillaries and create **filtration slits. Mesangial cells** are associated with the glomerular capillaries. (p. 620; Fig. 19-4)
12. One-fifth of renal plasma flow filters into the tubule lumen. The percentage of total plasma volume that filters is called the **filtration fraction**. (p. 621; Fig. 19-5)
13. Hydrostatic pressure in glomerular capillaries averages 55 mm Hg, favoring filtration. Opposing filtration are colloid osmotic pressure of 30 mm Hg and hydrostatic capsule fluid pressure averaging 15 mm Hg. The net driving force is 10 mm Hg, favoring filtration. (pp. 621–622; Fig. 19-6)
14. The **glomerular filtration rate** (GFR) is the amount of fluid that filters into Bowman's capsule per unit time. Average GFR is 125 mL/min, or 180 L/day. (p. 622)
15. Hydrostatic pressure in glomerular capillaries can be altered by changing resistance in the afferent and efferent arterioles. (p. 624; Fig. 19-8)
16. Autoregulation of glomerular filtration is accomplished by a **myogenic response** of vascular smooth muscle in response to pressure changes and by **tubuloglomerular feedback.** When fluid flow through the distal tubule increases, the **macula densa** cells send a paracrine signal to the afferent arteriole, which constricts. (p. 624; Fig. 19-10)
17. Reflex control of GFR is mediated through systemic signals, such as hormones, and through the autonomic nervous system. (p. 625)

Reabsorption

IP Urinary System: Early Filtrate Processing

18. Most reabsorption takes place in the proximal tubule. Finely regulated reabsorption takes place in the more distal segments of the nephron. (p. 626)
19. The active transport of Na^+ and other solutes creates concentration gradients for passive reabsorption of urea and other solutes. (p. 626; Fig. 19-11)
20. Most reabsorption involves transepithelial transport, but some solutes and water are reabsorbed by the paracellular pathway. (p. 626)
21. Glucose, amino acids, ions, and various organic metabolites are reabsorbed by Na^+-linked secondary active transport. (p. 627; Fig. 19-13)
22. Most renal transport is mediated by membrane proteins and exhibits saturation, specificity, and competition. The **transport maximum T_m** is the transport rate at saturation. (p. 628; Fig. 19-14)
23. The **renal threshold** is the plasma concentration at which a substance first appears in the urine. (p. 629; Fig. 19-14)
24. Peritubular capillaries reabsorb fluid along their entire length. (p. 629)

Secretion

25. Secretion enhances excretion by removing solutes from the peritubular capillaries. K^+, H^+, and a variety of organic compounds are secreted. (p. 631)
26. Molecules that compete for renal carriers slow the secretion of a molecule. (p. 631)

Excretion

27. The excretion rate of a solute depends on (1) its filtered load and (2) whether it is reabsorbed or secreted as it passes through the nephron. (p. 631)
28. **Clearance** describes how many milliliters of plasma passing through the kidneys have been totally cleared of a solute in a given period of time. (p. 632)
29. **Inulin** clearance is equal to GFR. In clinical settings, **creatinine** is used to measure GFR. (p. 632; Fig. 19-16)
30. Clearance can be used to determine how the nephron handles a solute filtered into it. (p. 633; Fig. 19-17)

Micturition

31. The external sphincter of the bladder is skeletal muscle that is tonically contracted except during urination. (p. 635; Fig. 19-18)
32. Micturition is a simple spinal reflex subject to conscious and unconscious control. Parasympathetic neurons cause contraction of the smooth muscle in the bladder wall. Somatic motor neurons leading to the external sphincter are simultaneously inhibited. (p. 635)

QUESTIONS

(Answers to the Review Questions begin on page A1.)

THE PHYSIOLOGY PLACE

Access more review material online at **The Physiology Place** website. There you'll find review questions, problem-solving activities, case studies, flashcards, and direct links to both *InterActive Physiology®* and PhysioEx™. To access the site, go to *www.physiologyplace.com* and select Human Physiology, Fourth Edition.

LEVEL ONE REVIEWING FACTS AND TERMS

1. List and explain the significance of the five characteristics of urine that can be found by physical examination.
2. List and explain the six major kidney functions.
3. At any given time, what percentage of cardiac output goes to the kidneys?
4. List the major structures of the urinary system in their anatomical sequence, from the kidneys to the urine leaving the body. Describe the function of each structure.
5. Arrange the following structures in the order that a drop of water entering the nephron would encounter them:
   (a) afferent arteriole
   (b) Bowman's capsule
   (c) collecting duct
   (d) distal tubule
   (e) glomerulus
   (f) loop of Henle
   (g) proximal tubule
   (h) renal pelvis
6. Name the three filtration barriers that solutes must cross as they move from plasma to the lumen of Bowman's capsule. What components of blood are usually excluded by these layers?
7. What force(s) promotes glomerular filtration? What force(s) opposes it? What is meant by the term *net driving force*?
8. What does the abbreviation GFR stand for? What is a typical numerical value for GFR in milliliters per minute? In liters per day?
9. Identify the following structures, then explain their significance in renal physiology:
   (a) juxtaglomerular apparatus
   (b) macula densa
   (c) mesangial cell
   (d) podocyte
   (e) sphincters in the bladder
   (f) renal cortex
10. In which segment of the nephron does most reabsorption take place? When a molecule or ion is reabsorbed from the lumen of the nephron, where does it go? If a solute is filtered and not reabsorbed from the tubule, where does it go?
11. Match each of the following ions or molecules with its primary mode(s) of transport across the kidney epithelium.
   (a) Na^+
   (b) glucose
   (c) urea
   (d) plasma proteins
   (e) water

   1. transcytosis
   2. primary active transport
   3. secondary active transport
   4. facilitated diffusion
   5. movement through open channels
   6. simple diffusion through the phospholipid bilayer
12. List three solutes secreted into the tubule lumen.
13. What solute that is normally present in the body is used to estimate GFR in humans?
14. What is micturition?

LEVEL TWO REVIEWING CONCEPTS

15. Map the following terms. You may add additional terms if you like.

α-receptor	glomerulus
afferent arteriole	JG cells
autoregulation	macula densa
basal lamina	mesangial cell
Bowman's capsule	myogenic autoregulation
capillary blood pressure	norepinephrine
capsule fluid pressure	paracrine
colloid osmotic pressure	plasma proteins
efferent arteriole	podocyte
endothelium	resistance
epithelium	vasoconstriction
GFR	

16. Define, compare, and contrast the items in the following sets of terms:
   (a) filtration, secretion, and excretion
   (b) saturation, transport maximum, and renal threshold
   (c) probenecid, creatinine, inulin, and penicillin
   (d) clearance, excretion, and glomerular filtration rate

17. What are the advantages of a kidney that filters a large volume of fluid and then reabsorbs 99% of it?
18. If the afferent arteriole of a nephron constricts, what happens to GFR in that nephron? If the efferent arteriole of a nephron constricts, what happens to GFR in that nephron? Assume that no autoregulation takes place.
19. Diagram the micturition reflex. How is this reflex altered by toilet training? How do higher brain centers influence micturition?
20. Antimuscarinic drugs are the accepted treatment for an overactive bladder. Explain why they work for this condition.

LEVEL THREE PROBLEM SOLVING

21. You have been asked to study kidney function in a new species of rodent found in the Amazonian jungle. You isolate some nephrons and expose them to inulin. The following graph shows the results of your studies. (a) How is the rodent nephron handling inulin? Is inulin filtered? Is it excreted? Is there net inulin reabsorption? Is there net secretion? (b) On the graph, accurately draw a line indicating the net reabsorption or secretion. (*Hint:* excretion = filtration − reabsorption + secretion)

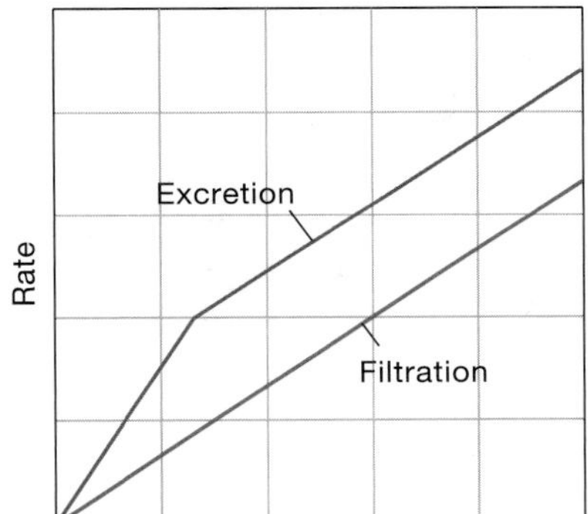

22. Draw a section of renal tubule epithelium showing three cells joined by cell junctions. Label the apical and basolateral membranes, the tubule lumen, and the extracellular fluid. Use the following written description of proximal tubule processes to draw a model cell.

The proximal tubule cells contain carbonic anhydrase, which promotes the conversion of CO_2 and water to carbonic acid. Carbonic acid then dissociates to H^+ and HCO_3^-. Sodium is reabsorbed by an apical Na^+-H^+ antiporter and a basolateral Na^+-K^+ATPase. Chloride is passively reabsorbed by movement through the paracellular pathway. Bicarbonate produced in the cytoplasm leaves the cell on a basolateral Na^+-HCO_3^- symporter.

23. Read the box on hemodialysis on p. 628 and see if you can create a model system that would work for dialysis. Draw two compartments (one to represent blood and one to represent dialysis fluid) separated by a semipermeable membrane. In the blood compartment, list normal extracellular fluid solutes and their concentrations (see the table with normal values of blood components inside the back cover of this book). What will happen to the concentrations of these solutes during kidney failure? Which of these solutes should you put in the dialysis fluid, and what should their concentrations be? (*Hint:* do you want diffusion into the dialysis fluid, out of the dialysis fluid, or no net movement?) How would you change the dialysis fluid if the patient was retaining too much water?

LEVEL FOUR QUANTITATIVE PROBLEMS

24. Darlene weighs 50 kg. Assume that her total blood volume is 8% of her body weight, that her heart pumps her total blood volume once a minute, and that her renal blood flow is 25% of her cardiac output. Calculate the volume of blood that flows through Darlene's kidneys each minute.
25. Dwight was competing for a spot on the Olympic equestrian team. As his horse, Nitro, cleared a jump, the footing gave way, causing the horse to somersault, landing on Dwight and crushing him. The doctors feared kidney damage and ran several tests. Dwight's serum creatinine level was 2 mg/100 mL. His 24-hour urine specimen had a volume of 1 L and a creatinine concentration of 20 mg/mL. A second specimen taken over the next 24 hours had the same serum creatinine value and urine volume, but a urine creatinine concentration of 4 mg/ml. How many milligrams of creatinine are in each specimen? What is Dwight's creatinine clearance in each test? What is his GFR? Evaluate these results and comment on Dwight's kidney function.
26. You are a physiologist taking part in an archeological expedition to search for Atlantis. One of the deep-sea submersibles has come back with a mermaid, and you are taking a series of samples from her. You have determined that her GFR is 250 mL/min and that her kidneys reabsorb glucose with a transport maximum of 50 mg/min. What is her renal threshold for glucose? When her plasma concentration of glucose is 15 mg/mL, what is its glucose clearance?

ANSWERS

Answers to Concept Check Questions

Page 615

1. If extracellular K^+ decreases, more K^+ leaves the neuron, and the membrane potential hyperpolarizes (becomes more negative, increases).
2. If plasma Ca^{2+} decreases, the force of contraction decreases.

Page 618

3. When net filtration out of the glomerular capillaries occurs, the capillary hydrostatic pressure must be greater than the capillary colloid osmotic pressure.
4. When net reabsorption into the peritubular capillaries occurs, the capillary hydrostatic pressure must be less than the capillary colloid osmotic pressure.

Page 620

5. Filtration and secretion both represent movement from the extracellular fluid into the lumen. Filtration takes place only at Bowman's capsule; secretion takes place all along the rest of the tubule.
6. Glomerulus → Bowman's capsule → proximal tubule → loop of Henle → distal tubule → collecting duct → renal pelvis → ureter → urinary bladder → urethra.

7. If reabsorption decreases to half the normal rate, the body would run out of plasma in under an hour.

Page 622

8. Osmotic pressure is higher in efferent arterioles because fluid volume is decreased there, leaving the same amount of protein in a smaller volume.

Page 624

9. This person's mean arterial pressure is 119 mm Hg. This person's GFR is 180 L/day.

Page 625

10. If the afferent arteriole constricts, the resistance in that arteriole increases, and blood flow through that arteriole is diverted to lower-resistance arterioles. GFR will decrease in the nephron whose arteriole constricted.
11. The primary driving force for GFR is blood pressure opposed by fluid pressure in Bowman's capsule and colloid osmotic pressure due to plasma proteins (Fig. 19-6). With fewer plasma proteins, the plasma has lower-than-normal colloid osmotic pressure. With less colloid osmotic pressure opposing GFR, GFR increases.

Page 633

12. Creatinine clearance = creatinine excretion rate/$[\text{creatinine}]_{\text{plasma}}$ = (1.5 mg creatinine/mL urine × 1.1 L urine/day)/1.8 mg creatinine/100 mL plasma. Creatinine clearance is about 92 L/day, and GFR is equal to creatinine clearance.

Q Answers to Figure and Graph Questions

Page 623

Figure 19-8: Capillary blood pressure, GFR, and renal blood flow all increase.

Page 629

Figure 19-14: The transport rate at 3 mg/mL is 3 mg/min; at 5 and 8 mg/mL, it is 4 mg/min. The transport rate is 4 mg/min at any plasma concentration equal to or greater than 4 mg/mL, the renal threshold for this substance.

At a 10% loss of body fluid, the patient will show signs of confusion, distress, and hallucinations and at 20%, death will occur.

—**Poul Astrup**, *in Salt and Water in Culture and Medicine, 1993*

20 Integrative Physiology II: Fluid and Electrolyte Balance

BACKGROUND BASICS

pH and buffers: **37** Control of blood pressure: **521** CO_2 excretion by lungs: **599** Membrane recycling: **149** Peptide hormones: **217** Membrane transport: **136** Carbonic anhydrase: **599** Osmolarity and tonicity: **155** Posterior pituitary hormones: **226** Body fluid compartments: **52** Steroid hormones: **219** Polarized epithelial cells: **151** Second messenger systems: **180** Glomerular filtration rate: **622** Protein structure: **31**

RUNNING PROBLEM

HYPONATREMIA

Lauren was competing in her first ironman-distance triathlon, a 140.6-mile race consisting of 2.4 miles of swimming, 112 miles of cycling, and 26.2 miles of running. At mile 22 of the run, approximately 16 hours after starting the race, she collapsed. After being admitted to the medical tent, Lauren complained of nausea, a headache, and general fatigue. The medical staff noted that Lauren's face and clothing were covered in white crystals. When they weighed her and compared that value with her pre-race weight recorded at registration, they realized Lauren had gained 2 kg during the race.

The American businesswoman in Tokyo finished her workout and stopped at the snack bar of the fitness club to ask for a sports drink. The attendant handed her a bottle labeled "Pocari Sweat®." Although the thought of drinking sweat is not very appealing, the physiological basis for the name is sound.

During exercise, the body secretes sweat, a dilute solution of water and ions, particularly Na^+, K^+, and Cl^-. To maintain homeostasis, the body must replace any substances it has lost to the external environment. Therefore, the replacement fluid a person consumes after exercise should resemble sweat.

In this chapter, we explore how humans maintain salt and water balance, also known as fluid and electrolyte balance. The homeostatic control mechanisms for fluid and electrolyte balance in the body are aimed at maintaining four parameters: fluid volume, osmolarity, the concentrations of individual ions, and pH.

FLUID AND ELECTROLYTE HOMEOSTASIS

The human body is in a state of constant flux. Over the course of a day we ingest about 2 liters of food and drink that contain 6–15 grams of NaCl. In addition, we bring in varying amounts of other electrolytes, including K^+, H^+, Ca^{2+}, HCO_3^-, and phosphate ions (HPO_4^{2-}). The body's task is to maintain *mass balance* [p. 129]: what comes in must be excreted if the body does not need it.

The body has several routes for excreting ions and water. The kidneys are the primary route for water loss and for removal of many ions. Under normal conditions, small amounts of both water and ions are lost in the feces as well. In addition, the lungs help remove H^+ and HCO_3^- by excreting CO_2.

Although physiological mechanisms that maintain fluid and electrolyte balance are important, behavioral mechanisms also play an essential role. *Thirst* is critical because drinking is the only normal way to replace lost water. *Salt appetite* is a behavior that leads people and animals to seek and ingest salt (sodium chloride, NaCl).

Why are we concerned with homeostasis of these substances? Water and Na^+ are associated with extracellular fluid volume and osmolarity. Disturbances in K^+ balance can cause serious problems with cardiac and muscle function by disrupting the membrane potential of excitable cells. Ca^{2+} is involved in a variety of body processes, from exocytosis and muscle contraction to bone formation and blood clotting, and H^+ and HCO_3^- are the ions whose balance determines body pH.

ECF Osmolarity Affects Cell Volume

Why is maintaining osmolarity so important to the body? The answer lies in the fact that water crosses most cell membranes freely. If the osmolarity of the extracellular fluid changes, water moves into or out of cells and changes intracellular volume. If ECF osmolarity decreases as a result of excess water intake, water moves into the cells and they swell. If ECF osmolarity increases as a result of salt intake, water moves out of the cells and they shrink.

Changes in cell volume—either shrinking or swelling—can impair cell function. When cells swell, for example, ion channels in the membrane open, disrupting membrane potential and cell signaling. The brain, encased in the rigid skull, is particularly vulnerable to damage from swelling. Some cells can regulate their volume in response to swelling or shrinking, but this capability is limited. In general, maintenance of ECF osmolarity within a normal range is essential to maintaining homeostasis.

EMERGING CONCEPTS

REGULATION OF CELL VOLUME

The regulation of cell volume is so important that many cells have independent mechanisms for regulating volume. Renal tubule cells in the medulla of the kidney, for example, are constantly exposed to high extracellular fluid osmolarity, yet these cells maintain normal cell volume. They do so by synthesizing organic solutes as needed so that their intracellular osmolarity matches that of the extracellular fluid. The organic solutes used to raise intracellular osmolarity include sugar alcohols and certain amino acids. In addition, cells can regulate their volume by changing their ionic composition. In some instances, changes in cell volume are believed to act as signals that initiate certain cellular responses. For example, swelling of liver cells activates protein and glycogen synthesis, whereas shrinkage of liver cells causes breakdown of protein and glycogen.

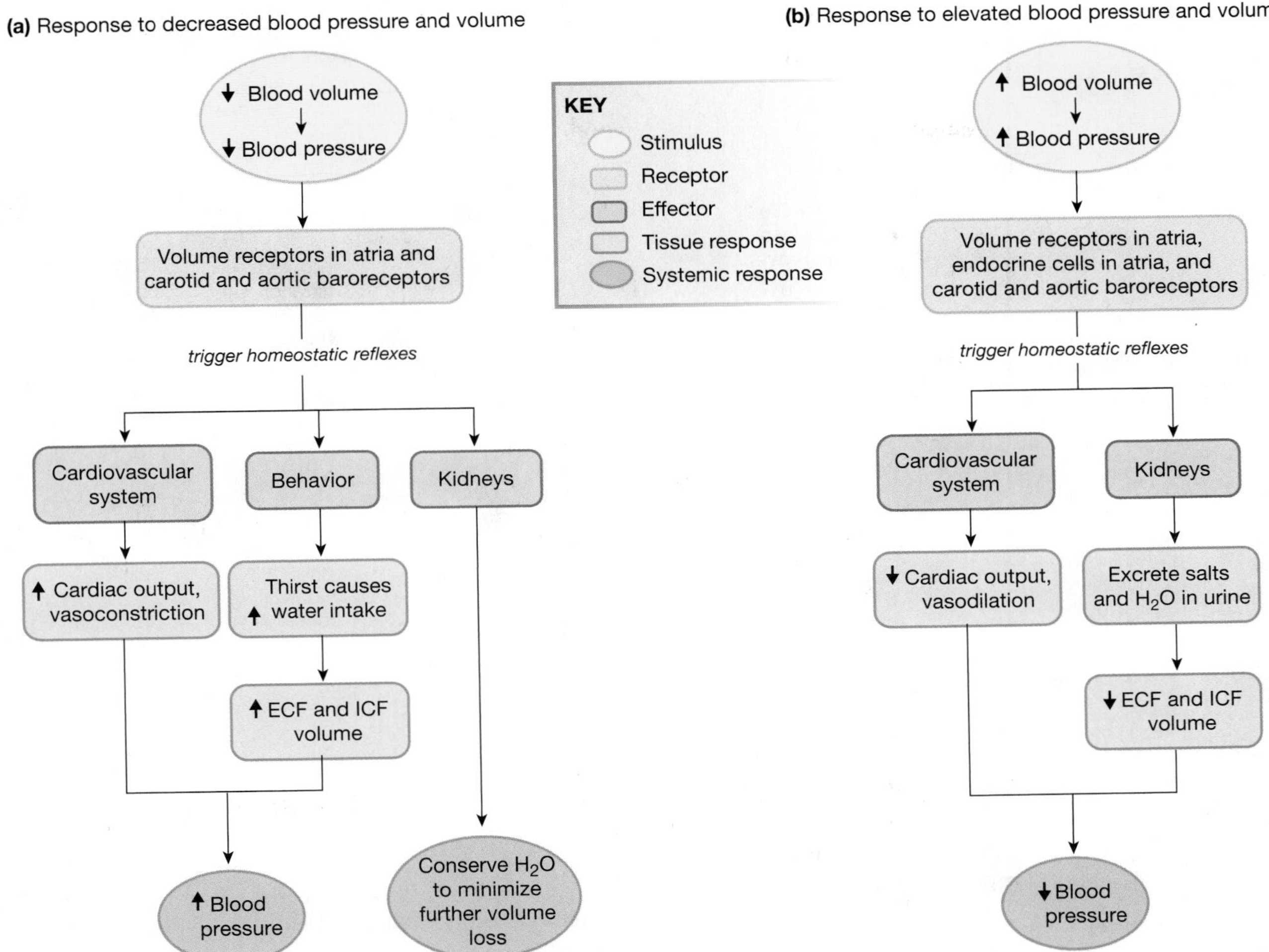

■ **FIGURE 20-1** ***The body's integrated responses to changes in blood volume and blood pressure***

Fluid and Electrolyte Balance Requires Integration of Multiple Systems

The process of fluid and electrolyte balance is truly integrative because it involves the respiratory and cardiovascular systems in addition to renal and behavioral responses. Adjustments made by the lungs and cardiovascular system are primarily under neural control and can be made quite rapidly. Homeostatic compensation by the kidneys occurs more slowly because the kidneys are primarily under endocrine and neuroendocrine control. For example, small changes in blood pressure that result from increases or decreases in blood volume are quickly corrected by the cardiovascular control center in the brain [p. 521]. If volume changes are persistent or of large magnitude, the kidneys step in to help maintain homeostasis.

Figure 20-1 ■ summarizes the integrated response of the body to changes in blood volume and blood pressure. Signals from carotid and aortic baroreceptors and atrial volume receptors initiate a quick neural response mediated through the cardiovascular control center, and a slower response elicited from the kidneys. In addition, low blood pressure stimulates thirst. In both situations, renal function integrates with the cardiovascular system to keep blood pressure within a normal range.

Because of the overlap in their functions, a change made by one system—whether renal or cardiovascular—is likely to have consequences that affect the other. Endocrine pathways initiated by the kidneys have direct effects on the cardiovascular system, for instance, and hormones released by myocardial cells act on the kidneys. Sympathetic pathways from the cardiovascular control center affect not only cardiac output and vasoconstriction but also glomerular filtration and hormone release by the kidneys.

Thus the maintenance of blood pressure, blood volume, and ECF osmolarity forms a network of interwoven control pathways. This integration of function in multiple systems is one of the more difficult concepts in physiology; it is also one of the most exciting areas of physiological research.

WATER BALANCE

Water is the most abundant molecule in the body, constituting about 50% of total body weight in females ages 17 to 39, and 60% of total body weight in males of the same age group.

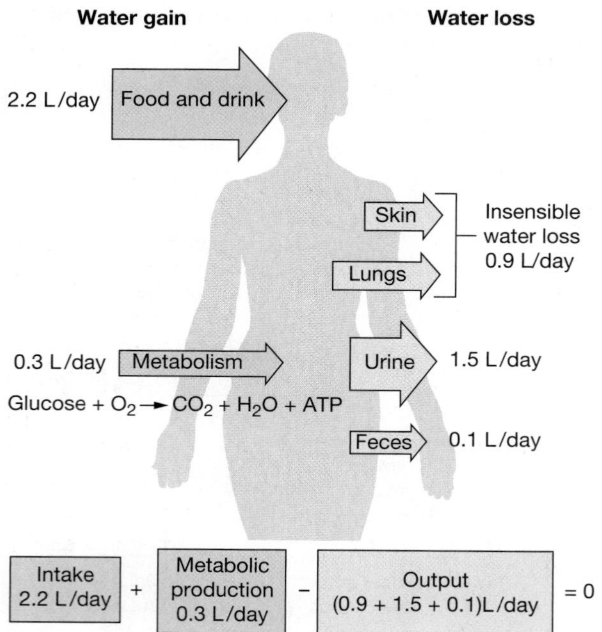

■ **FIGURE 20-2** ***Water balance in the body***

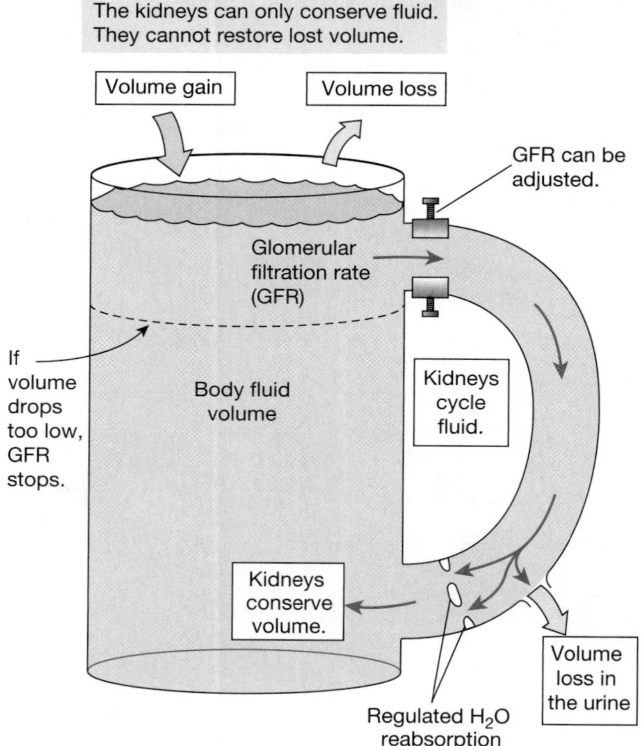

■ **FIGURE 20-3** ***A model of the role of the kidneys in water balance***

A 60-kg (132-lb) woman therefore contains about 30 liters of body water, and the "standard" 70-kg man contains about 42 liters. Two-thirds of his water (about 28 liters) is inside the cells, about 3 liters are in the plasma, and the remaining 11 liters are in the interstitial fluid [Fig. 5-28, p. 155].

Daily Water Intake and Excretion Are Balanced

To maintain a constant volume of water in the body, we must take in the same amount of water that we excrete: intake must equal output. There are multiple sources for water gain and loss during a day (Fig. 20-2 ■). On average, an adult ingests a little more than 2 liters of water in food and drink in a day. Normal cellular respiration (glucose + $O_2 \rightarrow CO_2 + H_2O$) adds about 0.3 liter of water, bringing the total daily intake to approximately 2.5 liters.

Notice that the only means by which water normally enters the body from the external environment is by absorption through the digestive tract. Unlike some animals, we cannot absorb significant amounts of water directly through our skin. If fluids must be rapidly replaced or an individual is unable to eat and drink, fluid can be added directly to the plasma by means of **intravenous (IV) injection**, a medical procedure.

The major route of water loss from the body is the urine, which has a daily volume of about 1.5 liters (Fig. 20-2). A small volume of water (about 100 mL) is lost in the feces. Additionally, water leaves the body through **insensible water loss**. This water loss, called *insensible* because we are not normally aware of it, occurs across the skin surface and during the exhalation of humidified air. Even though the human epidermis is modified with an outer layer of keratin to reduce evaporative water loss in a terrestrial environment [p. 83], we still lose about 900 mL of water insensibly each day. Thus the 2.5 liters of water we take in are balanced by the 2.5 liters that leave the body. Only water loss in the urine can be regulated.

Although urine is normally the major route of water loss, in certain situations other routes of water loss can become significant. Excessive sweating is one example. Another way in which water is lost is through diarrhea, a condition that can pose a major threat to the maintenance of water balance, particularly in infants.

Pathological water loss disrupts homeostasis in two ways. Volume depletion of the extracellular compartment decreases blood pressure. If blood pressure cannot be maintained, the tissues do not get adequate oxygen. If the fluid lost is hyposmotic to the body (as is the case in excessive sweating), the solutes left behind in the body raise osmolarity, potentially disrupting cell function.

Normally, water balance takes place automatically. Salty food makes us thirsty. Drinking 42 ounces of a soft drink means an extra trip to the bathroom. Salt and water balance is a subtle process that we are only peripherally aware of, like breathing and the beating of the heart.

Now that we have seen *why* regulation of osmolarity is important, let's see *how* the body accomplishes that goal.

The Kidneys Conserve Water

Figure 20-3 ■ summarizes the role of the kidneys in water balance. The mug represents the body, and its hollow handle

RUNNING PROBLEM

The medical staff was concerned with Lauren's large weight increase during the race. They asked her to recall what she ate and drank during the race. Lauren reported that to avoid getting dehydrated in the warm weather, she had drunk large quantities of water in addition to sports gel and sports drinks containing carbohydrates and electrolytes.

Question 1:
What are the names of the fluids found in the two major body compartments and the major ions in each fluid?

Question 2:
Based on Lauren's history, give a reason for why her weight increased during the race.

represents the kidneys, where body fluid filters into the nephrons and then may or may not be reabsorbed into the body. Some solutes and water leave the body in the urine, but the volume that leaves can be regulated, as indicated at the bottom of the handle.

The normal range for fluid volume in the mug lies between the dashed line and the open top. Fluid in the mug enters the handle (equivalent to being filtered into the kidney) and cycles back into the body of the mug to maintain the mug's volume. If fluid is added to the mug and threatens to overflow, the extra fluid is allowed to drain out of the handle (comparable to excess water excreted in urine). If a small volume is lost from the mug, fluid still flows through the handle, but all fluid loss from the handle is turned off to prevent additional fluid loss. The only way to replace the lost fluid is to add water from a source outside the mug. Translating this model to the body underscores the fact that the kidneys cannot replenish lost water: all they can do is conserve it. And as shown in the mug model, if fluid loss is severe and volume falls below the dashed line, fluid no longer flows into the handle, just as a major decrease in blood volume and blood pressure shuts down renal filtration.

Urine Concentration Is Determined in the Loop of Henle and Collecting Duct

The concentration, or osmolarity, of urine is a measure of how much water is excreted by the kidneys. When the body needs to eliminate excess water, the kidneys put out copious amounts of dilute urine with an osmolarity as low as 50 mOsM. Removal of excess water in urine is known as **diuresis** [*diourein,* to pass in urine]. (This is why drugs that promote the excretion of urine are called *diuretics.*) When the kidneys are conserving water, the urine becomes quite concentrated, up to four times as concentrated as the blood (1200 mOsM versus the blood's 300 mOsM).

The kidneys alter urine concentration by varying the amounts of water and Na^+ reabsorbed in the distal nephron. (For a review of renal anatomy, see Figure 19-1, p. 616.) To produce dilute urine, the kidney must reabsorb solute without allowing water to follow by osmosis. This means that the cell membranes across which solute is transported must not be permeable to water. To produce concentrated urine, the nephron must reabsorb water while leaving solute in the tubule lumen. At one time, scientists believed that water was actively transported on carriers, just as Na^+ and other ions are. However, once micropuncture techniques for sampling fluid inside kidney tubules were developed, scientists discovered that water is reabsorbed only by osmosis.

Osmosis will not take place unless a concentration gradient exists. Through an unusual arrangement of blood vessels and renal tubules, to be discussed later, the renal medulla maintains a high osmotic concentration in its interstitial fluid. This high *medullary interstitial osmolarity* allows urine to be concentrated.

Let's follow some filtered fluid through a nephron to see where these changes in osmolarity take place (Fig. 20-4 ■). Recall from Chapter 19 that reabsorption in the proximal tubule is isosmotic [p. 619]. Filtrate entering the loop of Henle has an osmolarity of about 300 mOsM. Fluid leaving the loop of Henle, however, is hyposmotic, with an osmolarity of around 100 mOsM. This hyposmotic fluid is created when cells in the thick portion of the ascending limb of the loop transport Na^+, K^+, and Cl^- out of the tubule lumen. These cells are unusual because their apical surface (facing the tubule lumen) is impermeable to water. Thus when these cells transport solute out of the lumen, water cannot follow, creating a hyposmotic solution.

Once the hyposmotic fluid leaves the loop of Henle and passes through the distal tubule and into a collecting duct, its concentration is determined by the water permeability of epithelial cells in the distal nephron. If the apical membrane of these cells is not permeable to water, water remains in the tubule and the filtrate remains dilute. A small amount of additional solute can be reabsorbed as fluid passes along the collecting duct, making the filtrate even more dilute. When this happens, the concentration of urine can be as low as 50 mOsM.

Conversely, if the urine that is excreted is to be more concentrated than 100 mOsM, the tubule epithelium in the distal nephron must become permeable to water through the insertion of water pores. When the collecting duct membrane is permeable to water, osmosis draws water out of the lumen and into the interstitial fluid. At maximal water permeability, removal of

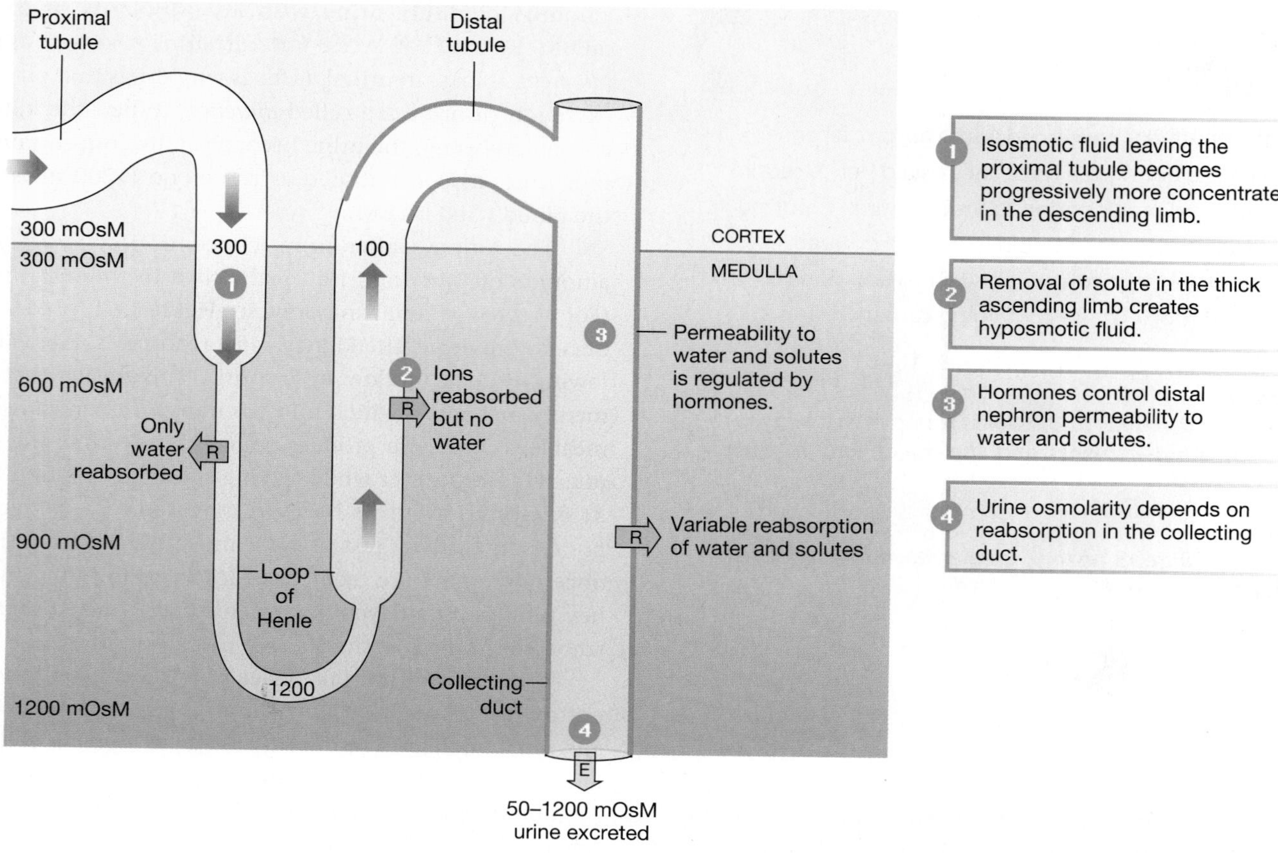

■ **FIGURE 20-4** ***Osmolarity changes as filtrate flows through the nephron***

20

water from the tubule leaves behind a concentrated urine with an osmolarity that can be as high as 1200 mOsM.

Water reabsorption in the kidneys conserves water and can decrease body osmolarity to some degree when coupled with excretion of solute in the urine. However, the kidney's homeostatic mechanisms can do nothing to restore lost fluid volume. Only the ingestion or infusion of water can replace water that has been lost.

Vasopressin Controls Water Reabsorption

How do the distal tubule and collecting duct cells alter their permeability to water? The process involves adding or removing water pores in the apical membrane under the direction of the posterior pituitary hormone vasopressin [p. 226]. Because vasopressin causes the body to retain water, it is also known as **antidiuretic hormone (ADH)**.

When vasopressin acts on target cells, water pores are present in the apical membrane, allowing water to move out of the lumen by osmosis (Fig. 20-5a ■). The water moves by osmosis because solute concentration in the cells and interstitial fluid of the renal medulla is higher than that of fluid in the tubule. In the absence of vasopressin, the collecting duct is impermeable to water (Fig. 20-5b). Although a concentration gradient is

CLINICAL FOCUS

DIABETES

OSMOTIC DIURESIS

The primary sign of diabetes mellitus is an elevated blood glucose concentration. In untreated diabetics, if blood glucose levels exceed the renal threshold for glucose reabsorption [p. 629], glucose will be excreted in the urine. This may not seem like a big deal, but any additional nonreabsorbable solute that remains in the lumen forces additional water to be excreted, causing *osmotic diuresis*. Suppose, for example, that the nephrons must excrete 300 milliosmoles of NaCl. If the urine is maximally concentrated at 1200 mOsM, the NaCl will be excreted in a volume of 0.25 L. However, if the NaCl is joined by 300 milliosmoles of glucose that must be excreted, the volume of urine doubles, to 0.5 L. Osmotic diuresis in untreated diabetics (primarily type 1) causes *polyuria* (excessive urination) and *polydipsia* (excessive thirst) [*dipsios*, thirsty] as a result of dehydration and high plasma osmolarity.

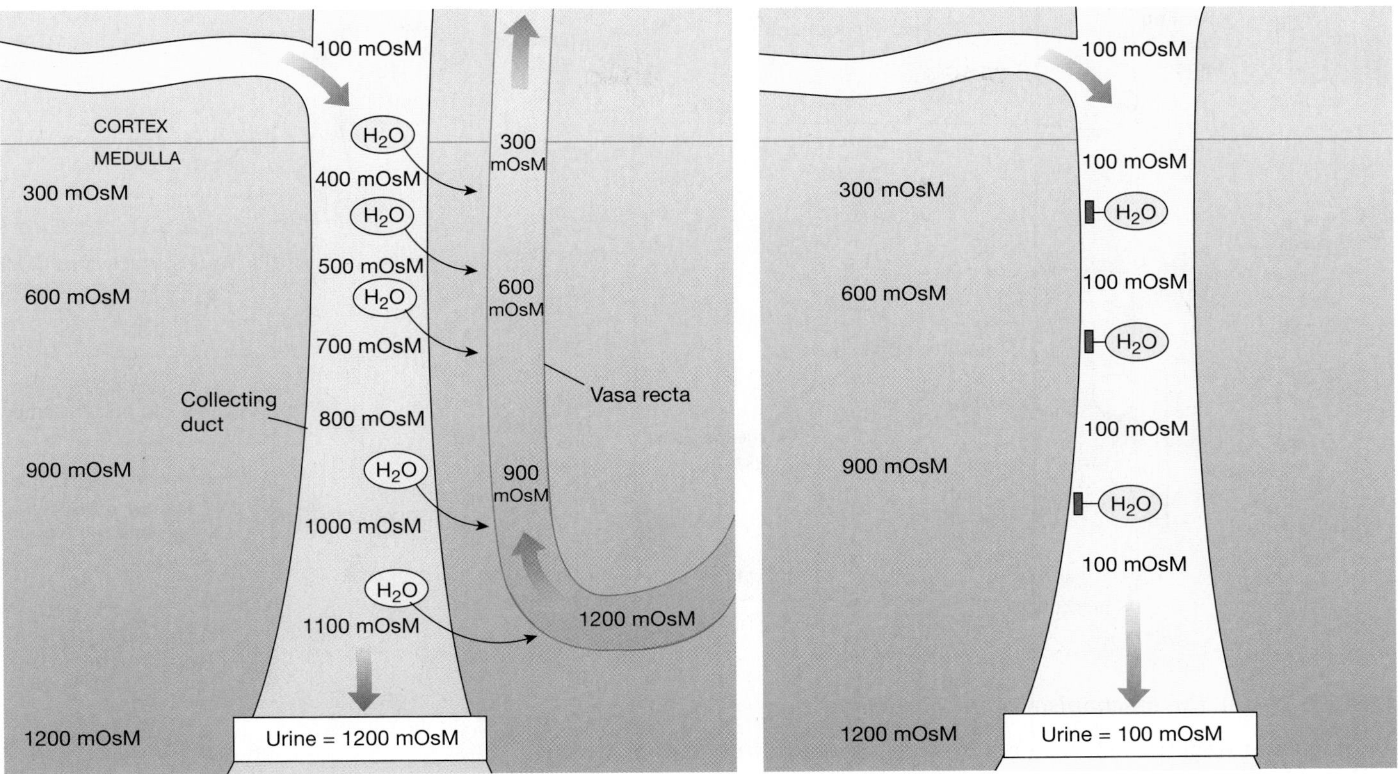

■ **FIGURE 20-5** ***Water movement in the collecting duct in the presence and absence of vasopressin***

present across the epithelium, water remains in the tubule, producing dilute urine.

The water permeability of the collecting duct is not an all-or-none phenomenon, as the previous paragraph might suggest. Permeability is variable, depending on how much vasopressin is present. The graded effect of vasopressin allows the body to match urine concentration closely to the body's needs.

Vasopressin and Aquaporins Most membranes in the body are freely permeable to water. What makes the cells of the distal nephron different? The answer lies with the *water pores* found in these cells. Water pores are **aquaporins**, a family of membrane channels with at least 10 different isoforms that occur in mammalian tissues. The kidney has multiple isoforms of aquaporins, including *aquaporin-2* (AQP2), the water channel regulated by vasopressin.

AQP2 in a collecting duct cell may be found in two locations: on the apical membrane facing the tubule lumen and in the membrane of cytoplasmic storage vesicles (Fig. 20-6 ■). (Two other isoforms of aquaporins are present in the basolateral membrane, but they are not regulated by vasopressin.) When vasopressin levels (and, consequently, collecting duct water permeability) are low, the collecting duct cell has few water pores in its apical membrane and stores its AQP2 water pores in cytoplasmic storage vesicles.

When vasopressin from the posterior pituitary arrives at its target, it binds to its receptor on the basolateral side of the cell (step 1 in Fig. 20-6). Binding activates a G-protein/cAMP second messenger system [p. 183]. Subsequent phosphorylation of intracellular proteins causes the AQP2 vesicles to move to the apical membrane and fuse with it. Exocytosis inserts the AQP2 water pores into the apical membrane. Now the cell is permeable to water. This process, in which parts of the cell membrane are alternately added by exocytosis and withdrawn by endocytosis, is known as **membrane recycling** [Fig. 5-24, p. 149).

CONCEPT CHECK

1. Will the apical membrane of a collecting duct cell have more water pores when vasopressin is present or when it is absent?
2. The interstitial fluid in contact with the basolateral side of collecting duct cells has an extremely high osmolarity, and yet the cells do not shrivel up. How can they maintain normal cell volume in the face of such high ECF osmolarity? (*Hint:* read the box on regulation of cell volume, p. 642.)

Answers: p. 675

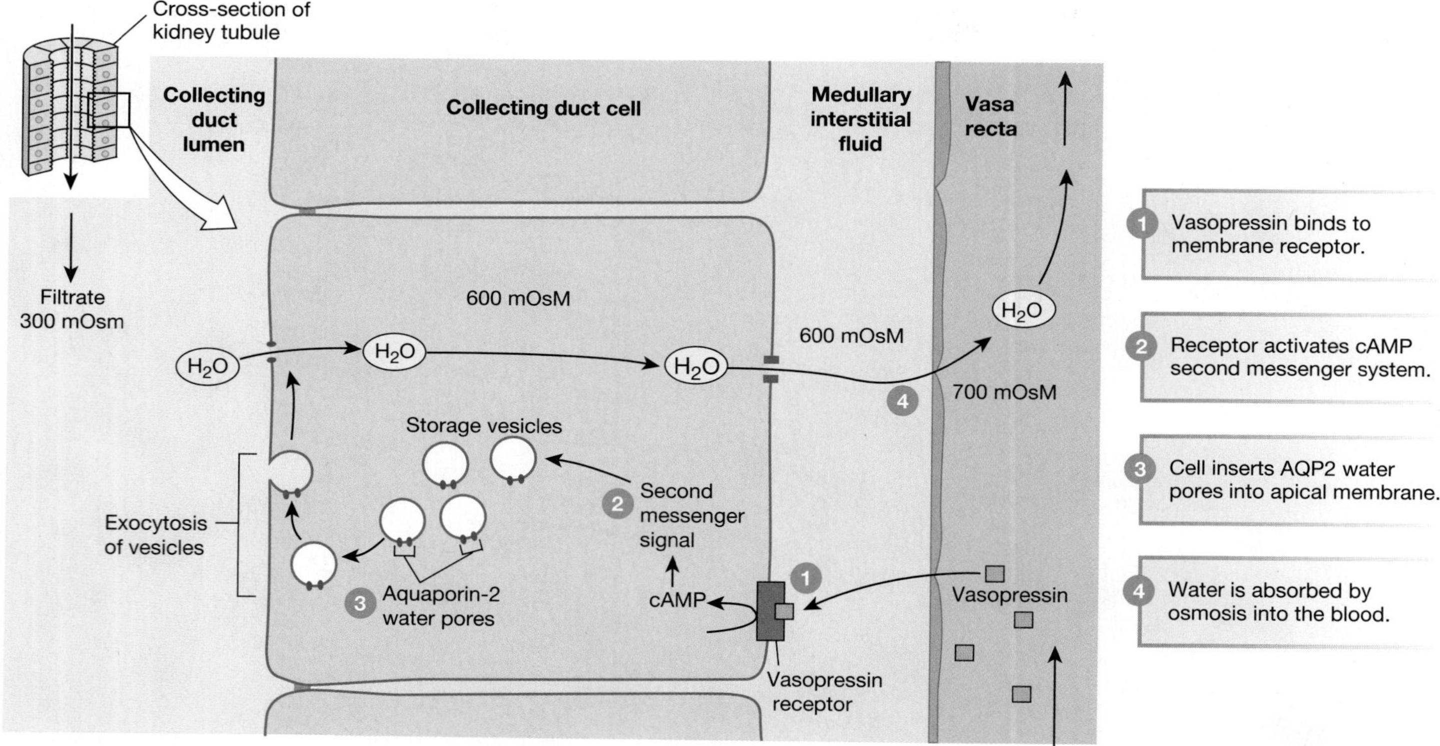

■ **FIGURE 20-6** ***The mechanism of vasopressin action***

In the absence of vasopressin, the water pores are withdrawn from the apical membrane by endocytosis and stored on cytoplasmic vesicles.

Changes in Blood Pressure, Volume, and Osmolarity Trigger Water Balance Reflexes

What stimuli control vasopressin secretion? There are three: plasma osmolarity, blood volume, and blood pressure (Fig. 20-7 ■). The most potent stimulus for vasopressin release is an increase in plasma osmolarity. Osmolarity is monitored by **osmoreceptors**, stretch-sensitive cells that activate sensory neurons when osmolarity increases above threshold.

The primary osmoreceptors for vasopressin release are found in the hypothalamus. When plasma osmolarity is below the threshold value of 280 mOsM, the osmoreceptors do not fire, and vasopressin release from the pituitary ceases (Fig. 20-8 ■). If plasma osmolarity rises above 280 mOsM, the osmoreceptors stimulate release of vasopressin.

Decreases in blood pressure and blood volume are less powerful stimuli for vasopressin release. The primary receptors for decreased volume are stretch-sensitive receptors in the atria. Blood pressure is monitored by the same carotid and aortic baroreceptors that initiate cardiovascular responses [p. 521]. When blood pressure or blood volume is low, these receptors signal the hypothalamus to secrete vasopressin and conserve fluid.

CLINICAL FOCUS

BED-WETTING AND VASOPRESSIN

Bed-wetting, or **nocturnal enuresis**, is a problem that affects about 8% of school-age children. For many years, nocturnal enuresis was thought to be of psychological origin, but now it is felt that most enuretic children have a physiological cause for their bed-wetting. In normal children, vasopressin secretion shows a circadian rhythm, with increased levels occurring at night; the result is that less urine is produced overnight than during the day. In many children with nocturnal enuresis, however, vasopressin secretion does not increase at night, so their urine output stays elevated, and the bladder fills to its maximum capacity and empties spontaneously during sleep. These children can be successfully treated with a nasal spray of desmopressin, a vasopressin derivative, administered at bedtime.

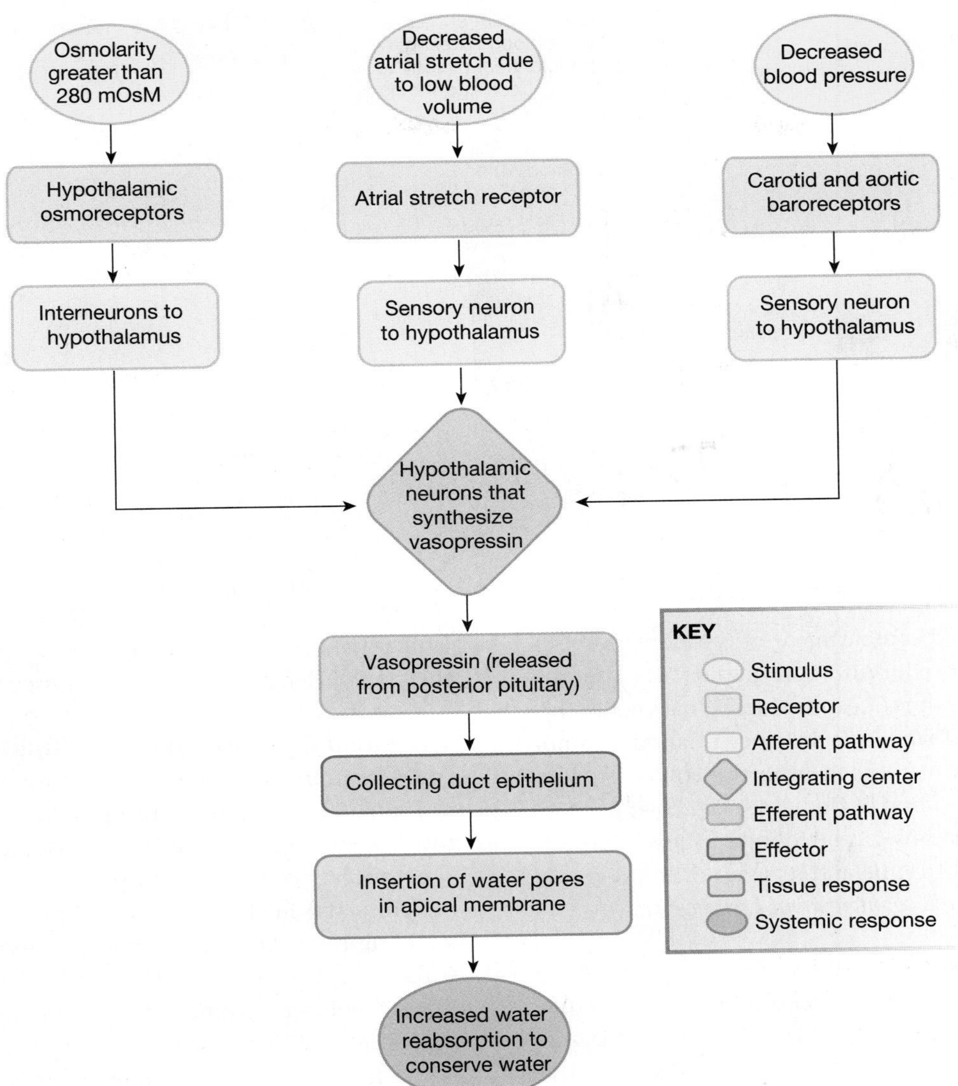

■ **FIGURE 20-7** ***Factors affecting vasopressin release***

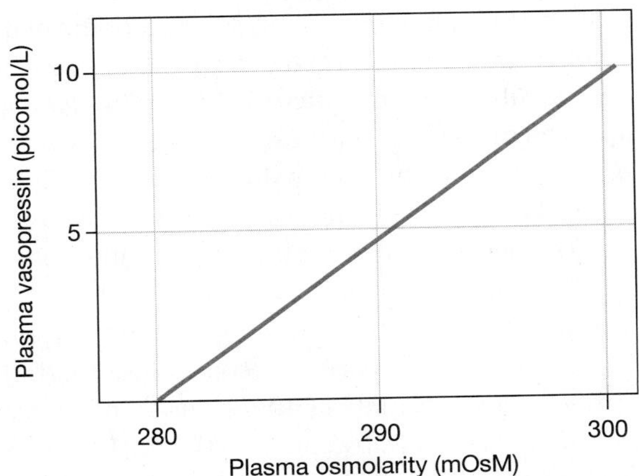

■ **FIGURE 20-8** ***The effect of plasma osmolarity on vasopressin secretion by the posterior pituitary***

CONCEPT CHECK

3. A scientist monitoring the activity of osmoreceptors notices that infusion of hyperosmotic saline (NaCl) causes increased firing of the osmoreceptors. Infusion of hyperosmotic urea (a penetrating solute) [p. 157] had no effect on the firing rate. If osmoreceptors fire only when cell volume decreases, explain why hyperosmotic urea did not affect them.
4. If vasopressin increases water reabsorption by the blood vessels of a nephron, would vasopressin secretion be increased or decreased with dehydration?
5. If vasopressin secretion is suppressed, will urine be dilute or concentrated?

Answers: p. 675

The Loop of Henle Is a Countercurrent Multiplier

Vasopressin is the signal for water reabsorption out of the nephron tubule, but the key to the kidney's ability to produce concentrated urine is the high osmolarity of the medullary

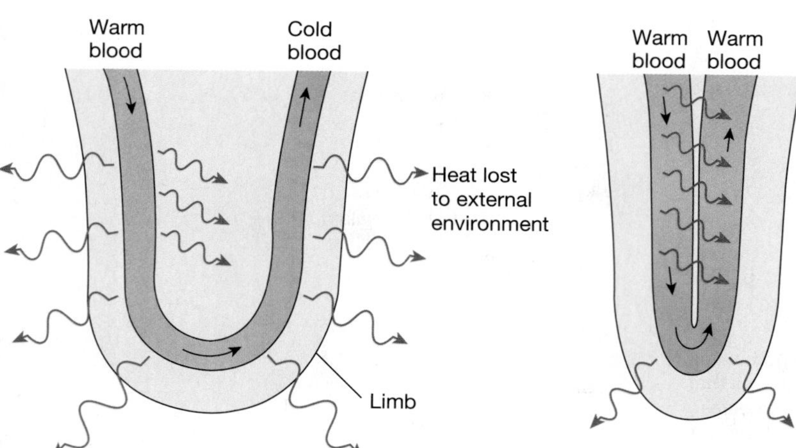
(a) If blood vessels are not close to each other, heat is dissipated to the external environment.
Warm blood
Cold blood
Heat lost to external environment
Limb
(b) Countercurrent heat exchanger allows warm blood entering the limb to transfer heat directly to blood flowing back into the body.
Warm blood
Warm blood

■ **FIGURE 20-9** ***A countercurrent heat exchanger***

interstitium (interstitial fluid compartment of the kidney). Without it, there would be no concentration gradient for osmotic movement of water out of the collecting duct. What creates this high ECF osmolarity? And why isn't the interstitial fluid osmolarity reduced as water is reabsorbed from the collecting duct and descending limb of the loop of Henle (see Fig. 20-4, p. 646)? The answers to these questions can be found in the anatomical arrangement of the loop of Henle and its associated blood vessels, the vasa recta, to form a *countercurrent exchange system.*

Countercurrent Exchange Systems **Countercurrent exchange systems** require arterial and venous blood vessels that pass very close to each other, with their fluid flow moving in opposite directions (the name *countercurrent* comes from the fact that the two flows run *counter to* each other). This anatomical arrangement allows the transfer of heat or molecules from one vessel to the other. Because the countercurrent heat exchanger is easier to understand, we first examine how it works and then translate the same principle to the kidney.

The countercurrent heat exchanger in mammals and birds evolved to reduce heat loss from flippers, tails, and other limbs that are poorly insulated and have a high surface-area-to-volume ratio. Without a heat exchanger, warm blood flowing from the body core into the limb would easily lose heat to the surrounding environment (Fig. 20-9a ■). With a countercurrent heat exchanger, warm arterial blood entering the limb transfers its heat to cooler venous blood flowing from the tip of the limb back into the body (Fig. 20-9b). This arrangement reduces the amount of heat lost to the external environment.

The countercurrent exchange system of the kidney—the loop of Henle—works on the same principle, except that it transfers solutes instead of heat. However, because the kidney forms a closed system, the solutes are not lost to the environment. Instead, the solutes concentrate in the interstitium. This process is aided by active transport of solutes out of the ascending limb, which makes the ECF osmolarity even greater. For this reason, the loop of Henle is known as a **countercurrent multiplier**.

The Renal Countercurrent Multiplier An overview of the countercurrent multiplier system in the renal medulla is shown in Figure 20-10 ■. Filtrate from the proximal tubule flows into the descending limb of the loop of Henle. The descending limb is permeable to water but does not transport ions. As the loop dips into the medulla, water moves by osmosis from the descending limb into the progressively more concentrated interstitial fluid, leaving solutes behind in the tubule lumen.

The filtrate becomes progressively more concentrated as it moves deeper into the medulla. At the tips of the longest loops of Henle, the filtrate reaches a concentration of 1200 mOsM. Filtrate in shorter loops (which do not extend into the most concentrated regions of the medulla) does not reach such a high concentration.

When the fluid flow reverses direction and enters the ascending limb of the loop, the properties of the tubule epithelium change. The tubule epithelium in this segment of the nephron is impermeable to water while actively transporting Na^+, K^+ and Cl^- out of the tubule into the interstitial fluid. The loss of solute from the lumen causes the filtrate osmolarity to decrease steadily, from 1200 mOsM at the bottom of the loop to 100 mOsM at the point where the ascending limb leaves the medulla and enters the cortex. The net result of the countercurrent multiplier in the kidney is to produce hyperosmotic interstitial fluid in the medulla, and hyposmotic filtrate leaving the loop of Henle.

Normally, about 25% of all Na^+ and K^+ reabsorption takes place in the ascending limb of the loop. Some transporters responsible for active ion reabsorption in the thick portion of the ascending limb are shown in Figure 20-11 ■. The *NKCC symporter* uses energy stored in the Na^+ concentration gradient to transport Na^+, K^+ and 2 Cl^- from the lumen into the epithelial cells of the ascending limb. The Na^+-K^+-ATPase removes Na^+ from

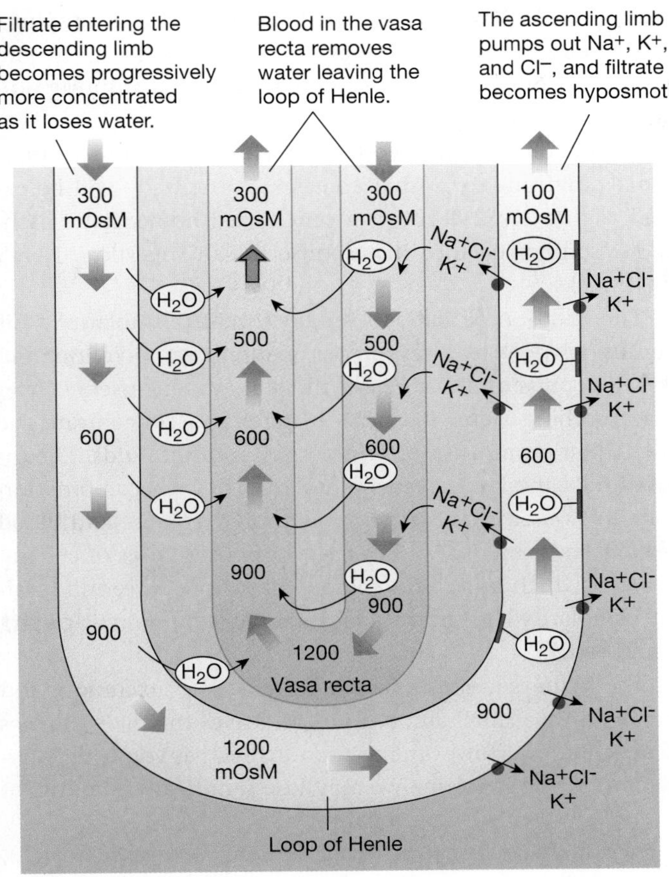

■ **FIGURE 20-10** ***Countercurrent exchange in the medulla of the kidney***

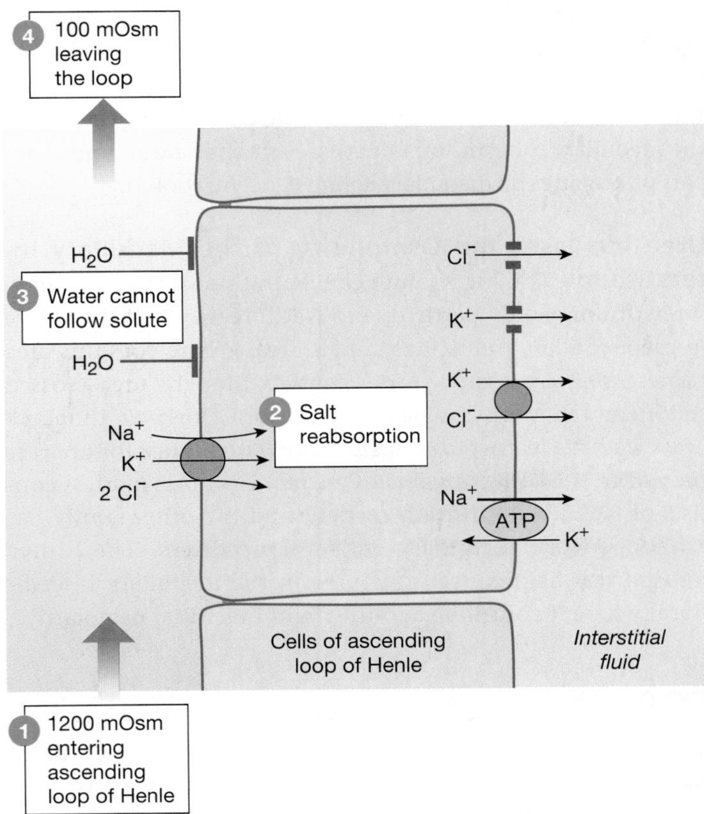

■ **FIGURE 20-11** ***Active reabsorption of ions in the thick ascending limb creates a dilute filtrate in the lumen***

the cells on the basolateral side of the epithelium, while K^+ and Cl^- leave the cells together on a cotransport protein or through open channels. NKCC-mediated transport can be inhibited by drugs known as "loop diuretics," such as furosemide (Lasix).

CONCEPT CHECK

6. Explain why a patient taking a loop diuretic that inhibits solute reabsorption will excrete greater-than-normal volumes of urine.
7. Loop diuretics that inhibit the NKCC symporter are sometimes called "potassium-wasting" diuretics. Explain why people who are on loop diuretics must increase their dietary K^+ intake. Answers: p. 675

The Vasa Recta Removes Water It is easy to see how transport of solute out of the ascending limb of the loop of Henle dilutes the filtrate and helps concentrate the interstitial fluid in the medulla. Still, why doesn't the water leaving the descending limb of the loop (see Fig. 20-10) *dilute* the interstitial fluid of the medulla? The answer lies in the close anatomical association of the loop of Henle and those peritubular capillaries known as the **vasa recta**.

These capillaries, like the loop of Henle, dip down into the medulla and then go back up to the cortex, forming hairpin loops. Although textbooks traditionally show a single nephron with a single loop of capillary (as we do in Fig. 20-10), each kidney has thousands of collecting ducts and loops of Henle packed between thousands of vasa recta capillaries, blurring the direct association between a nephron and its vascular supply. Functionally, the direction of blood flow in the vasa recta is opposite the direction of filtrate flow in the loops of Henle, as shown in Figure 20-10.

Water or solutes that leave the tubule move into the vasa recta if an osmotic or concentration gradient exists between the medullary interstitium and the blood in the vasa recta. For example, assume that at the point at which the vasa recta enter the medulla, the blood in the vasa recta is 300 mOsM, isosmotic with the cortex. As the blood flows deeper and deeper into the medulla, it loses water and picks up solutes transported out of the ascending limb of the loop of Henle, carrying these solutes farther into the medulla. By the time the blood reaches the bottom of the vasa recta loop, it has a high osmolarity, similar to that of the surrounding interstitial fluid (1200 mOsM).

Then, as blood in the vasa recta flows back toward the cortex, the high plasma osmolarity attracts the water that is being lost from the descending limb, as Figure 20-10 shows. The movement of this water into the vasa recta decreases the osmolarity of the blood while simultaneously preventing the water from diluting the concentrated medullary interstitial fluid.

The end result of this arrangement is that blood flowing through the vasa recta removes the water reabsorbed from the loop of Henle. Without the vasa recta, water moving out of the descending limb of the loop of Henle would eventually dilute the medullary interstitium. The vasa recta thus are an important part of keeping the medullary solute concentration high.

Urea Increases the Osmolarity of the Medullary Interstitium The high solute concentration in the medullary interstitium is only partly due to NaCl. Nearly half the solute in the medullary interstitial fluid is urea. Where does this urea come from? For many years scientists thought urea crossed cell membranes only by passive transport. However, in recent years we have learned that membrane transporters for urea are present in the collecting duct. One family of transporters consists of facilitated diffusion carriers, and the other family has Na^+-dependent secondary active transporters. These urea transporters help concentrate urea in the medullary interstitium, where it contributes to the high interstitial osmolarity.

SODIUM BALANCE AND ECF VOLUME

As noted in the introduction to this chapter, we ingest a lot of NaCl—an average of 9 grams per day. This is about 2 teaspoons of salt, or 155 milliosmoles of Na^+ and 155 milliosmoles of Cl^-. Let's see what would happen to our bodies if the kidneys could not get rid of this Na^+. (Remember from Chapter 19 that Cl^- follows the electrical gradient created by Na^+ transport. [p. 626])

Our normal plasma Na^+ concentration is 135–145 milliosmoles Na^+ per liter of plasma. Because sodium distributes freely between plasma and interstitial fluid, this value also represents our ECF Na^+ concentration. If we add 155 milliosmoles Na^+ to the ECF, how much water would we have to add to keep the ECF Na^+ concentration at 140 mOsM? One form of an equation asking this question is

$$155 \text{ mosmol}/X \text{ liters} = 140 \text{ mosmol/liter}$$
$$X = 1.1 \text{ liters}$$

We would have to add more than a liter of water to the ECF to compensate for the addition of the Na^+. Normal ECF volume is about 14 liters, and so that increase in volume would represent about an 8% gain! Imagine what that volume increase would do to blood pressure.

Suppose, however, that instead of adding water to keep plasma concentrations constant, we add the NaCl but don't drink any water. What happens to osmolarity now? If we assume that normal total body osmolarity is 300 mOsM and that the volume of fluid in the body is 42 L, the addition of 155 milliosmoles of Na^+ and 155 milliosmoles of Cl^- would increase total body osmolarity to 307 mOsM*—a substantial increase. In addition, because NaCl is a nonpenetrating solute, it would stay in the ECF. Higher osmolarity in the ECF would draw water from the cells, shrinking them and disrupting normal cell function.

Fortunately, our homeostatic mechanisms maintain mass balance: anything extra that comes into the body will be excreted. Figure 20-12 ■ shows a generalized homeostatic pathway for sodium balance in response to salt ingestion. Here's how it works:

The addition of NaCl to the body raises osmolarity. This stimulus triggers two responses: vasopressin secretion and thirst. Vasopressin release causes the kidneys to conserve water (by reabsorbing water from the filtrate) and concentrate the urine. Thirst prompts us to drink water or other fluids. The increased fluid intake decreases osmolarity, but the combination of salt and water intake increases both ECF volume and blood pressure. These increases then trigger another series of control pathways, which bring ECF volume, blood pressure, and total-body osmolarity back into the normal range by excreting extra salt and water.

The kidneys are responsible for most Na^+ excretion, and normally only a small amount of Na^+ leaves the body in feces and perspiration. However, in situations such as vomiting, diarrhea, and heavy sweating, we may lose significant amounts of Na^+ and Cl^- through non-renal routes.

Although we speak of ingesting and losing salt (NaCl), only renal Na^+ absorption is regulated, and the stimuli that set the Na^+ balance pathway in motion are more closely tied to blood volume and blood pressure than to Na^+ levels. Chloride movement usually follows Na^+ movement, either indirectly via the electrochemical gradient created by Na^+ transport or directly via membrane transporters such as the NKCC transporter of the loop of Henle or the Na^+-Cl^- symporter of the distal tubule.

Aldosterone Controls Sodium Balance

The regulation of blood Na^+ levels takes place through one of the most complicated endocrine pathways of the body. The reabsorption of Na^+ in the distal tubules and collecting ducts of the kidney is regulated by the steroid hormone **aldosterone**: the more aldosterone, the more Na^+ reabsorption. Because one target of aldosterone is increased activity of the Na^+-K^+-ATPase, aldosterone also causes K^+ secretion.

Aldosterone is a steroid hormone synthesized in the adrenal cortex, the outer portion of the adrenal gland that sits atop each kidney [p. 221]. Like other steroid hormones, aldosterone is secreted into the blood and transported on a protein carrier to its target.

The primary site of aldosterone action is the last third of the distal tubule and the portion of the collecting duct that runs through the kidney cortex (the *cortical collecting duct*). The primary target of aldosterone is **principal cells**, or **P cells**

*$(155 \text{ mosmol } Na^+ + 155 \text{ mosmol } Cl^-)/42 \text{ L} = 7.4 \text{ mosmol/L added}$
$300 \text{ mOsM initial} + 7.4 \text{ mOsM added} = 307 \text{ mOsM final}$

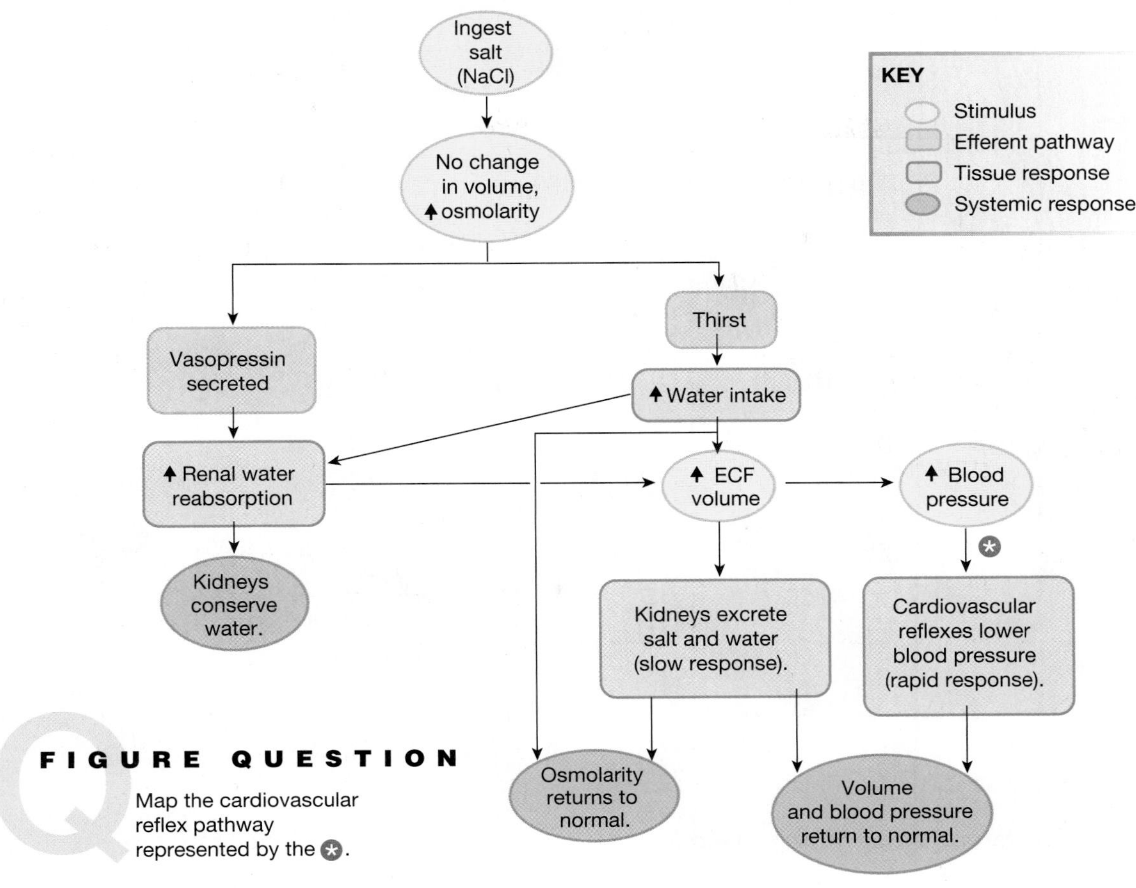

■ **FIGURE 20-12** ***Homeostatic responses to salt ingestion***

(Fig. 20-13 ■). Principal cells are arranged much like other polarized transporting epithelial cells, with Na^+-K^+-ATPase pumps on the basolateral membrane, and various channels and transporters on the apical membrane [p. 151]. In principal cells, the apical membranes contain leak channels for Na^+ (called ENaC, for *e*pithelial *Na*$^+$ *c*hannel) and for K^+ (called ROMK, for *r*enal *o*uter *m*edulla *K*$^+$ channel).

Aldosterone enters P cells by simple diffusion. Once inside, it combines with a cytoplasmic receptor (Fig. 20-13 ①). In the early response phase, apical Na^+ and K^+ channels increase their open time under the influence of an as-yet-unidentified signal molecule. As intracellular Na^+ levels rise, the Na^+-K^+-ATPase speeds up, transporting cytoplasmic Na^+ into the ECF and bringing K^+ from the ECF into the P cell. The net result is a rapid increase in Na^+ reabsorption and K^+ secretion that does not require the synthesis of new channel or ATPase proteins. In the slower phase of aldosterone action, newly synthesized channels and pumps are inserted into epithelial cell membranes (Fig. 20-13 ④).

Note that Na^+ and water reabsorption are separately regulated in the distal nephron. Water does not automatically follow Na^+ reabsorption: vasopressin must be present to make the distal-nephron epithelium permeable to water. In contrast, in the proximal tubule, Na^+ reabsorption is automatically followed by water reabsorption because the proximal tubule epithelium is always freely permeable to water.

Blood Pressure Is the Primary Stimulus for Aldosterone Secretion

What controls physiological aldosterone secretion from the adrenal cortex? There are two primary stimuli: increased extracellular K^+ concentration and decreased blood pressure. Elevated K^+ concentrations act directly on the adrenal cortex in a reflex that protects the body from hyperkalemia. Decreased blood pressure initiates a complex pathway that results in release of a trophic hormone, **angiotensin II**, that stimulates aldosterone secretion in most situations.

Two additional factors modulate aldosterone release in pathological states: an increase in ECF osmolarity acts directly on adrenal cortex cells to inhibit aldosterone secretion during dehydration, and a severe (10–20 meq/L) decrease in plasma Na^+ can directly stimulate aldosterone secretion.

The Renin-Angiotensin-Aldosterone Pathway **Angiotensin II** (ANG II) is the usual signal controlling aldosterone release from the adrenal cortex. ANG II is one component of the **renin-angiotensin-aldosterone system (RAAS)**, a complex, multistep pathway for maintaining blood pressure. The

20

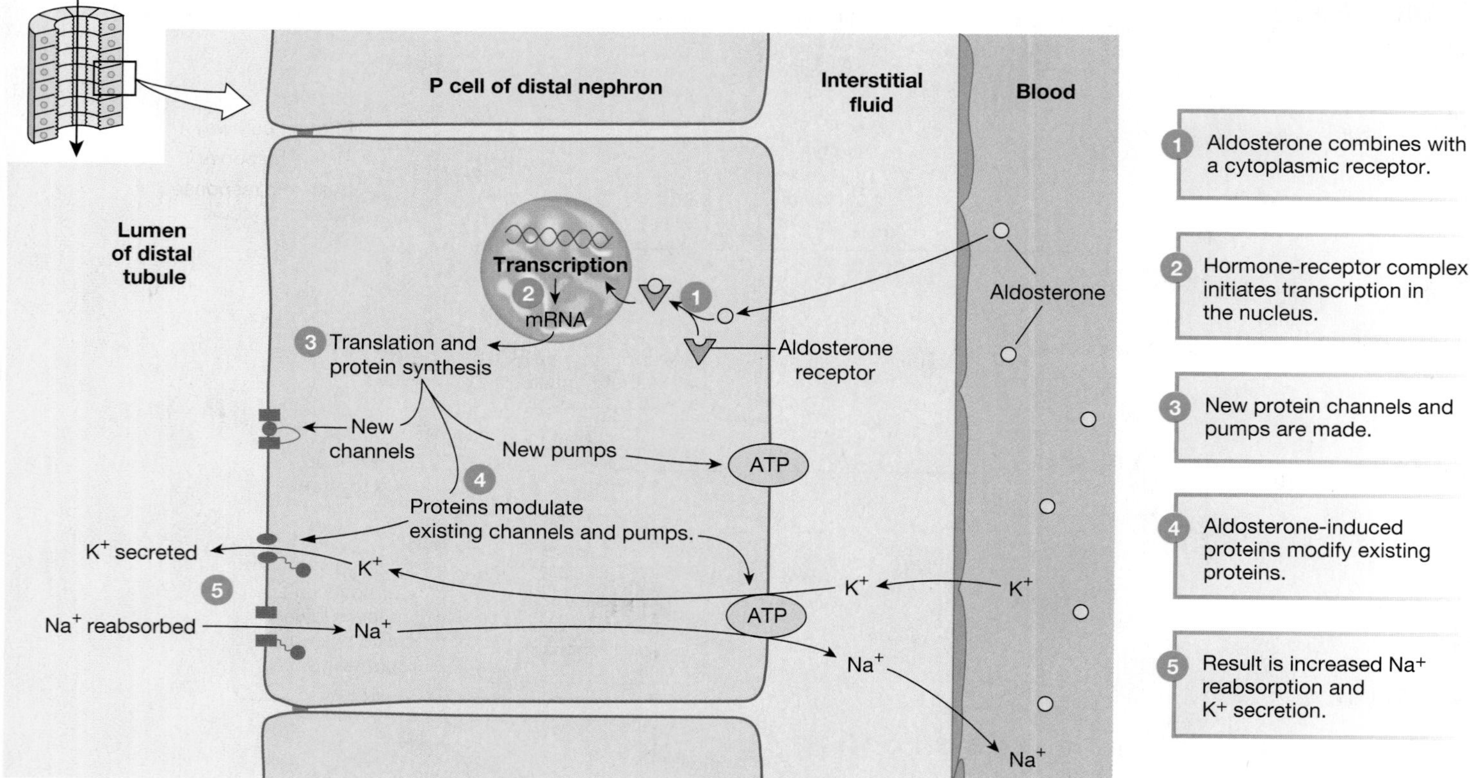

■ **FIGURE 20-13** *Aldosterone action in principal cells*

RAAS pathway begins when juxtaglomerular granular cells in the afferent arterioles of a nephron [p. 618] secrete an enzyme called **renin** (Fig. 20-14 ■). Renin converts an inactive plasma protein, **angiotensinogen**, into **angiotensin I (ANG I)**. (The suffix *-ogen* indicates an inactive precursor.) When ANG I in the blood encounters an enzyme called **angiotensin converting enzyme (ACE)**, ANG I is converted into ANG II.

This conversion was originally thought to take place only in the lungs, but ACE is now known to occur on the endothelium of blood vessels throughout the body. When ANG II in the blood reaches the adrenal gland, it causes synthesis and release of aldosterone. Finally, at the distal nephron, aldosterone initiates a series of intracellular reactions that cause the tubule to reabsorb Na^+.

The stimuli that begin the RAAS pathway are all related either directly or indirectly to low blood pressure (Fig. 20-15 ■):

1. The *granular cells* are directly sensitive to blood pressure. They respond to low blood pressure in renal arterioles by secreting renin.
2. *Sympathetic neurons,* activated by the cardiovascular control center when blood pressure decreases, terminate on the granular cells and stimulate renin secretion.
3. *Paracrine feedback*—from the macula densa in the distal tubule to the granular cells—stimulates renin release [p. 624]. When fluid flow through the distal tubule is relatively high, the macula densa cells release paracrines, which inhibit renin release. When fluid flow in the distal tubule decreases, macula densa cells signal the granular cells to secrete renin.

Sodium reabsorption does not directly raise low blood pressure, but retention of Na^+ increases osmolarity, which stimulates thirst. Fluid intake when the person drinks more water increases ECF volume (see Fig. 20-12). When blood volume increases, blood pressure also increases.

The effects of RAAS pathway are not limited to aldosterone release, however. Angiotensin II is a remarkable hormone with additional effects directed at raising blood pressure. These actions make ANG II an important hormone in its own right, not merely an intermediate step in the aldosterone control pathway.

CONCEPT CHECK

8. In Figure 20-13, what force(s) cause(s) Na^+ and K^+ to cross the apical membrane? Answers: p. 675

Angiotensin II Influences Blood Pressure Through Multiple Pathways

Angiotensin II has significant effects on fluid balance and blood pressure beyond stimulating aldosterone secretion, underscoring the integrated functions of the renal and cardiovascular systems. ANG II increases blood pressure both directly and indirectly through four additional pathways (Fig. 20-14):

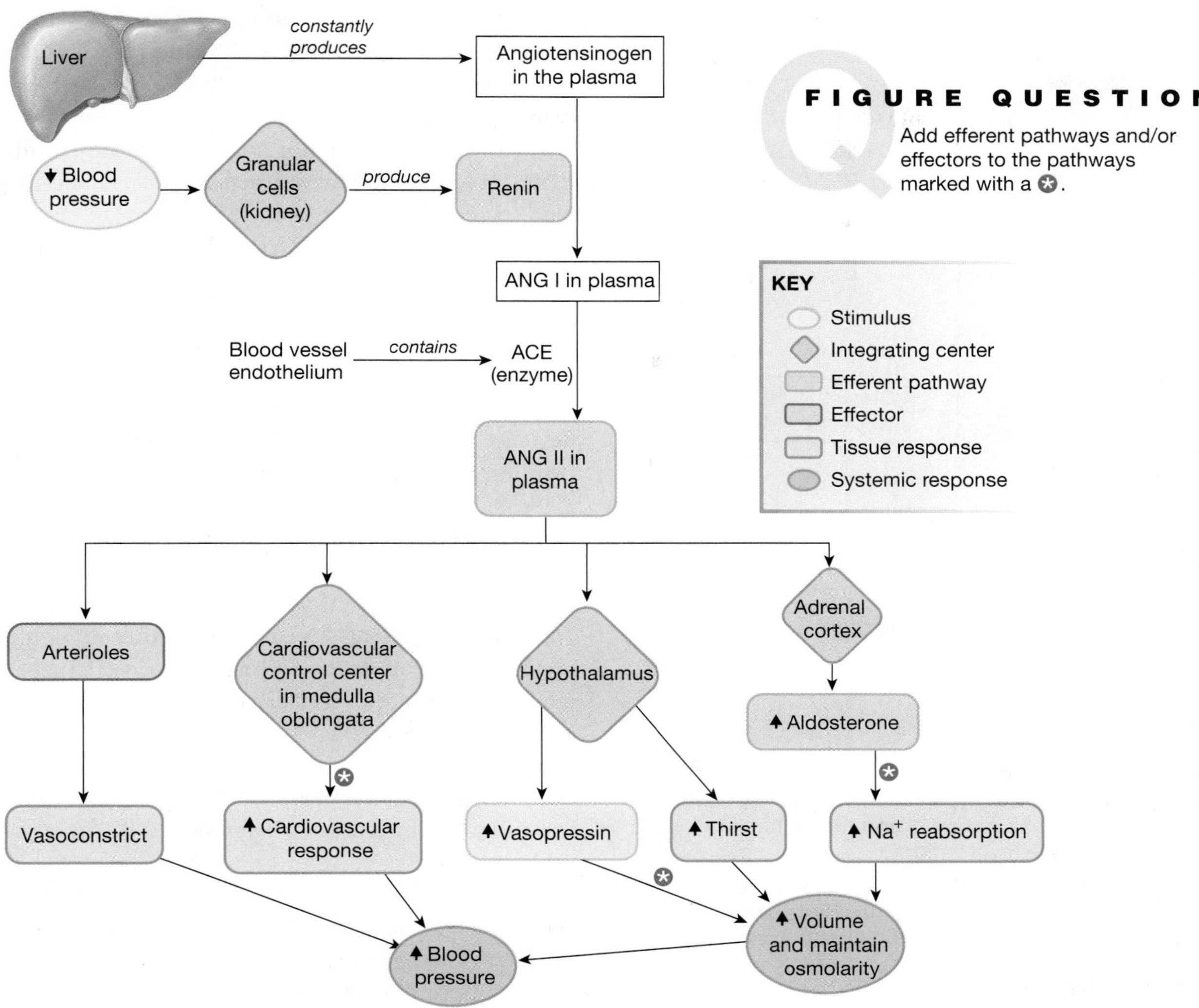

FIGURE 20-14 ***The renin-angiotensin-aldosterone pathway***

This map outlines the control of aldosterone secretion as well as the blood pressure-raising effects of ANG II.

1. *ANG II increases vasopressin secretion.* ANG II receptors in the hypothalamus initiate this reflex. Fluid retention in the kidney under the influence of vasopressin helps conserve blood volume, thereby maintaining blood pressure.
2. *ANG II stimulates thirst.* Fluid ingestion is a behavioral response that expands blood volume and raises blood pressure.
3. *ANG II is one of the most potent vasoconstrictors* known in humans. Vasoconstriction causes blood pressure to increase without a change in blood volume.
4. *Activation of ANG II receptors in the cardiovascular control center increases sympathetic output to the heart and blood vessels.* Sympathetic stimulation increases cardiac output and vasoconstriction, both of which increase blood pressure.

Once these blood-pressure-raising effects of ANG II became known, it was not surprising that pharmaceutical companies started looking for drugs to block ANG II. Their research produced a new class of antihypertensive drugs called *ACE inhibitors*. These drugs block the ACE-mediated conversion of ANG I to ANG II, thereby helping to relax blood vessels and lower blood pressure. Less ANG II also means less aldosterone release, a decrease in Na^+ reabsorption and, ultimately, a decrease in ECF volume. All these responses contribute to lowering blood pressure.

However, the ACE inhibitors are not without side effects. ACE inactivates a cytokine called *bradykinin*. When ACE is inhibited by drugs, bradykinin levels increase, and in some patients this creates a dry, hacking cough. One solution has been the development of drugs called *sartans* that block the blood-pressure-raising effects of ANG II by binding to *AT_1 receptors,* a subtype of ANG II receptor.

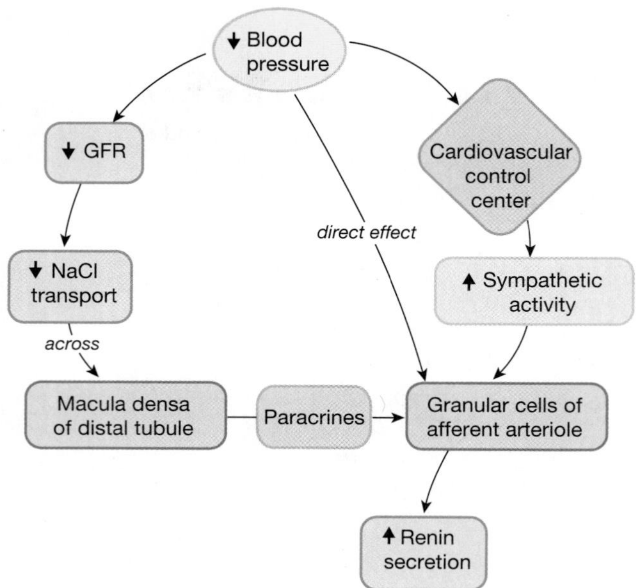

■ **FIGURE 20-15** ***Decreased blood pressure stimulates renin secretion***

CONCEPT CHECK

9. If a person experiences hyperkalemia, what happens to resting membrane potential and the excitability of neurons and the myocardium?
10. A man comes to the doctor with high blood pressure. Tests show that he also has elevated plasma renin levels and atherosclerotic plaques that have nearly blocked blood flow through his renal arteries. How does decreased blood flow in his renal arteries result in elevated renin levels?
11. Describe the pathways through which elevated renin causes high blood pressure in the man mentioned in Concept Check 10.

Answers: p. 675

Atrial Natriuretic Peptide Promotes Na^+ and Water Excretion

Once it was known that aldosterone and vasopressin increase Na^+ and water reabsorption, scientists speculated that other hormones might cause Na^+ loss, or **natriuresis** [*natrium,* sodium + *ourein,* to urinate] and water loss (diuresis) in the urine. If found, these hormones might be used clinically to lower blood volume and blood pressure in patients with essential hypertension [p. 525]. During years of searching, however, evidence for the other hormones was not forthcoming.

Then, in 1981, a group of Canadian researchers found that injections of homogenized rat atria caused rapid but short-lived excretion of Na^+ and water in the rats' urine. They hoped they had found the missing hormone, one whose activity would complement that of aldosterone and vasopressin. As it turned out, they had discovered the first natriuretic peptide (NP), one member of a family of hormones that appear to be endogenous RAAS antagonists.

Atrial natriuretic peptide (ANP; also known as *atriopeptin*) is a peptide hormone produced in specialized myocardial cells in the atria of the heart. It is synthesized as part of a large prohormone that is cleaved into several active hormone fragments [p. 218]. A related hormone, **brain natriuretic peptide** (BNP), is synthesized by ventricular myocardial cells and certain brain neurons. Both natriuretic peptides are released by the heart when myocardial cells stretch more than normal, as would occur with increased blood volume. The peptides bind to membrane receptors that work through a cGMP second messenger system.

At the systemic level, natriuretic peptides enhance Na^+ and water excretion (Fig. 20-16 ■), but the exact mechanisms by which they do so are not clear. The NPs increase GFR, apparently by making more surface area available for filtration. In addition, they directly decrease NaCl and water reabsorption in the collecting duct. The cellular mechanism by which NPs affect tubular reabsorption is not known.

Natriuretic peptides also act indirectly to increase Na^+ and water excretion by inhibiting the release of renin, aldosterone, and vasopressin (Fig. 20-16), actions that reinforce the natriuretic-diuretic effect. In addition, natriuretic peptides act directly on the cardiovascular control center of the medulla to lower blood pressure.

Brain natriuretic peptide is now recognized as an important biological marker for heart failure because production of this substance increases with ventricular dilation and increased ventricular pressure. According to one estimate in 2004, more than 70% of U.S. hospitals test for BNP levels to assist in the diagnosis of ventricular failure. This peptide has also been shown to be an independent predictor of heart failure and sudden death from cardiac arrhythmias.

POTASSIUM BALANCE

Aldosterone (but not other factors in the RAAS pathway) also plays a critical role in potassium homeostasis. Only about 2% of the body's K^+ load is in the ECF, but regulatory mechanisms keep plasma K^+ concentrations within a narrow range (3.5–5 meq/L). Under normal conditions, mass balance matches K^+ excretion to K^+ ingestion. If intake exceeds excretion and plasma K^+ goes up, aldosterone is released into the blood through the direct effect of hyperkalemia on the adrenal cortex. Aldosterone acting on distal-nephron P cells keeps the cells' apical ion channels open longer and speeds up the Na^+-K^+-ATPase, enhancing renal excretion of K^+.

The regulation of body potassium levels is essential to maintaining a state of well-being. As you learned in Chapter 8, changes in extracellular K^+ concentration affect the resting membrane potential of all cells [Fig. 8-19, p. 269]. If plasma (and ECF) K^+ concentrations decrease (hypokalemia), the concentration gradient between the cell and the ECF becomes larger, more K^+ leaves the cell, and the resting membrane potential becomes more negative. If ECF K^+ concentrations increase

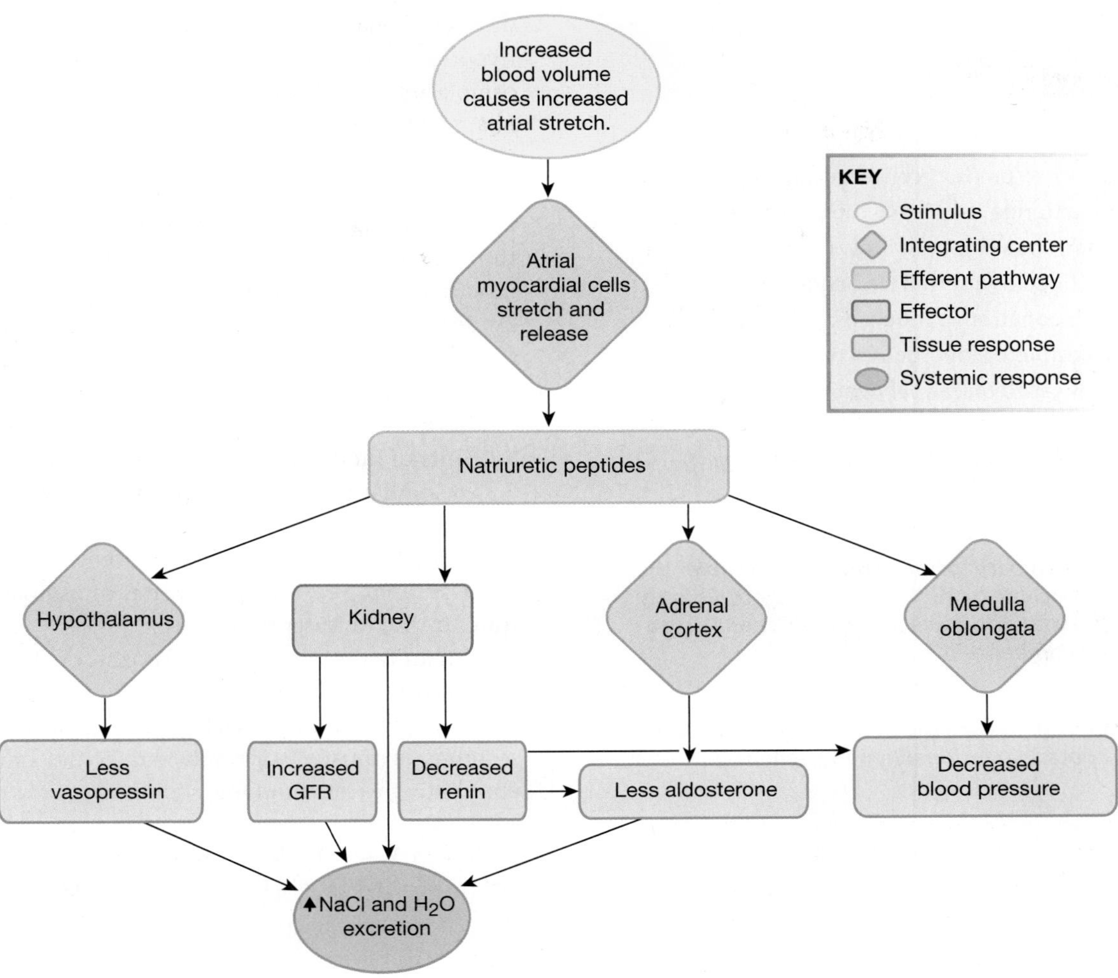

■ **FIGURE 20-16** ***Actions of natriuretic peptides***

(hyperkalemia), the concentration gradient decreases and more K^+ remains in the cell, depolarizing it. (Remember that when plasma K^+ concentrations change, anions such as Cl^- are also added to or subtracted from the ECF in a 1:1 ratio, maintaining overall electrical neutrality.)

Because of the effect of plasma K^+ on excitable tissues, such as the heart, clinicians are always concerned about keeping plasma K^+ within its normal range. If K^+ falls below 3 meq/L or rises above 6 meq/L, the excitable tissues of muscle and nerve begin to show altered function. For example, hypokalemia causes muscle weakness because it is more difficult for hyperpolarized neurons and muscles to fire action potentials. The danger in this condition lies in the failure of respiratory muscles and the heart. Fortunately, skeletal muscle weakness is usually significant enough to lead patients to seek treatment before cardiac problems occur. Mild hypokalemia may be corrected by oral intake of K^+ supplements and K^+-rich foods, such as orange juice and bananas.

Hyperkalemia is a more dangerous potassium disturbance because in this case depolarization of excitable tissues makes them more excitable initially. Subsequently, the cells are unable to repolarize fully and actually become *less* excitable. In this state, they have action potentials that are either smaller than normal or nonexistent. Cardiac muscle excitability affected by changes in plasma K^+ can lead to life-threatening cardiac arrhythmias.

Disturbances in K^+ balance may result from kidney disease, loss of K^+ in diarrhea, or the use of certain types of diuretics that prevent the kidneys from fully reabsorbing K^+. Inappropriate correction of dehydration can also create K^+ imbalance. Consider a golfer playing a round of golf when the temperature was above 100°F. He was aware of the risk of dehydration, so he drank lots of water to replace fluid lost through sweating. The replacement of lost sweat with pure water kept his ECF volume normal but dropped his total blood osmolarity and his K^+ and Na^+ concentrations. He was unable to finish the round of golf because of muscle weakness, and he required medical attention that included ion replacement therapy. A more suitable replacement fluid would have been one of the sports drinks that include salt and K^+.

Potassium balance is also closely tied to acid-base balance, as you will learn in the final section of this chapter. Correction

RUNNING PROBLEM

The medical staff analyzed Lauren's blood for electrolyte concentrations. Her serum Na^+ concentration was 124 mEq/L. The normal range is 135–145 mEq/L. Lauren's diagnosis was hyponatremia [*hypo-*, below + *natri-*, sodium + *-emia*, blood], defined as a serum Na^+ concentration below 135 mEq/L. Hyponatremia induced by the consumption of large quantities of low-sodium or sodium-free fluid is sometimes called *dilutional hyponatremia*.

Question 3:
Which fluid—ECF or ICF—is being diluted in dilutional hyponatremia?

Question 4:
One way to estimate osmolarity is to double the plasma Na^+ concentration. If normal body osmolarity is 280 mOsM, what effect will Lauren's dilutional hyponatremia have on her cells?

Question 5:
Which organ or tissue are the medical personnel most concerned about in dilutional hyponatremia?

of a pH disturbance requires close attention to plasma K^+ levels. Similarly, correction of K^+ imbalance may alter body pH.

BEHAVIORAL MECHANISMS IN SALT AND WATER BALANCE

Although neural, neuroendocrine, and endocrine reflexes play key roles in salt and water homeostasis, behavioral responses are critical in restoring the normal state, especially when ECF volume decreases or osmolarity increases. Drinking water is normally the only way to restore lost water, and eating salt is the only way to raise the body's Na^+ content. Both behaviors are essential for normal salt and water balance. Clinicians must recognize the absence of these behaviors in patients who are unconscious or otherwise unable to obey behavioral urges, and must adjust treatment accordingly. The study of the biological basis for behaviors, including drinking and eating, is a field known as *physiological psychology*.

Drinking Replaces Fluid Loss

Thirst is one of the most powerful urges known in humans. In 1952, the Swedish physiologist Bengt Andersson showed that stimulating certain regions of the hypothalamus triggered drinking behavior. This discovery led to the identification of hypothalamic osmoreceptors that initiate drinking when body osmolarity rises above 280 mOsM. This is an example of a behavior initiated by an internal stimulus.

It is interesting to note that, although increased osmolarity triggers thirst, the act of drinking is sufficient to relieve thirst. The ingested water need not be absorbed in order for thirst to be quenched. As-yet-unidentified receptors in the mouth and pharynx (*oropharynx receptors*) respond to cold water by decreasing thirst and decreasing vasopressin release even though plasma osmolarity remains high. This oropharynx reflex is one reason surgery patients are allowed to suck on ice chips: the ice alleviates their thirst without putting significant amounts of fluid into the digestive system.

A similar reflex exists in camels. When led to water, they will drink just enough to replenish their water deficit. Oropharynx receptors apparently act as a feedforward "metering" system that helps prevent wide swings in osmolarity by matching water intake to water need.

In humans, the reflex response of drinking to counter increased osmolarity is complicated by cultural rituals. Drinking takes place during social events, not just in response to the stimulus of thirst. As a result, our bodies must be capable of eliminating excess fluid ingested in various social situations.

CONCEPT CHECK

12. Incorporate the thirst reflex into Figure 20-7.

Answers: p. 675

Low Na^+ Stimulates Salt Appetite

Thirst is not the only urge associated with fluid balance. **Salt appetite** is a craving for salty foods that occurs when plasma Na^+ concentrations drop. It can be observed in deer and cattle attracted to salt blocks or naturally occurring salt licks. In humans, salt appetite is linked to aldosterone and angiotensin, hormones that regulate Na^+ balance. The centers for salt appetite are in the hypothalamus close to the center for thirst.

Avoidance Behaviors Help Prevent Dehydration

Other behaviors play a role in fluid balance by preventing or promoting dehydration. Desert animals avoid the heat of the day and become active only at night, when environmental temperatures fall and humidity rises. Humans, especially now that we have air conditioning, are not always so wise.

The midday nap, or *siesta,* is a cultural adaptation in tropical countries that keeps people indoors during the hottest part of the day, thereby helping prevent dehydration and overheating. In the United States, we have abandoned this civilized custom and are active continuously during daylight hours, even when the temperature soars during summer in the South and Southwest. Fortunately, our homeostatic mechanisms usually keep us out of trouble.

Volume	Osmolarity: Decrease	Osmolarity: No change	Osmolarity: Increase
Increase	Drinking large amount of water	Ingestion of isotonic saline	Ingestion of hypertonic saline
No change	Replacement of sweat loss with plain water	Normal volume and osmolarity	Eating salt without drinking water
Decrease	Incomplete compensation for dehydration	Hemorrhage	Dehydration (e.g., sweat loss or diarrhea)

■ **FIGURE 20-17** ***Disturbances in volume and osmolarity***

INTEGRATED CONTROL OF VOLUME AND OSMOLARITY

The body uses an integrated response to correct disruptions of salt and water balance. The cardiovascular system responds to changes in blood volume, and the kidneys respond to changes in blood volume or osmolarity. Maintaining homeostasis throughout the day is a continuous process in which the amounts of salt and water in the body shift, according to whether you just drank a soft drink or sweated through an aerobics class.

In that respect, maintaining fluid balance is like driving a car down the highway: small adjustments keep the car in the center of the lane. However, just as exciting movies feature wild car chases, not sedate driving, the exciting part of fluid homeostasis is the body's response to crisis situations, such as severe dehydration or hemorrhage. In this section we examine challenges to salt and water balance.

Osmolarity and Volume Can Change Independently

Normally, volume and osmolarity are homeostatically maintained within an acceptable range. Under some circumstances, however, fluid loss exceeds fluid gain or vice versa, and the body goes out of balance. Common pathways for fluid loss include excessive sweating, vomiting, diarrhea, and hemorrhage. All of these situations may require medical intervention. In contrast, fluid gain is seldom a medical emergency, unless it is pure water that decreases osmolarity below an acceptable range.

Volume and osmolarity of the ECF can each have three possible states: normal, increased, or decreased. The relation of volume and osmolarity changes can be represented by the matrix in Figure 20-17 ■. The center box represents the normal state, and the surrounding boxes represent the most common examples of the variations from normal.

In all cases, the appropriate homeostatic compensation for the change acts according to the principle of mass balance: whatever fluid and solute were added to the body must be removed, or whatever was lost must be replaced. However, perfect compensation is not always possible. Let's begin at the upper right corner of Figure 20-17 and move right to left across each row.

1. *Increased volume, increased osmolarity.* A state of increased volume and increased osmolarity might occur if you ate salty food and drank liquids at the same time, such as popcorn and a soft drink at the movies. The net result could be ingestion of hypertonic saline that increases ECF volume and osmolarity. The appropriate homeostatic response is excretion of hypertonic urine. For homeostasis to be maintained, the osmolarity and volume of the urinary output must match the salt and water input from the popcorn and soft drink.
2. *Increased volume, no change in osmolarity.* Moving one cell to the left in the top row, we see that if the proportion of salt and water in ingested food is equivalent to an isotonic NaCl solution, volume will increase but osmolarity will not change. The appropriate response is excretion of isotonic urine whose volume equals that of the ingested fluid.
3. *Increased volume, decreased osmolarity.* This situation would occur if you drank pure water without ingesting any solute. The goal here would be to excrete very dilute urine to maximize water loss while conserving salts. However, because our kidneys cannot excrete pure water, there will always be some loss of solute in the urine. In this situation, urinary output cannot exactly match input, and so compensation is imperfect.
4. *No change in volume, increased osmolarity.* This disturbance (middle row, right cell) might occur if you ate salted popcorn without drinking anything. The ingestion of salt without water increases ECF osmolarity and causes some water to shift from cells to the ECF. The homeostatic response is intense thirst, which prompts ingestion of water to dilute the added solute. The kidneys help by creating highly concentrated urine of minimal volume, conserving water while removing excess NaCl. Once water is ingested, the disturbance becomes that described in situation 1 or situation 2.
5. *No change in volume, decreased osmolarity.* This scenario (middle row, left cell) might occur when a person who is dehydrated replaces lost fluid with pure water, like the golfer described earlier. The decreased volume resulting from the dehydration is corrected, but the replacement fluid has no solutes to replace those lost. Consequently, a new imbalance is created.

This situation led to the development of electrolyte-containing sports beverages. If people working out in hot weather replace lost sweat with pure water, they may restore volume but run the risk of diluting plasma K^+ and Na^+ concentrations to dangerously low levels (*hypokalemia* and *hyponatremia,* respectively).

20

TABLE 20-1 Responses Triggered by Changes in Volume, Blood Pressure, and Osmolarity

STIMULUS	ORGAN OR TISSUE INVOLVED	RESPONSE(S)	FIGURE(S)
Decreased blood pressure			
Direct effects			
	Granular cells	Renin secretion	20-14
	Glomerulus	Decreased GFR	19-7, 20-15
Reflexes			
Carotid and aortic baroreceptors	Cardiovascular control center	Increased sympathetic output, decreased parasympathetic output	15-23, 20-15
Carotid and aortic baroreceptors	Hypothalamus	Thirst stimulation	20-1a
Carotid and aortic baroreceptors	Hypothalamus	Vasopressin secretion	20-7
Atrial baroreceptors	Hypothalamus	Thirst stimulation	20-1a
Atrial baroreceptors	Hypothalamus	Vasopressin secretion	20-7
Increased blood pressure			
Direct effects			
	Glomerulus	Increased GFR (transient)	19-8
	Myocardial cells	Natriuretic peptide secretion	20-16
Reflexes			
Carotid and aortic baroreceptors	Cardiovascular control center	Decreased sympathetic output, increased parasympathetic output	15-22
Carotid and aortic baroreceptors	Hypothalamus	Thirst inhibition	—
Carotid and aortic baroreceptors	Hypothalamus	Vasopressin inhibition	—
Atrial baroreceptors	Hypothalamus	Thirst inhibition	—
Atrial baroreceptors	Hypothalamus	Vasopressin inhibition	—
Increased osmolarity			
Direct effects			
Pathological dehydration	Adrenal cortex	Decreased aldosterone secretion	20-18
Reflexes			
Osmoreceptors	Hypothalamus	Thirst stimulation	20-12
Osmoreceptors	Hypothalamus	Vasopressin secretion	20-7
Decreased osmolarity			
Direct effects			
Pathological hyponatremia	Adrenal cortex	Increased aldosterone secretion	—
Reflexes			
Osmoreceptors	Hypothalamus	Decreased vasopressin secretion	—

20

RUNNING PROBLEM

During exercise in the heat, sweating rate and sweat composition are quite variable among athletes. Fluid losses can range from less than 0.6 L/h to more than 2.5 L/h, and sweat Na^+ concentrations can range from less than 20 mEq/L to more than 90 mEq/L. The white salt crystals noted on Lauren's face and clothing suggest that she is a "salty sweater" who probably lost a large amount of salt during the race. Follow-up testing revealed that Lauren's sweat Na^+ concentration was 70 mEq/L.

Question 6:
Assuming a sweating rate of 1.0 L/h and a sweat Na^+ level of 70 mEq/L, how much Na^+ did Lauren lose during the 16-hour race?

Question 7:
Total body water for a 60-kg female is approximately 30 L, and her ECF volume is 10 L. Based on the information given in the problem so far, what volume of fluid did Lauren ingest during the race?

642 645 658 661 665 671

6. *Decreased volume, increased osmolarity.* Dehydration is a common cause of this disturbance (bottom row, right cell). Dehydration has multiple causes. During prolonged heavy exercise, water loss from the lungs can double while sweat loss may increase from 0.1 liter to as much as 5 liters! Because the fluid secreted by sweat glands is hyposmotic, the fluid left behind in the body becomes hyperosmotic.

   Diarrhea [*diarhein,* to flow through], excessively watery feces, is a pathological condition involving major water and solute loss, this time from the digestive tract. In both sweating and diarrhea, if too much fluid is lost from the circulatory system, blood volume decreases to the point that the heart can no longer pump blood effectively to the brain. In addition, cell shrinkage caused by increased osmolarity disrupts cell function.
7. *Decreased volume, no change in osmolarity.* This situation (bottom row, middle cell) occurs with hemorrhage. Blood loss represents the loss of isosmotic fluid from the extracellular compartment, similar to scooping a cup of seawater out of a large bucketful. If a blood transfusion is not immediately available, the best replacement solution is one that is isosmotic and remains in the ECF, such as isotonic NaCl.
8. *Decreased volume, decreased osmolarity.* This situation (bottom row, left cell) might also result from incomplete compensation of dehydration, but it is uncommon, so we will ignore it.

Dehydration Triggers Renal and Cardiovascular Responses

To understand the body's integrated response to changes in volume and osmolarity, you must first have a clear idea of which pathways become active in response to various stimuli. Table 20-1 ■ is a summary of the many pathways involved in the homeostasis of salt and water balance. For details of individual pathways, refer to the figures cited in Table 20-1.

The homeostatic response to severe dehydration is an excellent example of how the body works to maintain blood volume and cell volume in the face of decreased volume and increased osmolarity. It also illustrates the role of neural and endocrine integrating centers. In dehydration, the adrenal cortex receives two opposing signals. One says, "Secrete aldosterone"; the other says, "Do not secrete aldosterone." The body has multiple mechanisms for dealing with diminished blood volume, but high ECF osmolarity causes cells to shrink and presents a more immediate threat to well-being. Thus, faced with decreased volume and increased osmolarity, the adrenal cortex will not secrete aldosterone. (If secreted, aldosterone would cause Na^+ reabsorption, which could worsen the already-high osmolarity associated with dehydration.)

In severe dehydration, compensatory mechanisms are aimed at restoring normal blood pressure, ECF volume, and osmolarity by (1) conserving fluid to prevent additional loss, (2) triggering cardiovascular reflexes to increase blood pressure, and (3) stimulating thirst so that normal fluid volume and osmolarity can be restored. Figure 20-18 ■ maps the interwoven nature of these responses. This figure is complex and intimidating at first glance, so we will discuss it step by step.

At the top of the map (in yellow) are the two stimuli caused by dehydration: decreased blood volume/pressure, and increased osmolarity. Decreased ECF volume causes decreased blood pressure. Blood pressure acts both directly and as a stimulus for several reflex pathways that are mediated through the carotid and aortic baroreceptors, atrial volume receptors, and the pressure-sensitive granular cells.

1. *The carotid and aortic baroreceptors signal the cardiovascular control center (CVCC) to raise blood pressure.* Sympathetic output from the CVCC increases while parasympathetic output decreases.
   (a) Heart rate goes up as control of the SA node shifts from predominantly parasympathetic to sympathetic.
   (b) The force of ventricular contraction also increases under sympathetic stimulation. The increased force of contraction combines with increased heart rate to increase cardiac output.
   (c) Simultaneously, sympathetic input causes arteriolar vasoconstriction, increasing peripheral resistance.
   (d) Sympathetic vasoconstriction of afferent arterioles in the kidneys decreases GFR, helping conserve fluid.
   (e) Increased sympathetic activity at the granular cells of the kidneys increases renin secretion.

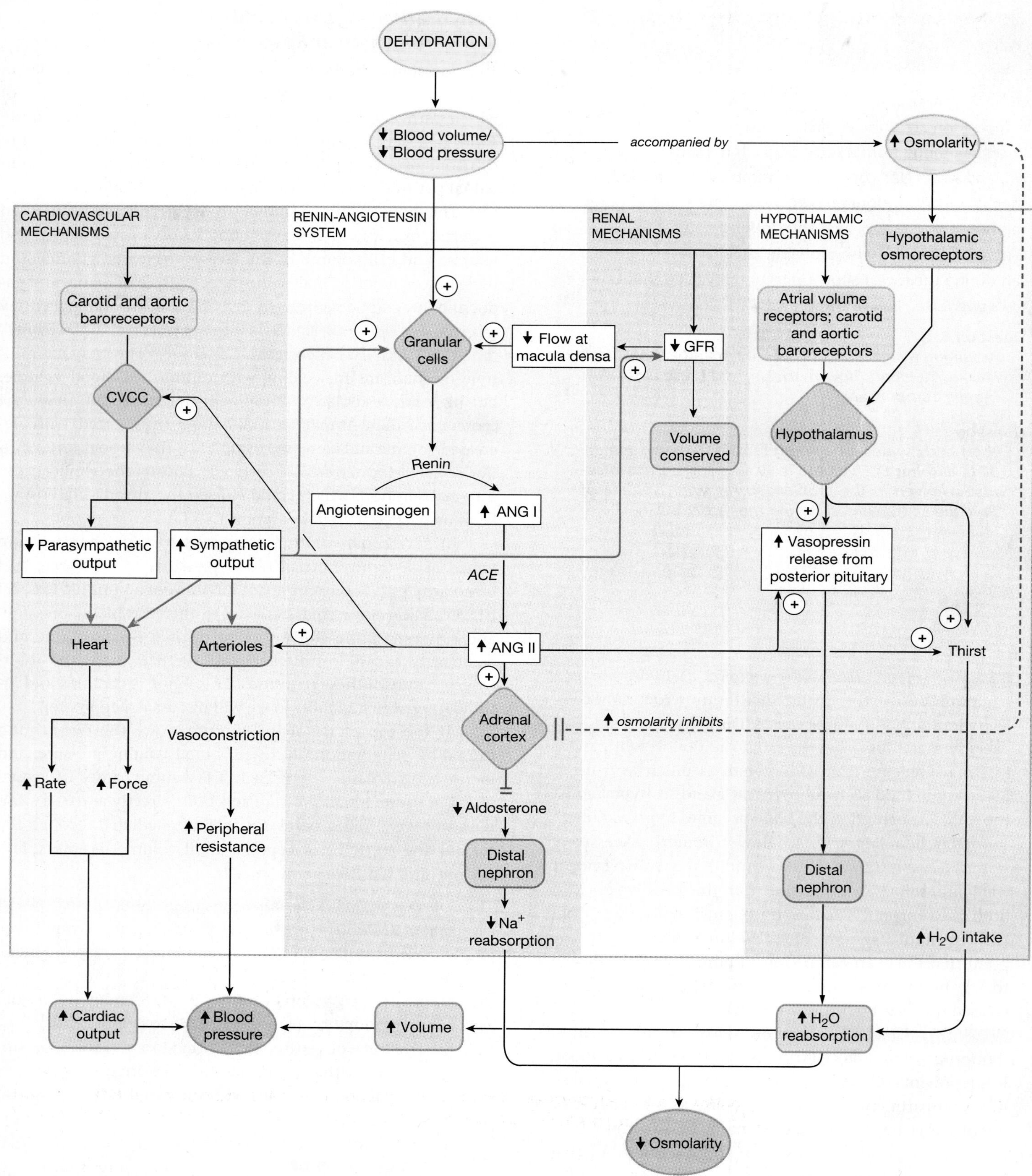

■ **FIGURE 20-18** ***Homeostatic compensation for severe dehydration***

2. *Decreased peripheral blood pressure directly decreases GFR.* A lower GFR conserves ECF volume by filtering less fluid into the nephron.
3. *Paracrine feedback causes the granular cells to release renin.* Decreased fluid flow past the macula densa as a result of lower GFR triggers renin release.
4. *Granular cells respond to decreased blood pressure by releasing renin.* The combination of decreased blood pressure, increased sympathetic input onto granular cells, and signals from the macula densa stimulates renin release and ensures increased production of angiotensin II.
5. *Decreased blood pressure, decreased blood volume, increased osmolarity, and increased ANG II production all stimulate vasopressin and the thirst centers of the hypothalamus.*

The redundancy in the control pathways ensures that all four main compensatory mechanisms are activated: cardiovascular responses, ANG II, vasopressin, and thirst.

1. *Cardiovascular responses* combine increased cardiac output and increased peripheral resistance to raise blood pressure. Note, however, that this increase in blood pressure does *not necessarily* mean that blood pressure returns to normal. If dehydration is severe, compensation may be incomplete, and blood pressure may remain below normal.
2. *Angiotensin II* has a variety of effects aimed at raising blood pressure, including stimulation of thirst, vasopressin release, direct vasoconstriction, and reinforcement of cardiovascular control center output. ANG II also reaches the adrenal cortex and attempts to stimulate aldosterone release. In dehydration, however, Na^+ reabsorption worsens the already-high osmolarity. Consequently, high osmolarity at the adrenal cortex directly inhibits aldosterone release, blocking the action of ANG II. The RAAS pathway in dehydration produces the beneficial blood-pressure-enhancing effects of ANG II while avoiding the detrimental effects of Na^+ reabsorption. This is a beautiful example of integrated function.
3. *Vasopressin* increases the water permeability of the renal collecting ducts, allowing water reabsorption to conserve fluid. Without fluid replacement, however, vasopressin cannot bring volume and osmolarity back to normal.
4. *Oral (or intravenous) intake of water* in response to thirst is the only mechanism for replacing lost fluid volume and for restoring ECF osmolarity to normal.

The net result of all four mechanisms is (1) restoration of volume by water conservation and fluid intake, (2) maintenance of blood pressure through increased blood volume, increased cardiac output, and vasoconstriction, and (3) restoration of normal osmolarity by decreased Na^+ reabsorption and increased water reabsorption and intake.

Using the pathways listed in Table 20-1, try to create reflex maps for the seven other disturbances of volume and osmolarity shown in Figure 20-17.

ACID-BASE BALANCE

Acid-base balance (also called pH homeostasis) is one of the essential functions of the body. The pH of a solution is a measure of its H^+ concentration [p. 37]. A normal arterial plasma sample has a H^+ concentration of 0.00004 meq/L, minute compared with the concentrations of other ions. (For example, the plasma concentration of Na^+ is about 135 meq/L.)

Because the body's H^+ concentration is so low, it is commonly expressed on a logarithmic pH scale of 0–14, in which a pH of 7.0 is neutral (neither acidic nor basic). If the pH of a solution is below 7.0, the solution has a H^+ concentration greater than 1×10^{-7} M and is considered acidic. If the pH is above 7.0, the solution has a H^+ concentration lower than 1×10^{-7} M and is considered alkaline (basic).

The normal pH of the body is 7.40, slightly alkaline. A change of 1 pH unit represents a 10-fold change in H^+ concentration. To review the concept of pH and the logarithmic scale on which it is based, see Appendix A.

Enzymes and the Nervous System Are Particularly Sensitive to Changes in pH

The normal pH range of plasma is 7.38–7.42. Extracellular pH usually reflects intracellular pH, and vice versa. Because monitoring intracellular conditions is difficult, plasma values are used clinically as an indicator of ECF and whole body pH. Body fluids that are "outside" the body's internal environment, such as those in the lumen of the gastrointestinal tract or kidney tubule, can have a pH that far exceeds the normal range. Acidic secretions in the stomach, for instance, may create a gastric pH as low as 1, and the pH of urine varies between 4.5 and 8.5, depending on the body's need to excrete H^+ or HCO_3^-.

20

The concentration of H^+ in the body is closely regulated. Intracellular proteins, such as enzymes and membrane channels, are particularly sensitive to pH because the function of these proteins depends on their three-dimensional shape [p. 31]. Changes in H^+ concentration alter the tertiary structure of proteins by interacting with hydrogen bonds in the molecules, disrupting the proteins' three-dimensional structures and activities.

Abnormal pH may significantly affect the activity of the nervous system. If pH is too low—the condition known as **acidosis**—neurons become less excitable and CNS depression results. Patients become confused and disoriented, then slip into a coma. If CNS depression progresses, the respiratory centers cease to function, causing death.

If pH is too high—the condition known as **alkalosis**—neurons become hyperexcitable, firing action potentials at the slightest signal. This condition shows up first as sensory changes, such as numbness or tingling, then as muscle twitches. If alkalosis is severe, muscle twitches turn into sustained contractions (*tetanus*) that paralyze respiratory muscles.

Disturbances of acid-base balance are associated with disturbances in K^+ balance. This is partly due to a renal transporter

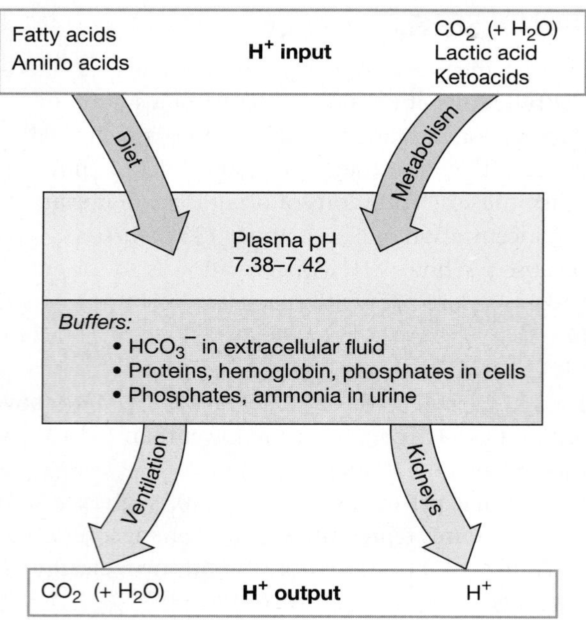

■ **FIGURE 20-19** ***Hydrogen balance in the body***

that moves K^+ and H^+ ions in an antiport fashion. In acidosis, the kidneys excrete H^+ and reabsorb K^+ using an H^+-K^+-ATPase. In alkalosis, the kidneys reabsorb H^+ and excrete K^+. Potassium imbalance usually shows up as disturbances in excitable tissues, especially the heart.

Acids and Bases in the Body Come from Many Sources

In day-to-day functioning, the body is challenged by intake and production of acids more than bases. Hydrogen ions come both from food and from internal metabolism. Maintaining mass balance requires that acid intake and production be balanced by acid excretion. Hydrogen balance in the body is summarized in Figure 20-19 ■.

Acid Input Many metabolic intermediates and foods are organic acids that ionize and contribute H^+ to body fluids.* Examples of organic acids include amino acids, fatty acids, intermediates in the citric acid cycle, and lactic acid produced by anaerobic metabolism. Metabolic production of organic acids each day creates a significant amount of H^+ that must be excreted to maintain mass balance.

Under extraordinary circumstances, metabolic organic acid production can increase significantly and create a crisis. For example, severe anaerobic conditions, such as circulatory collapse, produce so much lactic acid that normal homeostatic mechanisms cannot keep pace, resulting in a state of *lactic acidosis*. In diabetes mellitus, abnormal metabolism of fats and amino acids creates strong acids known as **ketoacids**. These acids cause a state of metabolic acidosis known as *ketoacidosis*.

The biggest source of acid on a daily basis is the production of CO_2 during aerobic respiration. Carbon dioxide is not an acid because it does not contain any hydrogen atoms. However, CO_2 from respiration combines with water to form carbonic acid (H_2CO_3), which dissociates into H^+ and HCO_3^-:

$$CO_2 + H_2O \rightleftharpoons H_2CO_3 \rightleftharpoons H^+ + HCO_3^-$$

This reaction takes place in all cells and in the plasma, but at a slow rate. However, in certain cells of the body, the reaction proceeds very rapidly because of the presence of large amounts of *carbonic anhydrase* [p. 599]. This enzyme catalyzes the conversion of CO_2 and H_2O to H_2CO_3.

The production of H^+ from CO_2 and H_2O is the single biggest source of acid input under normal conditions. By some estimates, CO_2 from resting metabolism produces 12,500 meq of H^+ each day. If this amount of acid were placed in a volume of water equal to the plasma volume, it would create a H^+concentration of 4167 meq/L, over one hundred million (10^8) times as concentrated as the normal plasma H^+concentration of 0.00004 meq/L!

These numbers show that CO_2 from aerobic respiration has the potential to affect pH in the body dramatically. Fortunately, homeostatic mechanisms normally prevent CO_2 from accumulating in the body.

Base Input Acid-base physiology focuses on acids for good reasons. First, our diet and metabolism have few significant sources of bases. Some fruits and vegetables contain anions that metabolize to HCO_3^-, but the influence of these foods is far outweighed by the contribution of acidic fruits, amino acids, and fatty acids. Second, in acid-base disturbances, those due to excess acid are more common than those due to excess base. For these reasons, the body expends far more resources removing excess acid.

pH Homeostasis Depends on Buffers, the Lungs, and the Kidneys

How does the body cope with minute-to-minute changes in pH? There are three mechanisms: (1) buffers, (2) ventilation, and (3) renal regulation of H^+ and HCO_3^-. Buffers are the first line of defense, always present and waiting to prevent wide swings in pH. Ventilation, the second line of defense, is a rapid, reflexively controlled response that can take care of 75% of most pH disturbances. The final line of defense lies with the kidneys. They are slower than buffers or the lungs but are very effective at coping with any remaining pH disturbance under normal conditions. These three mechanisms help the body balance acid so effectively that normal body pH varies only slightly. Let's take a closer look at each of them.

*The anion forms of many organic acids end with the suffix *–ate,* such as pyruvate and lactate.

Buffer Systems Include Proteins, Phosphate Ions, and HCO_3^-

A buffer is a molecule that moderates but does not prevent changes in pH by combining with or releasing H^+ [p. 38]. In the absence of buffers, the addition of acid to a solution causes a sharp change in pH. In the presence of a buffer, the pH change is moderated or may even be unnoticeable. Because acid production is the major challenge to pH homeostasis, most physiological buffers combine with H^+.

Buffers are found both within cells and in the plasma. Intracellular buffers include cellular proteins, phosphate ions (HPO_4^{2-}), and hemoglobin. As we have seen, hemoglobin in red blood cells buffers the H^+ produced by the reaction of CO_2 with H_2O (Fig. 18-14, p. 600).

Each H^+ ion buffered by hemoglobin leaves a matching bicarbonate ion inside the red blood cell. The HCO_3^- then leaves the red blood cell by exchanging with a plasma Cl^-. This exchange is the *chloride shift* described in Chapter 18 [p. 601].

The large amounts of bicarbonate produced from metabolic CO_2 create the most important extracellular buffer system of the body. Plasma HCO_3^- concentration averages 24 meq/L, which is approximately 600,000 times as concentrated as plasma H^+. Although H^+ and HCO_3^- are created in a 1:1 ratio from CO_2 and H_2O, intracellular buffering of H^+ by hemoglobin is a major reason the two ions do not appear in the plasma in the same concentration. The HCO_3^- in plasma can then buffer H^+ from nonrespiratory sources, such as metabolism.

The relationship between CO_2, HCO_3^-, and H^+ in the plasma is expressed by the equation we just looked at:

$$CO_2 + H_2O \rightleftharpoons \underset{\text{carbonic acid}}{H_2CO_3} \rightleftharpoons H^+ + HCO_3^- \qquad (1)$$

According to the law of mass action, any change in the amount of CO_2, H^+, or HCO_3^- in the reaction solution will cause the reaction to shift until a new equilibrium is reached. (Water is always in excess in the body and does not contribute to the reaction equilibrium.) For example, if CO_2 increases, the equation shifts to the right, creating one additional H^+ and one additional HCO_3^- from each CO_2 and water:

$$\uparrow CO_2 + H_2O \rightarrow H_2CO_3 \rightarrow \uparrow H^+ + \uparrow HCO_3^- \qquad (2)$$

Once a new equilibrium is reached, both H^+ and HCO_3^- levels have increased. The addition of H^+ makes the solution more acidic and therefore lowers its pH. In this reaction, it does not matter that a HCO_3^- buffer molecule has also been produced because HCO_3^- acts as a buffer only when it binds to H^+ and becomes carbonic acid.

Now suppose H^+ is added to the plasma from some metabolic source, such as lactic acid:

$$CO_2 + H_2O \rightleftharpoons H_2CO_3 \rightleftharpoons \uparrow H^+ + HCO_3^- \qquad (3)$$

In this case, plasma HCO_3^- *can* act as a buffer by combining with some of the added H^+ until the reaction reaches a new equilibrium state. The increase in H^+ shifts the equation to the left:

$$CO_2 + H_2O \leftarrow H_2CO_3 \leftarrow \uparrow H^+ + HCO_3^- \qquad (4)$$

Converting some of the added H^+ and bicarbonate buffer to carbonic acid means that at equilibrium, H^+ is still elevated, but not as much as it was initially. The concentration of HCO_3^- is decreased because some has been used as a buffer. The buffered H^+ is converted to CO_2 and H_2O, increasing the amounts of both. At equilibrium, the reaction looks like this:

$$\uparrow CO_2 + \uparrow H_2O \rightleftharpoons H_2CO_3 \rightleftharpoons \uparrow H^+ + \downarrow HCO_3^- \qquad (5)$$

The law of mass action is a useful way to think about the relationship between changes in the concentrations of H^+, HCO_3^-, and CO_2, as long as you remember certain qualifications. First, a change in HCO_3^- concentration (as indicated in reaction 5) may not show up clinically as a HCO_3^- concentration outside the normal range. This is because HCO_3^- is 600,000 times as concentrated in the plasma as H^+ is. If both H^+ and HCO_3^- are added to the plasma, you may observe changes in pH (but not in HCO_3^- concentration), because so much HCO_3^- was present initially. Both H^+ and HCO_3^- experience an *absolute* increase in concentration, but because so many HCO_3^- were in the plasma to begin with, the *relative increase* in HCO_3^- goes unnoticed.

As an analogy, think of two football teams playing in a stadium packed with 80,000 fans. If 10 more players (H^+) run out onto the field, everyone notices. But if 10 people (HCO_3^-) come into the stands at the same time, no one pays any attention because there were already so many people watching the game that 10 more make no significant difference.

The second qualification for the law of mass action is that when the reaction shifts to the left and increases plasma CO_2, a nearly instantaneous increase in ventilation takes place (in a normal person). If extra CO_2 is ventilated off, arterial P_{CO_2} may remain normal or even fall below normal as a result of hyperventilation.

RUNNING PROBLEM

The human body attempts to maintain fluid and sodium balance via several hormonal mechanisms. During exercise sessions, increased sympathetic output causes increased production of aldosterone and vasopressin, which promote the retention of Na^+ and water by the kidneys.

Question 8:

What would you expect to happen to vasopressin and aldosterone production in response to dilutional hyponatremia?

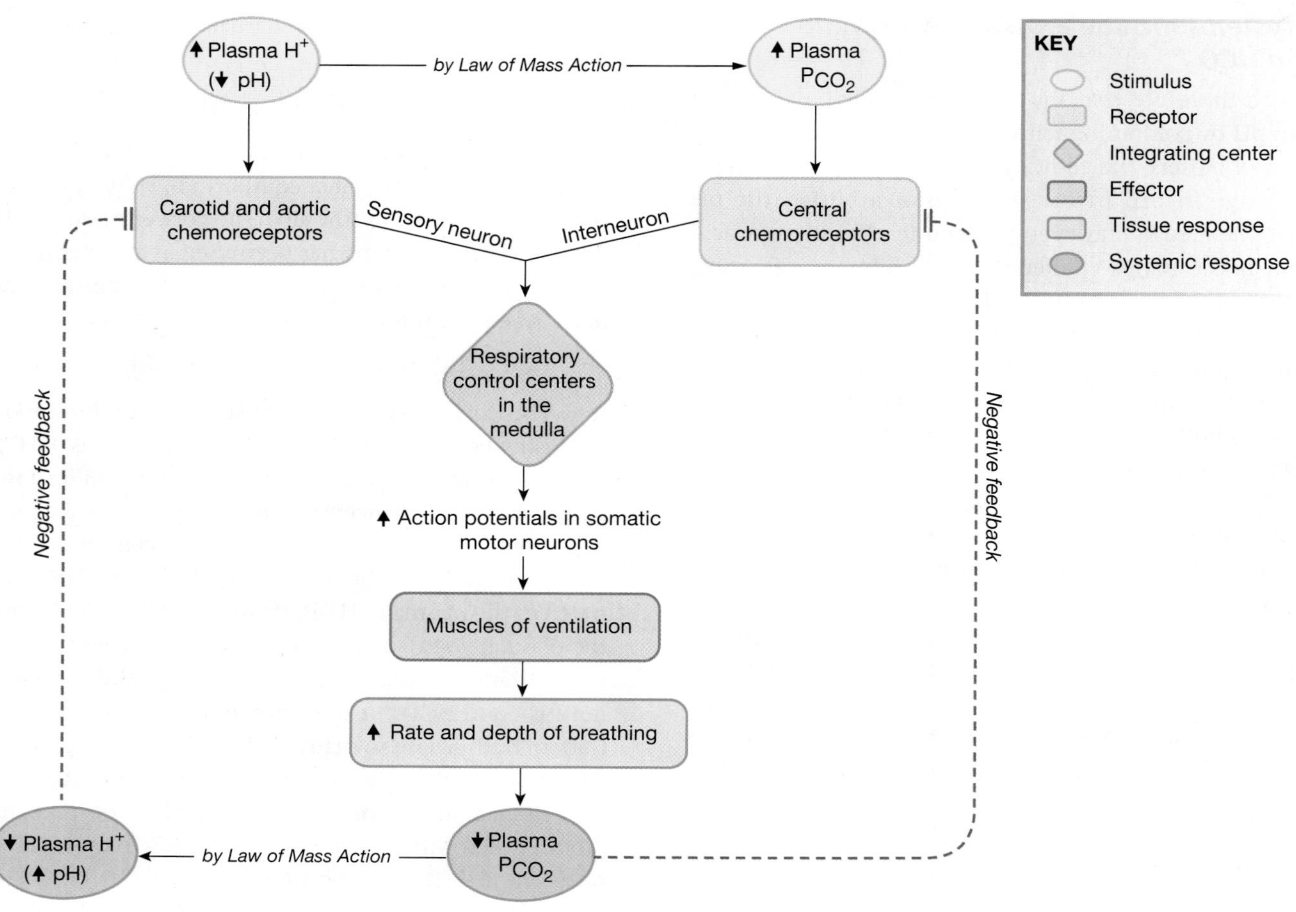

■ **FIGURE 20-20** ***The reflex pathway for respiratory compensation of metabolic acidosis***

20

Ventilation Can Compensate for pH Disturbances

The increase in ventilation just described is a *respiratory compensation* for acidosis. Ventilation and acid-base status are intimately linked, as shown by the equation

$$CO_2 + H_2O \rightleftharpoons H_2CO_3 \rightleftharpoons H^+ + HCO_3^-$$

Changes in ventilation can correct disturbances in acid-base balance, but they can also cause them. Because of the dynamic equilibrium between CO_2 and H^+, any change in plasma P_{CO_2} will affect both H^+ and HCO_3^- content of the blood. For example, if a person hypoventilates and P_{CO_2} increases, the equation shifts to the right. More carbonic acid is formed, and H^+ goes up, creating a more acidotic state:

$$\uparrow CO_2 + H_2O \rightarrow H_2CO_3 \rightarrow \uparrow H^+ + \uparrow HCO_3^- \quad (6)$$

If a person hyperventilates, blowing off CO_2 and thereby decreasing the plasma P_{CO_2}, the equation shifts to the left, which means that H^+ combines with HCO_3^- and becomes carbonic acid, thereby decreasing the H^+ concentration and so raising the pH:

$$\downarrow CO_2 + H_2O \leftarrow H_2CO_3 \leftarrow \downarrow H^+ + \downarrow HCO_3^- \quad (7)$$

In these two examples, you can see that a change in P_{CO_2} will affect the H^+ concentration and therefore the pH of the plasma. The body uses ventilation as a method for adjusting pH only if a stimulus associated with pH triggers the reflex response. Two stimuli can do so: H^+ and CO_2.

Ventilation is affected directly by plasma H^+ levels through carotid and aortic chemoreceptors (Fig. 20-20 ■). These are located in the aorta and carotid arteries along with the oxygen sensors and blood pressure sensors we discussed previously [p. 604]. An increase in plasma H^+ stimulates the chemoreceptors, which in turn signal the medullary respiratory control centers to increase ventilation. Increased alveolar ventilation allows the lungs to excrete more CO_2 and convert H^+ to carbonic acid.

The central chemoreceptors of the medulla oblongata cannot respond directly to changes in plasma pH because H^+ does not cross the blood-brain barrier. However, changes in pH change P_{CO_2}, and CO_2 stimulates the central chemoreceptors [Fig. 18-19, p. 605]. Dual control of ventilation through the central and peripheral chemoreceptors helps the body respond rapidly to changes in either pH or plasma CO_2.

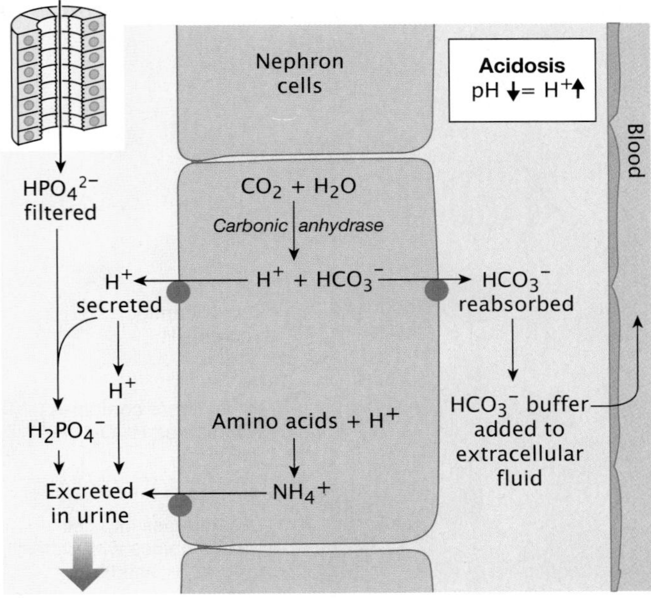

■ **FIGURE 20-21** ***Overview of renal compensation for acidosis***

The transporters represented in this figure are depicted in greater detail in Figures 20-22 and 20-23.

CONCEPT CHECK

13. Name the muscles of ventilation that might be involved in the reflex represented in Figure 20-20.
14. In equation 6, the amount of HCO_3^- present is increased at equilibrium. Why doesn't this HCO_3^- act as a buffer and prevent acidosis from occurring?

Answers: p. 675

Kidneys Use Ammonia and Phosphate Buffers

The kidneys take care of the 25% of compensation that the lungs cannot handle. They alter pH two ways: (1) directly, by excreting or reabsorbing H^+ and (2) indirectly, by changing the rate at which HCO_3^- buffer is reabsorbed or excreted.

In acidosis, the kidney secretes H^+ into the tubule lumen using direct and indirect active transport (Fig. 20-21 ■). Ammonia from amino acids and phosphate ions (HPO_4^{2-}) in the kidney act as buffers, trapping large amounts of H^+ as NH_4^+ and $H_2PO_4^-$ and allowing more H^+ to be excreted. Phosphate ions are present in filtrate and combine with H^+ secreted into the nephron lumen:

$$HPO_4^{2-} + H^+ \rightleftharpoons H_2PO_4^-$$

Ammonia is made from amino acids, as described in the next section.

Even with these buffers, urine can become quite acidic, down to a pH of about 4.5. While H^+ is being excreted, the kidneys make new HCO_3^- from CO_2 and H_2O. The HCO_3^- is reabsorbed into the blood to act as a buffer and increase pH.

In alkalosis, the kidney reverses the general process just described for acidosis, excreting HCO_3^- and reabsorbing H^+ in an effort to bring pH back into the normal range. Renal compensations are slower than respiratory compensations, and their effect on pH may not be noticed for 24–48 hours. However, once activated, renal compensations effectively handle all but severe acid-base disturbances.

The cellular mechanisms for renal handling of H^+ and HCO_3^- resemble transport processes in other epithelia. However, these mechanisms involve some membrane transporters that you have not encountered before:

1. The **apical Na^+-H^+ antiport** is an indirect active transporter that brings Na^+ into the epithelial cell in exchange for moving H^+ against its concentration gradient into the lumen. This is the same transporter that is active in proximal tubule Na^+ reabsorption [p. 627].
2. The **basolateral Na^+-HCO_3^- symport** moves Na^+ and HCO_3^- out of the epithelial cell and into the interstitial fluid. This indirect active transporter couples the energy of HCO_3^- diffusing down its concentration gradient to the uphill movement of Na^+ from the cell to the ECF.
3. The **H^+-ATPase** uses energy from ATP to acidify the urine, pushing H^+ against its concentration gradient into the lumen of the distal nephron.
4. The **H^+-K^+-ATPase** puts H^+ into the urine in exchange for reabsorbed K^+. This exchange contributes to the potassium imbalance that sometimes accompanies acid-base disturbances.
5. A **Na^+-NH_4^+ antiport** moves NH_4^+ from the cell to the lumen in exchange for Na^+.

In addition to these transporters, the renal tubule also uses the ubiquitous Na^+-K^+-ATPase and the same HCO_3^--Cl^- antiport protein that is responsible for the chloride shift in red blood cells.

The Proximal Tubule Secretes H^+ and Reabsorbs HCO_3^-

The amount of bicarbonate ion the kidneys filter each day is equivalent to the bicarbonate in a pound of baking soda ($NaHCO_3$)! Most of this HCO_3^- must be reabsorbed to maintain the body's buffer capacity. The proximal tubule reabsorbs most filtered HCO_3^- by indirect methods because there is no apical membrane transporter to bring HCO_3^- into the tubule cell.

Figure 20-22 ■ shows the two pathways by which bicarbonate is reabsorbed in the proximal tubule. (The numbers in the following lists correspond to the steps shown in the figure.) By following this illustration, you will see how the transporters listed in the previous section function together.

The first pathway converts filtered HCO_3^- into CO_2, then back into HCO_3^-:

1. H^+ is secreted from the proximal tubule cell into the lumen in exchange for filtered Na^+, which moves from the lumen into the tubule cell.

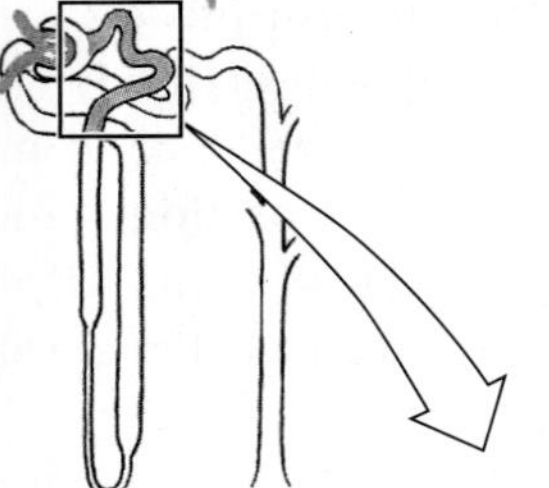

FIGURE 20-22 ***Proximal tubule H^+ secretion and the reabsorption of filtered HCO_3^-***

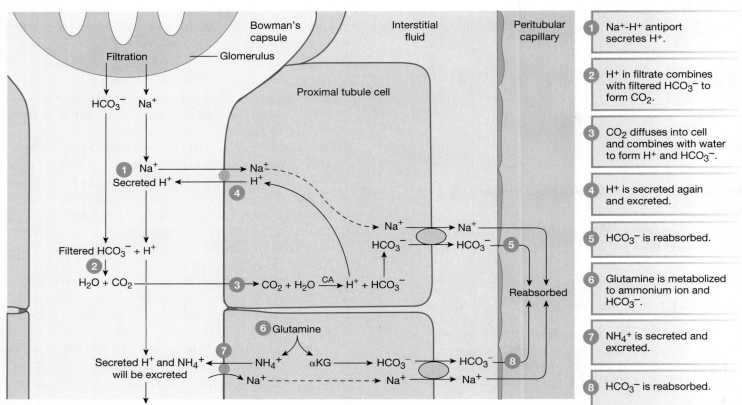

1. Na^+-H^+ antiport secretes H^+.
2. H^+ in filtrate combines with filtered HCO_3^- to form CO_2.
3. CO_2 diffuses into cell and combines with water to form H^+ and HCO_3^-.
4. H^+ is secreted again and excreted.
5. HCO_3^- is reabsorbed.
6. Glutamine is metabolized to ammonium ion and HCO_3^-.
7. NH_4^+ is secreted and excreted.
8. HCO_3^- is reabsorbed.

2. The secreted H^+ combines with filtered HCO_3^- to form CO_2 in the lumen.
3. This CO_2 diffuses into the tubule cell and combines with water to form H_2CO_3, which dissociates to H^+ and HCO_3^- in the cytoplasm.
4. The H^+ created in step 3 is secreted, replacing the luminal H^+ that combined with filtered HCO_3^- in step 2.
5. The HCO_3^- created in step 3 is transported out of the cell on the basolateral side by the HCO_3^--Na^+ symporter.

The net result of this process is reabsorption of filtered Na^+ and HCO_3^- and secretion of H^+.

A second way to reabsorb bicarbonate and excrete H^+ comes from metabolism of the amino acid glutamine:

6. Glutamine in the proximal tubule cell loses its two amino groups, which become ammonia (NH_3). The ammonia buffers H^+ to become ammonium ion.
7. The ammonium ion is transported into the lumen in exchange for Na^+.
8. The α-ketoglutarate molecule made from deamination of glutamine is metabolized further to HCO_3^-, which is transported into the blood along with Na^+.

The net result of these pathways is reabsorption of sodium bicarbonate—baking soda, $NaHCO_3$.

The Distal Nephron Controls Acid Excretion

The distal nephron plays a significant role in the fine regulation of acid-base balance. The **intercalated cells** (or **I cells**) interspersed among the principal cells are responsible for acid-base regulation.

Intercalated cells are characterized by high concentrations of carbonic anhydrase in their cytoplasm. This enzyme allows them to rapidly convert CO_2 and water into H^+ and HCO_3^-. The H^+ ions are pumped out of the intercalated cell either by the H^+-ATPase or by an ATPase that exchanges one H^+ for one K^+. Bicarbonate leaves the cell by means of the HCO_3^--Cl^- antiport exchanger.

■ **FIGURE 20-23** ***Role of intercalated cells in acidosis and alkalosis***

Intercalated cells in the collecting duct secrete or reabsorb H^+ and HCO_3^- according to the needs of the body.

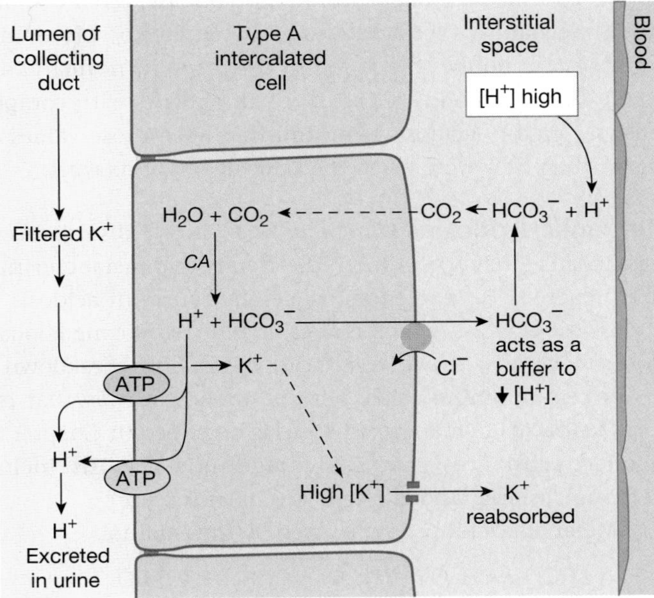

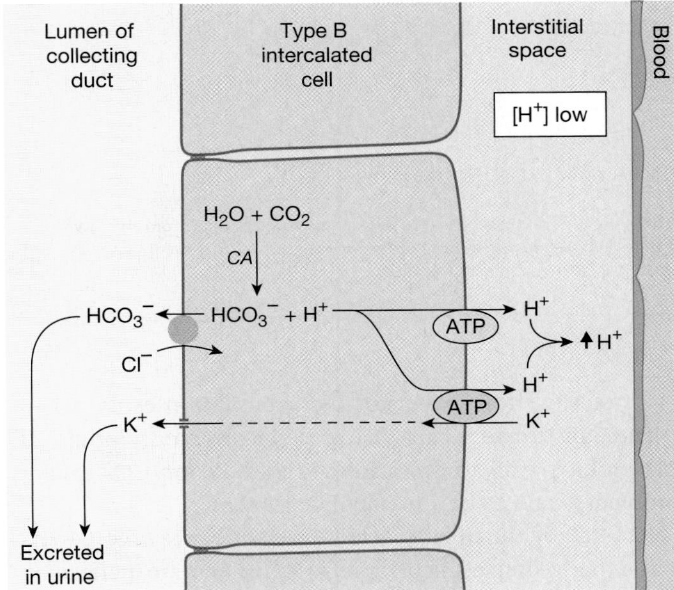

There are two types of intercalated cells, and their transporters are found on different faces of the epithelial cell. During periods of acidosis, type A intercalated cells secrete H^+ and reabsorb bicarbonate. During periods of alkalosis, type B intercalated cells secrete HCO_3^- and reabsorb H^+.

Fig. 20-23a ■ shows how type A intercalated cells work during acidosis, secreting H^+ and reabsorbing HCO_3^-. The process is similar to H^+ secretion in the proximal tubule except for the specific H^+ transporters. The distal nephron uses H^+-ATPase and H^+-K^+-ATPase rather than the Na^+-H^+ antiport protein found in the proximal tubule.

During alkalosis, when the H^+ concentration of the body is too low, H^+ is reabsorbed and HCO_3^- buffer is excreted in the urine (Fig. 20-23b). Once again, the ions are produced by the dissociation of H_2CO_3 formed from H_2O and CO_2. Hydrogen ions are reabsorbed into the ECF on the basolateral side of the nephron cell while HCO_3^- is secreted into the lumen. The polarity of the two types of I cells is reversed, with the transport proteins found on the opposite sides of the cell.

The H^+-K^+-ATPase of the distal nephron helps create parallel disturbances of acid-base balance and K^+ balance. In acidosis, when plasma H^+ is high, the kidney secretes H^+ and reabsorbs K^+. Thus, acidosis is often accompanied by hyperkalemia. (Certain nonrenal events also contribute to elevated ECF K^+ concentrations in acidosis.) The reverse is true for alkalosis, when blood H^+ levels are low. The mechanism that allows the distal nephron to reabsorb H^+ simultaneously causes it to secrete K^+, with the result that alkalosis goes hand in hand with hypokalemia.

CONCEPT CHECK

15. Why does the K^+-H^+ transporter in the distal nephron require ATP to secrete H^+ but the Na^+-H^+ exchanger in the proximal tubule does not?
16. In hypokalemia, the intercalated cells of the distal nephron reabsorb K^+ from the tubule lumen. What happens to blood pH as a result? Answers: p. 675

Acid-Base Disturbances May Be Respiratory or Metabolic in Origin

The three compensatory mechanisms (buffers, ventilation, and renal excretion) take care of most variations in plasma pH. But under some circumstances, the production or loss of H^+ or HCO_3^- is so extreme that compensatory mechanisms fail to maintain pH homeostasis. In these states, the pH of the blood moves out of the normal range of 7.38–7.42. If the body fails to keep pH between 7.00 and 7.70, acidosis or alkalosis can be fatal.

Acid-base problems are classified both by the direction of the pH change (acidosis or alkalosis) and by the underlying cause (metabolic or respiratory). As you learned earlier, changes

TABLE 20-2 Plasma P_{CO_2}, Ions, and pH in Acid-Base Disturbances

DISTURBANCE	P_{CO_2}	H^+	pH	HCO_3^-
Acidosis				
Respiratory	↑	↑	↓	↑
Metabolic	Normal* or ↓	↑	↓	↓
Alkalosis				
Respiratory	↓	↓	↑	↓
Metabolic	Normal* or ↑	↓	↑	↓

*These values are different from what you would expect from the law of mass action because almost instantaneous respiratory compensation keeps P_{CO_2} from changing significantly.

in P_{CO_2} resulting from hyper- or hypoventilation cause pH to shift. These disturbances are said to be of respiratory origin. If the pH problem arises from acids or bases of non-CO_2 origin, the problem is said to be a metabolic problem.

Note that by the time an acid-base disturbance becomes evident as a change in plasma pH, the body's buffers are ineffectual. The loss of buffering ability leaves the body with only two options: respiratory compensation or renal compensation. And if the problem is of respiratory origin, only one homeostatic compensation is available—the kidneys. If the problem is of metabolic origin, both respiratory and renal mechanisms can compensate.

20

The combination of an initial pH disturbance and the resultant compensatory changes is one factor that makes analysis of acid-base disorders in the clinical setting so difficult. In this book we will concentrate on simple scenarios with a single underlying cause. Changes that occur in the four simple acid-base disturbances are listed in Table 20-2 ■.

Respiratory Acidosis A state of respiratory acidosis occurs when alveolar hypoventilation results in CO_2 retention and elevated plasma P_{CO_2}. Some situations in which this occurs are respiratory depression due to drugs (including alcohol), increased airway resistance in asthma, impaired gas exchange in fibrosis or severe pneumonia, and muscle weakness in muscular dystrophy and other muscle diseases. The most common cause of respiratory acidosis is *chronic obstructive pulmonary disease* (COPD), such as emphysema, in which inadequate gas exchange is compounded by loss of alveolar exchange area.

No matter what the cause of respiratory acidosis, plasma CO_2 levels increase, leading to elevated H^+ and HCO_3^-:

$$\uparrow CO_2 + H_2O \rightarrow H_2CO_3 \rightarrow \uparrow H^+ + \uparrow HCO_3^-$$

The hallmark of respiratory acidosis is decreased pH and elevated bicarbonate levels (Table 20-2). Because the problem is of respiratory origin, the body cannot carry out respiratory compensation. (However, depending on the problem, mechanical ventilation can be used to assist breathing.)

Any compensation for respiratory acidosis must occur through renal mechanisms that excrete H^+ and reabsorb HCO_3^-. The excretion of H^+ raises plasma pH. Reabsorption of HCO_3^- provides additional buffer that combines with H^+, lowering the H^+ concentration and therefore raising the pH.

In chronic obstructive pulmonary disease, renal compensation mechanisms for acidosis can moderate the pH change, but they may not be able to return the pH to its normal range. If you look at pH and HCO_3^- levels in patients with compensated respiratory acidosis, you find that both those values are higher than they were when the acidosis was at its worst.

Metabolic Acidosis Metabolic acidosis is a disturbance of mass balance that occurs when the dietary and metabolic input of H^+ exceeds H^+ excretion. Metabolic causes of acidosis include lactic acidosis, which is a result of anaerobic metabolism, and ketoacidosis, which results from excessive breakdown of fats or certain amino acids. The metabolic pathway that produces ketoacids in diabetes mellitus is described in Chapter 21. Ingested substances that cause metabolic acidosis include methanol, aspirin, and ethylene glycol (antifreeze).

Metabolic acidosis is expressed by the equation

$$\uparrow CO_2 + H_2O \leftarrow H_2CO_3 \leftarrow \uparrow H^+ + \downarrow HCO_3^- \quad (8)$$

Hydrogen ion concentration increases because of the H^+contributed by the metabolic acids. This increase shifts the equilibrium represented in the equation to the left, increasing CO_2 levels and using up HCO_3^- buffer.

Metabolic acidosis can also occur if the body loses HCO_3^-. The most common cause of bicarbonate loss is diarrhea, during which HCO_3^- is lost from the intestines. The pancreas produces HCO_3^- from CO_2 and H_2O by a mechanism similar to the renal mechanism illustrated in Figure 20-21. The H^+ made at the same time is released into the blood. Normally, the HCO_3^- is released into the small intestine, then reabsorbed into the blood, buffering the H^+. However, if HCO_3^- is not reabsorbed because a person is experiencing diarrhea, a state of acidosis results.

Whether HCO_3^- concentration is elevated or decreased is an important criterion for distinguishing metabolic acidosis from respiratory acidosis (Table 20-2).

You would think from looking at equation 8 that metabolic acidosis would be accompanied by elevated P_{CO_2}. However, unless the individual also has a lung disease, respiratory compensation takes place almost instantaneously. Both elevated CO_2 and elevated H^+ stimulate ventilation through the pathways described earlier. As a result, P_{CO_2} decreases to normal or even below-normal levels via hyperventilation.

Uncompensated metabolic acidosis is rarely seen clinically. Indeed, a common sign of metabolic acidosis is hyperventilation, evidence of respiratory compensation occurring in response to the acidosis.

The renal compensations discussed for respiratory acidosis also take place in metabolic acidosis: secretion of H^+ and reabsorption of HCO_3^-. Renal compensations take several days to reach full effectiveness, and so they are not usually seen in acute disturbances.

Respiratory Alkalosis States of alkalosis are much less common than acidotic conditions. Respiratory alkalosis occurs as a result of hyperventilation, when alveolar ventilation increases without a matching increase in metabolic CO_2 production. Consequently, plasma P_{CO_2} falls and alkalosis results when the equation shifts to the left:

$$\downarrow CO_2 + H_2O \leftarrow H_2CO_3 \leftarrow \downarrow H^+ + \downarrow HCO_3^-$$

The decrease in CO_2 shifts the equilibrium to the left, and consequently both plasma H^+ and plasma HCO_3^- decrease. Low plasma HCO_3^- levels in alkalosis indicate a respiratory disorder.

The primary clinical cause of respiratory alkalosis is excessive artificial ventilation. Fortunately, this condition is easily corrected by adjusting the ventilator. The most common physiological cause of respiratory alkalosis is hysterical hyperventilation caused by anxiety. When this is the cause, the neurological symptoms caused by alkalosis can be partially reversed by having the patient breathe into a paper bag. In doing so, the patient rebreathes exhaled CO_2, a process that raises arterial P_{CO_2} and corrects the problem.

Because this alkalosis has respiratory cause, the only compensation available to the body is renal. Filtered bicarbonate, which if reabsorbed could act as a buffer and increase pH even more, is not reabsorbed in the proximal tubule and is secreted in the distal nephron. The combination of HCO_3^- excretion and H^+ reabsorption in the distal nephron decreases the body's HCO_3^- and increases its H^+, both of which help correct the alkalosis.

Metabolic Alkalosis Metabolic alkalosis has two common causes: excessive vomiting of acidic stomach contents and excessive ingestion of bicarbonate-containing antacids. In both cases, the resulting alkalosis reduces H^+ concentration:

$$\downarrow CO_2 + H_2O \rightarrow H_2CO_3 \rightarrow \downarrow H^+ + \uparrow HCO_3^-$$

The decrease in H^+ shifts the equilibrium to the right, meaning that carbon dioxide (P_{CO_2}) decreases and HCO_3^- goes up.

Just as in metabolic acidosis, respiratory compensation for metabolic alkalosis is rapid. The increase in pH and drop in P_{CO_2} depress ventilation. Less CO_2 is blown off, raising the P_{CO_2} and creating more H^+ and HCO_3^-. This respiratory compensation helps correct the pH problem but elevates HCO_3^- levels even more. However, the compensation is limited because hypoventilation causes hypoxia. Once the arterial P_{O_2} drops below 60 mm Hg, hypoventilation ceases.

The renal response to metabolic alkalosis is the same as that for respiratory alkalosis: HCO_3^- is excreted and H^+ is reabsorbed.

This chapter has used fluid balance and acid-base balance to illustrate functional integration in the cardiovascular, respiratory, and renal systems. Changes in body fluid volume, reflected by changes in blood pressure, trigger both cardiovascular and renal homeostatic responses. Disturbances of acid-base balance are met with compensatory responses from both the respiratory and renal systems. Because of the interwoven responsibilities of these three systems, a disturbance in one system is likely to cause disturbances in the other two. Recognition of this fact is an important aspect of treatment for many clinical conditions.

RUNNING PROBLEM CONCLUSION

HYPONATREMIA

In acute cases of dilutional hyponatremia such as Lauren's, the treatment goal is to correct the body's depleted Na^+ load and raise the plasma osmolarity to reduce cerebral swelling. The physicians in the emergency medical tent started a slow intravenous drip of 3% saline and restricted Lauren's oral fluid intake. Over the course of several hours, the combination of Na^+ intake and excretion of dilute urine returned Lauren's plasma Na^+ to normal levels.

Hyponatremia has numerous causes, including inappropriate secretion of antidiuretic hormone (a condition known as SIADH, which stands for *s*yndrome of *i*nappropriate *a*nti*d*iuretic *h*ormone secretion). To learn more about medical causes of hyponatremia, Google *hyponatremia*. To learn more about exercise-associated hyponatremia, visit the Gatorade Sports Science Institute at *www.gssiweb.com*.

(This problem was developed by Matt Panke while he was a kinesiology graduate student at the University of Texas.)

	QUESTION	FACTS	INTEGRATION AND ANALYSIS
1.	What are the names of the fluids found in the two major body compartments and the major ions in each fluid?	The two major body compartments are the intracellular space and the extracellular space. Intracellular fluid (ICF) is found in the former, extracellular fluid (ECF) in the latter. The primary ICF ion is K^+, and the major ECF ions are Na^+ and Cl^-.	N/A*

RUNNING PROBLEM CONCLUSION (continued)

	QUESTION	FACTS	INTEGRATION AND ANALYSIS
2.	Based on Lauren's history, give a reason for why her weight increased during the race.	Lauren reported drinking lots of water and sports drinks. One liter of pure water has a mass of 1 kg.	Lauren's fluid intake was greater than her fluid loss from sweating. A 2-kg increase in body weight means she drank an excess of about 2 L.
3.	Which fluid—ECF or ICF—is being diluted in dilutional hyponatremia?	Ingested water distributes itself throughout the ECF and ICF. Sodium is one of the major extracellular cations.	Lauren consumed a large amount of Na-free fluid and therefore diluted her Na^+ stores. Both ECF and ICF have lower osmolarities, but the diluted Na^+ is most noticeable in the ECF.
4.	One way to estimate osmolarity is to double the plasma Na^+ concentration. If normal body osmolarity is 280 mOsM, what effect will Lauren's dilutional hyponatremia have on her cells?	Lauren's plasma Na^+ is 124 mEq/L. For Na^+, 1 mEq = 1 milliosmole, and therefore doubling this value tells you that Lauren's estimated plasma osmolarity is 248 mOsM. Water distributes according to tonicity.	At the start of the race, Lauren's cells were at 280 mOsM. The water she ingested distributed according to tonicity, so water entered the ICF from the ECF, resulting in cell swelling.
5.	Which organ or tissue are the medical personnel most concerned about in dilutional hyponatremia?	All cells in Lauren's body will swell as a result of excess water ingestion. The brain is encased in the rigid skull.	The bony skull restricts the swelling of brain tissue, causing neurological symptoms, including confusion, headache, and loss of coordination. With lower Na^+ concentrations, death can result.
6.	Assuming a sweating rate of 1.0 L/h and a sweat Na^+ level of 70 mEq/L, how much Na^+ did Lauren lose during the 16-hour race?	1.0 L sweat lost/h × 16 h × 70 mEq Na^+/L sweat = 1120 mEq Na^+ lost during the 16-hour race.	Without Na^+ intake to match the amount of Na^+ lost in her sweat, Lauren's Na^+ concentration will fall as she ingests fluid.
7.	Total body water for a 60-kg female is approximately 30 L, and her ECF volume is 10 L. Based on the information given so far, what volume of fluid did Lauren ingest during the race?	From the sweating rate given in Question 6, you know that Lauren lost 16 liters of sweat during the race. You also know that she gained 2 kg in weight. One liter of water weighs 1 kg.	Lauren must have ingested at least 18 liters of fluid. You have no information on routes of fluid loss, such as urine and insensible water lost during breathing.
8.	What would you expect to happen to vasopressin and aldosterone production in response to dilutional hyponatremia?	Vasopressin secretion is inhibited by a decrease in osmolarity. The usual stimuli for renin or aldosterone release are low blood pressure and hyperkalemia.	Vasopressin secretion increases with hyponatremia. The usual stimuli for aldosterone secretion are absent, but a pathological decrease in plasma Na^+ of 10 mEq/L can stimulate the adrenal cortex to secrete aldosterone. Thus, Lauren's plasma Na^+ may be low enough to increase her aldosterone secretion.

*Not applicable

642 645 658 661 665 671

CHAPTER SUMMARY

Homeostasis of body fluid volume, electrolytes, and pH follows the principle of *mass balance*: whatever comes into the body must be excreted. The *control systems* that regulate these parameters are among the most complicated reflexes of the body because of the overlapping functions of the kidneys, lungs, and cardiovascular system. At the cellular level, however, the *movement of molecules across membranes* follows familiar patterns, as transfer of water and solutes from one *compartment* to another depends on osmosis, diffusion, and protein-mediated transport.

Fluid and Electrolyte Homeostasis

1. The renal, respiratory, and cardiovascular systems control fluid and electrolyte balance. Behaviors such as drinking also play an important role. (p. 642; Fig. 20-1)
2. Pulmonary and cardiovascular compensations are more rapid than renal compensation. (p. 643)

Water Balance

IP Urinary: Early Filtrate Processing

3. Most water intake comes from food and drink. The largest water loss is 1.5 liters/day in urine. Smaller amounts are lost in feces, by evaporation from skin, and in exhaled humidified air. (p. 644; Fig. 20-2)
4. Renal water reabsorption conserves water but cannot restore water lost from the body. (p. 644; Fig. 20-3)
5. To produce dilute urine, the nephron must reabsorb solute without reabsorbing water. To concentrate urine, the nephron must reabsorb water without reabsorbing solute. (p. 645)
6. Filtrate leaving the ascending limb of the loop of Henle is dilute. The final concentration of urine depends on the water permeability of the collecting duct. (p. 645; Fig. 20-4)
7. The hypothalamic hormone **vasopressin** controls collecting duct permeability to water in a graded fashion. When vasopressin is absent, water permeability is nearly zero. (p. 646; Fig. 20-5)
8. Vasopressin causes distal nephron cells to insert **aquaporin** water pores in their apical membrane. (p. 647; Fig. 20-6)
9. An increase in ECF osmolarity or a decrease in blood pressure will stimulate vasopressin release from the posterior pituitary. Osmolarity is monitored by hypothalamic **osmoreceptors.** Blood pressure and blood volume are sensed by receptors in the carotid and aortic bodies, and in the atria, respectively. (p. 648; Figs. 20-7, 20-8)
10. The loop of Henle is a **countercurrent multiplier** that creates high osmolarity in the medullary interstitial fluid by actively transporting Na^+, Cl^-, and K^+ out of the nephron. This high medullary osmolarity is necessary for formation of concentrated urine as filtrate flows through the collecting duct. (pp. 650–651; Figs. 20-9, 20-10)
11. The **vasa recta** capillaries carry away water leaving the nephron tubule so that the water does not dilute the medullary interstitium. (p. 651; Fig. 20-10)
12. Urea contributes to the high osmolarity in the renal medulla. (p. 652)

Sodium Balance and the Regulation of ECF Volume

IP Urinary: Late Filtrate Processing

13. The total amount of Na^+ in the body is a primary determinant of ECF volume. (p. 652; Fig. 20-12)
14. The steroid hormone **aldosterone** increases Na^+ reabsorption and K^+ secretion. (p. 652; Fig. 20-13)
15. Aldosterone acts on **principal cells** (P cells) of the distal nephron. This hormone enhances Na^+-K^+-ATPase activity and increases open time of Na^+ and K^+ leak channels. It also stimulates the synthesis of new pumps and channels. (p. 652; Fig. 20-13)
16. Aldosterone secretion can be controlled directly at the adrenal cortex. Increased ECF K^+ stimulates aldosterone secretion, but increased ECF osmolarity inhibits it. (p. 652; Tbl. 20-1)
17. Aldosterone secretion is also stimulated by **angiotensin II.** Granular cells in the kidney secrete **renin**, which converts **angiotensinogen** in the blood to **angiotensin I. Angiotensin converting enzyme (ACE)** converts ANG I to ANG II. (pp. 653–654; Fig. 20-14)
18. The stimuli for the release of renin are related either directly or indirectly to low blood pressure. (p. 654; Fig. 20-15)
19. ANG II has additional effects that raise blood pressure, including increased vasopressin secretion, stimulation of thirst, vasoconstriction, and activation of the cardiovascular control center. (pp. 654–655; Fig. 20-14)
20. **Atrial natriuretic peptide** (ANP) and **brain natriuretic peptide** (BNP) enhance Na^+ excretion and urinary water loss by increasing GFR, inhibiting tubular reabsorption of NaCl, and inhibiting the release of renin, aldosterone, and vasopressin. (p. 656; Fig. 20-16)

Potassium Balance

21. Potassium homeostasis keeps plasma K^+ concentrations in a narrow range. **Hyperkalemia** and **hypokalemia** cause problems with excitable tissues, especially the heart. (p. 656)

Behavioral Mechanisms in Salt and Water Balance

22. Thirst is triggered by hypothalamic osmoreceptors and relieved by drinking. (p. 658)
23. **Salt appetite** is triggered by aldosterone and angiotensin. (p. 658)

Integrated Control of Volume and Osmolarity

IP Fluids & Electrolytes: Water Homeostasis

24. Homeostatic compensations for changes in salt and water balance follow the law of mass balance. Fluid and solute added to the body must be removed, and fluid and solute lost from the body must be replaced. However, perfect compensation is not always possible. (pp. 659–661; Fig. 20-18; Tbl. 20-2)

Acid-Base Balance

IP Fluids & Electrolytes: Acid/Base Homeostasis

25. The body's pH is closely regulated because pH affects intracellular proteins, such as enzymes and membrane channels. (p. 663)
26. Acid intake from foods and acid production by the body's metabolic processes are the biggest challenge to body pH. The most significant source of acid is CO_2 from respiration, which combines with water to form carbonic acid (H_2CO_3). (p. 664; Fig. 20-19)
27. The body copes with changes in pH by using buffers, ventilation, and renal secretion or reabsorption of H^+ and HCO_3^-. (p. 664; Fig. 20-19)
28. Bicarbonate produced from CO_2 is the most important extracellular buffer of the body. Bicarbonate buffers organic acids produced by metabolism. (p. 665)
29. Ventilation can correct disturbances in acid-base balance because changes in plasma P_{CO_2} affect both the H^+ content and the HCO_3^- content of the blood. An increase in P_{CO_2} stimulates central chemoreceptors. An increase in plasma H^+ stimulates carotid and aortic chemoreceptors. Increased ventilation excretes CO_2 and plasma decreases H^+. (p. 666; Fig. 20-20)
30. In **acidosis**, the kidneys secrete H^+ and reabsorb HCO_3^-. (p. 669; Figs. 20-21, 20-22, 20-23a)
31. In **alkalosis**, the kidneys secrete HCO_3^- and reabsorb H^+. (p. 669; Fig. 20-23b)
32. **Intercalated cells** in the collecting duct are responsible for the fine regulation of acid-base balance. (p. 668; Fig. 20-23)

QUESTIONS

(Answers to the Review Questions begin on page A1.)

THE PHYSIOLOGY PLACE

Access more review material online at **The Physiology Place** website. There you'll find review questions, problem-solving activities, case studies, flashcards, and direct links to both *InterActive Physiology®* and PhysioEx™. To access the site, go to *www.physiologyplace.com* and select Human Physiology, Fourth Edition.

LEVEL ONE REVIEWING FACTS AND TERMS

1. What is an electrolyte? Name five electrolytes whose concentrations must be regulated by the body.
2. List five organs and four hormones important in maintaining fluid and electrolyte balance.
3. Compare the routes by which water enters the body with the routes by which the body loses water.
4. List the receptors that regulate osmolarity, blood volume, blood pressure, ventilation, and pH. Where are they located, what stimulates them, and what compensatory mechanisms are triggered by them?
5. How do the two limbs of the loop of Henle differ in their permeability to water? What makes this difference in permeability possible?
6. Which ion is a primary determinant of ECF volume? Which ion is the determinant of extracellular pH?
7. What happens to the resting membrane potential of excitable cells when plasma K^+ concentrations decrease? Which organ is most likely to be affected by changes in K^+ concentration?
8. Appetite for what two substances is important in regulating fluid volume and osmolarity?
9. Write out the words for the following abbreviations: ADH, ANP, ACE, ANG II, JG apparatus, P cell, I cell.
10. Make a list of all the different membrane transporters in the kidney. For each transporter, tell (a) which section(s) of the nephron contain(s) the transporter; (b) whether the transporter is on the apical membrane only, on the basolateral membrane only, or on both; (c) whether it participates in reabsorption only, in secretion only, or in both of these processes.
11. List and briefly explain three reasons why monitoring and regulating ECF pH are important. What three mechanisms does the body use to cope with changing pH?
12. Which is more likely to accumulate in the body, acids or bases? List some sources of each.
13. What is a buffer? List three intracellular buffers. Name the primary extracellular buffer.
14. Name two ways the kidneys alter plasma pH. Which compounds serve as urinary buffers?
15. Write the equation that shows how CO_2 is related to pH. What enzyme increases the rate of this reaction? Name two cell types that possess high concentrations of this enzyme.
16. When ventilation increases, what happens to arterial P_{CO_2}? To plasma pH? To plasma H^+ concentration?

LEVEL TWO REVIEWING CONCEPTS

17. **Concept map:** Map the homeostatic reflexes that occur in response to each of the following situations:
    (a) decreased blood volume, normal blood osmolarity
    (b) increased blood volume, increased blood osmolarity
    (c) normal blood volume, increased blood osmolarity
18. Figures 20-20 and 20-21 show the respiratory and renal compensations for acidosis. Draw similar maps for alkalosis.
19. Explain how the loop of Henle and vasa recta work together to create dilute renal filtrate.
20. Diagram the mechanism by which vasopressin alters the composition of urine.
21. Make a table that specifies the following for each substance listed: hormone or enzyme? steroid or peptide? produced by which cell or tissue? target cell or tissue? target has what response?
    (a) ANP (d) ANG II
    (b) aldosterone (e) vasopressin
    (c) renin (f) angiotensin-converting enzyme
22. Name the four main compensatory mechanisms for restoring low blood pressure to normal. Why do you think there are so many homeostatic pathways for raising low blood pressure?
23. Compare and contrast the terms in each set:
    (a) principal cells and intercalated cells
    (b) renin, angiotensin II, aldosterone, ACE
    (c) respiratory acidosis and metabolic acidosis, including causes and compensations
    (d) water reabsorption in proximal tubule, distal tubule, and ascending limb of the loop of Henle
    (e) respiratory alkalosis and metabolic alkalosis, including causes and compensations

LEVEL THREE PROBLEM SOLVING

24. (a) A 45-year-old man visiting from out of town arrives at the emergency room having an asthma attack caused by pollen. Blood drawn before treatment showed the following: $HCO_3^- = 30$ meq/L (normal: 24), $P_{CO_2} = 70$ mm Hg, pH = 7.24. What is the man's acid-base state? Is this an acute or a chronic situation?
    (b) The man was treated and made a complete recovery. Over the next ten years he continued to smoke a pack of cigarettes a day, and a year ago his family doctor diagnosed chronic obstructive pulmonary disease (emphysema). The man's most recent blood test showed the following: $HCO_3^- = 45$ meq/L, $P_{CO_2} = 85$ mm Hg, pH = 7.34. What is the man's acid-base state now? Is this an acute or a chronic situation?
    (c) Explain why in his second illness his plasma bicarbonate level and P_{CO_2} are higher than in the first illness but his pH is closer to normal.
25. Karen has bulimia, in which she induces vomiting to avoid weight gain. When the doctor sees her, her weight is 89 lb and her respiration rate is 6 breaths/min (normal 12). Her blood HCO_3^- is 62 meq/L (normal: 24–29), arterial blood pH is 7.61, and P_{CO_2} is 61 mm Hg.
    (a) What is her acid-base condition called?
    (b) Explain why her plasma bicarbonate level is so high.
    (c) Why is she hypoventilating? What effect will this have on the pH and total oxygen content of her blood? Explain your answers.

26. Hannah, a 31-year-old woman, decided to have colonic irrigation, a procedure during which large volumes of distilled water were infused into her rectum. During the treatment she absorbed 3000 mL of water. About 12 hours later, her roommate found her in convulsions and took her to the emergency room. Her blood pressure was 140/90, her plasma Na^+ concentration was 106 meq/L (normal: 135 meq/L), and her plasma osmolarity was 270 mOsM. In a concept map or flow chart, diagram all the homeostatic responses her body was using to attempt compensation for the changes in blood pressure and osmolarity.

LEVEL FOUR QUANTITATIVE PROBLEMS

27. The Henderson-Hasselbalch equation is a mathematical expression of the relationship between pH, HCO_3^- concentration, and dissolved CO_2 concentration. One variant of the equation uses P_{CO_2} instead of dissolved CO_2 concentration:

$$pH = \frac{6.1 + \log [HCO_3^-]}{0.03 \times P_{CO_2}}$$

(a) If arterial blood has a P_{CO2} of 40 mm Hg and its HCO_3^- concentration is 24 mM, what is its pH? (You will need a log table or calculator with a logarithmic function capability.)

(b) What is the pH of venous blood with the same HCO_3^- concentration but a P_{CO_2} of 46 mm Hg?

28. In extreme dehydration, urine can reach a concentration of 1400 mOsM. If the minimum amount of waste solute that a person must excrete daily is about 600 milliosmoles, what is the minimum urine volume that will be excreted in one day?

29. Hyperglycemia in a diabetic patient leads to osmotic diuresis and dehydration. Given the following information, answer the questions.

Plasma glucose = 400 mg/dL	Normal urine flow = 1 L per day
GFR = 130 mL/min	Normal urine osmolarity = 300 mOsM
Glucose T_m = 400 mg/min	Molecular mass of glucose = 180 daltons
Renal plasma flow = 500 mL/min	

(a) How much glucose filters into the nephron each minute?
(b) How much glucose is reabsorbed each minute?
(c) How much glucose is excreted in the urine each day?
(d) Assuming that dehydration causes maximal ADH secretion and allows the urine to concentrate to 1200 mOsM, how much additional urine will this diabetic patient excrete in a day?

ANSWERS

Answers to Concept Check Questions

Page 647

1. Apical membranes will have more water pores when vasopressin is present.
2. The collecting duct cells concentrate organic solutes that counteract the hypertonic effect of the cells' environment.

Page 649

3. Hyperosmotic NaCl is hypertonic and causes the osmoreceptors to shrink, but hyperosmotic urea is hypotonic and causes them to swell. Because only cell shrinkage causes firing, osmoreceptors exposed to urea will not fire.
4. Because vasopressin enhances water reabsorption, vasopressin levels would increase with dehydration.
5. If vasopressin secretion is suppressed, the urine will be dilute.

Page 651

6. Solutes that remain in the lumen when the NKCC symporter is inhibited force water to remain in the lumen with them because urine can be concentrated only to 1200 mOsM. Thus each 12 milliosmoles of un-reabsorbed solute will "hold" an additional 10 mL of water in the urine.
7. Diuretics that inhibit the NKCC symporter leave K^+ in the tubule lumen, where it is likely to be excreted, thus increasing urinary K^+ loss.

Page 653

8. Na^+ and K^+ are moving down their electrochemical gradients.

Page 656

9. In hyperkalemia, resting membrane potential depolarizes. Excitable tissues fire one action potential but are unable to repolarize to fire a second one.
10. Atherosclerotic plaques block blood flow, which decreases GFR and decreases pressure in the afferent arteriole. Both events are stimuli for renin release.
11. Renin secretion begins a cascade that produces angiotensin II. This powerful hormone then causes vasoconstriction, acts on the medullary cardiovascular control center to increase blood pressure, increases production of vasopressin and aldosterone, and increases thirst, resulting in drinking and an increased fluid volume in the body. All these responses may contribute to increased blood pressure.

Page 658

12. On the left side of Figure 20-7, interneurons also lead from hypothalamic osmoreceptors to the hypothalamic thirst centers.

Page 667

13. The muscles of ventilation involved are the diaphragm, the external intercostals, and the scalenes.
14. The bicarbonate level increases as the reaction shifts to the right as a result of added CO_2. Once a new equilibrium state is achieved, bicarbonate cannot act as a buffer because the system is at equilibrium.

Page 669

15. In the distal nephron, both K^+ and H^+ are being moved against their concentration gradients, which requires ATP. In the proximal tubule, Na^+ is moving down its concentration gradient, providing the energy to push H^+ against its gradient.
16. When intercalated cells reabsorb K^+, they secrete H^+, and therefore blood pH increases.

Answers to Figure Questions

Page 653

Figure 20-12: See Fig. 15-22, p. 523.

Page 655

Figure 20-14: See Fig. 15-21, p. 522, for the cardiovascular pathway, Fig. 20-13 for the effector cell involved in aldosterone action, and Fig. 20-6 for the effector cell involved in vasopressin action.

Answers to End-of-Chapter Review Questions

CHAPTER 1

LEVEL ONE REVIEWING FACTS AND TERMS

1. Physiology is the study of the normal functioning of a living organism and its component parts. Anatomy is the study of structure.
2. See Figure 1-1.
3. See Table 1-1.
4. Physiology integrates body function across all levels of organization, from cells to organs, and emphasizes the coordinated function of body systems.
5. Homeostasis is the maintenance of internal stability. Body temperature and water balance are two homeostatically maintained functions.
6. Four major themes are homeostasis and control systems, structure-function relationships, biological energy, and communication.

LEVEL TWO REVIEWING CONCEPTS

7. Mapping: Maps are highly individual. The best way to evaluate your map is to compare it with one done by a classmate or to ask your instructor for comments.
8. (a) Tissues are collections of cells that carry out related functions. Organs are collections of tissues that form structural and functional units.
   (b) The *x*-axis is the independent variable, and the *y*-axis is the dependent variable.
   (c) The dependent variable changes when the independent variable is manipulated or altered during the experiment.
   (d) The teleological approach is a functional approach that is concerned with the "why" of a physiological system. The mechanistic approach is concerned with the physiological mechanisms of physiology (the "hows" of a physiological system).
   (e) The internal environment of the human body is the extracellular fluid. The external environment is the world outside the body.
   (f) In a blind study, the subjects do not know the treatment they are receiving. In a double-blind study, neither the subject nor the administrator of the experiment knows which treatment is the control and which is the active treatment. In a crossover study, one subject serves as both the control and the experimental subject.
9. Lumens that are in contact with the external environment include nasal and oral cavities, external ear, lacrimal ducts, ducts of the integumentary system (sweat, sebaceous, and mammary glands), urethra, anus, and vagina. Lumens that are not in contact with the external environment include organs of the digestive tract (esophagus, stomach, small and large intestines), accessory digestive organs (ducts of the salivary glands, pancreas, liver and gall bladder, and the gall bladder itself), urinary organs (renal tubules and renal pelvis of the kidneys, ureters), reproductive organs (seminiferous tubules, epididymis, ductus deferens, ejaculatory duct, ducts of prostate, bulbourethral glands, and seminal vesicles), cardiovascular organs (heart chambers, blood vessels), lymphatic vessels, deeper respiratory organs (larynx, trachea, bronchi, bronchioles, alveoli), canals and ventricles in central nervous system, cavities in bones, and hollow organelles.
10. The endocrine and nervous systems coordinate functions in all organ systems. Protection of the body is provided by integumentary, digestive, cardiovascular, and immune systems. The respiratory system exchanges oxygen and carbon dioxide with the external environment. The digestive system takes in nutrients, and the digestive and urinary systems eliminate digestive and metabolic waste products and water. The integumentary system loses water and solutes to the environment.

LEVEL THREE PROBLEM SOLVING

11. (a) "Because of gravity" is an incorrect mechanistic answer.
    (b) "To bring oxygen and nutrients to the cells" is a correct teleological answer.
    (c) "Because if it didn't, we would die" is a concrete teleological answer.
    (d) "Because of the pumping action of the heart" is a correct mechanistic answer.
12. Other problems that terrestrial animals have had to overcome include the requirement of an aqueous environment for fertilization (internal fertilization in mammals; many other terrestrial animals return to water to breed); requirement for aqueous environment for embryonic development (eggs in birds, some reptiles and insects); internal development in mammals, some reptiles, and insects; physical support (exoskeletons in insects, internal skeletons in vertebrates).

LEVEL FOUR QUANTITATIVE PROBLEMS

13. (a) The independent variable was time (*x*-axis). The dependent variable was body length (*y*-axis).
    (b) There was no control. A proper control would have been a similar group of fish treated identically except for being fed a diet with normal levels of vitamin D.
    (c) A graph should have time in days on the *x*-axis and body length on the *y*-axis. A line graph is most appropriate for these data.
    (d) Growth was slowest from days 0–3 (1 mm/3 days) and most rapid for days 6–9 and days 18–21 (each 3 mm/3 days).
14. (a) The independent variable was the concentration of the soaking solution. The dependent variable was volume change of the potato slices.
    (b) The volume measurements before soaking provide a baseline but there is no control in this test.
    (c) A bar graph or a scatter plot with best-fit line could be used to graph these data. A best-fit-line graph would allow you to estimate volume change at intermediate salt concentrations, such as 5%.
15. (a) This graph is a scatter plot.
    (b) The investigators were asking if there is a relationship between midarm muscle circumference and aerobic fitness.
    (c) There appears to be no relationship between midarm muscle circumference and aerobic fitness.

16. (a) This question has no "correct" answer. For peer critiques of the study, read the editorials published in the same issue: *New England Journal of Medicine* 347(2):132–33 and 137–39, 2002, July 11.
    (b) The placebo group could have reported decreased pain because they believed that the surgery had helped (a placebo effect) or because other interventions (the anesthesia and incision of the surgery, pain medication, physical therapy) had helped.
    (c) The study is directly applicable to a limited population: male veterans, under age 76, predominantly white, with osteoarthritis or degenerative joint disease.
    (d) This was a blind study.
    (e) The investigators were trying to determine whether a placebo effect could account for post-surgical improvement.

CHAPTER 2

LEVEL ONE REVIEWING FACTS AND TERMS

1. Three major essential elements in the human body are carbon, hydrogen, and oxygen.
2. Atoms bind to form molecules.
3. (a) proton (b) neutron (c) electron
4. The number of protons determines the atomic number.
5. Calcium, carbon, oxygen, sodium, nitrogen, potassium, hydrogen, and phosphorous.
6. Isotopes have the same number of *protons* and *electrons* but variable numbers of *neutrons*.
7. Unstable isotopes emit *radiation*. *Nuclear medicine* uses radiation for diagnosis and treatment of disease.
8. Paired electrons are stable. Atoms with unpaired electrons have a higher probability of gaining or losing electrons to other atoms.
9. An atom that gains or loses one or more electrons is called an *ion*.
10. (a) 2 (b) 4 (c) 1 (d) 3
11. *Nonpolar* compounds have even distribution of electrons; *polar* compounds have their electrons distributed unevenly. Polar compounds dissolve more readily in water and are said to be hydrophylic (water loving).
12. pH indicates the H^+ concentration. *Acidic* solutions have a pH less than 7; *basic* or *alkaline* solutions have a pH greater than 7.
13. *Buffers* help prevent changes in pH.
14. The four kinds of biomolecules are proteins (collagen, keratin, hemoglobin), carbohydrates (glucose, sucrose, fructose), lipids (cholesterol, phospholipids), and nucleic acids (ATP, DNA, RNA).
15. (a) 4 (b) 5 (c) 6 (d) 1 (e) 3
16. *Lipoproteins* are proteins plus fatty components. *Glycoproteins* are proteins plus carbohydrates.
17. (a) 1 (b) 5 (c) 4 (d) 2 (e) 3
18. (a) 3 (b) 1 (c) 5 (d) 2 (e) 4, 6
19. A nucleotide is composed of one or more phosphate groups, a five-carbon sugar, and a carbon-nitrogen ring called a base.
20. Any molecule that binds to another molecule is called a *ligand*.
21. (a) 4 (b) 3 (c) 2
22. A *cofactor* is an ion or small organic function group that must be present in order for an enzyme to work.
23. A protein which loses its conformation is said to be *denatured*.

LEVEL TWO REVIEWING CONCEPTS

24. Maps will be different. Figure 2-1 is a good starting map for List 1. Check your map against your classmate's, or ask your instructor to look for omissions and errors.
25. (a) Na has 11 electrons.
    (b) The net electrical charge on a sodium atom is zero.
    (c) Na has 12 neutrons.
    (d) If the atom loses one electron, it would be called an ion, or more specifically, a cation.
    (e) The Na ion has a charge of +1.
    (f) Na^+
    (g) If Na loses a proton, it becomes a neon atom.
    (h) Ne
26. $[H^+] = 10^{-3}$ M = *pH 3; acidic.* $[H^+] = 10^{-10}$ M = *pH 10; basic*
27. ATP has usable energy in a high-energy bond. DNA stores genetic information in cells. RNA translates the genetic information of DNA into proteins. cAMP assists transfer of signals from outside of cells to the inside of cells.
28. Primary structure is the sequence of amino acids in a peptide chain. The secondary structure folds the chain into either an α-helix or β-pleated sheet. Tertiary structure is the final three-dimensional shape of the protein (globular or fibrous). Quaternary structure is the combination of two or more protein subunits to form a larger molecule.
29. DNA contains the bases adenine, guanine, cytosine, and thymine. RNA substitutes uracil for thymine. DNA has the sugar deoxyribose; RNA has the sugar ribose. DNA is a doubled stranded molecule with two chains of bases linked in an alpha helix. RNA is a single stranded molecule.
30. Purines (adenine and guanine) are larger and consist of two carbon rings. Pyrimidines are smaller and have only one carbon ring.
31. Isoforms are structurally related proteins whose functions are similar but whose affinities for ligands differ.
32. (a) 4, 5 (b) 3 (c) 2, 1

LEVEL THREE PROBLEM SOLVING

33. Nucleotides contain all of the elements listed. Pure carbohydrates would have a C:H:O ratio of 1:2:1. Fats would have mostly carbon and hydrogen and little oxygen. Proteins would not have phosphorus and would have less nitrogen relative to carbon. The nitrogenous bases have larger proportions of N than amino acids do; the phosphate groups of nucleotides are mostly oxygen and phosphorus.
34. According to the equation, carbon dioxide combines with water to ultimately produce H^+ and HCO_3^- (bicarbonate ion). An increase in H^+ results in a decrease in the pH, as the blood becomes more acidic. Any negatively charged ion (anion) that attracts and binds H^+ has the potential to act as a buffer.
35. The atomic mass would remain the same while the atomic number would increase to 54. The resulting atom would be xenon.

LEVEL FOUR QUANTITATIVE PROBLEMS

36. (a) $C_6H_{12}O_6$ (glucose); m.w. 180
    (b) CO_2; m.w. 44
    (c) H_2O; m.w. 18
    (d) $C_3H_7O_2N$ (alanine); m.w. 89
    (e) $C_5H_{10}O_5$ (a pentose); m.w. 150
37. 0.9% solution = 0.9 g/100 mL. Weigh out 9 g NaCl, place into a 1 liter flask, and dissolve in enough water to yield 1 L of solution.
38. (a) 1 M = 6.02×10^{23} molecules of NaCl
    (b) A 1 M solution contains 1000 millimoles.
    (c) 1 M contains one equivalent of Na^+.
    (d) 58.5 g/liter = 5.85 g/100 mL = 5.85% solution.

39. 5% glucose = 5 g/100 mL or 10 g in 200 mL of solution. Molarity: 5 g/100 mL = 50 g/L × 1 mole/180 g = 0.278 moles/L or 278 millimoles/L (278 mM). 500 mL of 5% glucose would have 25 g glucose × 1 mole/180 g = 139 millimoles glucose in 500 mL.

40. Myoglobin has a higher affinity for oxygen than hemoglobin because at lower oxygen concentrations, more myoglobin has oxygen bound to it.

CHAPTER 3

LEVEL ONE REVIEWING FACTS AND TERMS

1. Four general functions of cell membranes are (1) to act as a barrier between cell and extracellular environment, (2) to regulate the exchange of material between cell and its environment, (3) to act as a point of transfer of information between the cell and other cells, and (4) to provide structural support.
2. The *fluid mosaic model* has a bilayer of *phospholipids* with embedded *proteins* and *carbohydrates* on the extracellular surface.
3. The cell membrane is mostly phospholipids and proteins.
4. Inclusions are particles of insoluble material in the cytosol, such as glycogen granules, protein fibers and ribosomes. Membranous organelles, such as mitochondria and the Golgi complex, are separated from the cytosol by one or more phospholipid membranes.
5. The cytoskeleton is a flexible, changeable, three-dimensional scaffolding of actin, microfilaments, intermediate filaments, and microtubules. The cytoskeleton (1) provides mechanical strength, (2) stabilizes the positions of organelles and membrane proteins, (3) transports material into the cell and throughout the cytoplasm, (4) links cells together and supports material outside cell, and (5) is responsible for various kinds of movement.
6. (a) 2 (b) 3 (c) 1 (d) 4
7. (a) 3 (b) 5 (c) 4 (d) 1 (e) 2
8. Lysosomal enzymes are activated by very acidic conditions.
9. Exocrine glands produce watery *serous secretions* and stickier *mucous secretions*.
10. *Endocrine* glands secrete hormones.
11. The four tissue types are connective tissue (such as tendons that hold muscles to bones); epithelial tissues (such as the protective epithelium of the skin); neural tissue (such as the brain); and muscular tissue (such as the heart and skeletal muscles).
12. The largest organ of the body is the skin.
13. (a) 1 (b) 1 (c) 4 (d) 3 (e) 4 (f) 4 (g) 4 (h) 1 (i) 1
14. Exocrine glands in the skin include sweat glands that secrete watery sweat, apocrine glands that secrete waxy or milky secretions, and sebaceous glands that secrete a mixture of lipids.
15. The matrix of a mitochondrion is the internal compartment of the organelle. The matrix of tissues is noncellular material found outside the cells.

LEVEL TWO REVIEWING CONCEPTS

16. Map: Check your map against Figures 3-11, 3-12, 3-13, and 3-14.
17. The three types of cell junctions are adhesive junctions, tight junctions, and gap junctions. They are all alike in that they link cells together and have proteins that are connected to the cell membrane. Adhesive junctions are designed to allow twisting and stretching of the tissues in which they are found. Tight junctions are designed to prevent movement of materials between the cells they link. Gap junctions are designed to allow material to pass from the cytoplasm of one cell directly into the cytoplasm of the connecting cell.
18. Pancreatic cells that manufacture insulin have more rough endoplasmic reticulum (RER); proteins are made on ribosomes bound to the RER membranes. Steroid hormones, such as cortisol, are lipids and are made on the smooth endoplasmic reticulum (SER), which lacks ribosomes.
19. Vesicles are bubbles or spheres made from phospholipid membranes similar to the cell membrane. Many vesicles are formed when ends of the Golgi apparatus are pinched off. Lysosomes and peroxisomes with enzymes remain in the cytoplasm, while the contents of secretory vesicles are released from the cell.
20. A stratified epithelium has many cell layers that offer more protection than the single-cell layer of a simple epithelium.
21. See Figure 3-25. Tight junctions prevent movement of material between the cells; leaky junctions allow some material to pass between the cells.
22. The glucose would enter the *intracellular fluid* of the intestinal cell, then move from the cell into *interstitial fluid* first, then into the *plasma*.
23. Cholesterol decreases membrane permeability to water by filling space between the interior tails of phospholipids.
24. Bone is a rigid connective tissue due to calcification; cartilage is firm but elastic. Bones are the primary support structure for the body; cartilage forms the ear, nose, larynx, and spine and helps hold bones together at the joints.
25. (a) A lumen is the hollow inside of an organ or tube. The wall is the layer of cells that make up the organ or tube.
    (b) Cytoplasm is everything inside the cell membrane except for the nucleus; cytosol is the semi-gelatinous, intracellular fluid that contains dissolved nutrients, ions, and waste products.
    (c) Myosin is a motor protein filament found in the cytoplasm. Keratin is a structural protein fiber made in connective tissue by keratinocytes.
26. This is an example of apoptosis because it is a normal part of development.
27. (a) cell junctions: 1 (flow through gap junctions), 2 (fusion of tight junction proteins), 4 (strength of desmosomes)
    (b) cell membrane: 1 (membrane receptors), 2 (membrane enzymes), 3 (phospholipid bilayer forms barrier), 4 (fluidity), 5 (ATP-dependent membrane protein transporters)
    (c) cytoskeleton: 2 (microtubules direct movement of chromosomes), 4 (strength), 5 (ATP required for actin-myosin interaction)
    (d) organelles: 2 (mRNA binds to ribosomes), 3 (membrane-bounded organelles), 5 (ATP-dependent processes like protein synthesis)
    (e) cilia: 2 (microtubules and dynein), 4 (strength and flexibility), 5 (ATP-dependent movement)
28. Though the extracellular matrix may be rigid, it is a dynamic structure. The proteins that comprise this matrix can be disassembled and re-assembled as necessary, to allow the tissues to change size and shape.

LEVEL THREE PROBLEM SOLVING

29. Cilia of the respiratory passages constantly sweep mucus and trapped particles away from the lungs, to the pharynx where they can be swallowed harmlessly. When they fail to beat, inhaled particulate matter and pathogens are more likely to reach the delicate lungs. Possible consequences include infections, inflammation due

to presence of irritants, cancer, and increased effort of breathing due to accumulation of mucus. The smoker's cough is necessary to remove the mucus that would otherwise be swept away by the cilia.

30. Epithelial cells have one of the highest rates of mitosis of any cell type in the body, because many are in vulnerable locations and need to be replaced frequently. For example, the epithelial lining of the stomach is frequently exposed to acids and enzymes which kill the cells after a few days. Tissues whose cells undergo mitosis more often are more likely to develop abnormal cell division.
31. Matrix metalloproteinases are enzymes secreted by cancer cells that dissolve the extracellular matrix, enabling cancer cells to escape from the original tumor and spread to other tissues. Blocking these enzymes may prevent metastasis (spread) of cancer cells from the organ where they arise, thus preventing them from interfering with normal physiology of other organs.

CHAPTER 4

LEVEL ONE REVIEWING FACTS AND TERMS

1. The three forms of work are transport work (moving substances across cell membranes); chemical work (making proteins for cell structures); and mechanical work, (muscle contraction).
2. Potential energy is stored energy, such as the energy stored in chemical bonds or concentration gradients. Kinetic energy is the energy of motion, such as muscles contracting.
3. The First Law says that there is a fixed amount of energy in the universe. The Second Law says that without input of energy, a system will become progressively less organized or ordered.
4. *Metabolism* is the sum of chemical processes in the cell.
5. Water and CO_2 are the *reactants* or *substrates*. The speed of a reaction is called the *reaction rate*.
6. *Enzymes* are proteins that speed up chemical reactions by *decreasing* their activation energy.
7. 1. (d) 2. (a) 3. (f) 4. (c)
8. *-ase* is the suffix added to most enzyme names.
9. Organic molecules that must be present for an enzyme to function are called *coenzymes*. Many coenzymes require dietary *vitamins* for their synthesis.
10. Molecules that gain electrons are said to be *reduced*; molecules that lose electrons are said to be *oxidized*.
11. Removal of water is *dehydration;* use of water to break down polymers is *hydrolysis*.
12. Removal of an amino acid group is *deamination*; transfer of an amino group to another molecule is *transamination*. Amino acids that are removed are broken down into urea and uric acid.
13. *Catabolic* reactions release energy; *anabolic* reactions synthesize large biomolecules. Metabolic energy is measured in kilocalories.
14. Accumulation of metabolic end products may result in *feedback inhibition*.
15. Transport of H^+ into the inner mitochondrial membrane creates a concentration gradient that stores energy. When the ions move back across the membrane, the energy that is released is trapped in the high-energy bond of ATP.
16. The two carrier molecules that bring electrons to the electron transport system are NADH and $FADH_2$.
17. The breakdown of lipids is *lipolysis*. Fatty acids are broken down through *beta-oxidation*. The acetyl CoA formed from lipids then can go into the citric acid cycle.
18. Carbohydrates and proteins have 4 kilocalories per gram; fat has 9.
19. The smooth endoplasmic reticulum is the primary organelle involved in lipid synthesis.

LEVEL TWO REVIEWING CONCEPTS

20. For map 1, use Figure 4-13 as a starting point. Use Figures 4-25 and 4-26 to help create map 2.
21. Potential energy stored in chemical bonds can be used to perform work, can be transferred to another molecule, or can be released as heat to the environment.
22. 1. (b) 2. (a) 3. (b) 4. (a) 5. (c) 6. (c)
23. It is better to store enzymes in an inactive form so that they cannot harm the cell if they are accidentally released.
24. Aerobic breakdown of one glucose yields 30–32 ATP, while anaerobic breakdown yields only 2 ATP. Anaerobic breakdown is much faster and does not require oxygen, but the energy yield is much less.
25. Conversion of glycogen to glucose to glucose 6-phosphate requires the energy of one ATP, but conversion of glycogen directly to glucose 6-phosphate does not use an ATP.
26. Transcription, which takes place in the nucleus, is the synthesis of mRNA from the sense strand of DNA. Translation is the conversion of information coded in mRNA into a string of amino acids; it takes place on cytoplasmic or RER ribosomes.
27. Anticodons are part of a tRNA molecule. Amino acids attach to tRNA at the opposite end of the molecule from the anticodon.
28. The energy in ATP is primarily within the high-energy bond holding the third phosphate group onto the rest of the molecule, and chemical bonds contain potential energy.
29. If the reaction cannot proceed without the contribution of energy from ATP, the activation energy must be large compared to a reaction that does not require ATP.

LEVEL THREE PROBLEM SOLVING

30. Cells that do not use glucose as their primary energy source could use certain amino acids or fatty acids instead. For example, the transporting epithelia of the intestine use the amino acid glutamate.
31. The mRNA sequence would be GCG<u>AUG</u>U<u>UCA</u>G<u>UCC</u>AUGG<u>CAU</u>-UGC. The anticodons would be UAC (tyrosine), AGU (serine), AGG (arginine), GUA (valine).

LEVEL FOUR QUANTITATIVE PROBLEMS

32. Exergonic.
33. The polypeptide will have 149 amino acids.

CHAPTER 5

LEVEL ONE REVIEWING FACTS AND TERMS

1. Membrane proteins act as structural proteins (link the cytoskeleton to fibers in the matrix); transporters (channels that allow water to cross the membrane); receptors (receptors for hormones); and enzymes (digestive enzymes in the intestine).
2. Active transport requires the direct or indirect use of energy. Passive transport uses only the energy stored in a concentration gradient.
3. Simple and facilitated diffusion and osmosis are examples of passive transport. Phagocytosis, exocytosis, and endocytosis are examples of active transport.

4. Four factors that speed up the rate of diffusion include a greater concentration difference, smaller distance, higher temperature, and smaller molecular size.
5. (a) 4 (b) 1, 6 (c) 3 (d) 5
6. Materials enter cells by simple diffusion through the phospholipid bilayer, by protein-mediated transport, or in vesicles (endocytosis/phagocytosis).
7. Cotransporters of molecules in the same direction are called *symport* carriers, in the opposite direction are called *antiport* carriers. A transport protein that moves only one molecule is a *uniport* carrier.
8. The two types of active transport are *direct* and *indirect*.
9. A molecule that moves freely between body compartments is said to be a *penetrating* solute. A molecule that is not able to enter cells is called a *nonpenetrating* solute.
10. The toddler has the highest percentage of body water (d), followed by the 25-year-old male (a), the 25-year-old female (b), and the 65-year-old female (c). Body weight has no direct effect on the percentage of body water, although people with more fat will have less water.
11. Osmolarity is the concentration of osmotically active particles in solution and is usually given in osmoles or milliosmoles per liter.
12. A hypotonic solution will cause net gain of water by the cell, whereas a hypertonic solution will cause net loss of water by the cell. Tonicity is determined by relative concentrations of nonpenetrating solutes in cell versus solution.
13. The four principles of electricity are: (1) like charges repel while opposite charges attract; (2) every positive ion has a matching negative ion; (3) energy must be used to separate ions or electrons and protons; and (4) conductors allow ions to move through them, while insulators keep ions separated.
14. (a) 7 (b) 1, 4 (c) 6 (d) 5 (e) 8 (f) 3 (g) 2
15. The equilibrium potential is the electrical gradient that is equal and opposite to a given concentration gradient.
16. Conductors allow free movement of electrical charge; insulators prevent movement of charge.

LEVEL TWO REVIEWING CONCEPTS

17. Use Figures 5-4, 5-7, 5-24, and 5-26 to help create your map.

Cell (67% of volume)	Interstitial fluid (25%)	Plasma (8%)
An^-, Proteins$^-$ $K^+ > Na^+$ $HCO_3^- > Cl^-$	$Na^+ > K^+$ $Cl^- > HCO_3^- >>>$ Proteins	$Na^+ > K^+$ $Cl^- > HCO_3^-$ Proteins

↑ Cell membrane ↑ Endothelium

19. The three factors that influence diffusion across a membrane are lipid solubility, thickness of the membrane, and surface area of the membrane. Diffusion across the membrane requires that a molecule pass through the lipid core of the membrane, so the more lipophilic a substance is, the faster it will diffuse. Diffusion is slower across thicker membranes and faster when there is more surface area.
20. Specificity is the ability of an enzyme or transporter to work on one specific molecule or class of molecules. Competition refers to the fact that the different substrates will compete for the binding site on the enzyme or transport protein. Saturation means that the protein will work at a maximum rate when all the binding sites are filled. Facilitated diffusion uses protein transporters, so each transporter can be described by its specificity (glucose transporter, amino acid transporter, etc.). If two or more different substrates are present, the substrates will compete for transport. And if enough substrate is present, transport rate will reach a maximum rate that cannot be exceeded.
21. (a) hypotonic (b) into the cells
22. The system started at equilibrium, so to disrupt the equilibrium requires input of energy. Therefore, some type of active transport has occurred.
23. (a) False. A 2 M NaCl solution = 4 OsM, but a 2 M glucose solution = 2 OsM.
    (b) True. See reasoning for 23a.
    (c) False. Water moves to dilute the more concentrated solute, therefore, water will move from the 2 OsM glucose to the 4 OsM NaCl.
    (d) False. As water moves out of the glucose solution, its volume decreases.
24. (a) A 1 M NaCl solution would be 2 OsM and isosmotic. (c) The glucose solution would have to have a molarity greater than 4 M for this statement to be true. (d) Once (c) is true, (d) becomes true.
25. An electrical gradient means the separation of electrical charge and is not concerned with what kinds of molecules are carrying those charges. An electrochemical gradient takes into account both the concentration gradient of a molecule and the electrical gradient.

LEVEL THREE PROBLEM SOLVING

26. Sodium leak channels on the apical side will allow Na^+ into the cell down its electrochemical gradient. There must be no water pores on the apical side or water will follow the Na^+. The removal of Na^+ but not water from the lumen makes the remaining fluid hypotonic. Na^+ entering the cell on the apical side is pumped out of the cell into the ECF on the basolateral side by the Na^+-K^+-ATPase.
27. Glucose moves into cells by facilitated diffusion using a protein carrier. Insulin could increase glucose uptake in a variety of ways. (1) It could increase the number of carrier proteins available for transport. (2) It could increase the affinity of the carrier for glucose. (3) Because diffusion depends on maintaining a concentration gradient for glucose, insulin could act on the cell's metabolism to keep the intracellular glucose concentration low. In reality, insulin uses methods 1 and 3.
28. The three terms apply to both enzymes and transporters. In one instance, the substrates are altered by the protein; and in the other, the substrates are simply moved unchanged across a membrane. In both instances, the substrate(s) binds to the protein at a specific binding site.
29. For all parts, note that the concentrations are given in mM rather than mOsM. 1 mM urea = 1 mOsM urea, but (assuming complete dissociation) 1mM NaCl = 2 mOsM NaCl.
    (a) Hyperosmotic (450 mOsM total) but isotonic (300 mOsM NaCl)
    (b) Hyposmotic (250 mOsM total) and hypotonic (200 mOsM NaCl)
    (c) Isosmotic (300 mOsM total) and hypotonic (200 mOsM NaCl)
    (d) Hyperosmotic (400 mOsM total) and isotonic (300 mOsM NaCl)
    (e) Hyperosmotic (350 mOsM total) and hypotonic (200 mOsM NaCl)

30. When sugars are added to membrane proteins in the ER and Golgi, they are added to proteins facing the lumen of these organelles, which will become the lumen of the secretory vesicles that bud off the Golgi. In Figure 5-24 on p. 149, you can see that whatever faces the inside of a vesicle will face the outside of the cell after being inserted into the membrane. Therefore the sugar tails of the membrane proteins will face the extracellular side once the proteins have been inserted into the membrane.

LEVEL FOUR QUANTITATIVE PROBLEMS

31. Plasma osmolarity = 296 mOsM
32. (a) ICF volume = 29.5 L; interstitial fluid volume = 9.8
    (b) Total solute = 12.432 osmoles; ECF solute = 3.7 osmoles; ICF solute = 8.732 osmoles; plasma solute = 0.799 osmoles.
33. Half-normal saline is approximately 154 mOsM.
34. (a) increases (b) decreases (c) increase (d) decrease
35. The graph shows simple diffusion (a). You know that it is not active transport because the concentration inside the cell does not increase past equilibrium (concentration in = concentration out). The graph is the same shape as the saturation graph in Figure 5-22 but the axes are not the same. There is only one solute being transported, so there is no evidence for competition.

CHAPTER 6

LEVEL ONE REVIEWING FACTS AND TERMS

1. The two routes for long-distance signal delivery are electrical signals carried by neurons and chemical signals that are distributed through the bloodstream.
2. The nervous and endocrine systems maintain homeostasis.
3. Chemical and electrical signals are sent throughout the body. Chemical signals are available to all cells because they are distributed through the blood.
4. Homeostasis is the process of maintaining a relatively stable internal environment.
5. Parameters that are maintained homeostatically include blood pressure, body temperature, heart rate, and blood glucose concentrations.
6. A sensory receptor receives information about changes in the environment and relays that information to an integrating center. A membrane receptor allows a chemical ligand to bind to a cell and start a reaction. Any cell with the receptor for a chemical will be a target of that chemical, but without the proper receptor, a cell cannot respond.
7. The signal ligand or first messenger binds to a receptor which activates and changes intracellular effectors.
8. The three amplifier enzymes are (a) adenylyl cyclase, (b) guanylyl cyclase, and (c) phospholipase C.
9. Protein kinases add phosphates from ATP to the substrate.
10. Stimulus, receptor, afferent pathway, integrating center, efferent pathway, effector, response.
11. Central receptors are located within the central nervous system; peripheral receptors are associated with sensory neurons of the peripheral nervous system.
12. (a) 3 (b) 1 (c) 4 (d) 5 (e) 2
13. Receptors for signal pathways are found in the nucleus, cytosol, or cell membrane.
14. Daily fluctuations in a parameter are called circadian rhythms. These cycles arise in special cells in the brain.
15. Down-regulation results in a decreased sensitivity to a prolonged signal.
16. Down-regulation occurs when receptor number or receptor affinity for the substrate decreases.
17. In negative feedback, the effector moves the system in the opposite direction from the stimulus.

LEVEL TWO REVIEWING CONCEPTS

18. (a) **Gap junctions** are formed when protein channels, called **connexons**, connect the cytoplasm of two cells. **Connexins** are the proteins that form the channels. When gap junctions are open, the cytoplasm of adjoining cells is continuous, forming a functional **syncytium**, or a unit that behaves like a single cell with multiple nuclei. Gap junctions can be found in the heart.
    (b) These are all chemicals secreted by cells into the extracellular space. **Paracrines** act on cells close to the cell that secreted them; **autocrines** act on the same cell that secretes them. Histamine is an example of a paracrine. **Cytokines** are peptides that can act as autocrines and paracrines or that can be distributed in the blood like **hormones**. Many growth factors are cytokines. **Neurocrines** are chemicals secreted by neurons, or nerve cells. Neurotransmitters, neurohormones, and neuromodulators are all neurocrines.
    (c) **Agonists** are molecules that have the same action as another molecule. Estrogens in birth control pills are examples of agonists. **Antagonists** are molecules whose action opposes that of another molecule. Antagonists to estrogens and androgens are used to treat hormone-dependent cancers.
    (d) **Transduction** is the process by which a signal molecule transfers its information from the extracellular fluid to the cytoplasm. Transduction often involves a **cascade**, or series, of steps, with **amplification** taking place at each step so that one signal molecule can result in a larger signal.
19. The four classes of membrane receptors are: (1) ligand-gated channels such as the ATP-gated K^+ channel (2) integrin receptors, e.g., receptors of platelets (3) receptor enzymes such as tyrosine kinase receptors, and (4) G-protein-coupled receptors such as those that activate adenylyl cyclase and subsequently cAMP.

20 Walter Cannon was the father of American physiology. His four postulates are:
   (a) The nervous system keeps body functions such as blood pressure and body temperature within normal limits.
   (b) Some body functions are regulated in an up-and-down (or tonic) fashion rather than in an on-off fashion.
   (c) Some functions are controlled by two signals that act in opposition: one signal enhances the function while the other signal inhibits it.
   (d) The response of a cell to a particular chemical signal depends on the receptor that the cell has for that signal. Different cells can have different receptors and therefore exhibit different responses.

21. Stimulus: a change that begins a response (example: touching a hot stove).
    Receptor: a cell or structure that senses the change of the stimulus (example: temperature receptor).
    Afferent pathway: the means by which information about the stimulus is conveyed to an integrating center, an input signal (example: a sensory nerve).
    Integrating center: a cell or group of cells that receives incoming information, decides whether and how it should be acted upon, and sends a signal that begins a response (example: the brain).

Efferent pathway: the signal that goes from the integrating center to the cell or tissue that will carry out the response (example: a nerve or a hormone).
Effector: the cell or tissue that will carry out the response (example: a muscle).
Response: what the cell or tissue does to react to the change caused by the stimulus (example: pull your hand away from the hot stove).

22. In negative feedback, the signal tells the response to turn off. Positive feedback reinforces the stimulus and keeps the response going. Both positive and negative feedback happen after the response has taken place; a feedforward response gets the response loop started before the stimulus does. Negative feedback helps keep a parameter within a range for homeostasis. Feedforward helps prevent big changes in the regulated function. Positive feedback makes a change bigger and keeps it going once started by a stimulus.
23. The primary advantage of neural control over endocrine control is speed. The primary advantage of endocrine control is the ability to affect widely separated tissues with a single signal. Neural is better for short-acting responses, endocrine for long-acting.
24. (a) negative feedback
    (b) positive feedback
    (c) negative feedback
    (d) negative feedback
25. (a) Tissues respond to glucagon by increasing blood glucose.
    (b) Breast tissues secrete and release milk.
    (c) the urinary bladder
    (d) sweat glands
26. (a) endocrine cells that secrete glucagon (the endocrine pancreas)
    (b) insufficient information given in question. The hormone oxytocin controls milk release (letdown) and the hormone prolactin regulates milk secretion.
    (c) the nervous system
    (d) the nervous system

LEVEL THREE PROBLEM SOLVING

27. (a) stimulus = cold wind causes body temperature to decrease; receptor = temperature receptors; afferent pathway = sensory nerve cells; integrating center = CNS; efferent pathway = efferent neurons; effectors = muscles used to pull an afghan around you; response = afghan conserves heat and causes body temperature to increase.
    (b) stimulus = smell of sticky buns; receptor = odor receptors in the nose; afferent path = sensory neurons; integrating center = CNS; efferent pathway = skeletal muscles; response = walk to bakery, buy, and devour buns.

LEVEL FOUR QUANTITATIVE PROBLEMS

28. (a) This paragraph describes amplification and a cascade.
    (b) One rhodopsin creates (1000 × 4000) or 4,000,000 GMP.

CHAPTER 7

LEVEL ONE REVIEWING FACTS AND TERMS

1. *Endocrinology* is the study of hormones.
2. Hormones alter the rate of enzymatic reactions, control transport of molecules into and out of the cell, or change gene expression and protein synthesis in their target cells.
3. See Figure 7-2 to check your answers.
4. (a) 4 (b) 5 (c) 1 (d) 2 (e) 3
5. d - b - c - a
6. Hormones are secreted into the *blood* for transport to a *distant target* and take effect at *very low* concentrations.
7. The half-life of a hormone is the amount of time required for half of a dose of hormone to disappear from the blood.
8. Hormones are broken down into their metabolites by the *kidneys* and *liver,* and the metabolites are excreted in the *urine* and *bile,* respectively.
9. Candidate hormones are often called *factors*.
10. Peptide hormones are made of three or more amino acids. Most hormones are peptides (see Figure 7-2). Steroid hormones are derived from cholesterol; examples include hormones made by the gonads, adrenal cortex, and placenta. Amine hormones are made from single amino acids; thyroid hormones, epinephrine, norepinephrine, and dopamine are examples.
11. (a) peptide hormones (some of the amines are lipophobic but some are lipophilic)
    (b) peptides and some amines
    (c) steroids
    (d) peptides and some amines
    (e) peptides
    (f) steroids
    (g) peptides
    (h) all classes
    (i) steroids and some amines
    (j) steroids
12. Steroids are not very water-soluble, or the carrier protects the hormone from being broken down and extends its half-life.
13. In the nucleus, steroid hormones act as a *transcription* factor, activating *genes* that control synthesis of new *proteins*.
14. Some steroid hormones also have receptors on the *cell membrane*.
15. Melatonin is made from *tryptophan,* and the other amines are made from *tyrosine*.
16. *Trophic* hormones control the secretion of other hormones.
17. In complex endocrine pathways, the hormones themselves may act as the *feedback* signals.
18. Neurosecretory hormones (or neurohormones) are synthesized and secreted from nerve cells or neurons.
19. The posterior pituitary secretes oxytocin and vasopressin, both peptide neurohormones.
20. The hypothalamic-hypophyseal portal system is composed of capillaries that pick up hormones secreted in the hypothalamus and deliver them directly to a set of capillaries in the adjacent anterior pituitary. The direct connection allows very small amounts of hypothalamic hormone to control the endocrine cells of the anterior pituitary.
21. Prolactin controls milk production by the breast and is not trophic. The remaining hormones are all trophic hormones. Growth hormone, or somatotropin, alters tissue metabolism and controls secretion of somatomedins. Corticotropin, or ACTH, controls cortisol secretion. Thyrotropin, or TSH, controls thyroid hormone secretion. Follicle-stimulating hormone (FSH) and luteinizing hormone (LH) control hormone secretion by the gonads as well as gamete production.
22. Long-loop negative feedback goes from a peripheral endocrine gland back to the pituitary and hypothalamus to shut off trophic hormone secretion. In short-loop negative feedback, the trophic hormone of the anterior pituitary has a negative feedback effect on the hypothalamus.

23. *Synergism* occurs when the effects of two hormones combined is greater than their individual effects added together. If two hormones must be present for a full effect to be demonstrated, the relationship is called *permissiveness*. If one hormone opposes the actions of another, the hormone is *antagonistic*.

LEVEL TWO REVIEWING CONCEPTS

24. Use Figure 7-3 to help with the map for List 1 and use Figures 7-12 and 7-13 for List 2.
25. (a) All these chemicals are secreted by cells for actions on other cells. Paracrines act on adjacent cells; cytokines act on adjacent or distant cells; hormones act on distant cells. Cytokines are always peptides; hormones may be peptides, steroids, or amines. Cytokines are made on demand; peptide hormones are made in advance and stored in the endocrine cell.
    (b) A primary endocrine pathology arises in the last endocrine gland of a complex endocrine reflex. Secondary pathologies arise in a gland secreting a trophic hormone. Either pathology may result in too much or too little hormone being secreted.
    (c) Hypersecretion is excess secretion of hormone; hyposecretion is secretion of less-than-normal amounts of hormone.
    (d) Both are part of the pituitary gland and both secrete peptide hormones. The anterior pituitary gland is a true endocrine gland, but the posterior pituitary is neural tissue. The signal for posterior pituitary neurohormone release is an action potential. Anterior pituitary hormones are released in response to hypothalamic trophic hormones.
26. See Table 7-1.

LEVEL THREE PROBLEM SOLVING

27. The meanings of the words given have not changed significantly. Endocrine receptors are membrane or intracellular proteins. Endocrine target cells may up- or down-regulate their responses. Specificity refers to the selective interaction between a protein and its ligand. Enzymes, hormone receptors, and transport proteins are all proteins that have a binding site in their structure.
28. In patient A, cortisol hypersecretion is a result of ACTH hypersecretion (a secondary pathology). When dexamethasone suppresses secretion of ACTH, the adrenal gland is no longer being stimulated and cortisol secretion decreases. Patient B has primary hypercortisolism, with the problem arising in the adrenal gland. His normal negative feedback pathways do not operate, and the adrenal gland continues oversecreting cortisol even though ACTH secretion has been suppressed by dexamethasone.
29. (a) See Figure 26-11.
    (b) Both LH and testosterone are necessary for gamete formation. Administering testosterone would not directly suppress gamete formation for birth control. However, testosterone does have a negative feedback effect on the anterior pituitary and would shut off LH secretion. Because LH is needed for gamete production, its absence would suppress gamete synthesis. Thus, administration of testosterone could be an effective means of birth control.

LEVEL FOUR QUANTITATIVE PROBLEMS

30. Half-life is 3 hours.
31. (a) Group A (b) Group B (c) Group A
32. x-axis is plasma glucose concentration. y-axis is insulin secretion. As X increases, Y increases.

CHAPTER 8

LEVEL ONE REVIEWING FACTS AND TERMS

1. Afferent neurons carry messages from sensory receptors to the CNS. Their cell bodies are located close to the CNS and long processes extend from the cell bodies to the receptors. Interneurons are completely contained within the CNS and are often extensively branched. Efferent neurons carry signals from the CNS to effectors. They tend to have short, branched dendrites and extended axons.
2. Somatic motor neurons control *skeletal muscles*. *Autonomic* neurons control smooth and cardiac muscles, glands, and some adipose tissue.
3. Autonomic neurons are classified as either *sympathetic* or *parasympathetic*.
4. (a) 3 (b) 1 (c) 2 (d) 5 (e) 4
5. Neurons and glial cells are the two primary cell types of the nervous system.
6. See Figures 8-2 and 8-4.
7. (c). Answer (b) is not correct because not all axonal transport uses microtubules and not all substances moved will be secreted.
8. (a) 1, 4 (b) 2, 3, 5, 6
9. d
10. The four major ion channels are (1) Na^+ channels, voltage-gated along the axon and ligand-gated or mechanically-gated Na^+ channels on dendrites, (2) voltage-gated K^+ channels along the axon, (3) voltage-gated Ca^{2+} channels in the axon terminal, and (4) chemically-gated Cl^- channels.
11. e - b - d - a - c
12. Answers b and d are correct.
13. The resting cell is more permeable to K^+ than Na^+. Although Na^+ contributes little to the resting potential, it is key to the action potential.
14. Na^+ is more concentrated outside the cell than inside.
15. K^+ is more concentrated inside the cell.
16. An action potential occurs when Na^+ enters the cell.
17. The resting membrane potential is due to the high K^+ permeability of the cell.
18. The myelin sheath is formed from cells that create multiple wraps of insulating membrane around neurons to prevents current from leaking out of the axon.
19. Factors that enhance conduction speed are the diameter of the axon and the presence or absence of insulating myelin.
20. Neurotransmitters are removed by enzymatic degradation, reabsorption and diffusion.
21. See Figures 8-16 and 8-18.

LEVEL TWO REVIEWING CONCEPTS

22. See Figures 8-1 and 8-5.
23. Answer d is correct.
24. The PNS has two types of glial cells: Schwann cells and satellite cells, and the CNS has four types: oligodendrocytes, microglia, astrocytes, and ependymal cells. Oligodendrocytes and Schwann cells form myelin. Satellite cells form supportive capsules around nerve cell bodies located in ganglia. Astrocytes transfer nutrients between the blood and neurons. Microglia are immune cells. Ependymal cells separate the fluid compartments of the CNS.

25. f - c - g - e - b - k - c - a - h - i - d.

26. (a) depolarize
    (b) hyperpolarize
    (c) repolarize
    (d) depolarize. See Figure 5-37 on p. 166.

27. (a) Na^+ entry depolarizes;
    (b) K^+ leaving hyperpolarizes;
    (c) Cl^- entry hyperpolarizes;
    (d) Ca^{2+} entry depolarizes

28. (a) Threshold level signals trigger action potentials. Suprathreshold will also trigger action potentials but subthreshold will not unless they are summed through either spatial or temporal summation. Action potentials are all-or-none events that cannot be summed. Overshoot is the portion of the action potential above 0 mV. Undershoot is the after-hyperpolarization portion of the action potential (see Figure 8-12).
    (b) Graded potentials may be depolarizing or hyperpolarizing. If the graded potential occurs in a postsynaptic cell, the depolarizing graded potential is an excitatory postsynaptic potential (EPSP) and a hyperpolarizing graded potential is inhibitory, or an IPSP. Refractory periods are the periods of time following an action potential during which an additional action potential cannot be fired. No stimulus can trigger another action potential during the absolute refractory period but a suprathreshold stimulus can trigger an action potential during the relative refractory period.
    (c) See answer to question 1.
    (d) Sensory neurons are afferent neurons; all others are efferent neurons. For classification and comparison, see answer to question 1.
    (e) Fast synaptic potentials result from the opening of ion channels by neurotransmitters; they occur rapidly and are short-lived. Slow synaptic potentials are mediated through second messengers and last longer. They may include changes in the open states of ion channels but may also alter cellular proteins.
    (f) Temporal summation occurs when multiple stimuli arrive at the trigger zone close together in time. Spatial summation occurs when multiple stimuli arriving on the neuron at different locations arrive simultaneously at the trigger zone.
    (g) Divergence is the pattern where a single neuron branches and its collaterals synapse on multiple target neurons. Convergence is the pattern where many presynaptic neurons provide input to a smaller number of postsynaptic neurons.

29. Information about strength is coded by the frequency of action potentials; duration is coded by the duration of a train of repeated action potentials.

30. b

LEVEL THREE PROBLEM SOLVING

31. Although the neurons are fully developed, all the necessary synapses have not yet been made between neurons and between neurons and effectors.

32. Closure of the voltage-gated Na^+ channels is also initiated by depolarization, but the inactivation gates close slower than the activation gates open, allowing ions to flow for a short period of time.

33. The correct answers are b, d, and h.

34. (a) thermal (b) chemical (c) chemical (d) chemical
    (e) chemical (f) chemical (g) mechanical

LEVEL FOUR QUANTITATIVE PROBLEMS

35. (a) An increase in sodium permeability will make alpha larger. That in turn will increase the numerator and make the membrane potential more positive.
    (b) Membrane potential is −78.5 mV.

36. (a) (12×2 mV = +24) + (3×-3 mV = −9) = signal strength of +15. Potential −70 + 15 = −55. Threshold is −50, so no action potential. (Potential must be equal to or more positive than threshold.)
    (b) (11×2 = +22) + (3×-3 = −9) = +13. Potential −70 + 13 = −57. Threshold is −60, so action potential will fire.
    (c) (14×2 = +28) + (−9) = +19. Potential −70 + 19 = −51. Threshold is −50, so no action potential.

CHAPTER 9

LEVEL ONE REVIEWING FACTS AND TERMS

1. *Plasticity* is the ability to change connections in response to sensory input and experience.
2. *Cognitive* functions deal with thought, and *affective* functions deal with emotion.
3. The *cerebrum* allows human reasoning and cognition.
4. The brain is inside the *skull,* and the spinal cord is inside the *vertebral column.*
5. From the bones inward, the meninges are the dura mater, the arachnoid membrane, and the pia mater.
6. CSF physically protects the brain: its buoyancy reduces the brain's weight, and the fluid provides a cushion between the brain and the bones. CSF also provides chemical protection by creating a closely regulated external environment for the cells of the brain.
7. (a) HCO_3^- is lower in CSF
   (b) Ca^{2+} is lower in CSF
   (c) glucose is lower in CSF
   (d) H^+ is higher in CSF
   (e) Na^+ is the same in CSF and plasma
   (f) K^+ is lower in CSF
8. Neurons normally metabolize *glucose.* Low glucose in the blood is *hypoglycemia.* Neurons have high *oxygen* consumption, and they receive about *15%* of the blood pumped by the heart.
9. (a) 5 (b) 7 (c) 9 (d) 3 (e) 1 (f) 2 (g) 6
   (h) 8 (i) 4
10. The blood-brain barrier consists of capillaries that are much less leaky and much more selective than capillaries elsewhere in the body due to tight junctions between endothelial cells. The function of this barrier is to closely regulate which substances are allowed out of the blood and into brain tissue.
11. Gray matter has nerve cell bodies, dendrites, and axon terminals; it forms clusters (nuclei) or layers in the brain and spinal cord. Gray matter is where information passes from neuron to neuron. White matter is mostly myelinated axons; tracts of white matter carry information up and down the spinal cord to the brain.
12. (a) Sensory fields direct perception. (b) The motor cortex directs movement. (c) Association areas integrate information and direct voluntary behavior.
13. Cerebral lateralization is the asymmetrical distribution of function between the two lobes of the cerebrum. The left brain is the center for language and verbal functions, while the right brain is the center for spatial skills.

14. Gamma-aminobutyric acid (GABA) in the brain and glycine in the spinal cord are inhibitory amino acid neurotransmitters that open Cl^- channels and hyperpolarize their target cells.
15. REM, or rapid eye movement sleep, is the period of sleep when most dreaming takes place. It is marked by rapid, low-amplitude EEG waves, flaccid paralysis, and depression of homeostatic function. Slow-wave sleep, or deep sleep, is marked by high amplitude, low frequency waves on the EEG and unconscious body movements.
16. The hypothalamus contains centers for homeostasis. Reflexes and behaviors controlled by the hypothalamus include body temperature, thirst, reproductive functions, hunger and satiety, and influence of cardiovascular function. Emotional input to the hypothalamus comes from the limbic system.
17. The *amygdala* appears to be the center of basic instincts.
18. Learning can be categorized into associative and nonassociative learning. In habituation, a person responds less and less to a repeated stimulus; in sensitization, a person experiences an enhanced response to a dangerous or unpleasant stimulus.
19. Integration of spoken language takes place in Broca's area and Wernicke's area of the cortex.

LEVEL TWO REVIEWING CONCEPTS

20. The map should include information contained in Table 9-1 and Figures 9-15 and 9-16.
21. Cerebrospinal fluid is secreted into the ventricles and flows into the subarachnoid space around the brain and spinal cord before being reabsorbed by special regions of the cerebral arachnoid membrane.
22. The sensory system, behavioral state system, and cognitive system regulate motor output by the CNS.
23. The receptor for the molecule determines whether it acts as a neurotransmitter (opens ion channels) or a neuromodulator (acts through a second messenger).
24. (a) The diffuse modulatory systems in the brain stem influence attention, motivation, wakefulness, memory, motor control, mood, and metabolism. The reticular formation in the brain stem influences arousal and sleep, muscle tone, breathing, blood pressure, and pain. The limbic system is the interior region of the cerebrum and links higher cognitive functions with more primitive emotions such as fear.
    (b) Memory is divided into short-term memory that disappears unless consolidated, and long-term memory that is stored for recall. Long-term memory includes reflexive, or unconscious, memory, and declarative, or conscious, memory.
    (c) Nuclei are clusters of nerve cell bodies in the CNS; ganglia (in vertebrates) are clusters of nerve cell bodies outside the CNS.
    (d) Tracts are bundles of axons within the CNS; nerves are bundles of axons outside the CNS. Horns are extensions of spinal cord gray matter that connect to peripheral nerves. Nerve fibers are bundles of axons. Roots are the two branches of a peripheral nerve that enter the spinal cord. Sensory neurons go to the dorsal root and efferent neurons exit the spinal cord through the ventral root.
25. Primary somatic sensory cortex is in the parietal lobe. The visual cortex processes information from the eyes. The auditory cortex processes information from the ears. The olfactory cortex processes information from the nose. The motor cortices in the frontal lobes control skeletal muscle movements. The association areas integrate sensory information into perception.
26. (a) Lower frequency waves would have peaks farther apart.
    (b) Larger amplitude waves would have taller peaks.
    (c) Higher frequency waves would have peaks closer together.
27. Those motivational states known as drives all create increased state of arousal, goal-oriented behavior, and coordination of disparate behaviors to achieve goals.
28. Changes that take place at synapses as memories are formed include up-regulation of receptors and formation of new synapses.

LEVEL THREE PROBLEM SOLVING

29. With expressive aphasia Mr. Anderson could understand people but was unable to communicate in any way that made sense. He might be able to select the correct words but cannot put them together appropriately. If he had receptive aphasia, he would be unable to understand communication from other people. Speech centers are in the left brain. If music centers are in the right brain, then perhaps information from Wernicke's area can be integrated by the right brain so that Mr. Anderson can musically string together words so that they make sense.
30. Learning probably occurred, but learning need not be translated into behavioral responses. The participants who didn't buckle their seat belts learned that wearing seat belts was important but did not consider this knowledge important enough to act on.
31. One conclusion might be that sleep-deprived dogs are producing a substance that induces sleep. Possible controls would be putting CSF from normal dogs into sleep-deprived dogs, CSF from normal dogs into normal dogs, and CSF from sleep-deprived dogs into other sleep-deprived dogs.
32. (1) No, other information that should be taken into consideration include genetics, age, and general health. (2) The application of this study would be limited to women of similar age, background, and health. Other factors you would be interested in would include the ethnicity of the participants, factors as listed in (1), and geographical location.

CHAPTER 10

LEVEL ONE REVIEWING FACTS AND TERMS

1. The afferent division carries information from sensory receptors to the CNS.
2. Proprioreception is the ability to tell where our body is in space and to sense the relative locations of different body parts.
3. All sensory pathways include a stimulus that acts on a sensory receptor and a sensory neuron that begins at the receptor and ends in the CNS.
4. Mechanoreceptors respond when they are physically deformed by pressure, sound, stretch, etc. Chemoreceptors respond to the presence of or changes in the concentration of specific chemicals, such as glucose or oxygen. Photoreceptors respond to photons of light. Thermoreceptors respond to varying degrees of heat.
5. Information is sensed within the *sensory field* of a neuron.
6. (a) 3 (b) 2 (c) 1, 2 (d) 2, 3 (e) 4
7. *Transduction* is the process by which stimulus energy is converted into a change in membrane potential. The form of energy to which a receptor responds best is called its *adequate stimulus*. The minimum stimulus required to activate a receptor is known as the *threshold*.
8. When a sensory receptor membrane depolarizes (or hyperpolarizes in a few cases), the change in membrane potential is called the *receptor potential*. These are graded potentials.

9. The adequate stimulus for a receptor is the form of energy to which the receptor is most sensitive.
10. The organization of sensory regions in the *cortex* preserves the topographical organization of sensory receptors so that perceptions are localized to the area where the stimulus occurred. The two exceptions to this rule are olfaction and hearing, where the brain uses timing of stimulus reception to compute a location.
11. Lateral inhibition occurs when the sensory neurons surrounding a sensory field are inhibited, which enhances the contrast between the stimulus and surrounding unstimulated areas.
12. Tonic receptors adapt slowly to stimuli and respond to stimuli that need to be constantly monitored, such as noxious stimuli. Phasic receptors adapt rapidly to stimuli and stop responding unless the stimulus changes. An example is smell. Phasic receptors allow new stimuli to be sensed while ignoring old stimuli that are presumably not important or a threat.
13. Pain in the arm from cardiac ischemia is an example of *referred pain*.
14. Sweet, salty, bitter, sour, and umami are the five basic taste sensations. Nutritious foods taste sweet (e.g., fruit) or umami (e.g., meat) or salty (e.g., salted popcorn); sour foods may be either nutritious (e.g., juice) or unsafe due to spoilage; bitter foods may contain toxins or may be nutritious (unsweetened chocolate).
15. The frequency of the sound waves per second is measured in *hertz (Hz)*. The loudness or intensity of sound is a function of the *wave amplitude* and is measured in *decibels (dB)*. The range of hearing for the average human ear is over the range of *20–20,000 Hz*, with the most acute hearing in the range of *1000–3000 Hz*.
16. The basilar membrane codes for pitch. Spatial coding refers to the translation of different wave frequencies into stimulation of different areas of the membrane.
17. Correct answer is a. (Action potentials have constant amplitude and refractory period).
18. Once sound waves have been transformed into electrical signals in the cochlea, sensory neurons transfer information to the *medulla*, with collaterals then taking information to the *reticular formation* and *cerebellum*. The main auditory pathway synapses in the *midbrain* and *thalamus* before finally projecting to the *auditory cortex* in the *cerebrum*.
19. The *semicircular canals* sense rotation, and the *otolith organs* respond to linear forces. Movement is the *dynamic* component, and head position while standing is the *static* component.
20. b, a, d, c, e
21. The three primary colors of vision are *red, blue*, and *green*. Seeing these colors stimulate photoreceptors called *cones*. Lack of the ability to distinguish some colors is called *color-blindness*.
22. The six types of retinal cells are rods and cones (the photoreceptors), bipolar cells, ganglion cells, horizontal cells, and amacrine cells. Photoreceptors transduce light energy into electrical signals. Signal processing takes place in the bipolar neurons and ganglion cells, modulated by input from horizontal and amacrine cells.

LEVEL TWO REVIEWING CONCEPTS

23. (a) Special senses (hearing, vision, smell, taste, and equilibrium) have receptors localized in the head. Somatic senses are more general senses (touch, pressure, vibration, temperature) with receptors are located all over the body.
    (b) See Table 10-4.
    (c) Sharp pain is transmitted by small, myelinated Aδ fibers. Dull, diffuse pain is transmitted through small, unmyelinated C fibers.
    (d) In conductive hearing loss, sound cannot be transmitted through the external or middle ear. In sensorineural hearing loss, the inner ear has been damaged. In central hearing loss, the auditory pathways from the inner ear or the auditory cortex have sustained damage.
24. The brain can distinguish up to seven distant sensory areas: 1, 2, 3, 1 + 2, 1 + 3, 2 + 3, and 1 + 2 + 3.
25. Ascending pathways for pain go to the limbic system and hypothalamus, which explains the link between pain, emotional distress, and symptoms such as nausea and vomiting.
26. Olfaction begins with the nasal olfactory receptors whose axons project through the cribriform plate of the ethmoid bone to the olfactory bulbs of the brain, where they synapse with secondary sensory neurons. Secondary and higher-order neurons project to the olfactory cortex. Parallel pathways go to the amygdala and hippocampus. G_{olf} is a special G protein in olfactory receptors, which, when activated by an odorant, increases intracellular cAMP. cAMP opens ion channels, leading to depolarization of the cell, and initiating the olfactory signal into the brain.
27. Bitter, sweet, and umami flavor chemicals bind to membrane receptors on taste buds, activating second messenger systems. Different G protein-linked receptors are involved for the three ligands, activating several different signal transduction pathways. Some trigger release of intracellular calcium while others open calcium channels. Salty and sour tastes are really just the ions Na^+ and H^+; these flavor ions enter the receptor through ion channels. Entry of these ions into the cell depolarizes the membrane potential, which in turn opens voltage-gated calcium channels. Calcium triggers exocytosis of neurotransmitter, which passes the signal to the next neuron in the pathway.
28. a, g, j, h, c, e, i, b, f, d
29. See Figures 10-23, 10-24, and 10-25.
30. In accommodation, the lens changes shape due to contraction/relaxation of the ciliary muscles. The change in lens shape keeps light focused on the retina as objects move toward and away from the eye. Loss of this reflex is called presbyopia.
31. Presbyopia is loss of accommodation due to stiffening of the lens with age. Myopia or near-sightedness is due to a longer-than-normal distance between lens and retina; hyperopia or far-sightedness is due to a shorter-than-normal distance. Color blindness is caused by a defect in the visual pigments of some of the cones.
32. Intensity can be coded by the frequency of action potentials, and duration by the duration of a train of action potentials.
33. Start with Figure 10-28 and the basic components of vision. Work in details and related terms from the text.
34. See Table 10-1 and the section for each special sense.

LEVEL THREE PROBLEM SOLVING

35. You are testing the somatic sense of touch-pressure, mediated through free nerve endings and Merkel receptors. When she only feels one probe, it is because both needles are within the same receptive field.
36. Some well-known tests include having people try to walk a straight line or stand on one leg with the eyes closed. Other tests include higher brain functions, such as reciting the alphabet backwards.
37. The first sense to test for a child with poor speech is hearing. If children cannot hear well, they cannot hear the sounds to imitate for speech.

38. Normally, shining a light in either eye should induce pupillary constriction in both eyes (the consensual reflex). Given the normal reflex upon shining light into the right eye, it appears that the motor components of the reflex to both eyes are intact. Absence of the reflex upon stimulating the left eye suggests damage to the left retina and/or to the left optic nerve.

CHAPTER 11

LEVEL ONE REVIEWING FACTS AND TERMS

1. The two divisions of the efferent part of the autonomic nervous system are the somatic motor division, which controls skeletal muscles, and the autonomic division, which controls smooth muscle, cardiac muscle, glands, and some adipose tissue.
2. The autonomic nervous system can also be called the *visceral* nervous system because it controls the internal organs, or viscera. Some functions controlled by the autonomic nervous system include heart rate, blood pressure, and digestive function.
3. The two divisions of the autonomic nervous system are the sympathetic and parasympathetic divisions. Anatomically, sympathetic neurons exit the spinal cord in the thoracic and lumbar regions and have ganglia close to the spinal cord; parasympathetic neurons exit from the brain stem or sacral region of the spinal cord and have ganglia on or close to their targets. The neurotransmitter released onto the target is norepinephrine for the sympathetic and acetylcholine for the parasympathetic divisions. Physiologically, sympathetic innervation controls fight-or-flight reactions while parasympathetic is in charge of rest-and-digest functions.
4. The adrenal medulla is a neuroendocrine gland that is considered to be a modified sympathetic ganglion. It secretes epinephrine primarily, along with a small amount of norepinephrine.
5. Neurons that secrete acetylcholine are described as *cholinergic;* those that secrete norepinephrine are called *adrenergic* or *noradrenergic* neurons.
6. Four things that can happen to autonomic neurotransmitters after they are released include diffusion away from the synapse, breakdown by enzymes in the synapse, reuptake into the presynaptic neuron, or combination with a membrane receptor.
7. The main enzyme responsible for catecholamine degradation is *monoamine oxidase,* abbreviated *MAO*.
8. Somatic motor pathways are excitatory, composed of a single neuron, and synapse with skeletal muscles.
9. Acetylcholinesterase is the enzyme that breaks down ACh in the synapse.
10. Nicotinic cholinergic receptors are found on the postsynaptic cell of the neuromuscular junction.

LEVEL TWO REVIEWING CONCEPTS

11. Use the information in Figures 11-10 and 11-11 to create this map.
12. Divergence of neural pathways in the autonomic nervous system allows a single signal to have effects on multiple targets.
13. (a) Neuroeffector junctions occur along the length of the autonomic axon anywhere that there is a varicosity; neuromuscular junctions (NMJs) of the somatic nervous system occur at the axon terminals of the somatic motor neuron. Transmitter release and activity in the synapse are similar at both types of junctions.
    (b) Alpha and beta receptors are adrenergic; nicotinic and muscarinic are cholinergic. Nicotinic are the only receptors found in the somatic motor division; autonomic divisions all have nicotinic receptors on the postganglionic neuron. Adrenergic and muscarinic receptors are found on autonomic targets.
14. (a) Autonomic ganglia contain the nerve cell bodies of postganglionic autonomic neurons. CNS nuclei are clusters of nerve cell bodies in the brain and spinal cord.
    (b) The adrenal and pituitary glands are complex glands composed of both true endocrine tissue (adrenal cortex and anterior pituitary) and neuroendocrine tissue (adrenal medulla and posterior pituitary).
    (c) Boutons are found at the ends of axons; varicosities are areas of neurotransmitter release strung out like beads along the length of the branched ends of autonomic neurons.
15. (a) 1, 2 (b) 3 (c) 4 (d) 3
16. (d), (e)

LEVEL THREE PROBLEM SOLVING

17. The electrochemical gradient for Na^+ is greater than that for K^+.
18. (a) Endocytosis probably brings the marker into the axon terminal.
    (b) Parasympathetic autonomic ganglia are located close to the target organ.
    (c) Postganglionic parasympathetic neurons secrete acetylcholine onto their targets.
19. Any animal poisoned by curare will experience a loss in function of skeletal muscles. The animal would become paralyzed and unable to move its limbs, so it could not flee. Respiratory muscles will also be affected, and if the dose of curare is sufficient, the animal will die by suffocation.

LEVEL FOUR QUANTITATIVE PROBLEMS

20. Cigarette smoking among high school students increased from 1991 to 1997, then began to decrease. (b) Males are more likely to be smokers than females, and whites smoke more than Hispanics, who smoke more than blacks. Therefore, white males are the most likely to smoke and black females are the least likely to smoke.

CHAPTER 12

LEVEL ONE REVIEWING FACTS AND TERMS

1. The three types of muscle are smooth, cardiac, and skeletal. Skeletal muscles are attached to bones.
2. The two striated muscles are cardiac and skeletal muscle.
3. Skeletal muscle is controlled strictly by somatic motor neurons.
4. (a) False, muscles comprise about 40% of body weight.
    (b) true
    (c) true
    (d) true
5. Skeletal muscle components are connective tissue sheath, sarcolemma, myofibrils, and myofilaments.
6. Modified endoplasmic reticulum of skeletal muscle is called *sarcoplasmic reticulum*. It stores and concentrates Ca^{2+} ions.
7. T-tubules allow *action potentials* to travel to the interior of the muscle fiber.
8. Myofibrils are made of actin, myosin, troponin, tropomyosin, titin and nebulin. Myosin produces the power stroke, by binding to and pulling on actin.
9. Z disk forms the boundaries of a sarcomere. I band has a Z disk in the middle; A band consists of the thick filaments; H zone is the lighter region of the A band; M line, which divides the A band in half, is where thick filaments link to each other.

10. Titin and nebulin keep myofilaments in alignment. In addition, titin is elastic and helps stretched muscles return to their resting length.
11. During muscle contraction, the *A band* (myosin) remains a constant length. The H zone and I band shorten during contraction, and the Z disks approach each other.
12. The sliding filament theory states that a muscle cell contracts by the increasing overlap of thin and thick filaments in each sarcomere of each myofibril. Myosin heads on the thick filament bind to actin. When myosin heads bend, they pull the actin filaments toward the center of the sarcomere.
13. Fast-twitch glycolytic fibers: a, b, e; Fast-twitch oxidative fibers: g, f, d, e; Slow-twitch oxidative fibers: c, d, f, h
14. An increase in intracellular free Ca^{2+} activates troponin, which repositions tropomyosin, uncovering actin's myosin-binding sites.
15. Somatic motor neurons release acetylcholine.
16. The motor end plate is the region of a muscle fiber where the synapse occurs. It contains ACh receptors. Influx of Na^+ at the motor end plate causes the cell to depolarize and fire an action potential.
17. A single contraction/relaxation cycle in a skeletal muscle fiber is known as a *twitch.*
18. ATP binding to myosin causes myosin to dissociate from actin. ATP hydrolysis causes the myosin head to swing and bind to a new actin molecule. Release of the inorganic phosphate initiates the power stroke.
19. The basic unit of contraction in an intact skeletal muscle is the *motor unit*. The force of contraction within a skeletal muscle is increased by *recruitment* of additional motor units.
20. The two types are single-unit (visceral) and multi-unit smooth muscle.

LEVEL TWO REVIEWING CONCEPTS

21. Use Figures 12-3 to 12-6 to help construct this map.
22. Use Figures 12-9 to 12-11 to help construct this map.
23. The action potential activates DHP receptors that open Ca^{2+} channels in the sarcoplasmic reticulum membrane. Calcium then diffuses out of the sarcoplasmic reticulum.
24. Muscle cells can make some ATP by energy transfer from phosphocreatine. Oxidative fibers that require oxygen can use glucose and fatty acids to make ATP; glycolytic fibers get their ATP primarily from anaerobic glycolysis.
25. Muscle fatigue is a state in which a muscle can no longer generate or sustain the expected force. The physical cause of fatigue is unclear and may involve changes in ion concentrations, depletion of nutrients, or effects of these on excitation-contraction coupling. Central fatigue is a subjective feeling of fatigue and may be a protective mechanism. Muscle cells can become more fatigue-resistant by increasing the size and number of mitochondria and by increasing blood supply to the muscle.
26. To vary force, the body uses different types of motor units and recruits different numbers of motor units. Small movements use motor units with fewer muscle fibers; gross movements use motor units with more fibers.
27. See Table 12-3.
28. The sarcoplasmic reticulum stores Ca^{2+} and releases it upon command. The Ca^{2+} for smooth muscle contraction enters the cell from the extracellular fluid.
29. (a) Fast-twitch oxidative-glycolytic are smaller, contain some myoglobin, use both oxidative and glycolytic metabolism for ATP production, and are more fatigue-resistant. Fast-twitch glycolytic fibers are largest in diameter, rely primarily on anaerobic glycolysis for ATP synthesis, and are least fatigue-resistant. Slow-twitch fibers develop tension more slowly and maintain tension longer, are the most fatigue-resistant, depend primarily on oxidative phosphorylation for ATP production, have more mitochondria, greater vascularity, large amounts of myoglobin, and are smallest in diameter.
    (b) A single contraction-relaxation cycle is a twitch. Tetanus is a contraction with little to no relaxation, which occurs at high stimulus rates.
    (c) Action potentials in both motor neurons and skeletal muscle cells are the result of inward sodium current and outward potassium current through voltage-gated ion channels. In a motor neuron the action potential triggers ACh release, which ultimately leads to muscle contraction. The muscle action potential triggers Ca^{2+} release from the sarcoplasmic reticulum; Ca^{2+} in turn triggers contraction.
    (d) In a motor neuron, temporal summation determines whether or not the neuron will produce an action potential. Summation in a muscle cell occurs when the peak force increases as the stimulation rate increases. This summation results as the concentration of free calcium inside the cell increases, thus more cross bridges can form and more force can be produced.
    (e) Isotonic contraction moves a load. Isometric contraction creates tension without moving a load. In most movements, there is an isotonic phase and an isometric phase. Concentric action occurs when a muscle shortens in a controlled movement of a load. Eccentric action occurs when a muscle lengthens in a controlled movement of a load. Doing a biceps curl would involve alternating concentric and eccentric actions.
    (f) Slow-wave potentials are cycles of depolarization and repolarization of membrane potential that occur in smooth muscle cells. Pacemaker potentials are repetitive slow depolarizations to threshold that occur in some types of smooth muscle cells and in cardiac muscle.
    (g) In skeletal muscle, Ca^{2+} from internal stores regulates contraction. In smooth muscle, Ca^{2+} for contraction comes from both internal stores and extracellular fluid.
30. Release of Ca^{2+} from the SR of smooth muscle involves an IP_3-activated channel. Ca^{2+} influx from the ECF occurs through channels that open in response to depolarization, stretch, or chemical signals. Depolarization results from slow-wave or pacemaker potentials. Stretch results from increasing volume of contents of the hollow organ whose wall contains smooth muscle, for example, the urinary bladder. Autonomic neurotransmitters, hormones, and paracrines are important chemical factors.

LEVEL THREE PROBLEM SOLVING

31. (a) Adding ATP will allow the cross bridges to detach, and myosin will be able to unbind from actin. If insufficient Ca^{2+} is available, the muscle will relax.
    (b) If both ATP and Ca^{2+} are available, the muscle will continue in the contraction cycle until it is completely contracted. The muscle will remain contracted as long as free calcium is present in sufficient concentrations.
32. Because curare does not interfere with secretion of acetylcholine but does prevent contraction of skeletal muscle, it must interfere with a process that follows ACh release. These include diffusion of

ACh across the synaptic cleft, ACh binding to muscle fiber receptors, opening of the receptor-linked ion channels, and ensuing ion flux to produce the muscle action potential. To interfere with ion flow, curare would either have to bind to a significant number of ions, or block ion channels. Curare has been shown to bind to the acetylcholine receptor, thereby preventing ACh activation of the associated channels.

33. The muscle characteristic most dependent upon an individual's height is muscle length, because it is related to bone length. Assuming these athletes are lean, differences in weight and therefore muscle mass are correlated with muscle strength, so heavier athletes should have stronger muscles. More important factors are the relative endurance and strength required for a given sport. Any given muscle will have a combination of three fiber types, with the exact ratios depending upon genetics and specific type of athletic training.
    (a) Running up and down the basketball court requires both endurance, because of the duration of the game, and strength, because players must run fast. Precisely passing or shooting the ball requires variable strength dependent upon the distance the ball must move, as the ball itself represents a minimal load. Jumping up to the basket while shooting the ball requires strength, as the load is the entire mass of the athlete, but the activity is not sustained, therefore endurance is not an issue here. The leg muscles would have a greater proportion of fast-twitch glycolytic fibers, which generate the most strength for jumping, and fast-twitch oxidative, which have more endurance for running. The arm and shoulder muscles will have a higher proportion of fast-twitch glycolytic, because shooting requires fast and precise contraction, and great force when shooting over a distance.
    (b) A steer wrestler requires great strength in both the upper and lower limbs and trunk, but the duration of the activity is relatively short. The muscles will have a greater proportion of fast-twitch glycolytic fibers.
    (c) Female figure skaters require both strength and endurance. The legs do most of the work, producing great force during jumps, and sustaining activity while traversing the ice. The trunk muscles must hold the skater in precise positions. The trunk muscles will have a higher proportion of slow-twitch oxidative fibers for endurance. The leg muscles will have a higher proportion of fast-twitch oxidative, for moving across the ice, and fast-twitch glycolytic, for powering jumps.
    (d) A gymnastics routine involves great strength in arms and legs, and great endurance in trunk and limb muscles. Arm and leg muscles will have higher proportions of fast-twitch glycolytic fibers, to generate strength on the balance beam, uneven parallel bars, and floor exercises. Slow-twitch oxidative fibers in limb and trunk muscles will maintain the precise positioning of the body during all routines.

LEVEL FOUR QUANTITATIVE PROBLEMS

34. The data suggest that muscle fatigue may result from lactate accumulation or loss of PCr. To read the original paper, go to *http://jap.physiology.org* and use the SEARCH function to find the paper.
35. (a) The biceps would need to exert 7.5 kg of force to hold the arm stationary, a 125% increase over a biceps inserted at 5 cm.
    (b) With a 7-kg weight at 20 cm, the biceps needs to exert an additional 28 kg of force. This is less than if the weight is placed in the hand.

CHAPTER 13

LEVEL ONE REVIEWING FACTS AND TERMS

1. All neural reflexes begin with a *stimulus.*
2. Somatic reflexes involve *skeletal* muscles; *autonomic,* or visceral, reflexes are controlled by autonomic neurons.
3. The pathway pattern that brings information from many neurons into a smaller number of neurons is *convergence.*
4. If a presynaptic modulatory neuron decreases the amount of neurotransmitter released by its target neuron, the modulation is termed *presynatic inhibition.*
5. Autonomic reflexes are also called *visceral* reflexes because many of them involve the internal organs known collectively as the viscera.
6. Spinal reflexes include urination and defecation. Cranial reflexes include control of heart rate, blood pressure, and body temperature.
7. The limbic system is involved in the conversion of emotion into visceral reflexes. Some reflexes that may be influenced by emotion include heart rate, gastrointestinal function, and breathing rate.
8. The simplest autonomic reflex has two neuron-neuron synapses and one neuron-target synapse. The neuron-neuron synapses are in the spinal cord between the sensory neuron and the preganglionic efferent neuron, and in the autonomic ganglia, between the pre- and postganglionic neurons.
9. The three types of sensory receptors for muscle reflexes are the Golgi tendon organ, the muscle spindle, and the proprioreceptors called joint capsule mechanoreceptors.
10. Even at rest, muscles maintain *tone.*
11. Increase. This reflex is useful because it prevents damage from overstretching.
12. (a) 2, 3, 5, 6 (b) 1, 2, 6 (c) 1, 2, 4
13. The Golgi tendon organ responds to both *stretch* and *contraction* but more strongly to contraction. Activation *decreases* muscle contraction via inhibition of the *alpha motor* neuron.
14. The simplest reflexes are skeletal muscle reflexes, with one synapse between two neurons (monosynaptic). The knee jerk (patellar tendon) reflex is an example.
15. The three types of movement are reflex movements, such as the knee jerk; voluntary movements, such as playing the piano; and rhythmic movements, such as walking. Reflex movements are integrated in the spinal cord; the other two types must involve the brain at some point. Reflex movements are involuntary; rhythmic movements are initiated and terminated by signals from the cerebral cortex but in between are involuntary.

LEVEL TWO REVIEWING CONCEPTS

16. Alpha-gamma coactivation allows muscle spindles to continue functioning when the muscle contracts and would otherwise release tension on the spindle. When the muscle contracts (under control of alpha motor neurons), the ends of the spindles also contract (under the control of gamma motor neurons) to maintain stretch on the central portion of the spindle.
17. If M is an inhibitory neuron, neurotransmitter release by P will decrease when M's neurotransmitter hyperpolarizes the postsynaptic membrane potential of P.
18. (a) The patellar reflex is used to assess function of the local reflex arc and the central nervous system components that regulate limb movement. A reduced or absent reflex could indicate damage to the quadriceps muscle, the nerves that control it, or

the area of the spinal cord where the nerves originate. A hyperactive reflex could indicate damage to the spinal cord at a level above the reflex arc, or damage to motor areas of the brain.

(b) This reflex is fairly easy to inhibit by conscious intent or if nervous, so the reflex would probably be less apparent. The origin of this inhibition is the primary motor cortex. The inhibitory cells will produce IPSPs in the spinal motor neuron.

(c) If the brain is distracted by some other task, the inhibitory signals will presumably stop, and the physician can more easily assess the reflex.

LEVEL THREE PROBLEM SOLVING

19. (a) Ca^{2+}-activated transmitter release is prevented.
    (b) Cell would hyperpolarize due to Cl^- entry, and voltage-gated Ca^{2+} channels in terminal would not open.
    (c) Same answer as (b), but because K^+ would leave cell.
20. See Figures 13-12 and 13-13. Parts of the brain include the brain stem, cerebellum, basal ganglia, thalamus, cerebral cortex (visual cortex, association areas, motor cortex).
21. (a) Fright activates the sympathetic nervous system, which regulates a multitude of physiological functions, including the heart rate, piloerector muscles of the skin, and other startle reflexes.
    (b) The limbic system is involved in emotions, including fear. Functions of the limbic system include regulating other primitive drives such as sex, rage, aggression and hunger, and reflexes including urination, defecation, blushing, blanching, and piloerection. The limbic system influences primarily autonomic motor output. Heart, blood vessels, respiratory muscles, smooth muscle, and glands are some of the target organs involved.
    (c) Piloerection occurs because there are smooth muscles called arrector pili muscles that attach to the base of each hair. Smooth muscles are controlled by the autonomic division.
22. Both toxins are produced by bacteria of the Clostridium genus. *Clostridium tetani* are in soil, and can enter the body through a cut. *Clostridium botulini* can be present in improperly canned food, and enter the body upon ingestion. Both toxins produce paralysis (lack of control) of skeletal muscles. Tetanus toxin inhibits secretion of glycine from interneurons that normally inhibit somatic motor neurons. This releases the neurons from inhibition, so they trigger prolonged contractions in skeletal muscles; this is called spastic paralysis. Botulinum toxin blocks secretion of acetylcholine from somatic motor neurons. Skeletal muscles do not contract unless acetylcholine is present, so this toxin produces flaccid paralysis.

CHAPTER 14

LEVEL ONE REVIEWING FACTS AND TERMS

1. (a) William Harvey was the first European to describe the closed circulatory system.
   (b) Frank and Starling described the relationship between stretch of ventricular muscle and the force of its contraction.
   (c) Malpighi described capillaries.
2. Three functions of the cardiovascular system are transport of materials entering and leaving the body, defense, and cell-to-cell communication.
3. a, e, d, b, f, c
4. The primary reason blood flows is a *pressure* gradient. In humans, this value is highest at the *left ventricle* and in the *aorta*; it is lowest in the *right atrium*. In a system in which fluid is flowing, pressure decreases over distance due to *friction*.
5. If vasodilation occurs in a blood vessel, pressure *decreases*.
6. Cell junctions between myocardial cells are *intercalated disks* that contain *gap junctions*.
7. SA node to internodal pathways of atrial conducting system to AV node to bundle of His (left and right branches) to Purkinje fibers to ventricular myocardium.
8. (a) End-systolic volume is the volume of blood left in ventricle after heart contracts; end-diastolic is volume in the ventricle as heart begin to contract.
   (b) Sympathetic control (epinephrine or norepinephrine on β_1-adrenergic receptors) increases heart rate. Parasympathetic control (ACh on muscarinic receptors) decreases heart rate.
   (c) Diastole is the relaxation phase of the heart; systole is the contraction phase.
   (d) Pulmonary circulation goes to the lungs; systemic circulation goes to the rest of the body.
   (e) Action potentials pass from the SA node, a group of autorhythmic cells at the "top" of the right atrium, to the AV node, which are autorhythmic cells in the floor of the right atrium.
9. (a) 11 (b) 12 (c) 3 (d) 14 (e) 8 (f) 1
   (g) 10 (h) 2 (i) 6 (j) 4.
   See chapter for definitions of unused terms.
10. Vibrations from AV closure cause the "lub" sound and semilunar valve closure causes the "dup" sound.
11. (a) heart rate
    (b) end-diastolic volume
    (c) stroke volume
    (d) cardiac output
    (e) blood volume

LEVEL TWO REVIEWING CONCEPTS

12. (a) Refer to Figure 14-1.
    (b) Use Figures 14-31 and 14-27 as a starting point for your map.
13. See Figures 14-24 and 14-26.
14. See Table 12-3. The unique properties of cardiac muscle that are essential include the strong cell-to-cell junctions, gap junctions for electrical conduction, and the modification of some muscle cells into autorhythmic cells for rapid conduction and acting as a pacemaker
15. Contractions in cardiac muscle cannot sum or exhibit tetanus because of the long refractory period that prevents a new action potential until the heart muscle has relaxed.
16. See Figure 14-21. Atrial relaxation and ventricular contraction overlap during the QRS complex. The mechanical events following the waves are either contraction or relaxation of the heart muscle.
17. (a) 3; 5 in the last part (b) 5 (c) 3 (d) 5 (e) 2
    (f) 2 (g) 5 (h) 6
18. An ECG provides information about heart rate, heart rhythm (regular or irregular), conduction velocity, and the electrical condition of heart tissue. By implication only, it suggests what mechanical events are occurring. An ECG does not give any direct information about force of contraction.
19. An inotropic effect is an effect on force of cardiac contraction. Norepinephrine and cardiac glycosides such as digitalis have a positive inotropic effect.

LEVEL THREE PROBLEM SOLVING

20. Calcium channel blockers decrease cardiac output by slowing heart rate and decrease force of contraction by blocking Ca^{2+} entry and decreasing Ca^{2+}-induced Ca^{2+} release. Beta blockers decrease cardiac output by blocking increased heart rate and force of contraction by norepinephrine and epinephrine.
21. (a) Cpt. Jeffers' heart muscle has been damaged by lack of oxygen and the cells are unable to contract as strongly. Thus, less blood is being pumped out of the ventricle each time the ventricle contracts.
    (b) Leads are two recording electrodes placed on the surface of the body to measure electrical activity.
    (c) Leads are effective because electricity is conducted through body fluids to the skin surface.
22. A longer than normal P-R interval in an ECG might result from a conduction problem at the AV node or in the ventricular conduction system.
23. A rapid atrial depolarization rate is dangerous because it can cause a rapid ventricular rate. Also, if the rate is too fast, not all action potentials can be conducted to the ventricles due to the refractory period of the heart muscle. This can result in an arrhythmia. The AV node is destroyed to prevent the rapid atrial signals from being passed to the ventricles, and the ventricular pacemaker is implanted so that the ventricles have an electrical signal that tells them to contract at an appropriate rate.

LEVEL FOUR QUANTITATIVE PROBLEMS

24. SV/EDV = 0.25. If SV = 40 mL, EDV = 160 mL. SV = EDV − ESV, so 40 mL = 160 mL − ESV, therefore ESV = 120 mL. CO = HR × SV = 100 bpm × 40 mL/beat = 4000 mL/min or 4 L/min.
25. (a) 162.2 cm H_2O (b) 108.1 cm H_2O
26. 5200 mL/min or 5.2 L/min
27. 85 mL
28. (a) 1 min (b) 12 sec

CHAPTER 15

LEVEL ONE REVIEWING FACTS AND TERMS

1. The first priority of blood pressure homeostasis is to maintain adequate perfusion to the brain and heart.
2. (a) 6, 9 (b) 1, 2 (c) 4, 7 (d) 3, 5, 6, 8 (e) 3, 4
3. Blood vessel walls have endothelium, where exchange takes place in capillaries and where important paracrines are secreted; elastic tissue, which allows the vessel walls to recoil after being stretched; smooth muscle, which provides resistance to stretch and which can also contract; fibrous connective tissue, which also provides resistance to stretch.
4. Arterioles regulates blood flow to individual tissues.
5. Aortic pressure reaches *120 mm Hg* during systole. During *diastole,* aortic pressure declines to a typical low value of *80 mm Hg*. This blood pressure reading would be written as *120/80*.
6. The rapid pressure increase can be felt as a *pulse*. The equation for pulse pressure is systolic pressure minus diastolic pressure.
7. Venous return is aided by one-way valves in the veins, the skeletal muscle pump, and low pressure in the thorax during breathing.
8. Hypertension, or elevated blood pressure, threatens well-being because high pressure in the blood vessels can cause a weakened blood vessel to rupture and bleed.
9. Korotkoff sounds result when cuff pressure is lower than systolic pressure but higher than diastolic pressure.
10. See Table 15-2 for paracrines that cause vasodilation. Two other ways to control arterioles are contraction by sympathetic neurons (α-receptors) and vasodilation by epinephrine (β_2-receptors in certain organs).
11. Hyperemia is a localized region of increased blood flow. In active hyperemia, the increased blood flow is in response to an increase in metabolism. Reactive hyperemia is an increase in flow that follows a period of decreased blood flow.
12. Most systemic arterioles have *sympathetic* innervation. Exceptions are brain arterioles (no neural regulation), and arterioles in the penis and clitoris, controlled by the parasympathetic division.
13. (a) 1, 5 (b) 2, 6 (c) 1, 2, 4 (d) 3, 8 (e) none of the above
14. The digestive tract, liver, kidneys, and skeletal muscles receive over two-thirds of the cardiac output at rest. The kidneys have the highest flow of blood, on a per unit weight basis.
15. Capillary density in a tissue is directly proportional to the tissue's metabolic rate. Cartilage has one of the lowest capillary densities, while muscles and glands have the highest.
16. (a) diffusion (b) diffusion or transcytosis
    (c) facilitated diffusion (d) osmosis
17. The lymphatic vessels participate in immune, circulatory, and digestive system functions.
18. Edema is excess fluid in the interstitial space. It arises when capillary filtration exceeds the ability of the lymphatic system to remove the filtered fluid. Causes for this might be lower capillary oncotic pressure due to decreased plasma proteins or blockage of the lymphatic vessels by a tumor or other pathology.
19. (a) Perfusion is blood flow though a tissue.
    (b) Colloid osmotic pressure is the contribution of plasma proteins to the osmotic pressure of the plasma.
    (c) Vasoconstriction is a decrease in blood vessel diameter (usually an arteriole or a vein).
    (d) Angiogenesis is the growth of new blood vessels, especially capillaries, into a tissue.
    (e) Metarterioles are small vessels that go between arterioles and venules. They can act as bypass channels when precapillary sphincters constrict to prevent blood flow into capillaries.
    (f) Pericytes are cells surrounding the capillary endothelium that regulate the capillary leakiness.
20. The two major lipoprotein carriers of cholesterol are *HDL* and *LDL*. LDL-C is bad in elevated amounts; elevated HDL-C is good.

LEVEL TWO REVIEWING CONCEPTS

21. Concept Map: Use Figure 15-10 as the starting point and add additional detail wherever possible.
22. (a) Lymphatic capillaries and systemic capillaries both have thin walls but the pores of lymphatic capillaries are larger. Lymphatic capillaries dead-end and have contractile fibers to help fluid flow, whereas systemic capillaries depend on systemic blood pressure for flow.
    (b) In general, the sympathetic division raises blood pressure by increasing cardiac output (heart rate and stroke volume) and causing vasoconstriction. The parasympathetic division can decrease blood pressure by decreasing heart rate, but has no effect on vasodilation/constriction.
    (c) Lymph fluid is similar to blood plasma minus most plasma proteins. Blood also has nearly half its volume occupied by blood cells.

(d) Continuous capillaries have small pores and regulate the movement of substances better than fenestrated capillaries, which have larger pores. The latter can also open large gaps to allow proteins and blood cells to pass into the circulation.

(e) Hydraulic (hydrostatic) pressure forces fluid out of capillaries; colloid osmotic pressure of plasma proteins draws fluid into capillaries. In systemic capillaries, hydraulic pressure over the length of the capillary exceeds colloid osmotic pressure, leading to net filtration of fluid out of the capillary.

23. Preventing Ca^{2+} entry into cardiac and smooth muscle decreases the ability of those muscles to contract. Decreasing Ca^{2+} entry into autorhythmic cells decreases heart rate and cardiac output. Neurons and other cells are unaffected by these drugs because they have different types of calcium channels with which the drugs do not interact.

24. Myogenic autoregulation refers to the ability of vascular smooth muscle to regulate its own contraction. It may result from Ca^{2+} influx when the muscle is stretched, which causes a reflex contraction, or it may be due to paracrine release from the endothelium.

25. Left ventricular failure will cause blood to pool in the lungs, increasing hydrostatic pressure in pulmonary capillaries. This may cause edema in the lungs, which results in shortness of breath when oxygen has trouble diffusing into the body. If the pressure increases back into the systemic venous circulation, the increased hydrostatic pressure will cause peripheral edema and increased venous pressure.

LEVEL THREE PROBLEM SOLVING

26. The sight of blood is integrated in cerebral cortex, which sends output to the CVCC in the medulla oblongata, which results in increased parasympathetic output and decreased sympathetic output, resulting in decreased heart rate and decreased blood pressure.

27. Cells in the intact arteriole wall (in the endothelium) detect changes in oxygen and communicate these changes via a paracrine to the smooth muscle.

28. (a) Robert's uncontrollable risk factors include being male, being middle-aged, and having a family history of cardiovascular disease on both sides of his family. His only controllable risk factor is his elevated blood pressure (hypertension).

(b) Robert has hypertension because he had systolic blood pressure greater than 140 or diastolic pressure greater than 90 on several occasions. It would be useful to confirm that this was not doctor-anxiety by having him take his blood pressure for a week or so at locations away from the doctor's office, such as at a drug store.

(c) Beta blockers may help lower blood pressure by preventing norepinephrine and epinephrine from combining with $\beta 1$ receptors in the heart, thus lowering cardiac output and MAP.

29. (a) MAP will increase (MAP $\propto$ R), flow through vessels 1 and 2 will decrease (F $\propto$ 1/R), and flow through vessels 3 and 4 will increase (F $\propto$ MAP).

(b) Stimulus = increase in pressure, receptor = baroreceptor in artery, control center = vasomotor center, response = systemic vasodilation to decrease pressure.

(c) Filtration pressure downstream from the constriction decreases, because flow is reduced and flow affects pressure.

30. Atropine increases heart rate by acting as a competitive inhibitor and binding to the muscarinic receptor, preventing ACh from binding.

31. (a) increases afterload

(b) resistance increases and pressure increases

32. (a) In Figure 14-1 you could draw the connection from pulmonary artery to aorta. In Figure 14-7d you can see the remnant of the closed ductus connecting the aorta and pulmonary artery.

(b) The lungs are not functioning.

(c) systemic

(d) Left side must generate more pressure

(e) Blood will flow from the aorta into the pulmonary artery.

LEVEL FOUR QUANTITATIVE PROBLEMS

33. If diameter goes from 2 to 4, flow increases 16-fold.

34. Answers will vary. For a 50-kg individual with a resting pulse of 70 bpm, her weight in blood will be pumped in approximately 10 minutes.

35. Mean arterial pressure (MAP) = 1/3 (115 − 73) + 73 = 87 mm Hg. Pulse pressure = 115 − 73 = 42 mm Hg.

36. 250 mL oxygen/min = CO × (200 − 160 mL oxygen/L blood). His cardiac output is 6250 mL/min or 6.25 L/min.

CHAPTER 16

LEVEL ONE REVIEWING FACTS AND TERMS

1. The fluid portion of blood, *plasma,* is composed mainly of *water*.

2. The three types of plasma proteins are albumins, globulins, and fibrinogen. For functions, see Table 16-1. Albumins are the most prevalent.

3. The cellular elements of blood include erythrocytes or red blood cells (transport O_2 and CO_2); leukocytes or white blood cells (defense); and platelets (clotting).

4. Blood cell production is *hematopoiesis*. It begins in the embryo in the yolk sac, liver, spleen, and bone marrow. By birth, hematopoiesis is restricted to the bone marrow, and by adulthood it occurs only in the axial skeleton and the proximal ends of the long bones.

5. Colony-stimulating factors stimulate hematopoiesis. Cytokines are released by one cell to act on another cell. Interleukins are cytokines released by leukocytes to act on other leukocytes. These three types of chemical signals influence growth and differentiation of blood cells. For examples, see Table 16-2.

6. Red blood cell production is erythropoiesis, white blood cell production is leukopoiesis and platelet production is thrombopoiesis.

7. The hormone that directs red blood cell synthesis is *erythropoietin*. It is primarily produced in the kidney when there is hypoxia, or low oxygen in the tissues.

8. The hematocrit is the percent of total blood volume occupied by packed (centrifuged) red cells. Normal hematocrit for men is 40–54% and for women, 37–47%.

9. An erythroblast is the immature large, nucleated precursor of the mature erythrocyte, which is smaller and lacks a nucleus. Three distinct characteristics of erythrocytes are the biconcave disk shape, the lack of a nucleus, and the red color created by hemoglobin.

10. Iron in the diet is important for hemoglobin synthesis.

11. (a) Jaundice is a yellow color to the skin and sclera of the eyes due to elevated levels of bilirubin, a hemoglobin metabolite, in the blood.

(b) Anemia is a low level of hemoglobin, usually reflected by a decreased hematocrit.

(c) Transferrin is the plasma protein that acts as a carrier for iron.

(d) Hemophilia is a group of inherited diseases in which some aspect of the coagulation cascade is abnormal, resulting in decreased ability of the blood to clot.

12. Chemicals that prevent blood clotting are called anticoagulants.

LEVEL TWO REVIEWING CONCEPTS

13. List 1: see Figure 16-11. List 2: see Figure 16-13. List 3: see Figure 16-7.
14. The intrinsic pathway is initiated when exposed collagen and other triggers, such as a glass test tube wall, activate plasma protein factor XII. The extrinsic pathway begins when damaged tissue exposes tissue factor (III) that activates factor VII. Factors III and VII work directly on the common pathway and also interact with the intrinsic pathway. The two pathways unite at the common pathway to initiate the formation of thrombin. See Figure 16-12.
15. Activated platelets cannot stick to undamaged regions of endothelium that release prostacyclin and nitric oxide (NO).

LEVEL THREE PROBLEM SOLVING

16. Rachel is pale and tired at the first test because she has a low red blood cell count and low hemoglobin content in her blood. Jen looks for bruising as a sign that Rachel's platelet count is too low. Jen recommends proteins and vitamins for hemoglobin synthesis and the production of new blood cell components. Iron is also necessary for hemoglobin synthesis. Rachel is advised to avoid crowds to prevent being exposed to infections such as viruses; her WBC count is low and her ability to fight infection is decreased. By 20 days post-chemotherapy, all of Rachel's blood counts are back into the low-normal range.
17. (a) The plasma protein transferrin is elevated in this disease.
    (b) The liver, which stores iron, may be damaged in hemochromatosis.
    (c) One simple way to decrease the body's overload of iron in hemochromatosis is to withdraw blood. This illustrates the principle of mass balance: if intake has exceeded output, restore the body load by increasing output.
18. Some other factor that is essential for red blood cell synthesis must be lacking. These would include iron for hemoglobin production, folic acid, and vitamin B_{12}.

LEVEL FOUR QUANTITATIVE PROBLEMS

19. Total blood volume in a 200-lb man is about 6.4 L; his plasma volume is about 3.1 L. A 130-lb woman has total blood volume of 4.1 L and plasma volume of about 2.4 L.
20. Her total blood volume is 3.5 L and her total erythrocyte volume is 1.4 L.

CHAPTER 17

LEVEL ONE REVIEWING FACTS AND TERMS

1. Four functions of the respiratory system are gas exchange, vocalization, pH regulation, and protection.
2. Cellular respiration is the metabolic process in which oxygen and nutrients are used for energy production. External respiration is the exchange of gases between the atmosphere and cells.
3. Quiet inspiration uses the external intercostals, scalenes, and diaphragm. Normal quiet expiration is generally passive and involves no significant muscle contraction. In active expiration, the internal intercostals and abdominal muscles contract. These are all skeletal muscles.
4. Pleural fluid allows the lungs to slide freely over the internal surface of the thoracic cage.
5. Atmosphere to nose and mouth, pharynx, larynx, trachea, main bronchus, secondary bronchi, bronchioles, epithelium of the alveoli, interstitial fluid, and capillary endothelium.
6. See Figure 17-2g for structure of an alveolus. Type I cells are for gas exchange; type II produce surfactant. Macrophages ingest foreign material. Capillary endothelium is almost fused to the alveolar epithelium to minimize diffusion distance, and the surface of an alveolus is almost covered with capillaries.
7. Pulmonary circulation: right ventricle to pulmonary trunk, to left and right pulmonary arteries, smaller arteries, arterioles, capillaries, venules, and small veins. The two pulmonary veins empty into the left atrium. The pulmonary circuit contains about 0.5 liter of blood at any given moment. Typical pulmonary arterial blood pressure is 25/8, compared with 120/80 for the systemic arterial pressure.
8. Inspired air is warmed, humidified, and cleaned (filtered) during its passage through the airways.
9. During inspiration, most of the volume change of the chest is due to movement of the diaphragm.
10. Intrapleural pressure is always subatmospheric; it is lower at the end of inspiration and highest near the end of expiration. Intra-alveolar is equal to atmospheric at the beginning and end of inspiration. It is below atmospheric during inspiration and above atmospheric during expiration. See Figure 17-11.
11. Surfactant lowers the surface tension of water. In the lungs, it makes it easier for the lungs to inflate and stay inflated.
12. Radius of the airways, especially the bronchioles, plays the largest role in changing resistance in the human respiratory system.
13. (a) 1 (b) 2 (c) 1 (d) 2
14. (a) V_T = the part that varies from 2.0 to 2.5 L, IRV = from 2.5 to 3.75 L, ERV = from 2.0 to 1.0 L, RV = from 0 to 1.0 L, VC = from 1.0 to 3.75 L, and TLC = from 0 to 3.75 L.
    (b) V_T = 0.5 L, IRV = 1.25 L, ERV = 1.0 L.
    (c) Ventilation rate is 3 breaths/15 seconds = 0.2 breath per second × 60 seconds/minute = 12 breaths per minute.

LEVEL TWO REVIEWING CONCEPTS

15. See Figures 17-9 and 17-11.
16. (a) Compliance refers to the ability of a substance to stretch; elastance is a measure of how well a stretched substance returns to its unstretched state.
    (b) Ventilation is the exchange of air between the atmosphere and the lungs. Inspiration is movement of air into the lungs. Expiration is movement of air out of the lungs.
    (c) Intrapleural pressure is always subatmospheric; intra-alveolar pressures vary from subatmospheric to above atmospheric.
    (d) Total pulmonary ventilation refers to how much air enters and leaves the airways in a given period of time. Alveolar ventilation refers to how much air enters and leaves the alveoli in a given period of time. Alveolar ventilation is a better indicator of the efficiency of breathing.
    (e) Type 1 alveolar cells refer to the thin alveolar cells for gas exchange while Type II alveolar cells are the cells that synthesize and secrete surfactants.
    (f) Pulmonary circulation carries the blood from the heart to the lung. Systemic circulation carries blood to and from most tissues of the body.
17. Bronchoconstrictors: histamine, leukotrienes, acetylcholine (muscarinic); bronchodilators: carbon dioxide, epinephrine (β_2)

18. (a) decrease (b) decrease (c) decrease (d) increase
(e) decrease (f) increase
19. **Pneumothorax** is presence of air in the pleural cavity. **Spirometer** is a device used to measure the volume of inhaled and/or exhaled air. **Auscultation** is listening for body sounds. **Hypoventilation** is decreased pulmonary ventilation. **Bronchoconstriction** is a decrease in the radius of the bronchioles. **Minute volume** is the total pulmonary ventilation. **Partial pressure** of gas is that portion of total pressure in a mixture of gases that is contributed by a specific gas.
20. (a) The volume of air in the balloon is equal to the coyote's *vital capacity*. This volume can be measured by adding tidal volume with expiratory and inspiratory reserve volumes.
(b) In ten years, the coyote will not be able to put as much air in the balloon because lung function tends to decrease with age as elasticity and compliance diminish.
21. b – b – d – d
22. The *x*-axis should be time, and the *y*-axis should be P_{O_2}. During inspiration, the P_{O_2} of the primary bronchi will increase, as fresh air (P_{O_2} = 160 mm Hg) pushes the stale air (P_{O_2} = 100 mm Hg) into the alveoli. During expiration, the P_{O_2} will decrease, as the oxygen-depleted air exits. The curve will vary from 100 mm Hg to 160 mm Hg.
23. (a) Decreased compliance (decreased ability to expand) requires more work to inflate the lungs.
(b) Lungs will inflate less readily.
(c) Elastance is not directly affected by changes in compliance.
(d) Airway resistance is not affected by changes in compliance.
24. (a) decreases (b) increases (c) decreases

LEVEL THREE PROBLEM SOLVING

25. Total pulmonary ventilation = ventilation rate × tidal volume. Her resting pulmonary ventilation is 400 mL/breath × 13 breaths/min = 5200 mL/min.
(a) 400 mL/breath × 20 breaths/min = 8000 mL/min
(b) 550 mL/breath × 13 breaths/min = 7150 mL/min
(c) 500 mL/breath × 15 breaths/min = 7500 mL/min
Increasing her respiratory rate to 20 breaths/min has the largest effect. In real life, both respiratory rate and tidal volume increase during exercise, so she would have an even higher total pulmonary ventilation.
26. (a) 600 mL/breath × 16 breaths/min = 9600 mL/min.
(b) Dilating the bronchioles reduces the resistance of the airways, allowing greater volume of air flow into and out of the lungs. The patient is able to force more air out of the lungs on expiration, which increases her ERV and decreases her RV.
(c) From Figure 17-7, normal values for a female are 12–20 breaths/min, V_T = 500 mL, ERV = 700 mL, RV = 1100 mL, IC = 2400 mL, VC = 3100 mL, IRV = 1900, FRC = 1800 mL, and TLC = 4200 mL. Her respiratory rate is normal, and her lung volumes are abnormal. Her high RV is confirmed by the X-ray data showing overinflation. In obstructive lung diseases such as asthma, the bronchioles tend to collapse on expiration, trapping air in the lungs and resulting in hyperinflation. Her IRV = VC − V_T − ERV = 2800 − 600 − 1000 = 1200 mL. Her low IRV accounts for most of the low vital capacity, and is to be expected in someone with asthma, where airway resistance is high, air flow is low, and the lungs are already overinflated at the beginning of inspiration. Her higher tidal volume may be the result of the constant effort she must exert to breathe.

LEVEL FOUR QUANTITATIVE PROBLEMS

27. $P_1V_1 = P_2V_2$ New volume = 200 mL
28. (a) 21% O_2 = 160 mm Hg, 78% nitrogen = 593 mm Hg, 0.3% CO_2 = 3 mm Hg
(b) 40% O_2 = 304 mm Hg, 13% nitrogen = 99 mm Hg, 45% CO_2 = 342 mm Hg, 2% H_2 = 15 mm Hg
(c) 10% O_2 = 76 mm Hg, 15% nitrogen = 114 mm Hg, 1% argon = 8 mm Hg, 25% CO_2 = 190 mm Hg
29. 400 mL/breath × 12 breaths/min = total pulmonary ventilation of 4800 mL/min. Before an exam, ventilation is 7200 mL/min. Alveolar ventilation is (400–120) × rate, or 3360 (at rest) and 5040 mL/min (before exam).
30. Tidal volume = 417 mL/breath. IRV = 3383 mL
31. Lung volume is 1.1 L. (Did you forget to subtract the volume of the spirometer?)

CHAPTER 18

LEVEL ONE REVIEWING FACTS AND TERMS

1. Pressure gradients for oxygen and carbon dioxide, solubility of gases in water, alveolar capillary perfusion, pH of blood, temperature.
2. 98% of oxygen is bound to hemoglobin. Remaining oxygen is dissolved in the plasma.
3. Factors that alter oxygen-hemoglobin binding are P_{O_2}, temperature, pH, and the amount of hemoglobin available for binding. Of these, amount of hemoglobin is the most important.
4. Hemoglobin has four globular protein chains, each wrapped around a central heme group that contains iron, the essential element.
5. The respiratory control centers are found in the *medulla* and *pons*. The dorsal respiratory group contains neurons for inspiration; the ventral respiratory group contains neurons for inspiration and for active expiration. A central pattern generator is a group of neurons that interact spontaneously to control rhythmic contraction of certain muscle groups.
6. The central chemoreceptors increase ventilation when P_{CO_2} increases. The peripheral chemoreceptors in the carotid and aortic bodies increase ventilation primarily in response to P_{O_2} less than 60 mm Hg. P_{CO_2} is the most important chemical signal for ventilation.
7. The protective reflexes of the respiratory system include an irritant-mediated bronchoconstriction and the Hering-Breuer reflex that prevents overinflation. The latter is initiated when tidal volume exceeds one liter.
8. Pressure gradients drive the exchange of respiratory gases.
9. Decreased atmospheric P_{O_2}, decreased alveolar perfusion, anemia and blood loss, decreased pulmonary ventilation, toxicity from carbon monoxide or cyanide, increased thickness of respiratory membrane as with pulmonary edema, decreased surface area of respiratory membrane as with emphysema.

LEVEL TWO REVIEWING CONCEPTS

10. Start with Figure 18-13.
11. Most oxygen is bound to hemoglobin, not dissolved in the plasma, (P_{O_2}).
12. (a) 98% of arterial O_2 is bound to hemoglobin, while the remaining 2% is dissolved in plasma. 70% of CO_2 is converted to bicarbonate and H^+, 23% is bound to Hb, and the remaining 7% is dissolved in plasma.

(b) Partial pressure of a gas in solution refers to the amount that dissolves at equilibrium when the solution is exposed to the same partial pressure. Concentration is amount of gas per volume of solution, measured in units such as moles per liter. While solution partial pressure and concentration are proportional, the concentration is affected by the gas solubility, and therefore is not the same as the gas concentration in air.

13. Decreased pH (increased acidity) promotes oxygen unloading from hemoglobin.

14. Hypoxia is low oxygen inside cells. COPD is chronic obstructive pulmonary disease, such as asthma, in which increased airway resistance results in decreased pulmonary ventilation. Hypercapnia is elevated carbon dioxide.

15. Oxygen is not very soluble in water, and the metabolic requirement for oxygen in most multicellular animals would not be met without an oxygen-transport molecule.

16. (a) Graph should have an *x*-axis of ventilation in liters/minute and a *y*-axis of arterial P_{O_2}, in mm Hg, resembling Figure 18-9. Relationship is direct, with an increase in ventilation producing an increase in arterial P_{O_2}. Because maximum arterial P_{O_2} will depend upon oxygen solubility in water, the slope of the graph should decrease as dissolved oxygen approaches saturation.
(b) Graph should have an *x*-axis of arterial P_{CO_2} in mm Hg, and a *y*-axis of ventilation in liters/minute. Relationship is direct, with an increase in arterial P_{CO_2} producing a reflexive increase in ventilation, mediated by both the central and peripheral chemoreceptors. Because there is a maximum ventilation determined by properties of the neurons and muscles involved in ventilation, slope of curve should decrease as it approaches this maximum.

17. (a) Amount of dissolved gas increases with P_{O_2}.
(b) As P_{O_2} increases, amount of oxygen bound to hemoglobin increases, until 100% saturation is reached.

18. Arterial P_{O_2} is not changed because P_{O_2} depends on the P_{O_2} of the alveoli, not on how much Hb is available for oxygen transport.

19. (a) See Figure 18-20. (b) See Figure 18-15.

LEVEL THREE PROBLEM SOLVING

20. The increase in his dead space decreases alveolar ventilation.
(a) increases (b) decreases (c) increases (d) decreases

21. Person (a) has slightly reduced oxygen pressure but at $P_{O_2} = 80$, saturation of hemoglobin will be about 95%. If oxygen content with normal hemoglobin at 100 mm Hg P_{O_2} is 197 mL O_2/L at 98% saturation, then oxygen content at $P_{O_2} = 80$ mm Hg is 190 mL O_2/L blood ($197 \times (0.95/0.98)$). Person (b) has reduced hemoglobin of 12 g/dL at 98% saturation, so oxygen content would be 157.6 mL O_2/L blood ($197 \times (12/15)$). The increased P_{O_2} did not compensate for the decreased hemoglobin content and (b) has less total oxygen.

22. (a) decrease (b) decrease (c) decrease

23. (a) Respiratory movements depend upon signals originating above the level of the cut, which could include any area of the brain.
(b) Ventilation depends upon signals originating in the medulla and/or pons.
(c) Respiratory rhythm is controlled by the medulla alone, but other important aspects of normal respiration such as depth depend upon signals originating in the pons or higher.

24. With chronic elevated P_{CO_2}, the central chemoreceptors adapt and CO_2 is no longer a chemical drive for ventilation. The primary chemical signal for ventilation becomes low oxygen (below 60 mm Hg). Thus, when the patient is given oxygen and the P_{O_2} goes above the threshold, there is no chemical drive for ventilation, so the patient stops breathing.

25. (a) Hemoglobin at the alveoli is about 96% saturated. At an exercising cell, it is about 23% saturated.
(b) Bzork does not consume much oxygen because he only uses about 20% of the oxygen that his hemoglobin can carry. With exercise, his oxygen consumption increases dramatically, and his hemoglobin releases more than 3/4 of the oxygen it can carry.

26. All three lines show that as P_{CO_2} increases, ventilation increases. Line A shows that a decrease in P_{CO_2} potentiates this increase in ventilation (when compared to Line B). Line C shows that ingestion of alcohol diminishes the effect of increasing P_{CO_2} on ventilation. Because alcohol is a CNS-depressant, we can hypothesize that the pathway that links increased P_{CO_2} and increased ventilation is integrated in the CNS.

LEVEL FOUR QUANTITATIVE PROBLEMS

27. The maximum O_2 carrying capacity is 1.65 mL O_2/gm Hb.

28. Oxygen consumption is 202.5 mL O_2/min.

29. Nothing happens to the curve. The percent of available Hb bound to O_2 is unchanged at any given PO_2. However, with less Hb available, less oxygen will be transported.

CHAPTER 19

LEVEL ONE REVIEWING FACTS AND TERMS

1. Five characteristics are color (concentration), odor (infection or excreted substances), clarity (presence of cells), taste (presence of glucose), and froth (presence of proteins)

2. Kidney functions are regulation of extracellular fluid volume (to maintain adequate blood pressure), regulation of osmolarity (so that cells don't shrink or swell too much), maintenance of ion balance (especially Ca^{2+} and K^+, both of which influence the function of neurons), regulation of pH (cells malfunction if pH homeostasis is not maintained), excretion of wastes and foreign substances (to prevent toxic effects), and production of hormones (that regulate red blood cell production, Ca^{2+} balance, and Na^+ balance).

3. At any given time, 20–25% of the cardiac output goes to the kidneys.

4. Urine flows into the paired ureters, urinary bladder, and urethra.

5. (a), (e), (b), (g), (f), (d), (c), (h)

6. The filtration barriers are the glomerular capillary endothelium, basal lamina, and the epithelium of Bowman's capsule. Blood cells and most plasma proteins are usually excluded by these layers.

7. Hydraulic pressure of flowing blood promotes glomerular filtration. The fluid pressure (hydrostatic pressure) of fluid in Bowman's capsule and the oncotic (osmotic) pressure created by plasma proteins oppose it. Net driving force is the arithmetic sum of these pressures.

8. GFR stands for glomerular filtration rate. A typical GFR is 125 mL/min or 180 L/day.

9. (a) Juxtaglomerular apparatus is a specialized group of cells found where the distal tubule passes between the afferent and efferent arterioles. It is composed of the macula densa cells in the distal tubule wall and granular cells in the arteriole wall. (b) Paracrine signals from the macula densa play a role in autoregulation of GFR and in the secretion of renin.

(c) Mesangial cells in the basal lamina of the glomerulus alter the size of the filtration slits formed by the interlacing "fingers" of
(d) podocytes, the specialized epithelial cells that surround the glomerular capillaries. Changes in slit size alter GFR.
(e) The urinary bladder has an internal smooth muscle sphincter that is passively contracted and an external skeletal muscle sphincter that is tonically (actively) contracted.
(f) The renal cortex is the outer layer of the kidney; it contains renal corpuscles, proximal and distal tubules, and parts of the loop of Henle and collecting ducts.

10. Most reabsorption (80%) occurs in the proximal tubule. When a molecule or ion is reabsorbed from the lumen of the nephron, it goes into the peritubular capillaries and from there into the systemic venous circulation, back to the right atrium. If a substance is filtered and not reabsorbed, it is excreted in the urine.
11. (a) 2, 3 (b) 3, 4 (c) 3, 5 (d) 1 (e) 5
12. Penicillin, K^+, and H^+ are secreted into the tubule lumen.
13. Creatinine is used to estimate GFR in humans.
14. Micturition is urination.

LEVEL TWO REVIEWING CONCEPTS

15. The map of factors that influence or control GFR should include information from Figures 19-4, 19-6, 19-7, 19-8, and 19-9.
16. (a) Filtration and secretion both involve movement of material from blood to tubule lumen, but filtration is a bulk flow process created by pressure gradients while secretion is usually a mediated transport process. Excretion is also bulk flow but involves movement from the lumen of the kidney to the outside world.
(b) Transport maximum for a transport system is the maximum rate at which the carriers can work due to saturation of available binding sites by substrate. The renal threshold is the plasma concentration at which saturation occurs; at this point, the solute begins to appear in the urine.
(c) These substances are used as examples of renal transport. Creatinine is an endogenous compound but the other three are xenobiotics (foreign substances). All but inulin are filtered, not reabsorbed, and are secreted. Inulin is filtered but neither reabsorbed nor secreted.
(d) Clearance refers to the rate at which plasma is cleared of a substance (mL plasma cleared of substance *X*/min). GFR is expressed as the filtration rate of plasma (mL plasma filtered/min). Excretion is removal of urine, expressed as mL urine/min.
17. This kidney allows rapid removal of foreign substances that are filtered but not reabsorbed. The clearance rate for these substances is equal to the GFR if the substances are not also secreted.
18. If the afferent arteriole of a nephron constricts, the GFR in that nephron decreases. If the efferent arteriole of a nephron constricts, the GFR in that nephron increases.
19. The micturition reflex is shown in Figure 19-18. With toilet training, higher brain centers monitor sensory input from the expanding bladder and inhibit the reflex until an appropriate time. Higher brain centers can inhibit micturition either consciously or unconsciously or can be used to initiate the reflex.
20. Bladder smooth muscle contracts under parasympathetic control, so blocking muscarinic receptors decreases bladder contraction.

LEVEL THREE PROBLEM SOLVING

21. (a) Filtration rate is proportional to plasma concentration of inulin. Filtration is a passive, bulk flow process that does not show saturation. The excretion rate of inulin exceeds the filtration rate, indicating that inulin is also secreted into the tubule lumen. The slope of the excretion rate is higher initially, then it decreases to match the slope of the filtration rate. The point where the slope changes represents saturation of transporters that secrete inulin. Inulin is thus filtered, secreted (transported from the peritubular capillaries into the lumen after filtration), and excreted (eliminated from the body). No evidence for reabsorption is presented.
(b) The line indicating net secretion will be approximately superimposed on the filtration line until the slope change, after which the secretion line is horizontal (no further increase in rate due to saturation).
22. Drawing should resemble Figure 19-12. Place transporters as described on apical and basolateral membranes. Cl^- moves between the cells.
23. The dialysis fluid can resemble plasma without any waste substances, such as urea. This will allow diffusion of solutes and water from the blood into the dialysis fluid but diffusion will stop at the desired concentration. To remove excess water from the blood, the dialysis fluid can be made more concentrated.

LEVEL FOUR QUANTITATIVE PROBLEMS

24. Renal blood flow (25%) is 1 L/min.
25. The first specimen contains 20,000 mg creatinine. Clearance = 1000 L plasma/day. Normally creatinine clearance = GFR. However, this value of 1000 L/day is not all realistic for GFR (normal average is 180 L/day). The repeat test has 4000 mg of creatinine and gives a clearance of 200 L/day, which is within normal limits. The abnormal values on the first test were probably a laboratory error. Dwight's kidney function is normal.
26. For any solute that filters: plasma concentration × GFR = filtration rate. At the transport maximum: filtration rate = reabsorption rate of T_m

By substitution: plasma concentration × GFR = T_m

The renal threshold represents the plasma concentration at which the transporters working at their maximum (T_m). By substitution:

$$\text{renal threshold} \times \text{GFR} = T_m$$

Mermaid's GFR is 250 mL/min and T_m is 50 mg/min, so renal threshold is 0.2 mg glucose/mL plasma.

Clearance = excretion rate/plasma concentration. At 15 mg glucose/mL plasma, 3750 mg/min filter and 50 mg/min reabsorb, so 3700 mg/min are excreted.

$$\text{Clearance} = \frac{3700 \text{ mg glucose/min}}{15 \text{ mg glucose/mL plasma}} = 246.7 \text{ mL plasma cleared/min}$$

CHAPTER 20

LEVEL ONE REVIEWING FACTS AND TERMS

1. Electrolytes are ions, which can conduct electric current through a solution. Some electrolytes whose concentrations the body must regulate are Na^+, K^+, Ca^{2+}, H^+, $HPO_4{}^{2-}$ and $HCO_3{}^-$.
2. Organs include the kidneys, lungs, heart, blood vessels, and organs of the digestive tract. Four important hormones are vasopressin (ADH), aldosterone, atrial natriuretic peptides (ANP), and the renin-angiotensin pathway.
3. Water enters the body only through ingested food and drink. A small amount of water is manufactured by the body as a product of metabolism. The body loses water in exhaled air, by evaporation and perspiration from the skin, through the kidneys, and in the feces.

4. See Table 20-2.
5. The descending limb of the loop of Henle is permeable to water but does not transport salts because its cells lack the appropriate membrane transporters. The ascending limb is impermeable to water; however, it does have the membrane transporters to transport NaCl from the lumen into interstitial fluid.
6. Na^+ is a primary determinant of extracellular fluid volume. H^+ is the determinant of extracellular pH.
7. When plasma concentrations of K^+ decrease, more K^+ leaves the cell, and the membrane potential becomes more negative (hyperpolarizes). The heart is most likely to be affected by changes in K^+ concentration.
8. Salt appetite and thirst are important in regulating fluid volume and osmolarity.
9. ADH = antidiuretic hormone; ANP = atrial natriuretic peptide; ACE = angiotensin-converting enzyme; ANGII = angiotensin II; JG (apparatus) = juxtaglomerular; P cell = principal cell; I cell = intercalated cell.
10. Use the information in the following figures to compile your list: Figures 19-10 and 19-12, 20-7, 20-8, 20-12, 20-19, 20-20, and 20-21.
11. pH homeostasis is important because pH alters protein structure and therefore enzyme activity, membrane transporters, and the nervous system. The body copes with changing pH by using buffers, renal compensatory mechanisms, and respiratory compensation.
12. Acids are more likely to accumulate in the body. Acid sources include CO_2 from cellular respiration, metabolic acids, and acids ingested as food. Sources of bases include some foods.
13. A buffer is a molecule that helps prevent or slow changes in pH. Three intracellular buffers are proteins, phosphate ions, and hemoglobin. The primary extracellular buffer is HCO_3^-.
14. The kidneys excrete or reabsorb H^+ or HCO_3^-. Ammonia and phosphates are urinary buffers.
15. $CO_2 + H_2O \rightleftharpoons H_2CO_3 \rightleftharpoons H^+ + HCO_3^-$. Carbonic anhydrase increases the rate of this reaction. Renal tubule cells and red blood cells have high concentrations of carbonic anhydrase.
16. Arterial P_{CO_2} decreases, pH increases, and plasma H^+ concentration decreases.

LEVEL TWO REVIEWING CONCEPTS

17. To map the homeostatic reflexes that occur in response to each of the situations, use the information in Table 20-2 as the starting point and compile all the different pathways into a single map similar to Figure 20-16. Be sure to include all the steps of the reflex pathways on your map (stimulus, receptor, etc.).
18. This map will combine information from Figures 20-18 through 20-21.
19. See Figure 20-4.
20. This diagram should combine Figures 20-5 and 20-6.
21. (a) ANP—peptide hormone from atrial myocardial cells. Causes excretion of Na^+ and water by its actions on the kidney and by inhibiting ADH release from hypothalamus.
    (b) Aldosterone—steroid from adrenal cortex. Causes increased Na^+ reabsorption and increased K^+ excretion by its action on the distal tubule.
    (c) Renin—enzyme/hormone (peptide) from JG cells. Acts on blood angiotensinogen, converting it to ANGI.
    (d) ANGII—peptide hormone made from precursor molecule made by liver. Increases blood pressure and tries to maintain or increase blood volume by actions on arterioles, brain, and adrenal cortex
    (e) ADH—peptide hormone from hypothalamus. Increases water reabsorption by the distal nephron.
    (f) Angiotensin-converting enzyme—enzyme (protein) found on vascular endothelium. Converts ANGI to ANGII (see Figure 20-14).
22. Compensatory mechanisms for restoring low blood pressure are vasoconstriction, increased cardiac output, conservation of water by the kidneys, and increased thirst to increase fluid volume. If blood pressure falls too low, blood supply to the brain will diminish, resulting in damage or death.
23. (a) Principal and intercalated cells are both in the distal tubule. P cells are associated with aldosterone-mediated Na^+ reabsorption; I cells are involved with acid-base regulation.
    (b) Renin, angiotensin II, aldosterone, and ACE are all parts of the RAAS system. Renin and ACE function primarily as enzymes, while ANGII and aldosterone are hormones. For more details, see Figure 20-14.
    (c) In both respiratory and metabolic acidosis, body pH falls below 7.38. Respiratory acidosis results from CO_2 retention (from any number of causes), while metabolic acidosis results from excessive production of metabolic acids. Respiratory acidosis is moderated by buffers and can be compensated for by renal excretion of H^+ and retention of HCO_3^-. Metabolic acidosis is moderated by buffers and can be compensated by increased ventilation (decreasing arterial P_{CO_2}) and increased renal excretion of H^+ and retention of HCO_3^-. In respiratory acidosis, arterial P_{CO_2} will be elevated; in metabolic acidosis, it is usually decreased.
    (d) Water reabsorption in the proximal tubule and ascending limb of the loop of Henle is not regulated by ADH; water reabsorption in the distal tubule is altered by ADH. The proximal and distal tubule cells have water pores, but the apical membrane of the cells of the ascending limb of the loop of Henle does not.
    (e) Respiratory and metabolic alkalosis are both conditions in which body pH goes above 7.42. Metabolic alkalosis may be caused by excessive ingestion of bicarbonate-containing antacids or by loss of acidic stomach contents due to vomiting; respiratory alkalosis may be caused by hyperventilation. Metabolic alkalosis can be compensated by decreased ventilation (increasing arterial P_{CO_2}) and by decreased renal excretion of H^+ and increased excretion of HCO_3^-. Respiratory alkalosis can only be compensated by the renal mechanisms.

LEVEL THREE PROBLEM SOLVING

24. (a) The man is in acidosis. Plasma bicarbonate ion is elevated, probably because of his elevated P_{CO_2}, which also causes elevated H^+. This is an acute situation, because the bronchoconstriction is a short-term event.
    (b) The man is in acidosis again, with greater elevation of HCO_3^- and P_{CO_2}. As he now has a chronic disease that contributes to his chemical imbalance, the imbalance is chronic.
    (c) Renal compensation has partially increased his pH by excretion of H^+ and reabsorption of HCO_3^-, which also acts as a buffer. His P_{CO_2} is elevated because of his emphysema.
25. (a) Karen is in metabolic alkalosis, for which her body is trying to compensate.
    (b) Her plasma bicarbonate is high because after vomiting acid (H^+), her body was left with bicarbonate ions.

(c) Hypoventilation increases PCO_2 and also increases HCO_3^- and H^+. The increase in H^+ decreases her pH (compensation) but her HCO_3^- goes up even more. Hypoventilation will also decrease her arterial Po_2, and therefore decrease the total oxygen content of her blood (for review, see Figure 18-20).

26. Hannah's blood pressure is high. Absorption of 3 L water will expand total body volume and therefore blood volume. Her plasma Na^+ concentration and plasma osmolarity are low. Use Table 20-2 to select the reflex pathways for your map.

LEVEL FOUR QUANTITATIVE PROBLEMS

27. (a) pH = 6.1 + log 24/(.03 × 40) = 7.40 (b) 7.34
28. 428.6 mL (600 mosml/? L = 1400 mosmol/L)
29. (a) 400 mg glucose/100 mL × 130 mL/min = 520 mg glucose/min filters.
    (b) Can reabsorb up to T_m therefore 400 mg/min reabsorbed.
    (c) Excreted = filtered − reabsorbed or 120 mg/min × 1440 min/day = 172.8 g/day excreted.
    (d) Must convert grams of glucose to milliosmoles: 172.8 g × 180 g/mole × 1000 mosmol/mole = 960 mosmol glucose excreted/day. Concentration = amount/volume. 1200 mOsM = 960 mosmol/? liters. To excrete the glucose will require 0.8 additional liter of urine.

CHAPTER 21

LEVEL ONE REVIEWING FACTS AND TERMS

1. Digestion is the chemical or mechanical breakdown of ingested nutrients (e.g., proteins) into a form that can be absorbed by the body. Absorption is movement from lumen to extracellular fluid (water); secretion is movement from ECF to lumen (enzymes). Motility is the movement of material through the digestive tract.
2. *Absorption* and *digestion* are not regulated, whereas *secretion* and *motility* are continuously regulated. Secretion and motility are necessary for proper digestion, without which the body cannot obtain food. By not regulating absorption and digestion, the body ensures that it will always absorb the maximum available nutrients.
3. (a) 2 (b) 3 (c) 4 (d) 7, 10 (e) 8 (f) 2, 3, 7 (g) 2
4. The layers (lumen outward) are mucosa (epithelium, connective tissue and smooth muscle), submucosa (connective tissue), muscularis (smooth muscle), and serosa (connective tissue).
5. Secretory epithelium (endocrine and exocrine) lines the stomach, while absorptive epithelium with a few secretory cells lines the intestines.
6. Peyer's patches are clusters or nodes of lymphoid tissue in the mucosal layer.
7. Motility moves food through the gastrointestinal tract (usually from mouth to anus) and helps mix food with GI secretions. Gut motility results from contraction of longitudinal and circular muscle layers to create either propulsive peristaltic movements or mixing segmental movements.
8. Zymogens are inactive proenzymes in the digestive system. They must have a segment of protein chain removed before the enzyme becomes active. Examples are pepsinogen-pepsin and trypsinogen-trypsin.
9. (a) 8, 9 (b) 3, 7 (c) 1, 3, 7 (d) 1, 3, 7 (e) 6 (f) 2 (g) 4 (h) 5
10. Temperature is the only factor that does not significantly affect digestion in humans. Emulsification of fats takes place in the stomach and small intestine with the aid of lipase, mechanical mixing, and bile salts. Neural activity plays an important role in motility and secretion along the length of the digestive tract. Acidic pH in the stomach helps break down food and digest microorganisms. Surface area of food is increased by mechanical digestion and increases the area upon which enzymes can act.
11. Most digested nutrients are absorbed into *capillaries* of the *hepatic portal* system, delivering nutrients to the *liver*. However, digested fats go into the *lymphatic* system because intestinal capillaries have a *basement membrane (basal lamina)* around them that most lipids are unable to cross.
12. The ENS is a network of neurons contained within the digestive tract that can sense a stimulus, integrate information, and create an appropriate response without integration or input from the CNS. Although the ENS can work independently, it also interacts with the CNS through sensory and autonomic neurons.
13. Short reflexes are reflexes mediated entirely within the enteric nervous system. They regulate endocrine and exocrine secretion and GI motility. Long reflexes are GI reflexes integrated in the CNS.
14. Paracrines in the GI tract help mediate secretion and motility. Two examples are serotonin (5-HT) and histamine.

LEVEL TWO REVIEWING CONCEPTS

15. Use Figure 21-22 as the basis for the map and add details to it.
16. (a) Mastication is chewing, deglutition is swallowing.
    (b) Villi are created by folds of the intestine, while microvilli are created by folds of the cell membrane on individual cells. Both increase the surface area.
    (c) Migrating motor complex, peristaltic contraction, and segmentation are all patterns of GI muscle contraction. Migrating motor complex contractions move food remnants and bacteria from the stomach to the large intestine between meals. Peristaltic contractions are progressive waves of contraction that move from one section of the GI tract to another. Segmental contraction is the contraction and relaxation of short segments of the intestine. Mass movements push a large bolus of material into the rectum, triggering defecation (excretion of feces). Vomiting, a protective reflex integrated in the medulla, is the forceful expulsion of gastric and duodenal contents from the mouth. Diarrhea is excessive amounts of watery stool.
    (d) Chyme is the watery combination of semidigested food and GI secretions in the GI tract. Feces are the usually-solid waste material that remains after digestion and absorption are complete. Chyme is produced in the stomach; feces are produced in the large intestine.
    (e) Short reflexes originate within and are integrated within the enteric nervous system. Long reflexes may originate in the GI tract or elsewhere and are integrated within the CNS.
    (f) The ENS is a unique division of the nervous system that controls digestive function. It consists of the submucosal plexus in the submucosal layer of the gut wall, and the myenteric plexis, which lies between the two muscle layers of the digestive tract wall. The vagus nerve carries sensory information and efferent signals between the brain and many internal organs, including the ENS.
    (g) Cephalic phase consists of digestive reflexes triggered by stimuli received in the brain, such as the smell, sight, or taste of food. Gastric phase begins with food entering the stomach, triggering a series of short reflexes. Intestinal phase begins when chyme enters the small intestine.
17. See Figures 21-6, 21-8, 21-9, and 21-21.

18. The ENS and cephalic brain use similar neurotransmitters and neuromodulators, including serotonin, VIP, and NO. Enteric support cells are similar to astroglia in the CNS. The GI capillaries are not very permeable, like the blood-brain barrier surrounding those in the brain. Both divisions act as integrating centers.
19. See Table 21-1 for specific hormones.
20. See Figure 21-26.

LEVEL THREE PROBLEM SOLVING

21. See Figure 21-17.
22. Severe diarrhea may be associated with loss of small intestine contents and bicarbonate, which results in metabolic acidosis.
23. (a) The liver and gall bladder produce and store bile salts needed for fat digestion. Ingestion of a fatty meal triggers reflex contraction of the gall bladder, but the blocked bile duct prevents secretion of the bile, causing pain.
    (b) Micelle formation will be decreased due to lack of bile salts, and carbohydrate digestion will be decreased due to lack of pancreatic secretions containing amylase. Protein absorption will be decreased some because of low pancreatic protease secretion, but protein digestion begins in the stomach and is continued by enzymes bound to the brush border, so it does not stop completely when the bile duct is blocked. Therefore, some digested proteins will be absorbed.
25. Apical membrane has Na^+ and K^+ leak channels. Basolateral membrane has the Na^+-K^+-ATPase. At high flow, saliva has more Na^+ and less K^+.

LEVEL FOUR QUANTITATIVE PROBLEMS

26. (a) MIT started out with equal concentrations in both solutions but by the end of the experiment, it was more concentrated on the serosal side. Therefore, MIT must be moving by active transport.
    (b) MIT moves apical to basolateral. This movement is absorption.
    (c) Transport across the apical membrane goes from the bath into the tissue. The tissue has more MIT than the bath. Therefore, this must be active transport.
    (d) Transport across the basolateral membrane goes from the tissue into the sac of intestine. The tissue has more MIT than fluid on the basolateral side. Therefore, this must be passive transport.

CHAPTER 22

LEVEL ONE REVIEWING FACTS AND TERMS

1. Metabolic pathways are all pathways used for synthesis or for energy production, use, or storage. Anabolic pathways are primarily synthetic; catabolic pathways break down large molecules into smaller ones.
2. Biological work includes transport (such as moving molecules across membranes), mechanical work (such as movement of muscles), and chemical work (such as protein synthesis).
3. A kilocalorie is the amount of heat required to raise the temperature of 1 liter of water by 1° C. In direct calorimetry, food is burned to see how much energy it contains.
4. The respiratory quotient is the ratio of CO_2 produced to O_2 used in cellular metabolism. A typical RQ value for an American diet is about 0.82.
5. BMR is an individual's lowest metabolic rate, measured at rest after sleep and a 12-hour fast. Average BMR is higher in adult males than in females because females have more adipose tissue with a lower respiration rate. Other factors that affect BMR are age, physical activity, amount of lean muscle mass, diet, hormones, and genetics.
6. Biomolecules will be broken down for energy, used for synthesis, or stored.
7. Absorptive state metabolism is dominated by anabolic reactions and nutrient storage. Postabsorptive state metabolism mobilizes stored nutrients and uses them for energy and synthesis.
8. A nutrient pool is a group of nutrients that are available for the cells to use; most are found in the blood. The three primary pools are glucose, free fatty acids, and amino acids.
9. The primary goal of metabolism during the fasted state is to maintain adequate levels of glucose for the brain.
10. Excess energy is stored in small amounts of glycogen and in larger amounts of adipose tissue fat.
11. Three fates of ingested proteins include protein synthesis, energy, and conversion to fat or glucose for storage. The fate of ingested fats includes lipid synthesis (such as for cell membranes), energy, and storage as fats.
12. Insulin decreases blood glucose and glucagon increases it.
13. Amino acids and the glycerol portion of fatty acids can be made into glucose through gluconeogenesis.
14. Ketone bodies are produced by excessive breakdown of fatty acids, as occurs in starvation. Ketones can be burned as fuel by the brain and many peripheral tissues. Many ketone bodies are strong acids, so high concentrations can create metabolic acidosis.
15. Two stimuli for insulin secretion are increased plasma glucose and parasympathetic input onto pancreatic beta cells. Sympathetic stimulation inhibits insulin secretion.
16. Type 1 diabetes mellitus results from an absolute lack of insulin production. In type 2 diabetes, the body produces insulin but the cells do not respond normally to the hormone. Both types are characterized by elevated fasting blood glucose levels. In type 1, the body uses fats and proteins for fuel, leading to muscle wasting, ketosis, polyuria, polydipsia, and osmotic diuresis. Type 2 is not as severe because the cells can use some glucose.
17. Glucagon release is stimulated by low plasma glucose or increased plasma amino acids. The liver is its primary target, and glucagon increases glycogenolysis and gluconeogenesis to increase plasma glucose.
18. (a) Lipoprotein lipase is a capillary endothelium enzyme that converts blood triglycerides into free fatty acids and monoglycerides.
    (b) Amylin is co-secreted with insulin and slows gastric emptying and gastric acid secretion.
    (c) Ghrelin is a "hunger hormone" secreted by the stomach.
    (d) NPY is produced by the hypothalamus and causes an increase in food intake.
    (e) Apoproteins are the protein components of lipoproteins. Apoprotein B on LDL-C facilitates transport into most cells. Defective apoproteins have been linked to some inherited hypercholesterolemia.
    (f) Leptin is a "satiety hormone" produced by adipocytes.
    (g) Osmotic diuresis is loss of water in the urine due to high amounts of urine solutes. Hyperglycemia, as in diabetes mellitus, causes dehydration through osmotic diuresis.
    (h) Insulin resistance is seen in type 2 diabetes when target cells fail to response to insulin.
19. (a) stimulates (b) inhibits (c) stimulates
    (d) stimulates (e) stimulates

LEVEL TWO REVIEWING CONCEPTS

20. Hints for your concept maps: Try to base your maps on a figure in the book, such as Figures 22-2, 22-5, or 22-6. Use different colors for each organ or hormone. These will probably be the most complex maps you've done yet!
21. The concentration of glucagon varies only slightly during the day, while the concentration of insulin cycles according to food intake. Thus it appears that it is the ratio rather than an absolute amount of hormone that determines the direction of metabolism.
22. (a) Glucose is a monosaccharide. Glycogenolysis is glycogen breakdown. Glycogenesis is glycogen production from glucose. Gluconeogenesis is glucose synthesis from amino acids and fats. Glucagon is a hormone that increases plasma glucose. Glycolysis is the first pathway in glucose metabolism for ATP production.
    (b) Thermogenesis is heat production by cells. Shivering thermogenesis occurs when muscles twitch, producing heat as a byproduct. Non-shivering thermogenesis occurs in all cells, but especially brown fat, proportional to their metabolic activity. Diet-induced thermogenesis represents the heat generated by the digestive and anabolic reactions that occur during the absorptive state.
    (c) Lipoproteins are transport molecules. Chylomicrons are lipoprotein complexes assembled in the intestinal epithelium and absorbed into the lymphatic system. Cholesterol is a steroid component of cell membranes and precursor to steroid hormones. HDL-C contains high-density lipoprotein and takes cholesterol into liver cells, where it is metabolized or excreted. LDL-C is the most prevalent form of cholesterol-based lipoprotein and elevated concentrations are associated with atherosclerosis. Apoprotein is the protein component of lipoproteins.
    (d) Calorimetry is measurement of energy content and is a means of determining metabolic rate. Direct calorimetry involves measuring actual heat production when food is burned. Indirect calorimetry measures oxygen consumption or CO_2 production.
    (e) Conductive heat loss is loss of body heat to a cooler object. Radiant heat loss results from production of infrared electromagnetic waves by any object above absolute zero temperature. Convective heat loss results from upward movement of warm air and its replacement by cooler air. Evaporative heat loss occurs when water evaporates.
    (f) The absorptive metabolic state exists when nutrients are absorbed and anabolic processes exceed catabolic processes. Postabsorptive state exists when catabolic processes exceed anabolic processes to maintain plasma glucose.
23. (a) Hyperglycemia results from the lack of insulin production.
    (b) Glucosuria results when the glucose concentration in filtrate exceeds the kidney's capacity to reabsorb glucose.
    (c) Polyuria results from osmotic diuresis caused by glucosuria.
    (d) Ketosis results from increased metabolism of fatty acids, in the absence of cells' ability to utilize glucose.
    (e) Dehydration is a consequence of polyuria due to osmotic diuresis.
    (f) Severe thirst is a consequence of dehydration.
24. If a person ingests a pure protein meal and only insulin is released, the person's blood glucose concentrations might fall too low due to insulin action. Glucagon secretion by the same stimulus ensures that glucose concentrations in the blood will remain within normal levels.
25. See Figure 22-1.
26. See Figures 22-19 and 22-20.

LEVEL THREE PROBLEM SOLVING

27. Once Scott's new muscle proteins are made and once the limited pool of free amino acids in the blood is filled, excess amino acids will be stored as glycogen or fat.
28. As insulin secretion (x-axis) increases, plasma glucose concentration (y-axis) decreases.
29. Graph should be very similar to Figure 18-9 on p. 597. (a) Acidosis promotes O_2 dissociation from hemoglobin, shifting the curve to the right (like Fig. 18-10 on p. 598). The effect of low DPG, however, would shift the curve to the left (like Fig. 18-11 on p. 599). The net effect of both conditions would be somewhere between the right shift expected from acidosis (increased unloading) and the left shift expected from low DPG (decreased unloading). (b) Bicarbonate would bind some of the free H^+, bringing pH back up. As pH approached normal, the dissociation curve would shift back to the left. With DPG still remaining low, the curve would be between the left shift for low DPG and normal. Oxygen release after treatment would therefore be depressed, and cells would be deprived, compared to the untreated condition.

LEVEL FOUR QUANTITATIVE PROBLEMS

30. Answers will vary. A 64-inch woman weighing 50 kg will have a BMI of approximately 19.
31. Fat: 6 g $\times$ 9 kcal/g = 54 kcal. Carbohydrate: 30 g $\times$ 4 kcal/g = 120 kcal. Protein: 8 g $\times$ 4 kcal/g = 32 kcal. Total = 206 kcal. 54/206 = 26% of calories from fat.

CHAPTER 23

LEVEL ONE REVIEWING FACTS AND TERMS

1. The zones are zona glomerulosa (aldosterone), zona fasciculata (glucocorticoids), and zona reticularis (sex steroids, primarily androgens).
2. (a) corticotropin releasing hormone (hypothalamus) → adrenocorticotropic hormone (anterior pituitary) → cortisol (adrenal cortex) feeds back to directly inhibit secretion of both CRH and ACTH.
   (b) growth hormone releasing hormone and growth hormone inhibiting hormone (hypothalamus) → growth hormone (anterior pituitary)
   (c) decreased blood Ca^{2+} → parathyroid (parathyroid glands) → increase in blood Ca^{2+} by increasing reabsorption of bone, among other effects → negative feedback inhibits secretion of PTH.
   (d) Thyrotropin releasing hormone (hypothalamus) → thyroid stimulating hormone (thyrotropin) (anterior pituitary) → triiodothyronine (T_3) and thyroxine (T_4) (thyroid gland) → negative feedback to hypothalamus and anterior pituitary
3. Conditions: adequate diet, absence of stress, and adequate amounts of thyroid and growth hormones. Other important hormones: insulin, somatomedins, and sex hormones at puberty.
4. Triiodothyronine (T_3) and tetraiodothyronine (T_4 or thyroxine). T_3 is the most active thyroid hormone; most of it is made from T_4 in peripheral tissues.
5. (a) Melanocortins include ACTH and melanocyte-stimulating hormone (MSH).
   (b) Osteoporosis is bone loss that occurs when bone reabsorption exceeds bone deposition.
   (c) Hydroxyapatite is the inorganic portion of the bone matrix, consisting mainly of calcium salts.

(d) Mineralocorticoids are steroid hormones that regulate minerals, i.e., aldosterone.
(e) Trabecular bone is small spicules of bone that surround red marrow cavities, in areas known as spongy bone.
(f) POMC is pro-opiomelanocortin, the inactive precursor to ACTH and other active molecules.
(g) Epiphyseal plates are growth zones in long bones, comprised of cartilage.

6. Functions: blood clotting, cardiac muscle excitability and contraction, skeletal and smooth muscle contraction, second messenger systems, exocytosis, tight junctions, strength of bones and teeth.
7. In this table, A indicates promotion of anabolism, C indicates promotion of catabolism.

METABOLIC TARGET	CORTISOL	THYROID HORMONES	GROWTH HORMONE	INSULIN	GLUCAGON
PROTEIN	C (in skeletal muscle)	A (children) C (adults)	A	A	C
CARBOHYDRATE	C	C	C	A	C
LIPID	C	C	C	A	C

LEVEL TWO REVIEWING CONCEPTS

8. (a) See Figure 7-20c, p. 234.
(b) See Figure 7-20b, p. 234.
(c) Substitute hormones of thyroid pathway into Figure 7-20c.
(d) Substitute hormones of thyroid pathway into Figure 7-21a, p. 235.

9. (a) CRH from hypothalamus stimulates secretion of ACTH from anterior pituitary which stimulates secretion of glucocorticoids such as cortisol from adrenal cortex, zona fasciculata.
(b) Follicle cells of thyroid gland secrete colloid from which thyroid hormones are produced; C cells secrete calcitonin.
(c) Thyroid hormone synthesis is controlled by TSH, whose release is controlled by TRH. In the thyroid gland tyrosine and iodine combine on thyroglobulin to make thyroid hormones. Thyroid-binding globulin (TBG) carries lipophilic thyroid hormones during transport in the blood. Deiodinase in target removes the iodine from T_4 to create T_3.
(d) Growth hormone releasing hormone (GHRH) stimulates secretion of growth hormone (GH or somatotropin) from the anterior pituitary. Somatostatin (also known as growth hormone inhibiting hormone) inhibits production of GH. Growth hormone binding protein binds about half the GH in the blood. Insulin-like growth factors (IGFs) from the liver act with GH to promote growth.
(e) Dwarfism results from severe GH deficiency in childhood. Gigantism results from hypersecretion of GH during childhood. Acromegaly is lengthening of jaw and growth in hands and feet, caused by hypersecretion of GH in adults.
(f) Hyperplasia is increased cell number. Hypertrophy is increased cell size.
(g) Osteoblasts are immature osteocytes, bone cells that secrete organic bone matrix. Chondrocytes are cartilage cells. Osteoclasts are bone-destroying cells.
(h) PTH increases blood calcium by stimulating bone reabsorption, renal reabsorption, and intestinal absorption of calcium. Calcitriol, also know as 1,25-dihydroxycholecalciferol, is a vitamin D derivative that mediates the PTH effect on intestinal absorption of calcium. Calcitonin decreases bone reabsorption of calcium. Estrogen promotes bone deposition.

10. Thyroid hormone effects on metabolic rate are apparent within a few minutes and are thought to be related to changes in ion transport across cell and mitochondrial membranes. Thyroid effects on growth in children would require more than an hour to be apparent.
11. An ion equivalent is its molarity times the number of charges/ion. For Ca^{2+}: 2.5 mmol/L × 2 = 5 mEq/L.
12. An osteoclast is illustrated in Fig. 23-21. The cell makes acid with the help of carbonic anhydrase: $CO_2 + H_2O \rightarrow H_2CO_3 \rightarrow HCO_3^- + H^+$. The apical membrane secretes HCl using a proton pump and the basolateral membrane secretes HCO_3^- with either a chloride-bicarbonate antiporter or a sodium-bicarbonate symporter

LEVEL THREE PROBLEM SOLVING

13. Physiological stress stimulates secretion of cortisol, increases blood glucose. An increase in insulin would oppose this effect.
14. A normal response to ACTH suppression by dexamethasone would be a decrease in plasma cortisol. Patient A shows no response to ACTH suppression, suggesting there may be an adrenal tumor that is insensitive to ACTH. Patient B does show a decrease in cortisol production following ACTH suppression, suggesting that the problem may be a pituitary tumor.
15. Mr. A would have elevated TSH. Ms. B would have low levels of TSH. Mrs. C would have elevated TSH. (a) It is not possible to determine if the lab slip has the results of Mr. A or Mrs. C, without being able to read the thyroid hormone levels. (b) Ms. B can be ruled out, because her TSH would be low, if the tentative diagnosis is correct.
16. (a) People in all age groups showed vitamin D insufficiency when measured at the end of winter. This deficiency was most pronounced in the 18–29 age group and least pronounced in the 50+ age group. At the end of summer, far fewer subjects were deficient in vitamin D. The variables are season when blood was collected, age group, and % of people with vitamin D insufficiency.
(b) Energy from the sun is required for precursors in the skin to be converted to vitamin D. Days are shorter in the winter, and at northern latitudes like Boston, people spend less time outside during the winter. This explains the difference in data between the two seasons. Fewer than half the people tested were deficient, however, suggesting that most people consumed enough vitamin D. The biggest seasonal difference occurred in the 18–29 age group. These younger people probably spent significantly more time outside in the summer than members of the other groups.
(c) Vitamin D is present in multivitamin supplements, therefore consumption of these supplements should reduce vitamin D insufficiency.

LEVEL FOUR QUANTITATIVE PROBLEMS

17. (a) 5 mg Ca^{2+}/L plasma × 125 mL plasma filtered/min × 1440 min/day = 900 mg Ca^{2+} filtered/day
(b) To remain in Ca^{2+} balance, he must excrete 170 mg/day.
(c) 900 mg filtered − 170 mg excreted = 730 mg reabsorbed. 730/900 = 81%.

CHAPTER 24

LEVEL ONE REVIEWING FACTS AND TERMS

1. Immunity is the body's ability to defend itself against disease-causing pathogens. Memory refers to cells that activate upon repeat exposure to an antigen, producing a heightened immune response. Specificity refers to antibody production that is tailored to bind specific antigens.
2. Anatomical components are thymus gland, bone marrow, spleen, lymph nodes, and diffuse lymphoid tissues.
3. Functions are to protect the body against foreign pathogens; to remove dead or damaged tissues and cells; to recognize and remove abnormal "self" cells.
4. Viruses bud off the host cell or kill and rupture the host cell. Viruses damage host cells by killing them, by taking over their metabolism, or by causing them to become cancerous and to reproduce uncontrollably.
5. The body must detect the pathogen, recognize it as foreign, organize a response, recruit assistance from other cells, and destroy the pathogen. If the pathogen cannot be destroyed, the body may suppress it to keep it from spreading.
6. (a) Anaphylaxis is a severe IgE-mediated allergic reaction characterized by widespread vasodilation, circulatory collapse, and bronchoconstriction.
   (b) Agglutinate means to clump together. When blood cells with one blood group antigen are exposed to the matching antibody, the antibody-antigen reaction causes the blood cells to agglutinate.
   (c) Many steps of the immune reaction take place extravascularly (outside the blood vessels).
   (d) Degranulation refers to the loss of intracellular granules when a cell releases chemicals stored in cytoplasmic granules.
   (e) Acute phase proteins are released in the early stages of injury or infection; they act as opsonins that coat pathogens.
   (f) Clonal expansion is the process by which one cell of a clone divides to make many identical cells.
   (g) Immune surveillance is the ability of the immune system to scan the body for abnormal cells (especially cancerous) and destroy these cells before they cause harm.
7. Histiocytes, Kupffer cells, osteoclasts, and microglia are the tissue-specific names given to specialized macrophages in the tissues.
8. The mononuclear phagocytic system includes monocytes and macrophages, which ingest and destroy invaders and abnormal cells.
9. (a) 5 (b) 1 (c) 3 (d) 6 (e) 2 (f) 4
10. Physical barriers include the skin, mucous membranes, and the mucociliary escalator of the respiratory tract. Chemical barriers include nonspecific chemicals such as lysozymes, opsonins, and enzymes, and specific chemicals such as antibodies.
11. B-lymphocytes secrete antibodies; T-lymphocytes, and natural killer cells kill infected cells either directly or indirectly. T-lymphocytes bind to antigen presented by MHC-complexes; natural killer cells can also bind to antibodies coating foreign cells.
12. Self-tolerance is the ability of the body's immune system to ignore the body's own cells. Self-tolerance occurs because normally T lymphocytes that would react with "self" cells die. If self-tolerance fails and the body makes antibodies against itself, autoimmune disease results.
13. Neuroimmunomodulation refers to the ability of the nervous system to influence immune function, either positively or negatively.
14. Stress is a nonspecific stimulus that disturbs homeostasis; a stressor is a stimulus that causes stress. The general adaptation syndrome is a response to stress that includes activation of the adrenal glands (both the fight-or-flight response of the adrenal medulla and the less dramatic response of cortisol secretion), followed by suppression of the immune system.

LEVEL TWO REVIEWING CONCEPTS

15. Use the figures and the tables of the chapter to help create your map.
16. Lymph nodes trap bacteria and other pathogens and immune cells then create a localized inflammatory response within the nodes as they fight off the pathogens. This response includes swelling and the secretion of substances that activate nociceptors, resulting in swollen, sore nodes.
17. Histamine is a vasodilator that opens pores in capillaries, making it easier for immune cells and proteins in the blood to get into the extracellular space. Interleukin-1 also increases capillary permeability, stimulates acute phase proteins, causes fever, and stimulates cytokine and endocrine secretions. Acute phase proteins act as opsonins and help prevent tissue damage. Bradykinin is another vasodilator and stimulates pain receptors. Complement is a group of proteins that act as opsonins and attractants for leukocytes, signal mast cells to release histamine, and form membrane attack complex that puts pores in pathogens. Gamma interferon activates macrophages. These molecules all work together so they are not antagonistic. If the effect of them working together is greater than the sum of them working alone, then they are considered synergistic.
18. (a) Pathogens are any organisms that cause disease. Pyrogens are fever-causing chemicals. Antigens are substances that trigger an immune response and react with the products of the response. Antibodies are disease-fighting chemicals produced by the body, but antibiotics are drugs that destroy bacteria and fungi.
    (b) An infection is an illness caused by a pathogen, especially a virus or bacterium; inflammation is a nonspecific response to cell damage or extracellular invaders, including nonpathogens such as a splinter. An allergy is an inflammatory response to a nonpathogenic invader, such as plant pollen. In autoimmune diseases, the body creates a specific antibody-mediated response to its own cells.
    (c) Allergens are nonpathogenic substances that create allergic reactions; the other substances are all pathogens. Bacteria are cellular organisms that reproduce in the body's extracellular space. Viruses and retroviruses are acellular parasites that must invade the host's cells to reproduce. Retroviruses cause the host cell to make viral DNA so that the virus can reproduce.
    (d) Chemotaxins are any chemicals that attract immune cells to a specific location. Cytokines are peptides made on demand and secreted by cells for action on other cells. Opsonins are proteins that coat and tag foreign material so that it can be recognized by the immune system. Interleukins are cytokines that initially were thought to act only on leukocytes. Interferons are lymphocyte cytokines that aid in the immune response. Bradykinin is a paracrine vasodilator.
    (e) The human immune response is divided into nonspecific (innate) immunity and specific (acquired) immunity. Innate immunity is present from birth. Acquired immunity, also called adaptive immunity, is directed at specific invaders. Acquired immunity can be divided into cell-mediated immunity and humoral immunity (presence of antibodies in the blood).

(f) Immediate hypersensitivity responses are mediated by antibodies and occur within minutes of exposure to the allergens. Delayed hypersensitivity reactions may take several days to develop and are mediated by helper T cells and macrophages.

(g) These are all chemicals of the immune response. Membrane attack complex and perforin are membrane pore proteins. Perforins specifically allow granzymes, which are cytotoxic enzymes, to enter the cell.

19. The diagram should resemble Figure 24-12. The Fc region determines which of the five antibody classes a given antibody belongs to. The Fab region contains the antigen-binding sites that confer the antibody's specificity.
20. See Figure 24-17.
21. See Figure 24-18.
22. See Figure 24-19.

LEVEL THREE PROBLEM SOLVING

23. Blood type O is the universal donor because these erythrocytes lack A or B surface antigens and therefore do not trigger an immune response. Blood type AB is the universal recipient because these erythrocytes have both the A and the B antigens and therefore no antibodies to A or B antigens.
24. Maxie's genotype must be OO, as must the baby's. Snidley's genotype can be either BB or BO. Baby received an O gene from Maxie, and could have received the other O gene from Snidely. Thus, it is possible that Snidley is the father of Maxie's baby.
25. Emotional stress causes increased secretion of cortisol, which suppresses the immune system. It is also likely that students are spending more time inside because they are studying more and they may be having closer contact with fellow students in study groups.
26. Autoimmune diseases occur when immune cells treat a normal self protein as if it were an antigen, and thus a specific tissue is attacked. Autoimmune diseases often begin in association with an infection, and are thought to represent cross-reactivity of the antibodies that developed because of the infection. Because stress suppresses the immune system, the associated infection may be prolonged.
27. An increase in neutrophils is associated with bacterial infection. An increase in eosinophils is associated with parasitic infection.

CHAPTER 25

LEVEL ONE REVIEWING FACTS AND TERMS

1. ATP and phosphocreatine store energy in muscles.
2. The most efficient ATP production comes through *aerobic* pathways. When these pathways are being used then *both glucose and fatty acids* can be metabolized to provide ATP.
3. Aerobic metabolism: oxygen required, glucose goes through glycolysis and the citric acid cycle. Energy transferred to ATP through mitochondrial oxidative phosphorylation in the mitochondria. Produces 30–32 molecules of ATP/glucose. Anaerobic metabolism: no oxygen used, glucose undergoes glycolysis to lactic acid. Produces only 2 ATP/glucose molecule consumed.
4. Three sources of glucose for cells are glycogen, plasma glucose, and glucose produced through gluconeogenesis.
5. Cortisol, growth hormone, epinephrine, and norepinephrine all promote conversion of triglycerides into fatty acids and increase plasma glucose levels.
6. At the beginning of exercise, muscle ATP use exceeds aerobic ATP production so cellular stores of ATP are used. This creates an oxygen deficit reflected by increased oxygen consumption after exercise ceases.
7. The cardiovascular system is thought to be the major limiting factor.
8. Normal body temperature is 37° C. Increases in body temperature trigger sweating and cutaneous vasodilation.

LEVEL TWO REVIEWING CONCEPTS

9. Figures whose information might be incorporated into the map can be found in Chapters 4, 15, 17, 18, 23, and 25.
10. Insulin secretion decreases during exercise because of sympathetic input on pancreatic beta cells. This decrease causes the liver to produce glucose and keeps insulin-sensitive tissues from taking up glucose, thus sparing glucose for the brain and exercising muscle, whose glucose uptake does not require insulin.
11. Two advantages of anaerobic glycolysis are that it is fast and it uses glucose, which is readily available. Two disadvantages are that it has a low ATP yield per glucose and that it contributes to metabolic acidosis.
12. (a) ATP is the energy source for muscle contraction. ADP can accept a high-energy phosphate from PCr and become ATP.
(b) Myoglobin is an intracellular muscle protein that aids diffusion of oxygen from the blood to the mitochondria. Hemoglobin is an oxygen-binding pigment in red blood cells that transports oxygen from lungs to cells.
13. (a) 3 (b) 1, 2, 3, 4, 5 (c) 1, 2, 4, 5, 6 (d) 6
(e) no match (f) 6 (g) 1 (venous return), 4
14. (a) increases (b) decreases (c) increases (d) increases
(e) increases (f) increases (g) stays the same (h) decreases
15. Increased heart rate during exercise shortens the filling time and helps offset the increased end diastolic volume that might be expected from increased venous return.
16. Baroreceptor reflex may be absent in exercise because (1) the baroreceptor reflex resets to a higher setpoint, (2) afferent signals from the baroreceptors are being blocked in transit up the spinal cord, or (3) chemo- and mechanoreceptor input from exercising tissues overrides the baroreceptor input.
17. People with a lifestyle that includes regular exercise have lower risk of heart attacks, lower blood pressure, better lipid profiles, and lower risk of developing type 2 diabetes.
18. Exercising muscle does not require insulin for glucose uptake, so regular exercise can help keep blood glucose levels normal.

LEVEL THREE PROBLEM SOLVING

19. A sports drink should contain water, NaCl, and K^+ to replace fluid and ions lost in sweat. In addition, a sports drink should contain a carbohydrate such as glucose that is easily absorbed and readily metabolized to form ATP.

LEVEL FOUR QUANTITATIVE PROBLEMS

20. 60 beats/minute $\times$ 70 ml/beat = 4200 ml/min cardiac output. If heart rate doubles to 120 beats/min, CO goes to 8400 ml/min, or doubles also.

CHAPTER 26

LEVEL ONE REVIEWING FACTS AND TERMS

1. (a) 3, 4, 5 (b) 8 (c) 2, 7 (d) 2, 6 (e) 2 (f) 1
2. The region for male sex determination is the *SRY* gene.
3. The gonads produce gametes and secrete sex hormones. The female gamete is the egg or ovum; the male is the sperm. Female gonadal hormones are estrogen, progesterone, androgens, and inhibin. Male gonadal hormones are androgens and inhibin.
4. Newly formed sperm: lumen of seminiferous tubule → epididymis → ductus (vas) deferens → ejaculatory duct (passing the seminal vesicles, prostate gland, and bulbourethral glands) → urethra. Ovulated egg: fallopian tube → uterine cavity → cervix → vagina
5. (a) Aromatase converts androgens to estrogens.
   (b) The blood-testis barrier is formed by tight junctions that prevent free movement of substances between the blood and lumen of the seminiferous tubule.
   (c) Androgen binding protein is made by Sertoli cells and secreted into the seminiferous tubule lumen, where it binds and concentrates androgens.
   (d) The first polar body is formed by the first meiotic division of a primary oocyte. It disintegrates and has no further function.
   (e) The acrosome is a lysosome-like structure in the head of a sperm whose enzymes are essential for fertilization.
6. (a) False. Some testosterone is produced in the adrenal glands of both genders.
   (b) False. Men produce estrogen, women produce androgens, and both genders produce FSH, LH, and inhibin.
   (c) True.
   (d) False. High levels of late follicular estrogen help prepare the uterus for implantation of a fertilized ovum and act as a negative feedback signal to the hypothalamus/pituitary.
   (e) True.
7. Semen is a sperm-fluid mixture made mostly by the accessory glands. See Table 26-3 for a list of components and their sources.
8. The most effective form of contraception is abstinence. The least effective forms of contraception rely on avoiding intercourse during times when the female thinks she might be fertile.

LEVEL TWO REVIEWING CONCEPTS

9. List 1: use Figures 26-3, 26-4, and 26-5 to create your map. List 2: use Figures 26-12, 26-13, and 26-14.
10. See Figure 26-11.
11. See Figure 26-14.
12. Males have one X chromosome and one Y chromosome, which often does not have a gene to match one found on the X chromosome. Thus, a male may inherit a recessive X trait and will exhibit it, while a female who inherits the same recessive trait will not exhibit it if her second X chromosome has the dominant gene for the trait.
13. (a) A gamete is a haploid germ cell: eggs and sperm. A diploid zygote is formed from the fusion of egg and sperm; as it undergoes mitosis, the zygote becomes an embryo. By the 8th week of pregnancy, the embryo becomes a fetus.
    (b) Coitus is the sex act, or intercourse. In erection, the penis becomes stiff and engorged with blood. During the male orgasm, sperm move into the urethra during emission, then move out of the body with the other components of semen during ejaculation. Erogenous zones are portions of the body that have receptors for sexually arousing stimuli.
    (c) Before sperm can fertilize an egg, they must undergo capacitation. When sperm reach an egg, they undergo an acrosomal reaction that helps the sperm penetrate the protective zona pellucida around the egg. Once a sperm fuses with the oocyte membrane, cortical granules in the egg cytoplasm release their contents to change the properties of the egg membrane (the cortical reaction).
    (d) Puberty is the period of time in which a person becomes sexually mature. In females, its onset is marked by menarche, the first menstrual period. In females, reproductive cycles cease during the time known as the menopause. In men, testosterone production decreases with age but the existence of andropause is still controversial.
14. (a) FSH in both sexes stimulates gamete production.
    (b) Inhibin in both sexes inhibits FSH secretion.
    (c) Activin in both sexes stimulates FSH secretion.
    (d) GnRH in both sexes acts on the anterior pituitary to stimulate release of FSH and LH.
    (e) LH in both sexes stimulates production of sex hormones by the gonads; in females, LH is also necessary for gamete maturation.
    (f) DHT is a metabolite of testosterone that is responsible for the development of the male genitalia in the fetus.
    (g) Estrogen is present in both sexes but has its predominant effect in females, where it is involved in gamete formation and some secondary characteristics.
    (h) Testosterone in males plays a role in gamete formation. In both sexes it is responsible for some secondary sex traits such as hair growth.
    (i) Progesterone is found in females only; it helps prepare the uterus for pregnancy.
15. The four phases are very similar in both genders. In the excitement phase, the male penis and the female clitoris become erect due to increased blood flow into the organ. The vagina also secretes fluids for lubrication. In male orgasm, ejaculation takes place, while in female orgasm the uterus and vaginal walls contract.
16. (a) hCG is secreted by the developing placenta and keeps the corpus luteum from dying.
    (b) LH is very similar to hCG but otherwise has no direct role in pregnancy and subsequent events.
    (c) HPL apparently plays a role in regulation of maternal metabolism during pregnancy.
    (d) Estrogen is needed for breast development and to act as a negative feedback to prevent new follicles from developing.
    (e) Progesterone is used for maintenance of the uterine lining and to prevent uterine contractions. It also has a role in mammary gland development.
    (f) Relaxin helps prevent uterine contractions.
    (g) PIH levels decrease so that prolactin levels will increase, allowing milk production.

LEVEL THREE PROBLEM SOLVING

17. Normally after fertilization the second polar body, containing a haploid set of chromosomes, is released from the zygote. If all or some of the second polar body chromosomes are retained, the embryo will have three copies of a chromosome instead of just two.
18. If the unovulated cysts continue to secrete estrogen and do not develop into corpora lutea, the uterine lining will continue to grow and the breasts will develop, just as during pregnancy.

19. (a) Male
    (b) nonfunctional testes
    (c) no ducts of either type
    (d) female
20. During pregnancy the mother's high blood glucose concentration is available to the fetus, which metabolizes the extra energy and gains weight. The fetus also up-regulates insulin secretion to handle the glucose coming across the placenta. After birth, when insulin is still high but glucose drops to normal, the baby may become hypoglycemic.

LEVEL FOUR QUANTITATIVE PROBLEMS

21. (a) Testosterone increased at point A because it was being administered to the subjects.
    (b) LH and FSH decreased at point A because of the negative feedback effect of testosterone.
    (c) Sperm production decreased in the A-B interval because FSH and LH decreased. It increased toward the end of the B-C interval because FSH allowed sperm production to resume. Sperm production did not increase significantly during the D-E interval.

Physics and Math

Richard D. Hill and Daniel Biller, *University of Texas*

INTRODUCTION

This appendix discusses selected aspects of **biophysics**, the study of physics as it applies to biological systems. Because living systems are in a continual exchange of force and energy, it is necessary to define these important concepts. According to the seventeenth-century scientist Sir Isaac Newton, a body at rest tends to stay at rest, and a body in motion tends to continue moving in a straight line unless the body is acted upon by some force (Newton's First Law). Newton further defined **force** as an influence, measurable in both intensity and direction, that operates on a body in such a manner as to produce an alteration of its state of rest or motion. Put another way, force gives **energy** to a quantity, or mass, thereby enabling it to do work. In general, a driving force multiplied by a quantity yields energy, or work. Some relevant examples of this principle include:

Mechanical force × distance = mechanical energy or mechanical work

Gas pressure × volume of gas = mechanical energy or mechanical work

Osmotic pressure × molar value = osmotic energy or osmotic work

Electrical potential × charge = electrical energy or electrical work

Temperature × entropy = heat energy or mechanical work

Chemical potential × concentration = chemical energy or chemical work

Energy exists in two general forms: kinetic energy and potential energy. **Kinetic energy** [*kinein*, to move] is the energy possessed by a mass in motion. **Potential energy** is energy possessed by a mass because of its position. Kinetic energy (*KE*) is equal to one-half the mass (*m*) of a body in motion multiplied by the square of the velocity (*v*) of the body:

$$KE = 1/2\ mv^2$$

Potential energy (*PE*) is equal to the mass (*m*) of a body multiplied by acceleration due to gravity (*g*) times the height (*h*) of the body above the earth's surface:

$$PE = mgh \quad \text{where } g = 10\ \text{m/s}^2$$

Both kinetic and potential energy are measured in joules.

BASIC UNITS OF MEASUREMENT

For physical concepts to be useful in scientific endeavors, they must be measurable and should be expressed in standard units of measurement. Some fundamental units of measure include the following:

Length (*l*): Length is measured in meters (m).

Time (*t*): Time is measured in seconds (s).

Mass (*m*): Mass is measured in kilograms (kg), and is defined as the weight of a body in a gravitational field.

Temperature (*T*): Absolute temperature is measured on the Kelvin (K) scale,

where K = degrees Celsius (°C) + 273.15

and °C = (degrees Fahrenheit −32)/1.8

Electric current (*I*): Electric current is measured in amperes (A).

Amount of substance (*n*): The amount of a substance is measured in moles (mol).

Using these fundamental units of measure, we can now establish standard units for physical concepts (Table B-1 ■). Although these are the standard units for these concepts at this time, they are not the only units ever used to describe them. For instance, force can also be measured in dynes, energy can be measured in calories, pressure can be measured in torr or mm Hg, and power can be measured in horsepower. However, all of these units can be converted into a standard unit counterpart, and vice versa.

The remainder of this appendix will discuss some biologically relevant applications of physical concepts. This discussion will

TABLE B-1 Standard Units for Physical Concepts

MEASURED CONCEPT	STANDARD (SI*) UNIT	MATHEMATICAL DERIVATION/ DEFINITION
Force	Newton (N)	$1\ \text{N} = 1\ \text{kg m/s}^2$
Energy/Work/Heat	Joule (J)	$1\ \text{J} = 1\ \text{N} \cdot \text{m}$
Power	Watt (W)	1 W = 1 J/s
Electrical charge	Coulomb (C)	$1\ \text{C} = 1\ \text{A} \cdot \text{s}$
Potential	Volt (V)	1 V = 1 J/C
Resistance	Ohm (Ω)	1 Ω = 1 V/A
Capacitance	Farad (F)	1 F = 1 C/V
Pressure	Pascal (Pa)	$1\ \text{Pa} = 1\ \text{N/m}^2$

*SI = Système International d'Unités

include topics such as bioelectrical principles, osmotic principles, and behaviors of gases and liquids relevant to living organisms.

BIOELECTRICAL PRINCIPLES

Living systems are composed of different molecules, many of which exist in a charged state. Cells are filled with charged particles such as proteins and organic acids, and ions are in continual flux across the cell membrane. Therefore, electrical forces are important to life.

When molecules gain or lose electrons, they develop positive or negative charges. A basic principle of electricity is that opposite charges attract and like charges repel. A force must act on a charged particle (a mass) to bring about changes in its position. Therefore, there must be a force acting on charged particles to cause attraction or repulsion, and this electrical force can be measured. Electrical force increases as the strength (number) of charges increases, and it decreases as the distance between the charges increases. This observation has been called **Coulomb's law**, and can be written:

$$F = \frac{q_1 q_2}{\varepsilon d^2}$$

where q_1 and q_2 are the electrical charges (coulombs), d is the distance between the charges (meters), ε is the dielectric constant, and F is the force of attraction or repulsion, depending on the type of charge on the particles.

When opposite charges are separated, a force acts over a distance to draw them together. As the charges move together, work is being done by the charged particles and energy is being released (Fig. B-1 ■). Conversely, to separate the united charges, energy must be added and work done. If charges are separated and kept apart, they have the potential to do work. This electrical potential is called **voltage**. Voltage is measured in **volts (V)**.

If electrical charges are separated and there is a potential difference between them, then the force between the charges will allow electrons to flow. Electron flow is called an electric **current**. The **Faraday constant (F)** is an expression of the electrical charge carried by one mole of electrons and is equal to 96,485 coulombs/mole.

The amount of current that flows depends on the nature of the material between the charges. If that material hinders the electron flow, then it is said to offer **resistance (R)**, measured in ohms. Current is inversely proportional to resistance, such that current decreases as resistance increases. If a material offers a high resistance, then that material is called an **insulator**. If resistance is low, and current flows relatively freely, then the material is called a **conductor**. Current, voltage, and resistance are related by **Ohm's law**, which states:

$$V = IR$$

where V = potential difference in volts
I = current in amperes
R = resistance in ohms

If you separate two opposite charges, there will be an electric force between them.

If you increase the number of charges that are separated, the force increases.

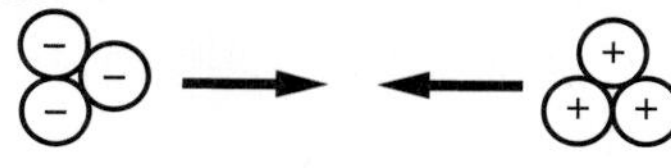

If you increase the distance between the charges, the force decreases.

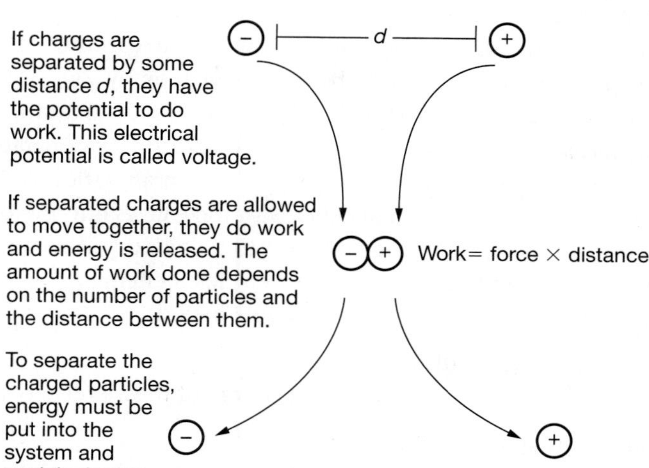

If charges are separated by some distance d, they have the potential to do work. This electrical potential is called voltage.
d
If separated charges are allowed to move together, they do work and energy is released. The amount of work done depends on the number of particles and the distance between them.
Work= force × distance
To separate the charged particles, energy must be put into the system and work is done.

■ **FIGURE B-1** ***Electrical force***

In biological systems, pure water is not a good conductor, but water containing dissolved NaCl is a fairly good conductor because ions provide charges to carry the current. In biological membranes, the lipids have few or no charged groups, so they offer high resistance to current flow across them. Thus, different cells can have different electrical properties depending on their membrane lipid composition and the permeability of their membranes to ions.

OSMOTIC PRINCIPLES

Freezing point, vapor pressure, boiling point, and osmotic pressure are properties of solutions collectively called **colligative properties**. These properties depend on the number of solute particles present in a solution. **Osmotic pressure** is the force that drives the diffusion of water across a membrane. Because there are no solutes in pure water, it has no osmotic pressure. However, if one adds a solute like NaCl, the greater the concentration (c) of a solute dissolved in water, the greater the osmotic pressure. The osmotic pressure (π) varies directly with the concentration of solute (number of particles (n) per volume (V)):

$$\pi = (n/V)RT$$

$$\pi = cRT$$

where R is the ideal gas constant (8.3145 joules/K mol) and T is the absolute temperature in Kelvin.

Osmotic pressure can be measured by determining the mechanical pressure that must be applied to a solution so that osmosis ceases.

Water balance in the body is under the control of osmotic pressure gradients (concentration gradients). Most cellular membranes allow water to pass freely because water is a small, uncharged molecule. Therefore, by making cellular membranes selectively permeable to solutes, the body can control the movement of water by controlling the movement of solutes.

RELEVANT BEHAVIORS OF GASES AND LIQUIDS

The respiratory and circulatory systems of the human body have developed according to the physical laws that govern the behaviors of gases and liquids. This section will discuss some of the important laws that govern these behaviors and how our body systems utilize these laws.

Gases The **ideal gas law** states:

$$PV = nRT$$

where P = pressure of gases in the system
V = volume of the system
n = number of moles in gas
T = temperature
R = ideal gas constant (8.3145 J/K mol)

If n and T are kept constant for all pressures and volumes in a system, then any two pressures and volumes in that system are related by Boyle's Law,

$$P_1V_1 = P_2V_2$$

where P represents pressure and V represents volume.

This principle is relevant to the human lungs because the concentration of gas in the lungs is relatively equal to that in the atmosphere. In addition, body temperature is maintained at a constant temperature by homeostatic mechanisms. Therefore, if the volume of the lungs is changed, then the pressure in the lungs will change inversely. For example, an increase in pressure causes a decrease in volume, and vice versa.

Liquids **Fluid pressure** (or hydrostatic pressure) is the pressure exerted by a fluid on a real or hypothetical body. In other words, the pressure exists whether or not there is a body submerged in the fluid. Fluid exerts a pressure (P) on an object submerged in it at a certain depth from the surface (h). **Pascal's law** allows us to find the fluid pressure at a specified depth for any given fluid. It states:

$$P = \rho gh$$

where: P = fluid pressure (measured in pascals, Pa)
ρ = density of the fluid
g = acceleration due to gravity (10 m/s^2)
h = depth below the surface of the fluid

Fluid pressure is unrelated to the shape of the container in which the fluid is situated.

REVIEW OF LOGARITHMS

Understanding logarithms ("logs") is important in biology because of the definition of pH:

$$\text{pH} = -\log_{10}[\text{H}^+]$$

This equation is read as "pH is equal to the negative log to the base 10 of the hydrogen ion concentration." But what is a logarithm?

A logarithm is the exponent to which you would have to raise the base (10) to get the number in which you are interested. For example, to get the number 100, you would have to square the base (10):

$$10^2 = 100$$

The base 10 was raised to the second power; therefore, the log of 100 is 2:

$$\log 100 = 2$$

Some other simple examples include:

$10^1 = 10$ The log of 10 is 1.
$10^0 = 1$ The log of 1 is 0.
$10^{-1} = 0.1$ The log of 0.1 is -1.

What about numbers that fall between the powers of 10? If the log of 10 is 1 and the log of 100 is 2, the log of 70 would be between 1 and 2. The actual value can be looked up on a log table or ascertained with most calculators.

To calculate pH, you need to know another rule of logs that says:

$$-\log x = \log(1/x)$$

and a rule of exponents that says:

$$1/10^x = 10^{-x}$$

Suppose you have a solution whose hydrogen ion concentration $[\text{H}^+]$ is 10^{-7} mEq/L. What is the pH of this solution?

$$\text{pH} = -\log[\text{H}^+]$$

$$\text{pH} = -\log(10^{-7})$$

Using the rule of logs, this can be rewritten as

$$\text{pH} = \log(1/10^{-7})$$

Using the rule of exponents, this can be rewritten as

$$\text{pH} = \log 10^7$$

The log of 10^7 is 7, so the solution has a pH of 7.

Natural logarithms (ln) are logs in the base e. The mathematical constant e is approximately equal to 2.7183.

Appendix C Genetics

Richard D. Hill, *University of Texas*

WHAT IS DNA?

Deoxyribonucleic acid (DNA) is the macromolecule that stores the information necessary to build structural and functional cellular components. It also provides the basis for inheritance when DNA is passed from parent to offspring. The union of these concepts about DNA allows us to devise a working definition of a gene. A **gene** (1) is a segment of DNA that codes for the synthesis of a protein, and (2) acts as a unit of inheritance that can be transmitted from generation to generation. The external appearance (**phenotype**) of an organism is determined to a large extent by the genes it inherits (**genotype**). Thus, one can begin to see how variation at the DNA level can cause variation at the level of the entire organism. These concepts form the basis of **genetics** and evolutionary theory.

NUCLEOTIDES AND BASE-PAIRING

DNA belongs to a group of macromolecules called **nucleic acids. Ribonucleic acid (RNA)** is also a nucleic acid, but it has different functions in the cell that are not discussed here (see Chapter 4, p. 115). Nucleic acids are polymers made from monomers [*mono-*, one] called **nucleotides.** Each nucleotide consists of a *nucleoside* (a pentose, or 5-carbon, sugar covalently bound to a nitrogenous base) and a phosphoric acid with at least one phosphate group (Fig. C-1a■). Nitrogenous bases in nucleic acids are classified as either **purines** or **pyrimidines**. The purine bases are **guanine (G)** and **adenine (A)**; the pyrimidine bases are **cytosine (C)**, **thymine (T)**, found in DNA only, and **uracil (U)**, found in RNA only. To remember which DNA bases are pyrimidines, look at the first syllable. The word "pyrimidine" and names of the DNA pyrimidine bases all have a "y" in the first syllable.

When nucleotides link together to form polymers such as DNA and RNA, the phosphate group of one nucleotide bonds covalently to the sugar group of the adjacent nucleotide (Fig. C-1b, c). The end of the polymer that has an unbound sugar is called the 3' ("three prime") end. The end of the polymer with the unbound phosphate is called the 5' end.

DNA STRUCTURE

In humans, many millions of nucleotides are joined together to form DNA. Eukaryotic DNA is commonly in the form of a double-stranded double helix (Fig. C-2■) that looks like a twisted ladder or twisted zipper. The sugar-phosphate sides, or backbone, are the same for every DNA molecule, but the sequence of the nucleotides is unique for each individual organism.

The backbone of the double helix is formed by covalent **phosphodiester bonds** that link a deoxyribose sugar from one nucleotide to the phosphate group on the adjacent nucleotide. The "rungs" of the double helix are created when the nitrogenous bases on one DNA strand form hydrogen bonds with nitrogenous bases on the adjoining DNA strand. This phenomenon is called **base-pairing**. The base-pairing rules are as follows:

1. Purines pair only with pyrimidines.
2. Guanine (G) forms three hydrogen bonds with cytosine (C) in both DNA and RNA.
3. Adenine (A) forms with two hydrogen bonds with thymine (T) in DNA or with uracil (U) in RNA.

The number of hydrogen bonds is directly related to the amount of energy necessary to break the base pair. Thus, more energy is required to break G:::C bonds (each ":" represents a hydrogen bond) than A::T bonds. This fact can be useful experimentally to make general conjectures about the similarity of two DNA samples.

The two strands of DNA are bound in **antiparallel** orientation, so that the 3' end of one strand is bound to the 5' end of the second strand (see Fig. C-1c). This organization has important implications for DNA replication.

DNA Replication Is Semi-Conservative

In order to be transmitted from one generation to the next, DNA must be replicated. Furthermore, the process of replication must be accurate and fast enough for a living system. The base-pairing rules for nitrogenous bases provide a means for making an appropriate replication system.

In DNA replication, special proteins unzip the DNA double helix and build new DNA by pairing new nucleotide molecules to the two existing DNA strands. The result of this replication is two double-stranded DNA molecules, such that each DNA molecule contains one DNA strand from the template and one newly synthesized DNA strand. This form of replication is called **semi-conservative replication**.

Replication of DNA is bidirectional. A portion of DNA that is "unzipped" and has enzymes performing replication is called a **replication fork** (Fig. C-2). Replication begins at many points (**replicons**), and it continues along both parent strands simultaneously until all the replication forks join.

Nucleotides bond together to form new strands of DNA with the help of an enzyme called **DNA polymerase**. DNA polymerase can only add nucleotides to the 3' end of a growing strand of DNA. For this reason, DNA is said to replicate in a 5' to 3' direction.

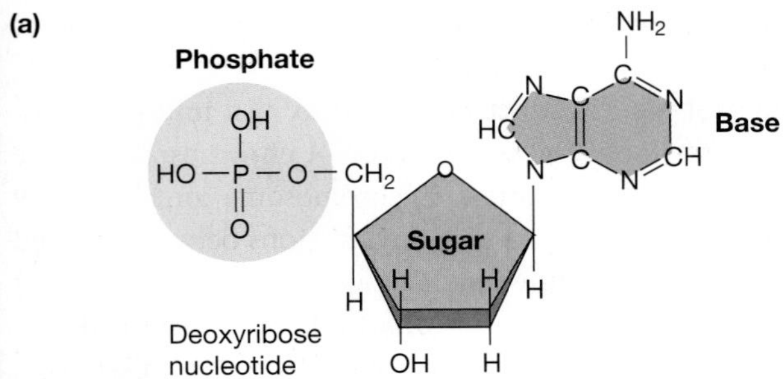

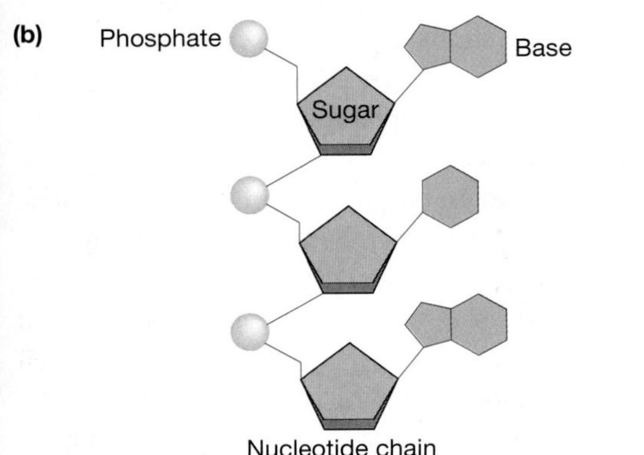

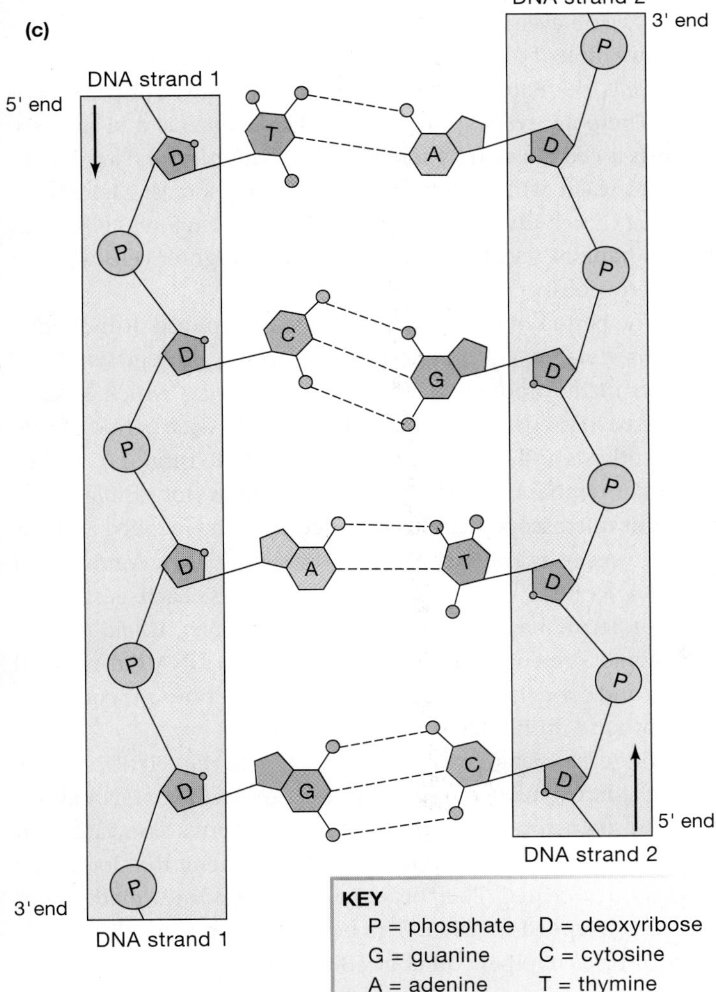

■ **FIGURE C-1** ***Nucleotides and DNA***

(a) A nucleotide is composed of a pentose sugar, a nitrogenous base, and a phosphate group. **(b)** Nucleotides link sugar to phosphate to form nucleic acids. The end of the nucleic acid with an unbound sugar is designated the 3' end; the end with the unbound phosphate is the 5' end. **(c)** Two nucleotide strands link by hydrogen binding between complementary base pairs to form the double helix of DNA. Adenine always pairs to thymine, and guanine pairs to cytosine.

The antiparallel orientation of the DNA strands and the directionality of DNA polymerase force replication into two different modes: **leading strand replication** and **lagging strand replication**. The DNA polymerase can replicate continuously along only one parent strand of DNA: the parent strand in the 3' to 5' orientation. The DNA replicated continuously is called the **leading strand**.

The DNA replication along the other parent strand is discontinuous because of the strand's 5' to 3' orientation. DNA replication on this strand occurs in short fragments called **Okazaki fragments** that are synthesized in the direction away from the replication fork. Another enzyme known as **DNA ligase** later connects these fragments into a continuous strand. The DNA replicated in this way is called the **lagging strand**. Because the 5' ends of the lagging strand of DNA cannot be replicated by DNA polymerase, a specialized enzyme called **telomerase** has arisen to replicate the 5' ends.

Much of the accuracy of DNA replication comes from base pairing, but on occasion, mistakes in replication happen. However, several quality control mechanisms are in place to keep the error rate at 1 error/10^9 to 10^{12} base pairs. **Genome** (the entire amount of DNA in an organism) sizes in eukaryotes range from 10^9 to 10^{11} base pairs per genome, so this error rate is low enough to prevent many lethal mutations, yet still allows genetic variation to arise.

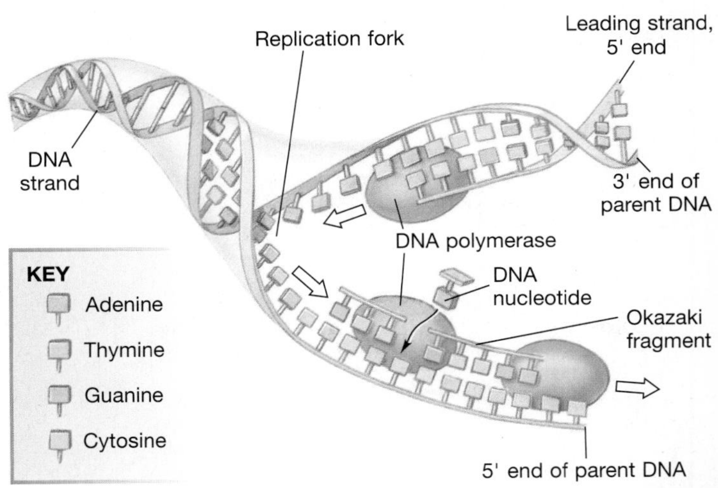

■ **FIGURE C-2** ***DNA replication***

FUNCTIONS OF DNA

One of the key functions of DNA is its ability to code for the synthesis of proteins that participate in structural or functional aspects of a cell. The information coded in DNA is *transcribed* into mRNA [p. 115], whose code then is *translated* into proteins with the help of tRNAs attached to specific amino acids (Table C-1). The other key function of DNA is its ability to act as a unit of inheritance when transmitted across generations.

TABLE C-1 The Amino Acids of the Human Body

Each amino acid has both a three-letter abbreviation of its name and a single-letter abbreviation, used to spell out the sequence of amino acids in large proteins. The essential amino acids are marked with a star. These nine amino acids cannot be made by the body and must be obtained from the diet.

AMINO ACID	THREE-LETTER ABBREVIATION	ONE-LETTER SYMBOL
Alanine	Ala	A
Arginine	Arg	R
Asparagine	Asn	N
Asparagine or aspartic acid	Asx	B
Aspartic acid	Asp	D
Cysteine	Cys	C
Glutamic acid	Glu	E
Glutamine	Gln	Q
Glutamine or glutamic acid	Glx	Z
Glycine	Gly	G
*Histidine	His	H
*Isoleucine	Ile	I
*Leucine	Leu	L
*Lysine	Lys	K
*Methionine	Met	M
*Phenylalanine	Phe	F
Proline	Pro	P
Serine	Ser	S
*Threonine	Thr	T
*Tryptophan	Trp	W
*Tyrosine	Tyr	Y
*Valine	Val	V

*Essential amino acids

Before we begin our discussion of DNA as a unit of inheritance, a few terms need to be introduced. A **chromosome** is one complete molecule of DNA, and each chromosome contains many genes. An **allele** is a form of a gene; interactions between the cell products of alleles determine how that gene will be expressed in the phenotype of an individual. **Somatic** [*soma,* body] **cells** are those cells that comprise the majority of the body (e.g., a skin cell, a liver cell); they are not directly involved with passing on genetic information to future generations. Each somatic cell in a human contains two alleles of each gene, one allele inherited from each parent. For this reason, human somatic cells are called **diploid** ("two chromosome sets"), meaning that they have two complete sets of all their chromosomes. In contrast, **germ cells** pass genetic information directly to the next generation. In human males, the germ cells are the **spermatozoa** (sperm), and in human females, the germ cells are the **oocytes** (eggs). Human germ cells are called **haploid** ("half of the chromosome sets") because each germ cell only contains one chromosome set, which is equal to half of the number of chromosome sets in somatic cells. When a human male germ cell joins with a human female germ cell, the result is a fertilized egg (zygote) containing the diploid number of chromosomes. If this zygote eventually develops into a healthy adult, that adult will have diploid somatic cells and haploid germ cells.

Cells alternate between periods of cell growth and cell division. There are two types of cell division: mitosis and meiosis. **Mitosis** is cell division by somatic cells that results in two daughter cells, each with a diploid set of chromosomes. **Meiosis,** in contrast, is cell division that results in four daughter cells, each with a haploid set of chromosomes. The daughter cells develop into germ cells.

The period of cell growth is called **interphase**. It is divided into three stages: $\mathbf{G_1}$, a period of cell growth, protein synthesis, and organelle production; **S**, the period during which DNA is replicated in preparation for cell division; and $\mathbf{G_2}$, a period of protein synthesis and final preparations for cell division (Fig. C-3). During interphase, the DNA in the nucleus is not visible under the light microscope without dyes because it is uncoiled and diffuse. However, as a cell prepares for division, it must condense all its DNA to form more manageable packages. Each eukaryotic DNA molecule has millions of base pairs, which, if laid end-to-end, could stretch out to about 6 cm. If this DNA did not coil tightly and condense for cell division, imagine how difficult moving it around during cell division would be.

There is a hierarchy of DNA packaging in the cell (Fig. C-4). Each chromosome begins with a linear molecule of DNA about 2 nm in diameter. Then proteins called **histones** associate with the DNA to form a fiber about 10 nm in diameter that looks like "beads on a string." The "beads" are **nucleosomes** made up of histones wrapped in DNA. The beaded string can twist into a **solenoid** [*solen,* pipe] coil about 30 nm in diameter, consisting

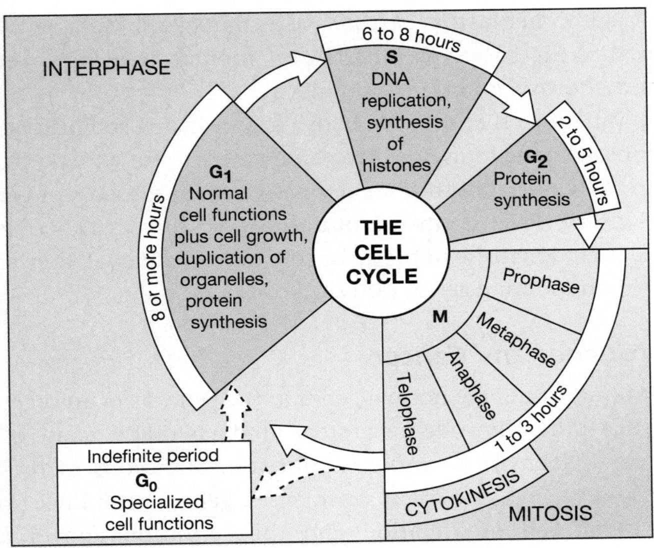

FIGURE C-3 *The cell cycle*

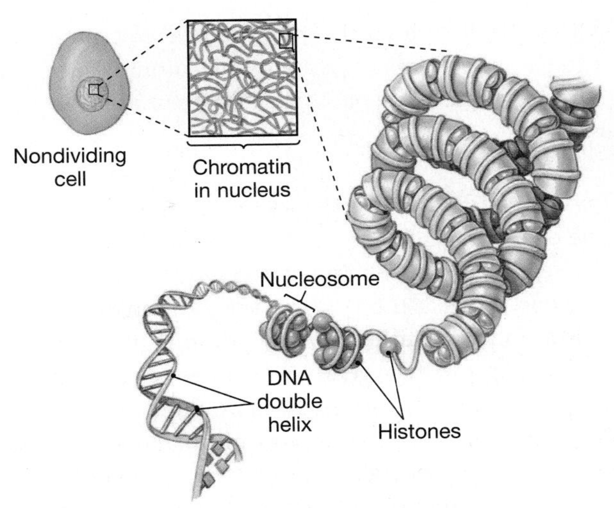

FIGURE C-4 *Levels of organization of DNA*

of about 6 nucleosomes per turn. The 30-nm solenoid structure can form looped domains, and these looped domains can attach to **nonhistone** (structural) **proteins** to form a 250–300-nm fiber called **chromatid fiber**. The chromatid fiber then coils to form the **chromosome fiber** (about 700 nm in diameter) that is visible during cell division. In this state of packaging, the cell is ready for division.

Mitosis Creates Two Identical Daughter Cells

As stated earlier, mitosis is the cellular division of a somatic cell that results in two diploid daughter cells. The steps of mitosis are **prophase, metaphase, anaphase**, and **telophase** (Fig. C-5■). The entire somatic cell cycle can be remembered by the acronym, IPMAT, in which the "I" stands for interphase and the other letters stand for the steps of mitosis that follow.

Prophase During prophase, chromatin becomes condensed and microscopically visible as duplicate chromosomes. The duplicated chromosomes form **sister chromatids**, which are joined to each other at the **centromere**. The centriole pair [p. 61] duplicates and the centriole pairs move to opposing ends of the cell. The **mitotic spindle**, composed of microtubules, assembles between them. The nuclear membrane begins to break down and disappears by the end of prophase.

Metaphase In metaphase, mitotic spindle fibers extending from the centrioles attach to the centromere of each chromosome. The forty-six chromosomes, each consisting of a pair of sister chromatids, line up at the "equator" of the cell.

Anaphase During anaphase, the spindle fibers pull the sister chromatids apart, so that an identical copy of each chromosome moves toward each pole of the cell. By the end of anaphase, an identical set of forty-six chromosomes is present at each pole. At this point, the cell has a total of ninety-two chromosomes.

Telophase The actual division of the parent cell into two daughter cells takes place during telophase. In **cytokinesis**, the cytoplasm divides when an actin contractile ring tightens at the midline of the cell. The result is two separate daughter cells,

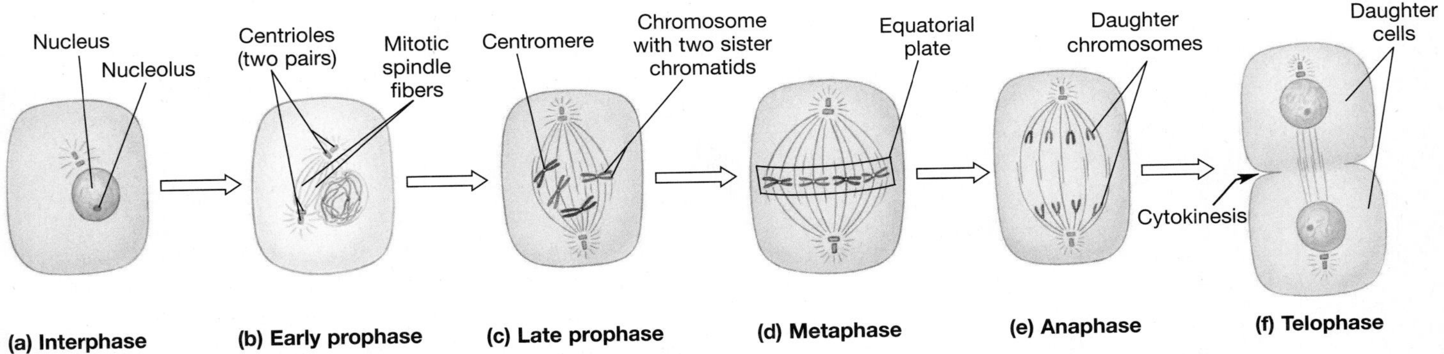

FIGURE C-5 *Mitosis*

each with a full diploid set of chromosomes. The spindle fibers disintegrate, nuclear envelopes are formed around the chromosomes in each cell, and the chromatin returns to its loosely coiled state.

Mutations Change the Sequence of DNA

Over the course of a lifetime, there are countless opportunities for mistakes to arise in the replication of DNA. A change in a DNA sequence, such as the addition, substitution, or deletion of a base, is a **point mutation**. If a mutation is not corrected, it may cause a change in the gene product. These changes may be relatively minor, or they may result in dysfunctional gene products that could kill the cell or the organism. Only rarely does a mutation result in a beneficial change in a gene product. Fortunately, our cells contain enzymes that can detect and repair damage to DNA.

Some mutations are caused by **mutagens**, which are factors that increase the rate of mutation. Various chemicals, ionizing radiation such as X-rays and atomic radiation, ultraviolet light, and other factors can behave as mutagens. Mutagens either alter the base code of DNA or interfere with repair enzymes, thereby promoting mutation.

Mutations that occur in body cells are called **somatic mutations**. Somatic mutations are perpetuated in the somatic cells of an individual, but they are not passed on to subsequent generations. However, **germ-line mutations** can also occur. Because these mutations arise in the germ cells of an individual, they are passed on to future generations.

Oncogenes and Cancer

Proto-oncogenes are normal genes in the genome of an organism that primarily code for protein products that regulate cell growth, cell division, and cell adhesion. Mutations in these proto-oncogenes give rise to **oncogenes**, genes that induce uncontrolled cell proliferation and the condition known as **cancer.** The mutations in proto-oncogenes that give rise to cancer-causing oncogenes are often the result of viral activity.

Appendix D Anatomical Positions of the Body

ANTERIOR (situated in front of): in humans, toward the front of the body (see VENTRAL) D-1■

POSTERIOR (situated behind): in humans, toward the back of the body (see DORSAL) D-2■

MEDIAL (middle, as in *median strip*): located nearer to the midline of the body (the line that divides the body into mirror-image halves)

LATERAL (side, as in a *football lateral*): located toward the sides of the body

DISTAL (distant): farther away from the point of reference or from the center of the body

PROXIMAL (closer, as in *proximity*): closer to the center of the body

SUPERIOR (higher): located toward the head or the upper part of the body

INFERIOR (lower): located away from the head or from the upper part of the body

PRONE: lying on the stomach, face downward

SUPINE: lying on the back, face up

DORSAL: refers to the back of the body

VENTRAL: refers to the front of the body

IPSILATERAL: on the same side as

CONTRALATERAL: on the opposite side from

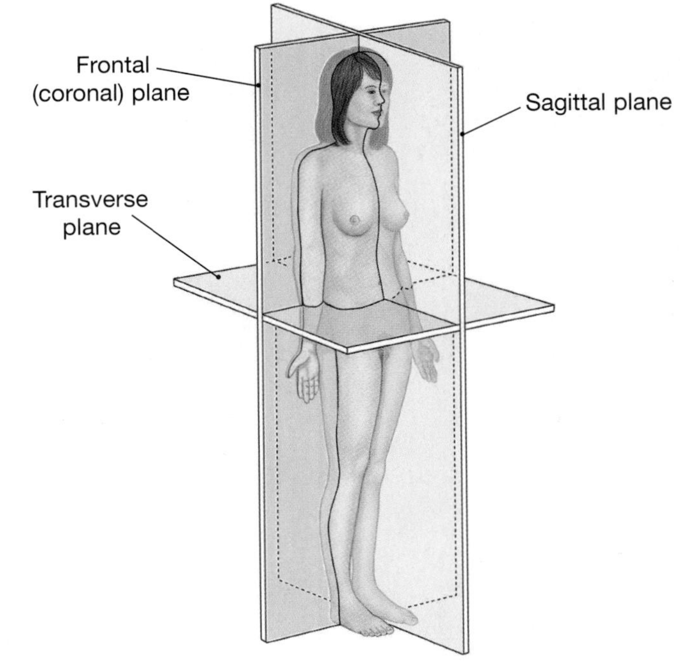

■ **FIGURE D-1** ***Sectional planes***

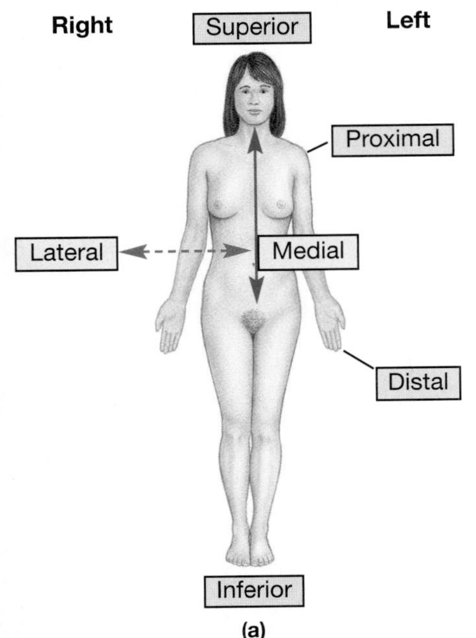

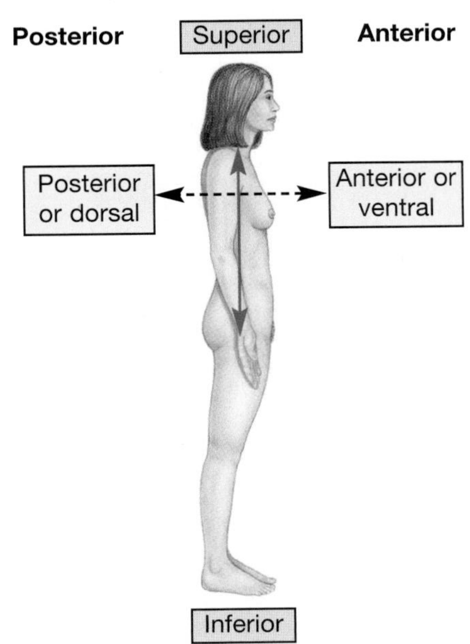

■ **FIGURE D-2** ***Body directions***

Glossary/Index

NOTE: A *t* following a page number indicates tabular material and an *f* indicates a figure.

active expiration Expiration that is assisted by contraction of abdominal and internal intercostal muscles (Ch 17), 572
active hyperemia An increase in blood flow that accompanies an increase in metabolism (Ch 15), 511, 512f
active immunity, 788
active reabsorption, 627–628, 627f
active site Region of an enzyme or transport protein to which the substrate binds. Synonym: binding site (Ch 2, 4), 39
  receptor, 189
    diseases/drugs associated with changes in, 191, 192t
active transport Movement across a membrane that requires the input of energy from ATP (Ch 5, 19), 132–133, 132f, 137, 142–145, 142f, 143f, 143t, 144f, 145f
  energy for, 145, 145f
  primary (direct), 142, 142–143, 143f, 143t
  renal tubular reabsorption and, 627–628, 627f
  secondary (indirect), 132f, 142, 144–145, 144f, 144t, 145f
    renal tubular reabsorption and, 627–628, 627f
activin Peptide hormone from the gonads that stimulates FSH secretion (Ch 26), 829
activity, physical. *See* exercise
activity level, metabolic rate and, 720
acuity Keenness of vision (Ch 10), 366, 369
acute inflammatory demyelinating polyneuropathy. *See* Guillain-Barré syndrome
acute motor axonal polyneuropathy (AMAN) (Ch 8), 283, 285
acute mountain sickness, 593
acute-phase protein Liver proteins that act as opsonins and enhance the inflammatory response (Ch 24), 786–787, 786t
acyl unit, 107, 107f, 108
adaptation of receptors Process in which sensory receptors decrease their response to a stimulus over time (Ch 10), 334, 335
adaptive immunity (acquired immunity), 779, 784, 787–793
adaptive significance, homeostasis and, 3
addictive behavior (Ch 9), 316
  nicotine and, 377, 390, 392
Addison's disease, 756
addition reaction Chemical reaction that adds a functional group to a molecule (Ch 4), 100–101, 100t
adenine Nucleotide base found in ATP, DNA, RNA, and cAMP (Ch 2, 4, Appendix C), 33, 33f, A-34
  amino acid coding and, 114, 115f
adenohypophyseal secretions/hormones, 225. *See also* anterior pituitary trophic hormones
adenohypophysis. *See* anterior pituitary gland
adenoma, 232
  ACTH secreting, 234f, 235
adenosine Nucleoside composed of adenine and ribose purine (Ch 8, 9, 15), 273t, 275, 315
  receptors for, 273t
  as vasodilator, 511t, 512
adenosine diphosphate (ADP) Precursor of ATP, composed of adenine, ribose, and two phosphate groups (Ch 2, 3, 12, 16), 32f, 33
  platelet aggregation and, 549, 550t
  ratio of to ATP, 103
adenosine monophosphate, cyclic (cyclic AMP/cAMP) Nucleotide that participates in the transfer of signals between the external environment and the cell (Ch 2, 6), 33, 181t, 182t
  as neurotransmitter, 275
adenosine triphosphate (ATP) An energy-storing compound composed of adenine, ribose, and three phosphate groups (Ch 2, 3, 4, 12, 25), 32f, 33, 94, 101, 181t
  for active transport, 145, 145f
  for anabolic reactions, 112–122
  ATP/ADP ratio and, 103
  from catabolic reactions, 101, 103, 104–112, 104f, 106t
  in coupled reactions, 95, 95f
  for endocytosis, 148
  energy transfer between reactions and, 103
  in exergonic reactions, 94
  for exocytosis, 150
  for muscle contraction, 404, 404–406, 405f, 410–411, 410f, 808–810, 809f, 810f
  as neurotransmitter, 275
  for phagocytosis, 148
  production of, 103–112, 104f, 106t
    by aerobic metabolism, 103, 104–109, 104f, 106t, 808
    by anaerobic metabolism, 103, 106–107, 106t, 107f, 808
    by citric acid cycle, 104f, 107–108, 108f
    by electron transport system, 104f, 108–109, 109f
    by glycogenolysis, 110–111, 110f
    by glycolysis, 104–106, 104f, 105f, 106t, 808
    hydrogen ion movement and, 109–110
    by lipolysis, 111–112, 112f
    maximum energy yield from glucose and, 106t, 110
    in mitochondria, 65
    by protein catabolism, 111, 111f
adenylyl cyclase Membrane-bound enzyme that converts ATP to cyclic AMP (Ch 6), 181t, 184
adenylyl cyclase-cAMP system The first signal transduction system discovered (Ch 6), 183–184, 184f
adequate stimulus The form of energy to which a particular receptor is most responsive (Ch 10), 330
ADH. *See* antidiuretic hormone
adherens junctions Bands that link actin microfilaments in adjacent cells together with the help of cadherins (Ch 3), 70f, 71, 71f
  in transporting epithelia, 151
adipocyte Fat cells (Ch 3, 16, 22), 77, 78f, 78t, 79f, 80f
adipose tissue, 77, 78t, 79f
  autonomic control of, 380f, 382–383
  in fasted state, 727, 728f
  hormones produced by, 214–215f
adjunct therapy, guided imagery as, 438
ADP. *See* adenosine diphosphate
adrenal cortex Outer portion of adrenal gland that produces steroid hormones (Ch 7, 11, 23), 214–215f, 219, 221f, 228f, 385–386, 385f, 751, 751–752, 752f
adrenal gland Endocrine and neuroendocrine gland that sits on top of the kidney (Ch 7, 11, 23), 219, 385, 385f, 751–752, 752f
  tumor of, cortisol produced by, 235, 755
adrenal glucocorticoids, 751–756
adrenaline. *See* epinephrine
adrenal medulla Modified sympathetic ganglion, the inner portion of the adrenal gland that produces catecholamines (Ch 7, 11), 214–215f, 385–386, 385f, 751, 752f
  autonomic control of, 380f, 731, 731t
adrenal sympathetic pathway, 388f
adrenergic Adjective pertaining to epinephrine (adrenaline) or norepinephrine (Ch 6, 11), 189, 274
  agonists and antagonists of, 386t
adrenergic neuron Neuron that secretes norepinephrine (Ch 8), 274
adrenergic receptor Receptor that binds to norepinephrine or epinephrine (Ch 6, 8, 11), 189, 190f, 193, 273t, 276, 379, 382, 382f, 383–384, 384t, 385t
  in smooth muscle control, 428
adrenocorticotropic hormone (ACTH) Anterior pituitary hormone that regulates secretion of cortisol from the adrenal cortex (Ch 7, 9, 10, 23, 24, 26), 215f, 227f, 228f, 230, 232–233, 232f, 234, 234f, 235, 235f, 753, 753f, 756
  for infantile spasms, 300, 315
  therapeutic steroid use and, 755
  tumors secreting, 234f, 235, 755–756
adrenogenital syndrome, 756
aequorin, 188
aerobic Adjective pertaining to a process that requires oxygen (Ch 4), 103
aerobic exercise, 808, 810, 811
aerobic metabolism, 103
  citric acid cycle, 104f, 106t, 107–108, 108f
  electron transport system, 104f, 108–109, 109f
  exercise and, 808, 809f
  glycolysis, 104–106, 104f, 105f, 106t
affective behavior Behaviors related to feeling and emotion (Ch 9), 292
afferent arteriole Renal arterioles that bring blood to the glomerulus (Ch 19), 616f, 617f, 618, 619f, 620f
  resistance in, glomerular filtration rate and, 623f, 624
afferent neuron. *See* sensory neuron
afferent pathway The pathway that connects a receptor to an integrating center (Ch 6), 195, 195f, 197, 198, 198f, 204f, 205t
affinity The degree to which a protein is attracted to its ligand (Ch 2), 39–40
  factors affecting, 40, 40f
AFM. *See* atomic force microscopy
after-hyperpolarization, 258, 259f
afterload, 493
agglutination Clumping of cells together (Ch 24), 799
aging, 854–855
  metabolic rate and, 720
agonist Molecules that combine with a receptor and mimic a response (Ch 2, 6, 11), 40, 189, 190f
  neurotransmitter, 273t, 275, 386–387, 386t
agouti mouse, 757
agouti protein Antagonist to the melanocortin-1 receptor (MC1R) that controls melanin synthesis (Ch 23), 757
AIDS, 777, 779, 793, 795, 798
  treatment for, 777, 779, 801, 803
AIDS cocktail, 777, 779, 801, 803
air flow, 565–566, 569–570. *See also* gas laws
airway Anatomical structures from mouth to bronchioles that carry air to the alveoli (Ch 17), 560, 561, 562f, 563f, 564f
  epithelia of, 73f, 74, 75f

functions of, 568–569, 569*f*
smooth muscle of, in asthma, 429
airway resistance, 576, 577*t*
alanine, A-36*t*
albumin Plasma protein made in the liver (Ch 2, 7, 15, 16), 220, 536, 538*t*
denaturation of, 42
alcohol, 273*t*, 282
alcohol consumption, erectile dysfunction and, 845–846
aldosterone A steroid hormone that stimulates Na^+ reabsorption and K^+ secretion in the kidney (Ch 7, 20, 23), 215*f*, 221*f*, 652–653, 653–654, 654*f*, 655*f*, 656*f*, 665, 829*f*
adrenal secretion of, 751–752, 752*f*, 753*f*
algorithm, 525
alkaline phosphatase, 96*t*
alkaline solution, 37, 663
alkaline tide, 685
alkalosis Extracellular pH greater than 7.42 (Ch 20), 663, 670*t*, 671
intercalated cells in, 669, 669*f*
renal compensation for, 667
allantois Extraembryonic membrane that becomes part of the umbilical cord (Ch 26), 849
allele, A-36
allergen Any substance capable of triggering an allergic reaction (Ch 24), 797, 797*f*
allergy (allergic response), 777, 797–798, 797*f*
eosinophils in, 782
all-or-none phenomenon, 258
allosteric activator, 41
allosteric inhibitor, 41
allosteric modulation, 41
allosteric modulator Bind to an enzyme away from the binding site and change the shape of the active site (Ch 2), 41, 52*f*
alpha-adrenergic receptor (α receptor) Membrane receptor that binds to norepinephrine and epinephrine (Ch 6, 11), 189, 190, 190*f*, 193, 273*t*, 276, 383–384, 384*t*, 385*t*
agonists and antagonists of, 386*t*
arteriole control and, 513, 514*f*
alpha-blockers, 386
alpha-bungarotoxin Snake toxin that is a nicotinic receptor antagonist (Ch 8), 270, 273*t*, 386*t*, 391
alpha cell pancreatic cell that secretes glucagon. Synonym: A cell (Ch 22), 730*f*, 734, 735*f*
alpha (α) chain, 595, 596*f*
alpha-gamma coactivation Simultaneous activation of alpha and gamma motor neurons so that during muscle contraction, the intrafusal fibers continue to monitor tension in the muscle (Ch 13), 440–442, 442*f*
alpha- (α) glucosidase inhibitors, 739*t*
alpha helix Spiral configuration formed by some amino acid chains (Ch 2), 30*f*, 31, 122
alpha interferon, 785–786, 795, 796*f*
alpha- (α) ketoglutarate, 668
alpha- (α) melanocyte-stimulating hormone (MSH), 718*t*, 756, 756*f*
alpha motor neuron Neurons that innervate extrafusal muscle fibers and cause muscle contraction (Ch 13), 439, 441*f*
$alpha_1$- (α_1) receptor, 384, 385*t*
$alpha_2$- (α_2) receptor, 384, 385*t*
5-alpha-reductase Enzyme that converts testosterone to DHT (Ch 26), 825–826
alpha wave Low amplitude, high-frequency brain waves characteristic of the awake-resting state (Ch 9), 314*f*
alternative splicing The processing of mRNA to make different proteins from a single strand of DNA (Ch 4), 116*f*, 118, 119*f*
alternative therapy, 802
altitude, 588, 591, 592, 593, 596
altitude hypoxia, 592, 593, 596, 601
altitude sickness, 592, 593
alveolar blood flow, 579–580, 580*t*, 581*f*
alveolar cells, types I and II, 561, 563*f*
alveolar epithelium, 561, 563*f*
alveolar macrophage Immune cells that patrol the alveoli (Ch 17), 563*f*, 574
alveolar membrane, gas exchange affected by changes in, 592–593, 592*f*
alveolar P_{CO_2}, 578–579, 579*f*, 590, 590*f*
alveolar P_{O_2}, 578–579, 579*f*, 590, 590*f*
decreased, 591–592, 591*f*
alveolar pressure, 570
expiration and, 572
inspiration and, 570–572, 571*f*
alveolar ventilation The volume of air that reaches the alveoli each minute (Ch 17, 18), 577, 578*f*, 579*t*
breathing pattern and, 577, 578–580, 578*t*, 579*f*, 580*t*, 581*f*
exercise and, 811
pathological conditions affecting, 591–592, 591*f*, 592–593
alveoli The exchange surface of the lungs, where oxygen and carbon dioxide transfer between air and the blood (Ch 17), 560, 561, 563*f*, 564*f*
Alzheimer's disease (Ch 9), 319–320
amacrine cells, in retina, 364, 365*f*
AMAN. *See* acute motor axonal polyneuropathy
ambiguous genitalia, 827
amenorrhea, 855
aminase, 100*t*
amination Addition of an amino group to a molecule (Ch 4), 101
amine hormone Derivatives of single amino acids, either tyrosine or tryptophan (Ch 7), 214–215*f*, 218*t*, 222, 223*f*
amine neurotransmitter Neurotransmitters made from amino acids, including the catecholamines, histamine, and serotonin (Ch 8), 273*t*, 274
amino acid Molecule with a central carbon atom linked to a hydrogen atom, an amino group, a carboxyl group, and a variable group of atoms designated "R." The building blocks of proteins (Ch 2, 4, 8, 21, 22, Appendix C), 30-31, 30*f*, 695, 695*f*, 724–725, A-36, A-36*t*
amine hormone synthesis and, 222, 223*f*
glucagon release and, 734, 735*f*
glucose synthesis and, 111, 112–113, 113*f*, 722–723, 723*f*, 727, 728*f*
insulin secretion and, 730, 733
mRNA translation in production of, 118–119, 120*f*
as neurotransmitter, 273*t*, 274–275
protein catabolism and, 103, 111, 111*f*, 695, 695*f*
protein synthesis and, 30, 30*f*, 104*f*, 722, 723*f*, 724–725
structure of, 30–31, 30*f*
substitution of, inherited diseases and, 114
amino acid pool, 722, 723*f*
amino acid supplements, 724–725
amino group Functional group whose composition is - NH_2 (Ch 2), 27*t*, 30*f*, 31, 111, 119
in exchange reaction, 101
aminopeptidase Digestive enzyme that removes amino acids from the NH_2 terminal end of a peptide (Ch 2, 21), 39, 695, 695*f*
ammonia, 111, 111*f*
ammonia buffer, 667
ammonium ion, 111, 111*f*, 668, 668*f*
amnesia, anterograde, 318
amnion Extraembryonic membrane that secretes amniotic fluid (Ch 26), 849, 851*f*
amniotic fluid, 849, 851*f*
AMPA receptor Glutamate receptor-channel that allows net Na^+ influx (Ch 8), 273*t*, 277
in long-term potentiation, 282, 282*f*
ampere (A), A-31
amphipathic (Ch 21), 696
amplification, 180, 180*f*
in sound transduction, 350
amplifier enzyme A membrane enzyme that creates two or more second messengers during signal transduction (Ch 6), 180, 181*f*, 181*t*
amplitude
of graded potential, 255, 256, 256*f*
of sound wave, 349, 349*f*
ampulla (vestibular apparatus) (Ch 10), 355, 356*f*
amu. *See* atomic mass unit
amygdala Portion of the brain linked to emotion and memory (Ch 9), 305*f*, 308, 308*f*, 315–316
amylase Enzyme that digests starch to maltose (Ch 4, 21), 97*t*, 694, 694*f*, 699
salivary, 699
amylin Peptide cosecreted with insulin (Ch 22), 728, 738–739
amylin analogs, 739*t*
amyloid protein (Ch 9), 319
anabolic metabolism/pathway, 101, 112–122, 721, 723–727. *See also* anabolism
anabolic steroids, 751, 836
anabolism Metabolic pathways that require a net input of energy and that synthesize small molecules into larger ones (Ch 4, 22), 101, 112–122, 721, 723–727
insulin and, 731–733, 732*f*, 733*f*, 734*f*
anaerobic Adjective pertaining to a process that does not require oxygen (Ch 4), 103
anaerobic glycolysis, 410
anaerobic metabolism, 103, 106–107, 106*t*, 107*f*
exercise and, 808, 809*f*
analgesia, 275, 342
analgesic drugs Drugs that relieve pain (Ch 10), 342
opiates/opioid peptides, 275, 342
anal sphincters, 679, 708, 708–709, 708*f*
anaphase, A-37, A-37*f*
anaphylactic shock (anaphylaxis) Allergic reaction marked by bronchoconstriction and vasodilation with hypotension (Ch 15), 189, 510, 787, 798
anatomical positions of human body, A-39
anatomic dead space The portions of the airways that do not exchange gases with the blood (Ch 17), 577
anatomy The study of structure (Ch 1, 9), 2. *See also specific organ, structure, system*
anaxonic neuron (Ch 8), 246, 248*f*

chromatin, 68, 68*f*
chromium, 20, 21, 23, 26, 38, 44–45
toxicity of, 35
chromium picolinate, 21, 38
chromosome, 822, 823*f*, A-36
chromosome fiber, A-37
chronic bronchitis, 559, 561, 569, 581, 582
chronic hypoxia, 598–599
chronic inflammatory disease, 786
chronic obstructive pulmonary disease (COPD) Pulmonary diseases characterized by nonreversible decreased air flow through bronchioles; emphysema and chronic bronchitis (Ch 17), 559, 561, 569, 574, 581, 582, 670
chronic pain, 342
chylomicron Large droplets of triglycerides, cholesterol, proteins, and lipoproteins that are synthesized in cells of the small intestine (Ch 21, 22), 697, 697*f*, 725, 726*f*
chylomicron remnant, 725
chyme A soupy substance produced by digestion in the digestive tract (Ch 21), 678, 704, 705, 706, 706*f*, 707, 708
chymotrypsin, 40*f*, 122, 695, 707*f*
chymotrypsinogen, 40, 40*f*, 707*f*
cigarette smoking. *See* smoking
cilia Short, hair-like structures whose movement creates currents that move fluids or secretions across the cell surface (Ch 3, 10, 17), 62, 62*f*, 63
ciliary muscle Muscle in the eye whose contraction slackens zonules and rounds the lens (Ch 10), 359*f*, 362
ciliated epithelia Epithelia covered with cilia that move fluid over the surface (Ch 3, 17, 26), 72, 73*f*, 74, 74*t*, 75*f*
respiratory, 569–570, 569*f*
smoking and, 569
cimetidine, 704
cingulate gyrus, 304*f*, 308, 308*f*
circadian rhythm Biological rhythm based on a 24-hour cycle (Ch 6, 9, 10), 201, 201*f*, 315, 370
body temperature and, 201, 740, 743
of cortisol secretion, 201, 201*f*, 753, 753*f*, 754*f*
of prolactin secretion, 854
circulatory system The heart and blood vessels (Ch 1, 14), 2, 3*f*, 4*t*, 52, 457, 459*f*, 501*f*. *See also* blood flow; blood vessel; cardiovascular system
circumcision Removal of the foreskin of the penis (Ch 26), 833
cis-face of Golgi complex, 121*f*, 122
cisternae
Golgi complex, 121*f*, 122
terminal, 398
citation formats, 15
citric acid, in semen, 836*t*
citric acid cycle Key metabolic pathway of aerobic respiration. Synonyms: Krebs cycle, tricarboxylic cycle, TCA cycle (Ch 4), 103, 104*f*, 107–108, 108*f*
insulin secretion and, 166, 167*f*
CK. *See* creatine kinase
Cl^-. *See* chloride ion
classic hormone, 213
-clast (suffix), 76
clathrin, 149, 149*f*
clathrin-coated pits, 149, 149*f*
claudin Protein in tight junctions (Ch 3), 69, 70*f*, 71*f*
clearance A measurement of the disappearance of a substance from the blood, expressed as milliliters of plasma cleared of solute per unit time (Ch 5, 19), 130, 632
excretion and, 634, 634*f*
glomerular filtration rate and, 632–633, 632*f*
renal handling of solutes and, 633–635, 633*t*, 634*f*
cleavage, protein, 122
clicks, 486
clitoral erection, 846
clitoris, 837, 838*f*
development of, 824*f*, 825*t*
clonal expansion Reproduction of one type of lymphocyte following exposure to an antigen (Ch 24), 788, 789
clone A group of cells that are genetically identical (Ch 24), 788, 788*f*
closed system, universe as, 93
Clostridium tetani, 439
clot, 77, 548. *See also* coagulation
integrin receptor defects and, 184
myocardial infarction and, 457, 461, 527–528
plaque rupture and, 526, 527*f*
clot buster, 548, 554
clotting factor, 551, 552*f*, 552*t*
disorders of, 554
clotting factor I. *See* fibrin
clotting factor II. *See* thrombin
clotting factor III. *See* tissue factor
clotting factor IV. *See* calcium
clotting factor VII, 551, 552*f*
clotting factor VIII deficiency, 554
clotting factor IX deficiency, 554
clotting factor XII, 551, 552*f*
clotting factor XIII (fibrin-stabilizing factor), 551, 552*f*, 553*t*
clotting protein, transport of in cardiovascular system, 458*t*
Cnidaria, nerve net of animals in, 292, 293*f*, 690
CNS. *See* central nervous system
CO. *See* carbon monoxide; cardiac output
coagulation Process in which fluid blood forms a gelatinous clot (Ch 16), 538, 549*f*, 550*f*, 551–554, 552*f*, 553*t*. *See also* hemostasis
chemicals in prevention of (anticoagulants), 551–554, 553*t*
disorders of, 554
coagulation cascade, 548, 549*f*, 551, 552*f*
calcium in, 552, 766
coagulation factor, 551, 552*f*, 552*t*. *See also specific type under factor*
disorders of, 554
coated pit Region of the cell membrane where endocytosis takes place (Ch 5), 149, 149*f*
cobalamin. *See* vitamin B_{12}
cocaine, 386, 386*t*
cocaine- and amphetamine-regulated transcript (CART), 718*t*
cochlea Coiled structure of ear that contains receptors for hearing (Ch 10), 329, 348, 348*f*, 350–353, 351*f*
cochlear duct, 350, 350*f*, 351*f*
cochlear implant, 354
cochlear nerve, 350, 350*f*, 351*f*, 353
codeine, 343
coding (stimulus), 203, 203*t*, 261, 263*f*, 332–335, 334*f*, 335*f*, 336*f*
for pitch, 353, 353*f*
codon Triplet of DNA or mRNA bases that encodes information for one amino acid (Ch 4), 114, 115*f*
coenzyme Organic cofactors that act as receptors and carriers for atoms or functional groups that are removed from substrates during the course of a reaction (Ch 4), 97
coenzyme A, 107, 108*f*
cofactor An inorganic or nonprotein organic molecule required for activation of protein (Ch 2), 40, 40*f*, 41*t*, 97
cognitive behavior Behaviors that deal with thought processes rather than emotion (Ch 9), 292
language and, 320, 320*f*
learning and, 317–318
memory and, 318–320, 318*f*, 319*t*
cognitive system, 308
coitus Synonym: intercourse (Ch 26), 844
cold, body's responses to, 743, 744*f*
cold receptor, 339
colipase A protein cofactor that allows lipase to break through the bile salt coating of an emulsion (Ch 21), 696, 697*f*, 707*f*
collagen Flexible but inelastic protein fibers of connective tissue (Ch 3, 16, 26), 77, 80*f*
exocytosis in release of, 150
hemostasis/platelet activation/coagulation and, 548, 549, 549*f*, 550*f*, 550*t*, 551, 552*f*, 553*t*
collagenase Enzyme that degrades collagen (Ch 26), 843
collateral Branch of an axon (Ch 8), 247
collateral circulation (Ch 15), 504
collecting duct Terminal region of the kidney tubule (Ch 19), 617*f*, 618, 619, 619*f*, 619*t*
cortical, 652
urine concentration determined in, 645–646, 646*f*
colligative property, 156, A-32
colloid, 757, 757*f*, 758*f*
colloid osmotic pressure (π) Osmotic pressure that is due to the presence of plasma proteins that cannot cross the capillary endothelium. Synonym: oncotic pressure (Ch 15, 19), 517–518, 518*f*
edema and, 519–520
glomerular filtration and, 622, 622*f*
colon Proximal portion of the large intestine. Divided into ascending, transverse, descending, and sigmoid regions (Ch 21), 679, 708, 708*f*
colonic bacteria, 709
colonocyte Transporting epithelial cell of the large intestine (Ch 21), 699
colony-stimulating factor (CSF) Cytokines made by endothelial cells and white blood cells that direct the production and development of white blood cells (Ch 16, 24), 540–541, 540*t*, 542, 793
color-blindness, 367
color vision, 366, 367
colostrum Watery, low-fat secretions of the mammary gland prior to delivery (Ch 26), 853
column (spinal cord), 301, 302*f*
columnar epithelia, 72
common bile duct, 688*f*, 689
common hepatic duct, 688*f*
common pathway, 551, 552*f*
compact bone, 765, 765*f*, 766*f*
comparative endocrinology, 236
compartment, 50
compartmentation The internal division of the body or cell into compartments so that functions can be isolated from one another (Ch 1, 3), 9, 50–88. *See also* cell; tissue

Edkins, J. S, 691
EDRF. *See* endothelium-derived relaxing factor
EDV. *See* end-diastolic volume
EEG. *See* electroencephalogram
effector The cell or tissue that carries out the homeostatic response (Ch 6, 24), 192, 192*f*, 195*f*, 196, 197, 198, 198*f*, 204*f*, 205*t*. *See also* target cell
in immune response, 788, 789*f*
in skeletal muscle reflex, 436, 439
efferent arteriole, 617*f*, 618, 619*f*, 620*f*
resistance in, glomerular filtration rate and, 623*f*, 624
efferent division of peripheral nervous system, 376–395
autonomic motor control and, 244*t*, 245*f*, 246, 311, 377–389
somatic motor control and, 246, 311, 389–391
efferent neuron A peripheral neuron that carries signals from the central nervous system to the target cells (Ch 8, 11), 245, 246, 247, 248*f*, 296
efferent pathway Outgoing signal that goes from the integrating center to an effector (Ch 6, 11), 195*f*, 196, 197, 198, 198*f*, 204*f*, 205*t*
efficiency, of energy conversion, 92–93
egg, 827, 828, 828*f*, 842. *See also* ovum
fertilization of, 822, 827, 828, 828*f*, 848–849, 848*f*, 849*f*, 850*f*
eicosanoid Modified 20-carbon fatty acids that act as regulators of physiological functions (Ch 2, 6, 7), 29*f*, 30, 176, 188–189, 188*f*, 216, 275
Einstein, Albert, 133
Einthoven, Walter, 480
Einthoven's triangle The triangle formed by the three lead electrodes of the simple ECG (Ch 14), 480, 480*f*
E_{ion}. *See* equilibrium potential
ejaculation Semen in the urethra is expelled to the exterior (Ch 26), 845
ejaculatory duct, 832*f*
ejection fraction, 493
EKG. *See* electrocardiogram
elastance Ability of a stretched substance to return to its unstretched state (Ch 1, 17), 9, 77
disease states affecting, 574
elastase, 574
elastic fibers, 77
in arteries, 502, 502*f*
elastic recoil, 502
elastin A coiled, wavy protein that returns to its original length after being stretched (Ch 3, 17), 77, 80*f*
in emphysema, 574
electrical charge, 160-161, 161*f*, A-32
law of conservation of, 160
separation of, 161–162, 161*f*
electrical disequilibrium, 131, 160, 161*f*, 162
electrical equilibrium, 161*f*, 162
electrical force, A-32, A-32*f*
electrical gradient Uneven distribution of electrical change, especially across a membrane (Ch 5), 135, 161*f*, 162
relative scale for, 161*f*, 162
electrical signal, 175, 176, 202, 271
chemical factors affecting, 269, 269*f*
ion movement causing, 253–254
light transduction to, 366–367. *See also* phototransduction
in neurons, 176, 177*f*, 244, 252–256
electrical synapse Synapse where electrical signals pass directly from cell to cell through gap junctions (Ch 8), 271
electric current, 271, A-31 to A-32
electricity review, 160–161
electrocardiogram (ECG) A recording of the summed electrical events of the cardiac cycle (Ch 14), 480–484, 480*f*, 481*f*, 482*f*, 483*f*, 488*f*
in myocardial infarction, 479, 484, 495
electrochemical gradient The combined concentration and electrical gradients for an ion (Ch 5), 135, 162, 254
electrodes, 162, 163*f*, 480, 480*f*
electroencephalogram/electroencephalography (EEG), 313, 314*f*, 315
electrogenic pump, 165
electrolyte An ion (Ch 21), 642, 677. *See also* ion
electrolyte balance, 642–643, 643*f*. *See also specific electrolyte*
electromagnetic spectrum, 364, 364*f*
electron Subatomic particle with one negative charge and negligible mass (Ch 2), 20, 20*f*, 160
bonds formed by, 22–23
covalent bond formation and, 22, 23–24, 23*f*
energy levels of, 22
high-energy, 22, 95, 101, 104*f*, 108–109, 109*f*
ionic bond formation and, 24–25, 25*f*
electron-dot shorthand, 23
electron transport system, 103, 104*f*, 108–109, 109*f*
electrophoresis, 97
element The simplest kind of matter, such as oxygen and carbon (Ch 2), 21
essential, 21
isotopes of, 21–22
major essential, 21
periodic table of, 21
trace (minor essential), 21
elephantiasis, 520
embryo, 822, 849
as stem cell source, 82
embryological development, 824*f*, 825–826. *See also specific structure*
emergent property Some property of a system that cannot be predicted from the simple sum of its parts (Ch 1, 4, 8, 9), 6, 90
nervous system and, 244, 292, 302
emesis Vomiting (Ch 21), 710
metabolic alkalosis and, 671, 710
emission Movement of sperm from vas deferens to the urethra (Ch 26), 845
emotion, 315–316, 316*f*
autonomic responses and, 379, 438
digestive system affected by, 689
hormone secretion/function affected by, 225
limbic system in, 308, 308*f*, 315–316
olfaction and, 343
ventilation affected by, 607
emphysema Lung disease characterized by loss of elastance and alveolar surface area (Ch 5, 16, 17, 18), 135, 559, 574, 581, 582, 670
alveolar ventilation/gas exchange and, 591*f*, 592
emulsion Small droplets suspended in a liquid (Ch 21), 697, 698*f*
ENaC (epithelial sodium channel) (Ch 20), 653
encapsulated bacteria, 778
encapsulated lymphoid tissue Lymph nodes and the spleen (Ch 24), 780*f*, 781
end-diastolic volume (EDV) The maximum volume of blood that the ventricles hold during a cardiac cycle (Ch 14), 487, 493
endergonic reaction A reaction that requires net input of energy from an outside source (Ch 4), 94–95, 94*f*
coupling with exergonic reaction and, 95, 95*f*
endocrine cell, 76
membrane potential as signal and, 166, 167*f*
in reflex control pathway, 197
endocrine gland A ductless gland or single cell that secretes a hormone (Ch 3, 7), 75–76, 77*f*, 213, 214–215*f*, 216. *See also* endocrine system
epithelial origin of, 76, 77*f*
tumors of, 232
endocrine pathology. *See* endocrine system, disorders of
endocrine reflex, 202, 202*f*, 202*t*, 203, 204*f*, 205*t*, 223–224, 224*f*
endocrine pathology related to complexity of, 234–235, 234*f*
nervous system and, 225. *See also* neuroendocrine reflex
endocrine system The cells and tissues of the body that secrete hormones (Ch 1, 6, 7, 23), 2, 3*f*, 4*t*, 176, 177*f*, 211–242, 214–215*f*, 750–775. *See also specific gland and* hormone
disorders of, 212–213, 212*f*, 232–235, 234*f*, 235*f*, 751
reflex complexity and, 234–235, 234*f*
immune system/nervous system interactions and, 800–802, 801*f*, 802*f*
metabolic control and, 728, 751. *See also* metabolism
reflex control systems and, 194–197, 195*f*, 202–205, 202*f*, 203*t*, 204*f*, 205*t*, 223–224, 224*f*, 751
endocrinology, 212, 236, 751. *See also* endocrine system; hormone
comparative, 236
endocytosis Process by which a cell brings molecules into the cytoplasm in vesicles formed from the cell membrane (Ch 5), 148–150, 149*f*
in receptor regulation, 190, 217
endogenous cortisol hypersecretion, 234*f*, 235, 755–756
endogenous opiates, 342
endolymph High K^+, low Na^+ fluid that fills the cochlear duct of the ear (Ch 10), 350*f*, 352, 355, 356*f*
endometrium The secretory inner lining of the uterus (Ch 26), 837, 839*f*
in uterine cycle, 837–841, 840*f*, 843
endopeptidase An enzyme that attacks peptide bonds in the interior of an amino acid chain (Ch 21), 694–695, 695*f*. *See also* protease
endoplasmic reticulum (ER) A network of interconnected membrane tubes in the cytoplasm; site of protein and lipid synthesis (Ch 3), 60*f*, 65–66, 65*f*
energy use by, 91–92
in peptide hormone synthesis/storage/release, 218, 219*f*
protein modification in, 122
in steroid hormone synthesis, 219, 222*f*
endorphin, 275, 342
endoscopy, 691
endosome Vesicle formed by endocytosis (Ch 5), 149, 149*f*
endostatin, 504

(continue

(continue

image projection onto, 364, 365*f*
phototransduction at, 364, 365*f*, 366*f*. *See also* phototransduction
signal processing in, 369–370, 369*f*
retinal The light-absorbing pigment of rhodopsin (Ch 10), 367, 368, 368*f*
retinal artery, 359*f*
retinal pigment epithelium, 364, 365*f*
retinal vein, 359*f*
retinitis pigmentosa, 192*t*
retinopathy, diabetic, 503
retrograde axonal transport, 250
retroperitoneal cavity, 615
retrospective study Study that compares people with a disease to healthy controls (Ch 1), 11–14
retrovirus, 779
reverse transcriptase Viral enzyme that allows viral RNA to make the complementary DNA (Ch 24), 779
reversible reaction A chemical reaction that can proceed in both directions (Ch 4), 95, 96*f*, 99, 99*f*, 102, 103*f*
review articles, 14
"R" group, 30*f*, 31
Rh blood group, 798
rheumatoid arthritis, 67, 799*t*
rhodopsin Visual pigment of rods (Ch 10), 367
in phototransduction, 366*f*, 367–368, 368*f*
receptor for, abnormal, 192*t*
rhythmic movement Combination of reflexes and voluntary movements that must be initiated and terminated by input from the cerebral cortex, but that once initiated, can be sustained by central pattern generators (Ch 13), 447–448, 447*t*
rib cage (ribs), 560
during expiration, 572
during inspiration, 570, 570*f*
ribonuclease Enzyme that breaks down mRNA (Ch 4), 119
ribonucleic acid. *See* RNA
ribose A pentose sugar (Ch 2), 27, 32, 33*f*
ribosomal RNA (rRNA) Cytoplasmic RNA where assembly of proteins takes place (Ch 4), 60*f*, 61, 115, 116*f*
ribosome Small dense granules of RNA and protein that assemble amino acids into proteins (Ch 3), 60*f*, 61
in protein synthesis, 61, 118, 120*f*
on rough endoplasmic reticulum, 67, 67*f*
right atrium Chamber of the heart that receives systemic venous blood (Ch 14), 459, 459*f*, 460, 466*f*, 467*f*
right ventricle Chamber of the heart that pumps blood to the lungs (Ch 14), 459*f*, 460, 466*f*, 467*f*
rigor mortis, 406
rigor state Tight binding between actin and myosin in the absence of ATP (Ch 12), 404, 405*f*, 406
ring, 26
rising phase of action potential, 258, 259*f*
RMR. *See* resting metabolic rate
RNA (ribonucleic acid) Nucleotide that interprets the genetic information stored in DNA and uses it to direct protein synthesis (Ch 2, Appendix C), 33, 33*f*, A-34
digestion of, 697–698
double-stranded, 118
messenger. *See* messenger RNA
ribosomal, 60*f*, 61, 115, 116*f*
small interfering, 118
transfer, 115, 116*f*, 118–119, 120*f*
in vaults, 61
RNA interference (RNAi) (Ch 4), 115, 116*f*, 118
RNA polymerase Enzyme needed for synthesis of mRNA from DNA (Ch 2, 4), 115, 116, 117*f*, 120*f*
RNA virus, 779
rod Receptors for monochromatic nighttime vision (Ch 10), 365*f*, 366–368, 366*f*, 367*f*, 368*f*
Rodbell, Martin, 183
ROMK (potassium channel) (Ch 20), 653
root, spinal nerve, 301, 302*f*
Rosenstein, Beryl, 151
rotational acceleration, 355, 357*f*
roughage, 694
rough endoplasmic reticulum (RER) Organelle that is the primary site of protein synthesis (Ch 3, 8), 60*f*, 65–66, 65*f*
of neuron, 244*t*
in peptide hormone synthesis/storage/release, 218, 219*f*
round window Membrane between cochlea and middle ear that disperses energy from fluid waves in the duct (Ch 10), 348, 348*f*, 351*f*
RQ. *See* respiratory quotient
rRNA. *See* ribosomal RNA
Ruffini corpuscle Cutaneous receptor for steady pressure (Ch 10), 339*f*, 339*t*
rugae Surface folds in the interior of the stomach (Ch 21), 679, 680*f*
RV. *See* residual volume
R wave The largest wave of the QRS complex (Ch 14), 481, 482*f*
ryanodine receptor-channel (RyR) Calcium-release channel of sarcoplasmic reticulum in striated muscles (Ch 12, 14), 408, 408*f*, 471, 472*f*
RyR. *See* ryanodine receptor-channel

S (phase of cell cycle), A-36, A-37*f*
S_1 (first heart sound), 485, 486, 488*f*
S_2 (second heart sound), 486, 488*f*
saccharin, 615
saccule One of the otolith organs of the vestibular apparatus (Ch 10), 351*f*, 355, 355–357, 356*f*
Sacks, Oliver, 343
sacral spinal cord/nerves, 297*f*, 301
SADD. *See* seasonal affective depressive disorder
sagittal plane, A-39
saline, 160*t*, 595
saliva Watery enzyme and mucous secretions of the mouth (Ch 21), 689, 699
salivary amylase, 699
salivary gland, 678, 680*f*, 689
autonomic control of, 380*f*, 689
salivary immunoglobulins, 699
salivary lipase, 699
salmonella, 710
salt appetite, 346, 642, 658
saltatory conduction The apparent leap-frogging of the action potential down myelinated axons (Ch 8), 267–268, 267*f*
salt balance, 614, 642, 652–656, 653*f*
aldosterone secretion and, 653
behavioral mechanisms in, 658
hyponatremia and, 642, 645, 658
salt ingestion, 652, 653*f*
salt and water balance, 614, 658. *See also* sodium balance; water balance
integrated control of, 659–663, 660*t*, 662*f*
salty taste, sensation of, 345, 346, 347*f*
SA node. *See* sinoatrial node
sarcolemma The cell membrane of a muscle fiber (Ch 12), 398, 398*t*, 400*f*, 401*f*
sarcomere The contractile unit of a myofibril (Ch 12), 399, 400*f*, 401*f*, 402*f*
changes in during contraction, 403–404, 404*f*
sarcoplasmic reticulum Modified endoplasmic reticulum in muscle that concentrates and stores Ca^{2+} (Ch 12, 14), 398, 398*t*, 400*f*, 401*f*, 402*f*
myocardial cell, 471
smooth muscle, 423
sarcoplasm The cytoplasm of a muscle fiber (Ch 12), 398, 398*t*, 400*f*
sargramostim, 542
SARS, 777
sartans, 655
satellite cell Glial cell that forms a supportive capsule around nerve cell bodies in ganglia (Ch 8), 250, 250*f*
satiety A sensation of fullness (Ch 9, 21, 22), 316, 690, 717
satiety center Hypothalamic center that decreases food intake (Ch 22), 717
saturated fatty acid Fatty acid with no double bonds between carbons (Ch 2), 28–29, 29*f*
saturation All active sites on a given amount of protein are filled with substrate and reaction rate is maximal (Ch 2, 4, 5, 6, 18, 19), 44, 98, 628
in carrier-mediated transport, 147, 147*f*
of hemoglobin, 596–598, 597*f*
receptor, 190–191
of renal transport, 628–629, 629*f*, 630*f*
scala media. *See* cochlear duct
scala tympani. *See* tympanic duct
scala vestibuli. *See* vestibular duct
scalene muscle Respiratory muscle than lifts the upper rib cage (Ch 17), 560, 562*f*, 569, 570, 571
scatter plot, 13
Schistosoma, 778, 782
schizophrenia, 282, 283, 321
Schlemm, canal of, 358, 359*f*
Schwann cell Cell that forms myelin around a peripheral neuron axon (Ch 8, 11), 248*f*, 250, 250*f*
axonal regeneration and, 284
in neuromuscular junction, 390, 390*f*
scientific inquiry, 9
scientific literature, 14–15
scientific theory, 10
sclera, 358*f*, 359*f*
scopolamine, 386*t*
scrotum The external sac into which the testes descend so that they can stay cooler than body temperature (Ch 26), 831, 832*f*, 833
development of, 824*f*, 825
sea anemone, 216, 690
nerve net of, 292, 690–691
search terms, defining, 15
seasonal affective depressive disorder (SADD), 237*f*
sebaceous gland, 83*f*
secondary active transport The energy for transport is the potential energy stored in a concentration gradient; indirectly depends on energy of ATP (Ch 5, 19), 132*f*, 142, 144–145, 144*f*, 144*t*, 145*f*
renal tubular reabsorption and, 627–628, 627*f*

Photo Credits

About the Author

Author: Dee Silverthorn

Chapter 1

Page 1: Niki Sianni/Photonica/Getty Images.

Chapter 2

Page 19: Edy Kieser, *www.edykieser.ch*

Chapter 3

Page 50: Todd Derksen; **3-8:** D. E. Saslowsky, J. Lawrence, X. Ren, D. A. Brown, R. M. Henderson, J. M. Edwardson, Placental alkaline phosphatase is efficiently targeted to rafts in supported lipid bilayers, Journal of Biological Chemistry, Pages 26966-70, Vol. 277:30, 26 July 2002. c.2002 Journal of Biological Chemistry, American Society for Biochemistry and Molecular Biology, Inc., Bethesda, MD, 20814. JBC Online, *http://www.jbc.org;* **3-13c:** Robert W. Riess; **3-14a:** Fawcett/Hirokawa/Heuser/Science Researchers, Inc.; **3-16:** CNRI/Science Source/Photo Researchers, Inc.; **3-17:** Robert W. Riess; **3-17:** Robert W. Riess; **3-18b:** Brad J. Marsh, David N. Mastronarde, Karolyn F. Buttle, Kathryn E. Howell, and J. Richard McIntosh, Inaugural Article: Organellar relationships in the Golgi region of the pancreatic beta cell line, HIT-T15, visualized by high resolution electron tomography. Proceedings of the National Academy of Sciences of the United States of America. Fig. 2, Pages 2399-2406, Vol. 98:5, 27 February 2001. c.2001 by the National Academy of Sciences; **3-19:** Dr. Don Fawcett/Photo Researchers, Inc.; 3-20 Biophoto Associates/Photo Researchers, Inc.; **3-21 (top):** Prof. H. Wartenberg/Dr. H. Jastrow's EM Atlas, *www.drjastrow.de;* **3-21 (bottom):** Photo Researchers, Inc.; **3-23:** Todd Derksen; **3-26b:** Custom Medical Stock Photo, Inc.; **3-27:** Todd Derksen; **3-29:** Ward's Natural Science Establishment, Inc.; **3-30c:** John D. Cunningham/Visuals Unlimited; **3-31:** Frederic H. Martini; **3-33a:** SPL/Photo Researchers; **3-33b:** SPL/Photo Researchers, Photo Researchers, Inc.

Chapter 4

Page 89: Photo Researchers, Inc.

Chapter 5

Page 128: Alex Gray/The Welcome Trust Medical Photographic Library.

Chapter 7

Page 211: CNRI/Phototake NYC; **17.01:** Dee Silverthorn.

Chapter 8

Page 243: Peter Brophy/The Welcome Trust Medical Photographic Library; **8-17a:** Todd Derksen, **8-17b:** David M. Phillips/Visuals Unlimited; **8-31:** Timothy M. Gomez, University of Wisconsin-Madison.

Chapter 9

Page 291: McGill University/CNRI/Phototake NYC; **9-12b:** Robert Brons/BPS/Stone; **9-17:** Marcus Raichle, Washington University School of Medicine.

Chapter 10

Page 327: E.S. Lein, X. Zhao, F.H. Gage Defining a molecular atlas of the hippocampus using DNA microarrays and high-throughput in situ hybridization. Journal of Neuroscience 2004 Apr 14; 24 (15):3879-89, (i); **10-15b:** Todd Derksen; **10-28:** Webvision, John Moran Eye Center, University of Utah.

Chapter 11

Page 376: Dr. Flora Love.

Chapter 12

Page 396: University of Texas at Austin; **12-1a:** Ward's Natural Science Establishment; **12-1b:** Phototake NYC; **12-1c:** Todd Derksen; **12-15 (left):** D. Comack, ed. Ham's Histology 9th ed. Philadelphia: J.B. Lippincott, 1987. By permission; **12-15 (top right):** Frederic H. Martini; **12-15 (bottom right):** Frederic H. Martini; **12-26:** Biophoto Associates/Photo Researchers, Inc.

Chapter 14

Page 456: Carole L. Moncman, Ph.D.

Chapter 15

Page 500: Amy Brock and Don Ingber, Harvard Medical School/Children's Hospital; **15-20:** World Health Organization.

Chapter 16

Page 535: Diane Gray Molecular Probes, Inc. Eugene, Oregon, USA; **16-5a:** Todd Derksen; **16-6a:** Visuals Unlimited; **16-6b:** Visuals Unlimited; **16-6c:** Visuals Unlimited; **16-8:** Photo Researchers, Inc.; **16-9b:** Todd Derksen; **16-9c:** Todd Derksen.

Chapter 17

Page 558: Barbara A. Danowski Department of Biology Union College Schenectady, New York, USA; **17-8**: Frederic H. Martini.

Chapter 18

Page 587: Phototake NYC.

Chapter 19

Page 613: Ruben M. Sandoval, Indiana Center for Biological Microscopy, Indiana University School of Medicine, Indianapolis, Indiana, USA; **19-1f:** Todd Derksen; **19-4b:** Todd Derksen.

Chapter 21

Page 676: Mark L. Tamplin, Anne L. Gauzens, and Rita R. Colwell.

Chapter 22

Page 716: Roland O. Marsh, Jr. Madigan Army Medical Center Tacoma, Washington, USA; **22-8c:** Ward's Natural Science Establishment, Inc.

Chapter 23

Page 750: CNRI/SPL/Photo Researchers, Inc.; **23-1c:** Ward's Natural Science Establishment, Inc.; **23-5a:** Biophoto Associates/ Science Source/Photo Researchers, Inc.; **23-5b:** Biophoto Associates/Photo Researchers, Inc.; **23-11:** Martin Rotker/Phototake NYC; **23-13:** Alison Wright/CORBIS; **23-15:** Ralph Eagle/Science Source/Photo Researchers, Inc.; **23-17:** American Journal of Medicine; **23-17:** American Journal of Medicine; **23-17:** American Journal of Medicine; **23-18:** Ralph T. Hutchings; **23-24:** Dr. Michael Klein/Peter Arnold, Inc.

Chapter 24

Page 776: Dr. Dennis Kunkel/Phototake NYC.

Chapter 26

Page 821: Vanessa Rawe, Ph.D., Laboratory of Reproductive Biology and Special Studies Center of Studies in Gynecology and Reproduction, Viamonte, Buenos Aires, ARGENTINA. Photographed at Pittsburgh Development Center, MWRI, University of Pittsburgh School of Medicine, Pittsburgh, PA; **26-01:** CNRI/ Science Photo Library/Photo Researchers, Inc. **26-16a:** Francis Leroy/Biocosmos/ Science Photo Library/Custom Medical Stock Photo, Inc.

easurements and Conversions

IXES

-	(d)	1/10	0.1	1×10^{-1}
ti-	(c)	1/100	0.01	1×10^{-2}
li-	(m)	1/1000	0.001	1×10^{-3}
ro-	(μ)	1/1,000,000	0.000001	1×10^{-6}
no-	(n)	1/1,000,000,000	0.000000001	1×10^{-9}
o-	(p)	1/1,000,000,000,000	0.000000000001	1×10^{-12}
o-	(k)		1000.	1×10^{3}

TRIC SYSTEM

neter (m)	=	100 centimeters (cm)	=	1000 millimeters (mm)
entimeter (cm)	=	10 millimeters (mm)	=	0.01 meters (m)
nillimeter (mm)	=	1000 micrometers (μm; also called micron, μ)		
ngstrom (Å)	=	1/10,000 micrometer	=	1×10^{-7} millimeters
iter (L)	=	1000 milliliters (mL)		
deciliter (dL)	=	100 milliliters (mL)	=	0.1 liters (L)
cubic centimeter (cc)	=	1 milliliter (mL)		
milliliter (mL)	=	1000 microliters (μL)		
kilogram (kg)	=	1000 grams (g)		
gram (g)	=	1000 milligrams (mg)		
milligram (mg)	=	1000 micrograms (μg)		

ONVERSIONS

yard (yd)	=	0.92 meter		
inch (in)	=	2.54 centimeters		
meter	=	1.09 yards		
centimeter	=	0.39 inch		
liquid quart (qt)	=	946 milliliters		
fluid ounce (oz)	=	8 fluid drams	=	29.57 milliliters (mL)
liter	=	1.05 liquid quarts		
1 pound (lb)	=	453.6 grams		
1 kilogram	=	2.2 pounds		

TEMPERATURE

FREEZING

0 degrees Celsius (°C)	=	32 degrees Fahrenheit (°F)	=	273 Kelvin (K)

To convert degrees Celsius (°C) to degrees Fahrenheit (°F):
(°C × 9/5) + 32

To convert degrees Fahrenheit (°F) to degrees Celsius (°C):
(°F − 32) × 5/9

NORMAL VALUES OF BLOOD COMPONENTS

SUBSTANCE OR PARAMETER	NORMAL RANGE	MEASURED IN
Calcium (Ca^{2+})	4.3–5.3 meq/L	Serum
Chloride (Cl^{-})	100–108 meq/L	Serum
Potassium (K^{+})	3.5–5.0 meq/L	Serum
Sodium (Na^{+})	135–145 meq/L	Serum
pH	7.35–7.45	Whole blood
P_{O_2}	75–100 mm Hg	Arterial blood
P_{CO_2}	34–45 mm Hg	Arterial blood
Osmolality	280–296 mosmol/kg water	Serum
Glucose, fasting	70–110 mg/dL	Plasma
Creatinine	0.6–1.5 mg/dL	Serum
Protein, total	6.0–8.0 g/dL	Serum

Modified from W. F. Ganong, *Review of Medical Physiology* (Norwalk: Appleton & Lange), 1995.